LEAVING CERTIFICATE MATHEMATICS
THE COMPLETE ORDINARY LEVEL COURSE

DESTINATION MATHS

Louise Boylan and Aisling Quirke

Gill Education
Hume Avenue
Park West
Dublin 12
www.gilleducation.ie

Gill Education is an imprint of M.H. Gill & Co.

ISBN: 978-0-7171-73389

Design: Compuscript
Illustrations: Maria Murray

Extracts from the booklet of *formulae and tables* were reproduced by kind permission of the State Examination Commission.

For permission to reproduce photographs, the authors and publisher gratefully acknowledge the following:
All images © iStock except the following: © Alamy: 168, 177, 283, 358, 374, 412; © Google Maps: 251;
© Premier League 2017: 491; Wikimedia: 467.

The authors and publisher have made every effort to trace all copyright holders, but if any have been inadvertently overlooked we would be pleased to make the necessary arrangement at the first opportunity.
The paper used in this book is made from the wood pulp of managed forests. For every tree felled, at least one tree is planted, thereby renewing natural resources.

Louise would like to thank friends and family, particularly Joe, Danny and Josh Heron, and Mairead and Christy Boylan for their continued support. Aisling would like to thank friends and family, particularly Ann and Seamie Quirke for their encouragement and support throughout the project and always.

Contents

Introduction

Welcome to *Destination Maths*, our Leaving Certificate Mathematics book. Written especially for Ordinary Level students, this book covers the complete Leaving Certificate course in a single volume.

The following features help hone mathematical skills and exam technique:

- **Learning outcomes** at the start of each section help focus learning
- **Keywords** develop mathematical literacy
- **Something to Think About questions** at the start of each chapter emphasise real-life applications and foster problem-solving skills
- **Post-it notes** provide helpful **hints** and **tips** to scaffold difficult questions and encourage sound mathematical technique
- Comprehensive, **fully worked examples** facilitate self-directed learning
- **Step-by-step approach** encourages all students to make attempts and thus earn partial credit marks in the exam
- **Links across the syllabus** reinforce learning by helping students to make connections between topics
- Wide selection of **practice questions**, with a strong emphasis on in-context applications
- **Graded revision and exam style questions** provide for effective revision and exam preparation
- **Discussion Time** activities facilitate discovery learning through pair and group work
- **Snapshots** of the **booklet of *formulae and tables*** familiarise students with the formulae they will use in the exam.

The *Destination Maths* package includes a textbook and an eBook with links to digital resources from the Project Maths website. Teachers also have access to a bank of exam style questions that require knowledge from multiple areas of the syllabus, as well as animated PowerPoints complete with fully worked solutions.

We hope teachers, as well as students enjoy using our book and that it will guide all students to fulfil their potential in the Leaving Certificate Ordinary Level Mathematics exam.

Louise Boylan and Aisling Quirke

CHAPTER 01

Number Systems

Sections covered within this chapter:

KEY WORDS

- Natural numbers
- Integers
- Real numbers
- Factor
- Rational numbers
- Composite number
- Irrational numbers
- Prime number
- Surds

SOMETHING TO THINK ABOUT…

Two athletes are running laps around a running track at a steady pace.

The first athlete can complete a lap in four minutes and the second athlete can complete a lap in six minutes. They both start at the same place and time and go in the same direction.

(i) After how many minutes will they meet again at the starting place?

(ii) How many laps will each athlete have completed at this point?

Section 1.1: Order of Operations

Learning Outcome:

You should be able to:

- understand and use order of operations

Numbers have limited value to us on their own. We need to be able to work with them using various different operations.

Operations are actions such as adding, subtracting, multiplying, dividing, squaring and taking the square root.

Discussion Time 

1. Work with a classmate, without using your calculator and decide which of the options given is the correct answer to the following sum: $7 + 6 \times 2^2 + 3$

   A: 55 B: 64 C: 34 D: 22

2. Enter the sum into your calculator. Did you get the same answer?
3. Does the order in which you do a sum matter?

The calculator is programmed a specific way according to the following order of operations. This is the order in which all operations should be done.

Order of operations

The following order of operations is based on the idea of doing the 'most powerful operations' first and working your way to the least powerful operations.

Step 1: Do things in **brackets** first.

Step 2: Next do the **exponents/indices** (powers), e.g. 5^2, 2^3, 3^4 etc.

Step 3: Next **multiply or divide** (these operations are equal in strength, so do them from left to right as you see them).

Step 4: Finally **add or subtract** (again, these operations are equal in strength, so do them in the order they appear)

In summary,

Brackets **E**xponents/**I**ndices **M**ultiplication/**D**ivision **A**ddition/**S**ubtraction

Most powerful → Least powerful

We use BEMDAS/BIMDAS to help us remember this. BEMDAS and BIMDAS are the same thing. It depends on whether you use the word exponent or index.

EXAMPLE

Evaluate each of the following:

(i) $4 \times (3 + 2)$ **(ii)** 2×3^2 **(iii)** $30 \div 5 \times 3$ **(iv)** $(7^2 + (14 \div 2 + 5^2)) + 3^2$

Solution

By following the rules of BEMDAS in each case, we get:

(i) $4 \times (3 + 2)$
$= 4 \times 5$
$= 20$

(ii) 2×3^2
$= 2 \times 9$
$= 18$

(iii) $30 \div 5 \times 3$
$= 6 \times 3$
$= 18$

(iv) $(7^2 + (14 \div 2 + 5^2)) + 3^2$
$= (7^2 + (14 \div 2 + 25)) + 3^2$
$= (49 + (7 + 25)) + 9$
$= (49 + 32) + 9$
$= 81 + 9$
$= 90$

Practice Questions 1.1

1. Evaluate the following and show all your workings:
   (i) $7 - 5 + 18 \div 2$
   (ii) $5 + 16 \times 14 \div 7$
   (iii) $13 + 6 \times 10 \div 2$
   (iv) $18 \times 9 + 2 - 1$
   (v) $8 \div 2 \times (7 + 3)$
   (vi) $(4 - 2)^2 + 7 \times 13$
2. Evaluate the following and show all your workings:
   (i) $(3^2 + 4) + 8 + 6^2$
   (ii) $(15 - 7) - (10 \div 2)^2 \times 5^2$
   (iii) $16 + (8 + (11 - 4)^2) - 5$
   (iv) $7^2 + (16 \div 2 + 5^2) - 2^2$
   (v) $7^2 + (10 \div 2 + 5^2) + 2^2$
   (vi) $(12 \div 2)^2 + ((13 - 2) \times 6^2)$
3. Evaluate the following and show all your workings:
   (i) $3^3 - (6 \times (3 - 7))$
   (ii) $((-4)^2 + 9) \times (-4) - 5$
   (iii) $(72 \div 2)^2 - 7 \times 4$
   (iv) $[(23 + 11) \times 2] - 4$
   (v) $[(-9) + ((-84) \div (-7))] \times (-4)^2$
4. Matt had €35 in cash and withdrew €200 from his bank account. He bought a pair of jeans for €34·00, two t-shirts for €16·00 each, and two pairs of shoes for €24·00 each. Write an expression, and use it determine how much money Matt had in his wallet at the end of the shopping day.
5. A small factory employs 98 workers. Of these, 10 receive a wage of €150 per day and the rest receive €85·50 per day. To the management, a week is equal to six working days. Write an expression for these wages and work out how much the factory pays out each week.
6. In a game Lillian scores 10 points less than Bob, who scores 40 points. Carol scores half as many points as Lillian. Write an expression for the number of points Carol scored and evaluate it.
7. Use the order of operations and at least three of the digits 2, 4, 6, and 8 to create an expression with a value of 2. You can use exponents and/or negatives if you like.
8. A carpet layer charges €15 per square metre to lay a carpet, and an installation fee of €50. If the room is square and each side measures 12 m, write an expression for the cost of carpeting the room and evaluate it.

Section 1.2: Commutative, Associative and Distributive Properties

Learning Outcome:

You should be able to:
- understand and use the commutative, associative and distributive properties of operations

Operations also follow three rules: the commutative, associative and distributive properties.

Links across the syllabus

These rules are used when simplifying algebraic equations, which is covered in Chapter 2: Algebra I and Chapter 3: Algebra II.

Commutative property

The 'commutative property' says we can swap numbers around and still get the same answer. For example, when we add: $\boldsymbol{a + b = b + a}$

e.g. $(-2) + (3) = (3) + (-2)$

$-2 + 3 = 3 - 2$

$1 = 1$

Why commutative?
Because the numbers can travel back and forth like a commuter.

So we say that addition is commutative. Multiplication is also commutative.

Subtraction and division are not commutative.

Associative property

The 'associative property' says that it doesn't matter how we group the numbers (i.e. which we calculate first).

For example, when we add: $a + (b + c) = (a + b) + c$

e.g. $-10 + (3 + 4) = ((-10) + 3) + 4$

$-10 + 7 = -7 + 4$

$-3 = -3$

So we say that addition is associative.

Multiplication is also associative.

Subtraction and division are not associative.

> Why associative?
> Comes from the word 'associate', which refers to groups.

Distributive property

The 'distributive property' says that multiplication distributes over addition. This can be a little more difficult to understand, so let's look at a concrete example:

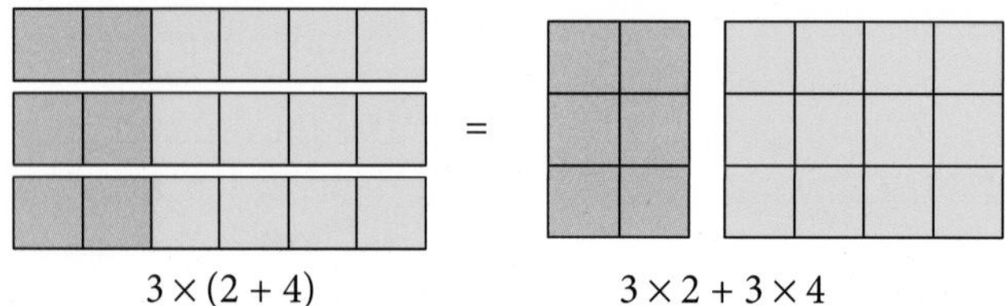

$3 \times (2 + 4)$ $\qquad$ $3 \times 2 + 3 \times 4$

3 lots of (2 + 4) is the same as 3 lots of 2 plus 3 lots of 4.

So, the 3× can be 'distributed' across the 2 + 4, into 3 × 2 and 3 × 4.

More formally, $a \times (b + c) = (a \times b) + (a \times c)$.

We say that multiplication distributes over addition and subtraction.

> Why distributive?
> Comes from the word 'distribute', which means to spread out

EXAMPLE

Use the numbers and the property to create an equation and verify that the property is true.

(i) Numbers: 9 and 7 — Property: Commutative property of addition

(ii) Numbers: 8, 5 and 9 — Property: Associative property of multiplication

(iii) Numbers: 5, 7 and 3 — Property: Distributive property of subtraction

Solution

(i) $9 + 7 = 7 + 9$

Verify: $16 = 16$

(ii) $(8 \times 5) \times 9 = 8 \times (5 \times 9)$

Verify: $40 \times 9 = 8 \times 45$

$360 = 360$

(iii) $5 \times (7 - 3) = (5 \times 7) - (5 \times 3)$

Verify: $5 \times 4 = 35 - 15$

$20 = 20$

Practice Questions 1.2

1. Identify the property being described in each of the following statements:
   (i) This property means the numbers can be swapped.
   (ii) This property refers to grouping.
   (iii) This property multiplies the value outside the brackets with each of the terms in the brackets.
   (iv) This property says that changing the grouping of numbers that are either being added or multiplied does **not** change the value of it.
   (v) This property says the brackets can be moved.

2. Use the numbers and the property in each of the questions below to create an equation and verify that the property is true for each of the following:
   (i) Numbers: 7 and 11 Property: Commutative property of addition
   (ii) Numbers: 15 and 6 Property: Commutative property of multiplication
   (iii) Numbers: 9, 11 and 4 Property: Associative property of addition
   (iv) Numbers: 12, 2 and 4 Property: Distributive property of addition

3. Rewrite the following expressions in a different way to get the same answer:
   (i) $2 + (6 + 8)$ (iii) $4(9 - 2)$ (v) $(9 + 3) + 5$
   (ii) $5 \times (8 \times 3)$ (iv) $(2 \times 3) + (4 \times 6)$ (vi) $(6 \times 7) \times 9$

4. Rewrite the expression using the distributive property of multiplication and then solve each expression:
   (i) $5 \times (5 + 7)$ (ii) $(9 - 2) \times 2$ (iii) $(2 + 7) \times - 3$

5. Determine which property of multiplication is shown in each of the following (commutative, associative or distributive).
   (i) $(5 \times 7) \times 4 = 5 \times (7 \times 4)$ (iii) $9 \times 2 = 2 \times (2 + 7)$ (v) $(10 \times 3) + (10 \times 0) = 10 \times (3 + 0)$
   (ii) $10 \times 8 = 8 \times 10$ (iv) $4 \times (5 + 6) = (4 \times 5) + (4 \times 6)$

6. (i) Using the associative and commutative properties of addition, write (at least three) expressions equivalent to the expression $(4x + 2y) + 3z$.
   (ii) Pick one of the expressions above that shows the commutative property of addition. Clearly explain how this property was used.
   (iii) Pick one of the expressions that shows the associative property of addition. Clearly explain how this property was used.

7. A soccer uniform costs €13 for the jersey, €11 for shorts, and €8 for socks. Write two equivalent expressions for the total cost of 12 uniforms, then find the cost.

8. The price of an apple is n. The number of apples bought by three different people is x, y and z. Write two equivalent expressions to represent the total cost of all the apples bought by the three people. What property did you use?

Section 1.3: Natural Numbers

Learning Outcomes:

You should be able to:
- recognise the set of natural numbers, $\mathbb{N}$
- perform operations using natural numbers

Natural numbers are positive, whole numbers starting at 1.

This is the set of counting numbers. All numbers in this set are positive and whole. They start at 1 (you wouldn't start with 0 if you were counting objects or people).

This set is represented by the letter $\mathbb{N}$.

Adding and multiplying natural numbers always gives natural number answers.

Factors

A **factor** is a number that will divide evenly (with no remainder) into another number.

1 is a factor of all numbers, and so is the number itself.
For example, the factors of 24 are 1, 2, 3, 4, 6, 8, 12 and 24.

A number which has more than 1 pair of factors is called a **composite number**.

A **composite number** is a whole number that can be divided evenly by numbers other than 1 or itself.

Discussion Time 

Work with a classmate to answer the following questions:

1. All numbers have an even number of factors: true or false?
2. Can you think of a counter-example to disprove this statement?

A **prime number** is a positive number that has *exactly* two distinct whole number factors which are 1 and the number itself.

There is often misunderstanding about whether 1 and 2 are prime. To avoid confusion, here are the facts:

- The number 1 is not prime.
- The number 2 is prime. (It is the only even prime.)

Prime factors

We can 'break apart' composite numbers into prime factors. Prime numbers are the basic building blocks of all numbers. Composite numbers are made up of prime numbers multiplied together.

For example:

12 can be written as $2 \times 2 \times 3$

290 can be written as $2 \times 5 \times 29$

To find prime factors we continuously divide by the lowest prime number that will go into the number evenly until we get to 1.

EXAMPLE 1

Find the prime factors of 5880.

Solution

Prime factors can also be found using your calculator.

$5880 \div 2 = 2940$
$2940 \div 2 = 1470$
$1470 \div 2 = 735$
$735 \div 3 = 245$
$245 \div 5 = 49$
$49 \div 7 = 7$
$7 \div 7 = 1$

The prime factors are all the numbers we divided by: $2 \times 2 \times 2 \times 3 \times 5 \times 7 \times 7 = 2^3 \times 3 \times 5 \times 7^2$

Number Systems

EXAMPLE 2

Find the highest common factor of 81, 126 and 234.

Solution

We express each of the given numbers as a product of its prime factors.

$81 = 3 \times 3 \times 3 \times 3 = 3^4$

$126 = 2 \times 3 \times 3 \times 7 = 2 \times 3^2 \times 7$

$234 = 2 \times 3 \times 3 \times 13 = 2 \times 3^2 \times 13$

We now take the highest power of each prime that is in common in our prime factors.

So the highest common factor is $3^2 = 9$.

The highest common factor (HCF) is simply the largest number which is common to all of the lists.

Multiples

The multiples of 6 are 6, 12, 18, 24, 30… etc. This is found by multiplying 6 by every natural number.

Common multiples

The common multiples of 7 and 8 are 56, 112, etc. These can be found by writing out as many of the multiples of each number until we arrive at a common number in each list.

7 = 7, 14, 21, 28, 35, 42, 49, 56, 63, 70, 77, 84, 91, 98, 105, 112…

8 = 8, 16, 24, 32, 40, 48, 56, 64, 72, 80, 88, 96, 104, 112…

Lowest common multiple (LCM)

Using the numbers from above, we can see that 56 is the lowest common multiple of both 7 and 8. It is the lowest number that is a multiple of both.

A quicker way to work this out is to use prime factorisation as shown in the next example.

EXAMPLE 3

Find the lowest common multiple of 81, 126 and 234.

Solution

Express each of the given numbers as a product of its prime factors.

$81 = 3^4$

$126 = 2 \times 3^2 \times 7$

$234 = 2 \times 3^2 \times 13$

This time we have to do something different to find the LCM. We now take the highest power of each of the prime numbers in our prime factors and we multiply them together.

$\text{LCM} = 2 \times 3^4 \times 7 \times 13$

$\text{LCM} = 2 \times 81 \times 7 \times 13$

$\text{LCM} = 14{,}742$

So, the lowest common multiple of 81, 126 and 234 is 14,742.

(This would take considerably longer if we wrote out lists of common multiples of each number!)

Practice Questions 1.3

1. Find the prime factors of the following numbers:
   (i) 120 (iii) 624 (v) 24,789
   (ii) 375 (iv) 1,450

2. (i) Find the prime factors of the following numbers:
   (a) 15,485,867 (c) 217,645,199
   (b) 32,452,843 (d) 694,847,539
   (ii) What do the answers in (i) tell you about each of these numbers?

3. Find the highest common factor of these numbers:
   (i) 18 and 30 (iii) 16 and 24
   (ii) 15 and 20 (iv) 12 and 36

4. Jack thinks of two numbers. The HCF of these numbers is 6 and one of the numbers is 24. Suggest what his other numbers may have been.

5. Find the HCF of each of the following:
   (i) 12, 15 and 18 (iii) 8, 16 and 24
   (ii) 15, 10 and 60 (iv) 4, 6 and 24

6. Danielle says that the bigger a number, the more factors it has. Is she right? Use examples to justify your answer.

7. Find the lowest common multiple of these numbers:
   (i) 6 and 7 (iii) 5 and 8 (v) 16 and 5
   (ii) 4 and 6 (iv) 10 and 4

8. The lowest common multiple of two numbers is 36. One number is 12. What might the other number be?

9. What is the LCM of 15 and 10 multiplied by the LCM of 6 and 20?

10. What is the LCM of 18 and 12 divided by their HCF?

11. Samantha has two pieces of cloth. One piece is 72 inches wide and the other piece is 90 inches wide. She wants to cut both pieces into strips of equal width that are as wide as possible. How wide should she cut the strips?

12. Rosa is making a game board that is 16 cm by 24 cm. She wants to use square tiles. What is the largest tile she can use?

Section 1.4: Integers

Learning Outcomes:

You should be able to:

- recognise the set of integers, $\mathbb{Z}$
- perform operations using integers

Integers are positive and negative whole numbers, including zero.

If we subtract natural numbers, we will sometimes end up with negative answers.

As integers include positive whole numbers, we can say that natural numbers are a subset of integers as shown in the Venn diagram on the right.

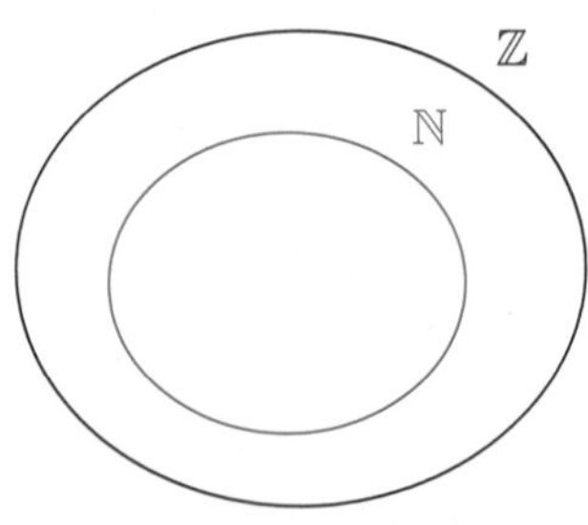

The set of integers contains all the positive and negative whole numbers. This set is represented by the letter $\mathbb{Z}$.

$$\mathbb{Z} = \{\ldots -3, -2, -1, 0, 1, 2, 3 \ldots\}$$

Adding, subtracting and multiplying integers will give integer answers.

$\mathbb{Z}$ comes from the German word 'Zahlen', meaning numbers.

Remember the rules of integers you learnt in your Junior Certificate.

Addition/subtraction

Same signs: add the numbers and keep the sign.

Different signs: subtract the smaller number from the bigger number and keep the sign of the bigger number.

Multiplication/division

Same signs: the answer is always positive.

Different signs: the answer is always negative.

Practice Questions 1.4

1. Evaluate the following without using a calculator
   (i) $-13 + 7$
   (ii) $-22 - 15$
   (iii) $29 - (-12)$
   (iv) $(17)(-3)$
   (v) $5 - 8 + 1$
   (vi) $-10 + 3 + 13$
   (vii) $-6 - (-8)$
   (viii) $(9)(-2)(-7)$
2. Evaluate the following without using a calculator
   (i) $6 \times (-5 + 3)$
   (ii) $-5 \times (-9 - 5)$
   (iii) $(-2 - 4)^2 \times (-7 - 4 + 3)$
   (iv) $\dfrac{(-12 + 6)}{(-3 + 5)}$
   (v) $\dfrac{-44}{-4 + 6}$
   (vi) $[((-96) \div (-4))^2 - (-11)] \times (-10)$
3. Emily has the following cards. She is going to choose two cards and multiply the numbers on them.

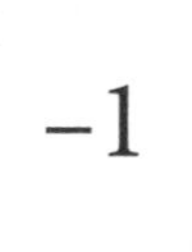

−1	−4	2	−6	4	5

   Which cards should Emily choose to make the largest possible answer?
4. Shamrock United started a football competition on 4 points.
   Each win is worth three points. Each loss loses one point. Each draw is worth 0 points. Over the season, Shamrock United won 11 matches, lost eight matches and drew three.
   How many points did they finish with at the end of the season?
5. (i) Fionn is playing a game. He throws eight balls at a target, one at a time. Each hit is worth five points. Each miss is worth minus three points.
   Fionn hits the target with five of the balls and misses with the rest.
   How many points does Fionn end up with?
   (ii) Chris throws nine balls at the target, one at a time.
   Is it possible for Chris to end up with the same number of points as Fionn?

Section 1.5: Rational Numbers

Learning Outcomes:

You should be able to:

- recognise the set of rational numbers, $\mathbb{Q}$
- perform operations using rational numbers

When we divide natural numbers and integers we do not always end up with whole numbers. For example, if you divided three bars of chocolate between six people, each person would get $\frac{1}{2}$ a bar of chocolate.

This number $\frac{1}{2}$ is not part of either $\mathbb{N}$ or $\mathbb{Z}$ as it is not a whole number.

It is part of the **rational numbers**.

This set is represented by $\mathbb{Q}$.

$\mathbb{Q}$ comes from the German word 'Quotient' meaning ratio – this word is now commonly used in English.

Rational numbers can be expressed as a fraction where both the numerator and the denominator are whole numbers.

This set includes positive and negative whole numbers and fractions, which means that all natural numbers and integers are rational numbers. (Remember, any whole number can be written as a fraction by placing it over 1.)

$\mathbb{N}$ and $\mathbb{Z}$ are subsets of $\mathbb{Q}$.

Addition, subtraction, multiplication and division (by a non-zero rational) of rational numbers will give rational answers.

1·5 is a rational number because $1{\cdot}5 = \frac{3}{2}$ (can be written as a fraction)

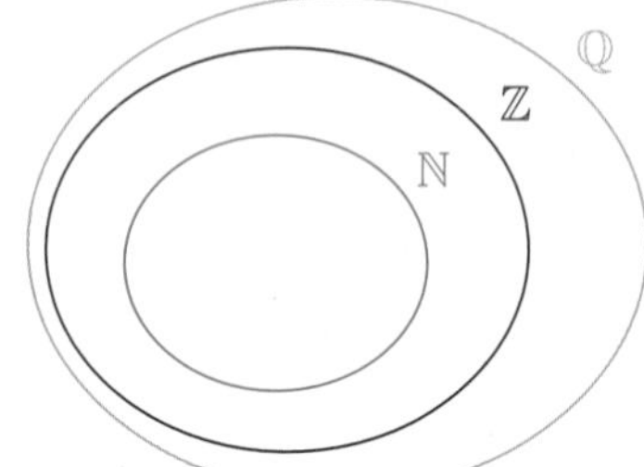

Your calculator allows you to easily convert between fractions and decimals.

Adding and subtracting rational numbers (fractions)

Numerator = top part of fraction
Denominator = bottom part of fraction

Links across the syllabus

These rules are used when simplifying algebraic fractions, which is covered in Chapter 2: Algebra I.

For your exam, it is possible to do some fraction questions on the calculator but it is really important that you spend time ensuring you can do this section without the use of a calculator. This is because when we move on to algebra later, we will have to use the same methods as we are using here.

To add or subtract fractions we use the lowest common multiple of the denominators method, as shown in the examples.

EXAMPLE 1

Express $\frac{2}{7} + \frac{8}{17}$ as a single fraction.

Solution

We need to have the same denominator in both fractions.

The easiest way to do this is to find the LCM of 7 and 17. These are already prime numbers so the LCM is the product of the two numbers, i.e. $7 \times 17 = 119$

$$\frac{?}{119} + \frac{?}{119}$$

We now change each of the numerators accordingly in the same ratio.

Just focus on the first fraction for now. What happened to the denominator? It is now 17 times bigger. Accordingly, make the numerator 17 times bigger.

Apply this method to the 2nd fraction:

$$= \frac{2(17)}{119} + \frac{8(7)}{119}$$

$$= \frac{34}{119} + \frac{56}{119}$$

$$= \frac{90}{119}$$

EXAMPLE 2

Express $\frac{1}{3}+\frac{2}{5}-\frac{3}{10}$ as a single fraction.

Solution

The LCM of 3, 5 and 10 is 30

To make all the fractions have a denominator of 30:

The first denominator is multiplied by 10, so multiply the numerator by 10

The second denominator is multiplied by 6, so multiply the numerator by 6

The third denominator is multiplied by 3, so multiply the numerator by 3

$$\frac{10(1)}{30}+\frac{6(2)}{30}-\frac{3(3)}{30}$$

$$=\frac{10}{30}+\frac{12}{30}-\frac{9}{30}$$

$$=\frac{22}{30}-\frac{9}{30}$$

$$=\frac{13}{30}$$

Multiplying fractions

To multiply fractions, multiply the tops by each other, and the bottoms by each other:

$$\frac{a}{b} \times \frac{c}{d} = \frac{ac}{bd}$$

Don't forget to give your answer in its simplest form. (Your calculator will do this if you type in the fraction and press =).

EXAMPLE 3

Simplify: **(i)** $\frac{3}{8}\times\frac{4}{13}$ **(ii)** $\frac{3p}{p-2}\times\frac{p}{2}$

Solution

(i) $\frac{3}{8}\times\frac{4}{13}$

$$=\frac{3\times 4}{8\times 13}$$

$$=\frac{12}{104}$$

$$=\frac{3}{26}$$

(ii) $\frac{3p}{p-2}\times\frac{p}{2}$

$$=\frac{3p(p)}{(p-2)(2)}$$

$$=\frac{3p^2}{2p-4}$$

Dividing fractions

Let's look at a problem.

A bottle of medicine contains 15 ml. Each dose of the medicine is $2\frac{1}{2}$ ml. How many doses are there in the bottle?

This question is asking us to find how many $2\frac{1}{2}$s are in 15. This is a division problem.

So we can write this as $15 \div 2\frac{1}{2}$.

We will look at two methods of solving this problem.

Method 1

You have probably already learned that when we divide fractions, we invert (turn upside down) the second fraction and multiply it by the first fraction.

$15 \div 2\frac{1}{2}$

Convert $2\frac{1}{2}$ into a top-heavy fraction:

$2\frac{1}{2} = \frac{5}{2}$

$15 \div 2\frac{1}{2}$

$= 15 \div \frac{5}{2}$

$= \frac{15}{1} \times \frac{2}{5}$ invert second fraction and multiply

$= \frac{30}{5}$

$= 6$

Method 2

Like the addition and subtraction problems, we must have the same denominators before we begin. We write all of the fractions as single fractions to start with:

$$\frac{\left(\frac{15}{1}\right)}{\left(\frac{5}{2}\right)}$$

$$= \frac{\left(\frac{15}{1}\right)}{\left(\frac{5}{2}\right)} \times \frac{2}{2}$$ multiply top and bottom by 2 (LCM of 2 and 1)

$$= \frac{2\left(\frac{15}{1}\right)}{2\left(\frac{5}{2}\right)}$$

$$= \frac{30}{5} = 6$$

This approach works all the time and is very helpful when we move on to using division of fractions in algebra.

Practice Questions 1.5

1. Evaluate each of the following questions without using a calculator.

(i) $\frac{2}{3} + \frac{5}{7}$ **(ii)** $\frac{5}{9} - 3\frac{1}{3}$ **(iii)** $\frac{1}{6} \times \frac{3}{5}$

(iv) $\frac{4}{5} - \frac{3}{4}$ **(v)** $3\frac{1}{2} - 1\frac{4}{7}$ **(vi)** $\frac{1}{2} \div \frac{3}{4}$

(vii) $2\frac{3}{8} \div \frac{1}{6}$ **(viii)** $10\frac{1}{7} \times 6\frac{2}{3}$ **(ix)** $2\frac{1}{3} \div 1\frac{3}{4}$

(x) $-\frac{2}{7} - \frac{2}{3}$ **(xi)** $\left(3\frac{2}{5} + \frac{3}{4}\right) \div \frac{1}{2}$ **(xii)** $\left(\frac{1}{6} + \frac{4}{9}\right)^2$

2. There are 96 children in a library. $\frac{5}{8}$ of them are girls. How many of the children are boys?

3. David had €40. He spent $\frac{1}{5}$ of the money on a book and $\frac{3}{10}$ on a calculator. How much did he spend altogether?

4. Scott had some eggs. He sold $\frac{5}{8}$ of them. If he sold 300 eggs, how many eggs did he have to begin with?

5. On a certain day, $\frac{1}{2}$ of the students in a school walked to school, $\frac{2}{5}$ of the students came to school by bus and the remaining 68 students came by car.
   (i) What fraction of the students came by car?
   (ii) How many students came to school by bus?

6. Alex, Betty, and Chris are trading marbles. First, Alex gives Betty $\frac{1}{2}$ of his marbles. Then Betty gives Chris $\frac{1}{3}$ of her marbles. Finally, Chris gives Alex two marbles. If everyone ends up with 12 marbles, how many marbles did each person start with?

7. Emma started with a certain amount of money. She spent $\frac{2}{5}$ of her money. She earned €5 the next day. Later, she lost $\frac{3}{7}$ of her money, but she still had €20 left. How much did she start with?

Section 1.6: Irrational Numbers

Learning Outcomes:

You should be able to:

- recognise the set of irrational numbers, $\mathbb{R}\backslash\mathbb{Q}$
- perform operations using irrational numbers

An **irrational number** is a number than cannot be expressed in the form $\frac{p}{q}$.

Some numbers can't be expressed in the form $\frac{p}{q}$. These numbers also cannot be represented as terminating or repeating decimals, which means the decimal part of irrational numbers never repeats and never terminates (ends).

Examples of irrational numbers include:

$\pi = 3{\cdot}1415926535...$ $\qquad e = 2{\cdot}7182818284...$ $\qquad \sqrt{2} = 1{\cdot}4142135623...$

Notice that the decimal part of these numbers doesn't repeat or terminate.

As irrational numbers are the real numbers that are not rational, we can use the symbol $\mathbb{R}\backslash\mathbb{Q}$ (real, not rational) to represent this set.

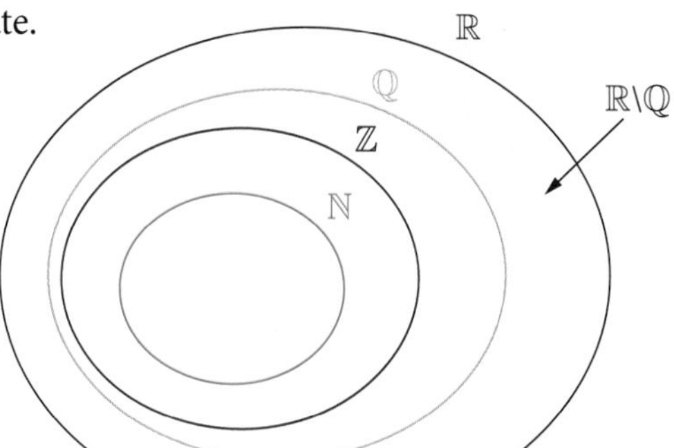

Many irrational numbers can be written as the root of a rational number. These numbers are called **surds**.

Not all numbers written as roots are surds. Consider the following:

$\sqrt{16} \qquad \sqrt[3]{8} \qquad \sqrt{3}$

$\sqrt{16} = 4$ which is rational, therefore $\sqrt{16}$ is not a surd

$\sqrt[3]{8} = 2$ which is rational, therefore $\sqrt[3]{8}$ is not a surd

$\sqrt{3} = 1{\cdot}732050808...$, which is a non-terminating decimal, that is an irrational number and a surd as it can be written as the root of a rational number. The calculator only shows a surd to nine decimal places. If you use your calculator to calculate $(1{\cdot}732050808)^2$, the answer will be $3{\cdot}000000001$.

Surds are irrational numbers that can be written as roots of a rational number.

Dealing with surds

As with fractions, you can simply use your calculator to get the answers to questions containing surds. However, these can also appear in algebra-style questions, so an understanding of the rules of surds is important.

Rule 1: $\sqrt{p \times q} = (\sqrt{p})(\sqrt{q})$

Let's firstly take a look at an example using familiar non-surd roots:

We know $\sqrt{4} = 2$ and $\sqrt{9} = 3$ so

$\sqrt{4} \times \sqrt{9} = 2 \times 3 = 6$ and also $\sqrt{4 \times 9} = \sqrt{36} = 6$

From the above example, we can say that:

$\sqrt{4 \times 9} = \sqrt{4} \times \sqrt{9}$; putting this in general terms, we get: $\sqrt{p \times q} = (\sqrt{p})(\sqrt{q})$

We can now use this rule to simplify surds. Once we have simplified the surds, we can then add or subtract surds using the like terms rule from algebra.

EXAMPLE 1

Simplify $3\sqrt{45} + \sqrt{20} + \sqrt{32}$

Solution

$= 3(\sqrt{9} \times \sqrt{5}) + (\sqrt{4} \times \sqrt{5}) + (\sqrt{16} \times \sqrt{2})$
$= 3(3 \times \sqrt{5}) + (2 \times \sqrt{5}) + (4 \times \sqrt{2})$
$= 9\sqrt{5} + 2\sqrt{5} + 4\sqrt{2}$ (remember, we can only add like terms, i.e. $9\sqrt{5} + 2\sqrt{5}$)
$= 11\sqrt{5} + 4\sqrt{2}$

This rule also allows us to multiply surds.

When we multiply surds, we:

1. multiply any whole numbers written in front of the $\sqrt{\ }$ sign.

2. multiply the numbers under the $\sqrt{\ }$ sign.

So, $6\sqrt{3} \times 2\sqrt{5} = 12\sqrt{15}$

EXAMPLE 2

Multiply $\sqrt{2}$ by $3\sqrt{2}$

Solution

$(1\sqrt{2})(3\sqrt{2})$
$= (1 \times 3)(\sqrt{2} \times \sqrt{2})$
$= (3)(\sqrt{2} \times \sqrt{2})$
$= 3 \times \sqrt{4}$ $\quad \sqrt{2} \times \sqrt{2} = \sqrt{2 \times 2}$
$= 3 \times 2 = 6$

In general, $\sqrt{a} \times \sqrt{a}$ or $(\sqrt{a})^2 = a$

Rule 2: $\sqrt{\frac{p}{q}} = \frac{\sqrt{p}}{\sqrt{q}}$

Now let's go back to our known roots to look at rule 2.

We know $\sqrt{64} = 8$ and $\sqrt{4} = 2$, so:

$\frac{\sqrt{64}}{\sqrt{4}} = \frac{8}{2} = 4$ and also $\sqrt{\frac{64}{4}} = \sqrt{16} = 4$

so, we can say that $\sqrt{\frac{64}{4}} = \frac{\sqrt{64}}{\sqrt{4}}$

Putting this into general terms gives us: $\sqrt{\frac{p}{q}} = \frac{\sqrt{p}}{\sqrt{q}}$

EXAMPLE 3

Simplify $4\sqrt{3} \times \frac{\sqrt{18}}{\sqrt{12}}$

Solution

$= 4\sqrt{3} \times \frac{\sqrt{9} \times \sqrt{2}}{\sqrt{4} \times \sqrt{3}}$ simplify the $\sqrt{\ }$

$= 4\sqrt{3} \times \frac{3(\sqrt{2})}{2(\sqrt{3})}$

$= \frac{4\sqrt{3}}{1} \times \frac{3(\sqrt{2})}{2(\sqrt{3})}$ express both as fractions

$= \frac{(4\sqrt{3})(3\sqrt{2})}{(1)(2\sqrt{3})}$ multiply the tops by each other and the bottoms by each other

$= \frac{(4 \times 3)(\sqrt{3} \times \sqrt{2})}{(1 \times 2)\sqrt{3}}$ multiply the numbers by the numbers and the $\sqrt{\ }$ by the $\sqrt{\ }$

$= \frac{12(\sqrt{3})(\sqrt{2})}{2\sqrt{3}}$ divide top and bottom by $\sqrt{3}$

$= \frac{12\sqrt{2}}{2} = 6\sqrt{2}$

Division of surds

When we divide surds, we:

1. divide any whole numbers written in front of the $\sqrt{\ }$ sign

2. divide the numbers under the $\sqrt{\ }$ sign.

So $8\sqrt{6} \div 2\sqrt{3} = 4\sqrt{2}$

To divide a rational number by a surd, we must convert the surd to a rational number. This process is called **rationalising the denominator**.

In order to do this we must recall that $\sqrt{a} \times \sqrt{a} = a$

EXAMPLE 4

Simplify $\frac{2}{\sqrt{3}}$

Solution

We must multiply the numerator (top) and the denominator (bottom) by $\sqrt{3}$ to rationalise the surd.

$\frac{2 \times \sqrt{3}}{\sqrt{3} \times \sqrt{3}}$

$= \frac{2\sqrt{3}}{3}$ (remember $\sqrt{3} \times \sqrt{3} = 3$)

Once our denominator is a rational number, we are finished.

Multiplying and dividing numbers of the form $a \pm b\sqrt{c}$, where a, b and c are positive rational numbers

Multiplication

Links across the syllabus

Expanding brackets is covered in Chapter 2: Algebra I.

We use the distributive law to multiply these numbers:

$$a \times (b + c) = a \times b + a \times c$$

We multiply each term first and then add or subtract.

EXAMPLE 5

Simplify $(2 - \sqrt{3})^2$

Solution

$(2 - \sqrt{3})^2$
$= (2 - \sqrt{3})(2 - \sqrt{3})$
$= 2(2 - \sqrt{3}) - \sqrt{3}(2 - \sqrt{3})$
$= 4 - 2\sqrt{3} - 2\sqrt{3} + 3$
$= 7 - 4\sqrt{3}$

Division

Links across the syllabus

A method similar to this is used in Chapter 28: Complex Numbers.

When dividing numbers in this form we must rationalise the denominator and simplify. To do this we multiply the numerator (top) and the denominator (bottom) by the denominator with the middle sign changed.

$$(a + \sqrt{b})(a - \sqrt{b}) = a^2 - b$$

EXAMPLE 6

Simplify $\frac{3}{7 - \sqrt{2}}$

Solution

To rationalise the denominator we must multiply the numerator and the denominator by $7 + \sqrt{2}$, i.e. the denominator with its middle sign changed:

$\frac{3(7 + \sqrt{2})}{(7 - \sqrt{2})(7 + \sqrt{2})}$

$= \frac{21 + 3\sqrt{2}}{7(7 + \sqrt{2}) - \sqrt{2}(7 + \sqrt{2})}$

$= \frac{21 + 3\sqrt{2}}{49 + 7\sqrt{2} - 7\sqrt{2} - 2}$

$= \frac{21 + 3\sqrt{2}}{47}$

Once the denominator is rationalised there should be no $\sqrt{\ }$ on the bottom

Practice Questions 1.6

1. Which of the following numbers are rational and which are irrational?
   (i) $4\frac{2}{3}$
   (ii) -7
   (iii) $\sqrt{64}$
   (iv) $\sqrt{5}$
   (v) $1\frac{5}{8}$

2. Simplify the following without using a calculator:
   (i) $\sqrt{96}$ (ii) $\sqrt{44}$ (iii) $\sqrt{54}$ (iv) $\sqrt{125}$ (v) $\sqrt{28}$ (vi) $\sqrt{200}$ (vii) $\sqrt{50}$ (viii) $\sqrt{72}$

3. (i) Express, in simplest form, $\sqrt{45}$ and $\sqrt{20}$.
   (ii) Hence, or otherwise, simplify $3\sqrt{45} + 2\sqrt{20}$.

4. Simplify the following:
   (i) $\sqrt{50} + \sqrt{8}$
   (ii) $\sqrt{5} + \sqrt{80}$
   (iii) $\sqrt{175} - \sqrt{28}$
   (iv) $\sqrt{99} - \sqrt{44}$

5. Calculate the area of the triangle, giving your answer as an integer. All sides' lengths are in metres.

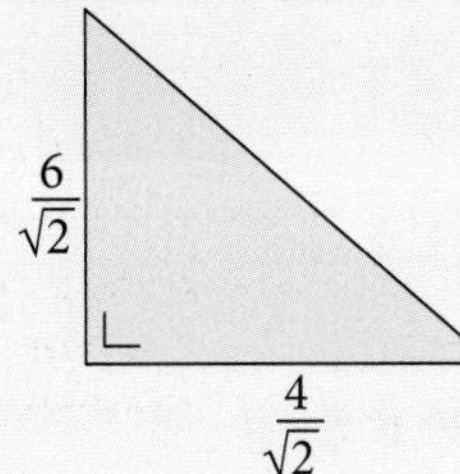

Recall: Area of a triangle = $\frac{1}{2}$ (base)(height)

6. A rectangular garden has length $6\sqrt{2}$ and width $1\sqrt{2}$. Find the area and the perimeter of the garden.

7. Rationalise the denominator in each of the following and express your answer in its simplest form:
   (i) $\frac{3}{\sqrt{2}}$ (ii) $\frac{7}{\sqrt{7}}$ (iii) $\frac{1}{\sqrt{5}}$ (iv) $\frac{\sqrt{3}}{\sqrt{2}}$

8. Express $\frac{6}{\sqrt{2}}$ in the form $a\sqrt{b}$, where a and b are positive integers.

9. Given the area of a circle is πr^2, find the area of a circle of radius $2\sqrt{7}$ cm, correct to two decimal places.

10. Expand and simplify the following expressions:
    (i) $\sqrt{2}(3 + \sqrt{5})$
    (ii) $\sqrt{6}(\sqrt{2} + \sqrt{8})$
    (iii) $4(\sqrt{5} + 3)$
    (iv) $(2 + \sqrt{3})(1 + \sqrt{3})$
    (v) $(3 - \sqrt{5})(3 - 2\sqrt{5})$
    (vi) $(5 - \sqrt{2})(5 + \sqrt{2})$
    (vii) $(2 + \sqrt{5})(2 + \sqrt{3})$
    (viii) $(1 - \sqrt{2})(1 + \sqrt{3})$
    (ix) $(8 - \sqrt{2})(8 + \sqrt{2})$
    (x) $(\sqrt{3} + \sqrt{5})(\sqrt{3} + \sqrt{5})$

11. Expand and simplify $(\sqrt{5} + \sqrt{15})^2$. Give your answer in the form $a + b\sqrt{3}$, where a and b are integers.

12. Expand and simplify $(\sqrt{3} - \sqrt{2})(\sqrt{3} + \sqrt{2})$.

13. Expand $(2 + \sqrt{3})(1 + \sqrt{3})$. Give your answer in the form $a + b\sqrt{3}$, where a and b are integers.

14. Rewrite the following expressions with rational denominators:
    (i) $\frac{3}{\sqrt{5}}$
    (ii) $\frac{4}{\sqrt{8}}$
    (iii) $\frac{9}{\sqrt{48}}$
    (iv) $\frac{\sqrt{2}+1}{\sqrt{2}}$
    (v) $\frac{\sqrt{3} - 1}{\sqrt{5}}$
    (vi) $\frac{-4}{3\sqrt{2}}$
    (vii) $\frac{\sqrt{3} + 3}{\sqrt{10}}$
    (viii) $\frac{\sqrt{2} - 1}{\sqrt{7}}$
    (ix) $\frac{1}{\sqrt{3} - 1}$
    (x) $\frac{4}{\sqrt{6} - 2}$
    (xi) $\frac{7}{\sqrt{7} - 2}$
    (xii) $\frac{-3}{\sqrt{5} + 1}$
    (xiii) $\frac{\sqrt{2} + 3}{\sqrt{5}}$
    (xiv) $\frac{\sqrt{5} - 1}{\sqrt{5} + 3}$
    (xv) $\frac{5 + 2\sqrt{3}}{\sqrt{5} + \sqrt{3}}$

15. Write $\frac{\sqrt{18} + 10}{2}$ in the form $p + q\sqrt{2}$, where p and q are integers.

16. Work out $\frac{(5 + \sqrt{3})(5 - \sqrt{3})}{\sqrt{22}}$. Give your answer in its simplest form.

17. Simplify:
    (i) $5\sqrt{12} + \sqrt{27}$
    (ii) $3\sqrt{20} - 3\sqrt{80} - 2\sqrt{45}$
    (iii) $\sqrt{15} \times \sqrt{3}$
    (iv) $2\sqrt{20} \times 3\sqrt{45}$
    (v) $(2 + \sqrt{3})(2 - \sqrt{3})$
    (vi) $(3\sqrt{5} - 2)(\sqrt{5} + 3)$
    (vii) $(2\sqrt{5} - \sqrt{3})(3\sqrt{3} + \sqrt{5})$
    (viii) $\frac{2}{\sqrt{3}}$
    (ix) $\frac{2}{\sqrt{5} + 1}$
    (x) $\frac{\sqrt{3} + 1}{\sqrt{3} - 1}$
    (xi) $\frac{\sqrt{5}}{2 + \sqrt{8}}$

Section 1.7: Real Numbers

Learning Outcome:

You should be able to:

- recognise the set of real numbers, $\mathbb{R}$

The set of **real numbers** contains both rational and irrational numbers.

It is represented by the letter $\mathbb{R}$.

$\mathbb{N}$, $\mathbb{Z}$, $\mathbb{Q}$ and the irrational numbers are all subsets of $\mathbb{R}$.

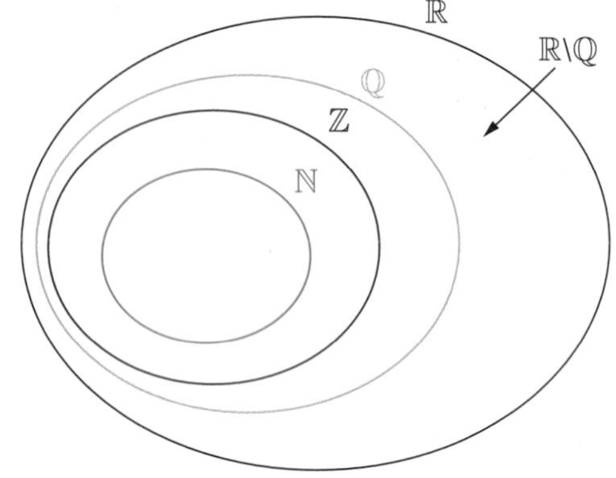

EXAMPLE

The columns in the table on the right represent the natural numbers ($\mathbb{N}$), integers ($\mathbb{Z}$), rational numbers ($\mathbb{Q}$), irrational numbers ($\mathbb{R}\backslash\mathbb{Q}$) and real numbers ($\mathbb{R}$).
Write 'yes' or 'no' in the space provided to indicate which set each of the listed numbers are part of. Explain your answer in each case.

	$\mathbb{N}$	$\mathbb{Z}$	$\mathbb{Q}$	$\mathbb{Q}\backslash\mathbb{R}$	$\mathbb{R}$
$\sqrt{3}$					
−6					
$\frac{3}{4}$					
$\sqrt{9}$					
7					

Solution

	$\mathbb{N}$	$\mathbb{Z}$	$\mathbb{Q}$	$\mathbb{Q}\backslash\mathbb{R}$	$\mathbb{R}$
$\sqrt{3}$	No. It is not a whole number.	No. It is not a whole number.	No. It can't be expressed as $\frac{p}{q}$.	Yes. It can't be expressed as $\frac{p}{q}$.	Yes. It is irrational and $\mathbb{R}$ includes both rational and irrational numbers.
−6	No. It is not positive.	Yes. It is a negative whole number.	Yes. It can be expressed as $-\frac{6}{1}$.	No. It can be expressed as $\frac{p}{q}$.	Yes. It is rational and $\mathbb{R}$ includes both rational and irrational numbers.
$\frac{3}{4}$	No. It is not a whole number.	No. It is not a whole number.	Yes. It is in the form $\frac{p}{q}$.	No. It can be expressed as $\frac{p}{q}$.	Yes. It is rational and $\mathbb{R}$ includes both rational and irrational numbers.
$\sqrt{9}$	Yes. $\sqrt{9} = \pm 3$ and $+3$ is a positive whole number.	Yes. $\sqrt{9} = \pm 3$, both whole positive or negative numbers.	Yes. It can be written as $\pm\frac{3}{1}$.	No. It can be expressed as $\frac{p}{q}$.	Yes. It is rational and $\mathbb{R}$ includes both rational and irrational numbers.
7	Yes. It is a positive whole number.	Yes. It is a positive whole number.	Yes. It can be written as $\frac{7}{1}$.	No. It can be expressed as $\frac{p}{q}$.	Yes. It is rational and $\mathbb{R}$ includes both rational and irrational numbers.

Discussion Time 

Work with a classmate to answer the following questions.

1. Is every natural number rational?
2. Is every rational number natural?
3. Is every natural number a real number?
4. Is every real number natural?

A summary of the sets of numbers is shown on page 23 of the booklet of *formulae and tables*.

	Number sets
$\mathbb{N} = \{1, 2, 3, 4, 5, 6, \cdots\}$	natural numbers
$\mathbb{Z} = \{\cdots -3, -2, -1, 0, 1, 2, 3, \cdots\}$	integers
$\mathbb{Q} = \left\{ \frac{p}{q} \middle\vert p \in \mathbb{Z},\ q \in \mathbb{Z},\ q \neq 0 \right\}$	rational numbers
$\mathbb{R}$	real numbers

Practice Questions 1.7

1. Which of these is not a rational number? Explain your answer.
   (i) 0·35 **(ii)** $\sqrt{25}$ **(iii)** $\sqrt{5}$ **(iv)** $-\frac{3}{8}$ **(v)** 16
2. Give an example to show that a positive integer is also a rational number.
3. Show why each of the following numbers are rational:
   (i) 0·125 **(ii)** −8 **(iii)** $6\frac{2}{3}$ **(iv)** −0·42
4. Pick the irrational numbers in the list below:
   (i) $\sqrt{2}$ **(ii)** $\sqrt{64}$ **(iii)** $\sqrt{7}$ **(iv)** $\sqrt{169}$ **(v)** $\sqrt{5}$
5. True or false:
   (i) $-2 \in \mathbb{N}$ **(ii)** $-\frac{3}{4} \in \mathbb{Z}$ **(iii)** $\sqrt{5} \in \mathbb{Q}$ **(iv)** $\sqrt{11} \in \mathbb{R}$
6. Name the set or sets that each of the following belong to:
   (i) −12
   (ii) 3·25
   (iii) $\sqrt{30}$
   (iv) $\frac{325}{475}$
   (v) 0
   (vi) 36
   (vii) π
   (viii) $-\sqrt{169}$
   (ix) 0·24
   (x) $\frac{-32}{-16}$
7. To which set or sets could each of the following belong? Justify your answers.
   (i) The number of students in a school.
   (ii) The bill for a meal.
   (iii) The average night-time temperature in January.
   (iv) The circumference of a circle divided by its diameter.
8. Answer true or false for each statement:
   (i) Real numbers are either rational or irrational.
   (ii) An irrational number can be a repeating decimal.
   (iii) Natural numbers include negative numbers.
   (iv) The number 12 is an integer.
   (v) The only integer not included in the natural numbers is 0.
   (vi) Irrational numbers are not real numbers.
   (vii) The fraction $\frac{1}{2}$ can be written as a terminating decimal.
9. Classify each of the following using one or more of the words from the list below:
   Natural, prime, integer, rational, terminating decimal, repeating decimal and irrational.
   (i) $\sqrt{11}$
   (ii) $\sqrt{14}$
   (iii) $\sqrt{49}$
   (iv) $\frac{2}{3}$
   (v) 0
   (vi) $\sqrt{2}$
   (vii) $-\sqrt{81}$
   (viii) 1
   (ix) $\frac{7}{11}$
   (x) $\frac{3}{7}$

10. The columns in the table below represent the natural numbers (ℕ), integers (ℤ), rational numbers (ℚ), irrational numbers (ℝ\ℚ) and real numbers (ℝ).
Copy the table below and write 'yes' or 'no' in the space provided to indicate which set each of the listed numbers are part of. Explain your answer in each case.

	ℕ (Natural)	ℤ (Integer)	ℚ (Rational)	ℝ/ℚ (Irrational)	ℝ (Real)
$\frac{3\pi}{2}$					
-4					
$\frac{6}{7}$					
$\sqrt{225}$					
$\sqrt{11}$					

11. Let $p = \sqrt{3}$
For each of the numbers in the table opposite, tick (✓) the correct box to say whether it is rational or irrational.

Number	Rational	Irrational
p		
$p - 2$		
$(-p)^2$		
$(p - 1)^2$		
$1 - p^2$		

Section 1.8: Significant Figures

Learning Outcome:

You should be able to:

- approximate numbers to a specified number of significant figures

Sometimes we wish to round numbers off to give an approximation of the answer. One method of giving an approximate answer is to round off using significant figures.

For example, if we want to know how many people attended a football match, a figure of 32,000 would be acceptable even if the exact number was 31,964. 32,000 is 31,964 rounded to two significant figures.

The first significant figure of a number is the first digit which is not zero.

Hence, the first significant figure of 20,499 is 2 and the first significant figure of 0·0020499 is also 2.

The second significant figure of a number is the digit after the first significant figure. This is true even if the digit is zero.

Hence, the second significant figure of 20,499 is 0, and is also the second significant figure of 0·0020499.

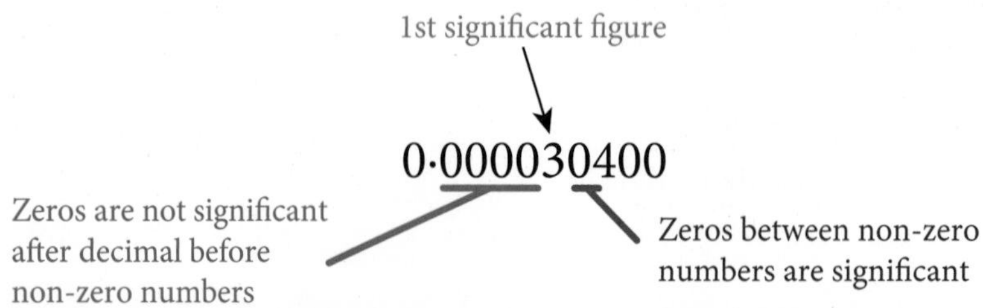

EXAMPLE 1

Round 742,396 to **(i)** four, **(ii)** three, and **(iii)** two significant figures:

If the next number is 5 or more, round up.

If the next number is 4 or less, do nothing.

Solution

(i) Four significant figures = 742,400 — Fourth figure is 3 but the 5th rounds it up to 4

(ii) Three significant figures = 742,000 — Third figure is 2 and 4th doesn't change it

(iii) Two significant figures = 740,000 — Second figure is 2 and 3rd doesn't change it

EXAMPLE 2

Round 0·0728431 to **(i)** four, **(ii)** three, and **(iii)** two significant digits:

Solution

(i) Four significant figures = 0·07284

(ii) Three significant figures = 0·0728

(iii) Two significant figures = 0·073

Practice Questions 1.8

1. How many significant figures are in each of the following numbers?
   - **(i)** 5·40
   - **(ii)** 210
   - **(iii)** 801·5
   - **(iv)** 1,000
   - **(v)** 101·0100
   - **(vi)** 12000
   - **(vii)** 0·00120
   - **(viii)** 0·0102
   - **(ix)** 2,370·0
   - **(x)** 0·000009010
2. Round these numbers to three significant figures:
   - **(i)** 1,566,311
   - **(ii)** 0·0027651
   - **(iii)** 84,592
   - **(iv)** 0·0011672
3. Perform the following calculations. Give your answer to two significant figures:
   - **(i)** 144·3854 + 8·04 – 165·32 + 30
   - **(ii)** 1 × 0·074 ÷ 2·014
   - **(iii)** 73·8967 × 9·03 ÷ 875·34
   - **(iv)** (410 × 63·91) ÷ (17·9 ÷ 0·002)
   - **(v)** $\dfrac{50{\cdot}31 + 70{\cdot}408}{13{\cdot}38 \times 0{\cdot}018}$
4. Round the following numbers to **(a)** one and **(b)** four significant figures:
   - **(i)** 26,895
   - **(ii)** 32·45653
   - **(iii)** 156·9823
   - **(iv)** 0·00023986
   - **(v)** 293·40235
   - **(vi)** 375·00876
5. An angler catches a fish that weighs 16·4 kg. If the fish weighs 0·232 times the weight of the angler, calculate the weight of the angler to two significant figures.

6. Serena measures a block of wood. The length is 5·6 cm, the width is 4·4 cm, and the thickness is 1·7 cm.
   - **(i)** Find the volume of the block of wood.

   Serena's friend Toby says that it would be better to give this answer to two significant figures.
   - **(ii)** Do you agree with Toby? Justify your answer.
7. Sam works in a factory and is packing boxes. He can fit 55 tins into one box. How many tins would there be altogether in 300 boxes? Give your answer correct to two significant figures.
8. A solid metal sphere has a radius of 7·5 cm.
   - **(i)** Calculate the volume of the sphere to the nearest cubic centimetre.

   Volume of a sphere = $\frac{4}{3}\pi r^3$
   - **(ii)** If one cubic centimetre of the metal has a mass of 4·9 grams, calculate the mass of the sphere to three significant figures.

Revision and Exam Style Questions – Section A

1. From the list below, pick out the number or numbers that satisfies the conditions stated in each part.

   13, 22, 27, 35, 8, 12, 19, 72, 48, 36, 25

   (i) Multiples of 7 **(iii)** Square numbers

   (ii) Factors of 36 **(iv)** Prime numbers

2. What are the prime factors of:

   (i) **(a)** 432 **(b)** 522.

   (ii) Hence, or otherwise, find the highest common factor of 432 and 522.

3. Show that $\frac{\sqrt{75}-\sqrt{27}}{\sqrt{3}}$ is an integer and find its value.

4. Jan ate $\frac{1}{3}$ of her lunch while walking to school and another $\frac{1}{4}$ at break time. What fraction of her lunch did she have left to eat at lunchtime?

5. Calculate $\frac{3}{7}$ of 98 and express your answer as a fraction of 56.

6. In a group of 20 students, three have red hair. In the school, there are 600 students. How many would you estimate have red hair?

7. Write 720 as a product of its prime factors.

8. Find the highest common factor of 60 and 96.

9. Find the lowest common multiple (LCM) of 24 and 36.

10. James thinks of two numbers. He says 'The highest common factor (HCF) of my two numbers is 3, the lowest common multiple (LCM) of my two numbers is 45.'
    Write down two numbers that James could be thinking of.

11. Which one of the following is not a rational number? Explain your answer.

    (i) $3\frac{1}{7}$ **(ii)** 3·142 **(iii)** $\frac{22}{7}$ **(iv)** π

12. Arrange the following in order from smallest to largest.

    (i) $\sqrt{2}$ **(ii)** $\frac{2}{3}$ **(iii)** 1·6 **(iv)** $(1{\cdot}19)^2$

Revision and Exam Style Questions – Section B

More challenging problems

1. The Venn diagram represents the sets $\mathbb{N}$, $\mathbb{Z}$, $\mathbb{Q}$ and $\mathbb{R}$. Copy the diagram and insert each of the following numbers into the correct region of the diagram:

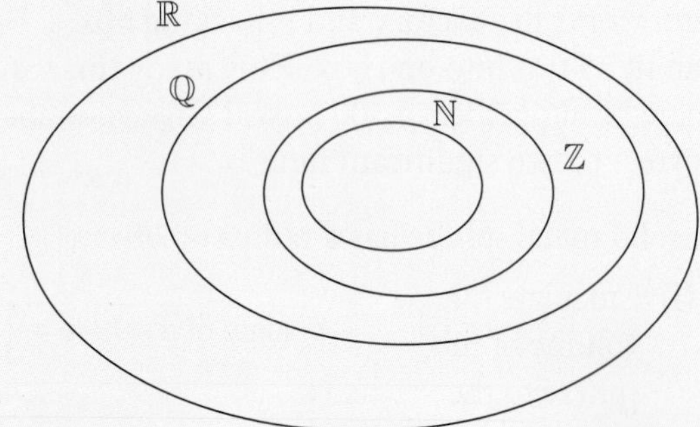

   (i) -3 **(iv)** $\sqrt{2}$ **(vii)** 0

   (ii) $\frac{3}{4}$ **(v)** $\sqrt{81}$ **(viii)** e

   (iii) $-6{\cdot}5$ **(vi)** 10·24

2. $n - 1$ is a natural number, for $n > 1$.

   (i) Write down the next three natural numbers in terms of n.

   (ii) Hence, or otherwise, show that the sum of any three consecutive natural numbers is divisible by three.

3. n is a natural number.

   (i) Write down the next three natural numbers, in terms of n.

   (ii) Hence, or otherwise, investigate whether the following is true or false:

   'The sum of four consecutive natural numbers is never divisible by four.'

4. Express $(4\sqrt{5} - 1)(\sqrt{5} + 3)$ in the form $p + q\sqrt{5}$, where p and q are integers.

5. At the beginning of every six-hour period, a patient is given 5 ml of a particular drug. During each of these six-hour periods, the patient's body partially breaks down the drug. Only $\frac{1}{3}$ of the total amount of the drug present in the patient's body at the beginning of each six-hour period remains at the end of that period.
   (i) How much of the drug is in the patient's body immediately after the second dose is given?
   (ii) Show that the total amount of the drug in the patient's body never exceeds 10 ml in the first day of treatment.

6. Find integers a and b such that $\frac{1}{\sqrt{5}-2} = a + b\sqrt{5}$.

7. The set $A = \left\{-8, \pi, \frac{1}{3}, -4{\cdot}5, \sqrt{3}\right\}$
   X = {integers}   Y = {irrational numbers}
   Z = {natural numbers}
   List the elements of:
   (i) $A \cap X$ (ii) $A \cap Y$ and (iii) $A \cap Z$

8. A right-angled triangle has a base length $4 + \sqrt{2}$ and a perpendicular height $4 - \sqrt{2}$ as shown in the diagram.
   Show that the total length of the three sides of the triangle is a natural number.

Use Pythagoras' Theorem

$4 - \sqrt{2}$

$4 + \sqrt{2}$

9. Two cyclists are cycling on a circular path. The first cyclist completes a lap in 12 minutes and the second cyclist completes it in 18 minutes. If they both started at the same place and at the same time and both go in the same direction, after how many minutes will they meet again at the starting point?

10. Ben exercises every six days and Isabel every eight days. Ben and Isabel both exercised today. How many days will it be until they exercise together again?

Now that you have completed the chapter, revisit the 'Something to think about…' question.

CHAPTER 02 Algebra I – Expressions

Sections covered within this chapter:

KEY WORDS

- Expression
- Expand
- Variable
- Factorising
- Constant
- Square number
- Coefficient

SOMETHING TO THINK ABOUT... 

The length of a rectangular swimming pool is $(x + 35)$. If the area of the swimming pool is $x^2 + 40x + 175$, find the width of the swimming pool, in terms of x.

Introduction

Algebra is a branch of maths that substitutes letters for numbers. It is about dealing with symbols and the rules for manipulating those symbols. It is also about finding the unknown or putting real-life problems into equations and then solving them.

Before we can solve equations, we must be able to work with algebraic expressions. The skills for working with algebraic expressions are covered in this chapter.

Section 2.1: Simplifying Expressions

Learning Outcomes:

You should be able to:

- simplify algebraic expressions by adding and subtracting like terms
- simplify algebraic expressions by expanding brackets

An **expression** consists of constants and variables, separated by mathematical operators. For example, $3x + 4 - x + 7$

In an expression, a letter, for example x, is called a **variable**. This is because its value can vary from one expression to the next. Think of it as an empty container that can be filled with any value.

In an expression, a number with no variable attached is called a **constant**. This is because its value remains the same in every expression.

In an expression, the number in front of a variable is called the **coefficient** of that variable.

To simplify an expression, follow these steps:

Step 1: Multiply out brackets, if there are any

Step 2: Identify like terms

Step 3: Simplify the expression, by adding or subtracting like terms

EXAMPLE 1

Simplify $7p - 6q + 8p - 2q - 2p$

Solution

$7p - 6q + 8p - 2q - 2p$

There are no brackets, so we skip step 1:

Step 2: $7p - 6q + 8p - 2q - 2p$ (identify like terms)

Step 3: $13p - 8q$ (simplify the terms)

EXAMPLE 2

Simplify $2a^2 - 3a + 4 - 4a + 5a^2 - 1$

Solution

$2a^2 - 3a + 4 - 4a + 5a^2 - 1$

There are no brackets, so we skip step 1:

Step 2: $2a^2 - 3a + 4 - 4a + 5a^2 - 1$ (identify like terms)

Step 3: $7a^2 - 7a + 3$ (simplify the terms)

a^2 and a are different variables.

EXAMPLE 3

Expand and simplify $7(p + 4) - (3p - 2)$

Expand means to multiply out brackets.

Solution

$7(p + 4) - (3p - 2)$

Step 1: $7(p + 4) - 1(3p - 2)$ (a negative sign in front of the bracket means to multiply the bracket by -1)

Step 2: $7p + 28 - 3p + 2$ (identify like terms)

Step 3: $4p + 30$ (simplify the terms)

Algebra I

EXAMPLE 4

Expand and simplify $(x-3)(4x-5)$

Solution

	$(x-3)(4x-5)$	(separate out the first bracket and multiply each part by the second bracket, using the distributive law)
Step 1:	$x(4x-5)-3(4x-5)$	(multiply out the brackets)
Step 2:	$4x^2-5x-12x+15$	(identify like terms)
Step 3:	$4x^2-17x+15$	(simplify each variable)

Links across the syllabus

The distributive law is covered in Chapter 1: Number Systems.

Alternative Method – Grid Method

	x	-3
$4x$	$4x^2$	$-12x$
-5	$-5x$	15

Listing the elements in the grid:

$4x^2-5x-12x+15$

$4x^2-17x+15$ (simplify the terms)

Practice Questions 2.1

1. Simplify each of the following expressions:
   - **(i)** $3x+5x-2x$
   - **(ii)** $-4y+8y-y$
   - **(iii)** $12+4n+5-2n-8$
   - **(iv)** $8a-2b+4a+3b-2a$
   - **(v)** $10x+2+6x-3+5x$
   - **(vi)** $8c-\mathrm{b}+4a-a+5b-3c$
2. Simplify each of the following expressions:
   - **(i)** $9p^2+3p-2p^2-7p$
   - **(ii)** $13y-3y^2+5y+4y^2-9y$
   - **(iii)** $5x^2+3-2x+3x^2+7x-5$
   - **(iv)** $-2a+4a^2+6-a^2+8a-5$
   - **(v)** $12+8p-4p^2-3p-5+p^2$
   - **(vi)** $7x^2-9x+13+5x-2x^2-6$
3. Expand the following brackets and simplify:
   - **(i)** $(2x)(4x)+3(4y)-5y$
   - **(ii)** $4(3p+1)-2(p-2)$
   - **(iii)** $7(k-1)-3(4k-1)$
   - **(iv)** $3x(x-2)+5(2x+3)$
   - **(v)** $3(2a-2)+4a(3a-1)+7$
   - **(vi)** $6a(2x+3)+7-(4a-4)$
   - **(vii)** $7x(3x-2)-14x+3(3x+2)$
   - **(viii)** $-4p(3p+1)+6-(7-8p)$
4. Expand the following brackets and simplify:
   - **(i)** $(x+1)(3x-2)$
   - **(ii)** $(p+5)(4p-3)$
   - **(iii)** $(2x-4)(3x+2)$
   - **(iv)** $(3k-4)(5k-1)$
   - **(v)** $(5x-2)(x+1)-(x^2+3x+4)$
   - **(vi)** $(2p^2-4p+6)+(3-p)(p+4)$
5. Expand the following brackets and simplify:
   - **(i)** $(x-5)^2$
   - **(ii)** $(3p+2)^2$
   - **(iii)** $(4a-2)^2$
   - **(iv)** $(3-7k)^2$
6. Simplify the following:
   - **(i)** $(x+3)(x+4)$
   - **(ii)** $3a-4+5+2a+4$
   - **(iii)** $4(2k+5)-k(2k+6)-3$
   - **(iv)** $(a+5)(a-1)$
   - **(v)** $3(2a-2)-5+4a(3a-1)$
   - **(vi)** $5(x+3)+2(4x-1)$
   - **(vii)** $-6p+2q-p+4r-4q+2r$
   - **(viii)** $(x-3)(x+3)$
   - **(ix)** $(y-2)^2$
   - **(x)** $3x^2+2x-(x+3)^2$
7. Find the sum of $(2x-1)$ and $(x+5)$

8. Find the product of $(p + 7)$ and $(3p - 2)$

To find the product means to multiply.

9. If the length of a rectangle is $(4x + 5)$ and its width is 7
   (i) find the area of the rectangle, in terms of x
   (ii) find the perimeter of the rectangle, in terms of x.

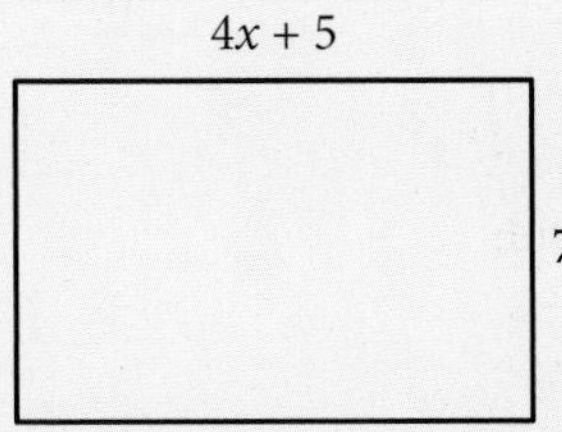

10. If the length of a rectangle is $(2a - 1)$ and its width is $(5 - a)$
   (i) find the area of the rectangle, in terms of a
   (ii) find the perimeter of the rectangle, in terms of a.

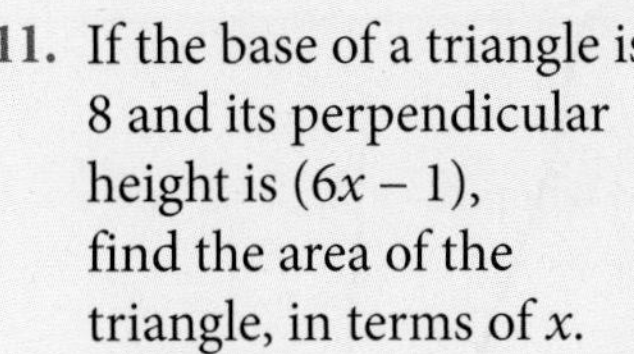

11. If the base of a triangle is 8 and its perpendicular height is $(6x - 1)$, find the area of the triangle, in terms of x.

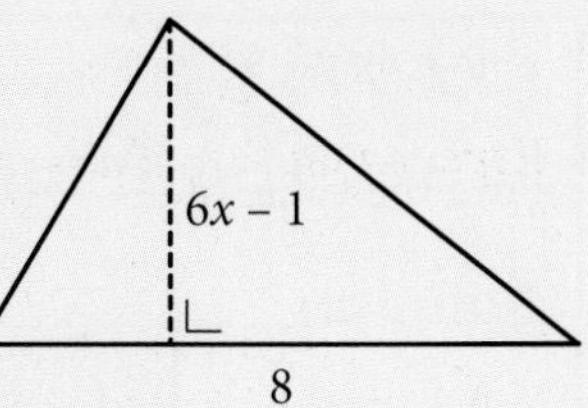

12. Find the area of a circle of radius $(3k - 2)$. Give your answer in terms of k and π.

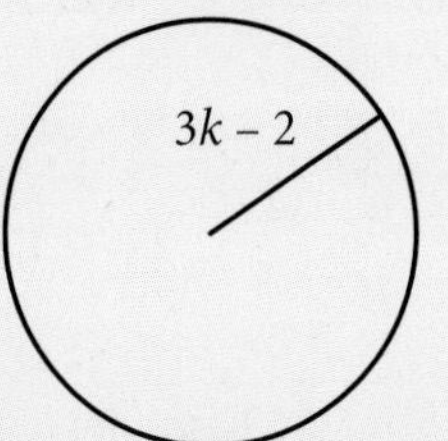

Links across the syllabus

Area of shapes is covered in Chapter 16: Area and Perimeter.

Section 2.2: Evaluating Expressions

Learning Outcome:

You should be able to:

- evaluate expressions when given the values of the variables

Evaluating an expression means finding the value of the expression when given the value of the variables.

To evaluate expressions, replace (or substitute) the variable or variables with the values given and work out the answer.

Links across the syllabus

Substituting values into formulae is an essential skill for you to have throughout your maths course.

EXAMPLE 1

Find the value of $3(p^2 - 5pq)$ when $p = 4$ and $q = -1$

Solution

$3(p^2 - 5pq)$

$3((4)^2 - 5(4)(-1))$ (let $p = 4$ and $q = -1$)

$3(16 - 5(-4))$

$3(16 + 20)$

$3(36)$

108

Always put the values into brackets and then simplify.

EXAMPLE 2

Find the value of $\left(\frac{7ab - b^2}{a^c}\right)$ when $a = -2$, $b = 3$ and $c = 6$

Solution

$\frac{7ab - b^2}{a^c}$

$\frac{7(-2)(3) - (3)^2}{(-2)^6}$ (let $a = -2$, $b = 3$ and $c = 6$)

$\frac{7(-6) - 9}{64}$

$\frac{-42 - 9}{64}$

$-\frac{51}{64}$

If using a calculator to find the value of $(-2)^6$, make sure to use brackets.

Practice Questions 2.2

1. Evaluate each of the following expressions given that $x = 4$, $y = -2$ and $z = 3$
   - (i) $x - z$
   - (ii) $3x + z$
   - (iii) $2x - y + 3z$
   - (iv) $2(x + y)$
   - (v) xz
   - (vi) $x^2 - 2y$
2. Evaluate each of the following expressions given that $a = 2$, $b = -1$, $c = 5$, $x = -2$, $y = -3$ and $z = 4$
   - (i) abx
   - (ii) $6c - b$
   - (iii) $\frac{a^2 + c}{3}$
   - (iv) $x^2 + 2b^2$
   - (v) $\frac{xy + a}{z}$
   - (vi) $(az - bc)^2$
   - (vii) $\frac{yz}{a} + c$
   - (viii) $\sqrt{ac + xy}$
   - (ix) $\frac{c^3 - 11z}{y^2}$
3. Evaluate each of the following expressions given that $p = \frac{2}{3}$, $q = -\frac{1}{2}$ and $r = -3$
   - (i) pr
   - (ii) $6pq$
   - (iii) $p + q - r$
   - (iv) $9p + 2r$
   - (v) q^2
   - (vi) pqr
4. Given $a = b + \frac{1}{c}$, find the value of a when $b = 3$ and $c = 5$.
5. Given $x = 4\left(\frac{v}{u}\right) - w$, find the value of x when $u = 8$, $v = 5$ and $w = -7$.
6. The area of a circle is given by the formula $A = \pi r^2$. Find the value of A when $\pi = 3{\cdot}14$ and $r = 5$.
7. The volume of a cylinder is given by the formula $V = \pi r^2 h$.
   Find the value of V when $\pi = \frac{22}{7}$, $r = 3$ and $h = 14$.
8. The volume of a sphere is given by the formula $V = \frac{4}{3}\pi r^3$.
   Find the value of V when $\pi = 3{\cdot}14$ and $r = 6$.
9. Pythagoras' Theorem is commonly used in Trigonometry.
   Its formula states that $c^2 = a^2 + b^2$.
   Find the value of c when $a = 12$ and $b = 5$.
10. The periodic time of a pendulum is calculated by using the following formula:

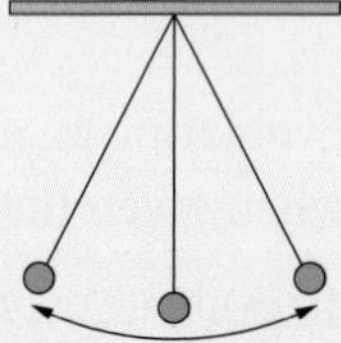

$$T = 2\pi\sqrt{\frac{l}{g}}$$

Where:
T = periodic time (time for the pendulum to swing over and back once)
l = length of the pendulum, in metres
g = acceleration due to gravity.

Find the periodic time of a pendulum, of length 82 cm, given that $g = 9{\cdot}8$ m/s^2.
Give your answer to one decimal place.

Section 2.3: Simplifying Algebraic Fractions

Learning Outcome:

You should be able to:

- simplify algebraic fractions, and express them as a single fraction

The method for adding or subtracting fractions is the same for simplifying numerical fractions or algebraic fractions.

Step 1: Find the lowest common multiple of the denominators.

Step 2: Divide each denominator into the LCM and multiply the top (numerator) by the result.

Step 3: Multiply out the brackets.

Step 4: Simplify the numerator.

Adding fractions is covered in Chapter 1: Number Systems.

EXAMPLE 1

Express as a single fraction $\frac{x}{2} - \frac{5x-2}{3}$ and verify your answer for $x = 4$.

Solution

Step 1: $\frac{x}{2} - \frac{5x-2}{3}$ (the LCM of 3 and 2 is 6)

Step 2: $\frac{3(x) - 2(5x-2)}{6}$ (divide each denominator into 6 and multiply the top by the result)

Step 3: $\frac{3x - 10x + 4}{6}$ (multiply out the brackets)

Step 4: $\frac{-7x + 4}{6}$ (simplify the numerator)

Verify $x = 4$:

Original expression:	Single fraction:
$\frac{x}{2} - \frac{5x-2}{3}$	$\frac{-7x+4}{6}$
$\frac{(4)}{2} - \frac{5(4)-2}{3}$	$\frac{-7(4)+4}{6}$
$\frac{4}{2} - \frac{20-2}{3}$	$\frac{-28+4}{6}$
$2 - \frac{18}{3}$	$\frac{-24}{6}$
$2 - 6$	-4
-4	

When we substitute $x = 4$ into the original expression and the simplified expression we get -4 in each case.

Therefore, we have verified that the original expression and the simplified expression are the same.

EXAMPLE 2

Express as a single fraction $\frac{4}{p+2} - \frac{1}{3p-4}$

Solution

Step 1: $\frac{4}{p+2} - \frac{1}{3p-4}$ (the LCM of $(p + 2)$ and $(3p - 4)$ is their product, $(p + 2)(3p - 4)$)

$\frac{4(\ ?\ ) - 1(\ ?\ )}{(p+2)(3p-4)}$

Step 2: Divide $(p + 2)$ into $(p + 2)(3p - 4)$ to get $(3p - 4)$, as shown: $\frac{\cancel{(p+2)}(3p-4)}{\cancel{(p+2)}} = (3p-4)$

Now, multiply the 4, on top of the first fraction, by $(3p - 4)$

$$\frac{4(3p-4) - 1(\ ?\ )}{(p+2)(3p-4)}$$

Divide $(3p - 4)$ into $(p + 2)(3p - 4)$ to get $(p + 2)$, as shown: $\frac{(p+2)\cancel{(3p-4)}}{\cancel{(3p-4)}} = (p+2)$

Now, multiply the -1, on top of the second fraction, by $(p + 2)$ $\quad \frac{4(3p-4) - 1(p+2)}{(p+2)(3p-4)}$

Step 3: $\frac{4(3p-4) - 1(p+2)}{(p+2)(3p-4)}$

$\frac{12p - 16 - p - 2}{(p+2)(3p-4)}$ (multiply out the brackets, on the numerator)

You are not expected to expand the brackets in the denominator.

Step 4: $\frac{11p - 18}{(p+2)(3p-4)}$ (simplify the numerator)

Practice Questions 2.3

1. Express the following as a single fraction:

(i) $\frac{x}{4} + \frac{2x}{3}$ (iv) $\frac{4t}{7} - \frac{t+1}{5}$ (vii) $\frac{m-2}{2} - \frac{3m-4}{8}$

(ii) $\frac{3a}{5} - \frac{a}{2}$ (v) $\frac{x+1}{3} + \frac{2x}{5}$ (viii) $\frac{k+4}{4} - \frac{k-1}{6}$

(iii) $\frac{4x}{3} + \frac{5x}{2}$ (vi) $\frac{3x}{2} - \frac{x-4}{6}$ (ix) $\frac{3x+2}{8} - \frac{x-5}{6}$

2. Express the following as a single fraction:

(i) $\frac{5}{x} + \frac{4}{3}$ (iv) $\frac{2}{k+1} - \frac{1}{6}$ (vii) $\frac{5}{2x} + \frac{4}{x}$

(ii) $\frac{1}{4} - \frac{3}{2a}$ (v) $\frac{3}{7} + \frac{5}{m+2}$ (viii) $\frac{3}{k} + \frac{4}{5k}$

(iii) $\frac{2}{3p} + \frac{4}{6}$ (vi) $\frac{2}{3} - \frac{4}{x+5}$ (ix) $\frac{7}{3x} - \frac{1}{2x}$

3. Show that $\frac{3}{x} + \frac{2}{x+4}$ simplifies to $\frac{5x+12}{x(x+4)}$

4. Show that $\frac{5}{k+2} - \frac{1}{k}$ simplifies to $\frac{4k-2}{k(k+2)}$

5. Express the following as a single fraction:

(i) $\frac{3}{x} + \frac{2}{x-1}$ (ii) $\frac{1}{2k+5} - \frac{4}{k}$ (iii) $\frac{1}{2m} + \frac{5}{m+3}$

6. Show that $\frac{2}{x+1} + \frac{1}{x+2}$ simplifies to $\frac{3x+5}{(x+1)(x+2)}$

7. Show that $\frac{8}{m+1} - \frac{5}{m-4}$ simplifies to $\frac{3m-37}{(m+1)(m-4)}$

8. Express the following as a single fraction:

(i) $\frac{3}{x+1} + \frac{4}{x+2}$ (iii) $\frac{3}{m-2} - \frac{5}{m+1}$ (v) $\frac{2}{4k-1} + \frac{5}{2k+1}$

(ii) $\frac{2}{x+4} - \frac{1}{x+3}$ (iv) $\frac{7}{3a+1} - \frac{9}{a-2}$ (vi) $\frac{2}{3x+4} + \frac{1}{x+3}$

9. Express $\frac{8}{x+3} - \frac{4}{2x-3}$ as a single fraction and verify your answer for $x = 1$.

10. Express $\frac{2}{3x-1} + \frac{3}{5x+5}$ as a single fraction and verify your answer for $x = 2$.

Section 2.4: Rearranging Formulae

Learning Outcome:

You should be able to:

- rearrange a formula to make a given variable the subject of the formula

The ability to rearrange formulae or rewrite them in different ways is an important skill in mathematics. If given a formula such as the one for the area of a rectangle, $A = (L)(W)$, A is written in terms of L and W.

We say that A is the **subject of the formula**. The subject of a formula is usually on its own on the left-hand side of the formula. Changing the subject of a formula means to rearrange the formula so that a different letter is on its own and hence it becomes the subject of the formula.

For example, $L = \frac{A}{W}$, is writing L in terms of A and W.

Rearranging a formula follows the same procedure as solving an equation. **Whatever operation you perform to one side, you must do to the other side.**

EXAMPLE 1

Make x the subject of the formula $z + 5x = y$

Solution

$z + 5x = y$

$z + 5x - z = y - z$ (subtract z from both sides)

$5x = y - z$ (simplify)

$\frac{5x}{5} = \frac{y-z}{5}$ (divide both sides by 5)

$x = \frac{y-z}{5}$ (simplify)

EXAMPLE 2

Make b the subject of the formula $p(x + b^2) = c$

Solution

$p(x + b^2) = c$ (multiply out brackets first, when present)

$px + pb^2 = c$

$px + pb^2 - px = c - px$ (subtract px from both sides)

$pb^2 = c - px$ (simplify)

$\frac{pb^2}{p} = \frac{c - px}{p}$ (divide both sides by p)

$b^2 = \frac{c - px}{p}$ (simplify)

$b = \sqrt{\frac{c - px}{p}}$ (square root both sides)

EXAMPLE 3

Express q in terms of p and r, where $\frac{1}{p} = r + \frac{1}{q}$

Solution

Eliminate fractions at the start, by multiplying all parts by the lowest common multiple of the denominators.

$\frac{1}{p} = \frac{r}{1} + \frac{1}{q}$ (denominator of r is 1)

$pq\left(\frac{1}{p}\right) = pq\left(\frac{r}{1}\right) + pq\left(\frac{1}{q}\right)$ (multiply all parts by pq, the LCM of the denominators.)

$\frac{\cancel{p}q}{\cancel{p}} = \frac{pqr}{1} + \frac{p\cancel{q}}{\cancel{q}}$

$q = pqr + p$ (simplify)

$q - pqr = pqr + p - pqr$ (subtract pqr from both sides)

$q - pqr = p$ (simplify)

$q(1 - pr) = p$ (take q out, as a common factor on the left-hand side)

$\frac{q(1 - pr)}{(1 - pr)} = \frac{p}{(1 - pr)}$ (divide both sides by $(1 - pr)$)

$q = \frac{p}{(1 - pr)}$ (simplify)

Recall factorising from Junior Certificate.

It is also covered later in this chapter.

Practice Questions 2.4

1. Rearrange the following formulae to make the letter in brackets the subject of the formula:

(i) $a = b + c$ (b) **(iii)** $pq - r = 4r$ (q) **(v)** $u = x^2 - wr$ (w)

(ii) $y = 3x + 5$ (x) **(iv)** $y = mx + c$ (m) **(vi)** $c = abc + a^2$ (b)

2. Rearrange the following formulae to make the letter in brackets the subject of the formula:

(i) $a + 2 = xy^2$ (y) **(iii)** $a = c + 5b^2$ (b) **(v)** $x = (r - 2)^3$ (r)

(ii) $s = r^2 + t$ (r) **(iv)** $a = (b + c)^2$ (c) **(vi)** $t = (2s + c)^4$ (s)

3. Rearrange the following formulae to make the letter in brackets the subject of the formula:

(i) $x = \sqrt{y - 4}$ (y) (iv) $3x = \sqrt{yz}$ (y)

(ii) $p = \sqrt{r + 3}$ (r) (v) $p = \sqrt{4q} - r$ (q)

(iii) $a = \sqrt{2b + 5}$ (b) (vi) $a = b - \sqrt{c}$ (c)

4. Rearrange the following formulae to make the letter in brackets the subject of the formula:

(i) $b = \frac{a + 5}{3}$ (a) (iv) $s = \frac{2t + 5}{t}$ (t)

(ii) $p = \frac{q - r}{5}$ (q) (v) $4p = \frac{3q - r}{q + 2}$ (q)

(iii) $4a = \frac{3b - c}{6}$ (c) (vi) $5a = \frac{b + 3c}{c - 1}$ (c)

5. Rearrange the following formulae to make the letter in brackets the subject of the formula:

(i) $2p = \frac{3}{q} + 4r$ (r) (iii) $\frac{4}{x} = 2y - \frac{3}{z}$ (z)

(ii) $b = \frac{2}{a} + \frac{1}{c}$ (c) (iv) $\frac{4}{p} = \frac{5}{q} - \frac{3}{r}$ (q)

---

6. The formula for the volume of a cylinder is $V = \pi r^2 h$, where r is the radius and h is the height. Rearrange this formula to make the radius the subject of the formula.

7. (i) Rearrange $(2x + 3)y = 6 - x$ to make x the subject of the formula.

   (ii) Hence, find the value of x when $y = 4$.

8. (i) Rearrange the formula $v = u + at$ to express a in terms of u, v and t.

   (ii) Hence, find the value of a when $v = 36$, $u = 12$ and $t = 4$.

9. The formula for the volume of a sphere is $V = \frac{4}{3}\pi r^3$, where r is the radius.

   (i) Rearrange the formula to make the radius the subject of the formula.

   (ii) Hence, find the radius when the volume of the sphere is 288π cm^3.

10. To convert degrees Celsius to degrees Fahrenheit we use the formula: $F = \frac{9}{5}C + 32°$

   (i) Convert 10°C into degrees Fahrenheit.

   (ii) Rearrange the formula to express C in terms of F.

   (iii) Hence, convert 104°F into degrees Celsius.

11. (i) Given $v = \sqrt{t^2 - 5}$, find the value of v when $t = 8$. Give your answer to one decimal place.

   (ii) Rearrange the formula to make t the subject of the formula.

   (iii) Hence, find the value of t when $v = 12$. Give your answer to one decimal place.

12. (i) Rearrange the formula $E = mc^2$ to make c the subject of the formula.

   (ii) Hence, find the value of c when $E = 900{,}000$ and $m = 0{\cdot}001$.

13. (i) Rearrange the formula $2s = 2ut + at^2$ to make u the subject of the formula.

   (ii) Hence, find the value of u when $s = 200$, $t = 5$ and $a = 10$.

Section 2.5: Factorising

Learning Outcome:

You should be able to:

- factorise expressions

Factorising means finding two (or more) expressions, which multiply out to give the original expression. These expressions are known as the factors of the original expression.

- Expanding brackets or simplifying means to start with an expression such as $5(x + 4)$ and end up with $5x + 20$.
- Factorising means to start with an expression such as $5x + 20$ and end up with $5(x + 4)$.

There are four methods for factorising. The elements given within an expression will determine which method you use. You will need to look very carefully at the given expression and decide which method of factorisation will work best.

1. Take out the highest common factor

If a number or a variable is common to all parts of an expression, we can factorise the expression by taking out the highest common factors (HCF).

Step 1: Find the highest common factor (HCF) of all the terms in the expression. This is the biggest value (constants and/or variables) which divides into all terms evenly.

Step 2: Put the HCF outside the brackets.

Step 3: Divide each term by the HCF to find the factor inside the brackets.

EXAMPLE 1

Factorise the following

(i) $5xy + 15xz$ **(ii)** $6p^2 - 8pq + 2p$

Solution

(i) $5xy + 15xz$

Step 1: The HCF of $(5xy + 15xz)$ is $5x$.

Step 2: $5x(? + ?)$ (put the HCF outside the brackets)

Step 3: $5x(y + 3z)$ (divide each term by the HCF to find the factor inside the brackets.)

Check your factors by multiplying out the brackets.

$5x(y + 3z)$

$= 5xy + 15xz$

Using the grid method:

	y	$3z$
$5x$	$5xy$	$15xz$

It is good practice to check your factors are correct, as shown.

Algebra I

(ii) $6p^2 - 8pq + 2p$

$6pp - 8pq + 2p \qquad (p^2 = pp)$

Step 1: The HCF $(6p^2 - 8pq + 2p)$ is $2p$.

Step 2: $2p(? + ? + ?)$ (put the HCF outside the brackets)

Step 3: $2p(3p - 4q + 1)$ (divide each term by the HCF to find the factor inside the brackets)

Check your factors by multiplying out the brackets.

$2p(3p - 4q + 1)$

$= 6p^2 - 8pq + 2p$

Using the grid method:

	$3p$	$-4q$	1
$2p$	$6p^2$	$-8pq$	$2p$

2. Grouping

Use this method when you have four terms, with no common factor.

Step 1: Group into pairs with a common factor.

Step 2: Take out the highest common factor (HCF) in each pair separately.

Step 3: Take out the new common factor.

EXAMPLE 2

Factorise the following **(i)** $6a + 3b + 2ac + bc$ **(ii)** $2mx + 7 - 7x - 2m$

Solution

(i) $6a + 3b + 2ac + bc$ is already grouped into pairs with a common factor, so we start at step 2.

Step 2: $3(2a + b) + c(2a + b)$ (3 is common to the first two parts and c is common to the second two parts)

We can see that $(2a + b)$ is common to both parts, so we factorise it out now:

Step 3: $(2a + b)(3 + c)$

Check your factors by multiplying out the brackets.

$(2a + b)(3 + c)$

$= 2a(3 + c) + b(3 + c)$

$= 6a + 2ac + 3b + bc$

$= 6a + 3b + 2ac + bc$

Using the grid method:

	$2a$	b
3	$6a$	$3b$
c	$2ac$	bc

(ii) $2mx + 7 - 7x - 2m$

Step 1: $2mx - 2m - 7x + 7$ (rearrange the expression so that each pair has common factors)

Step 2: $2m(x - 1) - 7(x - 1)$ ($2m$ is common to the first two parts and -7 is common to the second two parts)

We can see that $(x - 1)$ is common to both parts, so we factorise it out now:

Step 3: $(x - 1)(2m - 7)$

Check your factors by multiplying out the brackets.

$(x - 1)(2m - 7)$

$= x(2m - 7) - 1(2m - 7)$

$= 2mx - 7x - 2m + 7$

$= 2mx + 7 - 7x - 2m$

Using the grid method:

	x	-1
$2m$	$2mx$	$-2m$
-7	$-7x$	7

3. Difference of two squares

A **square number** is a value which has been obtained by multiplying a number by itself.

It is important that you can quickly recognise if a number is a square number. The main square numbers, which we will deal with, are shown in the note on the right.

When two expressions are subtracted, we are said to find their 'difference'.

Thus, the 'difference of two squares' is an expression in the form

$$(\text{1st term})^2 - (\text{2nd term})^2$$

This can be factorised as: (1st term + 2nd term)(1st term − 2nd term)

Step 1: Write the expression in the form $(a)^2 - (b)^2$

Step 2: Factorise as: $(a + b)(a - b)$

Make sure that you are familiar with the following squares:

$1^2 = 1$	$7^2 = 49$
$2^2 = 4$	$8^2 = 64$
$3^2 = 9$	$9^2 = 81$
$4^2 = 16$	$10^2 = 100$
$5^2 = 25$	$11^2 = 121$
$6^2 = 36$	$12^2 = 144$

EXAMPLE 3

Factorise the following **(i)** $x^2 - 9$ **(ii)** $4a^2 - 25b^2$

Solution

(i) $x^2 - 9$

Step 1: $(x)^2 - (3)^2$ (rewrite the expression as the difference of two squares)

Step 2: $(x + 3)(x - 3)$ (factorise)

Check your factors by multiplying out the brackets.

$(x + 3)(x - 3)$

$= x(x - 3) + 3(x - 3)$

$= x^2 - 3x + 3x - 9$

$= x^2 - 9$

Using the grid method:

	x	3
x	x^2	$3x$
-3	$-3x$	-9

(ii) $4a^2 - 25b^2$

Step 1: $(2a)^2 - (5b)^2$ (rewrite the expression as the difference of two squares)

Step 2: $(2a + 5b)(2a - 5b)$ (factorise)

Check your factors by multiplying out the brackets.

$(2a + 5b)(2a - 5b)$

$= 2a(2a - 5b) + 5b(2a - 5b)$

$= 4a^2 - 10ab + 10ab - 25b^2$

$= 4a^2 - 25b^2$

Using the grid method:

	$2a$	$5b$
$2a$	$4a^2$	$10ab$
$-5b$	$-10ab$	$-25b^2$

4. Quadratic trinomials

An expression in the form $ax^2 + bx + c$, where a, b and c are constants, is called a quadratic trinomial. This is because the highest power of x, in the expression, is 2 (quadratic) and it contains three terms (trinomial).

For factorising, quadratic trinomials can be broken into two types:

1. **Final term is positive**

   When the final term is positive, the signs inside the middle of the brackets will be the **same**, either two pluses or two minuses. Keep the sign of the middle term given in the question.

2. **Final term is negative**

   When the final term is negative, the signs inside the middle of the brackets will be **different**.

EXAMPLE 4

Factorise $x^2 + 7x + 12$

Solution

Method 1: Using the guide number

$1x^2 + 7x + 12$

Step 1: Multiply the coefficient of x^2 by the constant: $1 \times 12 = 12$. This is the guide number. Because it is **positive**, we know that both signs will be the **same**.

Step 2: We need factors of +12 which add to give +7.

We take each pair of factors of +12 and find their sum, until they result in +7.

From the table, we see that the factors which fit this criteria are 3 and 4.

Multiply to give +12	Add to give +7	
$1 \times 12 = 12$	$1 + 12 = 13$	×
$2 \times 6 = 12$	$2 + 6 = 8$	×
$3 \times 4 = 12$	$3 + 4 = 7$	✓

Step 3: Rewrite the trinomial, replacing $7x$ with $3x$ and $4x$.

$1x^2 + 7x + 12$

$1x^2 + 3x + 4x + 12$

Step 4: Factorise by grouping: $1x^2 + 3x + 4x + 12$

$x(x + 3) + 4(x + 3)$

$(x + 3)(x + 4)$

Method 2: Trial and improvement

$x^2 + 7x + 12$ (final term is **positive**, so the signs in the brackets are the **same**)

We need factors of +12 which add to give +7.

$(x + 3)(x + 4)$ (use trial and improvement to find the correct factors)

Check: outside terms $= (x)(4) = 4x$

inside terms $= (3)(x) = \underline{3x}$

sum $= 7x$ = middle term of original quadratic trinomial

Therefore, factors $(x + 3)(x + 4)$ are correct.

outside terms

$(x + 3)\ (x + 4)$

inside terms

Check your factors by multiplying out the brackets.

$(x + 3)(x + 4)$

$= x(x + 4) + 3(x + 4)$

$= x^2 + 4x + 3x + 12$

$= x^2 + 7x + 12$

Using the grid method:

	x	3
x	x^2	$3x$
4	$4x$	12

EXAMPLE 5

Factorise $4a^2 + 4a - 15$

Solution

Method 1: Using the guide number

$4a^2 + 4a - 15$

Step 1: Multiply the coefficient of a^2 by the constant $4 \times -15 = -60$

This is the guide number; it tells you that the signs are **different**.

Step 2: We need factors of -60 which add to give $+4$

We take each pair of factors of -60 and find their sum, until they result in $+4$.

From the table, we see that the factors which fit this criteria are -6 and $+10$.

Multiply to give −60	Add to give +4	
$1 \times -60 = -60$	$1 - 60 = -59$	✗
$2 \times -30 = -60$	$2 - 30 = -28$	✗
$3 \times -20 = -60$	$3 - 20 = -17$	✗
$4 \times -15 = -60$	$4 - 15 = -11$	✗
$6 \times -10 = -60$	$6 - 10 = -4$	✗
$-6 \times 10 = -60$	$-6 + 10 = 4$	✓

Step 3: Rewrite the trinomial, replacing $4a$ with $-6a$ and $+10a$

$4a^2 + 4a - 15$

$4a^2 - 6a + 10a - 15$

Step 4: Factorise by grouping: $4a^2 - 6a + 10a - 15$

$2a(2a - 3) + 5(2a - 3)$

$(2a - 3)(2a + 5)$

Method 2: Trial and improvement

$4a^2 + 4a - 15$ (final term is **negative**, so the signs in the brackets are **different**)

We need factors of -15 which add to give $+4$.

$(2a - 3)(2a + 5)$ (use trial and improvement to find the correct factors)

Check: outside terms = $(2a)(5) = +10a$

inside terms = $(-3)(2a) = \underline{-6a}$

sum = $+4a$ = middle term of original quadratic trinomial

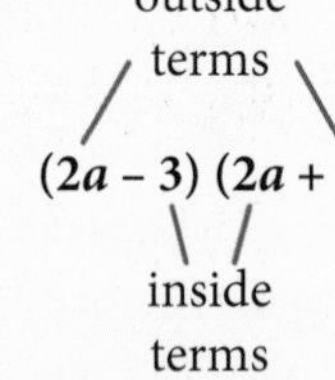

Therefore, factors $(2a - 3)(2a + 5)$ are correct.

Check your factors by multiplying out the brackets.

$(2a - 3)(2a + 5)$

$= 2a(2a + 5) - 3(2a + 5)$

$= 4a^2 + 10a - 6a - 15$

$= 4a^2 + 4a - 15$

Using the grid method:

	$2a$	-3
$2a$	$4a^2$	$-6a$
5	$10a$	-15

The following flowchart can be used to help you factorise an expression.
Start at the top and work your way down the chart.

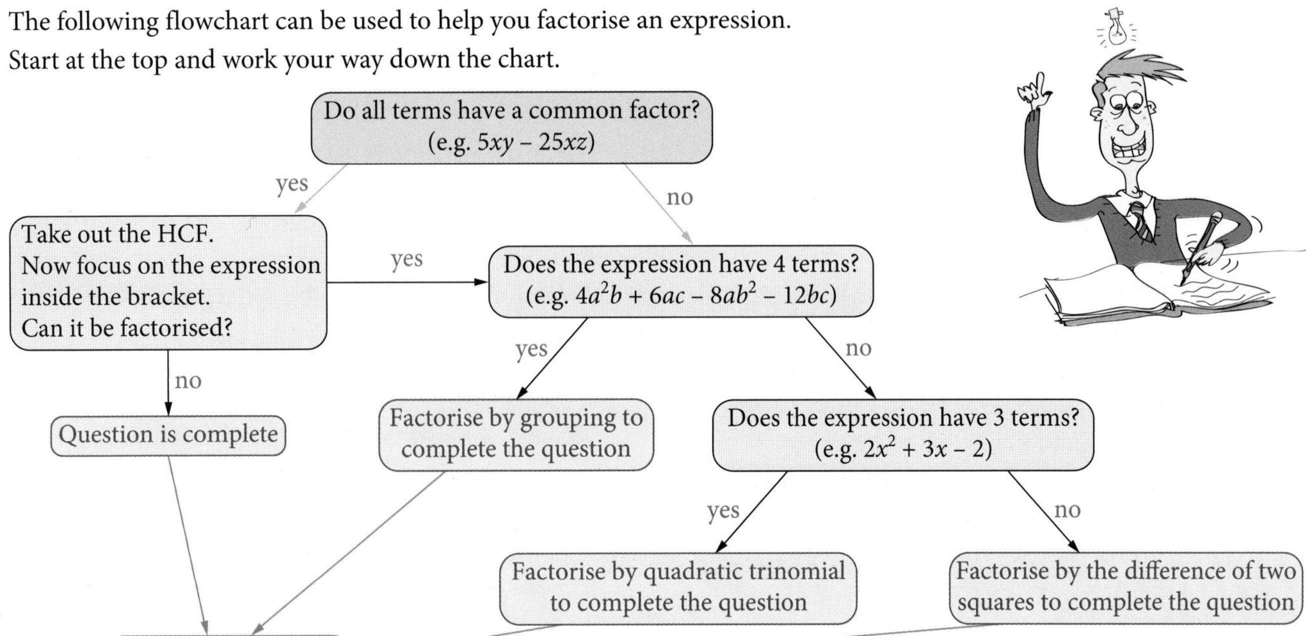

Practice Questions 2.5

1. Copy and complete the following factorisations:

   (i) $3a + ab = a(\qquad)$
   (ii) $5x^2 - 10x = 5x(\qquad)$
   (iii) $x^2 + 8x + 15 = (x + 3)(\qquad)$
   (iv) $x^2 - 16 = (x + 4)(\qquad)$
   (v) $8p^2 - 12pq = 4p(\qquad)$
   (vi) $x^2 - 7x + 10 = (x - 5)(\qquad)$
   (vii) $x^2 + 6x - 16 = (x - 2)(\qquad)$
   (viii) $9a^2 - 64b^2 = (3a + 8b)(\qquad)$
   (ix) $4x^2 + 21x + 5 = (4x + 1)(\qquad)$
   (x) $3x^2 + x - 14 = (3x + 7)(\qquad)$

2. Factorise each of the following expressions:

   (i) $15xy - 35x$
   (ii) $16x^2 + 20x$
   (iii) $ax + bx + ay + by$
   (iv) $6mt^2 - 3pt$
   (v) $14p + 21pq$
   (vi) $ms + 2mt^2 - ns - 2nt^2$
   (vii) $28xy + 25 + 35x + 20y$
   (viii) $4xy + 6 - x - 24y$

3. Factorise each of the following expressions:

   (i) $a^2 - 25$
   (ii) $36x^2 - y^2$
   (iii) $x^2 + 9x + 18$
   (iv) $m^2 + 13m + 40$
   (v) $x^2 + 7x - 18$
   (vi) $49m^2 - 64k^2$
   (vii) $k^2 - 10k + 24$
   (viii) $81 - 4a^2$
   (ix) $9k^2 - 1$

4. Factorise each of the following expressions:

   (i) $3x^2 + 10x + 8$
   (ii) $2a^2 + 11a + 12$
   (iii) $3k^2 + 14k + 8$
   (iv) $2x^2 - 17x - 30$
   (v) $2p^2 + p - 45$
   (vi) $6x^2 + 11x - 10$
   (vii) $10t^2 + 17t + 3$
   (viii) $14a^2 - 9a + 1$
   (ix) $12x^2 - 8x - 15$

5. By first taking out any common factors, express each of the following as three factors:

   (i) $2x^2 - 20x + 48$
   (ii) $3x^2 - 18x + 27$
   (iii) $2x^2 + 2x - 144$
   (iv) $12x^2 - 26x - 10$
   (v) $2x^2 + 10x - 48$
   (vi) $4x^2 - 20x - 96$

6. Factorise the following expressions:

(i) $6ax - 3bx + 2ay - by$
(ii) $3m^2 + 13m - 10$
(iii) $1 - p^2$
(iv) $x^2 - 7x - 30$
(v) $5b^2c - 10bc$
(vi) $x^2 - 4x - 77$
(vii) $16mn - 4m^2 + 28n - 7m$
(viii) $6x^2 - 13x - 5$
(ix) $24ab + 16ac$

7. The length of a rectangular picture frame is $(x + 5)$. If the area of the frame is $x^2 + 7x + 10$, find the width of the frame, in terms of x

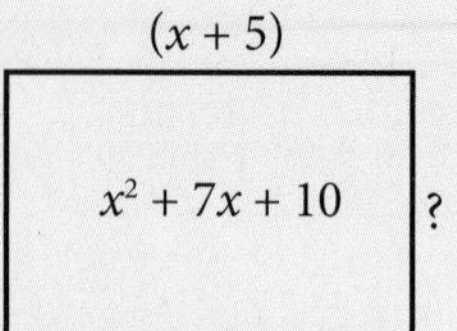

8. (i) The length of a rectangular garden is $(x + 4)$. If the area of the garden is $x^2 - 6x - 40$, find the width of the garden, in terms of x.

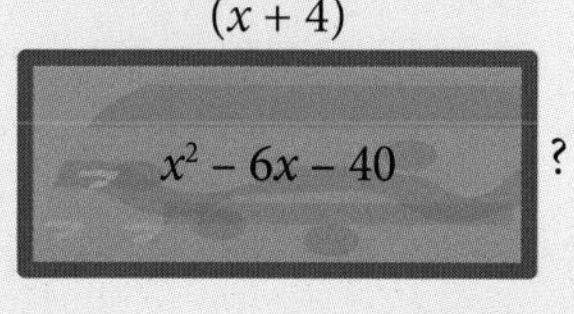

(ii) Verify your answer for $x = 12$.

9. A car travelled a distance of $(2x^2 + 11x + 15)$ m in a time of $(x + 3)$ seconds.

(i) Find the speed of the car, in terms of x.

(ii) Verify your answer for $x = 10$.

Links across the syllabus

Speed is covered in Chapter 8: Arithmetic I.

10. A body travelled a distance of $(6x^2 + 10x - 4)$ m at a speed of $(2x + 4)$ m/s.

(i) Find the time taken for the body to travel this distance, in terms of x.

(ii) Verify your answer for $x = 5$.

Revision and Exam Style Questions – Section A

1. Simplify $5(3x + 4) - (3x - 1)$
2. Factorise $8x^2 - 28xy$
3. Simplify $(5a - 4)(3 + 2a)$
4. Find the value of $4(2a - b)$ when $a = 5$ and $b = -3$
5. Express as a single fraction $\frac{x-1}{3} + \frac{2x}{5}$
6. Factorise $p^2 - 100q^2$
7. Find the value of $p^2 - 4pq$ when $p = -3$ and $q = 2$.
8. Given that $ab + 5 = c$ express b in terms of a and c, where $a \neq 0$.
9. Express as a single fraction $\frac{x}{6} - \frac{2x-5}{4}$
10. Given that $p(k - 7) = 11$ express k in terms of p.
11. Factorise $x^2 + 5x - 24$
12. (i) If x is an even integer, write an expression for the next even integer.

    (ii) If half of the smallest even number is subtracted from one third of the bigger even number, write an expression for this in terms of x.
13. Simplify $p(5p + 4) - 3(p - 2)$
14. Factorise $x^2 - 7x - 18$
15. A picture frame has a width of 44 cm and a height of 34 cm. The wooden frame has a thickness of T cm.

    (i) Find the width and height of the glass, within the frame, in terms of T.

    (ii) Hence, find the area of the glass, in terms of T.

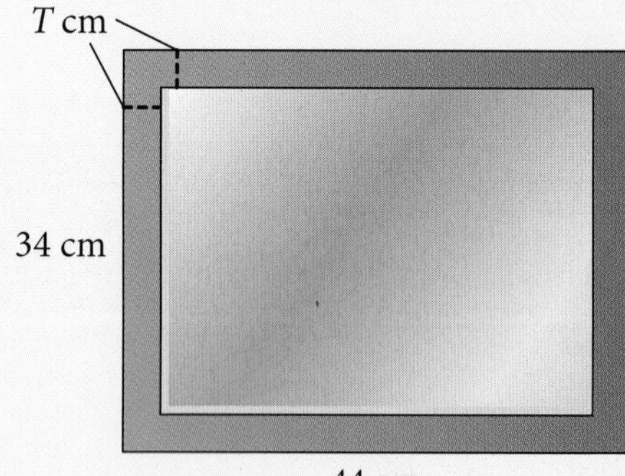

16. x is a real number. One new number is formed by increasing x by 2. A second number is formed by decreasing x by 4.

    (i) Write each of the new numbers, in terms of x.

    (ii) Find the product of these new numbers in the form $x^2 + bx + c$, where $b, c \in \mathbb{Z}$.

Revision and Exam Style Questions – Section B

More challenging problems

1. Given that $3p(q + 5) = 51$, find the value of q when $p = -2$.

2. Simplify $(2x - 1)(3 + 5x) - (x + 2)^2$

3. Find the value of $\frac{3ab - 4c}{2}$ when $a = 4$, $b = \frac{2}{3}$ and $c = -1$

4. Factorise $12bc - 4bd - 15xc + 5xd$

5. Express as a single fraction $\frac{5}{x - 1} + \frac{3}{x + 4}$

6. Find the value of $\frac{4x + 3y - 3}{5}$ when $x = 6$ and $y = -2$.

7. (i) Rearrange $5x - 3y = 5$, to make y the subject of the formula.
   (ii) Hence, find the value of y when $x = -2$.

8. Factorise $9ma - 4nc + 3mc - 12na$

9. (i) Rearrange $4(5 + a) = t(3 - a)$ to make a the subject of the formula.
   (ii) Hence, find the value of a when $t = 7$.

10. Factorise $5a^2 - 12a + 4$

11. Express $\frac{4}{3p + 4} + \frac{3}{p - 2}$ as a single fraction and verify your answer for $p = 4$

12. (i) Express q in terms of p and r where $\frac{3p - 5q}{q} = r$
    (ii) Hence, or otherwise, find the value of q when $p = -2$ and $r = 7$.

13. Factorise $12x^2 - 7x - 10$

14. Find the value of $\frac{4x + 6y + 4}{2x + 9y}$ when $x = \frac{5}{2}$ and $y = \frac{1}{3}$

15. Express the following as three factors: $8x^2 + 36x - 72$

16. Body mass index (BMI) is a value which can be used as a measure of body fat. It is based on a person's height and weight.
    (i) BMI is calculated by dividing a person's weight, in kilograms, by the square of their height, in metres. Write a formula you could use for calculating BMI. Explain any letters used.
    (ii) Robbie has a weight of 80 kg and height of 1·75 m. Calculate Robbie's BMI.
    (iii) Rose has a BMI of 22·5 and a height of 162 cm. Find Rose's weight, correct to two decimal places.
    (iv) Jim has a BMI of 28 and a weight of 92 kg. Find Jim's height, correct to the nearest centimetre.
    (v) Beth has a weight of 79 kg and height of 158 cm. Calculate Beth's BMI.

Now that you have completed the chapter, revisit the 'Something to think about…' question.

CHAPTER 03 Algebra II – Linear Relations

Sections covered within this chapter:

KEY WORDS

- Function
- Equation
- Domain
- Linear equation
- Range
- Simultaneous equations
- Rate of change
- Inequality

SOMETHING TO THINK ABOUT…

Calum is now one-quarter of his father's age.
In seven years, Calum will be one-third the age of his father at this time.
Use algebraic methods to find out how old Calum is now.

Section 3.1: Linear Functions

Learning Outcomes:

You should be able to:

- recognise a linear function
- graph a function of the form $ax + b$
- represent linear functions, set in context, graphically

We often hear expressions such as 'the profit is a function of the number of objects sold'. This means that the profit depends on the number of objects sold.

A **function** is a relation for which there is only one output value corresponding to any input value.

The **domain** is the set of inputs or x coordinates.

The **range** is the set of outputs or y coordinates.

Discussion Time 

Work with a classmate to carry out the following tasks:

1. Given the function **output = 2(input) + 4**, find the outputs for each of the inputs from −3 to 3.
2. Plot each (input, output) pair on a coordinated plane.
3. Join these points to form the graph of the function.
4. Repeat tasks **1** to **3** using the function **output = 8 − input** and inputs from −3 to 3.
5. Study each graph drawn and comment on their shape.

A **linear function** can be written in the form $f(x) = y = ax + b$ and, when graphed, is a straight line.

When graphed,

- the value of b is the point where the function crosses the y-axis (the y-intercept).
- the value of a is the rate of change of the function (the slope of the line).

The **rate of change** is a measure of how much the graph rises or falls, for every one unit it goes across.

A linear function, in the form $f(x) = y = ax + b$, is the same as the equation of a line $y = mx + c$ where m = rate of change (slope of the line) and c = initial value (y-intercept).

 **Links across the syllabus**

Linear functions are also covered in Chapter 7: Further Functions and Chapter 11: Coordinate Geometry II.

Graph showing the balance in a savings account, each month after the account is opened

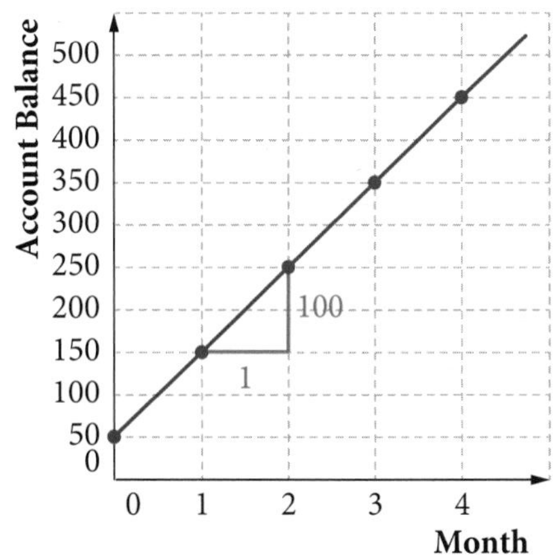

- This graph crosses the y-axis at 50.
- This graph rises by 100 units for every 1 unit across. Therefore, the rate of change of the function is 100.

Graph is **increasing.**
Rate of change is **positive.**

Equation of the function:

Account balance = €100(month number) + €50

Output = 100(input) + 50

$y = 100x + 50$

Graph showing the temperature of a container of warm liquid, each minute after it is put into a freezer

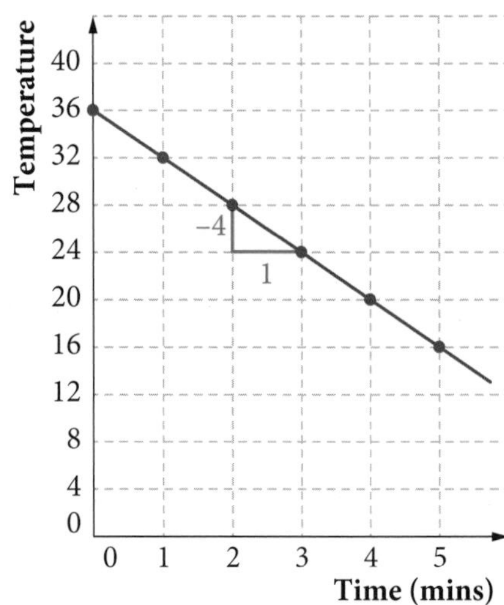

- This graph crosses the y-axis at 36.
- This graph drops by 4 units for every 1 unit across. Therefore, the rate of change of the function is −4.

Graph is **decreasing.**
Rate of change is **negative.**

Equation of the function:

Temperature = −4(number of minutes) + 36

Output = −4(input) + 36

$y = -4x + 36$

Graph of a linear function, $f(x) = ax + b$

Graphs are always read from left to right.

If the coefficient of the x part is positive ($a > 0$), the graph is **increasing**:

E.g. $y = 2x + 3$

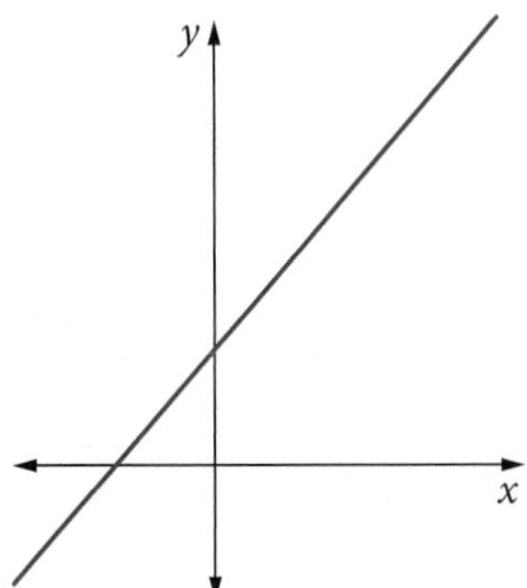

If the coefficient of the x part is zero ($a = 0$), the graph is **horizontal**:

E.g. $y = 3$

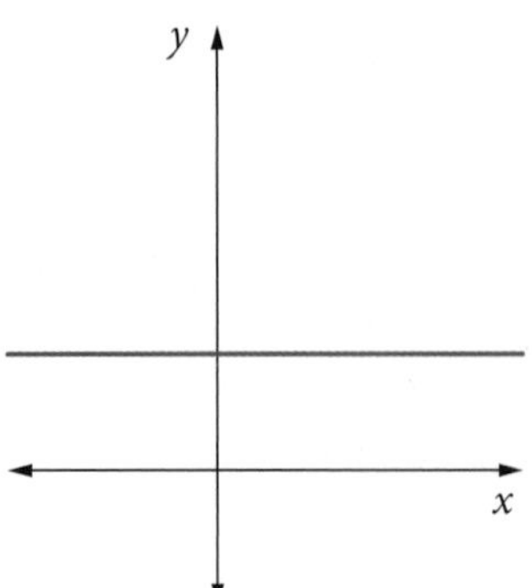

If the coefficient of the x part is negative ($a < 0$), the graph is **decreasing**:

E.g. $y = -2x + 3$

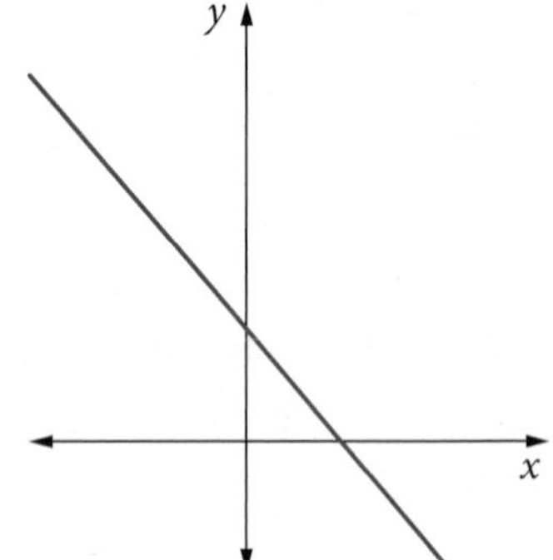

EXAMPLE 1

Tamzin has a jar of sweets. The jar initially contains 32 sweets and Tamzin eats four sweets per day.

(i) Copy and complete the table on the right:

(ii) What is the rate of change of this function?

(iii) Write down a function to represent the number of sweets remaining, in terms of the day number.

(iv) Hence, or otherwise, graph the function.

(v) Use your graph to find the number of sweets remaining in the jar after five days.

(vi) After how many days will the jar be empty?

Day number	Number of sweets remaining
0	32
1	
2	
3	

Solution

(i) The number of sweets are reducing by four every day, so the completed table is as follows:

Day number	Number of sweets remaining
0	32
1	28
2	24
3	20

(ii) The initial value for the number of sweets is 32 and this is reducing by four sweets every day.

This means that the rate of change for this function is -4.

(iii) The function can be represented as:

output = initial value + (rate of change) input

Number of sweets remaining = 32 – 4(day number)

$$n = 32 - 4d$$

Where n = number of sweets remaining

d = day number

This is the equation of a line. It can be presented as:

$f(x) = ax + b$

$y = mx + c$

$n = -4d + 32$

(iv) From the function, we can see that the initial value is 32.

The rate of change is −4, therefore, the graph drops by 4 units for every 1 unit across.

Therefore, we graph a line which starts at 32 and has a slope of −4.

Alternatively, plot the points found by completing the table in part **(i)**.

Since the graph is a straight line, you only need two points to be able to plot the graph of a linear function.

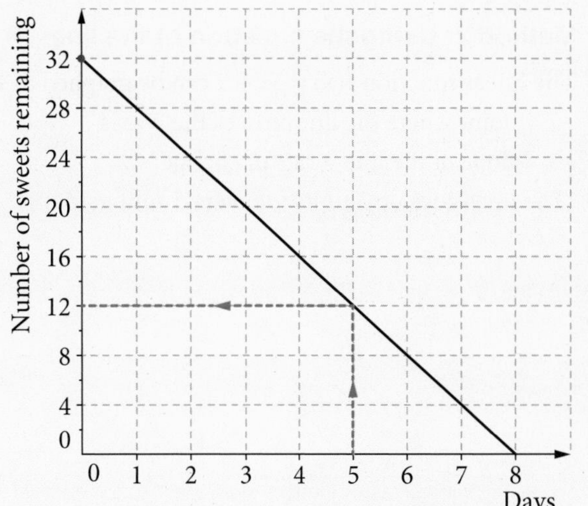

(v) From the graph, we can see that on day 5 there are 12 sweets remaining (marked in red on the graph).

(vi) From the graph we can see that on day 8, there are 0 sweets remaining and so the jar is empty.

EXAMPLE 2

A function is defined as $f(x) = 3x + 2$. Find:

(i) $f(1)$ **(ii)** $f(3)$ **(iii)** $f(-2)$

(iv) Hence, or otherwise, graph this function.

Solution

(i) $f(x) = 3x + 2$

Replace x with 1:

$f(1) = 3(1) + 2$

$f(1) = 3 + 2$

$f(1) = 5$

$f(1)$ means to substitute 1 into the $f(x)$ function, in place of x.

(ii) $f(x) = 3x + 2$

Replace x with 3:

$f(3) = 3(3) + 2$

$f(3) = 9 + 2$

$f(3) = 11$

(iii) $f(x) = 3x + 2$

Replace x with −2:

$f(-2) = 3(-2) + 2$

$f(-2) = -6 + 2$

$f(-2) = -4$

(iv) Method 1: Using ordered pairs

Parts **(i)**, **(ii)** and **(iii)** give us three ordered pairs, which are three points on the graph of the function:

(1, 5), (3, 11) and (−2, −4)

Plotting these points and joining them up gives us the graph of the function:
$f(x) = 3x + 2$

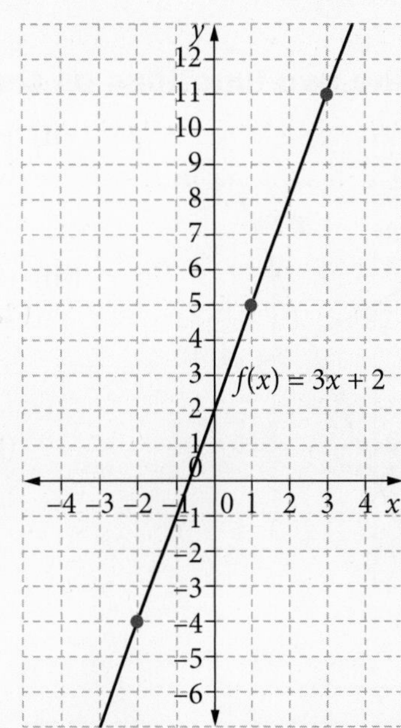

Method 2: Using the equation of the line

The linear function $f(x) = 3x + 2$ can be graphed as follows:
$+2$ = point where the line crosses the y-axis
$+3$ = slope of the line = rate of change
(The lines goes up 3 units for every 1 unit across.)

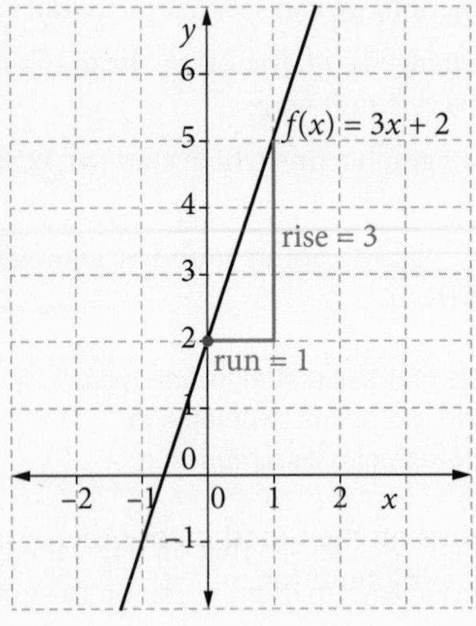

EXAMPLE 3

(i) Graph the functions $g(x) = 2x + 1$ and $h(x) = 6 - \frac{1}{2}x$ in the domain $-2 \leq x \leq 4$ using the same axes and scale.

(ii) Hence, find the coordinates of the point where $g(x) = h(x)$.

(iii) Use your graph to find the value of **(a)** $h(1)$ **(b)** x when $g(x) = 7$.

Solution

(i) We know that the functions are linear and so will be graphed as straight lines. We need to find the end points of each line:

$g(x) = 2x + 1$, in the domain $-2 \leq x \leq 4$

Starts at $x = -2$	Ends at $x = 4$
$g(-2) = 2(-2) + 1$	$g(4) = 2(4) + 1$
$g(-2) = -4 + 1$	$g(4) = 8 + 1$
$g(-2) = -3$	$g(4) = 9$
Start point: $(-2, -3)$	End point: $(4, 9)$

$h(x) = 6 - \frac{1}{2}x$, in the domain $-2 \leq x \leq 4$

Starts at $x = -2$	Ends at $x = 4$
$h(x) = 6 - \frac{1}{2}x$	$h(x) = 6 - \frac{1}{2}x$
$h(-2) = 6 - \frac{1}{2}(-2)$	$h(4) = 6 - \frac{1}{2}(4)$
$h(-2) = 6 + 1$	$h(4) = 6 - 2$
$h(-2) = 7$	$h(4) = 4$
Start point: $(-2, 7)$	End point: $(4, 4)$

Graphing the two functions on the same axes and scale gives:

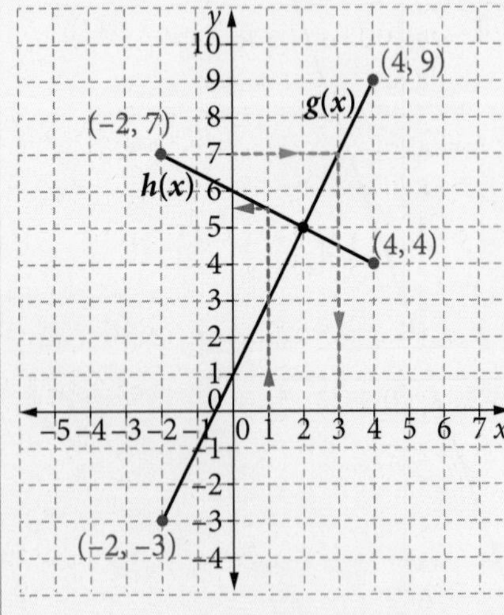

(ii) From looking at the graph, we can see that the point where $g(x) = h(x)$ is the point where the two lines intersect.

Therefore, $g(x) = h(x)$ at the point $(2, 5)$.

(iii) (a) $h(1)$ means to find y when $x = 1$.
Start at 1 on the x-axis, move up to the $h(x)$ graph. Once you touch the graph, go across to the y-axis and read the value off the scale (marked in red on the graph). $h(1) = 5{\cdot}5$

(b) To find x when $g(x) = 7$.
$g(x) = y$, therefore start at 7 on the y-axis, move across to the $g(x)$ graph. Once you touch the graph, go down to the x-axis and read the value off the scale (marked in green on the graph).

When $g(x) = 7$, $x = 3$

Practice Questions 3.1

1. A function is defined as $f(x) = 3x - 1$. Find:
   (i) $f(-3)$
   (ii) $f(0)$
   (iii) $f(2)$
   (iv) $f(4)$
   (v) Hence, or otherwise, graph the function $f(x)$.

2. A function is defined as $g(x) = 5 - 2x$. Find:
   (i) $g(-2)$
   (ii) $g(-1)$
   (iii) $g(2)$
   (iv) $g(3)$
   (v) Hence, or otherwise, graph the function $g(x)$.

3. By finding points on the function, or otherwise, graph the following functions:
   (i) $f(x) = x + 3$
   (ii) $g(x) = 2x + 4$
   (iii) $h(x) = 6 - x$
   (iv) $k(x) = -2x - 3$

4. By finding the point where the line crosses the y-axis (y-intercept) and the rate of change of each line, hence or otherwise, write down the function represented by each of the following graphs:

(i)

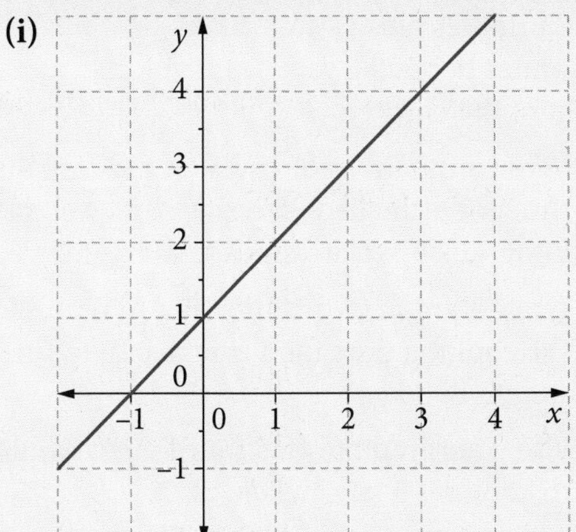

(ii)

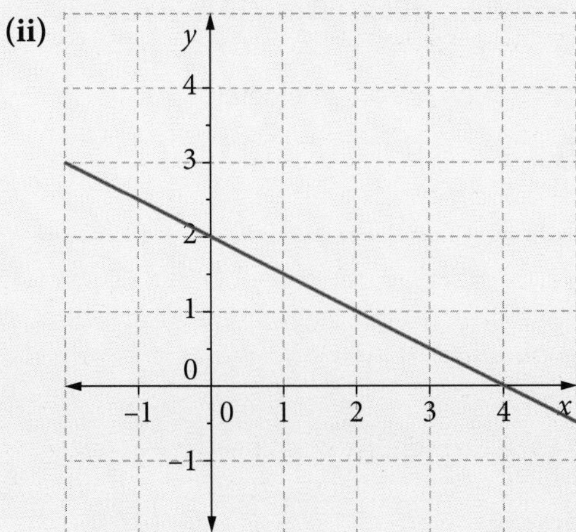

(iii)

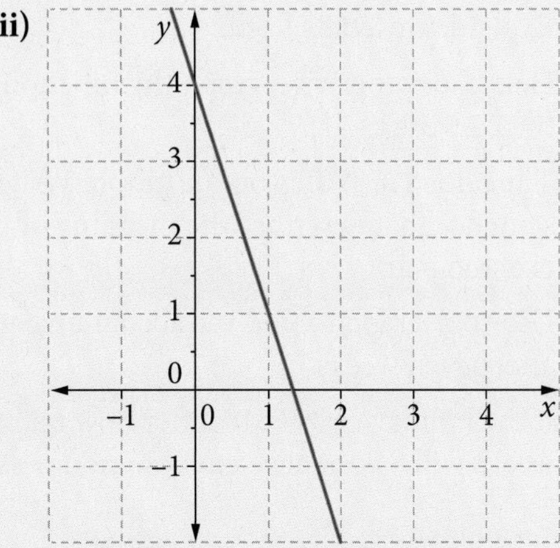

(iv)

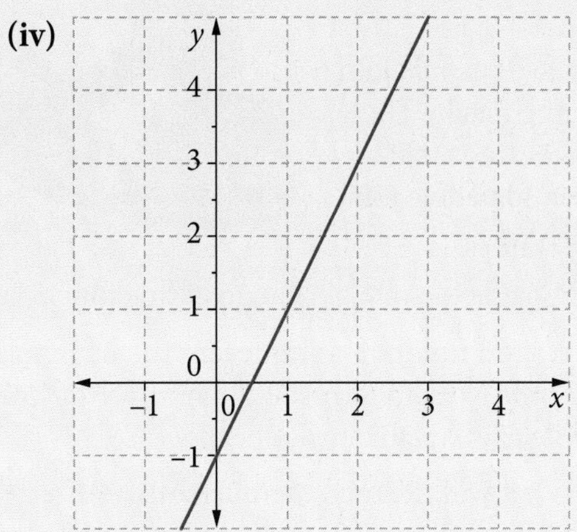

5. Using the same axes and scale, graph the functions: $f(x) = x + 2$ and $g(x) = 2x - 1$ in the domain $-2 \leq x \leq 5$.
   Hence, or otherwise, find the coordinates of the point where $f(x) = g(x)$.

6. Using the same axes and scale, graph the functions: $h(x) = 2x - 3$ and $k(x) = 2 - \frac{1}{2}x$ in the domain $-1 \leq x \leq 4$.
   Hence, or otherwise, find the coordinates of the point where $h(x) = k(x)$.

7. Sakthi is saving for a holiday. He opens a savings account and deposits €100. He then deposits €30 per week for the next 25 weeks (week number 1 is the first week).
   (i) Copy and complete the following table:

Week number	Account balance
0	100
1	
2	
3	

(ii) Write a function to represent the account balance, in terms of the week number. Explain any letters used.

(iii) Hence, or otherwise, graph the function for the 25 weeks.

(iv) The point (9, 370) is on the graph. Write a sentence that describes the meaning of this ordered pair.

(v) Use your graph to find the account balance after seven weeks.

(vi) If the holiday costs €610, after how many weeks will Sakthi have enough money saved?

8. A gym can take a maximum of 2,500 members. When it first opens, 670 people join up immediately. The manager finds that a further 30 people join up each week.

(i) What is the rate of change of this function?

(ii) Write a function to represent the membership of the gym, in terms of the number of weeks. Clearly explain any letters you use.

(iii) What will the total membership be after 12 weeks?

(iv) How many weeks will it take before the gym is at maximum membership?

(v) Do you think the function you found in part **(i)** is an accurate description for the membership numbers of a gym? Give a reason for your answer.

9. A taxi company charges a flat fee of €4·50 and then €1·50 per kilometre travelled.

(i) What is the rate of change (slope) of this function?

(ii) Write a function to represent the cost of a journey with this taxi company. Clearly explain any letters used.

(iii) Draw a graph of this function, to represent the cost of a journey up to 30 km.

(iv) The point (5, 12) is on the graph. Write a sentence that describes the meaning of this ordered pair.

(v) Use this graph to find the cost of a 16 km journey.

(vi) Bertrand takes a trip with this taxi company and he is charged €37·50.

Use your graph to find the length of Bertrand's trip.

10. Cooking instructions for roasting a chicken are 20 minutes plus 25 minutes per 500 g weight of the chicken.

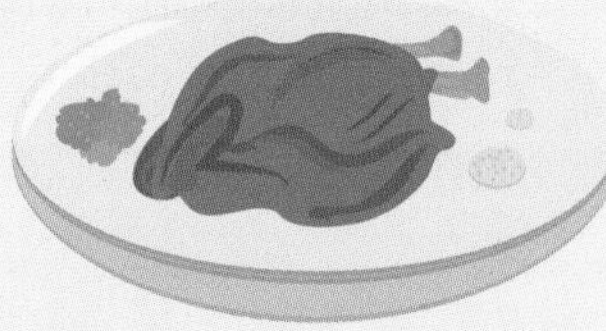

(i) Write a function to represent the cooking time for a chicken, in terms of its weight in kilograms. Explain any letters used.

(ii) Draw a graph of this function to represent the cooking time for a chicken up to the weight of 3 kg.

(iii) Use your graph to find how long it would take to cook a 1·5 kg chicken.

(iv) Use your graph to estimate the weight of a chicken, which takes 130 minutes to cook.

Section 3.2: Linear Equations

Learning Outcomes:

You should be able to:

- solve linear equations
- use linear equations to solve problems in real-life contexts

$2x + 3 = 9$, $\frac{2x - 3}{5} = 3$ and $3p - 5 = 2p + 7$ are all examples of equations.

Solving an equation means finding the value or values of the variable that makes the equation true or balances the equation. That is, the left-hand side equals the right-hand side. We say that this value **satisfies** the equation.

An **equation** is an expression which has an equals (=) sign. For all equations, the left-hand side (LHS) **equals** the right-hand side (RHS).

Links across the syllabus

Being able to solve equations is a vital skill for you to have throughout your maths course.

A **linear equation** is an algebraic equation in which the highest power of the variables is 1.
When graphed, a linear equation is represented by a straight line.

When solving equations, we could use a trial and improvement method. This would involve trying different values in the equation until we find the one which makes the equation balance. This may be a quick approach to solving some questions, but it is difficult to use if the required answer is a fraction or a decimal. Thus, it is important that we follow a clear method for solving equations.

When solving a linear equation, we must perform operations until the variable is on its own on one side. It is very important to remember that **whatever operation you perform on one side of the equation, you must also perform on the other side.**

EXAMPLE 1

(i) Solve the linear equation $7x - 3 = 18$.

(ii) Verify your answer.

Solution

(i)

$7x - 3 = 18$

$7x - 3 + 3 = 18 + 3$ (add 3 to both sides)

$7x = 21$

$\frac{7x}{7} = \frac{21}{7}$ (divide both sides by 7)

$x = 3$

(ii) Verify that $x = 3$ satisfies the equation: $7x - 3 = 18$

Substitute $x = 3$ into the left side of the equation:

$7(3) - 3$

$21 - 3$

18

Since the left side of the equation equals the right side of the equation, for $x = 3$, we can say that $x = 3$ satisfies the equation.

EXAMPLE 2

Solve $2y - 8 = 6y + 4$

Solution

$2y - 8 = 6y + 4$

$2y - 8 - 4 = 6y + 4 - 4$ (subtract 4 from both sides)

$2y - 12 = 6y$

$2y - 12 - 2y = 6y - 2y$ (subtract $2y$ from both sides)

$-12 = 4y$

$\frac{-12}{4} = \frac{4y}{4}$ (divide both sides by 4)

$-3 = y$

We could have brought the *y*s to the left-hand side, but that would have resulted in a negative sign in front of the variable, which is less desirable.

EXAMPLE 3

Solve the equation $5(1 + 2x) = 4x - (2x - 9)$

Solution

$$5(1 + 2x) = 4x - (2x - 9)$$

$5 + 10x = 4x - 1(2x) - 1(-9)$ (multiply out the brackets)

$5 + 10x = 4x - 2x + 9$

$5 + 10x = 2x + 9$

$5 + 10x - 2x = 2x + 9 - 2x$ (subtract $2x$ from both sides)

$5 + 8x = 9$

$5 + 8x - 5 = 9 - 5$ (subtract 5 from both sides)

$8x = 4$

$\frac{8x}{8} = \frac{4}{8}$ (divide both sides by 8)

$x = \frac{4}{8} = \frac{1}{2}$

Linear equations involving fractions

When an equation involves fractions, we must multiply both sides by the lowest common multiple of the denominators. That is the smallest number that all denominators divide into evenly.

 **Links across the syllabus**

Adding fractions was covered in Chapter 1: Number Systems.

You should be able to recognise that fractions can be presented in different forms, as shown:

$$-\frac{2}{3} = \frac{-2}{3} = \frac{2}{-3}$$

$$\frac{2}{3}(x + 1) = \frac{2(x + 1)}{3} = \frac{2x}{3} + \frac{1}{3}$$

EXAMPLE 4

Solve the following equation $\frac{(5x + 1)}{3} - 8 = \frac{1}{2}(x + 1)$

Solution

$\frac{(5x + 1)}{3} - 8 = \frac{1}{2}(x + 1)$ (simplify $\frac{1}{2}(x + 1)$ by multiplying top by top and bottom by bottom)

$\frac{5x + 1}{3} - \frac{8}{1} = \frac{x + 1}{2}$ (denominator of 8 is 1)

The lowest common multiple of 3, 1 and 2 is 6.

$6\left(\frac{5x + 1}{3}\right) - 6\left(\frac{8}{1}\right) = 6\left(\frac{x + 1}{2}\right)$ (multiply all parts by 6)

$2(5x + 1) - 6(8) = 3(x + 1)$

$10x + 2 - 48 = 3x + 3$ (multiply out the brackets)

$10x - 46 = 3x + 3$

$10x - 46 - 3x = 3x + 3 - 3x$ (subtract $3x$ from both sides)

$7x - 46 = 3$

$7x - 46 + 46 = 3 + 46$ (add 46 to both sides)

$7x = 49$

$\frac{7x}{7} = \frac{49}{7}$ (divide both sides by 7)

$x = 7$

Practice Questions 3.2

1. Solve the following equations:
   - **(i)** $2x - 5 = 11$
   - **(ii)** $4y - 3 = 21$
   - **(iii)** $25 = 13 + 6p$
   - **(iv)** $5a + 7 = 9a - 13$
   - **(v)** $6k - 1 = 3k + 14$
   - **(vi)** $2t + 1 = 8t - 35$
   - **(vii)** $12p - 21 = 7p + 9$
   - **(viii)** $b + 17 = 32 - 9b$
   - **(ix)** $5x - 1 - 2x - 4 = x$
2. $f(x) = 2x + 7$. Find:
   - **(i)** the value of x when $f(x) = 9$
   - **(ii)** the value of x when $f(x) = 1$.
3. Solve the following, given $f(x) = 15x - 1$ and $g(x) = 9x - 19$.
   - **(i)** By letting $f(x) = g(x)$, form an equation in terms of x.
   - **(ii)** Hence, solve this equation to find the value of x, for which $f(x) = g(x)$.
   - **(iii)** If $f(x)$ and $g(x)$ were graphed using the same axes and scale, what would be the relationship between their graphs and the answer to part **(ii)**?
4. Given $h(x) = 16 - 2x$ and $k(x) = 4x + 4$, find:
   - **(i)** the value of x, for which $h(x) = k(x)$
   - **(ii)** the value of x, for which $h(x) + k(x) = 8$.
5. Your friend thinks of a number, multiplies it by five, then adds 12. The result is 52. What is the number?
6. A number is trebled and added to 11. The result is 50. What is the number?
7. The three angles of a triangle are θ, $\theta - 25$ and $\theta + 85$. Find θ.

   The three angles of a triangle add up to 180°.

8. Solve the following equations:
   - **(i)** $3(x - 1) = 2x$
   - **(ii)** $4(a + 1) = 16 - 2a$
   - **(iii)** $3(4p - 7) = 7p + 9$
   - **(iv)** $4(x - 1) = 2x + 3$
   - **(v)** $2(k + 7) - 5(k - 1) = 13$
   - **(vi)** $2(3t + 7) = 7(4t - 1) - 1$
   - **(vii)** $5(7x + 3) = 2(3 - x) - 3 + x$
   - **(viii)** $11 = 7(y + 1) - 2(3 - 8y) - 3y$
9. Find the value of x, which satisfies the equation $3(4x + 2) - x = -2x - 7$ and verify your solution.
10. Find the value of y, which satisfies the equation $7 + 4y = 3(y - 5)$ and verify your solution.
11. Find the value of k, which satisfies the equation $9(3 - k) + 5 + 4k = -k$ and verify your solution.
12. When 7 times a certain number is subtracted from 15, the result is -6. Find the number.
13. Solve the following equations:
    - **(i)** $\frac{x}{6} + 11 = 19$
    - **(ii)** $\frac{1}{3}(k + 2) = \frac{2k - 1}{5}$
    - **(iii)** $\frac{b + 1}{2} = \frac{b + 4}{3}$
    - **(iv)** $\frac{x - 5}{3} + \frac{1}{2}(x - 2) = 4$
    - **(v)** $\frac{5p - 1}{7} - 1 = \frac{p + 2}{2}$
    - **(vi)** $\frac{x}{6} - \frac{2(x + 1)}{5} = \frac{5(x - 10)}{2}$
14. Find the value of x, which satisfies the equation $\frac{2x - 1}{3} + 2 = \frac{5x - 6}{6}$ and verify your solution.
15. Find the value of p, which satisfies the equation $\frac{3p - 2}{5} - \frac{3}{10} = \frac{p - 1}{2}$ and verify your solution.
16. The perimeter of the rectangle shown is 18 cm. Write an equation for the perimeter of the rectangle and solve it to find the length of all the sides.

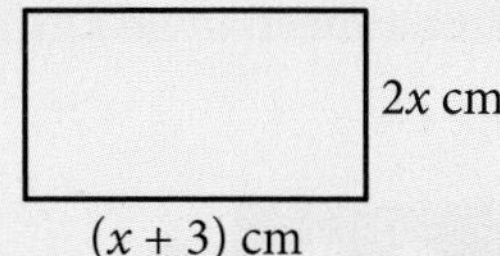

17. A wedding band charges €250 plus €180 per hour that they play. The cost of the band can be represented by the equation $C = 180h + 250$, where C is the total cost and h is the time played, in hours.

Find how many hours the band played, if the total cost is €1,060.

18. An airline allows each person to carry 15 kg of baggage. Extra baggage is charged at €7·50 per kilo. The airline uses the following formula to calculate the cost, C, for extra luggage: $C = 7{\cdot}5(w - 15)$.
    - (i) Write down what you think w stands for.
    - (ii) Josh has a suitcase, which weighs 17·5 kg. How much will Josh have to pay for his excess baggage?
    - (iii) Leo is charged €82·50 for extra baggage. How much extra baggage did he have?
    - (iv) Donna is charged €30 for extra baggage. Find the total weight of Donna's luggage.

19. Ida is an estate agent. She charges a flat fee of €800 plus 2% of the sales price of the home.
    The total commission that Ida earns on the sale of a home can be found by using the following function: $C = 800 + 0{\cdot}02P$.
    Where C is the commission earned, in euro, P is the sale price of the home, in euro.
    - (i) Find the commission that Ida would receive on a home that sold for €325,000.
    - (ii) If the total commission paid was €4,100, what was the sale price of the home?
    - (iii) If the total commission paid was €6,200, what was the sale price of the home?

20. Nikoli is making a journey from town A to C, via town B. When travelling from A to B, he travels a distance of x km at a speed of 60 km/h. He travels from B to C, a distance which is 30 km longer than that of A to B, at a speed of 40 km/h.
    - (i) Find the time taken for Nikoli to travel from A to B, in terms of x.

    $$\text{Speed} = \frac{\text{Distance}}{\text{Time}}$$

    - (ii) Find the time it takes him to travel from B to C, in terms of x.
    - (iii) Given the total travel time is 3 hours 15 minutes, find the distance from town A to town B and, hence, the total distance from town A to town C.

21. On a particular day, the gate receipts for a soccer match were €27,472. Tickets for the match cost €6 for children, €10 for students and €15 for all other adults.

    There were twice as many children as there were students. The number of students was 1,200 less than the number of all other adults present. Solve the following, by letting x equal the number of students.
    - (i) Write an expression for the number of children who attended the match, in terms of x.
    - (ii) Write an expression for the number of other adults, who attended the match, in terms of x.
    - (iii) Hence, write an equation for the ticket sales, in terms of x.
    - (iv) Find x and, hence, write down how many of each type of ticket was sold.

Section 3.3: Simultaneous Equations – Two Linear Equations

Learning Outcome:

You should be able to:

- solve simultaneous linear equations with two unknowns and interpret the results

Simultaneous equations are two equations, each containing two variables. The method of solving these equations simultaneously (at the same time) gives the pair of answers which satisfy both equations at the same time.

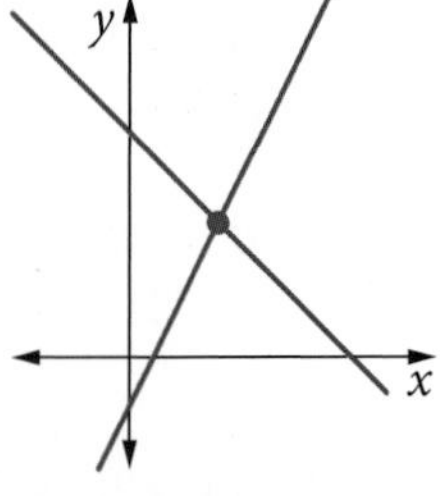

We have already seen that when we graph two linear functions using the same axes and scale, we can find the point of intersection of these lines.

These are the x and y values which satisfy both of the linear equations.

It may not always be practical to graph the linear functions. When this is the case, we can solve these equations using algebra. This is known as solving simultaneous equations.

To solve simultaneous equations, we can use the **elimination method** or the **substitution method**, whichever is more appropriate for the question. The steps for each method are outlined below.

If the question asks for the equations to be solved using algebra, then the method of graphing the lines is not an acceptable solution.

Elimination method

Step 1: Decide which letter to eliminate. Bearing in mind that in order to be able to eliminate a letter, the coefficients must be the same value, but of opposite sign.

Step 2: Place the equations one under the other.

Step 3: Multiply or divide one equation, as required, in order to be able to eliminate a variable.

Step 4: Add the two equations, and eliminate one variable. Hence solve for the other variable.

Step 5: Take the known value and substitute it back into one of the equations, to find the other variable.

EXAMPLE 1

Solve the following pair of simultaneous equations: $2x + y = 8$ and $3x - 2y = 19$

Solution

Step 1: Decide which letter to eliminate.
In this case, since they are already opposite signs, we will eliminate the *y*s:

Step 2: Put the equations one under the other

$$2x + y = 8$$
$$3x - 2y = 19$$

Step 3: To make the coefficients of the *y*s the same value, multiply the top equation by 2:

$$4x + 2y = 16$$
$$+\ 3x - 2y = 19$$

Step 4: Add the rows, to eliminate the *y*s:

$$7x \quad = 35 \qquad \text{(divide both sides by 7)}$$
$$x = 5$$

Step 5: Take the value for x and substitute it back into the first equation:

$$2x + y = 8$$
$$2(5) + y = 8$$
$$10 + y = 8$$
$$y = 8 - 10$$
$$y = -2$$

Therefore, solution is $x = 5$, $y = -2$.

Substitution method

Step 1: Rearrange one equation to get the variable whose coefficient is 1, on its own.

Step 2: Substitute the result of step 1 in to the other equation. This equation will now be in terms of one variable only.

Step 3: Solve the resulting equation.

Step 4: Take the known value and substitute it back into the simpler equation, to find the other variable.

The substitution method is best used when it is possible to get one of the variables on its own, without introducing fractions. That is, when the coefficient of one of the variables is 1.

EXAMPLE 2

Solve the following pair of simultaneous equations: $2p + 3q = 5$ and $p - 4q = -14$

Solution

Looking at the second equation, we can see that it will be easy to rearrange it to get p on its own:

Step 1: Rearrange the second equation to get p alone, by adding $4q$ to both sides:

$$p - 4q = -14$$
$$p = -14 + 4q$$

Step 2: Substitute $p = -14 + 4q$ into the first equation:

$$2p + 3q = 5$$
$$2(-14 + 4q) + 3q = 5$$

Step 3: Solve the resulting equation:

$$-28 + 8q + 3q = 5$$
$$-28 + 11q = 5$$
$$11q = 5 + 28$$
$$11q = 33$$
$$q = 3$$

Step 4: Take the value for q and substitute it back into the second equation:

$$p - 4q = -14$$
$$p - 4(3) = -14$$
$$p - 12 = -14$$
$$p = -2$$

Therefore, solution is $p = -2$, $q = 3$.

EXAMPLE 3

Solve the simultaneous equations: $\frac{1}{3}f + \frac{1}{2}g = 0$ and $\frac{5}{4}f + g = 7$

To solve equations involving fractions, multiply each equation by the lowest common multiple of the denominators. Then rearrange each in the form $ax + by = c$.

Solution

Get the equations in the form $ax + by = c$:

Equation 1: Multiply $\frac{1}{3}f + \frac{1}{2}g = 0$ by the LCM i.e. 6

$$6\left(\frac{1}{3}f\right) + 6\left(\frac{1}{2}g\right) = 6(0)$$
$$2f + 3g = 0$$

Equation 2: Multiply $\frac{5}{4}f + g = 7$ by the LCM i.e. 4

$$4\left(\frac{5}{4}f\right) + 4(g) = 4(7)$$
$$5f + 4g = 28$$

Rearranging to get one of the variables on its own will introduce more fractions.
So we will solve the equations using the elimination method:

Eliminate gs:

$$2f + 3g = 0 \quad (\times 4)$$
$$5f + 4g = 28 \quad (\times -3)$$
$$8f + 12g = 0$$
$$+\ -15f - 12g = -84$$
$$-7f = -84 \quad (\div -7)$$
$$f = 12$$

To find the value for g, let $f = 12$ in either of the equations:

$$2f + 3g = 0$$
$$2(12) + 3g = 0$$
$$24 + 3g = 0$$
$$3g = -24$$
$$g = -8$$

Therefore, solution is $f = 12$, $g = -8$.

Practice Questions 3.3

1. Use a suitable method to solve the following pairs of simultaneous equations.

 (i) $x + 2y = 20$
 $9x - 2y = 80$

 (ii) $5p - 3q = -3$
 $7p + 3q = 39$

 (iii) $2a + 5b = 26$
 $5a + 5b = 35$

 (iv) $7x - 2y = 22$
 $5x - 2y = 14$

 (v) $3m + 2n = 26$
 $4m - n = 20$

 (vi) $4a + 3b = 20$
 $3a - 4b = -10$

 (vii) $5x - 3y = 14$
 $9x - 4y = 28$

 (viii) $2x + 9y = 69$
 $x + 3y = 24$

 (ix) $6p + 2q = 14$
 $5p + 5q = 5$

2. Use a suitable method to solve the following simultaneous equations.
 In some cases it may be necessary to write the equation in the form $ax + by = c$, before solving.

 (i) $4x = 7 + 3y$
 $y + 3 = x$

 (ii) $6x = 52 - 2y$
 $70 - 7y = 5x$

 (iii) $6x = 5y$
 $4x = 5y - 10$

 (iv) $4x - 5 = 3y$
 $2y + 1 = -2x$

 (v) $4y = 5 - 5x$
 $3x + 34 = 5y$

 (vi) $2y = 7x - 13$
 $4x = 13 + 3y$

3. Solve the following simultaneous equations, involving fractions.

 (i) $2x - y = 18$
 $\frac{1}{3}x - \frac{1}{4}y = 2$

 (ii) $3a - \frac{2}{5}b = 6$
 $\frac{1}{2}a + \frac{2}{3}b = 1$

 (iii) $\frac{5}{3}x - \frac{1}{2}y = 12$
 $\frac{1}{4}x - \frac{3}{8}y = 3$

 (iv) $\frac{2}{5}x - \frac{1}{2}y = \frac{13}{2}$
 $\frac{3}{4}x - \frac{1}{5}y = \frac{17}{2}$

 (v) $\frac{a + b}{2} = 1$
 $\frac{a - 3b}{3} = 2$

 (vi) $\frac{2p - 5}{3} + \frac{q}{5} = 6$
 $\frac{3p}{10} + 2 = \frac{3q - 5}{2}$

4. The diagram shows a rectangle.

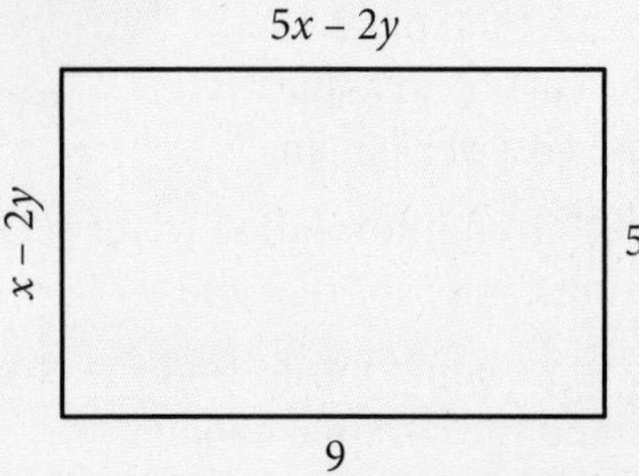

 (i) Form two equations, in terms of x and y.
 (ii) Solve these equations to find the values of x and y.
 (iii) Hence, verify that the perimeter of the rectangle is 28 units.

5. The diagram shows a parallelogram.

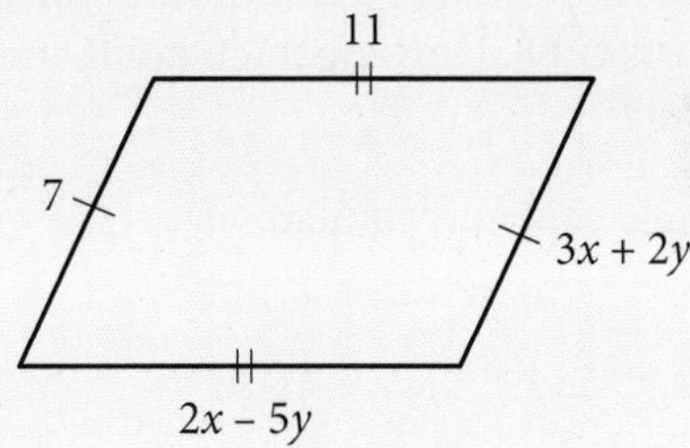

 (i) Form two equations, in terms of x and y.
 (ii) Solve these equations to find the values of x and y.

6. p and q are two numbers. Their sum is 15 and their difference is 7. Find p and q.

7. a and b are two numbers. Their sum is 28 and half of their difference is 2. Find a and b.

8. Seven shirts and three jumpers cost €168.
 Four shirts and five jumpers cost €165.
 Let x be the cost of a shirt and y be the cost of a jumper.
 (i) Use the given information to form two equations, in terms of x and y.
 (ii) Solve these equations to find the cost of a shirt and the cost of a jumper.

9. Five apples and six bananas cost a total of €2·50, whereas seven apples and three bananas cost a total of €2·15. Let x be the cost of an apple and y be the cost of a banana.

(i) Use the given information to form two equations, in terms of x and y.

(ii) Solve these equations to find the cost of an apple and the cost of a banana.

10. Ilva bought two bottles of cola and one bag of crisps for €1·40. Karina bought one bottle of cola and three bags of crisps for €1·70. How much does each cost?

11. Five adult tickets and three child tickets to a concert costs €99. Eight adult tickets and six child tickets costs €168. How much do adult and child tickets cost?

12. The triangle shown is equilateral.

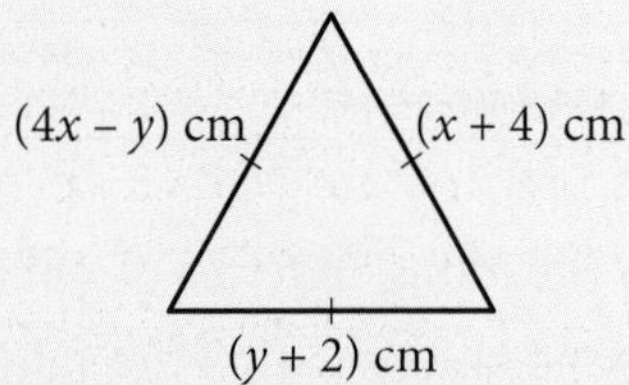

(i) Write two equations in terms of x and y.

(ii) Hence, solve these equations to find the values of x and y.

13. $h(x) = 3x + 2$ and $k(x) = \frac{1}{3}x - 3$.

(i) Using the same axes and scale, graph the functions $h(x)$ and $k(x)$ in the domain $-4 \leq x \leq 2$.

(ii) Use your graph to estimate the value of x, for which $h(x) = k(x)$.

(iii) Use algebra to verify your solution to part **(ii)**.

14. The diagram shows the graphs of two functions, $f(x)$ and $g(x)$.

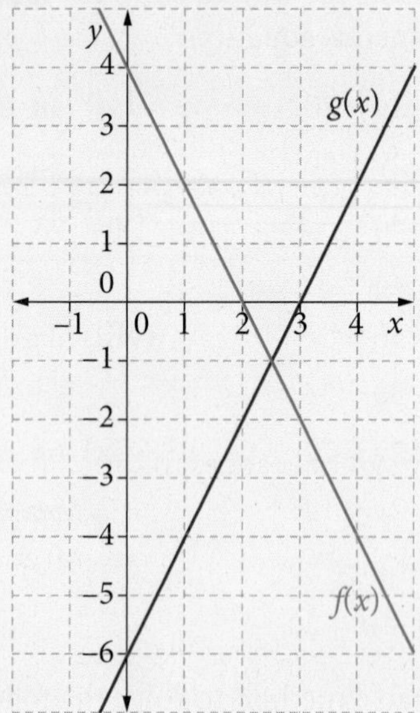

(i) Use the graphs to write down an expression for $f(x)$ and $g(x)$, in terms of x.

(ii) Use the graph to estimate the value of x, for which $f(x) = g(x)$.

(iii) Use algebra to verify your solution to part **(ii)**.

15. Jill needs to have trees removed from her garden. She contacts two different companies for their prices. Company A charge a flat fee of €50, plus €30 for each tree removed. Company B charge €35 for each tree removed and no flat fee.

(i) Write a function to represent the cost of using company A. Explain any letters you use in your function.

(ii) Write a function to represent the cost of using company B. Explain any letters you use in your function.

(iii) Using the same axes and scale, graph each function to show the cost of removing 20 trees with each company. Clearly indicate which graph represents which company.

(iv) If Jill is planning to remove seven trees, which company should she use? Justify your answer.

(v) If Jill is planning to remove 16 trees, which company should she use? Justify your answer.

(vi) Using the graphs, or otherwise, find the number of trees that will have the same removal cost with both companies.

Section 3.4: Linear Inequalities

Learning Outcome:

You should be able to:

- solve linear inequalities and graph the solution set on a number line

An **inequality** is a relationship between two expressions that are not equal. The equals sign is replaced by one of the inequality symbols: $<$, $>$, $\leq$ or $\geq$.

The inequality symbols are as follows:

$<$	Means less than	$\leq$	Means less than or equal to
$>$	Means greater than	$\geq$	Means greater than or equal to

Much like solving equations, when solving a linear inequality we must perform operations until the variable is on its own on one side. It is very important to remember that whatever operation you perform on one side of the inequality, you must also perform on the other side.

When you multiply or divide both sides of an inequality by a negative number, you must change the direction of the inequality.

Graphing a solution set

Links across the syllabus

You must be familiar with the types of numbers. These are covered in Chapter 1: Number Systems.

There are three types of numbers which we can graph on a number line:

Natural numbers (ℕ): positive whole numbers

When we graph natural numbers on a number line, we put dots on the whole numbers and leave the spaces between the whole numbers blank:

The following number line illustrates $x > 1, x \in \mathbb{N}$:

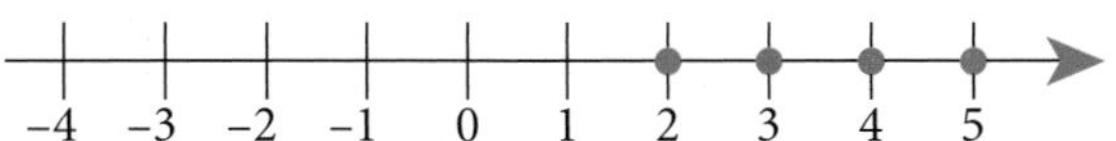

The arrow at the end of the number line indicates that the values continue on forever in that direction.

The following number line illustrates $3 \leq x < 8, x \in \mathbb{N}$:

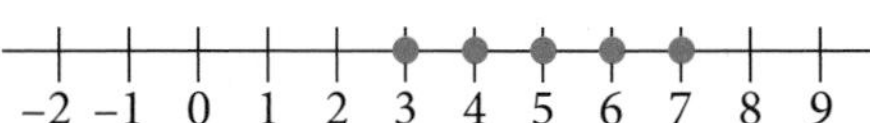

Integers (ℤ): positive and negative whole numbers

When we graph integers on a number line, we put dots on the whole numbers and leave the spaces between the whole numbers blank:

The following number line illustrates $x \leq 2, x \in \mathbb{Z}$:

When the inequality has an equals in it, the value is included in the solution set.

The following number line illustrates $-4 < x \leq 1,\ x \in \mathbb{Z}$:

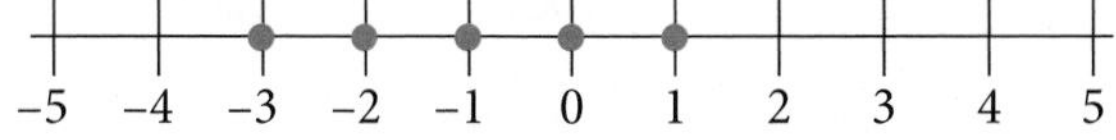

Real number ($\mathbb{R}$): all numbers, positive and negative, decimals, fractions and whole numbers

When we graph real numbers on a number line, we put a dot at the starting value and shade in the line, to show that all values between whole numbers are included.

The following number line illustrates $x \geq -1, x \in \mathbb{R}$:

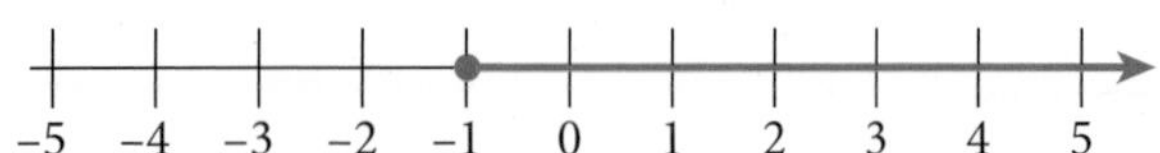

The following number line illustrates $x < 4, x \in \mathbb{R}$:

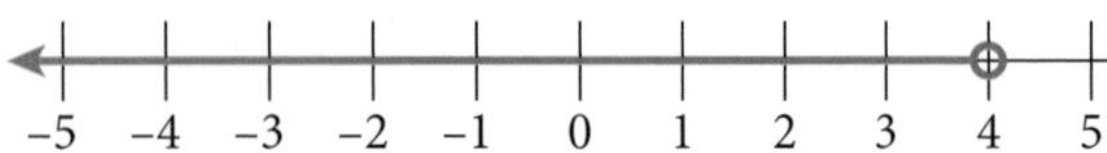

The following number line illustrates $-3 < x \leq 4, x \in \mathbb{R}$:

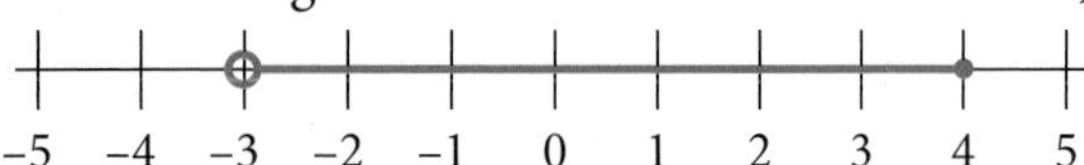

For real numbers, when the inequality has an equals in it, a dot is drawn at the starting value and the line is shaded from that point onwards.
When the inequality has no equals in it, an open circle is drawn at the starting value and the line is shaded from that point onwards.

EXAMPLE 1

Find the range of values of x for which $8x - 5 \leq 2x + 19, x \in \mathbb{N}$.
Graph your solution on the number line.

Solution

$8x - 5 \leq 2x + 19$

$8x - 5 + 5 \leq 2x + 19 + 5$ (add 5 to both sides)

$8x \leq 2x + 24$

$8x - 2x \leq 2x + 24 - 2x$ (subtract $2x$ from both sides)

$6x \leq 24$

$\frac{6x}{6} \leq \frac{24}{6}$ (divide both sides by 6)

$x \leq 4$

As $x \in \mathbb{N}$, this is the set of natural numbers less than or equal to 4.
Thus, the values of x are 1, 2, 3 and 4.

Number line: 0 1 2 3 4 5

$x \in \mathbb{N}$, so dots are used on the number line.

EXAMPLE 2

Find the range of values of k for which $3(k - 4) < 5(k - 2) - 7, k \in \mathbb{R}$ and graph your solution on the number line.

Solution

$3(k - 4) < 5(k - 2) - 7$

$3k - 12 < 5k - 10 - 7$ (multiply out the brackets)

$3k - 12 < 5k - 17$

$3k - 12 + 12 < 5k - 17 + 12$ (add 12 to both sides)

$3k < 5k - 5$

$3k - 5k < 5k - 5 - 5k$ (subtract $5k$ from both sides)

$-2k < -5$

$\frac{-2k}{-2} > \frac{-5}{-2}$ (divide both sides by -2 and **reverse the inequality**, i.e. turn $<$ into $>$)

$k > 2{\cdot}5$

Number line: 0 1 2 3 4 5 6 7 8 9

$k \in \mathbb{R}$, so we use full heavy shading on the number line. An open circle is put around 2·5 to indicate that it is **not** included in the solution.

EXAMPLE 3

(i) Find the solution set P of $3x - 4 \leq 2, x \in \mathbb{Z}$.

(ii) Find the solution set Q of $5 - 4x < 13, x \in \mathbb{Z}$.

(iii) Find $P \cap Q$ and graph your solution on the number line.

Solution

We solve each inequality separately and then combine the solutions.

(i) P: $3x - 4 \leq 2$

$3x \leq 2 + 4$ (add 4 to both sides)

$3x \leq 6$

$x \leq 2$ (divide both sides by 3)

(ii) Q: $5 - 4x < 13$

$-4x < 13 - 5$ (subtract 5 from both sides)

$-4x < 8$

$x > -2$ (divide both sides by -4)

(iii) Combining the two inequalities gives:

The set of positive and negative whole numbers between -2 and 2, including 2 but not including -2.

$P \cap Q$: $-2 < x \leq 2, x \in \mathbb{Z}$

Number line:

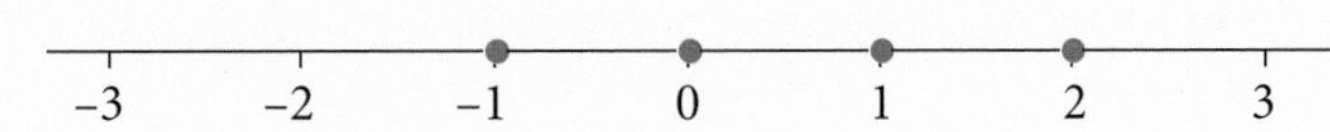

$x \in \mathbb{Z}$, so dots are used on the number line.

Practice Questions 3.4

1. Solve the following inequalities and graph your solution set on a number line.

(i)	$x + 3 < 7$,	$x \in \mathbb{N}$	**(vii)**	$x + 4 \geq 3(x - 1)$,	$x \in \mathbb{R}$
(ii)	$5a - 6 > 4$,	$a \in \mathbb{Z}$	**(viii)**	$2(p + 4) < 2 - p$,	$p \in \mathbb{R}$
(iii)	$5 - 3p < 8$,	$p \in \mathbb{R}$	**(ix)**	$3(k - 3) < 2(k - 1)$,	$k \in \mathbb{N}$
(iv)	$2x - 4 > 10x$,	$x \in \mathbb{R}$	**(x)**	$2(z - 1) \leq 5(z + 2)$,	$z \in \mathbb{R}$
(v)	$3z + 2 > z + 4$,	$z \in \mathbb{R}$	**(xi)**	$2x - 5 < \frac{1}{3}(x + 3)$,	$x \in \mathbb{Z}$
(vi)	$7 - 3x \leq 3 - x$,	$x \in \mathbb{N}$	**(xii)**	$2(x - 1) + 5x > 3x - 10$,	$x \in \mathbb{R}$

2. Write an inequality to represent each of the following shaded sections of the number line. Note that there may be more than one correct inequality to describe each solution set.

(i)
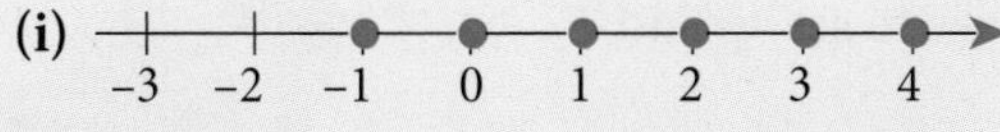

(ii)
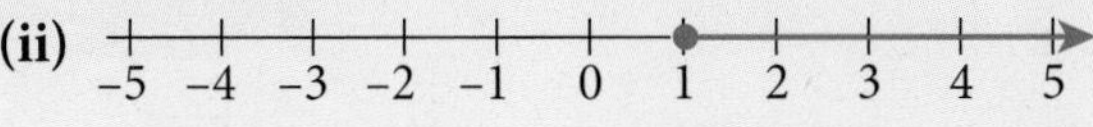

(iii)
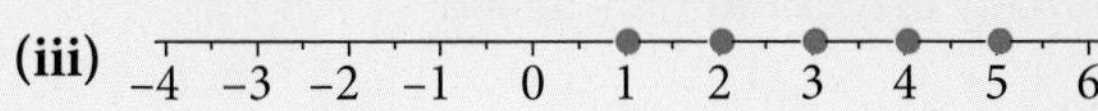

(iv)
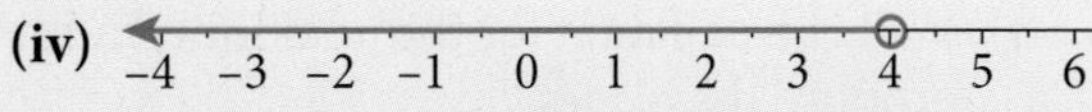

(v)
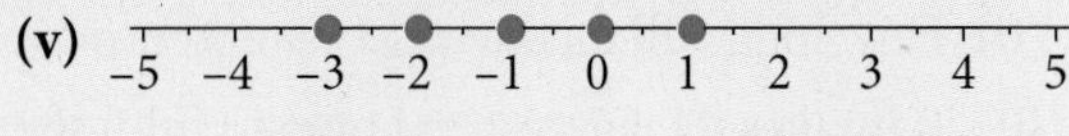

(vi)
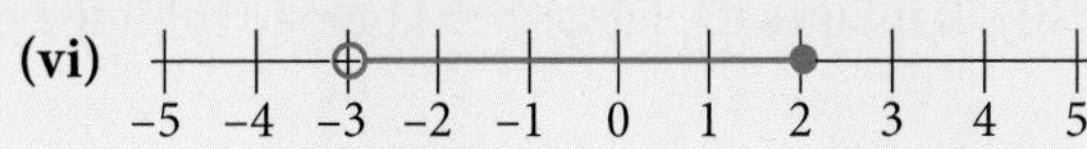

3. Write down the values of x that satisfy each of the following:
   (i) $x - 2 < 6$, where x is a positive, even number.
   (ii) $x + 4 > 7$, where x is a square number, less than 100.
   (iii) $2x - 13 < 37$, where x is a prime number.
   (iv) $3x + 5 < 26$, where x is a positive, odd number.

4. The width of a rectangle is $2x$ cm and its length is $(10 - x)$ cm, where $x \in \mathbb{N}$.

   (i) If the perimeter of the rectangle must be greater than 21 cm, find the smallest possible value of x.
   (ii) Hence, find the area of the rectangle for this value of x.

5. (i) Find the solution set of **(a)** P: $2x - 3 < 5, x \in \mathbb{Z}$ **(b)** Q: $5x + 2 \geq 2x - 1, x \in \mathbb{Z}$
   (ii) Find $P \cap Q$ and graph your solution on the number line.

6. (i) Find the solution set M of $4 - x < 6, x \in \mathbb{R}$.
   (ii) Find the solution set N of $3x - 1 \leq x + 9, x \in \mathbb{R}$.
   (iii) If $M \cap N = a < x \leq b$, write down the value of a and the value of b.
   (iv) Hence, find the value of $a(a + b)$.

7. (i) Find the solution set P of $3(x - 1) \leq x + 8, x \in \mathbb{R}$.
   (ii) Find the solution set Q of $5(x + 2) > 2(x - 1)$, $x \in \mathbb{R}$.
   (iii) If $P \cap Q = a < x \leq b$, write down the value of a and the value of b.
   (iv) Hence, find the value of $\sqrt{(a^2 + b^2)}$ correct to one decimal place.

8. Given $f(x) = 7x + 2$ and $g(x) = 3x + 22$.
   (i) Write down the values of x, for which $f(x) < g(x), x \in \mathbb{N}$.
   (ii) Solve the inequality $f(x) - g(x) \leq 6, x \in \mathbb{R}$ and, hence, graph the solution set on the number line.
   (iii) Solve the inequality $f(x) + 2g(x) \geq 7, x \in \mathbb{R}$ and, hence, graph the solution set on the number line.

Revision and Exam Style Questions – Section A

1. The function $f(x) = 3x - 2$ where $x \in \mathbb{R}$. Find:
   (i) $f(4)$
   (ii) the value of x for which $f(x) = -11$.

2. Solve $x = 3(8 - x)$.

3. List the solution set of $5k - 4 < 16, k \in \mathbb{N}$

4. Let $g(x) = 6 - kx$. Given $g(-3) = 21$, find the value of k.

5. Solve the following inequality and graph the solution set on a number line:

$$5x + 1 \geq 4x - 3, x \in \mathbb{R}$$

6. Solve the following pair of simultaneous equations: $3x + y = 5$ and $4x + 5y = 3$

7. Solve the following inequality and graph the solution set on a number line:

$$5x - 2 \geq 18, x \in \mathbb{R}$$

8. A factory produces custom-made machine parts. A lawnmower manufacturer orders blades from this factory. The factory manager determines that it will take eight hours to set up the manufacturing process and then 12 minutes per blade to manufacture.

   (i) Write an equation for the total time, in minutes, it will take to set up and produce the blades.
   (ii) How long will it take to set up and produce 72 blades?
   (iii) If it takes the factory 29 hours to fulfil the order, how many blades did they make?

9. Solve $5(x-3)-2(x+5)=-4$, where $x \in \mathbb{R}$.

10. Solve $\frac{k-7}{2}=\frac{k+3}{6}$

11. Solve the following inequality and graph the solution set on a number line: $2(3+4x) \leq 38$, $x \in \mathbb{Z}$

12. List all the values of x that satisfy the inequality $7x+4<2x+40$, where $x \in \mathbb{N}$.
Hence, graph this solution set on a number line.

Revision and Exam-Style Questions – Section B

More challenging problems

1. Find the value of x, which satisfies the equation $2(x+10)=12-3(x-6)$ and verify your solution.

2. Find the value of x, which satisfies the equation $\frac{2x-7}{3}-1=\frac{x-4}{6}$ and verify your solution.

3. The temperature, C, in degrees Celsius, of a liquid in an insulated container is related to time, t, in hours by the following function: $C=78-8t$
   - **(i)** Find the temperature of the liquid in the container after 2·5 hours.
   - **(ii)** Draw a graph of this function for $0 \leq t \leq 7$.
   - **(iii)** Use this graph to estimate how long it will take for the liquid to reach 42 °C.
   - **(iv)** Use your graph to estimate the time it takes for the temperature to drop from 65°C to 25°C.

4. Solve the following pair of simultaneous equations:
   $\frac{3}{4}x+\frac{1}{3}y=-\frac{1}{2}$ and $\frac{1}{2}x-\frac{5}{6}y=-\frac{7}{2}$

5. Solve the equation $\frac{1}{2}(2x-5)-6=\frac{1}{4}(8-12x)$ and verify your answer.

6. Kathy has a weight of 115 kg. After joining a weight-loss club Kathy has a steady weight loss of 1·5 kg per week.
   - **(i)** Write a function to represent Kathy's weight after W weeks.
   - **(ii)** What is the rate of change (slope) of this function?
   - **(iii)** Draw a graph of this function, to represent weight for the first 30 weeks.
   - **(iv)** The point (5, 107·5) is on the graph. Write a sentence that describes the meaning of this ordered pair.
   - **(iv)** Use this graph to find Kathy's weight after eight weeks.
   - **(v)** Use your graph to find how many weeks it takes Kathy to get to a weight of 82 kg.
   - **(vi)** Do you think this graph is a good representation of a person's weight loss? Give a reason for your answer.

7. Solve the following inequality and graph the solution set on a number line:
   $\frac{2-x}{4}-\frac{3}{8} \geq \frac{2}{5}$, $x \in \mathbb{R}$

8. Solve the equations below to find the values of p and q.
   $3p-4q=6$ and $p=3q+2$

9. Two couples, the Murphys and the O'Briens, have babies born in the same year. Soon after the birth, each couple opens a savings account to start saving for their child's future.
The Murphys initially deposit €1,000 and they then add a further €450 at the beginning of each subsequent year.
The O'Briens initially deposit €100 and they then add a further €600 at the beginning of each subsequent year.

(i) Copy and complete the following table to show the savings of each couple over an eight year period.

Year	1	2	3	4	5	6	7	8
Murphys account balance (€)	1,000	1,450						
O'Briens account balance (€)								

(ii) In what year will both couples have the same account balance?

(iii) Find, in terms of n, formulae that give the balance in each of the bank accounts in the nth year.

(iv) Use the formulae from part **(iii)** to verify your answer to part **(ii)** algebraically.

(v) If the couples continue to save at the same rate, how much will be in each account in the 15th year (i.e. when $n = 15$)?

10. (i) Find P, the solution set of $2x - 3 \leq 5, \quad x \in \mathbb{Z}$.

(ii) Find Q, the solution set of $\frac{-2 - 3x}{7} < 1, x \in \mathbb{Z}$.

(iii) List the elements of $P \cap Q$.

11. Pawel is hosting a party. He plans to use a catering company. He gets a quote from two different companies:
Company A charge a flat fee of €300, plus an additional €15 for every guest in attendance.
Company B charge €25 per person in attendance, with no flat fee.

(i) Write a function to represent the cost of using company A. Explain any letters you use in your function.

(ii) Write a function to represent the cost of using company B. Explain any letters you use in your function.

(iii) Using the same axes and scale, graph each function to show the cost of catering for up to 50 people. Clearly indicate which graph represents which company.

(iv) If Pawel is inviting 22 people, which company should he use? Justify your answer.

(v) If Pawel is inviting 45 people, which company should he use? Justify your answer.

(vi) Using the graphs, or otherwise, find how many guests Pawel could invite so that the cost incurred would be the same from both companies.

Now that you have completed the chapter, revisit the 'Something to think about…' question.

Algebra III – Quadratic Relations

CHAPTER 04

Sections covered within this chapter:

KEY WORDS

- Quadratic function
- Parabola
- Roots

SOMETHING TO THINK ABOUT… 

A sports club runs a weekly lottery draw, with a jackpot prize of €1,500.
On a given week, the jackpot prize was divided evenly between n people.
The following week the jackpot prize was divided evenly between $(n + 2)$ people.

In the second week, each winner received €25 **less** than those who won in the first week.
Find how many people shared the jackpot prize in the first week.

Section 4.1: Quadratic Functions

Learning Outcomes:

You should be able to:

- recognise a quadratic function
- graph a function of the form $ax^2 + bx + c = 0$
- use the graph of a quadratic function to find the roots of an equation

A **quadratic function** is a function wherein the greatest power of the variable is 2. It can be described by an equation of the form $f(x) = ax^2 + bx + c$ where $a \neq 0$.

Discussion Time

Work with a classmate to carry out the following tasks:

1. Given the function **output = (input)^2 – 3**, find the outputs for each of the inputs from –3 to 3.
2. Plot each (input, output) pair on a coordinated plane.
3. Join these points to form the graph of the function.
4. Repeat tasks **1** to **3** using the function **output = 6 – (input)^2** and inputs from –3 to 3.
5. Study each graph drawn and comment on their shape.

The graph of a quadratic function is either a ∪–shaped or an ∩–shaped curve, better known as a parabola.

A **parabola** is a two-dimensional, symmetrical curve.

The shape of the graph is determined by the coefficient of the x^2 part of the function:

If the coefficient of the x^2 part is positive ($a > 0$), the graph has a ∪ shape and ends by increasing:

For example: $y = 2x^2 - 10x + 7$

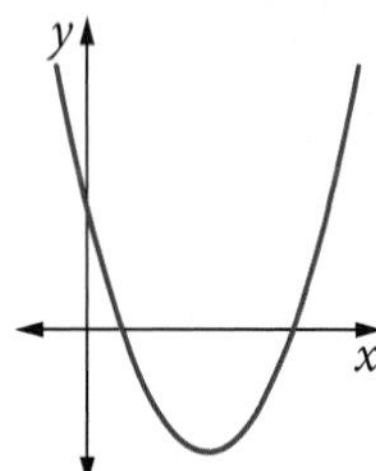

If the coefficient of the x^2 part is negative ($a < 0$), the graph has an ∩ shape and ends by decreasing:

For example: $y = -3x^2 + 18x - 14$

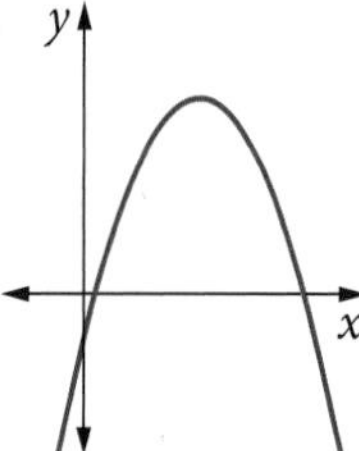

To draw the graph of a quadratic function, we must find a series of points (ordered pairs) along the curve. We find the coordinates of these points by substituting x-values into the function and finding the corresponding y-values. These values are known as the domain and the range.

Roots of a quadratic function

The **roots** of a quadratic function are the points where the graph of the function crosses the x-axis (the x-intercepts).

For a quadratic function $f(x)$, the roots are the values which satisfy the equation $f(x) = y = 0$.

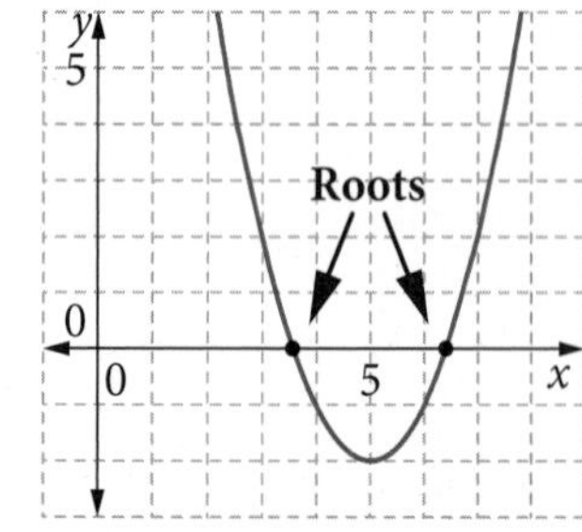

The position of the graph determines how many roots the function has.

If the graph intersects the x-axis twice, then the function has two distinct real roots.

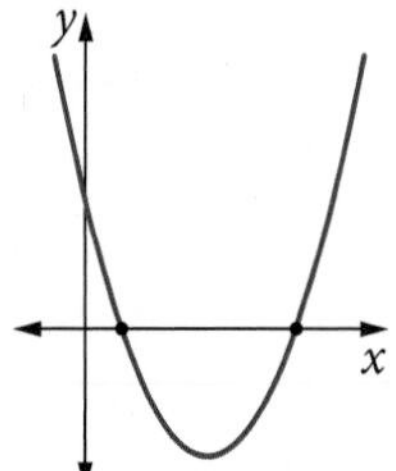

If the graph intersects the x-axis once, then the function has two equal real roots.

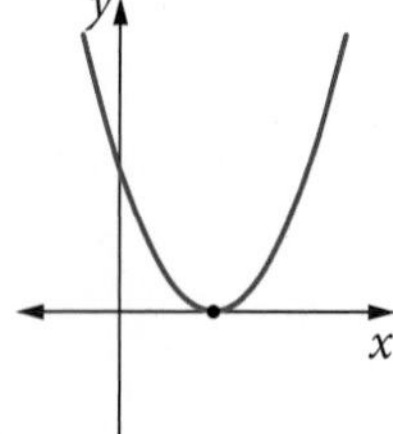

If the graph does not intersect the x-axis at all, then the function has no real roots.

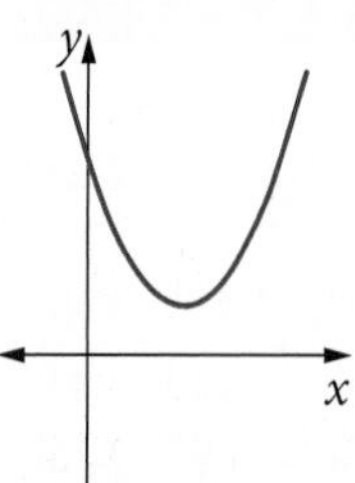

Links across the syllabus

You will encounter functions of this type when you are working on Chapter 28: Complex Numbers.

EXAMPLE 1

(i) Graph the function $f(x) = x^2 - 2x - 4$ in the domain $-2 \leq x \leq 4$.

(ii) Use your graph to estimate the roots of $f(x)$.

(iii) List the elements of the domain and the range.

Solution

(i) When asked to graph a function, we must find the coordinates of the points on the curve, then plot these points and draw the curve accurately.

Put x values into $f(x)$ and find y values:	Points
$f(-2) = (-2)^2 - 2(-2) - 4 = 4$	$(-2, 4)$
$f(-1) = (-1)^2 - 2(-1) - 4 = -1$	$(-1, -1)$
$f(0) = (0)^2 - 2(0) - 4 = -4$	$(0, -4)$
$f(1) = (1)^2 - 2(1) - 4 = -5$	$(1, -5)$
$f(2) = (2)^2 - 2(2) - 4 = -4$	$(2, -4)$
$f(3) = (3)^2 - 2(3) - 4 = -1$	$(3, -1)$
$f(4) = (4)^2 - 2(4) - 4 = 4$	$(4, 4)$

Plot the points and join with a curved line:

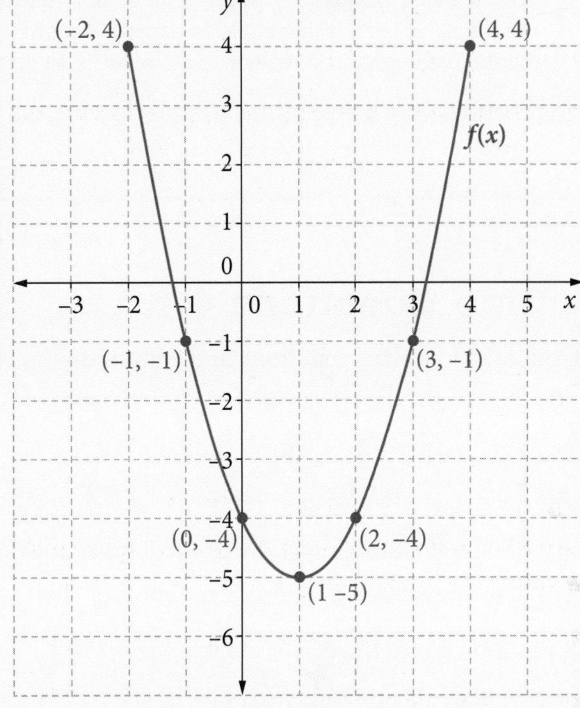

It is possible to use your calculator to generate the y values for the given x values.

(ii) The roots of the function are the values on the x-axis where the graph crosses the axis. That is, where $f(x) = 0$.

Looking closely at this section of the graph, we can mark in the position of the roots:

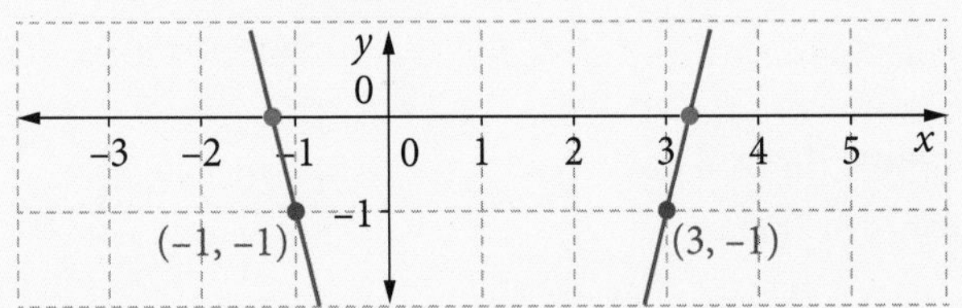

When the question says 'using the graph…' we must show work done on the graph. It is not acceptable to use algebra to solve the problem.

Reading from the x-axis, the roots are estimated to be at: $-1{\cdot}25$ and $3{\cdot}25$

These are the values where $f(x) = 0$.

(iii) Domain = x-values = $\{-2, -1, 0, 1, 2, 3, 4\}$

Range = y-values = $\{-5, -4, -1, 4\}$

Algebra III

EXAMPLE 2

Draw a sketch of the quadratic function which has a negative coefficient on the x^2 and roots -2 and $4\cdot5$.

Solution

- The fact that this function has a negative coefficient on the x^2 tells us that the curve has an $\cap$ shape and ends by decreasing.
- Roots of -2 and $4\cdot5$ tells us that the curve crosses the x-axis at these values.

Put these two pieces of information together to get the sketch shown:

When asked to **sketch** a function, we do not need to find a lot of points on the curve, or to scale the axes exactly. A drawing of the position and shape of the graph, in relation to the axes, is all that is required.

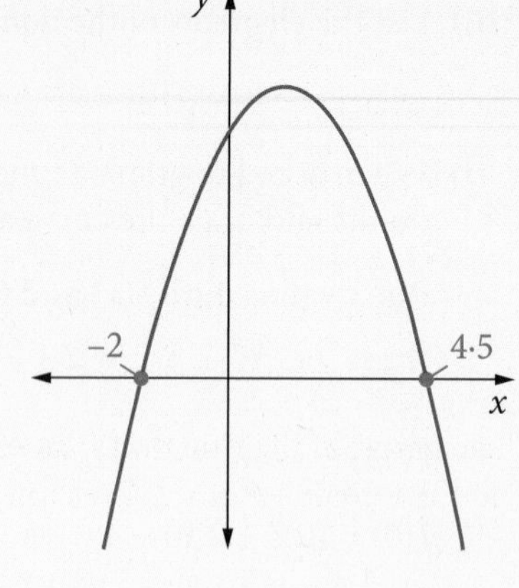

Practice Questions 4.1

1. Graph the following functions in the given domains.
   (i) $f(x) = x^2 - 4x - 5$ in the domain $-2 \leq x \leq 6$.
   (ii) $f(x) = 2x^2 - 12x + 9$ in the domain $0 \leq x \leq 6$.
   (iii) $f(x) = 7 - 3x^2$ in the domain $-2 \leq x \leq 2$.
   (iv) $f(x) = -x^2 + 3x + 12$ in the domain $-3 \leq x \leq 4$.
   (v) $f(x) = -2x^2 - 4x + 9$ in the domain $-4 \leq x \leq 1$.
2. (i) Graph the function $g(x) = x^2 + 6x + 2$ in the domain $-8 \leq x \leq 2$.
   (ii) Use your graph to estimate the roots of $g(x)$.
3. A function k is defined as $k: x \rightarrow x^2 - 4x + 4$.
   (i) Find $k(-1), k(0), k(1), k(2), k(3), k(4)$.
   (ii) Use your answers to part **(i)** to graph the function $k(x)$.
   (iii) Use your graph to estimate the roots of $k(x)$.
4. (i) Graph the function $h(x) = -3x^2 + 12x + 5$ in the domain $-1 \leq x \leq 5$.
   (ii) Use your graph to estimate the roots of $h(x)$.
   (iii) List the elements of the domain and range.
5. (i) Graph the function $f(x) = x^2 - 4x + 5$ in the domain $-1 \leq x \leq 5$.
   (ii) Use your graph to determine the nature of the roots of $f(x)$.
6. Sketch the functions which have the following properties:
   (i) Positive x^2 and roots -1 and 4
   (ii) Negative x^2 and roots 2 and $5\cdot5$
   (iii) Negative x^2 and roots $-3\cdot5$ and 0
   (iv) Positive x^2 and roots -6 and $-0\cdot5$
   (v) Positive x^2 and roots 1 and 1

Section 4.2: Reading and Interpreting Graphs

Learning Outcomes:

You should be able to:

- use graphical methods to find approximate solutions to $f(x) = 0$ and $f(x) = k$, where $k \in \mathbb{R}$
- use graphical methods to find approximate solutions to $f(x) = g(x)$, where $f(x)$ and $g(x)$ are both functions

It is important that you are able to use the graph to read required information. This is a particularly important skill to have when the graph is representing a real-life situation. For example, the height of a ball as time passes.

EXAMPLE 1

The graph of the function $f: x \to 3 + 2x - x^2$ in the domain $-2 \leq x \leq 4$ is shown.

Use the graph to find:

(i) the values of x for which $f(x) = 0$

(ii) the values of x for which $f(x) = -4$

(iii) estimate the value of $f(2\cdot5)$

(iv) the coordinates of the maximum point.

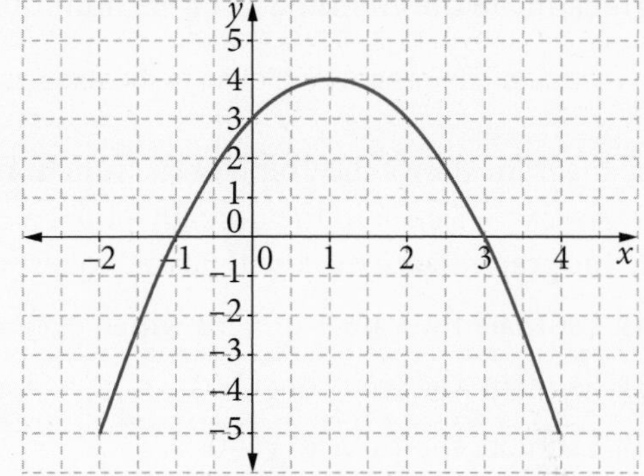

Solution

(i) To find the values of x for which $f(x) = 0$ means to find the values of x when $y = 0$.

Go to 0 on the y-axis and move across horizontally in both directions until you touch the graph.

You touch the graph at $x = -1$ and $x = 3$.

(shown in orange on the graph).

Therefore, when $f(x) = 0$, $x = -1$ and 3.

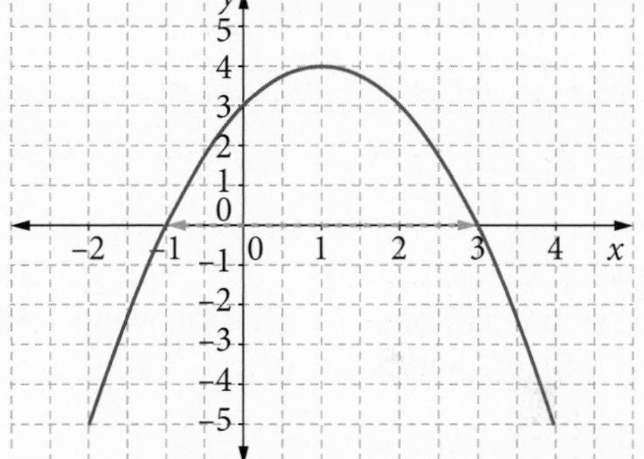

(ii) To find the values of x for which $f(x) = -4$ means to find the values of x when $y = -4$.

Go to -4 on the y-axis and move across horizontally in both directions until you touch the graph. Go up to the x-axis from there.

You touch the graph at $x = -1\cdot8$ and $x = 3\cdot8$

(shown in red on the graph).

Therefore, when $f(x) = -4$, $x = -1\cdot8$ and $3\cdot8$.

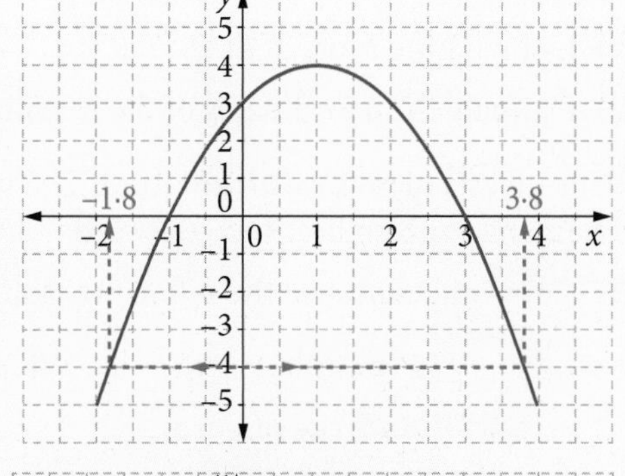

(iii) To find the values of $f(2\cdot5)$ means to find the values of y when $x = 2\cdot5$:

Go to $2\cdot5$ on the x-axis and move vertically until you touch the graph (shown in green on the graph). Go across to the y-axis from there.

You touch the graph at $y = 1\cdot8$.

Therefore, $f(2\cdot5) = 1\cdot8$.

(iv) The maximum point is the highest point that the curve reaches.

For this function, the coordinates of the maximum point are $(1, 4)$.

(shown in purple on the graph)

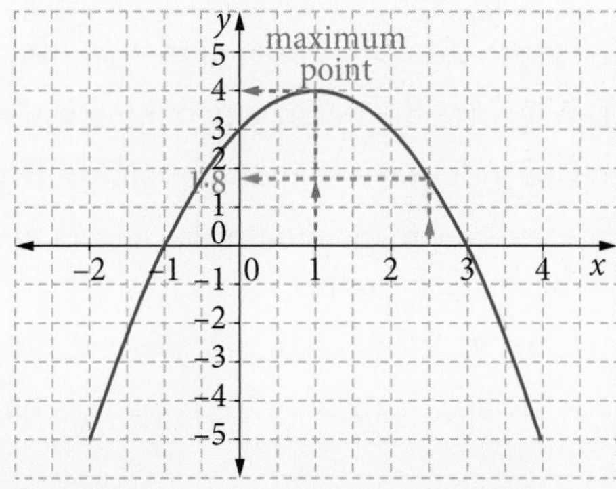

Practice Questions 4.2

1. The diagram shows the graph of the function $f(x) = x^2 - x - 8$ in the domain $-3 \leq x \leq 4$.
Use the graph to answer the following questions:
   (i) Find the values of x for which $f(x) = 4$.
   (ii) Estimate the values of x for which $f(x) = -4$.
   (iii) Estimate the value of $f(2{\cdot}5)$.
   (iv) Estimate the value of $f(-0{\cdot}5)$.
   (v) Estimate the roots of $f(x)$ (i.e. the values of x for which $f(x) = 0$).
   (vi) Estimate the coordinates of the minimum point on the graph.

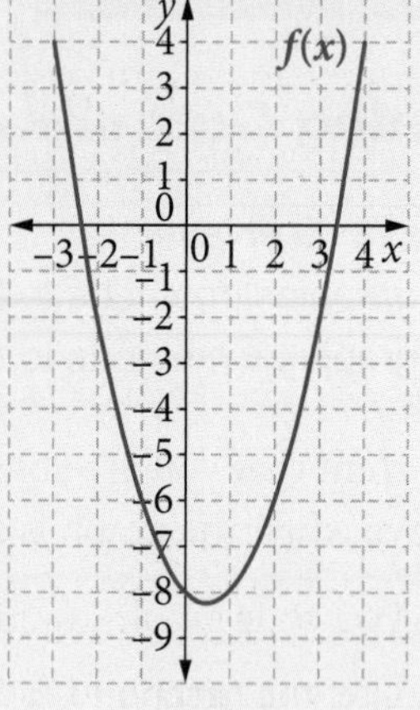

2. The diagram shows the graph of the function $g(x) = -2x^2 + 3x + 6$ in the domain $-1{\cdot}5 \leq x \leq 3$.
Use the graph to answer the following questions:
   (i) Estimate the values of x for which $g(x) = 2$.
   (ii) Estimate the value of $g(1{\cdot}5)$.
   (iii) Estimate the value of $g(-0{\cdot}5)$.
   (iv) Estimate the roots of $g(x)$.
   (v) Estimate the coordinates of the maximum point on the graph.

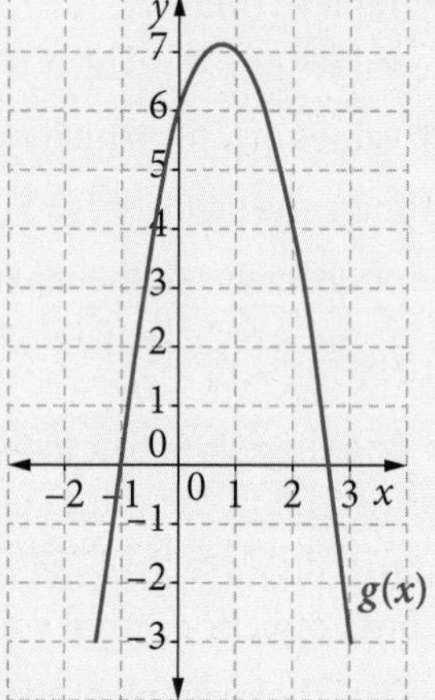

3. Graph the function $h(x) = -3x^2 + 2x + 7$ in the domain $-2 \leq x \leq 3$.
Use your graph to answer the following questions:
   (i) Estimate the values of x for which $h(x) = -2$.
   (iii) Estimate the value of $h(0{\cdot}5)$.
   (iv) Estimate the value of $h(-0{\cdot}5)$.
   (v) Estimate the roots of $h(x)$.
   (vi) Estimate the coordinates of the maximum point on the graph.

4. Dhafir invests in an investment fund. The value of the fund, v, in hundreds of euro, after t months of investment, is given by: $v(t) = 50 + 73t - 3t^2$.
   (i) Copy and complete the following table:

t (months)	0	4	8	12	16	20	24	28
$v(t)$ (hundreds of euro)								

   (ii) Hence, draw the graph of the $v(t)$ function.
   (iii) What was the initial sum of money that Dhafir invested?
   (iv) Use your graph to find the value of Dhafir's fund after 10 months.
   (v) After how many months is Dhafir's fund at a value of €25,000 for the *second* time? Give your answer to the nearest month.
   (vi) Estimate the maximum value that Dhafir's fund reaches.
   (vii) After how many months is Dhafir's fund worthless? Give your answer to the nearest month.

5. A company makes a weekly profit of p euro by selling x items, according to the equation

$$p(x) = -0{\cdot}5x^2 + 40x$$

(i) Copy and complete the following table:

x items sold (in 100s)	0	5	10	15	20	25	30	35	40
$p(x)$ (profit in 1,000s of euro)									

(ii) Draw a graph of the profit function, $p(x)$, in the domain $0 \leq x \leq 40$.

(iii) Use your graph to estimate the profit made on the sale of 2,200 items.

(iv) Use your graph to estimate the number of items the company would sell, in order to make a profit of €450,000.

6. During training, a tennis player hits a ball straight up into the air. The height of the ball, h, in metres, after t seconds is modelled by the following quadratic function:

$$h(t) = -12t^2 + 36t + 1$$

(i) Copy and complete the following table:

t (sec)	0	0·5	1	1·5	2	2·5	3
$h(t)$ (m)							

(ii) Hence, draw the graph of the $h(t)$ function.

Using your graph:

(iii) find the maximum height the ball reached

(iv) estimate how long it takes until the ball hits the ground

(v) estimate the two times when the height of the ball is 10 m. Give your answers to one decimal place.

7. A diver jumps off a spring board. He starts by going up into the air and then dives down into the swimming pool below.
The height of the diver, h, in metres, above the water in the pool, t seconds after he leaves the spring board, is modelled by the following quadratic function:

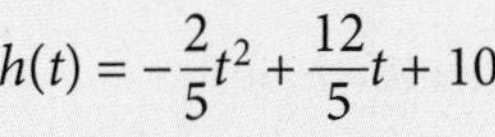

$$h(t) = -\frac{2}{5}t^2 + \frac{12}{5}t + 10$$

(i) Graph the function $h(t)$ in the domain $0 \leq t \leq 9$.

Use your graph to solve the following:

(ii) Estimate the maximum height that the diver reaches.

(iii) Find the height of the diver after five seconds.

(iv) Estimate the height of the diver after 7·5 seconds.

(v) How long is the diver in the air for? Give your answer to one decimal place.

8. The average daytime temperature, T, in Paris can be modelled by:

$$T(m) = -0{\cdot}8m^2 + 10m - 1$$

where $T(m)$ represents the average temperature (in degrees celsius) in Paris during month m of the year.

(i) Given that $m = 1$ represents the **start** of January, find the average temperature at the start of each month for a year and hence draw the graph of this model.

Use your graph to solve the following:

(ii) Write down the value of $T(4)$ and explain its meaning in words.

(iii) During which two months is the average temperature 18°C?

(iv) Estimate the highest average temperature that is reached in Paris and state during which month it occurs.

Section 4.3: Solving Quadratic Equations

Learning Outcomes:

You should be able to:

- solve an equation of the form $ax^2 + bx + c = 0$, $a \neq 0$ by factorising
- solve an equation of the form $ax^2 + bx + c = 0$, $a \neq 0$, which cannot be easily factorised (using the quadratic formula)

In section 4.1 of this chapter, we learnt how to read the approximate roots of an equation from a graph. Now we will learn how to solve a quadratic equation algebraically, to find the exact values of the roots.

Any equation of the form $ax^2 + bx + c = 0$, $a \neq 0$, is called a quadratic equation. Solving a quadratic equation gives us the two values which satisfy the equation. These are known as the roots of the equation.

To solve a quadratic equation, follow these steps:

Step 1: Rearrange the equation into the form $ax^2 + bx + c = 0$.

Step 2: Factorise the quadratic.

Step 3: Let each factor equal zero.

Step 4: Solve each linear equation.

Links across the syllabus

Factorising is an essential skill to have here. Factorising is covered in Chapter 2: Algebra I.

EXAMPLE 1

Solve the following quadratic equations:

(i) $3x^2 = 15x$ (ii) $4x^2 - 49 = 0$

Solution

(i) $3x^2 = 15x$

Step 1: $3x^2 - 15x = 0$ (rearrange)

Step 2: Factorise by HCF:

$$3x(x - 5) = 0$$

Step 3: $3x = 0$ or $x - 5 = 0$

Step 4: $x = 0$ or $x = 5$

These values for x are called the **roots of the quadratic equation.** These values are the points where the graph of the quadratic function crosses the x-axis.

(ii) $4x^2 - 49 = 0$

Step 1: $(2x)^2 - (7)^2 = 0$

Step 2: Factorise by difference of two squares:

$$(2x + 7)(2x - 7) = 0$$

Step 3: $2x + 7 = 0$ or $2x - 7 = 0$

$2x = -7$ or $2x = 7$

Step 4: $x = -\frac{7}{2}$ or $x = \frac{7}{2}$

EXAMPLE 2

Solve the following quadratic equations:

(i) $x^2 + 4x - 21 = 0$

(ii) $2x^2 = 3 - 5x$

Solution

(i) ***Step 1:*** $x^2 + 4x - 21 = 0$

Step 2: Factorise by trial and improvement:

$$(x - 3)(x + 7) = 0$$

Step 3: $x - 3 = 0$ or $x + 7 = 0$

Step 4: $x = 3$ or $x = -7$

(ii) $2x^2 = 3 - 5x$

Step 1: $2x^2 + 5x - 3 = 0$

Step 2: Factorise by trial and improvement:

$$(2x - 1)(x + 3) = 0$$

Step 3: $2x - 1 = 0$ or $x + 3 = 0$

Step 4: $2x = 1$ or $x = -3$

$x = \frac{1}{2}$

Quadratic formula

Some quadratic equations, $ax^2 + bx + c$ cannot be easily factorised. When this is the case, we can use a formula to solve the equation.

The roots of the quadratic equation $ax^2 + bx + c = 0$ are found using the formula:

The quadratic formula can be used to solve **any** quadratic equation, not only ones which cannot be easily factorised.

$$x = \frac{-b \pm \sqrt{b^2 - 4ac}}{2a}$$

The quadratic formula appears on page 20 of the booklet of *formulae and tables* as follows:

$$x = \frac{-b \pm \sqrt{b^2 - 4ac}}{2a}$$

roots of the quadratic equation $ax^2 + bx + c = 0$

EXAMPLE 3

(i) Solve the equation $2x^2 - 5x - 6 = 0$, giving your answers in surd form.

(ii) Hence, express the answers for part **(i)**, correct to two decimal places.

When the question asks you to leave your answer in surd or decimal form, this generally means you will not be able to factorise easily and so need to use the quadratic formula.

Solution

(i) $2x^2 - 5x - 6 = 0$

$$x = \frac{-b \pm \sqrt{b^2 - 4ac}}{2a}, \text{ where } a = 2, b = -5, c = -6$$

$$= \frac{-(-5) \pm \sqrt{(-5)^2 - 4(2)(-6)}}{2(2)}$$

$$= \frac{5 \pm \sqrt{25 + 48}}{4}$$

$$= \frac{5 \pm \sqrt{73}}{4}$$

(ii) We find $\sqrt{73} = 8{\cdot}544$, therefore:

$$x = \frac{5 \pm 8{\cdot}544}{4}$$

$$x = \frac{5 + 8{\cdot}544}{4} \quad \text{or} \quad x = \frac{5 - 8{\cdot}544}{4}$$

$$x = \frac{13{\cdot}544}{4} \quad \text{or} \quad x = \frac{-3{\cdot}544}{4}$$

$$x = 3{\cdot}386 \quad \text{or} \quad x = -0{\cdot}886$$

Therefore, $x = 3{\cdot}39$ or $-0{\cdot}89$ correct to two decimal places.

Practice Questions 4.3

1. Factorise and hence solve the following quadratic equations:

(i) $8x^2 - 16x = 0$ **(vi)** $a^2 - a - 12 = 0$
(ii) $6x^2 + 3x = 0$ **(vii)** $5k^2 - 35k = 0$
(iii) $16x^2 - 9 = 0$ **(viii)** $b^2 + 10b + 16 = 0$
(iv) $p^2 - 8p + 12 = 0$ **(ix)** $x^2 + 15x + 36 = 0$
(v) $4x^2 - 36 = 0$

2. Factorise and hence solve the following quadratic equations:

(i) $2c^2 - 5c - 12 = 0$ **(vi)** $4t^2 + 12t + 9 = 0$
(ii) $3x^2 + 10x + 8 = 0$ **(vii)** $4x^2 - 23x + 15 = 0$
(iii) $11t^2 - 32t - 3 = 0$ **(viii)** $9a^2 + 12a + 4 = 0$
(iv) $3a^2 + 10a - 8 = 0$ **(ix)** $12x^2 + 32x + 5 = 0$
(v) $4x^2 + 10x + 6 = 0$

3. Rearrange the following quadratic equations into the form $ax^2 + bx + c = 0$, and hence factorise and solve.

(i) $4x^2 - 46 = 3$ **(vi)** $2x^2 = 3x + 2$
(ii) $k^2 - 7 = 9$ **(vii)** $9a^2 = 73a - 8$
(iii) $6x^2 = 24x$ **(viii)** $9h^2 + 4 = 15h$
(iv) $7x^2 = 15x - 2$ **(ix)** $5x^2 - 11x - 3 = 2x + 3$
(v) $7k = 15 - 2k^2$

4. Use the quadratic formula to solve the following quadratic equations.
Leave your answer in simplest surd form.

(i) $x^2 + 2x - 2 = 0$
(ii) $a^2 + 6a - 1 = 0$
(iii) $x^2 - 7x - 4 = 0$
(iv) $p^2 + 8p - 4 = 0$
(v) $2x^2 + 5x + 1 = 0$
(vi) $3k^2 - 10k + 5 = 0$

5. Rearrange the following quadratic equations into the form $ax^2 + bx + c = 0$ and hence solve using the quadratic formula. Give your answer to two decimal places.

(i) $x^2 + 5x = -1$ **(iv)** $k^2 - 4 = 7k$
(ii) $x^2 = 3x + 1$ **(v)** $8x = 2 - 5x^2$
(iii) $9a = 4 - a^2$ **(vi)** $4p^2 = 3 - 5p$

6. **(i)** The function $f(x) = x^2 - x - 6$. Solve the equation $f(x) = 0$.
(ii) Hence draw a sketch of the graph of $f(x)$.

7. **(i)** The function $g(x) = -x^2 + 3x + 4$. Solve the equation $g(x) = 0$.
(ii) Hence draw a sketch of the graph of $g(x)$.

8. **(i)** The function $h(x) = 2x^2 - 3x - 5$. Solve the equation $h(x) = 0$.
(ii) By replacing $h(x)$ with $2x^2 - 3x - 5$, express $h(x) = 9$ in terms of x.
(iii) Hence, solve the equation $h(x) = 9$.
(iv) Draw a sketch of the graph of $h(x)$.

9. **(i)** The function $f(x) = -3x^2 + 2x + 8$. Solve the equation $f(x) = 0$.
(ii) By replacing $f(x)$ with $-3x^2 + 2x + 8$, express $f(x) = 3$ in terms of x.
(iii) Find the values of x for which $f(x) = 3$.
(iv) Draw a sketch of the graph of $f(x)$.

10. Given the function $f(x) = x^2 + 2x - 3$

(i) Solve $f(x) = 0$.

(ii) Hence, identify which of the following graphs represents the function $f(x)$. Give a reason for your answer.

(a)

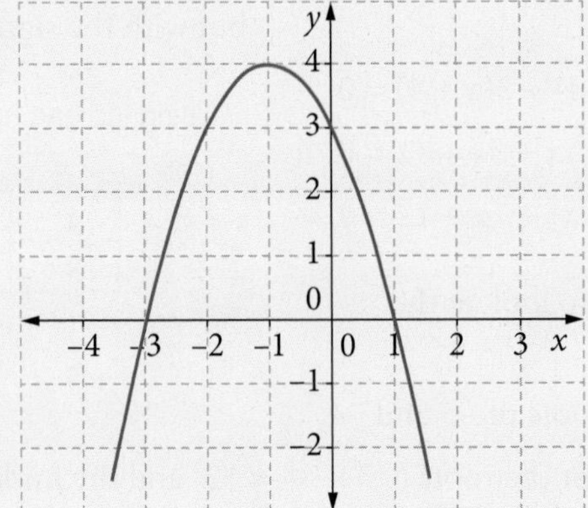

(c)

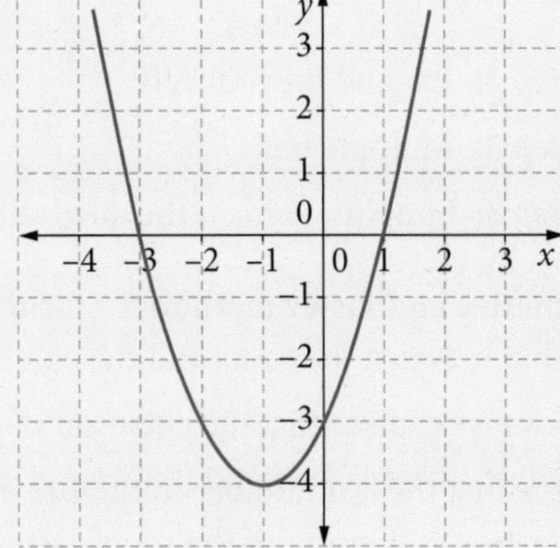

(b)

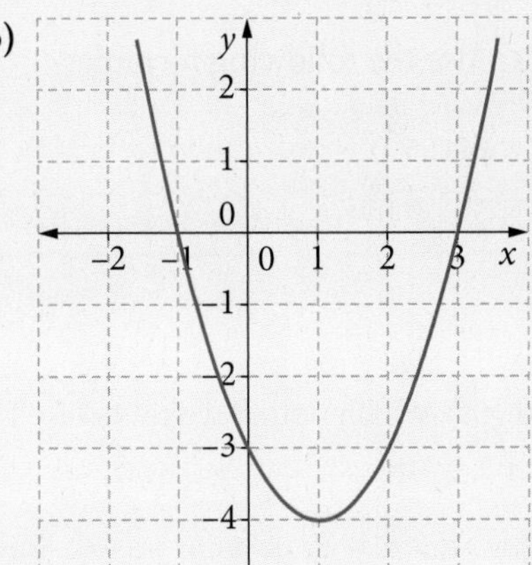

(d)

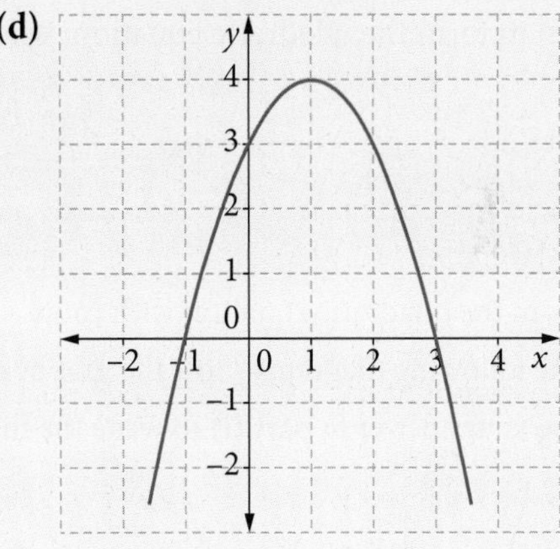

11. **(i)** Verify that $1 + \sqrt{7}$ is a root of the function $f(x) = x^2 - 2x - 6$.

(ii) Find the other root of $f(x) = 0$.

(iii) Hence draw a sketch of the graph of $f(x)$.

12. **(i)** Verify that $1 - \sqrt{10}$ is a root of the function $f(x) = -x^2 + 2x + 9$.

(ii) Find the other root of $f(x) = 0$.

(iii) Hence draw a sketch of the graph of $f(x)$.

Putting the roots into decimal form will make it easier to graph.

Section 4.4: Forming a Quadratic Equation, When Given its Roots

Learning Outcome:

You should be able to:

- form quadratic equations, given whole number roots

If we examine the quadratic equation: $x^2 + 7x + 12 = 0$

factorising gives: $(x + 3)(x + 4) = 0$

solving gives: $x = -3$ or $x = -4$

Therefore, the roots of $x^2 + 7x + 12 = 0$ are $x = -3$ or $x = -4$.

If we are given the roots and asked to form the quadratic equation, we simply reverse the order of the steps shown on the previous page.

Step 1: Start with the roots: $x = -3$ or $x = -4$

Step 2: Form the factors: $(x + 3)(x + 4) = 0$ (the same values as the roots, but with the signs changed)

Step 3: Expand the brackets: $x(x + 4) + 3(x + 4) = 0$

Step 4: Multiply out: $x^2 + 4x + 3x + 12 = 0$

Step 5: Simplify to form the quadratic equation: $x^2 + 7x + 12 = 0$

Using the grid method:

	x	3
x	x^2	$3x$
4	$4x$	12

An alternative and faster method for forming the equation is to look at the relationship between the roots and the values in the equation.

From above we can see that the equation $x^2 + 7x + 12 = 0$ has roots of -3 and -4.

We can see that the last number in the equation is the product of the roots ($-3 \times -4 = 12$) and the middle number in the equation is the sum of the roots, but with the opposite sign ($-3 - 4 = -7$).

Therefore, to form the quadratic equation, when given the roots, we can use the following formula:

$$x^2 - (\text{sum of roots})x + (\text{product of roots}) = 0$$

EXAMPLE 1

(i) Form the quadratic equation with roots -2 and 5.

(ii) The following diagrams show the graphs of the functions, $f(x)$ and $g(x)$, which both have roots of -2 and 5. Use your answer to part **(i)** to write the functions $f(x)$ and $g(x)$.

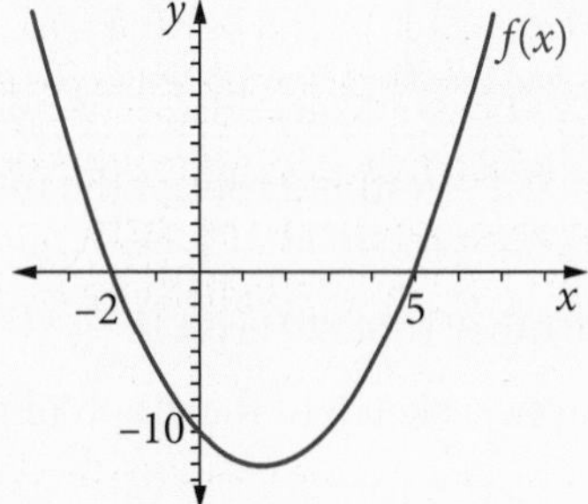

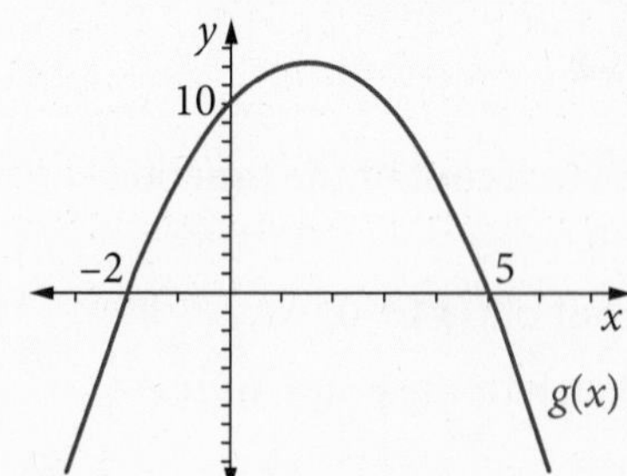

Solution

(i) Method 1:

Step 1: $x = -2$ or $x = 5$ (let x equal each of the roots)

Step 2: $(x + 2)(x - 5) = 0$ (form the factors)

Step 3: $x(x - 5) + 2(x - 5) = 0$ (expand the brackets)

Step 4: $x^2 - 5x + 2x - 10 = 0$

Step 5: $x^2 - 3x - 10 = 0$ (simplify to form the quadratic equation)

Method 2:

Sum of the roots: $-2 + 5 = +3$

Product of the roots: $(-2)(5) = -10$

$x^2 - (\text{sum of roots})x + \text{product of roots} = 0$

$x^2 - (3)x + (-10) = 0$

$x^2 - 3x - 10 = 0$

(ii) Since the $f(x)$ graph is a ∪ shape, the coefficient of the x^2 part must be positive.
Therefore, $f(x) = x^2 - 3x - 10$.

Since the $g(x)$ graph is an ∩ shape, the coefficient of the x^2 part must be negative.
Therefore, we must multiply the $f(x)$ function by -1, giving $g(x) = -x^2 + 3x + 10$.

Practice Questions 4.4

1. Form the quadratic equations with the following roots:
   - (i) 2 and 4
   - (ii) 7 and 3
   - (iii) 4 and 6
   - (iv) −1 and 3
   - (v) −2 and 9
   - (vi) 8 and −2
   - (vii) 12 and −3
   - (viii) −2 and −6
   - (ix) −7 and −4

2. The quadratic equation $x^2 + px + q = 0$ has roots 7 and 2. Find the values of p and q.

3. The quadratic equation $x^2 + cx + d = 0$ has roots −6 and −4. Find the values of c and d.

4. (i) Form the quadratic equation with roots −3 and 8.
   (ii) Verify your result by factorising and solving this quadratic equation.

5. For each of the following graphs:
   (i) identify the roots of the function
   (ii) form the equation
   (iii) verify the roots of the equation, algebraically
   (iv) given each graph is illustrating a function $f(x)$, write the function in each case.

(a)

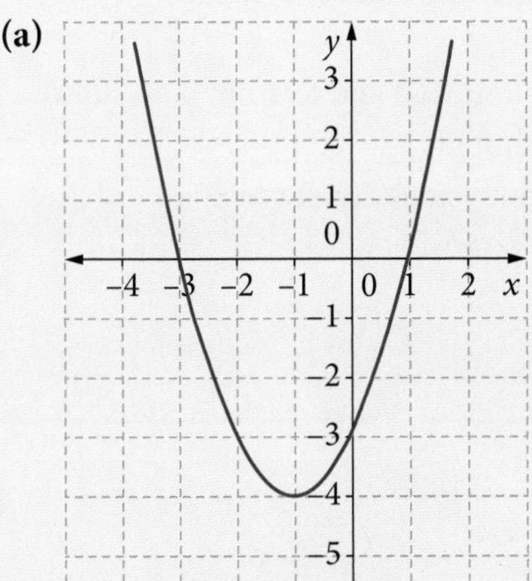

(b)

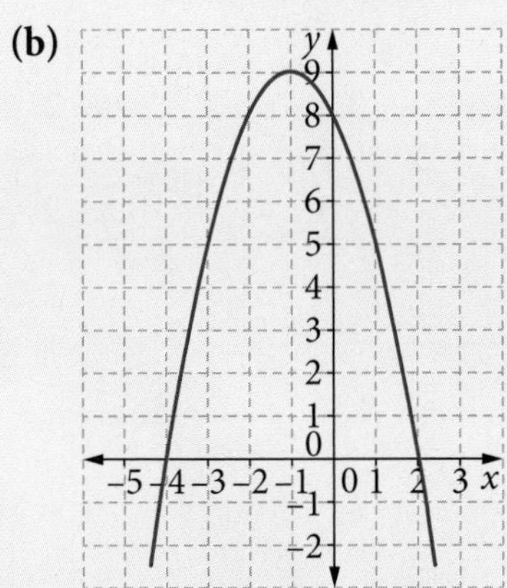

(c)

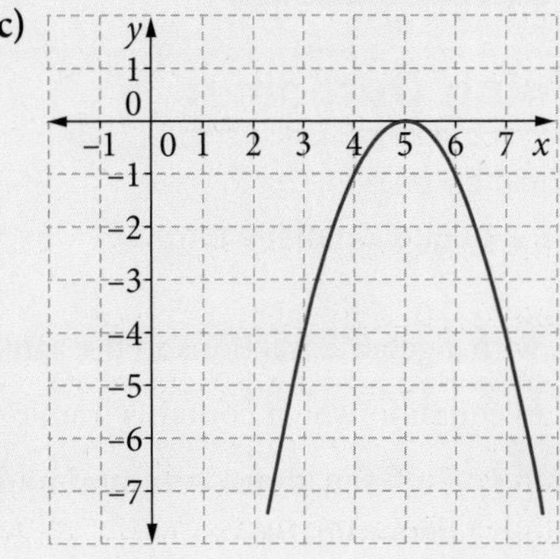

(d)

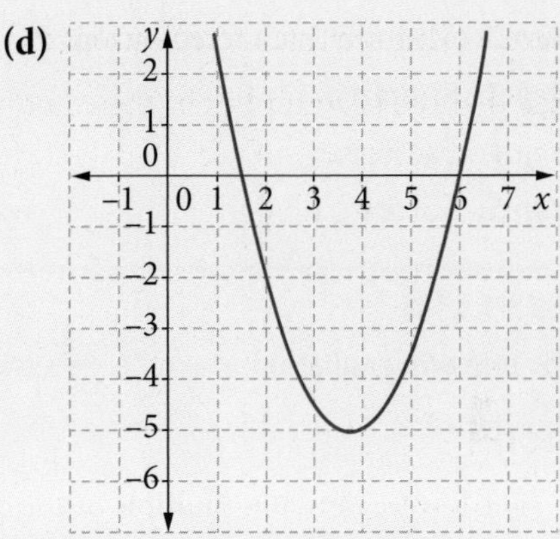

6. (i) Form the quadratic equation with roots 5 and −9.
   (ii) Verify your result by factorising and solving this quadratic equation.
   (iii) The graph of a function, $k(x)$, has roots 5 and −9 and crosses the y-axis at the point (0, −45). Draw a sketch of the graph of $k(x)$.
   (iv) Write down the function, $k(x)$.

7. (i) Form the quadratic equation with roots −4 and −11.
   (ii) Verify your result by factorising and solving this quadratic equation.
   (iii) The graph of a function, $g(x)$, has roots −4 and −11 and crosses the y-axis at the point (0, −44). Draw a sketch of the graph of $g(x)$.
   (iv) Write down the function, $g(x)$.

Section 4.5: Equations Involving Fractions

Learning Outcome:

You should be able to:

- solve an equation of the form $ax^2 + bx + c = 0$, $a \neq 0$, where a, b or c are fractions

We work with algebraic fractions in the same way as we work with numerical fractions.

To solve an equation which contains fractions, follow these steps:

> **Links across the syllabus**
>
> Adding fractions is covered in Chapter 1: Number Systems.

Step 1: Find the lowest common multiple (LCM) of the denominators

Step 2: Multiply each term by this LCM

Step 3: Simplify

Step 4: Factorise

Step 5: Solve

EXAMPLE 1

Solve the following equation: $\frac{1}{x} + \frac{5}{x+4} = 2$

Solution

Step 1: The lowest common multiple of the denominators is: $(x)(x+4)$

Step 2: $(\cancel{x})(x+4)\left(\frac{1}{\cancel{x}}\right) + (x)(\cancel{x+4})\left(\frac{5}{\cancel{x+4}}\right) = (x)(x+4)(2)$ (multiply all parts by $(x)(x+4)$)

Step 3:

$(x+4)(1) + (x)(5) = (x)(x+4)(2)$ (simplify each fraction)

$x + 4 + 5x = (x^2 + 4x)(2)$ (multiply out the brackets)

$4 + 6x = 2x^2 + 8x$

$0 = 2x^2 + 8x - 6x - 4$ (subtract 4 and $6x$ from both sides)

$0 = 2x^2 + 2x - 4$ (simplify)

$0 = x^2 + x - 2$ (both sides divided by 2)

Step 4: $0 = (x+2)(x-1)$ (factorise)

$x + 2 = 0$ or $x - 1 = 0$

Step 5: $x = -2$ or $x = 1$

Practice Questions 4.5

1. Solve the following equations:

   (i) $\frac{3}{x} + \frac{3}{2x} = 2$

   (ii) $\frac{3}{2x} + \frac{4}{x+1} = 5$

   (iii) $\frac{5}{4a} + \frac{3}{2a} = \frac{11}{16}$

   (iv) $\frac{3}{s} - \frac{2}{2s-1} = 1$

   (v) $\frac{1}{a-4} + \frac{1}{a} = \frac{2}{3}$

   (vi) $\frac{1}{x} + \frac{3}{x-1} = \frac{7}{2}$

2. Solve the following equations:

   (i) $\frac{3}{2x-1} - \frac{4}{3x-1} = 1$

   (ii) $\frac{6}{x-3} - \frac{3}{x-1} = \frac{7}{5}$

   (iii) $\frac{7}{p+2} + \frac{1}{p-1} = 4$

   (iv) $\frac{8}{z-2} + \frac{8}{z+2} = 3$

3. Solve the following equations and leave your answer correct to two decimal places.

(i) $\frac{9}{x+3}+\frac{4}{x}=\frac{1}{6}$ (iii) $\frac{4}{m-2}+\frac{7}{m+1}=3$

(ii) $\frac{5}{z}-\frac{4}{z+2}=\frac{3}{5}$ (iv) $\frac{3}{4x+1}-\frac{4}{x+2}=2$

4. Solve the following equations and leave your answer in surd form.

(i) $\frac{4}{z-4}-\frac{5}{z}=1$ (iii) $\frac{6}{x+1}+\frac{3}{x-1}=\frac{7}{2}$

(ii) $\frac{3}{n+1}+\frac{1}{n-1}=1$ (iv) $\frac{2}{y+1}+\frac{1}{y-1}=2$

Section 4.6: Simultaneous Equations – One Linear and One Quadratic Equation

Learning Outcome:

You should be able to:

- solve one linear equation and one quadratic equation with two unknowns and interpret the results

To solve one linear equation and one quadratic equation simultaneously, we use the **substitution method**. The steps involved in using the substitution method are outlined as follows:

Step 1: Rearrange the linear equation to get one variable on its own.

Step 2: Substitute this expression for the variable into the quadratic equation. This equation will now be in terms of one variable only.

Step 3: Solve the resulting quadratic equation.

Step 4: Take the known values and substitute back into the linear equation, to find the values of the other variable.

Graphically, solving a linear and a quadratic equation simultaneously gives the point(s) of intersection between a line (linear function) and a curve (quadratic equation), if they exist.

Two points of intersection

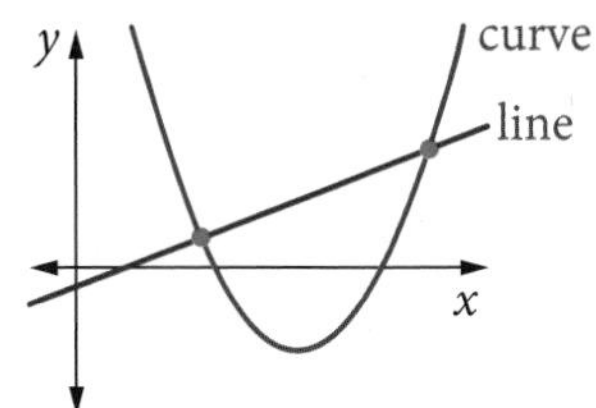

One point of intersection

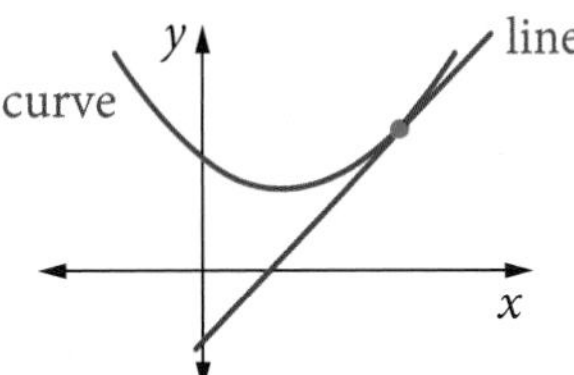

No points of intersection

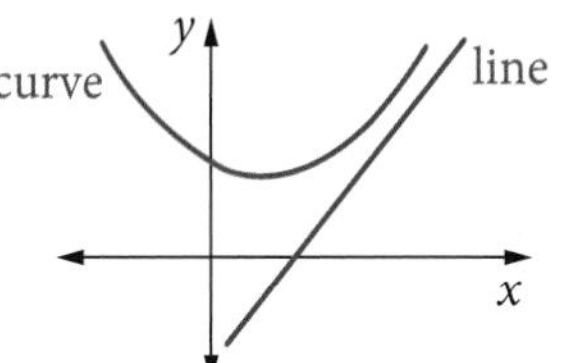

EXAMPLE 1

Solve the following pair of simultaneous equations: $2x - y = 2$ and $x^2 + 2y^2 = 12$

Solution

Step 1: Rearrange the linear equation to get y alone:

$2x - y = 2$

$-y = 2 - 2x$ (subtract $2x$ from both sides)

$y = -2 + 2x$ (multiply both sides by -1)

$y = 2x - 2$ (rearrange)

Step 2: Substitute $y = 2x - 2$ into the quadratic equation:

$$x^2 + 2y^2 = 12$$

$$x^2 + 2(2x - 2)^2 = 12 \qquad \text{(replace } y \text{ with } (2x - 2))$$

$$x^2 + 2(2x - 2)(2x - 2) = 12$$

$$x^2 + 2[2x(2x - 2) - 2(2x - 2)] = 12$$

$$x^2 + 2(4x^2 - 4x - 4x + 4) = 12$$

$$x^2 + 2(4x^2 - 8x + 4) = 12 \qquad \text{(multiply out the brackets)}$$

$$x^2 + 8x^2 - 16x + 8 = 12$$

$$9x^2 - 16x + 8 - 12 = 0 \qquad \text{(simplify)}$$

$$9x^2 - 16x - 4 = 0$$

Step 3: Solve the resulting equation:

$$9x^2 - 16x - 4 = 0$$

$$(9x + 2)(x - 2) = 0 \qquad \text{(factorise)}$$

$$9x + 2 = 0 \quad \text{or} \quad x - 2 = 0 \qquad \text{(let each bracket equal zero)}$$

$$9x = -2 \quad \text{or} \quad x = 2 \qquad \text{(solve each equation)}$$

$$x = -\frac{2}{9} \quad \text{or} \quad x = 2$$

Step 4: Take these values for x and substitute them back into the linear equation: $2x - 2 = y$

$x = -\frac{2}{9}$:

$$2x - 2 = y$$

$$2\left(-\frac{2}{9}\right) - 2 = y$$

$$-\frac{4}{9} - 2 = y \qquad \text{(multiply by 9)}$$

$$-4 - 18 = 9y$$

$$-22 = 9y$$

$$-\frac{22}{9} = y \qquad \text{(both sides divided by 9)}$$

$x = 2$:

$$2x - 2 = y$$

$$2(2) - 2 = y$$

$$4 - 2 = y$$

$$2 = y$$

Therefore, the solutions are $x = -\frac{2}{9}$, $y = -\frac{22}{9}$ and $x = 2$, $y = 2$

Practice Questions 4.6

1. Use a suitable method to solve the following pairs of simultaneous equations:
   (i) $x = y + 1$, $x + y^2 = 3$
   (ii) $x = y$, $x^2 + 2xy = 3$
   (iii) $x + y = 5$, $x^2 + y^2 = 13$
2. Use a suitable method to solve the following pairs of simultaneous equations:
   (i) $a - b = -4$, $a^2 + 4b^2 = 37$
   (ii) $2x - y = 5$, $2x^2 - y^2 = 7$
   (iii) $p - 2q = -4$, $p^2 + q^2 = 16$
3. Use a suitable method to solve the following pairs of simultaneous equations:
   (i) $x - y = 6$, $x^2 - 2x - y = 10$
   (ii) $a - 2b = -5$, $a^2 + ab - b^2 = 5$
   (iii) $x + y = -2$, $x^2 + 2xy + 2y^2 = 8$

Algebra III

4. **(i)** Solve the following simultaneous equations: $3x - y = -2$ and $y = x^2 + 3x + 2$

   (ii) Which of the sketches below represents the graphs of the equations in part **(i)**? Give a reason for your answer.

(a)

(b)

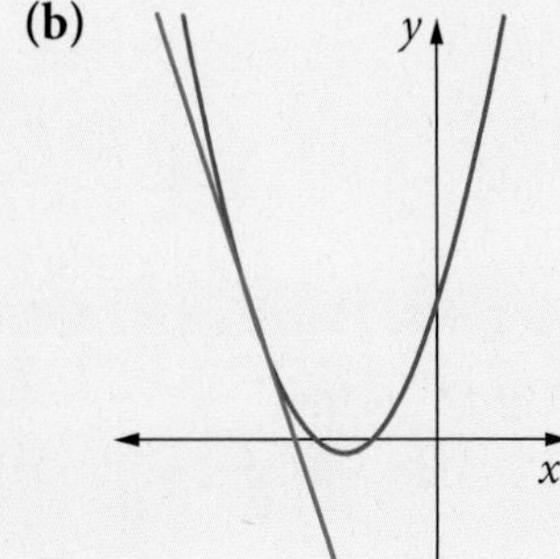

(c)

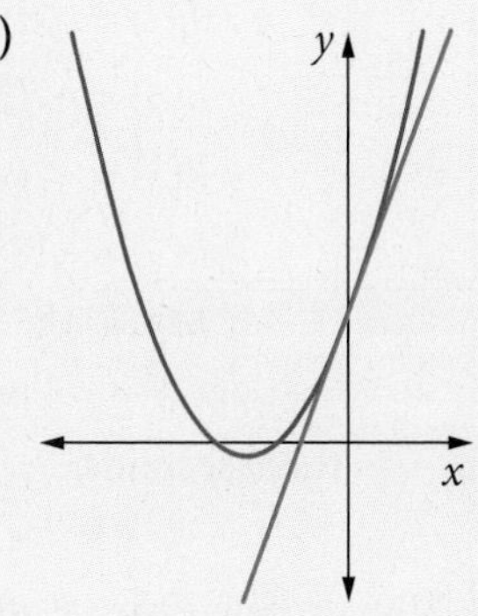

5. **(i)** Solve the following simultaneous equations: $x - 3y = -5$ and $x^2 + y^2 = 25$

   (ii) Which of the sketches below represents the graphs of the equations in part **(i)**? Give a reason for your answer.

(a)

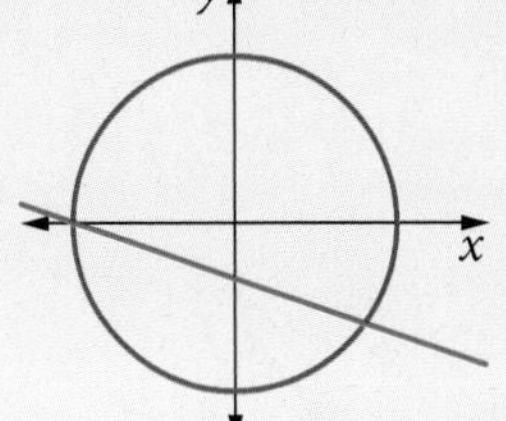

(b)

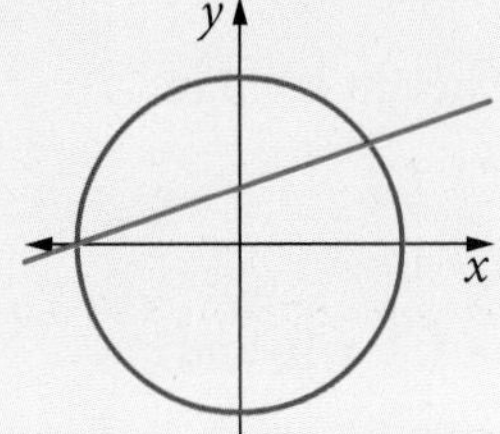

(c)

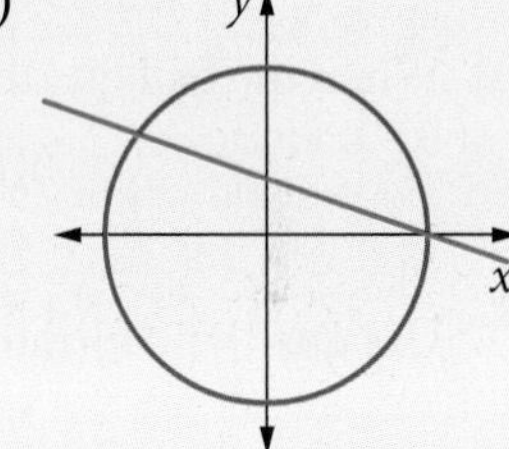

Links across the syllabus

Using simultaneous equations to find the point of intersection between a circle and a line is covered in Chapter 15: Coordinate Geometry II.

Section 4.7: Quadratic Equations in the Real World

Learning Outcome:

You should be able to:

- solve equations set in a context

Many real-world problems involve the use of quadratic equations. We can model situations using algebraic expressions and equations and then solve these equations to find the required information.

EXAMPLE 1

Ben kicks a football upwards into the air. The height h, in metres, of the ball above the ground t seconds after being kicked is given by

$$h(t) = -2t^2 + 10t + 1.$$

(i) Find the height of the football after three seconds.

(ii) Find the times when the height of the ball is 9 m. Explain why you get two possible answers.

(iii) After how many seconds does the ball hit the ground? Give your answer to one decimal place.

Solution

(i) Find h when $t = 3$:

$$h(t) = -2t^2 + 10t + 1$$
$$h(3) = -2(3)^2 + 10(3) + 1$$
$$h(3) = -2(9) + 30 + 1$$
$$h(3) = -18 + 31$$
$$h(3) = 13$$

Therefore, the ball is at a height of 13 m after three seconds.

(ii) Find t when $h = 9$:

$$h(t) = -2t^2 + 10t + 1$$
$$9 = -2t^2 + 10t + 1$$
$$0 = -2t^2 + 10t + 1 - 9$$
$$0 = -2t^2 + 10t - 8 \quad \text{(divide both sides by } -2)$$
$$0 = t^2 - 5t + 4$$
$$0 = (t - 4)(t - 1)$$
$$t - 4 = 0 \quad \text{or} \quad t - 1 = 0$$
$$t = 4 \quad \text{or} \quad t = 1$$

Therefore, the ball is at a height of 9 m after one second and again after four seconds.

There are two possible answers, as the ball reaches 9 m on its way upwards and again when it is falling back downwards.

(iii) When the ball hits the ground, the height $h = 0$ m

$$h(t) = -2t^2 + 10t + 1$$
$$0 = -2t^2 + 10t + 1$$

Use quadratic formula, where: $a = -2$, $b = 10$ and $c = 1$

$$t = \frac{-b \pm \sqrt{b^2 - 4ac}}{2a}$$
$$t = \frac{-(10) \pm \sqrt{(10)^2 - 4(-2)(1)}}{2(-2)}$$
$$t = \frac{-10 \pm \sqrt{100 + 8}}{-4}$$
$$t = \frac{-10 \pm \sqrt{108}}{-4}$$

$$t = \frac{-10 + \sqrt{108}}{-4} \quad \text{or} \quad t = \frac{-10 - \sqrt{108}}{-4}$$
$$t = \frac{0{\cdot}3923}{-4} \quad \text{or} \quad t = \frac{-20{\cdot}3923}{-4}$$
$$t = -0{\cdot}098 \quad \text{or} \quad t = 5{\cdot}098$$

We reject the negative value, since time cannot be a negative value, so the ball hits the ground when $t = 5{\cdot}098$ seconds.

Therefore, the ball hit the ground after 5·1 seconds, correct to one decimal place.

EXAMPLE 2

Jack and Holly are modelling the motion of a train. They decide to track its distance from a given point, P, after t seconds.

Jack models its distance, in metres, $f(t)$ as: $\quad f(t) = \frac{1}{20}t^2 + 4$

Holly models its distance, in metres, $h(t)$ as: $\quad h(t) = \frac{3t + 8}{2}$

Algebra III

(i) Complete the following table:

t	0	5	10	15	20	25	30
$f(t)$							
$h(t)$							

(ii) Graph each of the functions using the same axes and scale.

(iii) If after 10 seconds, the actual location of the train is 12 m from P, whose model is more accurate?

(iii) If after 25 seconds, the actual location of the train is 40 m from P, whose model is more accurate?

(iv) At what two points do the two models agree?

Solution

(i) Using your calculator or by substituting into the function, we get the following table:

t	0	5	10	15	20	25	30
$f(t)$	4	5·25	9	15·25	24	35·25	49
$h(t)$	4	11·5	19	26·5	34	41·5	49

(ii) Plotting these points on a coordinated plane gives:

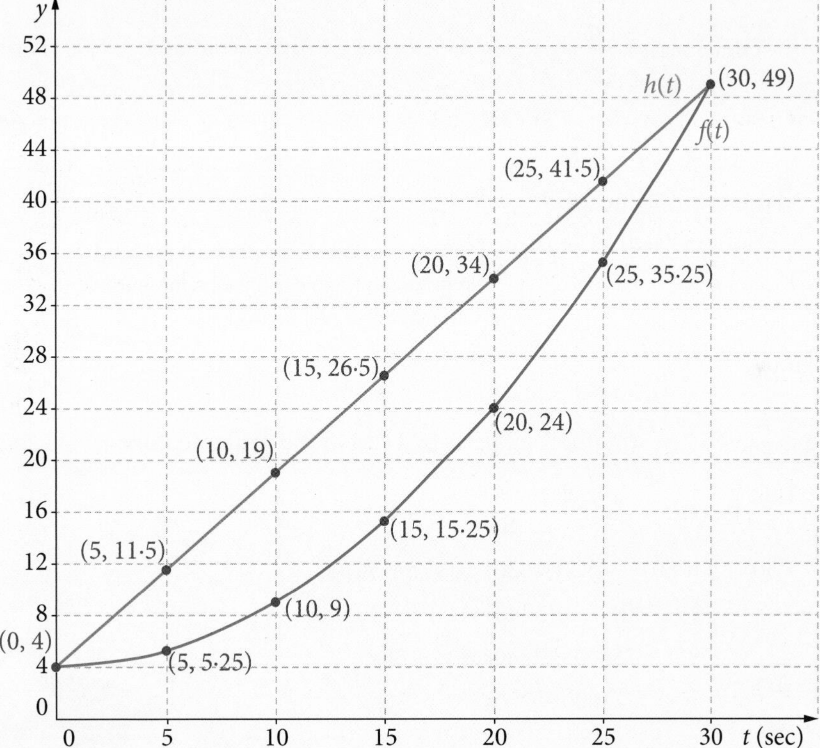

(iii) At $t = 10$ seconds: $h(10) = 19$ m and $f(10) = 9$ m

If the true location of the train at this time is 12 m from P, then the $f(t)$ function is a more accurate model for its position at this time.

(iv) At $t = 25$ seconds: $h(25) = 41{\cdot}5$ m and $f(25) = 35{\cdot}25$ m

If the true location of the train at this time is 40 m from P, then the $h(t)$ function is a more accurate model for its position at this time.

(v) The two models agree at the points where the graphs intersect.

$$h(t) = f(t) \text{ at } (0, 4) \text{ and } (30, 49).$$

This means that both models agree that at $t = 0$ seconds, the train is 4 m from P and after 30 seconds the train is 49 m from P.

EXAMPLE 3

Airplane A travels a distance of 1,260 km at a speed of s km/hr. Airplane B travels a distance 1,620 km at a speed of 30 km/hr faster than airplane A.

(i) Write an expression for the time it takes for airplane A to travel the 1,260 km, in terms of s.

(ii) Write an expression for the time it takes for airplane B to travel the 1,620 km, in terms of s.

(iii) Given that airplane A completed its journey 30 minutes faster than airplane B, form an equation, in terms of s.

(iv) Hence, solve this equation to find the speed of airplane A.

Solution

(i) Airplane A is travelling at s km/hr:

$$\text{Speed} = \frac{\text{Distance}}{\text{Time}}$$

By rearranging: $$\text{Time} = \frac{\text{Distance}}{\text{Speed}}$$

$$\text{Time for } A = \frac{1260}{s}$$

(ii) Airplane B is travelling 30 km/hr faster than airplane A.

Therefore, speed of airplane $B = s + 30$

$$\text{Speed} = \frac{\text{Distance}}{\text{Time}}$$

By rearranging: $$\text{Time} = \frac{\text{Distance}}{\text{Speed}}$$

$$\text{Time for } B = \frac{1620}{s+30}$$

(iii) Time for A – 30 minutes = Time for B

Time for A – Time for B = half an hour

$$\frac{1260}{s} - \frac{1620}{s+30} = \frac{1}{2}$$

Speed is in km/hr, so we must put time in hours, to keep dimensions the same. 30 minutes is half an hour.

(iv) Solve the equation:

$$\frac{1260}{s} - \frac{1620}{s+30} = \frac{1}{2}$$ (multiply all parts by LCM of the denominators: $(s)(s+30)(2)$)

$$(\cancel{s})(s+30)(2)\left(\frac{1260}{\cancel{s}}\right) - (s)(\cancel{s+30})(2)\left(\frac{1620}{\cancel{s+30}}\right) = (s)(s+30)(\cancel{2})\left(\frac{1}{\cancel{2}}\right)$$

$$(s+30)(2)(1260) - (s)(2)(1620) = (s)(s+30)(1)$$

$$(s+30)(2520) - (s)(3240) = (s)(s+30)$$

$$2520s + 75600 - 3240s = s^2 + 30s$$

$$75600 - 720s = s^2 + 30s$$

$$0 = s^2 + 30s + 720s - 75600$$

$$0 = s^2 + 750s - 75600$$

$$0 = (s+840)(s-90)$$

$$s + 840 = 0 \quad \text{or} \quad s - 90 = 0$$

$$s = -840 \quad \text{or} \quad s = 90$$

We reject the negative value, therefore the speed of airplane A is 90 km/hr.

Practice Questions 4.7

1. An advertising billboard is 5 m wider than it is high. The billboard is 204 m^2 of advertising space.

   (i) Letting x be the height of the billboard, write down the width of the billboard, in terms of x.

   (ii) Form an equation for the area of the billboard, in terms of x.

   (iii) Hence, find the dimensions of the billboard.

2. A triangle has a height that is equal to its base. If the area of the triangle is 32 cm^2, find the base and height of the triangle.

3. The length of a rectangle is 7 cm, and the width is 4 cm.

   (i) Find the area of the rectangle.

   If both the length and the width are increased by k cm, the area of the rectangle is increased by 102 cm^2.

   (ii) Form an equation, in terms of k.

   (iii) Solve this equation and hence find the length and width of the larger rectangle.

4. A garden has outside dimensions of 35 m in length and 27 m wide. A concrete path, of width w m, is installed all around the inside wall of the garden, leaving a rectangular lawn in the middle of the garden, as shown in the diagram.

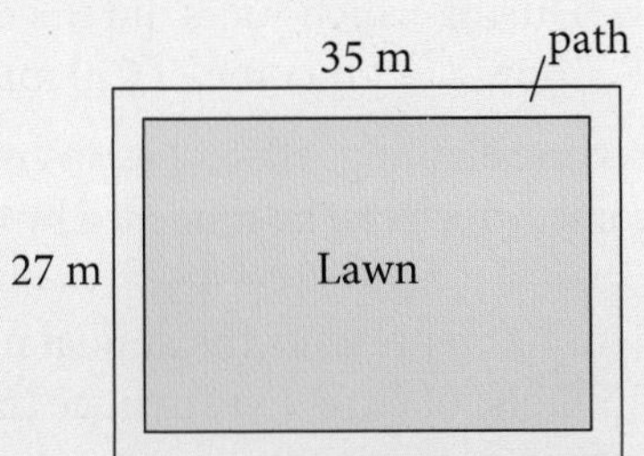

   (i) Find the length and width of the lawn, in terms of w.

   (ii) Write an expression for the area of the lawn, in terms of w.

   (iii) If the area of the lawn is 660 m^2, find the value of w.

5. (i) If x is an even integer, write down the next consecutive even integer, in terms of x.

   (ii) If the product of half the smaller number and three times the larger number is 72, find x.

6. A rectangular piece of cardboard is 10 cm longer than it is wide. Squares, of side length 2 cm, are cut from each corner and then the sides are folded up to make an open box.

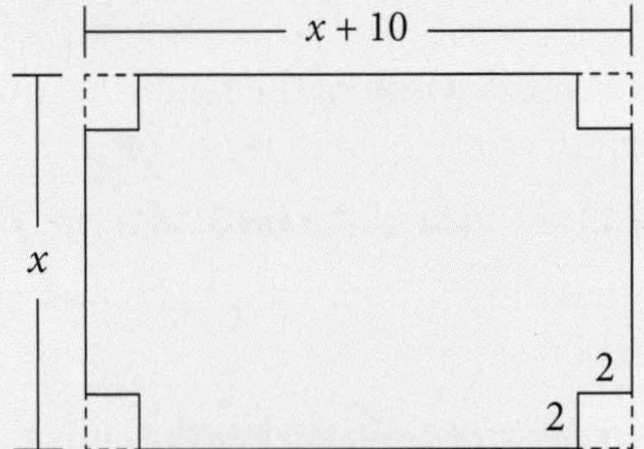

   (i) Write down the height of the box.

   (ii) Write the length and width of the box, in terms of x.

   (iii) Find the volume of the box, in terms of x.

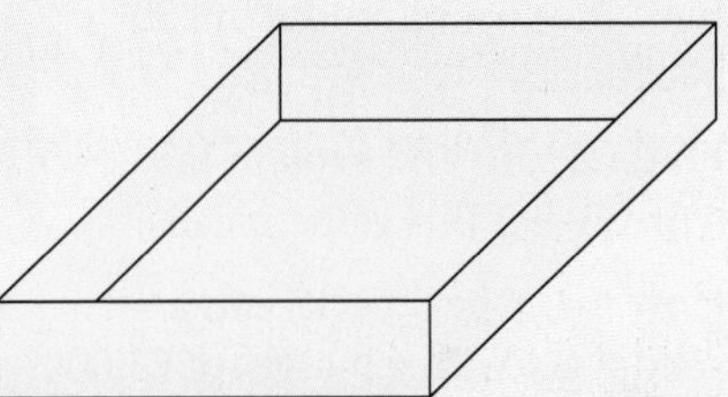

   (iv) If the volume of the box is 112 cm^3, find the value of x.

   (v) Hence, write down the length and width of the original piece of cardboard.

Volume of a box is covered in Chapter 17: Volume and Surface Area.

7. Three hundred metres of fencing is available to enclose a rectangular field alongside a river. The river forms one side of the field, as shown in the diagram.

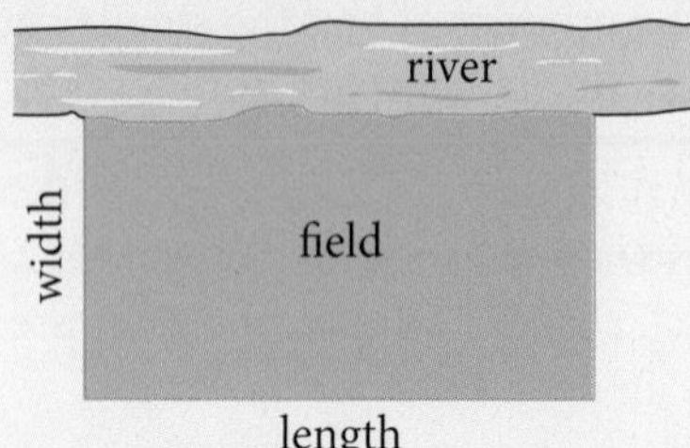

   (i) Given the width of the field is w, find the length of the field in terms of w.

   (ii) Find the area of the field, in terms of w.

   (iii) What dimensions will produce an area of 10,000 m^2?

8. The cost of producing backpacks with a school's logo can be modelled by:

$$C(b) = \frac{2}{5}b^2 - 12b + 500$$

   where $C(b)$ represents the cost, in euro, to produce b backpacks.

   (i) Find the cost of producing 50 backpacks.

   (ii) Find $C(150)$ and explain in words what this value means.

   (iii) How many backpacks can a school get with a budget of €3,000?

9. A cyclist travels 45 km at a speed of x km/hr. A jogger runs 24 km at a speed which is 6 km/hr slower than the cyclist.

   (i) Write an expression for the time it takes the cyclist to complete his journey, in terms of x.

   (ii) Write an expression for the time it takes the jogger to complete his journey, in terms of x.

   (iii) The cyclist completes his journey 20 minutes ahead of the jogger. Use this information to form an equation, in terms of x.

   (iv) Solve this equation to find the speed of the cyclist.

10. The revenue from selling digital cameras can be modelled by

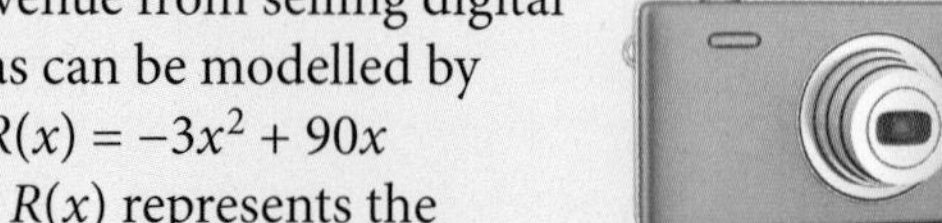

$$R(x) = -3x^2 + 90x$$

   Where $R(x)$ represents the revenue, in thousands of euro, from selling x thousand digital cameras.

   (i) Find the revenue from selling five thousand digital cameras.

   (ii) Find $R(4)$ and explain in words what this value means.

   (iii) How many cameras must the company sell to have a revenue of €600,000?

11. A rock is dropped from a 180-metre-high cliff, so that it falls into the sea below.
   The height of the rock, h, in metres, above the surface of the water, after t seconds, is given by the following function:

$$h(t) = -5t^2 + 180$$

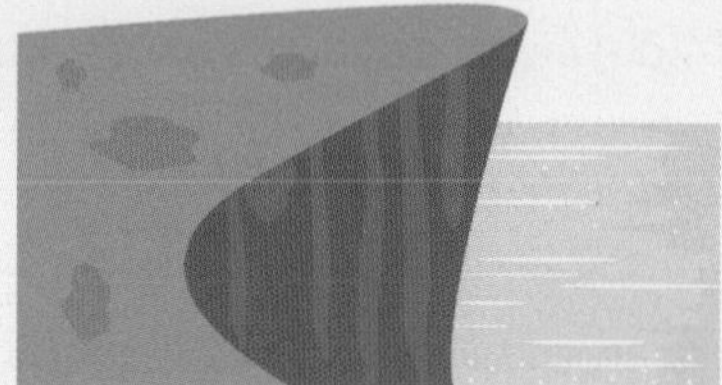

   (i) Find the height of the rock after 2 seconds.

   (ii) Find the height of the rock after 3·5 seconds.

   (iii) After how many seconds will the rock be at a height of 65 m? Give your answer to one decimal place.

   (iv) After how many seconds will the rock hit the surface of the water?

12. **(a)** The annual net income for a clothing retailer can be modelled by the function:

$$I(t) = -1{\cdot}5t^2 + 32t - 140$$

   where $I(t)$ represents the annual net income, in millions of euro, t years since the company was founded in 2000.

   (i) Use this model to find the net income the company took in in 2005. Explain your answer in words.

   (ii) Use this model to find the net income the company took in in 2012. Explain your answer in words.

   (iii) During which years did the company show a net income of €20 million?

   (b) A second clothing retailer has an annual net income, which can be modelled by the function

$$f(t) = 2t + 4$$

   where $f(t)$ represents the annual net income, in millions of euro, t years since the company was founded in 2000.

   (i) Use this model to find the net income this company took in 2005. Explain your answer in words.

   (ii) In which year(s) did the two companies have the same net income? Justify your answers.

13. The density of a substance is defined as its 'mass per unit volume'. The density is calculated by dividing the mass of a sample of the substance by its volume.

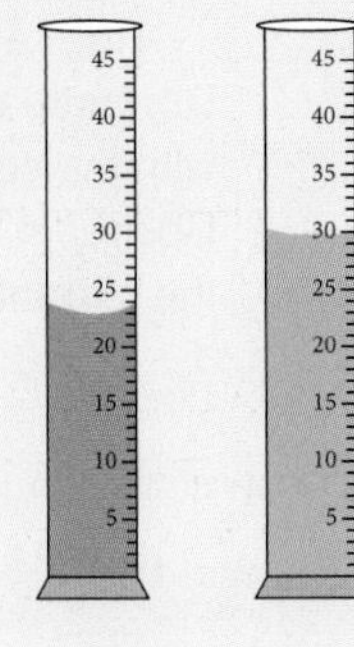

(i) Based on the information given above, write a formula for finding the density of a substance.

(ii) Rearrange this formula to make volume the subject of the formula.

(iii) Liquid A has a density of D kg/litre. Write an expression, in terms of D, for the volume of 3 kg of liquid A.

(iv) Liquid B has a density 0·2 kg/litre greater than liquid A. Write an expression, in terms of D, for the volume of 5·25 kg of liquid B.

(v) When 3 kg of liquid A is combined with 5·25 kg of liquid B, the total volume of liquid present is 6·25 litres. Use this information to write an equation, in terms of D.

(vi) Hence, find the value of D.

14. A circle has equation $x^2 + y^2 = 100$ and a line has equation $x + y = -2$.
Solve these equations simultaneously to find the points where the line intersects the circle.

15. (a) During testing, a missile is launched vertically upwards. The height of the missile h, after t seconds, can be modelled by the following function:

$$h(t) = -5t^2 + 50t + 7$$

(i) Copy and complete the following table, showing the height of the missile at the indicated times:

t (sec)	0	1	2	3	4	5	6	7	8	9	10
$h(t)$ (m)											

(ii) Draw a graph of the height of the missile for the first 10 seconds of its flight.

(iii) The point (3, 112) is on this graph. Explain in words what the coordinates of this point mean.

(iv) Use your graph to estimate the greatest height that the missile reaches.

(v) Use your graph to estimate two times that the height of the missile is at 100 m.

(vi) Use algebra to verify your answers to part **(v)**.

(b) Another missile is launched and it follows the path of the function $f(t) = 10t + 7$.

(i) What shape is formed by the graph of $f(t)$?

(ii) Using the same axes and scale as above, graph the function $f(t)$ in the domain $0 \leq t \leq 10$.

(iii) Find the points where the paths of the two missiles meet.

(iv) Use algebra to verify your answer to part **(iii)**.

16. The total amount of fresh vegetables consumed per person per year can be modelled by

$$v(t) = 4(t - 2{\cdot}5)^2 + 40$$

where $v(t)$ is the total amount of fresh vegetables consumed per person in kilograms per year, for t years since 2005 (i.e. $t = 0$ is 2005, $t = 1$ is 2006, etc.)

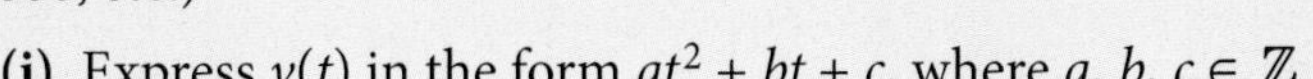

(i) Express $v(t)$ in the form $at^2 + bt + c$, where $a, b, c \in \mathbb{Z}$.

(ii) Draw a graph of this model for the years 2005 to 2015, inclusive.

(iii) The point (6, 89) is on the curve. Explain in words what the coordinates of this point represent.

(iv) Use the graph to estimate when the vegetable consumption was at 110 kg per person per year.

(v) Use your graph to estimate the vegetable consumption halfway between 2011 and 2012.

17. A cargo boat travels along a river, moving logs of wood from one location to another, a distance 75 km away. The boat then returns to its original site, to be loaded up for the next day. The boat is able to travel at a speed of V km/hr in still water and the river has a steady current of 5 km/hr.

Downstream means that the boat is going with the current.
Upstream means that the boat is going against the current.

(i) Write an expression for the time it takes the boat to travel the 75 km **downstream**.

(ii) Write an expression for the time it takes the boat to travel the 75 km **upstream**.

(iii) If the boat is travelling for a total of eight hours, find the value of V, the speed of the boat in still water.

(iv) On a given day, the current of the river was 2 km/hr. What difference will this make to the travelling time of the boat? Give your answer to the nearest minute.

18. A circle has equation $x^2 + y^2 = 169$ and a line has equation $x - 5y = -13$.
Solve these equations simultaneously to find the points where the line intersects the circle.

Revision and Exam Style Questions – Section A

1. Form the quadratic equation, whose roots are −3 and 4.

2. Solve the following quadratic equations:

(i) $2x^2 - 7x - 15 = 0$

(ii) $6x^2 = 1 - x$

3. Solve $k(k + 6) = 16$ and hence find the two possible values of $3k^2 + 2k - 1$.

4. Solve $\frac{6}{y+1} + \frac{1}{y-1} = 3$

5. Solve the following simultaneous equations $x + 3 = 2y$ and $xy - 7y + 8 = 0$.

6. When a number x is subtracted from its square, the result is 42.
Write down an equation in x to represent this information and solve it to calculate two possible values for x.

7. Solve the equation $x^2 - 6x - 18 = 0$, giving your answer in the form $a \pm a\sqrt{a}$, where $a \in \mathbb{Z}$.

8. A ball rolls down a slope and travels a distance $d = 6t + \frac{t^2}{2}$ metres in t seconds.

(i) Find the distance, d, when the time is 3 seconds.

(ii) Find the time taken for the ball to travel 17 m.
Give your answer correct to two decimal places.

9. A man jogs at an average speed of x km/hr for $(x - 5)$ hours.
If the man jogged a distance of 24 km,

(i) use the information to form an equation.

(ii) Hence, solve the equation to find x.

10. A quadratic function has a positive coefficient on the x^2 term and roots of −5 and 0.
Draw a sketch of this function.

11. Find the roots of the function $f(x) = 3x^2 + 4x - 6$. Give your answers to two decimal places.

Revision and Exam Style Questions – Section B

More challenging problems

1. **(i)** Find the roots of the function $f(x) = x^2 - 2x - 2$
   (ii) Hence draw a sketch of the graph of $f(x)$.

2. A closed rectangular box has a square base of side x cm.
   The height of the box is 7 cm.
   The total surface area of the box is 240 cm^2.
   Write down an equation in x to represent this information and use it to calculate x.

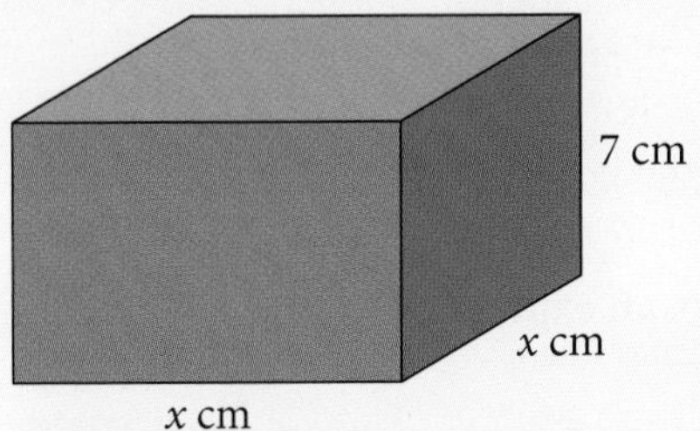

Links across the syllabus

Surface area of a box is covered in Chapter 17: Volume and Surface Area.

3. **(i)** Solve the following simultaneous equations $p + q = 1$ and $p^2 + q^2 = 13$
   (ii) Hence find the two possible values of $2p - 3q$.

4. Five hundred metres of fencing is available to enclose a rectangular site along the side of a motorway, as shown in the diagram. The motorway forms one side of the site, so fencing is only needed for three sides of the site.

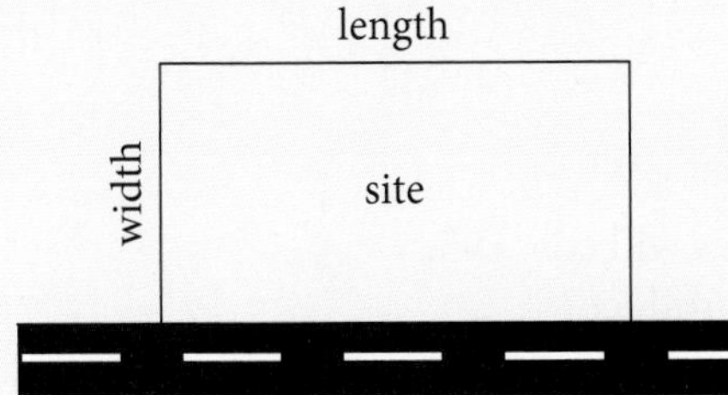

   (i) Given the width of the site is w, find the length of the field in terms of w.
   (ii) Find the area of the site, in terms of w.
   (iii) What dimensions will produce an area of 20,000 m^2?

5. A packet of raisins costs € 4·00.

   (i) If the packet contains x grams of raisins, write an expression in x to represent the cost, in cent, of one gram of raisins.

   During a promotion, the manufacturer adds an extra 50 grams of raisins into the packets. The cost of the packet of raisins remains at € 4·00.

   (ii) Write an expression in x to represent the cost, in cent, of 1 gram of the raisins during the promotion.

   During the promotion, each gram of raisins costs 0·4 c less than before the promotion.

   (iii) Write an equation in x to represent the above information.
   (iv) Solve this equation to find how many grams of raisins are in the box during the promotion.

6. A square sheet of cardboard measures 8 cm by 8 cm. A square of side x cm is removed from each corner. The remaining piece of cardboard is folded to form an open box, as shown.

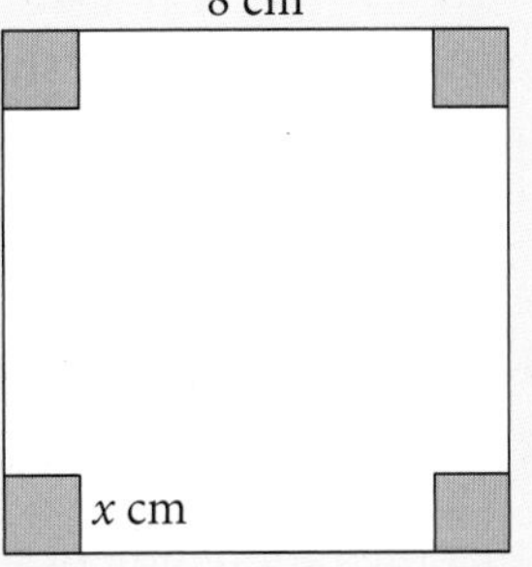

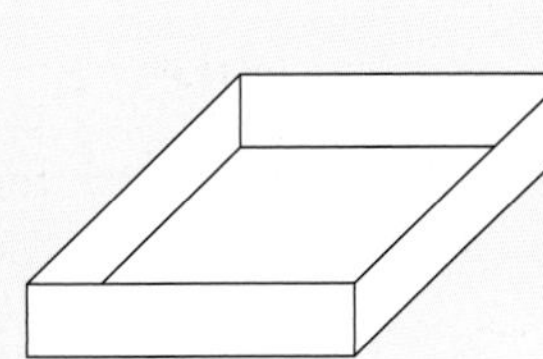

   (a) Show that the area, in cm^2, of each side of the box is $8x - 2x^2$.
   (b) Let f be the function $f(x) = 8x - 2x^2$.
   Evaluate $f(x)$ when $x = 0, 1, 2, 3, 4$.
   Hence, draw the graph of f for $0 \leq x \leq 4, x \in \mathbb{R}$.
   (c) Use your graph from part **(b)** to estimate:
   (i) the area of a side when $x = 0·5$
   (ii) the maximum possible area of a side
   (iii) the value of x that gives sides of maximum area
   (iv) the length and height of a side of maximum area.

Algebra III

7. **(i)** Solve the following simultaneous equations: $x + y = 4$ and $y = -x^2 + 5x - 1$

(ii) Which of the sketches below represents the graphs of the equations in part **(i)**? Give a reason for your answer.

(a)

(b)

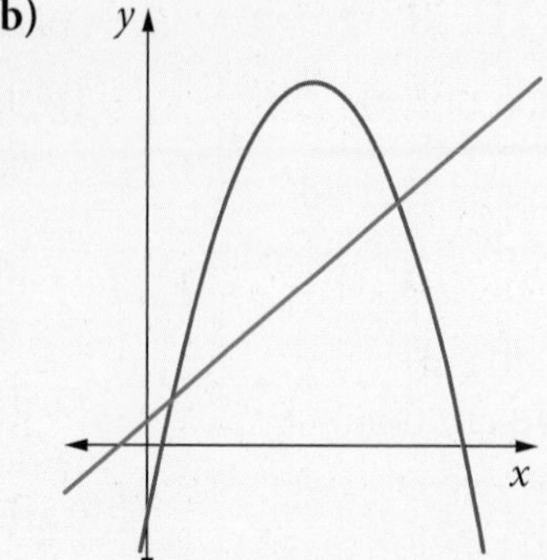

(c)

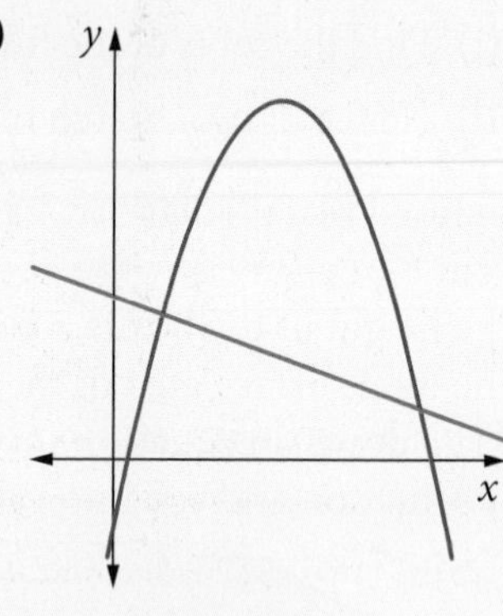

8. A teacher is organising an outing for her class. The total cost for the trip comes to €210. This covers the cost of a bus and entry to a museum.

(i) Taking x to be the total number of students in the class, write an expression in x to represent the cost of the trip per student.

If three members of the class decide not to go on the trip, then the total cost drops to €200.

(ii) Write an expression in x to represent the cost of the trip per student in this case.

The cost of the trip per student, in this case, would be increased by 50 c.

(iii) Write an equation in x to represent the above information.

(iv) Solve this equation to find the number of students in the class.

9. A picture frame manufacturer finds that the cost €C of making x picture frames per day is given by

$$C(x) = x^2 - 22x + 200$$

(i) Complete the following table, showing the cost of making each number of picture frames per day.

x	0	2	4	6	8	10	12	14	16	18	20
$C(x)$ (€)											

(ii) Hence, sketch the graph of the $C(x)$ function.

(iii) What is the cost if no picture frames are made on a particular day?

(iv) The graph shows that the production of seven picture frames will cost €95. What other number of picture frames will also cost €95 to produce?

(v) If the manufacturer wants to keep his costs to a minimum, how many picture frames should he produce each day?

(vi) On a given day, the manufacturer produces 17 picture frames. He sells them for €12 each. Find the profit he has made that day.

(vii) Given that the manufacturer sells all of his picture frames for €12, write an expression for the income he receives, per day, by selling x frames.

(viii) Hence, write an expression for the profit he makes if he produces and sells x picture frames on a given day.

Now that you have completed the chapter, revisit the 'Something to think about…' question.

Indices and Index Notation

Sections covered within this chapter:

KEY WORDS

- Index
- Exponential equations
- Scientific notation
- Order of magnitude

SOMETHING TO THINK ABOUT… 

A section of a river is 12 km long, 270 m wide and 38 m deep.

(i) How many millilitres of water are in this section of the river? Express your answer in scientific notation to two decimal places.

The river flows into a lake 30 km long, 12 km wide and 54 m deep.

(ii) Find an order of magnitude comparison between the number of millilitres of water in the full lake and the 12 km section of the river.

Section 5.1: Index Laws 1 and 2

Learning Outcome:

You should be able to:

- use index laws 1 and 2

We have already learned how to express numbers in the form of prime factors. Recall:

$$32 = 2 \times 2 \times 2 \times 2 \times 2, \text{ which we can simplify to } 2^5.$$

2^5 is known as **index form**.

The index can also be referred to as the exponent or power.

The big number is called the base and the small number is called the **index**.

When dealing with indices, there are a number of laws that can be employed to make our calculations simpler.
We will now discover and learn how to use these laws.
You do not have to remember these laws as they are given to you on page 21 of the booklet of *formulae and tables* as shown:

$a^p a^q = a^{p+q}$ $\quad a^{\frac{1}{q}} = \sqrt[q]{a}$

$\dfrac{a^p}{a^q} = a^{p-q}$ $\quad a^{\frac{p}{q}} = \sqrt[q]{a^p} = \left(\sqrt[q]{a}\right)^p$

$\left(a^p\right)^q = a^{pq}$ $\quad (ab)^p = a^p b^p$

$a^0 = 1$ $\quad \left(\dfrac{a}{b}\right)^p = \dfrac{a^p}{b^p}$

$a^{-p} = \dfrac{1}{a^p}$

Index law 1

We will look at what happens when we have a number or letter base which is raised to a power multiplied by another term with a power and the **same base.**

Consider the following: $a^2 \times a^3$

If we write this in expanded form, we get $(a \times a) \times (a \times a \times a)$.

If we now convert this back to index form, we get a^5.

Let's try another one: $a^3 \times a^4 = (a \times a \times a) \times (a \times a \times a \times a) = a^7$.

Hopefully you have noticed that we are adding the indices (small numbers) each time.

In words we say, 'add indices when multiplying numbers with the same base'.

In mathematical terms, this is written: $a^p a^q = a^{p+q}$

This rule only works if the bases are the same.

When a number and a letter are involved we deal with them separately.

For example: $2a^2 \times 3a^5 = 2 \times 3 \times a^2 \times a^5 = 6a^7$

Index law 2

We will now look at what happens when we have a number or letter base which is raised to a power divided by another term with a power and the **same base.**

Consider: $\dfrac{a^5}{a^2} = \dfrac{\cancel{a \times a} \times a \times a \times a}{\cancel{a \times a}} = a^3$

Let's try another: $\dfrac{a^7}{a^5} = \dfrac{\cancel{a \times a \times a \times a \times a} \times a \times a}{\cancel{a \times a \times a \times a \times a}} = a^2$

Hopefully you have noticed that we are subtracting the indices each time.

In words we say, 'subtract indices when dividing numbers with the same base'.

In mathematical terms, this is written: $\dfrac{a^p}{a^q} = a^{p-q}$

This rule only works if the bases are the same.

As before, when a number and a letter are involved we deal with them separately.

For example: $\dfrac{4a^3}{2a} = \dfrac{4}{2} a^{3-1} = 2a^2$

Practice Questions 5.1

1. Simplify the following and leave your answers in index form:
   (i) $6^3 \times 6^7$
   (ii) $4^5 \times 4^2$
   (iii) $m^4 \times m^6$
   (iv) $c^7 \times c^9$
   (v) $3a^8 \times 8a^{-4}$
   (vi) $2y^5 \times 7y^{-2}$

2. Multiply each of the following and leave your answers in index form:
   (i) $(6^3)(6^2)$
   (ii) $(11c^8)(-10c^4d)$
   (iii) $(7q^5)(12q^3r^2)$
   (iv) $(4r^5)(2r^7)$
   (v) $(3c^2)(5d^3)$
   (vi) $(2a^3)(7a^4)$

3. What is the area of a square with the length of a side equalling $3a^5$?

4. What is the area of the rectangle with the width of $3x^3$ and length $5x^4$?

5. Simplify the following and leave your answers in index form:

(i) $\frac{3^5}{3^2}$ (iii) $\frac{2^4}{2^2}$ (v) $\frac{k^4}{k^3}$

(ii) $\frac{10^6}{10^4}$ (iv) $\frac{5^4}{5^{-3}}$ (vi) $\frac{s^{-1}}{s^{-4}}$

6. Simplify the following and leave your answers in index form:

(i) $\frac{3^{y+1}}{3^y}$ (iii) $\frac{8^{r+4}}{8^{r+1}}$ (v) $\frac{a^2b^5}{ab^3}$

(ii) $\frac{-16w^7x^2}{-4wx}$ (iv) $\frac{10c^3d^2}{5c^5d}$ (vi) $\frac{48x^2y^6}{6x^7y^3}$

7. The area of a rectangle is $24x^7$. If the width of the rectangle is $4x^2$, find the length of the rectangle.

Section 5.2: Index Laws 3, 4 and 5

Learning Outcome:

You should be able to:

- understand and use index laws 3, 4 and 5

Index law 3

We will look at what happens when we have a number or letter base which is raised to a power then raised to another power.

Consider $(a^2)^3$

When we expand this we get: $(a \times a) \times (a \times a) \times (a \times a) = a \times a \times a \times a \times a \times a = a^6$.

Let's look at another example:

$(a^3)^4 = (a \times a \times a) \times (a \times a \times a) \times (a \times a \times a) \times (a \times a \times a) = a^{12}$.

Hopefully you have noticed that we are multiplying the indices.

In words, we say that 'when a number or letter base is raised to a power and then raised to another power, we multiply the powers'.

In mathematical terms: $(a^p)^q = a^{pq}$

When a number and a letter are involved we apply the power to both parts separately.

For example: $(3a)^2 = 3^2 \times a^2 = 9a^2$

Index law 4

We can now use index law 2 to show how we can arrive at another law. Firstly, recall that any number divided by itself is 1.

Consider $\frac{a^3}{a^3} = 1$

Also using law 2: $\frac{a^3}{a^3} = a^{3-3} = a^0$

Therefore, we can say that $a^0 = 1$.

In words, we say 'any number or letter to the power of zero equals 1'.

In mathematical terms: $a^0 = 1$

Index law 5

We will now see what happens if the power to which a number or letter is raised is a negative number.

First, let's look at the following example: $\dfrac{a^2}{a^5}$

If we expand this, we get: $\dfrac{\cancel{a \times a}}{\cancel{a \times a} \times a \times a \times a} = \dfrac{1}{a^3}$

If we use index law 2: $\dfrac{a^2}{a^5} = a^{2-5} = a^{-3}$

So $\dfrac{1}{a^3} = a^{-3}$

In words, we say that 'when a term is moved up or down over a fraction line, we change the sign of the index'.

In mathematical terms:

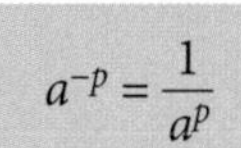

$$a^{-p} = \frac{1}{a^p}$$

Practice Questions 5.2

1. Evaluate each of the following:
   (i) 100^0 (ii) -5^0 (iii) a^0 (iv) $2^{-3} \times 2^3$ (v) $4^6 \times 4^{-6}$ (vi) $\dfrac{7^8}{7^8}$ (vii) $\dfrac{5^6 \times 5^{-2}}{5^{-3} \times 5^7}$ (viii) $\dfrac{2^{-3} \times 2^{-2}}{2^2 \times 2^{-7}}$
2. Express the following in simplest index form.
   (i) $(w^3)^4$ (ii) $(t^{-3})^2$ (iii) $(4^6)^7$ (iv) $(5^4)^5$ (v) $(2^9)^3$ (vi) $(2a^3)^3$ (vii) $(7r^4)^2$ (viii) $(3h^4)^3$ (ix) $(5w^7)^3$ (x) $(10b^5)^4$
3. Find the value of each of the following in the form $\frac{1}{a}$, $a \in \mathbb{N}$.
   (i) 2^{-4} (ii) 3^{-2} (iii) 5^{-2} (iv) 7^{-2} (v) 2^{-5}
4. Express the following in index form, such that the index is always positive.
   (i) $\dfrac{1}{5^{-4}}$ (ii) $\dfrac{1}{7^{-3}}$ (iii) $\dfrac{1}{(xy)^{-6}}$ (iv) $\dfrac{1}{a^{-2}b^{-3}}$ (v) $\dfrac{1}{3rs^{-8}}$
5. Express the following in index form, such that the index is always positive.
   (i) $\dfrac{p^4}{p^6}$ (ii) $\dfrac{t}{t^5}$ (iii) $\dfrac{x^4 \times x^3}{(x^2)^6}$ (iv) $(4a^{-3})^3$
6. Express the following in simplest index form.
   (i) $(3p^2 \times 2p)^5$ (ii) $\left(\dfrac{12x^8}{-2x^3}\right)^3$ (iii) $(5p^3q^2)(2p^4q)^2$ (iv) $\dfrac{(6m^2)^2}{3m^6}$ (v) $(u^{-3})\left(\dfrac{9u^{-5}}{3u^6}\right)$ (vi) $\left(\dfrac{(s^{-2}t^7)}{s^3t^{-5}}\right)^{-4}$ (vii) $(4u^2v)^{-3}(u^{-5}v^6)^2$ (viii) $\dfrac{(2a^{-3}b)(6b^5c^{-7})}{4c^{-9}}$

Indices and Index Notation

Section 5.3: Index Laws 6 and 7

Learning Outcome:

You should be able to:
- understand and use index laws 6 and 7

Index law 6

We will now look at what happens when we have a number or letter base which is raised to a power that is a fraction.

Look at the following examples and see if you can come up with a mathematical way to write this law.

$4^{\frac{1}{2}} = \sqrt{4} = 2$

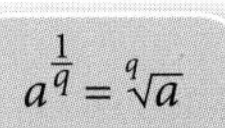

$16^{\frac{1}{4}} = \sqrt[4]{16} = 2$

$8^{\frac{1}{3}} = \sqrt[3]{8} = 2$

$32^{\frac{1}{5}} = \sqrt[5]{32} = 2$

Looking at the examples above, complete the following $a^{\frac{1}{q}} = ?$

Hopefully you can see that: $a^{\frac{1}{q}} = \sqrt[q]{a}$

Index law 7

What happens if the numerator (top) of the fraction is not 1?

Consider $4^{\frac{3}{2}}$

$\frac{3}{2}$ can be expressed as $3 \times \frac{1}{2}$, so

$4^{\frac{3}{2}} = (4^{\frac{1}{2}})^3 = (\sqrt{4})^3 = 2^3 = 8$

Let's try another:

$(125)^{\frac{2}{3}} = (125^{\frac{1}{3}})^2 = (\sqrt[3]{125})^2 = 5^2 = 25$

In words, we say that 'the numerator (top) becomes the power and the denominator (bottom) becomes the root'.

In mathematical terms: $a^{\frac{p}{q}} = \sqrt[q]{a^p} = (\sqrt[q]{a})^p$

Practice Questions 5.3

1. Rewrite the following using the $\sqrt[q]{a^p}$ sign:

(i) $y^{\frac{1}{2}}$ (ii) $r^{\frac{1}{4}}$ (iii) $a^{\frac{1}{5}}$ (iv) $m^{\frac{1}{5}}$ (v) $q^{\frac{1}{6}}$ (vi) $x^{\frac{3}{4}}$ (vii) $c^{\frac{3}{5}}$ (viii) $t^{\frac{3}{2}}$ (ix) $k^{\frac{5}{6}}$ (x) $h^{\frac{3}{2}}$

2. Find the value of:

(i) $64^{\frac{1}{2}}$ (ii) $125^{\frac{1}{3}}$ (iii) $81^{\frac{3}{2}}$ (iv) $27^{\frac{2}{3}}$ (v) $64^{\frac{4}{3}}$

Section 5.4: Index Laws 8 and 9

Learning Outcome:

You should be able to:
- understand and use index laws 8 and 9

Index law 8

We will now consider what happens if a product is raised to a power.

Consider the following: $(6)^3 = 216$

If we express 6 as a product (2×3),

then $(6)^3$ becomes $(2 \times 3)^3$

$= (2 \times 3) \times (2 \times 3) \times (2 \times 3) = 2 \times 2 \times 2 \times 3 \times 3 \times 3$

$= 2^3 \times 3^3$

$= 8 \times 27$

$= 216$

Let's try another one:

$(xy)^3 = (xy)(xy)(xy) = x \times x \times x \times y \times y \times y = x^3y^3$

In words, we say that 'each factor of the product gets raised to the power'.

In mathematical terms: $(ab)^p = a^pb^p$

When a number and a letter are involved, we apply the power to both parts separately.

For example: $(2x)^3 = 2^3 \times (x^3) = 8x^3$

Index law 9

Finally, we will consider what happens when a quotient is raised to a power.

Consider the following: $\left(\frac{4}{2}\right)^3 = 2^3 = 8$

Also,

$\left(\frac{4}{2}\right)^3 = \left(\frac{4^3}{2^3}\right) = \frac{64}{8} = 8$

Therefore,

$\left(\frac{4}{2}\right)^3 = \left(\frac{4^3}{2^3}\right)$

Let's look at another one: $\left(\frac{2xy}{x}\right)^2 = \frac{2^2x^2y^2}{x^2}$

$= \frac{4x^2y^2}{x^2} = 4y^2$

In words, we say that 'each part of the quotient is raised to the power'.

In mathematical terms: $\left(\frac{a}{b}\right)^p = \frac{a^p}{b^p}$

When a number and a letter are involved, we deal with them in a similar way.

For example: $\left(\frac{3x}{4y}\right)^3 = \frac{(3x)^3}{(4y)^3} = \frac{3^3x^3}{4^3y^3} = \frac{27x^3}{64y^3}$

Practice Questions 5.4

1. Simplify each of the following:
   - (i) $(6x^3)^2$
   - (ii) $(2yz)^6$
   - (iii) $(8h^5w^3)^4$
   - (iv) $(-3x^3y^2)^4$
   - (v) $(-7a^4b)^2$
   - (vi) $(3d^3 \times 2d^2)^3$
   - (vii) $(4x^3)^5(2x^2)^3$
   - (viii) $(2s^3t^{-3})^3$
2. Simplify each of the following:
   - (i) $\left(\frac{x^2}{y}\right)^6$
   - (ii) $\left(\frac{2b}{3a}\right)^2$
   - (iii) $\left(\frac{7y^2}{4y^4}\right)^3$
   - (iv) $\left(\frac{4u^2v}{2u^3v^2}\right)^5$
   - (v) $\left(\frac{9r^2s^3}{4r^5s}\right)^4$
   - (vi) $\left(\frac{5p^2q^{-3}}{3p^{-1}q^2}\right)^2$
   - (vii) $\left(\frac{2g^2h^5}{4gh^{-3}}\right)^{-2}$
   - (viii) $\left(\frac{5a^{-2}b^3}{a^{-5}b^{-3}}\right)^{-4}$

The following questions combine laws 1–9

3. Express each of the following in simplest index form:
   - (i) $x^{12} \times x^{25}$
   - (ii) $c^4 \times c^8$
   - (iii) $d^9 \times d^{10}$
   - (iv) $a^5 \times a^{11}$
   - (v) $w^{-3} \times w^{-1}$
   - (vi) $g^3 \times g^6 \times g^{-5}$
   - (vii) $2^a \times 2^b$
   - (viii) $r^4 \times s^3$
4. Simplify each of the following products:
   - (i) $(2x^2)(4x^3y^2)$
   - (ii) $(-3a^2b)(6ab^4c)$
   - (iii) $(11c^8)(-10c^4d)$
   - (iv) $(9x^{10}z^2)(-x^5y^3)$
5. Express each of the following in simplest index form:
   - (i) $(x^2)^3$
   - (ii) $(a^7)^5$
   - (iii) $(y^5)^4$
   - (iv) $(5^2)^3$
   - (v) $(4y^3)^2$
   - (vi) $(8c^5)^2$
   - (vii) $(-3h^9)^3$
   - (viii) $(-c^5h^6)^4$
   - (ix) $(y^4d^6)^8$
   - (x) $(k^9)^5(k^3)^2$

6. Simplify the following and leave in index form:

(i) $\frac{y^8}{y^3}$ (v) $\frac{8s^7t^{12}}{2s^3t^7}$

(ii) $\frac{b^5}{b^2}$ (vi) $\frac{45e^8f^8}{5ef^2}$

(iii) $\frac{m}{m^{-4}}$ (vii) $\frac{a^6 \times a^{14}}{a^5}$

(iv) $\frac{c^2d^9}{cd^3}$ (viii) $\frac{3q^4 \times 2q^5}{q^3}$

7. Simplify each of the following without using the calculator:

(i) $9^{\frac{1}{2}}$ (iii) $16^{\frac{1}{2}}$ (v) $27^{\frac{-2}{3}}$

(ii) $27^{\frac{1}{3}}$ (iv) $16^{\frac{-1}{2}}$

8. Rewrite each of the following in index form:

(i) $\sqrt{8}$ (iii) $(m^6)^{\frac{1}{2}}$ (v) $(16^{\frac{1}{2}})^{-2}$

(ii) $3\sqrt{m}$ (iv) $(10^{\frac{1}{2}})^3$

9. (i) Express $3 \times 3 \times 3 \times 2 \times 2$ using indices.

(ii) Write 27 in index form using base three.

(iii) Calculate each of the following and determine which are the same.

(a) $2^2 \times 3^2$ (c) $2^2 + 3^2$ (e) $\frac{2^3}{3^2}$

(b) $(2 + 3)^2$ (d) $(2 \times 3)^2$ (f) $\left(\frac{2}{3}\right)^2$

10. Simplify each of the following. Leave your answer in index form.

(i) $2^3 \times 2^4$ (vi) $\frac{4^8}{4^{12} \times 4^{-3}}$

(ii) $(3^2)^5$ (vii) $\frac{2}{2^{-3} \times (2^2 \times 2)^2}$

(iii) $\frac{12^5}{12^7}$ (viii) $\left(\frac{10a^3b^{-2}}{5a^{-1}b^2}\right)^{-1}$

(iv) $(2 \times 3)^2 (2 \times 3)^{-4}$ (ix) $x^2 z^{-3} \times (xz^2)^2$

(v) $8^{-\frac{1}{3}}$

11. Without using a calculator, find the value of $25^1 - 25^0$.

12. (i) Explain why $64^{\frac{1}{3}} = 4$.

(ii) Hence, or otherwise, find the value of $64^{-\frac{2}{3}}$, without using a calculator.

13. Given $a^{\frac{1}{2}} = b^{\frac{1}{4}}$, where $a > 0$ and $b > 0$:

(i) Find an expression for a in terms of b.

(ii) Hence, or otherwise, find an expression for a^3 in terms of b.

Section 5.5: Exponential Equations

Learning Outcome:

You should be able to:

- understand and solve exponential equations

Exponential equations are equations in which the exponent is unknown.

If you can express both sides of the equation as indices with the same base number, you can equate the indices to solve for the unknown.

To solve exponential equations, follow these steps:

Step 1: Express both sides of the equation as indices with the same base number.

Step 2: Use the indices laws to produce a single index (if necessary).

Step 3: Equate the indices.

Step 4: Solve for the unknown.

EXAMPLE 1

Solve for x in each of the following:

(i) $7^{3x-2} = 7^{2x+1}$ **(ii)** $3^{2x-1} = 27^x$ **(iii)** $\left(\frac{1}{25}\right)^{2x} = 5^{3x-28}$

Solution

(i) $7^{3x-2} = 7^{2x+1}$

Step 1:	$7^{3x-2} = 7^{2x+1}$	base number is already the same on both sides
Step 2:	$7^{3x-2} = 7^{2x+1}$	not needed in this example
Step 3:	$3x - 2 = 2x + 1$	equate indices
Step 4:	$3x - 2x - 2 = 2x - 2x + 1$	subtract $2x$ from both sides
	$x - 2 = 1$	
	$x - 2 + 2 = 1 + 2$	add 2 to both sides
	$x = 3$	

(ii) $3^{2x-1} = 27^x$

Step 1:	$3^{2x-1} = (3^3)^x$	$27 = 3^3$
Step 2:	$3^{2x-1} = 3^{3x}$	by index law 3
Step 3:	$2x - 1 = 3x$	equate indices
Step 4:	$2x - 2x - 1 = 3x - 2x$	subtract $2x$ from both sides
	$-1 = x$	

(iii) $\left(\frac{1}{25}\right)^{2x} = 5^{3x-28}$

Step 1:	$(5^{-2})^{2x} = 5^{3x-28}$	$\frac{1}{25} = \frac{1}{5^2} = 5^{-2}$ by index law 5
Step 2:	$5^{-4x} = 5^{3x-28}$	by index law 3
Step 3:	$-4x = 3x - 28$	equate indices
Step 4:	$-4x - 3x = 3x - 3x - 28$	subtract $3x$ from both sides
	$-7x = -28$	
	$\frac{-7x}{-7} = \frac{-28}{-7}$	divide both sides by -7
	$x = 4$	

Practice Questions 5.5

The most common bases chosen are 2, 3, 5 and 7.

1. Write each of the following in the form 2^k, where $k \in \mathbb{Z}$.
   (i) 64 **(ii)** $\frac{1}{16}$ **(iii)** 1 **(iv)** $\sqrt{2}$ **(v)** $\frac{1}{\sqrt{2}}$ **(vi)** $\sqrt{32}$

2. **(a)** Write each of the following in the form 3^k, where $k \in \mathbb{Z}$.
   (i) $\sqrt{27}$ **(ii)** $\frac{1}{81}$ **(iii)** $\frac{1}{\sqrt{243}}$

   (b) Write each of the following in the form 5^k, where $k \in \mathbb{Z}$.
   (i) $\sqrt{5}$ **(ii)** $\frac{1}{625}$ **(iii)** $\frac{1}{\sqrt{125}}$

3. Solve for x in each of the following:
   (i) $5^x = 5^3$ **(ii)** $3^8 = 3^x$ **(iii)** $2^{5x} = 2^{15}$ **(iv)** $7^{3x} = 7^{33}$ **(v)** $4^{x+3} = 4^2$ **(vi)** $3^x = 9$ **(vii)** $81 = 9^{x-4}$ **(viii)** $64 = 2^{2x}$

4. Solve for x in each of the following:

(i) $5^{3x-8} = 25^{2x}$ (v) $4^{x+1} = \frac{1}{64}$

(ii) $3^{2x-1} = 27^{x}$ (vi) $9^{2x+1} = 27$

(iii) $2^{x-1} = \frac{1}{4}$ (vii) $4^{3x+1} = 16$

(iv) $8^{x-2} = \sqrt{8}$ (viii) $9(3^{x}) = 27^{x-1}$

5. (i) Express the following equation in simplest index form:

$$k^{x+1} = (\sqrt{k})(k^{2x})$$

(ii) Hence, or otherwise find the value of x.

6. Find two values for x in each of the following:

(i) $3^{x^2-3x} = 81$ (iii) $2^{x^2} = 16^{2x-3}$

(ii) $4^{2x^2+2x} = 8$

7. (a) Find the value of p, q and r given that:

(i) $64 = 8^{p}$ (ii) $\frac{1}{64} = 8^{q}$ (iii) $\sqrt{8} = 8^{r}$

(b) Find the value of x for which $\frac{8^{x}}{\sqrt{8}} = \frac{1}{64}$

8. (a) Write as a power of 2

(i) 8 (ii) $8^{\frac{4}{3}}$

(b) Solve for x in the equation $8^{\frac{4}{3}} = \frac{2^{5x-4}}{\sqrt{2}}$

9. Write as a power of 3

(i) 243 (ii) $\sqrt{27}$

Hence, or otherwise, solve for x in the equation

$$\sqrt{3}(3^{x}) = \left(\frac{243}{\sqrt{27}}\right)^{2}$$

10. Solve each of the following equations for p:

(i) $9^{p} = \frac{1}{\sqrt{3}}$ (ii) $2^{3p-7} = 2^{6} - 2^{5}$

11. (i) Evaluate $36^{\frac{1}{2}}$.

(ii) Express $\sqrt{32}$ in the form 2^{k}, $k \in \mathbb{Q}$.

(iii) Solve for x in the equation $36^{x} = 6^{6-x}$.

12. Write $2^{4} - 2^{2}$ in the form $a(2^{n})$, where a, $n \in \mathbb{N}$. Hence, or otherwise, solve for x the equation $6(8^{x-1}) = 2^{4} - 2^{2}$.

Section 5.6: Scientific Notation

Learning Outcome:

You should be able to:

- express numbers in scientific notation

Scientific notation is a method of writing or displaying numbers in terms of a number between 1 and 10, multiplied by a power of 10.

In mathematical terms this is written as: $a \times 10^{n}$, where $1 \le a < 10$ and n is any integer.

This is very useful when dealing with very large or very small numbers.

For example: Number between 1 and 10 — Power of 10

$$6623{\cdot}5 = 6{\cdot}6235 \times 10^{3}$$

So the number is written in two parts:

1. Just the digits (with the decimal point placed after the first digit), followed by:
2. ×10 to a power that puts the decimal point where it should be (shows how many places to move the decimal point).

To figure out the power of 10, think 'how many places do I move the decimal point?'

When the number is **10 or greater**, the decimal point has to move to the **left**, and the power of ten is **positive**.

When the number is **smaller than 1**, the decimal point has to move to the **right**, and the power of ten is **negative**.

EXAMPLE 1

Write 5,900,000,000 in scientific notation.

Solution

Step 1: The number between 1 and 10 is 5·9

Step 2: The decimal needs to move 9 places to the left

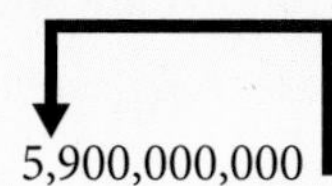

5,900,000,000

5,900,000,000 = $5{\cdot}9 \times 10^9$ in scientific notation

EXAMPLE 2

Write 0·0000000436 in scientific notation.

Solution

Step 1: The number between 1 and 10 is 4·36

Step 2: The decimal needs to move 8 places to the right = $4{\cdot}36 \times 10^{-8}$ in scientific notation

0·0000000436

0·0000000436 = $4{\cdot}36 \times 10^{-8}$ in scientific notation

What about converting from scientific notation back to regular numbers?

EXAMPLE 3

Write in non-scientific notation: $3{\cdot}6 \times 10^{12}$.

Solution

Since the power of 10 is positive, we know they are looking for a number that is greater than 10, so we'll need to move the decimal point to the right to make the number bigger.

Since the power of 10 is '12', we'll need to move the decimal point twelve places to the right.

There is one number after the decimal place so this counts as one move.

After that we must add a zero for every move, therefore we must add 11 zeros.

In non-scientific notation, $3{\cdot}6 \times 10^{12}$ = 3,600,000,000,000.

EXAMPLE 4

Convert $4{\cdot}2 \times 10^{-7}$ to non-scientific notation.

Solution

Since the power of 10 is negative, we are looking for a number that is less than 1, so we'll need to move to the left to make it smaller.

As the power is seven, we will be moving the decimal point seven places to the left.

Since the 4 counts as one place, we need to add six zeros after the decimal point.

In non-scientific notation, $4{\cdot}2 \times 10^{-7}$ = 0·00000042

Your calculator has a scientific notation setting, which can be used to verify your answers.

Practice Questions 5.6

1. Write the following as powers of 10:
   - **(i)** 100
   - **(ii)** 1000
   - **(iii)** 10
   - **(iv)** 100,000
   - **(v)** 0·1
   - **(vi)** 0·01
   - **(vii)** 0·00001
   - **(viii)** 100,000,000

2. Express the following in scientific notation:
   - **(i)** 357
   - **(ii)** 357,000
   - **(iii)** 3·57
   - **(iv)** 0·357
   - **(v)** 0·000357
   - **(vi)** 2060
   - **(vii)** 0·00206
   - **(viii)** 2,060,000

3. Write the following in non-scientific notation:
   - **(i)** 4×10^3
   - **(ii)** 5×10^2
   - **(iii)** $2{\cdot}1 \times 10^3$
   - **(iv)** $7{\cdot}8 \times 10^4$
   - **(v)** $3{\cdot}8 \times 10^{-5}$
   - **(vi)** $8{\cdot}6 \times 10^{-1}$
   - **(vii)** $4{\cdot}33 \times 10^{-7}$
   - **(viii)** $6{\cdot}32 \times 10^{-9}$

4. Express the following quantities in the form $a \times 10^n$, where $1 \leq a < 10$ and $n \in \mathbb{Z}$.
   - **(i)** The distance from the earth to the sun is 149,500,000,000 m.
   - **(ii)** A speck of dust is 0·001 mm wide.

(iii) The probability that your six numbers will be selected for the Lotto on Monday night is 0·000 000 141 62.

(iv) The central temperature of the sun is 15 million degrees Celsius.

5. Express the following quantities in non-scientific notation:

(i) There are approximately 4×10^6 red blood cells in a drop of blood.

(ii) The thickness of a coin is 8×10^{-4} m.

(iii) The earth's radius is $6{\cdot}38 \times 10^6$ metres.

(iv) A bacterium has a diameter of 4×10^{-7} cm.

(v) Twenty weeks is $1{\cdot}2096 \times 10^7$ seconds.

(vi) A piece of plastic wrap is 7×10^{-6} m thick.

6. A pollen sample weighs 14 grams and contains $1{\cdot}6 \times 10^{12}$ pollen grains. Calculate the weight of one pollen grain in grams. Give your answer in scientific notation.

7. A single red blood cell lives for about four months and during this time it will circulate around the body 300,000 times.

(i) Express the number of times the blood cell circulates the body in scientific notation.

(ii) If the total length of the circulatory system is 100,000 km, express in scientific notation the distance travelled by a red blood cell in four months.

(iii) Taking a month as four weeks, calculate the average speed of the red blood cell in m/s. Express your answer in scientific notation.

8. A planet takes 88 days to travel round the sun. The approximate path of the planet round the sun is a circle with diameter $1{\cdot}2 \times 10^7$ kilometres.
Find the speed of the planet as it travels around the sun. Give your answer in kilometres per hour, correct to two significant figures.

Length of a circle = $2\pi r$

Section 5.7: Order of Magnitude

Learning Outcome:

You should be able to:

- understand and find the order of magnitude estimation

Order of magnitude is the number of powers of ten that are in a number.

Order of magnitude is an estimate and it can be used when comparing very large or very small numbers.

A number rounded to the nearest power of 10 is called an order of magnitude.

To find the order of magnitude, estimate follow these steps:

Step 1: Write the number in scientific notation, $a \times 10^n$.

Step 2: If a is less than 5, the order of magnitude is n. If a is greater than or equal to 5, we add one to n to get the order of magnitude.

EXAMPLE 1

Find an order of magnitude estimate for:

(i) the mass of a raindrop which is approximately 0·003 g

(ii) the radius of the Earth, which is 6,371,000 m.

Solution

(i) ***Step 1:*** $0{\cdot}003\text{ g} = 3 \times 10^{-3}$

Step 2: $3 < 5$, so the order of magnitude $= n$

Order of magnitude $= -3$

(ii) ***Step 1:*** $6{,}371{,}000 = 6{\cdot}371 \times 10^{6}$

Step 2: $6 > 5$, so the order of magnitude $= n + 1$

Order of magnitude $= 6 + 1 = 7$

If a is less than 5, the order of magnitude is n. If a is greater than or equal to 5, we add one to n to get the order of magnitude.

EXAMPLE 2

The average height of a human is 1·7 m and the average height of an ant is 0·0008 m.
Find an order of magnitude comparison between the height of a human and the height of an ant.

Solution

Human: $1{\cdot}7 = 1{\cdot}7 \times 10^{0}$ Since 1·7 is less than 5, order of magnitude $= 0$

Ant: $0{\cdot}0008 = 8 \times 10^{-4}$ Since 8 is greater than 5, order of magnitude $= -4 + 1 = -3$

$$\frac{\text{height of human}}{\text{height of an ant}} = \frac{10^{0}}{10^{-3}} = 10^{0-(-3)} = 10^{3}$$

A human being is roughly 10^3 times (or 1,000 times) taller than an ant.
In other words, a human being is three orders of magnitude (three powers of 10) taller than an ant.

Practice Questions 5.7

1. How many orders of magnitude are in the following numbers?

   (i) 567,230,356
   (ii) 123,456
   (iii) 20,987
   (iv) 0·000567
   (v) 0·00298
   (vi) 0·00000323
   (vii) 0·085
   (viii) 0·0000076
   (ix) 116
   (x) 89

2. Find the order of magnitude estimate for each of the following:

   (i) The length of a virus is $2{\cdot}8 \times 10^{-3}$ m.
   (ii) The number of atoms in 12 g of carbon is 6×10^{23}.
   (iii) A google is 10^{100}.
   (iv) The age of the universe is 14·6 billion years.
   (v) The diameter of a human hair is 25×10^{-6} m.

3. The mass of an electron is $9{\cdot}11 \times 10^{-31}$ kg. The mass of a proton is $1{\cdot}67 \times 10^{-27}$ kg.

   (i) What is the order of magnitude for both the mass of a proton and the mass of an electron?
   (ii) Find the order of magnitude comparison between the mass of a proton and the mass of an electron.

4. The population of the Earth in 2015 was 7,324,782,225. The population of Ireland was 4,635,400.

   (i) What is the order of magnitude for each population?
   (ii) Find the order of magnitude comparison for the population of Earth to the population of Ireland.

5. Make an order of magnitude estimate for the following:
   (i) Your age in hours.
   (ii) The number of breaths you take in a year, given an average breathing rate of 16 breaths per minute.
   (iii) The number of heartbeats in a lifetime, given an average pulse rate of 72 beats per minute and an average life expectancy of 80 years.

6. (i) The area of Australia is 7·692 million km^2. The area of Ireland is 84,421 km^2. Find the order of magnitude comparison between the area of Australia and the area of Ireland.
   (ii) The population of Australia in 2013 was 23·13 million. The population of Ireland in 2013 was 4·595 million. Find the order of magnitude comparison between the population of Australia and the population of Ireland in 2013.

Revision and Exam Style Questions – Section A

1. (i) Find the value of $49^{\frac{1}{2}}$.
   (ii) Simplify $(s^3)^4$.
   (iii) Find the value of $\left(\frac{7^3 \times 7^4}{7^5}\right)^{-1}$ without using your calculator.

2. (i) Write $3 \times 3 \times 3 \times 3 \times 3 \times 3$ in the form 3^x, where $x \in \mathbb{N}$.
   (ii) If $3^p \times 3^4 = 3^{-2}$, write down the value of p.
   (iii) Write $\frac{3^5 \times 3^6}{3^4 \times 3^3}$ in the form 3^n, where $n \in \mathbb{Z}$.

3. The mass of water on the earth's surface is $1{\cdot}41 \times 10^{18}$ tonnes. The total mass of the earth is $5{\cdot}97 \times 10^{21}$ tonnes.
   (i) Find the order of magnitude comparison for the mass of water to the total mass of the earth.
   (ii) Express the mass of water on the earth's surface as a percentage of the total mass of the earth. Express your answer in scientific form.

4. The speed of light is 299,792,458 metres per second.
   (i) Write this number in the form $a \times 10^n$, where $1 \leq a \leq 10$ and $n \in \mathbb{Z}$, correct to one significant figure.
   (ii) Find the order of magnitude estimate for the speed of light.

5. Simplify $(n^2)^3 \times n^{-10}$. Give your answer with a positive power.

6. Calculate the value of $\frac{4{\cdot}2 \times 10^6 - 3{\cdot}1 \times 10^3}{6{\cdot}1 \times 10^4}$

   Write your answer in the form $a \times 10^n$, where $1 \leq a \leq 10$ and $n \in \mathbb{Z}$, correct to three significant figures.

7. (i) The earth is approximately spherical with a radius of 6,400 km. Calculate the volume of the earth, giving your answer in scientific notation, correct to two significant figures.
   (ii) The approximate volume of the moon is $2{\cdot}2 \times 10^{10}$ cubic kilometres. Calculate how many times the earth's volume is greater than the moon's.

   Volume of a sphere $= \frac{4}{3}\pi r^3$

8. (i) Express 9 and 27 in the form 3^n where $n \in \mathbb{Z}$.
   (ii) Hence or otherwise, solve for x if $9(3^x) = 27^{x-1}$.

9. Solve for x in the following equation:

$$5^{x+2} = 125\sqrt{5}$$

Revision and Exam Style Questions – Section B

More challenging problems

1. Simplify $\dfrac{\sqrt[3]{27} \times 3}{9^{\frac{1}{2}} \times 3^4}$ into the form 3^n where $n \in \mathbb{Z}$.

2. The average speed of an airplane is 885 kilometres per hour.
How many kilometres will the plane travel in 15 seconds? Express your answer in the form $a \times 10^n$, where $n \in \mathbb{N}$ and $1 \leq a < 10$.

3. Bruce is planning a flight to Australia. On average, the plane burns 102·8 litres of fuel an hour, and Bruce estimates the trip will require 37·6 hours of flying time.
   - **(i)** Estimate the amount of fuel required by rounding each value correct to one significant figure.
   - **(ii)** Calculate the exact amount of fuel needed and express your answer in the form $a \times 10^n$, where $1 \leq a \leq 10$ and $n \in \mathbb{Z}$, correct to three significant figures.
   - **(iii)** Comment on the difference between the two answers.

4. A pet shop uses a variety of ventilated boxes to safely transport their animals. The lid of the box used for the small animals measures 76 cm long by 20 cm wide. Along the lid of the box are 162 ventilation holes, which each have a radius of 1·2 cm.

   - **(i)** Using the formula, $A = \pi r^2$, calculate the area of one ventilation hole, correct to two decimal places.
   - **(ii)** Determine the amount of surface area that remains on the lid after the ventilation holes are removed.
   - **(iii)** The company that manufacture the boxes prefers to work in millimetre measurements. Convert your remaining surface area to millimetres squared.

     $1 \text{ cm}^2 = 100 \text{ mm}^2$
   - **(iv)** Record your answer to part **(iii)** in scientific notation.

5. A virus has an approximate mass of 1×10^{-20} kg. Which of the following items has a mass 10,000,000,000 times smaller than that of the virus?
   - **(i)** A hydrogen atom (mass = 1×10^{-27} kg)
   - **(ii)** An electron (mass = 1×10^{-30} kg)
   - **(iii)** A bacterium (mass = 1×10^{-15} kg)
   - **(iv)** An ant (mass = 1×10^{-6} kg)
   - **(v)** A grain of fine sand (mass = 1×10^{-9} kg)

6. Write the following as a power of 2:
   - **(i)** 16 and $\sqrt{8}$
   - **(ii)** Hence, solve for x in the equation:

     $$2^{x-5} = \left(\frac{16}{\sqrt{8}}\right)^3$$

7. If $5^{2x+1} = \dfrac{125}{\sqrt{5}}$, find the value of x.

8. Write $\dfrac{243}{\sqrt{3}}$ as a power of 3 and hence, or otherwise, solve for x in the equation

   $$3^{x-2} = \left(\frac{243}{\sqrt{3}}\right)^3$$

9. **(a)** Express each of the following in terms of 2^k, where $k \in \mathbb{Q}$.

   (i) 4 **(ii)** $\dfrac{1}{64}$

   (b) Hence, or otherwise, find the value of x if

   $$4^{x^2+4x} = \frac{1}{64}$$

10. If $27^{2a-b} = \frac{1}{9}$ and $49^{3a-2b} = 7$, find the value of a and b.

Now that you have completed the chapter, revisit the 'Something to think about…' questions.

Pattern

Sections covered within this chapter:

KEY WORDS

- Pattern
- Series
- Sequence
- Quadratic pattern
- Term
- Geometric sequence
- Linear pattern

SOMETHING TO THINK ABOUT…

Sven is asked to do some structural work on a ski jump.

He needs to develop a mathematical model of the ski jump.

To do this, he takes the height of the slope, in metres, at regular intervals along its length and graphs them as shown.

(i) Use the graph to determine the height of the slope at the marked positions.

(ii) Sven thinks that he can model the ski slope by using a quadratic equation. Investigate whether or not he is correct.

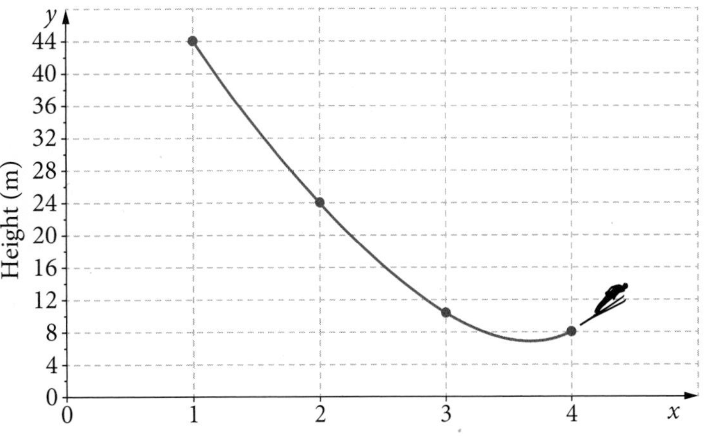

Section 6.1: Patterns

Learning Outcomes:

You should be able to:
- understand what a pattern is
- look at a pattern and predict what comes next
- generalise and explain patterns in words

A **pattern** is a list of objects, or terms, which are arranged following a rule or rules.

A **sequence** is a list of terms which are in a particular order. For example, 2, 5, 8, 11, 14, …

Patterns can be made up of letters, numbers, symbols or objects (e.g. tiles or blocks).

If we study a pattern we will be able to see the rule which describes the pattern and hence be able to predict the terms which follow.

In a pattern or sequence of numbers, each number is called a **term**.
The nth term of the sequence is written as T_n.

For example, the pattern −12, −8, −4, 0, 4, … is starting with the number −12 and increasing by 4 each time. Therefore the next terms are 8, 12, 16, etc.

For numerical patterns, finding the gap between consecutive terms can help to determine the rule used to generate the pattern.

For the sequence 3, 7, 11, 15, 19, … the first term, T_1, is 3, the second term, T_2, is 7, the third term, T_3, is 11, etc.

The gap between the numbers is called the difference. In this case, the difference = 7 − 3 = 4.

Difference = Any term − Previous term

$$d = T_n - T_{n-1}$$

EXAMPLE

Describe the following patterns in words and, hence, write out the next three terms of each pattern.

(i) ■, ■, ■, ■, ■, ■, … **(ii)** 3, 8, 5, 10, 7, 12, …

Solution

(i) This pattern consists of five different coloured squares, repeated: ■, ■, ■, ■, ■, ■, …

The colours are in the order: black, red, green, yellow, blue.

Since the last square shown was black, the next three terms are red, green and yellow: ■, ■, ■

(ii) Find the difference between each term: 3, 8, 5, 10, 7, 12, …

Terms:	3	8	5	10	7	12
	8 − 3	5 − 8	10 − 5	7 − 10	12 − 7	
Differences:	= 5	= −3	= 5	= −3	= 5	

We can see the first term is increased by 5 to get the second term. The second term is reduced by 3 to get the third term. The third term is increased by 5, the fourth term is reduced by 3, etc.,

The next three terms are: 9, 14, 11, …

Practice Questions 6.1

1. Study the following patterns and describe, in words, the rule that is used to generate each term.
Hence, draw the next four terms of each pattern.
   (i) □, O, Δ, □, O, ...
   (ii) ⊂, ∩, ⊃, ∪, ⊂, ...
   (iii) ■, ■, ■, ■, ■, ...
   (iv) ☺, ☺, ☹, ☺, ...

2. Study the following patterns and describe, in words, the rule that is used to generate each term.
Hence, write out the next four terms of each pattern.
   (i) 5, 7, 9, 11, ...
   (ii) 24, 12, 6, 3, ...
   (iii) 10, 5, 0, −5, −10, ...
   (iv) 3, 9, 5, 11, 7, 13, ...

3. Study the following patterns and describe, in words, the rule that is used to generate each term.
Hence, write out the next four terms of each pattern.
   (i) 1, 3, 9, 27, ...
   (ii) 1, 4, 9, 16, ...
   (iii) 1, 1, 2, 3, 5, ...
   (iv) Z, W, T, Q, ...

4. In your copybook, draw the next two terms of the following patterns:
   (i)
   (ii)
   (iii)

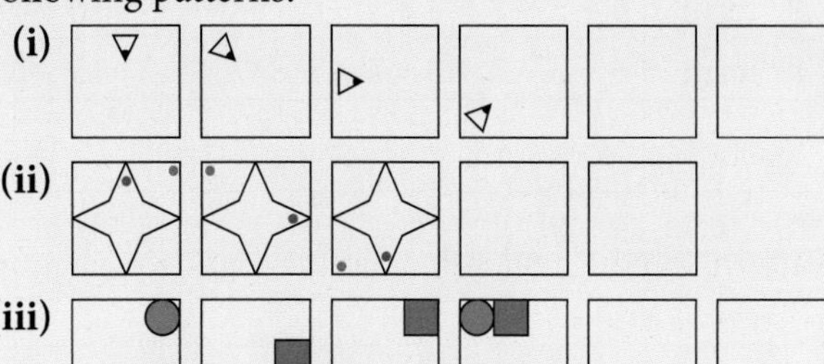

Section 6.2: Linear Patterns (Arithmetic Sequences)

Learning Outcomes:

You should be able to:

- recognise a linear pattern (arithmetic sequence)
- write an expression for a particular term in an arithmetic sequence (find T_n)
- generalise and explain linear patterns and relationships in algebraic form
- find the sum to n terms of an arithmetic series

A **linear pattern** is a sequence of numbers in which the differences between any two consecutive terms (the first difference) are all equal. A linear pattern is also called an arithmetic sequence.

A linear pattern or sequence is one where the values go up or down by the same fixed amount every time. When a linear sequence is graphed, the pattern forms a straight line graph.

Links across the syllabus

The graphs of linear patterns are covered in Chapter 3: Algebra II and Chapter 7: Further Functions.

EXAMPLE 1

A sequence is as follows: 7, 4, 1, −2, −5, −8, ...

(i) Prove that the sequence is arithmetic (linear).
(ii) Write down the next two terms of the sequence.

Solution

(i) Find the difference between each term.

Terms:	7		4		1		−2		−5		−8
Differences:		−3		−3		−3		−3		−3	

Since all the differences are equal, the sequence is arithmetic (linear).

When this is the case, we refer to the difference as the 'common difference'.

(ii) 6th term = −8 7th term = −8 − 3 = −11 8th term = −11 − 3 = −14

Generating a rule for a linear (arithmetic) sequence

In a linear sequence, the pattern starts with the first term and then the common difference is added on to generate the next term.

If a sequence starts with the number four and the common difference is three, then the sequence would be generated as follows:

1st term	4	4
2nd term	$4 + 3 = 4 + 1(3)$	7
3rd term	$4 + 3 + 3 = 4 + 2(3)$	10
4th term	$4 + 3 + 3 + 3 = 4 + 3(3)$	13
⋮	⋮	⋮
10th term	$4 + 9(3)$	31
⋮	⋮	⋮
n^{th} term	$4 + (n - 1)(3)$	

In mathematical terms:

n^{th} term = First term + $(n - 1)$(common difference)

$$T_n = a + (n - 1)d$$

Where, a = first term
d = common difference

Finding the sum of n terms in a series

A **series** is the sum of a sequence. For example, $2 + 5 + 8 + 11 + 14 + \ldots$

In certain situations we may want to find the sum of a number of terms in a sequence. If there is only a small number of terms to add up, then that is easily done. However, if you wish to add up a large number of terms then the simplest way to do so is to use the formula in the box to the right:

Sum of the first n terms:

$$S_n = \frac{n}{2}[2a + (n - 1)d]$$

where,
a = first term
d = common difference

The formulae for T_n and S_n appear on page 22 of the booklet of *formulae and tables* as shown.

Arithmetic sequence or series

$$T_n = a + (n - 1)d$$

$$S_n = \frac{n}{2}[2a + (n - 1)d]$$

where:
a is the first term
d is the common difference

EXAMPLE 2

The graph shows a linear (arithmetic) pattern.

(i) Use the graph to determine the first term, a, and the common difference, d.

(ii) Find an expression for T_n, the nth term of the sequence.

(iii) Use your answer to part **(ii)**, to verify the value for T_5.

(iv) Find S_{15}, the sum of the first 15 terms.

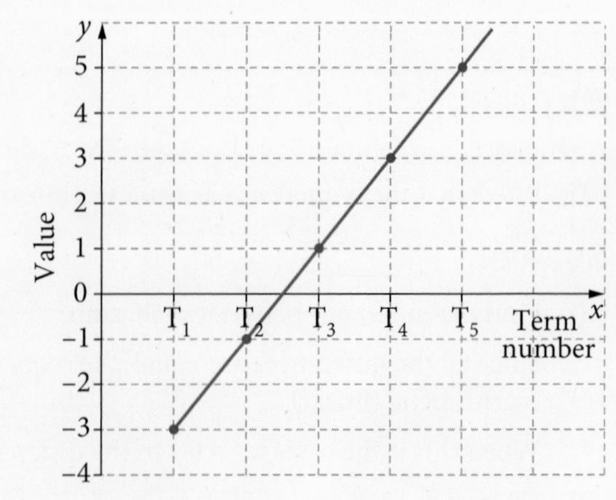

Solution

(i) From the graph, the first term, T_1, is -3.

Therefore, $a = -3$

The second term, T_2, is -1

Common difference, $d = T_2 - T_1$

$d = -1 - (-3)$

$d = 2$

(ii) $T_n = a + (n-1)d; \quad a = -3, d = 2$

$T_n = -3 + (n-1)2$

$T_n = -3 + 2n - 2$

$T_n = 2n - 5$

(iii) $T_n = 2n - 5$

$T_5 = 2(5) - 5 \qquad (n = 5)$

$T_5 = 10 - 5$

$T_5 = 5$

This agrees with the value for T_5, on the graph.

(iv) $S_n = \frac{n}{2}[2a + (n-1)d]; \qquad n = 15, a = -3, d = 2$

$S_{15} = \frac{15}{2}[2(-3) + (15-1)(2)]$

$S_{15} = \frac{15}{2}[-6 + (14)(2)]$

$S_{15} = \frac{15}{2}[-6 + 28]$

$S_{15} = \frac{15}{2}[22]$

$S_{15} = 165$

Therefore, the sum of the first 15 terms is 165.

EXAMPLE 3

The following patterns are made using matchsticks:

(i) Draw the next two patterns.

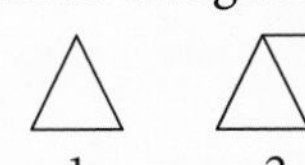

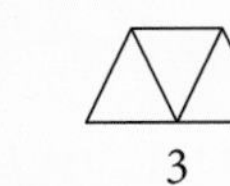

1 2 3

(ii) Copy and complete the following table:

Pattern number	Number of matchsticks
1	3
2	
3	
4	
5	

(iii) Investigate whether the number of matchsticks forms an arithmetic (linear) pattern.

(iv) Write a rule which describes the number of matchsticks, in terms of the pattern number.

(v) Hence, or otherwise, find the number of matchsticks in the 21st pattern.

(vi) Which pattern number contains 73 matchsticks?

(vii) A box of matchsticks contains 150 matchsticks. What's the largest pattern number which can be made using this box?

(viii) How many matchsticks are used to create the first 18 patterns?

Solution

(i) The fourth and fifth patterns are as follows:

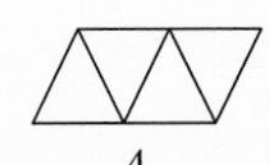

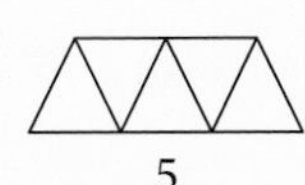

4 5

(ii) Complete the table:

Pattern number	Number of matchsticks
1	3
2	5
3	7
4	9
5	11

(iii) Find the differences:

Pattern number	Number of matchsticks	Difference
1	3	
2	5	2
3	7	2
4	9	2
5	11	2

Since all the differences are equal, the pattern is arithmetic (linear).

(iv) Number of matchsticks = First term + $(n - 1)$(difference)

Number of matchsticks = $3 + (n - 1)(2)$

Number of matchsticks = $3 + 2n - 2$

Number of matchsticks = $1 + 2n$

(v) For the 21st term, $n = 21$: Number of matchsticks = $1 + 2n$

Number of matchsticks = $1 + 2(21)$

Number of matchsticks = $1 + 42$

Number of matchsticks = 43

(vi) Find n when the number of matchsticks is 73:

Number of matchsticks = $1 + 2n$

$73 = 1 + 2n$

$72 = 2n$ (subtract 1 from both sides)

$36 = n$ (divide both sides by 2)

Therefore, the 36th pattern has 73 matchsticks.

(vii) Find the biggest value n can be for 150 matchsticks.

Number of matchsticks ≤ 150

$1 + 2n \leq 150$

$2n \leq 149$ (subtract 1 from both sides)

$n \leq 74{\cdot}5$ (divide both sides by 2)

Since n must be a whole number, the largest pattern number possible to create is the 74th pattern.

(viii) To find the total number of matchsticks needed to make the first 18 patterns, we use the formula for finding the sum of the first n terms in a sequence.

$S_n = \frac{n}{2}[2a + (n - 1)d]$ Let $n = 18$, $a = 3$ and $d = 2$

$S_{18} = \frac{18}{2}[2(3) + (18 - 1)(2)]$

$S_{18} = 9[6 + (17)(2)]$

$S_{18} = 9[6 + 34]$

$S_{18} = 9[40]$

$S_{18} = 360$

Therefore, 360 matchsticks in total are used to create the first 18 patterns.

Practice Questions 6.2

1. Find the missing terms of the following linear (arithmetic) patterns:
   (i) 3, 8, 13, __, 23, 28, __, __, 43
   (ii) −20, −17, __, __, −8, −5, __, __, __
   (iii) −2, __, 6, 10, __, __, __, __
2. Determine which of the following sequences and series are arithmetic (linear):
   (i) 2, 4, 6, 8, 10 …
   (ii) 8, 6, 3, 1, −3, −5 …
   (iii) −5, −3, −1, 1, 3, 5 …
   (iv) 18 + 15 + 12 + 9 + 6 + …
   (v) −12 −10 −7 −3 + 2 + …
   (vi) −3 + 2 + 9 + 14 + 21 + …
3. For each of the given graphs,
   (i) List the first three terms of the sequence.
   (ii) Investigate whether each sequence is a linear pattern.

(a)

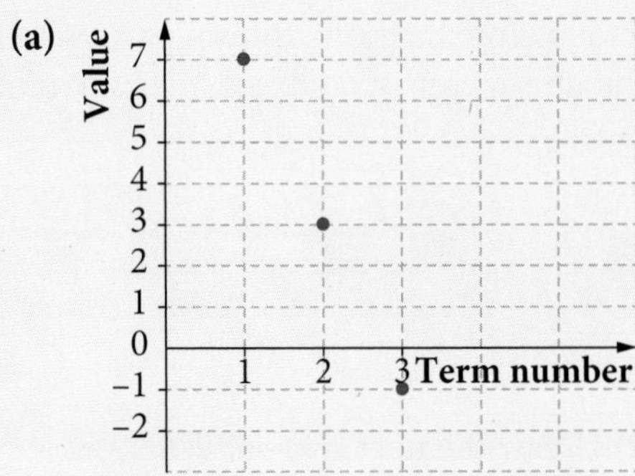

(b)

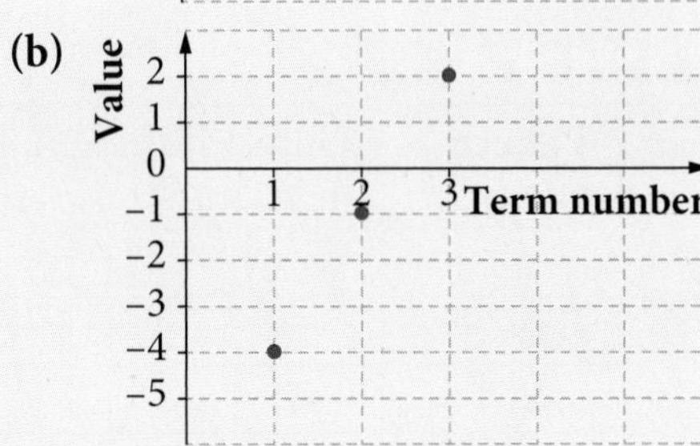

(c)

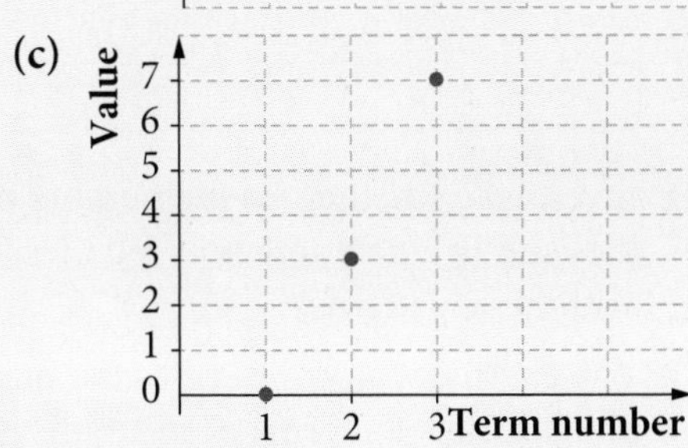

4. A sequence is as follows: −15, −8, −1, 6, …
   - **(i)** Prove that the sequence is arithmetic.
   - **(ii)** Find an expression for T_n, the nth term in the sequence.
   - **(iii)** Hence, or otherwise, write down the next four terms of the sequence.

5. A sequence is as follows: −9, −5·5, −2, 1·5, …
   - **(i)** Prove that the sequence is linear.
   - **(ii)** Hence, or otherwise, write down the next four terms of the sequence.

6. **(i)** Write out the first five terms of the linear pattern defined as 'start at 8 and add 2 each time'.
   - **(ii)** Find S_{20}, the sum of the first 20 terms of this sequence.

7. **(i)** Write out the first five terms of the arithmetic pattern defined as 'start at 12 and subtract 4 each time'.
   - **(ii)** Write an expression for T_n, the nth term of the sequence.
   - **(iii)** Find T_7 and T_{15}.
   - **(iv)** Find S_{14}, the sum of the first 14 terms of the sequence.

8. The graph shows a linear pattern.

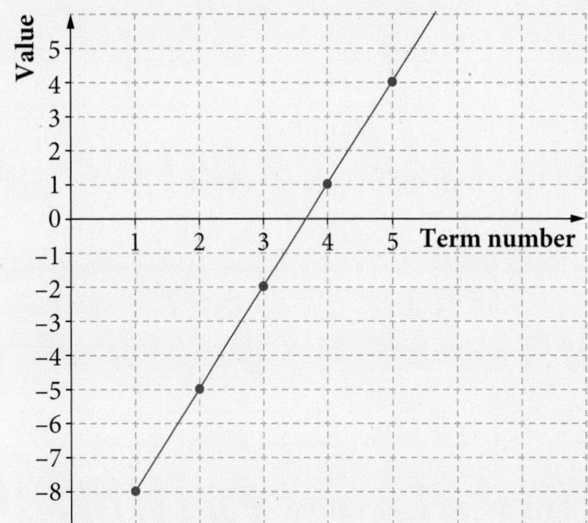

   - **(i)** Identify the first term, a.
   - **(ii)** Find d, the common difference.
   - **(iii)** Describe this pattern in words.
   - **(iv)** Hence, or otherwise, find, in terms of n, an expression for T_n, the nth term of the sequence.
   - **(v)** Find T_{21} and T_{40}.
   - **(vi)** Which term of the sequence is 28?

9. The following is an arithmetic series:

   $$22 + 15 + 8 + 1 + \ldots$$

   - **(i)** Find d, the common difference.
   - **(ii)** Describe this pattern in words.
   - **(iii)** Hence, or otherwise, find, in terms of n, an expression for T_n, the nth term of the sequence.
   - **(iv)** Which term of the series is −41?
   - **(v)** Find S_{18}.

10. The first term of an arithmetic sequence is 12 and the common difference is 3.
    - **(i)** Find, in terms of n, an expression for T_n, the nth term of the sequence.
    - **(ii)** How many terms of the sequence are less than 100?
    - **(iii)** Find the sum of these terms.

11. The following diagram shows a pattern of blocks:

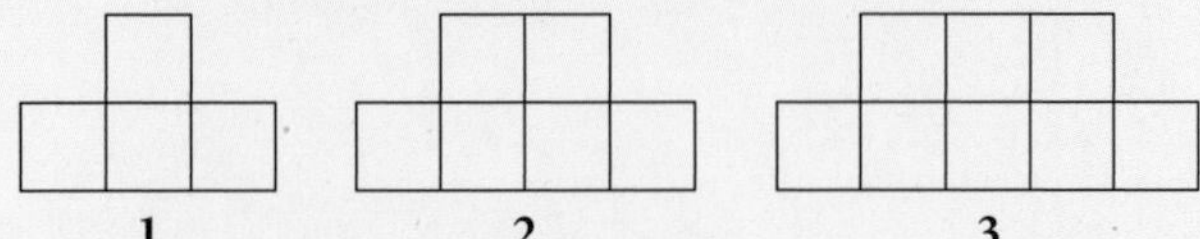

(i) Draw the next two patterns.

(ii) Copy and complete the following table:

Pattern number	Number of blocks
1	4
2	
3	
4	
5	

(iii) Investigate whether the number of blocks form a linear pattern.

(iv) Write a rule which describes the number of blocks, in terms of the pattern number.

(v) Hence, or otherwise, find the number of blocks in the 12th pattern.

(vi) Which pattern number contains 116 blocks?

(vii) What is the largest pattern number which can be made using 225 blocks?

(viii) How many blocks are needed in total to make the first 17 patterns?

12. The following diagram shows a pattern of 50 c coins:

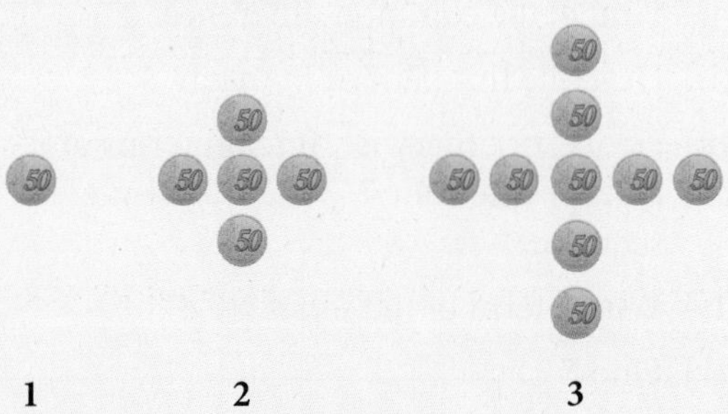

(i) Draw the next two patterns.

(ii) Write out the number of coins in the first five patterns.

(iii) Investigate whether the number of coins form a linear pattern.

(iv) Write a rule which describes the number of coins, in terms of the pattern number.

(v) Hence, or otherwise, find the number of coins in the 28th pattern.

(vi) Which pattern number contains 65 coins?

(vii) How many coins are needed in total to make the first 15 patterns?
What is the total value of these coins?

13. The following diagrams show a pattern of tiles. Each pattern consists of black tiles surrounded by red tiles.

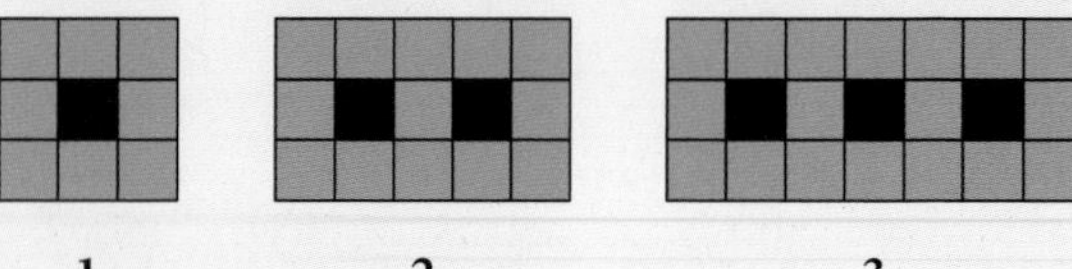

(i) Draw the next two patterns.

(ii) Copy and complete the following table:

Pattern number	Number of black tiles	Number of red tiles
1	1	8
2		
3		
4		
5		

(iii) Investigate whether **(a)** the number of black tiles and **(b)** the number of red tiles form arithmetic patterns.

(iv) Write a rule which describes the number of black tiles, in terms of the pattern number.

(v) Write a rule which describes the number of red tiles, in terms of the pattern number.

(vi) Hence, write an expression for the total number of tiles in a pattern, in terms of the pattern number.

(vii) Find the number of black tiles and red tiles in the 18th pattern.

(viii) Which pattern number contains 68 red tiles?

(ix) How many red tiles will be needed in total to make the first 16 patterns?

Section 6.3: Finding the First Term, *a*, and the Common Difference, *d*

Learning Outcome:

You should be able to:

- write an algebraic expression for a particular term in a linear sequence

In some problems you may be given a specific term or the sum of a number of terms in the sequence or series, and asked to find the value of the first term, *a*, and the common difference, *d*.

If this is the case, follow these steps to solve the problem:

Step 1: Use the formula for T_n or S_n to form equations in terms of *a* and *d*.

Step 2: Solve these equations to find the values of *a* and *d*.

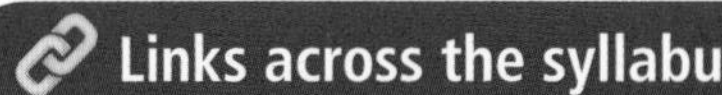

Solving simultaneous equations with two unknowns are covered in Chapter 3: Algebra II.

EXAMPLE 1

The fifth term of an arithmetic series is 15 and the tenth term is 5.

(i) Find the first term, *a*, and the common difference, *d*.

(ii) Find the sum of the first 18 terms.

(iii) For what values of *n* is the sum of the first *n* terms equal to 128?

(iv) Give a reason why there are two possible answers to part **(iii)**.

Solution

(i) ***Step 1:*** Fifth term is 15.

Therefore, $T_5 = 15$ and $n = 5$:

$T_5 = a + (5 - 1)d$

$15 = a + 4d$ ①

Tenth term is 5.

Therefore, $T_{10} = 5$ and $n = 10$:

$T_{10} = a + (10 - 1)d$

$5 = a + 9d$ ②

Step 2: Solve these equations simultaneously:

① $a + 4d = 15$ $(\times -1$ to eliminate $a)$

② $a + 9d = 5$

$-a - 4d = -15$

$a + 9d = 5$

$5d = -10$

$d = -2$

Substitute $d = -2$ into the first equation and hence find the value of *a*:

$a + 4d = 15$

$a + 4(-2) = 15$

$a - 8 = 15$

$a = 15 + 8$

$a = 23$

(ii) $S_n = \frac{n}{2}[2a + (n - 1)d]$ $a = 23$, $d = -2$, find S_{18}:

$S_{18} = \frac{18}{2}[2(23) + (18 - 1)(-2)]$

$S_{18} = 9[46 + 17(-2)]$

$S_{18} = 9[46 - 34]$

$S_{18} = 9[12]$

$S_{18} = 108$

(iii) $S_n = \frac{n}{2}[2a + (n-1)d]$ $S_n = 128, a = 23, d = -2$

$$128 = \frac{n}{2}[2(23) + (n-1)(-2)]$$
$$128 = \frac{n}{2}[46 - 2n + 2]$$
$$128 = \frac{n}{2}[48 - 2n]$$
$$128 = n[24 - n]$$
$$128 = 24n - n^2$$
$$n^2 - 24n + 128 = 0 \quad \text{(rearrange)}$$
$$(n-16)(n-8) = 0 \quad \text{(factorise)}$$
$$n - 16 = 0 \text{ or } n - 8 = 0$$
$$n = 16 \text{ or } n = 8$$

(iv) From part **(iii)**, we see that the first eight terms sum to 128 and also the first 16 terms sum to 128.

This is because the arithmetic sequence starts at 23 and decreases by 2 for each term.

Therefore, the sequence will eventually go into negative values and so the sum of the values will start to decrease.

Using S_n to find T_n

If we have a formula for finding the sum of n terms of a sequence, S_n, we can use this formula to find a value for T_n, the nth term in the sequence.

Let's say that we want to find the 6th term in a sequence:

T_1 T_2 T_3 T_4 T_5 T_6

$S_5 = T_1 + T_2 + T_3 + T_4 + T_5$

$S_6 = T_1 + T_2 + T_3 + T_4 + T_5 + T_6$

S_6 is the sum of the first six terms and S_5 is the sum of the first five terms, then $T_6 = S_6 - S_5$.

In mathematical terms: $T_n = S_n - S_{n-1}$

EXAMPLE 2

The sum of the first n terms of an arithmetic series is given by $S_n = 3n^2 - 4n$.
Use S_n to find the value of the 8th term in the series.

Solution

The 8th term will be found as $T_8 = S_8 - S_7$

Find S_8:
$S_8 = 3(8)^2 - 4(8)$
$S_8 = 3(64) - 32$
$S_8 = 192 - 32$
$S_8 = 160$

Find S_7:
$S_7 = 3(7)^2 - 4(7)$
$S_7 = 3(49) - 28$
$S_7 = 147 - 28$
$S_7 = 119$

The sum of the first 8 terms is 160 and the sum of the first 7 terms is 119.
Therefore, $T_8 = 160 - 119 = 41$

Practice Questions 6.3

1. The first term of an arithmetic series is −1 and the second term is 5.
   (i) Find d, the common difference.
   (ii) Find T_8, the eighth term of the series.
   (iii) The kth term of the series is 113. Find k.
   (iv) Find S_{18}, the sum of the first 18 terms of the series.

2. In an arithmetic sequence, the first term is 3 and the fifth term is 19. Find:
   (i) d, the common difference
   (ii) T_{12}, the 12th term of the sequence
   (iii) S_{25}, the sum of the first 25 terms.

3. The first term of an arithmetic series is 5 and the eighth term is 33. Find:
   (i) T_3, the third term of the series
   (ii) S_{28}, the sum of the first 28 terms.

4. The fourth term of an arithmetic series is 2 and the 12th term is 34.
   (i) Find the first term, a, and the common difference, d.
   (ii) Find the sum of the first 16 terms.
   (iii) For what values of n is the sum of the first n terms equal to 80?

5. The following diagram shows the second and fourth patterns in a sequence. Each pattern is made from toothpicks.

Pattern 1	Pattern 2	Pattern 3	Pattern 4

   (i) Draw the first and third steps of the pattern.
   (ii) Find an expression for T_n, the nth term of the sequence.
   (iii) How many toothpicks will be needed to make the 22nd pattern?
   (iv) Eamon wants to make the first 15 patterns of this sequence. How many toothpicks will he need in total?

6. The sum of the first n terms of an arithmetic series is given by $S_n = n^2 - 12n$.
   (i) Use S_1 and S_2 to find the first term and the second term of the series.
   (ii) Find d, the common difference.
   (iii) Find an expression for T_n, the nth term of the series.
   (iv) Find the values of n for which $S_n = 28$.
   (v) After how many terms of the series will S_n equal zero?

7. The third term of an arithmetic series is 2 and the ninth term is −16.
   (i) Find the first term, a, and the common difference, d.
   (ii) Find the sum of the first 15 terms.
   (iii) For what value of n is the sum of the first n terms equal to −55?

8. The second term of an arithmetic series is −8 and the seventh term is 12.
   (i) Find the first term, a, and the common difference, d.
   (ii) Find the sum of the first 22 terms.
   (iii) For what value of n is the sum of the first n terms equal to zero?

9. The sum of the first n terms of an arithmetic series is given by $S_n = n(2n + 1)$. Use S_n to find the value of the fourth term in the series.

10. The sum of the first n terms of an arithmetic series is given by $S_n = 3n^2 + 4n$. Use S_n to find the value of the 12th term in the series.

11. The sum of the first n terms of an arithmetic series is given by $S_n = 5n^2 - 3n$. Use S_n to find the value of the eighth term in the series.

12. Scarlet is investigating the number of tiles needed to make patterns in a sequence. The first three patterns are shown below, and the sequence continues in the same way.

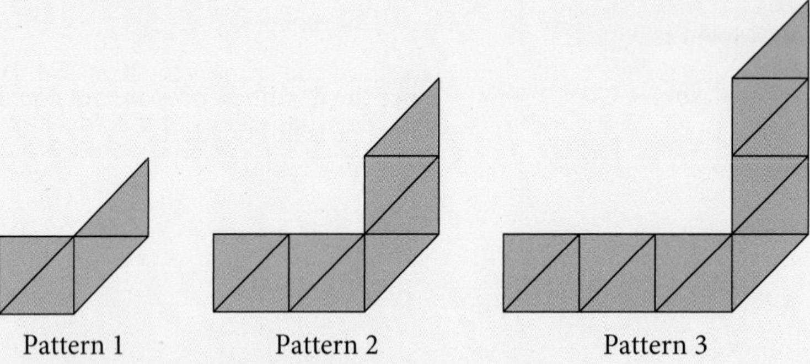

(i) Draw the next pattern in the sequence.

(ii) Copy the table on the right and write the number of tiles needed for each of the first five patterns:

Pattern	1	2	3	4	5
No. of tiles	4				

(iii) Find, in terms of n, a formula that gives the number of tiles needed to make the nth pattern.

(iv) Using your formula, or otherwise, find the number of tiles in the 12th pattern.

(v) Scarlet has 480 tiles. What is the biggest pattern in the sequence that she can make?

(vi) Find, in terms of n, a formula for the total number of tiles in the first n patterns (S_n).

(vii) Scarlet starts at the beginning of the sequence and makes as many patterns as she can. She does not break up the earlier patterns to make the new ones. For example, after making the first two patterns, she has used up 16 tiles (4 + 12).
How many patterns can she make in total with her 480 tiles?

Section 6.4: Quadratic Patterns

Learning Outcomes:

You should be able to:

- identify a quadratic pattern or sequence
- use patterns to continue a quadratic sequence
- generalise and explain patterns and relationships in algebraic form
- write an expression for a particular term in a quadratic sequence (find T_n)

A **quadratic pattern** is a sequence of numbers in which the differences of the differences (the second difference) are all equal.

EXAMPLE 1

Investigate whether the following patterns (sequences) are quadratic:

(i) −2, 4, 12, 22, … **(ii)** 5, 11, 29, 83, …

Solution

(i) Find the differences between each term:

Terms:	−2		4		12		22
1st differences:		6		8		10	
2nd differences			2		2		

Since all the 2nd differences are equal, the sequence is quadratic.

(ii) Find the difference between each term:

Terms:	5		11		29		83
1st differences:		6		18		54	
2nd differences			12		36		

Since the 2nd differences are **not** equal, the sequence is **not** quadratic.

EXAMPLE 2

A quadratic sequence is as follows: 6, 9, 14, 21, …

(i) Graph these terms on a coordinated plane.

(ii) Write down the next two terms of the sequence.

Solution

(i) Graphing the terms gives:

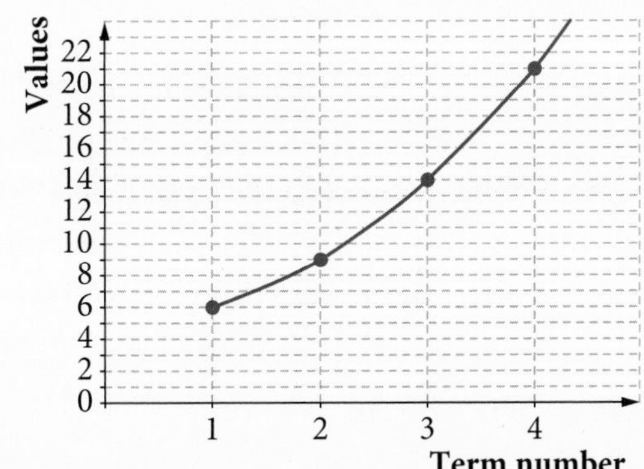

(ii) To continue the pattern, find the 1st and 2nd difference. We find that the 2nd difference is 2 (see below). Then, fill in the next two 2nd differences as being 2 (shown in red below), then work out the 1st differences (shown in blue below) and finally work out the missing terms:

Terms:	6		9		14		21		21 + 9 = 30		30 + 11 = 41
1st differences:		3		5		7		7 + 2 = 9		9 + 2 = 11	
2nd differences:			2		2		2		2		

Therefore, from the above we can see that the 5th term = 30 and the 6th term = 41

Pattern

Generating a rule for a quadratic sequence

Any term in a quadratic sequence or pattern can be written in the form:

$$T_n = an^2 + bn + c \qquad \text{where, } a = \frac{2^{\text{nd}} \text{ difference}}{2}.$$

To find the values of b and c, follow these steps:

Step 1: Take two known terms of the sequence.

Step 2: Substitute the values for T_n and n into $T_n = an^2 + bn + c$ to get two equations in terms of b and c.

Step 3: Use simultaneous equations to solve for b and c.

EXAMPLE 3

The following patterns are made using blocks:

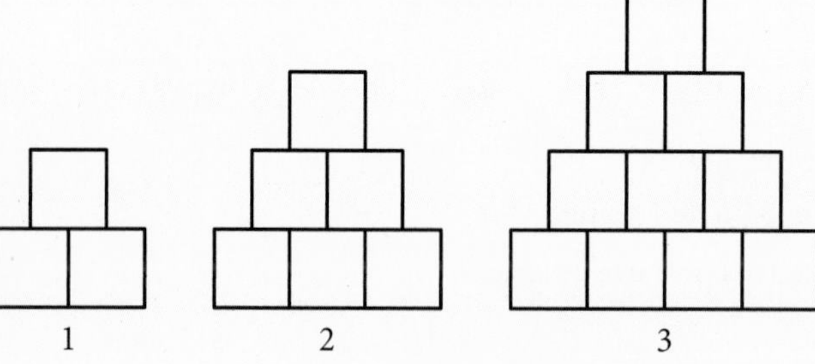

(i) Draw the next pattern.

(ii) Copy and complete the following table:

Pattern number	Number of blocks
1	3
2	
3	
4	

(iii) Investigate the type of pattern formed by the number of blocks.

(iv) Write a rule which describes the number of blocks, in terms of the pattern number.

(v) Hence, or otherwise, find the number of blocks in the 12th pattern.

(vi) Which pattern number contains 55 blocks?

Solution

(i) Fourth pattern:

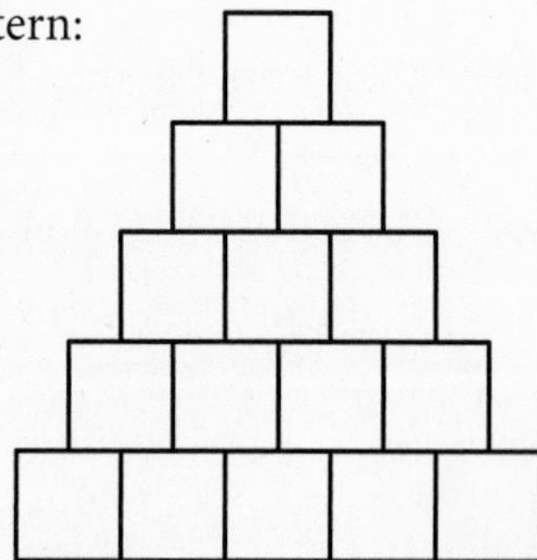

(ii)

Pattern number	Number of blocks
1	3
2	6
3	10
4	15

(iii) Find the differences between the numbers of blocks in each pattern.

Pattern number	Number of blocks
1	3
2	6
3	10
4	15

1st difference: 3, 4, 5

2nd difference: 1, 1

Since the 2nd differences are equal, the pattern is quadratic.

(iv) The quadratic pattern is in the form $T_n = an^2 + bn + c$ where, $a = \frac{2^{\text{nd}} \text{ difference}}{2}$

Since the 2nd difference is 1, $a = \frac{1}{2}$

Therefore, $T_n = \frac{1}{2}n^2 + bn + c$

For the 1st term, $n = 1$ and $T_1 = 3$:

$T_n = \frac{1}{2}n^2 + bn + c$

$3 = \frac{1}{2}(1)^2 + b(1) + c$

$3 = \frac{1}{2} + b + c$ (× 2 to eliminate fraction)

$6 = 1 + 2b + 2c$

$5 = 2b + 2c$ ①

For the 2nd term, $n = 2$ and $T_2 = 6$:

$T_n = \frac{1}{2}n^2 + bn + 8$

$6 = \frac{1}{2}(2)^2 + b(2) + c$

$6 = \frac{1}{2}(4) + 2b + c$

$6 = 2 + 2b + c$

$4 = 2b + c$ ②

Solve these equations simultaneously:

$2b + 2c = 5$

$2b + c = 4$ (× −1 to eliminate b)

$2b + 2c = 5$

$-2b - c = -4$

$c = 1$

substitute $c = 1$ to find b:

$2b + c = 4$

$2b + 1 = 4$

$2b = 3$

$b = \frac{3}{2}$

Therefore: $T_n = \frac{1}{2}n^2 + \frac{3}{2}n + 1$

(v) Find T_n when $n = 12$:

$T_{12} = \frac{1}{2}(12)^2 + \frac{3}{2}(12) + 1$

$T_{12} = \frac{1}{2}(144) + 18 + 1$

$T_{12} = 72 + 18 + 1$

$T_{12} = 91$

(vi) Find n when $T_n = 55$:

$55 = \frac{1}{2}n^2 + \frac{3}{2}n + 1$ (× 2 to eliminate the fractions)

$110 = n^2 + 3n + 2$

$0 = n^2 + 3n - 108$ (subtract 110 from both sides)

$0 = (n + 12)(n - 9)$

$n + 12 = 0$ or $n - 9 = 0$

$n = -12$ or $n = 9$

Since you cannot have a negative term number, we reject $n = -12$.

And so the 9th term contains 55 blocks.

Pattern

Practice Questions 6.4

1. Determine which of the following sequences and series are quadratic. Give a reason for your answer.

(i) 6, 11, 18, 27, …
(ii) $-4 - 1 + 2 + 5 + \ldots$
(iii) 3, 0, −5, −12, …
(iv) $1 - 3 - 9 - 17 - \ldots$
(v) 3, 9, 15, 21, …
(vi) 3, 9, 27, 81, …
(vii) $5 + 20 + 45 + 80 + \ldots$
(viii) 2, 10, 24, 44, …
(ix) $2 + 6 + 18 + 54 + \ldots$

2. For each of the given graphs:

(a)
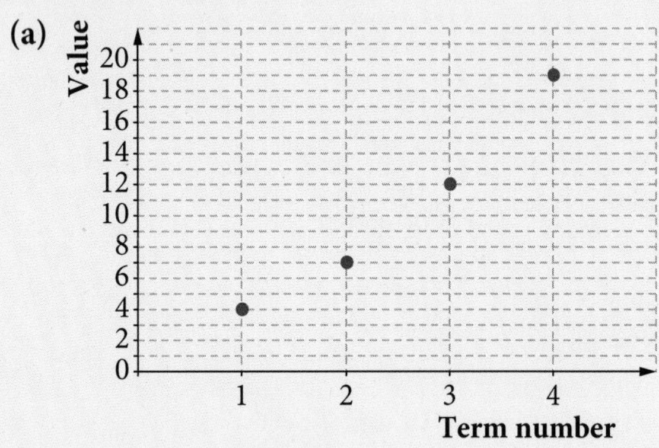

(b)
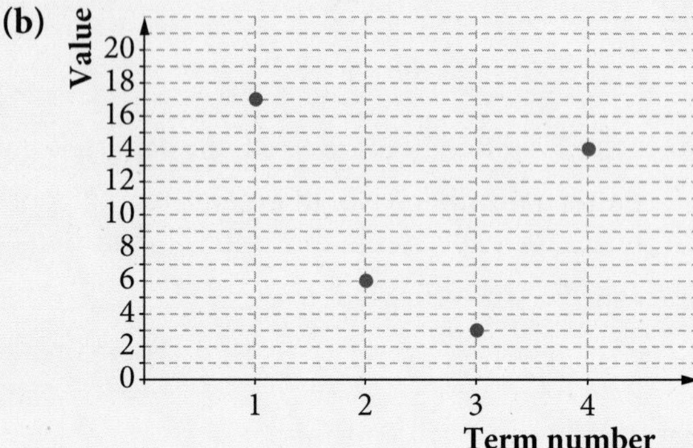

(i) list the first four terms of the sequence.
(ii) investigate whether each sequence is a quadratic pattern.

3. A sequence is as follows: 3, 3, 5, 9, …

(i) Graph these terms on a coordinated plane.
(ii) Show that this sequence is quadratic.
(iii) Find an expression for T_n, the nth term of the sequence.
(iv) Hence, or otherwise, find the tenth term in the sequence.

4. For each of the following sequences and series:

(a) 6, 11, 18, 27, 38, …
(b) $2 + 12 + 30 + 56, \ldots$
(c) −2, −3, −6, −11, …

(i) Show that the pattern is quadratic.
(ii) Find an expression for T_n, the nth term of the sequence.
(iii) Hence, or otherwise, find T_{12}, the 12th term in each sequence.

5. The following patterns are made using tiles:

Pattern 1

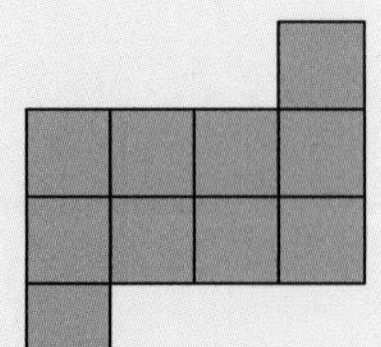
Pattern 2

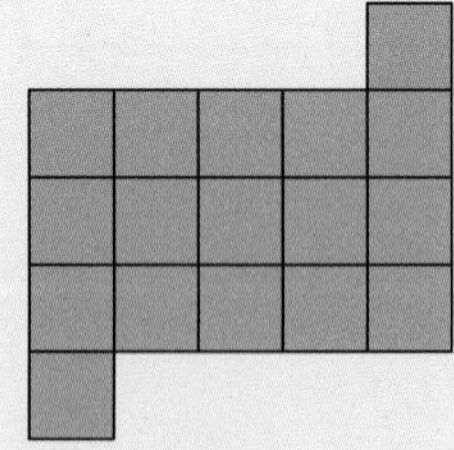
Pattern 3

(i) Draw the next pattern.
(ii) Copy and complete the following table:

Pattern number	Number of tiles
1	5
2	
3	
4	

(iii) Investigate the type of pattern formed by the number of tiles.
(iv) The nth term in the sequence is given by: $T_n = an^2 + bn + c$, where $a, b, c \in \mathbb{Z}$. Find the values of a, b and c.
(v) Hence, or otherwise, find the number of tiles in the 17th pattern.
(vi) Which pattern number contains 101 blocks?

6. The following patterns are made using tiles:

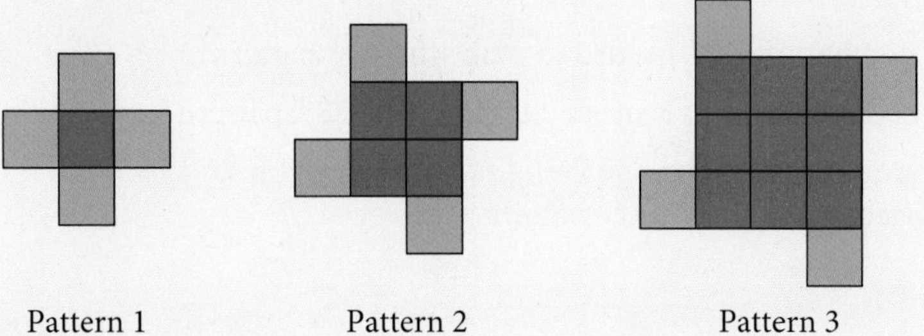

Pattern 1 Pattern 2 Pattern 3

(i) Draw the next pattern.

(ii) Copy and complete the following table:

Pattern number	No. of green tiles	No. of red tiles	Total no. of tiles
1			
2			
3			
4			

(iii) Determine the type of pattern formed by the number of red tiles.

(iv) Find a rule which describes the number of red tiles, in terms of the pattern number.

(v) Hence, write a rule which describes the total number of tiles, in terms of the pattern number.

(vi) Hence, or otherwise, find the total number of tiles in the 44th pattern.

(vii) Which pattern number contains 104 blocks?

7. The first three patterns of a sequence of coloured discs are shown as follows:

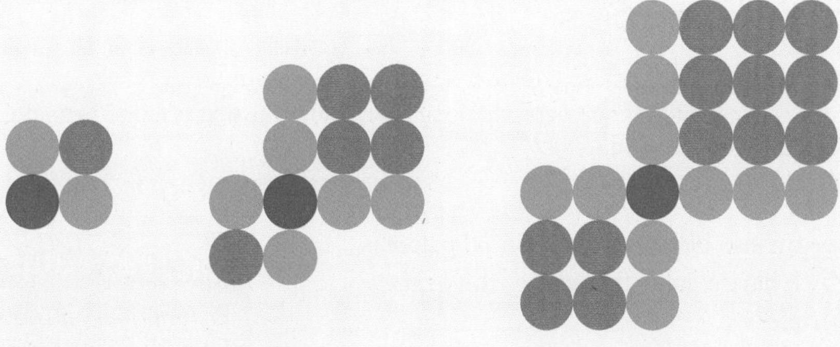

Pattern 1 Pattern 2 Pattern 3

(i) Draw the fourth pattern.

(ii) Copy and complete the following table:

Pattern no.	Number of red discs	Number of green discs	Number of blue discs	Total number of discs
1				
2				
3				
4				

(iii) Determine the type of pattern formed by the number of green discs.

(iv) Find a rule which describes the number of green discs, in terms of the pattern number.

(v) Determine the type of pattern formed by the total number of discs.

(vi) The total number of discs in the nth pattern is given by: $T_n = an^2 + bn + c$, where $a, b, c \in \mathbb{Z}$. Find the values of a, b and c.

(vii) Find the total number of discs needed to make the 28th pattern.

(viii) How many of each colour disc is needed to make the 28th pattern?

(ix) Using your answers to parts **(iv)** and **(vi)**, find an expression for the number of red discs and the number of blue discs together in terms of the pattern number.

Section 6.5: Recognising if a Sequence is Arithmetic (Linear), Geometric or Neither

Learning Outcome:

You should be able to:

- recognise whether a sequence is arithmetic (linear), geometric or neither

Arithmetic (linear) sequences

As covered in Section 6.2 of this chapter, an arithmetic (linear) sequence is one where there is a common first difference between consecutive terms. When this is the case, any term minus the previous term is a constant.

If a sequence is arithmetic:

$$T_n - T_{n-1} = \text{a constant}$$

Geometric sequences

A **geometric sequence** is a sequence of numbers where each term after the first is found by multiplying the previous term by a fixed number called the common ratio.

Geometric sequences can also be called exponential patterns. They are patterns which have a value that causes the next term to half/double/triple, etc.

When this is the case, any term divided by the previous term is a constant.

Exponential patterns are covered in Chapter 7: Further Functions.

If a sequence is geometric:

$$\frac{T_n}{T_{n-1}} = \text{a constant}$$

To determine whether a sequence is arithmetic, geometric or neither:

Step 1: Find the first difference between each of the terms. If these are equal, then the sequence is arithmetic.

Step 2: Find the ratio between all given terms. If these are equal, then the sequence is geometric.

Step 3: If neither the first differences are the same nor the ratios are equal, then the sequence is neither arithmetic (linear) nor geometric.

We can use the following flowchart to help us determine if a sequence is arithmetic, geometric or neither:

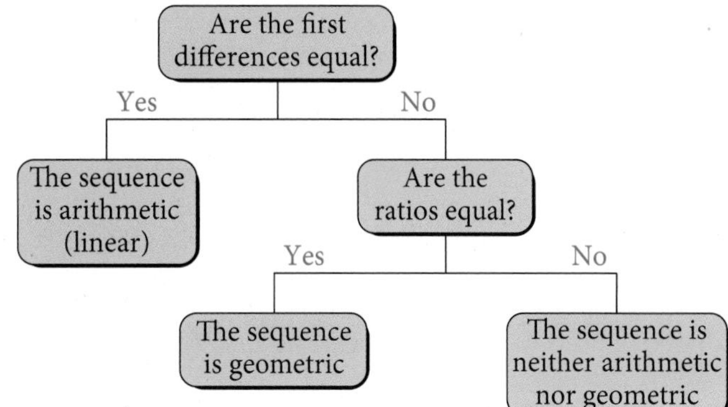

EXAMPLE

Determine whether each of the following sequences are arithmetic, geometric or neither.

(i) $\frac{1}{2}$, 2, 8, 32, … **(ii)** 3, 8, 15, 24, … **(iii)** 12, 7, 2, −3, …

Solution

(i) ***Step 1*:** Check the first difference: Difference = any term − previous term

Terms: $\frac{1}{2}$ 2 8 32

Differences: 1·5 6 24

The first differences are not equal, therefore the **sequence is not arithmetic.**

***Step 2*:** Check the ratios: Ratio = $\dfrac{\text{any term}}{\text{previous term}}$

Terms: $\frac{1}{2}$ 2 8 32

Ratio: $\dfrac{2}{\left(\frac{1}{2}\right)} = 4$ $\quad \frac{8}{2} = 4$ $\quad \frac{32}{8} = 4$

The ratios are equal, therefore the sequence $\frac{1}{2}$, 2, 8, 32, … is geometric.

(ii) ***Step 1*:** Check the first difference: Difference = any term − previous term

Terms: 3 8 15 24

Differences: 5 7 9

The first differences are not equal, therefore the **sequence is not arithmetic**.

***Step 2*:** Check the ratios: Ratio = $\dfrac{\text{any term}}{\text{previous term}}$

Terms: 3 8 15 24

Ratio: $\frac{8}{3}$ $\quad \frac{15}{8}$ $\quad \frac{24}{15}$

The ratios are not equal, therefore the **sequence is not geometric**.

***Step 3*:** Therefore, the sequence 3, 8, 15, 24, … is neither arithmetic nor geometric

(iii) ***Step 1*:** Check the first difference: Difference = any term − previous term

Terms: 12 7 2 −3

Differences: −5 −5 −5

The first differences are equal, therefore the sequence 12, 7, 2, −3, … is arithmetic.

Discussion Time 

The diagram shows the graph of three patterns, A, B and C.

Work with a classmate to:

1. use the graphs to identify the first four terms of each pattern
2. hence determine whether the patterns are arithmetic (linear), quadratic or geometric.

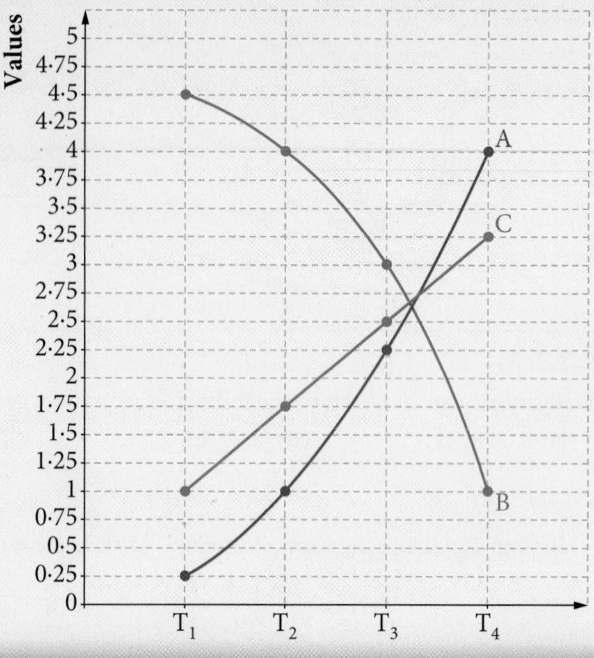

Practice Questions 6.5

1. Determine which of the following patterns are arithmetic, geometric or neither. Give reason for your answer.
   - **(i)** 3, 6, 12, 24, …
   - **(ii)** 2, 8, 18, 32, …
   - **(iii)** 9, 3, 1, $\frac{1}{3}$, …
   - **(iv)** 11, 7, 3, −1, …
   - **(v)** 1, 5, 25, 125, …
   - **(vi)** −4, 3, 22, 59, …
   - **(vii)** −3, −8, −2, −7, −1, …
   - **(viii)** −9, −4, 1, 6, …
   - **(ix)** 24, −12, 6, −3, …

2. For each of the given graphs:

(a)

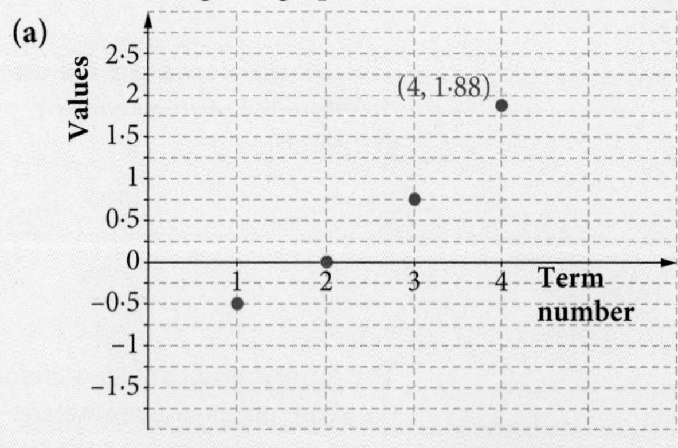

(b)

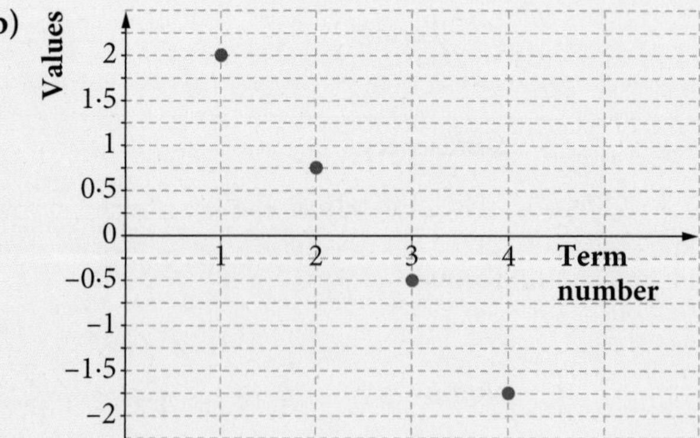

   - **(i)** List the first four terms of the sequence.
   - **(ii)** Investigate whether the patterns are arithmetic or geometric.

3. The first three terms of a sequence are: $3p + q$, $2p + 2q$, $p + 3q$, where p and q are real numbers. Verify that this sequence is arithmetic.

4. The first three terms of an arithmetic sequence are: $k + 3$, $5k - 2$, $6k - 13$, where k is a real number.
   (i) Find the value of k.
   (ii) Hence, write down the value of the first three terms.
   (iii) Find the value of the eighth term.

5. Three terms of a sequence are: $2x - 3$, $4x - 6$, $8x - 12$, where x is a real number.
   Determine whether this sequence is arithmetic, geometric or neither.

6. Three terms of a sequence are: $p - q$, $3p - 2q$, $6p - 3q$, where p and q are real numbers.
   Determine whether this sequence is arithmetic, geometric or neither.

7. Three terms of a sequence are: $(2a + b - 5c)$, $(3a - 4c)$ and $(4a - b - 3c)$, where a, b and c are real numbers. Determine whether this sequence is arithmetic, geometric or neither.

Revision and Exam Style Questions – Section A

1. The first term of a linear pattern is 25 and the common difference is −4.
   Write down the first six terms of the pattern.

2. The nth term of an arithmetic series is given by $T_n = 2n - 5$
   (i) Find a, the first term of the series.
   (ii) Find d, the common difference.
   (iii) Find the value of n, for which $T_n = 31$.
   (iv) Find S_{14}, the sum of the first 14 terms.

3. The table shows the first five terms of an arithmetic sequence.
   (i) Find an expression for T_n, the nth term of the sequence.
   (ii) Hence, or otherwise, find the value of T_{35}, the 35th term.

Term	Value
T_1	5
T_2	8
T_3	11
T_4	14
T_5	17

4. The graph shows part of the graph of a sequence.
   (i) Write out the first four terms of the sequence.
   (ii) Is the pattern quadratic? Justify your answer.

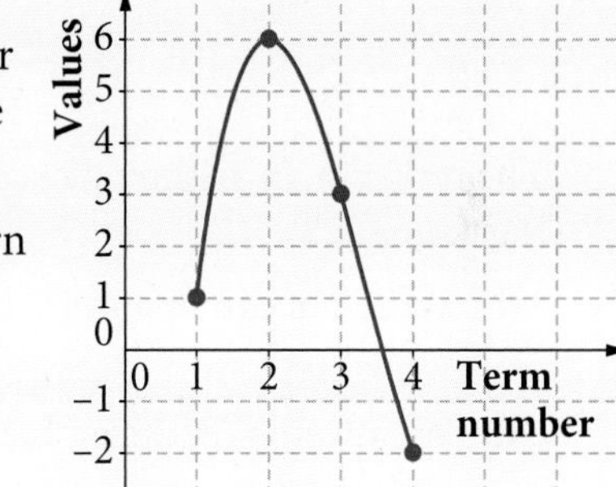

5. The first term of an arithmetic sequence is −2 and the second term is 2. Find:
   (i) d, the common difference
   (ii) the third and the fourth term of the sequence.

6. Write down the next three terms in each of the following arithmetic sequences:
   (i) −15, −13, −11, … (ii) 5·1, 5·7, 6·3, …

7. Determine whether the following sequence is arithmetic, geometric or neither: 18, 13, 9, 6, …

8. The nth term of a sequence is given by $T_n = 5 + 2n$. Find:
   (i) T_3, the third term of the sequence
   (ii) T_7, the seventh term of the sequence
   (iii) $T_{10} - T_7$.

9. The first term of an arithmetic sequence is 21 and the common difference is −6.
   Find, in terms of n, an expression for T_n, the nth term.

Pattern

10. The following diagram shows the second and fourth patterns in a sequence.
Each pattern is made from matches.

Pattern 1	Pattern 2	Pattern 3	Pattern 4

(i) Draw the first and third steps of the pattern.

(ii) Find an expression for T_n, the nth term of the sequence.

(iii) How many matches will be needed to make the 18th pattern?

(iv) A box contains 100 matches. What is the largest pattern number that can be made, using this box of matches?

(v) Aoibhe wants to make the first 23 patterns of this sequence.
How many matches will she need?

Revision and Exam Style Questions – Section B

More challenging problems

1. The terms in an arithmetic sequence are given by the formula $T_n = 26 - 4n$.
   - **(i)** Write out the first three terms in the sequence.
   - **(ii)** What is the first negative term in the sequence?
   - **(iii)** Find the sum of the first 15 terms of the sequence.
   - **(iv)** Find the value of n for which the sum of the first n terms of the sequence is zero.

2. The graph shows part of the graphs of two sequences.
   - **(i)** Write out the first four terms of each sequence.
   - **(ii)** Determine whether the patterns are arithmetic or geometric. Justify your answer.

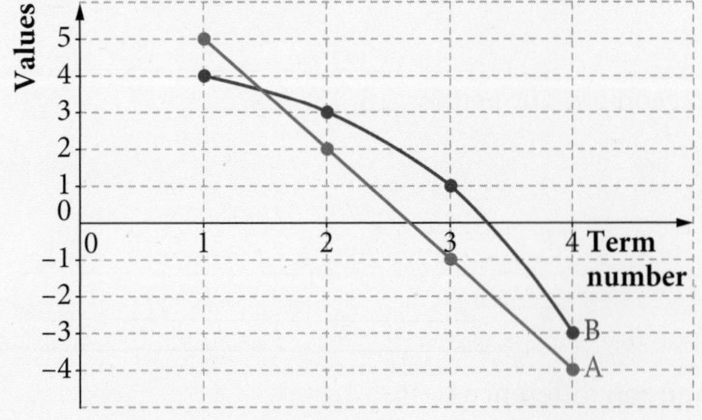

3. The sum of the first n terms of an arithmetic series is given by $S_n = 3n^2 - n$
   - **(i)** Find a, the first term.
   - **(ii)** Find S_2, the sum of the first two terms.
   - **(iii)** Find d, the common difference.
   - **(iv)** Write down the first six terms of the series.

4. The first four terms of a sequence are: 5, 11, 13, 11, …
   - **(i)** Verify that the sequence is quadratic.
   - **(ii)** The nth term in the sequence is given by: $T_n = an^2 + bn + c$ where $a, b, c \in \mathbb{Z}$.
     Find the values of a, b and c.

5. The sum of the first n terms of an arithmetic series is given by $S_n = n^2 + 4n$.
   Use S_n to find the value of the ninth term in the series.

6. The terms of a linear sequence are given by the formula $T_n = 8 - 2n$ for $n = 1, 2, 3, 4, \ldots$
   - **(i)** Write out the first four terms of the sequence.
   - **(ii)** Find the value of n for which $T_n = -46$.
   - **(iii)** Find S_{14}, the sum of the first 14 terms of the series.

7. Find the 12th term of the arithmetic sequence 4, 12, 20, …

8. Three terms of a sequence are: $(3x + y)$, $(x + 2y)$ and $(-x + 4y)$, where x, y and z are real numbers. Determine whether this sequence is arithmetic, geometric or neither.

9. The first four numbers in a pattern are shown in the table.
   (i) Follow the pattern to write the next three numbers into the table.
   (ii) Use the data in the table to show that the pattern is quadratic.
   (iii) $T_n = n^2 + bn + c$, where $b, c \in \mathbb{Z}$.
   Find the values of b and c.

Term	Value
T_1	1
T_2	6
T_3	13
T_4	22
T_5	
T_6	
T_7	

10. The sum of the first n terms of an arithmetic series is given by $S_n = 4n^2 - n$. Use S_n to find the value of the fifth term in the series.

11. The first three patterns in a sequence of patterns are shown below:

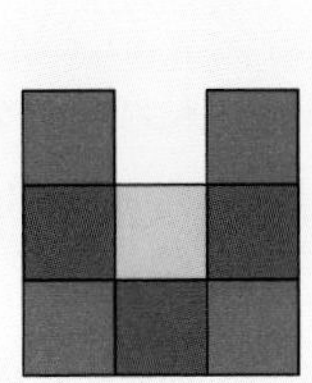

Pattern 1

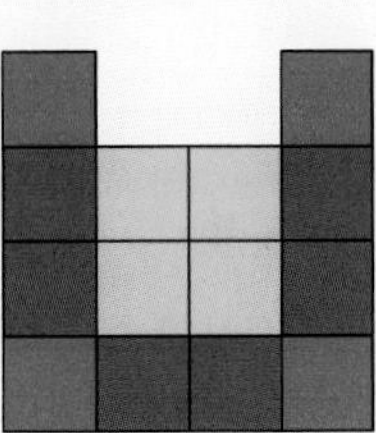

Pattern 2

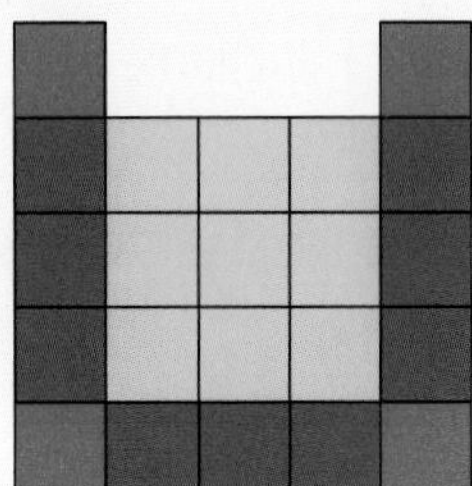

Pattern 3

(i) Draw the fourth pattern in the sequence.
(ii) Copy and complete the following table:

	Number of red tiles	Number of blue tiles	Number of yellow tiles	Total number of tiles
Pattern 1				
Pattern 2				
Pattern 3				
Pattern 4				

(iii) What type of pattern is formed by the yellow tiles? Justify your answer.
(iv) **(a)** How many red tiles are in the 12th sequence?
(b) How many blue tiles are in the 12th sequence?
(c) How many yellow tiles are in the 12th sequence?
(d) Hence, find how many tiles there are in total in the 12th sequence.
(v) The total number of tiles in the nth pattern is given by $T_n = an^2 + bn + c$ where $a, b, c \in \mathbb{Z}$. Find the values of a, b and c.
(vi) One particular pattern has a total of 554 tiles. Find the number of red tiles, blue tiles and yellow tiles in that pattern.

Now that you have completed the chapter, revisit the 'Something to think about…' questions.

CHAPTER 07

Further Functions

Sections covered within this chapter:

KEY WORDS

- Function
- Cubic function
- Domain
- Exponential function
- Range
- Composite function
- Co-domain

SOMETHING TO THINK ABOUT…

A nuclear power station has a leak, resulting in a nearby lake being contaminated with three tonnes of iodine-131.

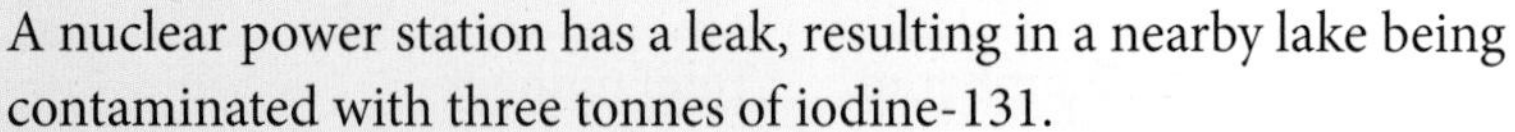

Iodine has a half-life of eight days, which means that after eight days, half of its mass will have disintegrated.

The mass, m, of iodine-131 remaining after n half-lives can be found by the function:

$$m(n) = 3000\left(\frac{1}{2}\right)^n$$

(i) Find the mass of iodine-131 remaining in the lake after 24 days.

(ii) The Department of the Environment declare the lake unsafe until the mass of iodine-131 present drops below 94 kg. How many days must pass before the lake can be declared safe?

Introduction

You will have studied functions at Junior Certificate level and so far, in this book, we have already covered linear functions and quadratic functions. In this chapter we are going to look at functions in more depth and also explore different types of functions and their graphs.

Links across the syllabus

Functions are covered in part in Chapter 3: Algebra II and Chapter 4: Algebra III.

Section 7.1: Recap on Functions

Learning Outcome:

You should be able to:

- recognise that a function assigns a unique output to each input

A **function** is a relation for which there is only one output value corresponding to any input value (i.e. each input has only one output). A function can also be considered as an algebraic representation of a graphical image (graph or mapping).

A function is like a machine, whereby you put in a number (input), it is transformed and some other number comes out (output).

For example, the image below shows a function f. When you put in a number, five times the number comes out the other end.

- When 2 goes in, 10 comes out
- When 4 goes in, 20 comes out
- When 9 goes in, 45 comes out, etc.

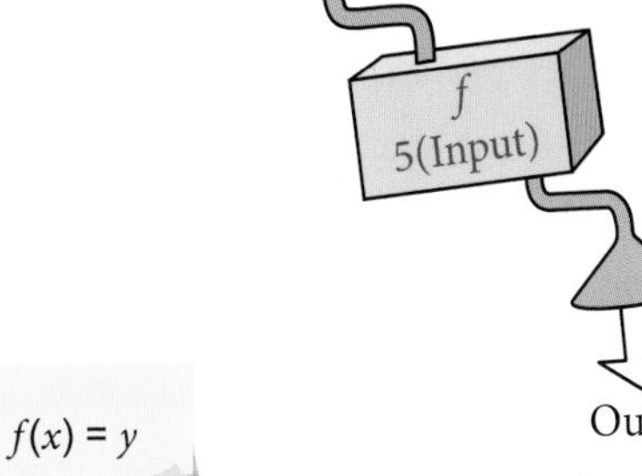

This function can be written in the following ways:

1. Output = 5(input)
2. $f : x \rightarrow 5x$, which is read as 'f maps x onto $5x$'
3. $f(x) = 5x$, which is read as 'f of x equals $5x$'
4. $y = 5x$, which is read as 'y equals $5x$'

$f(x) = y$

The couples of the function can be listed as a set of ordered pairs, or points, as follows:

$$\{(1, 5), (2, 10), (3, 15), (4, 20), \ldots\}$$

It is important that you are familiar with the terminology used in describing functions:

The **domain** is the set of all first elements of the ordered pairs (the inputs or x coordinates).

The **range** is the set of all second elements of the ordered pairs (the outputs or y coordinates).

The **co-domain** is the set of all possible outputs. In general, the range is a subset of the co-domain. However, sometimes the range and the co-domain are the same.

The following function notation can be broken down and explained by the bullet points:

- The function is called g.
- Its domain is the set of all integers.
- Its co-domain is the set of all integers.
- Its range then will be some of the integers in the co-domain.
- Its input is x.
- Its output is $2x + 1$ (doubles the input and adds 1).

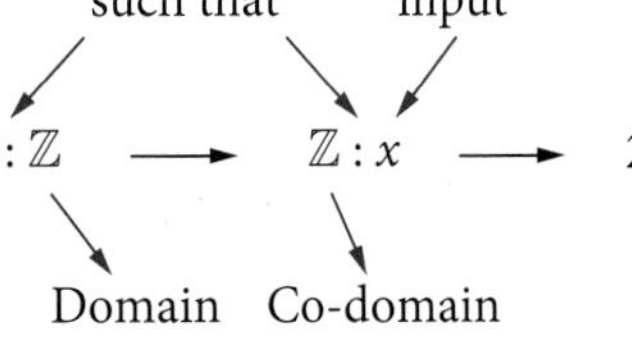
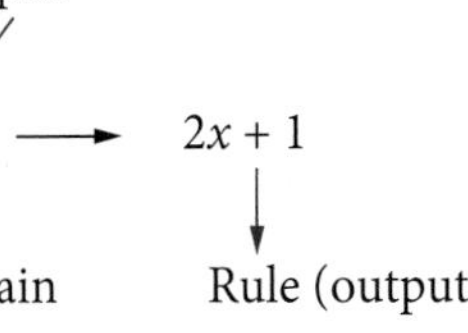

A function can be represented in different ways, as follows:

An equation: $f(x) = x^2 + 1$ or output = $(\text{input})^2 + 1$

Ordered pairs of numbers: [(1, 2), (2, 5), (3, 10), (4, 17)]

Table of inputs (x) and outputs (y):

Input (x)	1	2	3	4
Output (y)	2	5	10	17

Graphical representations:

Mapping

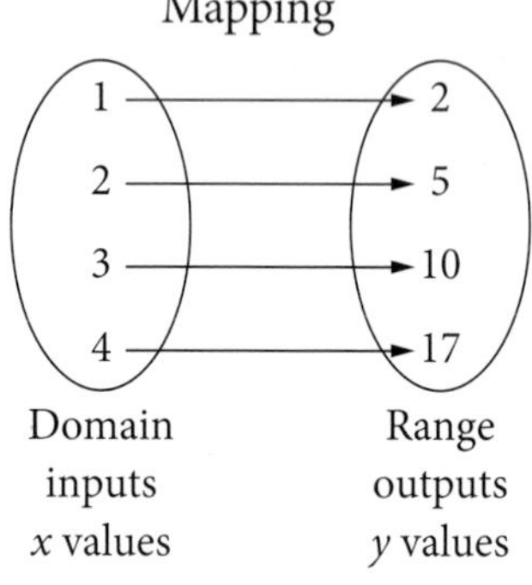

Graph

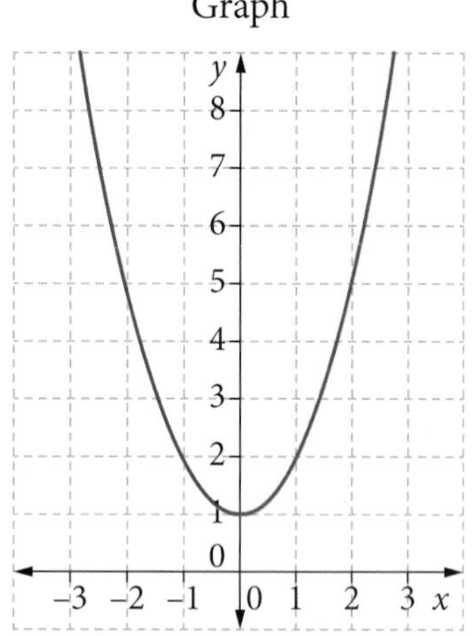

Identifying a function from a mapping or a graph

As already mentioned, for a function, each input value has exactly one corresponding output value. We can use this fact to determine whether a mapping or a graph represents a function.

Mapping

If there is more than one arrow leaving any of the elements in the domain, then the mapping does not represent a function.

The following mapping **represents a function** as there is **one arrow only leaving** each element in the domain:

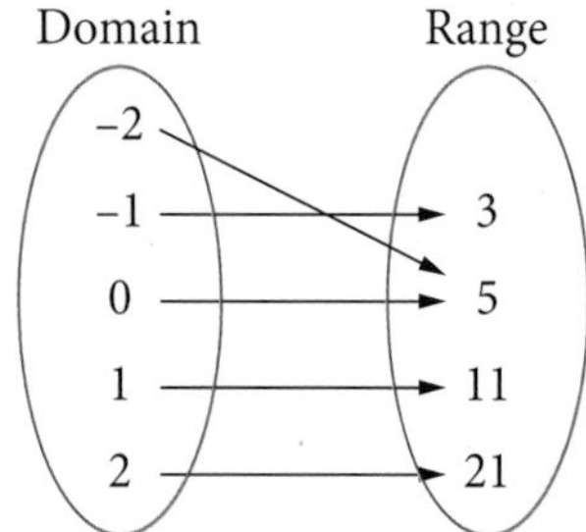

The following mapping **does not represent a function** as there are two arrows leaving the number −1 in the domain:

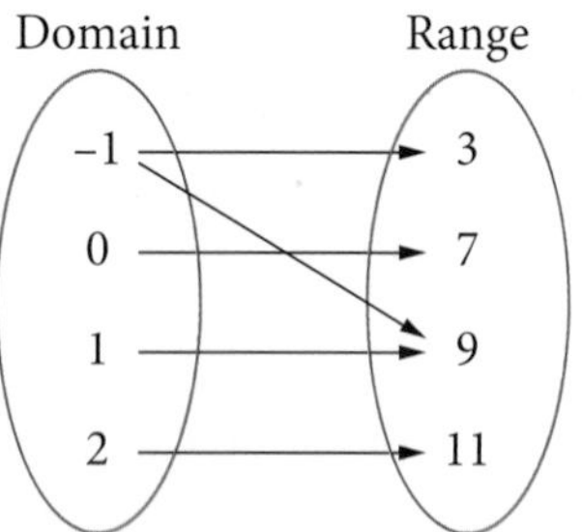

Graph

Each x value in the domain must have only one corresponding y-value.

You can use the 'vertical line' test to check if a graph represents a function.

Vertical line test
If a vertical line passes through the graph more than once, at any point along the graph, then the graph does not represent a function.

The following graph **represents a function** as a vertical line will, at most, pass through the graph once.

As we can see, the x-value indicated has only one corresponding y-value.

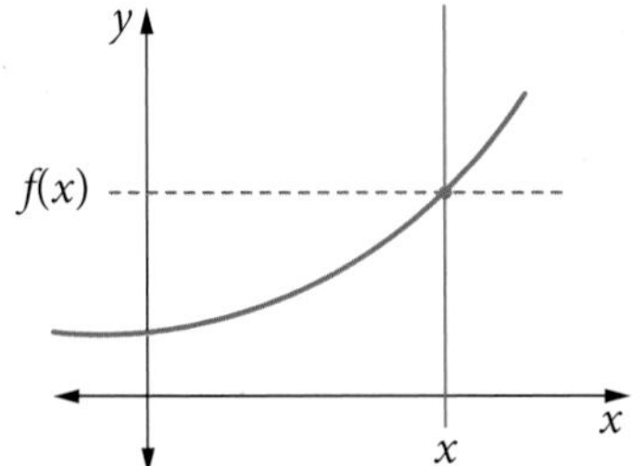

The following graph **does not represent a function** as a vertical line will pass through the graph more than once, in some places.

As we can see, the x-value indicated has more than one corresponding y-value.

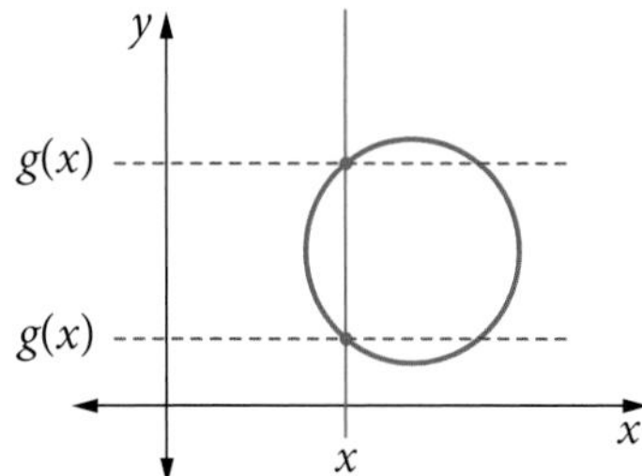

EXAMPLE 1

A mapping is shown on the right.
Use the diagram to answer the following:

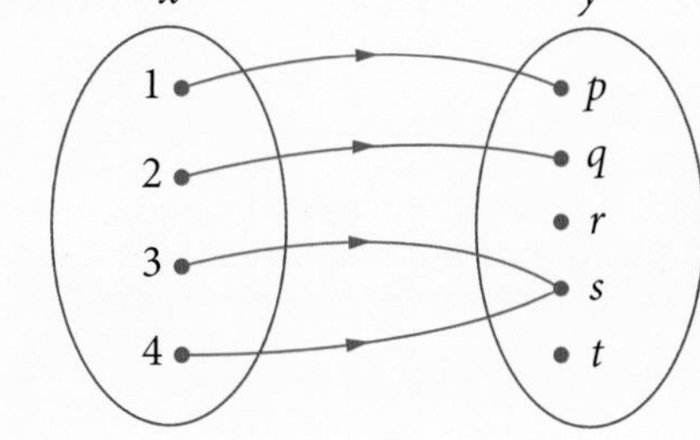

(i) List the set of ordered pairs.

(ii) Write out the domain.

(iii) Write down the range.

(iv) Write down the co-domain.

(v) Does this mapping represent a function? Give a reason for your answer.

Solution

(i) Ordered pairs: $\{(1, p), (2, q), (3, s), (4, s)\}$

(ii) Domain is the set of elements from which the arrows leave: $\{1, 2, 3, 4\}$

(iii) Range is the set of elements where the arrows arrive: $\{p, q, s\}$

(iv) Co-domain is the possible set of elements into which the arrows go: $\{p, q, r, s, t\}$

(v) This mapping represents a function since there is **one arrow only, leaving** each element in the domain.

EXAMPLE 2

The graph of a function is shown.
Study the graph and write down:

(i) the domain of the function **(ii)** the range of the function.

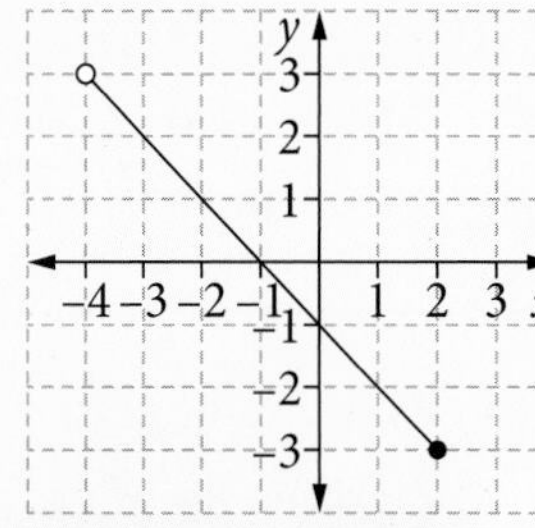

Solution

(i) The empty circle around one end of the line indicates that -4 is not included in the x-values.

The dot at the other end of the line indicates that 2 is included in the x-values.

The x-values start at -4 (but not including -4) and increase until they get to 2.

Domain: $-4 < x \leq 2$

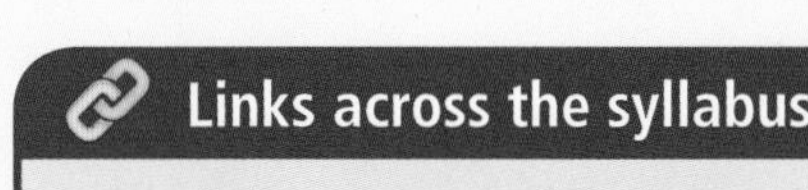

Inequalities are covered in Chapter 3: Algebra II.

(ii) The empty circle around one end of the line indicates that 3 is not included in the y-values.

The dot at the end of the line indicates that -3 is included in the y-values.

The y-values start at 3 (but not including 3) and decrease until they get to -3.

Range: $-3 \leq x < 3$

Always write a domain or range from smallest value to largest value.

EXAMPLE 3

The given mapping represents the function: $g:x \to 8 - 2x$
Complete the mapping.

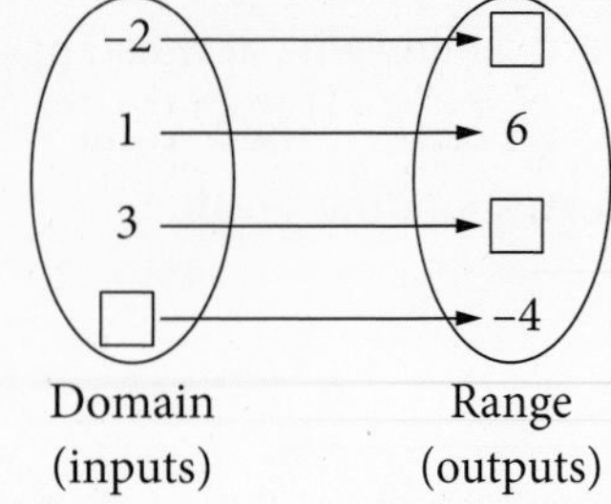

Solution

The function $g:x \to 8 - 2x$ means output = 8 – 2(input).

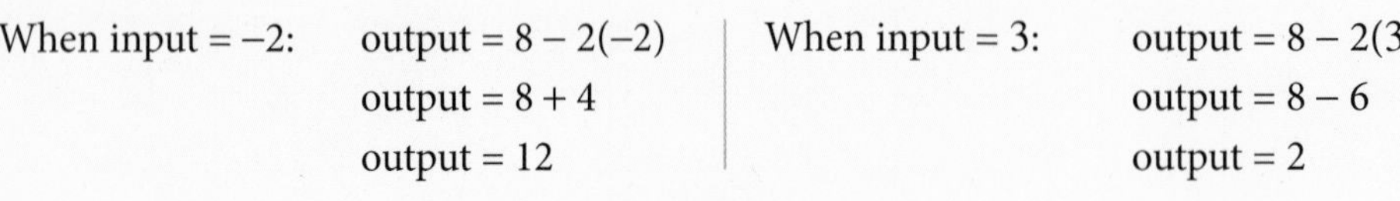

When input = –2: output = 8 – 2(–2), output = 8 + 4, output = 12

When input = 3: output = 8 – 2(3), output = 8 – 6, output = 2

When output = –4:

$$-4 = 8 - 2(\text{input})$$
$$-4 - 8 = 8 - 2(\text{input}) - 8 \quad \text{(subtract 8 from both sides)}$$
$$-12 = -2(\text{input})$$
$$6 = \text{input} \quad \text{(divide both sides by } -2\text{)}$$

Completed mapping is:

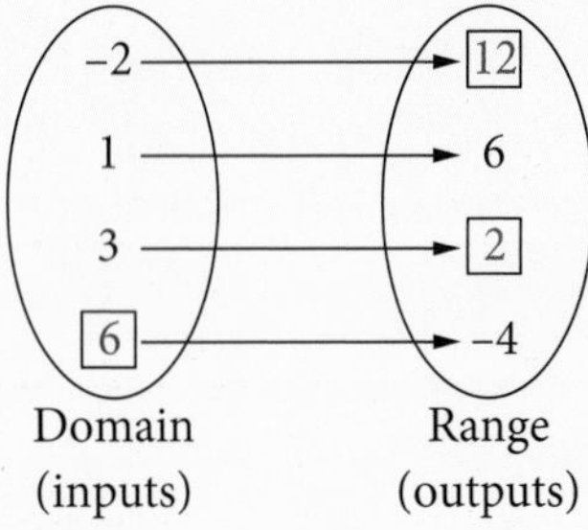

EXAMPLE 4

A function is defined as follows: $g(x) = 8 - x$

Find: **(i)** $g(0)$ **(ii)** $g(5)$ **(iii)** $g(-3)$ **(iv)** Find the value of x for which $g(x) = -4$

Solution

For parts **(i)** to **(iii)** we are given the value of x and asked to find $g(x)$.
In each case, replace x with the given value and simplify.

(i) $g(x) = 8 - x$
$g(0) = 8 - 0 \quad (x = 0)$
$g(0) = 8$

(ii) $g(x) = 8 - x$
$g(5) = 8 - 5 \quad (x = 5)$
$g(5) = 3$

(iii) $g(x) = 8 - x$
$g(-3) = 8 - (-3) \quad (x = -3)$
$g(-3) = 8 + 3$
$g(-3) = 11$

(iv) Given value of $g(x)$ and asked to find x. Replace $g(x)$ with the given value and solve for x.

$$g(x) = 8 - x$$
$$-4 = 8 - x \quad (g(x) = -4)$$
$$-4 - 8 = -x \quad \text{(subtract 8 from both sides)}$$
$$-12 = -x$$
$$12 = x \quad \text{(multiply both sides by } -1\text{)}$$

Read the question carefully to see if you are looking for the value of $g(x)$ or the value of x. Then ensure that you are using the correct method.

Practice Questions 7.1

1. Identify which of the following mappings and graphs represent functions.
   Give a reason for your answer in each case.

(i)

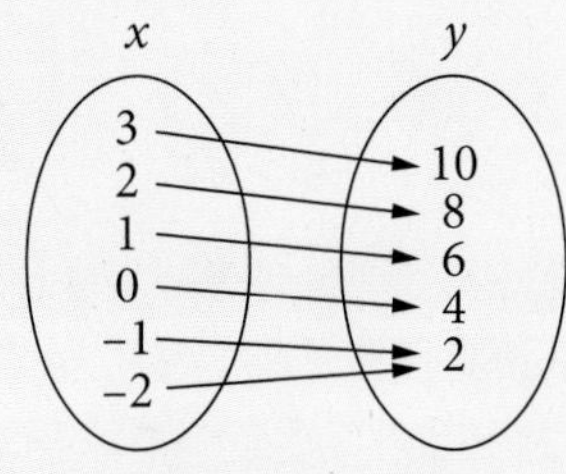

(iii)

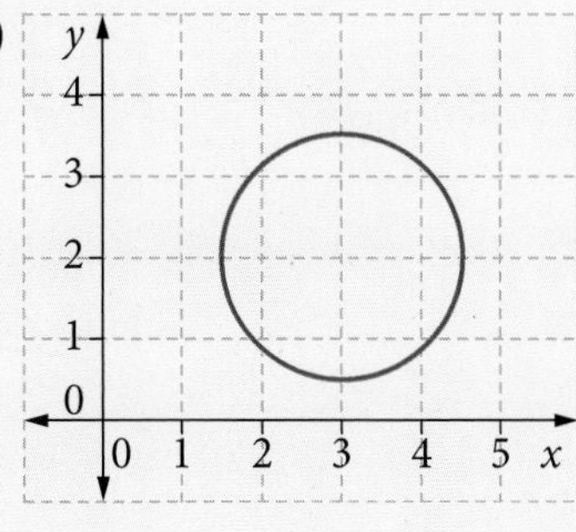

(v)

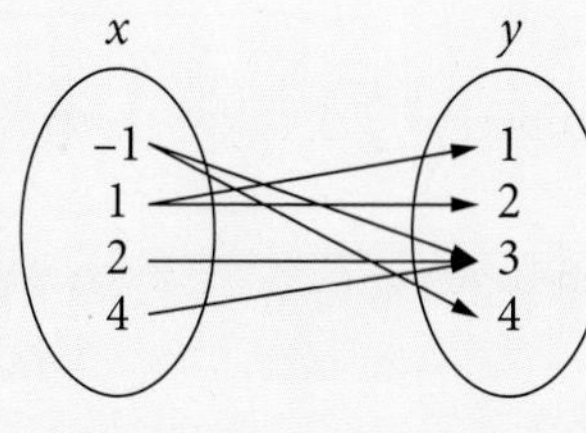

(ii)

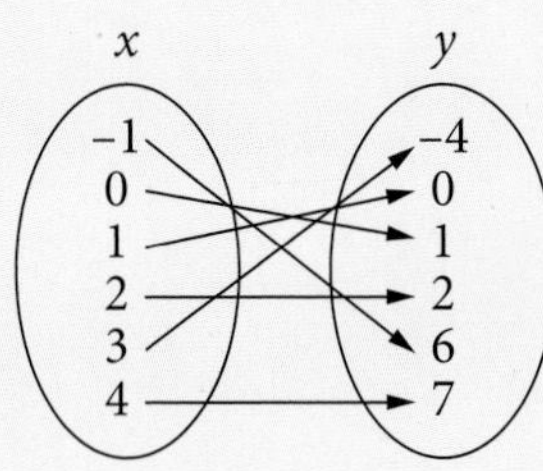

(iv)

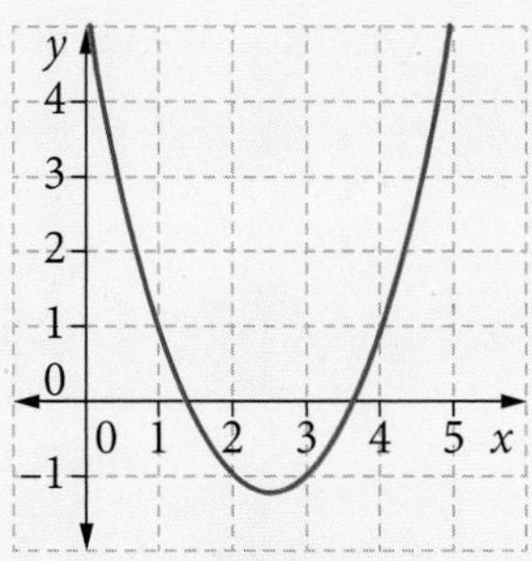

(vi)

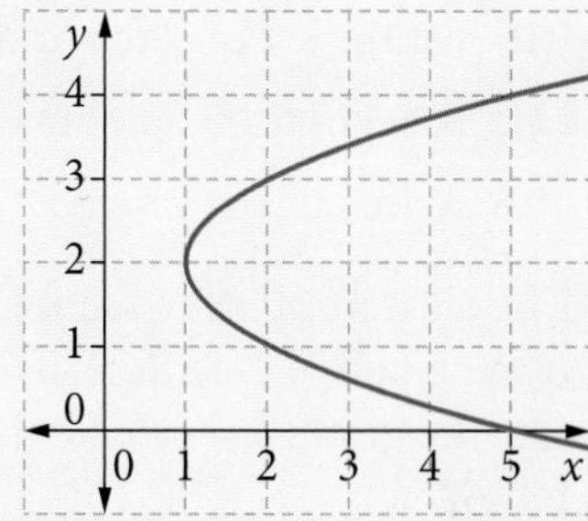

2. The diagram shows a function, f.
   Evaluate the output for each of the following inputs: −3, −1, 0, 4, 6, 7

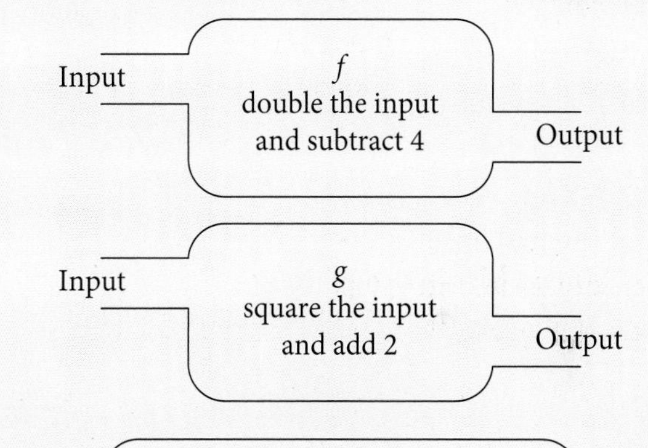

3. The diagram shows a function, g.
   Evaluate the output for each of the following inputs: 6, 3, 1, 0, −2, −4, −5

4. The diagram shows a function, h.
   Write down the output for each of the following inputs: A, B, C, D, E, F, G, H, I, J

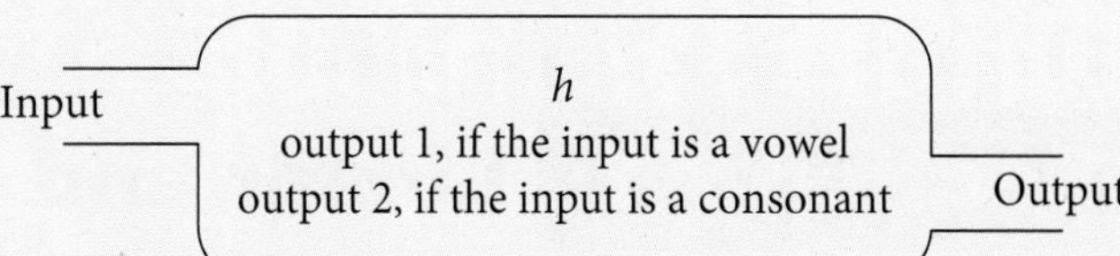

5. A function is defined as follows:

$$f(x) = \begin{cases} 1, \text{ when } x \text{ is odd} \\ 3, \text{ when } x \text{ is even} \end{cases}, \text{ where } x \in \mathbb{N}$$

   (i) Find:

   (a) $f(1)$ (b) $f(2)$ (c) $f(3)$ (d) $f(4)$ (e) $f(5)$

   (ii) Represent these couples on a graph.

6. A function is defined as follows: $h(x) = 7 - x$
   Find:

   (i) $h(2)$ (ii) $h(5)$ (iii) $h(10)$ (iv) $h(-3)$ (v) $h(-4)$

   (vi) the value of x for which $h(x) = 18$.

7. The following mappings represent functions.

(a) Function: output = 4(input) – 2

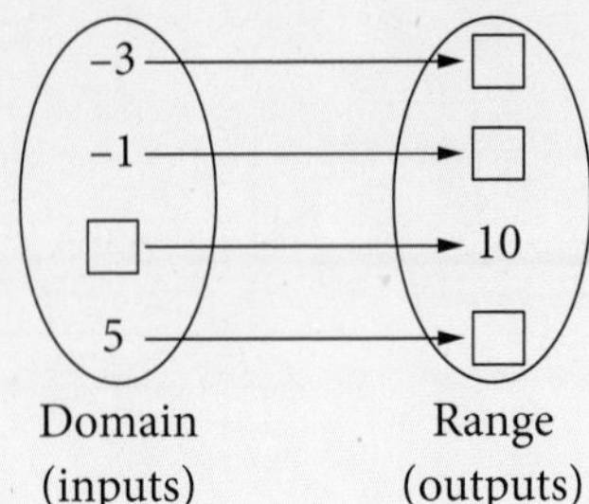

(b) Function: output = 5 – 2(input)

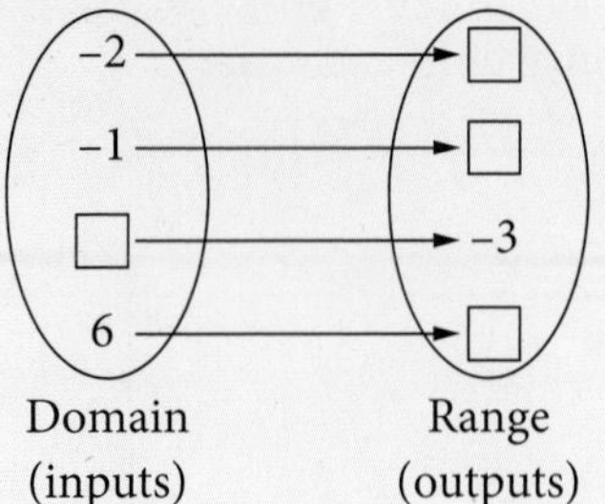

In each case:

(i) complete the mapping

(ii) list the set of ordered pairs

(iii) write out the domain

(iv) write out the range.

8. The diagram shows a section of the graph of the function $f(x)$. Use the graph to evaluate the following:

(i) $f(-1)$

(ii) $f(2)$

(iii) The value of x for which $f(x) = 2$

(iv) Using your answers to parts (i)–(iii), or otherwise, write out the rule which the $f(x)$ function is applying.

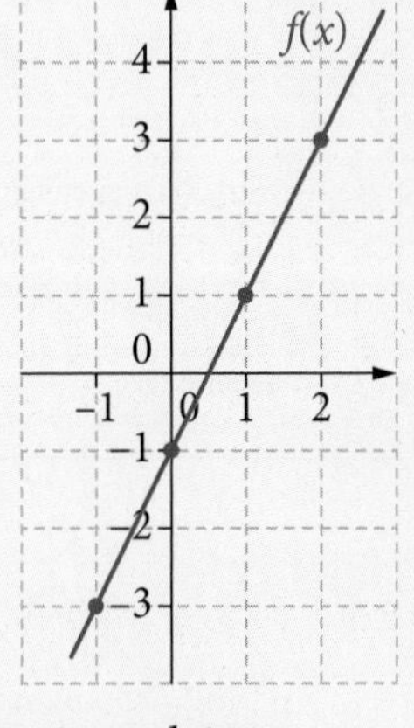

9. The diagram shows a blank mapping for the function: $f(x) = x^2 + 1$

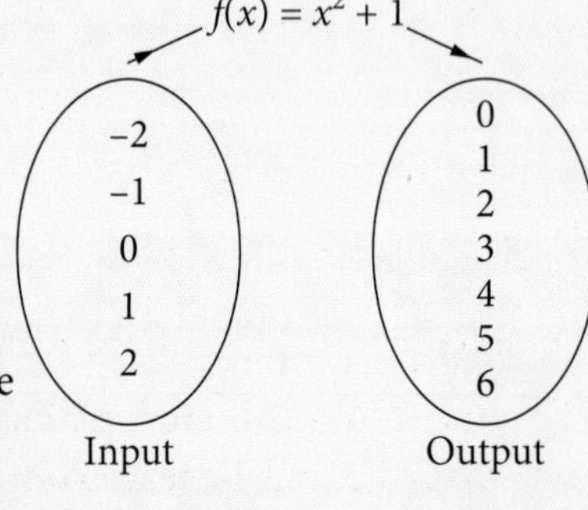

(i) Copy this mapping and complete it by adding in arrows from the inputs to the outputs, as appropriate.

(ii) Write out the domain.

(iii) Write out the range.

(iv) Write out the co-domain.

Section 7.2: Linear and Quadratic Functions

Learning Outcomes:

You should be able to:

- graph functions in the form $ax + b$ where $a, b, \in \mathbb{Q}$ and $x \in \mathbb{R}$
- graph functions in the form $ax^2 + bx + c$ where, $a, b, c, \in \mathbb{Z}$ and $x \in \mathbb{R}$
- solve problems involving linear and quadratic functions

Linear functions

A linear function is in the form: $f(x) = ax + b$

When graphed, a linear function is a straight line where

a = slope of the line

b = point where the line crosses the y-axis (y-intercept)

Links across the syllabus

Linear functions are covered in Chapter 3: Algebra II and Chapter 14: Coordinate Geometry I.

If the coefficient of the x part is positive (**slope, $a > 0$**), the graph is **increasing**:
For example: $y = 2x + 3$

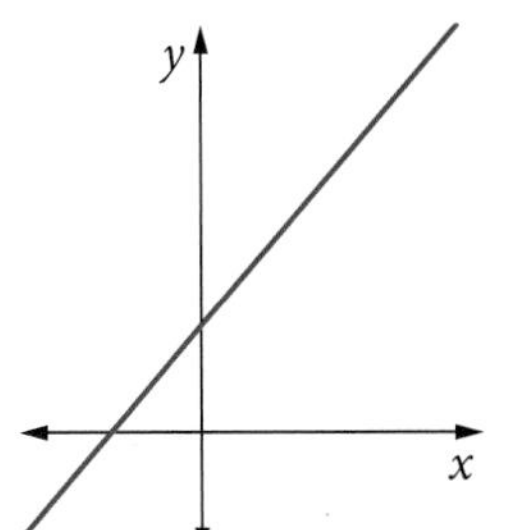

If the coefficient of the x part is zero (**slope, $a = 0$**), the graph is **horizontal**:
For example: $y = 3$

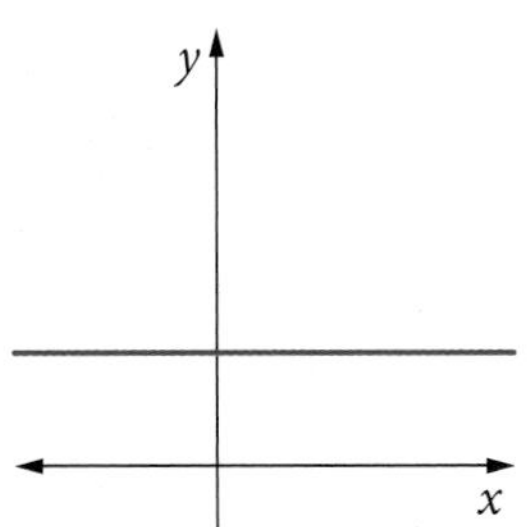

If the coefficient of the x part is negative (**slope, $a < 0$**), the graph is **decreasing**:
For example: $y = -2x + 3$

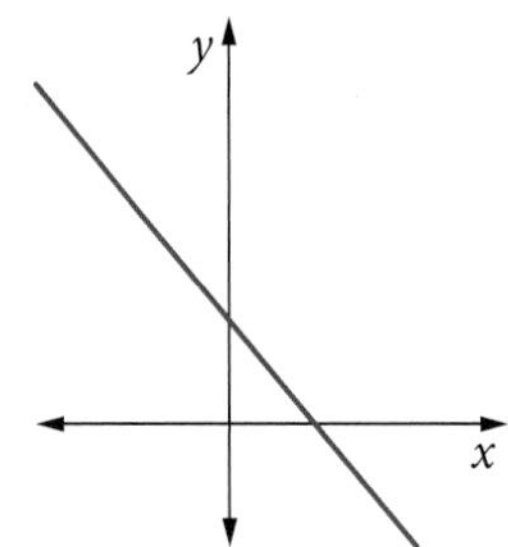

A linear function can be represented by the following formula:

output = initial value on y-axis + (rate of change) input

Function: Output = initial value on y-axis + (rate of change) input

Relation: $f(x) = b + ax$

Equation Line: $y = c + mx$

Note the similarities between the equations. A linear function is the same as an equation of a line and the linear relation formula, the order is just written differently.
Rate of change = slope = $a = m$
Initial value = y-intercept = $b = c$

Quadratic functions

A quadratic function is in the form: $f(x) = ax^2 + bx + c$

The graph of a quadratic function is either a ∪ shaped or an ∩ shaped curve, better known as a parabola.
c = y-intercept. Therefore the graph will cross the y-axis at the point $(0, c)$.

Links across the syllabus

Quadratic functions are covered in Chapter 4: Algebra III.

The shape of the graph is determined by the coefficient of the x^2 part of the function:

If the coefficient of the x^2 part is positive (**$a > 0$**), the graph has a ∪ shape and ends by increasing:
For example: $y = 2x^2 - 10x + 7$

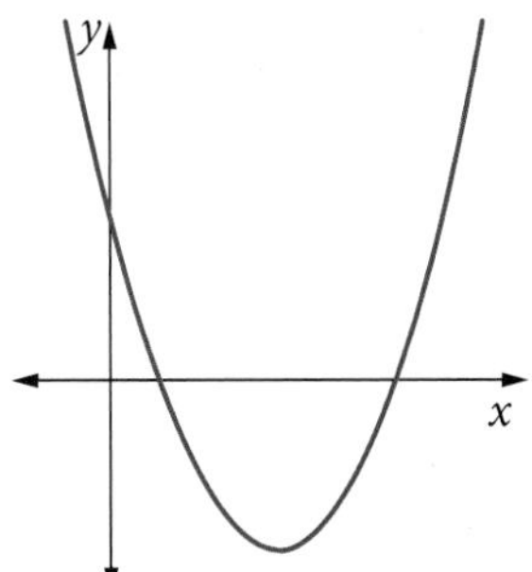

If the coefficient of the x^2 part is negative (**$a < 0$**), the graph has an ∩ shape and ends by decreasing:
For example: $y = -3x^2 + 18x - 14$

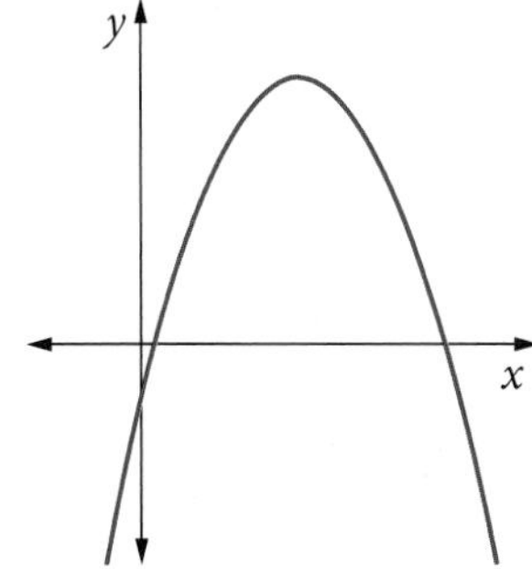

Roots of a quadratic equation

For a quadratic function, $f(x)$, the position of the graph determines how many roots the equation $f(x) = 0$ has.

If the graph intersects the x-axis twice, then the equation, $f(x) = 0$, has two distinct real roots.

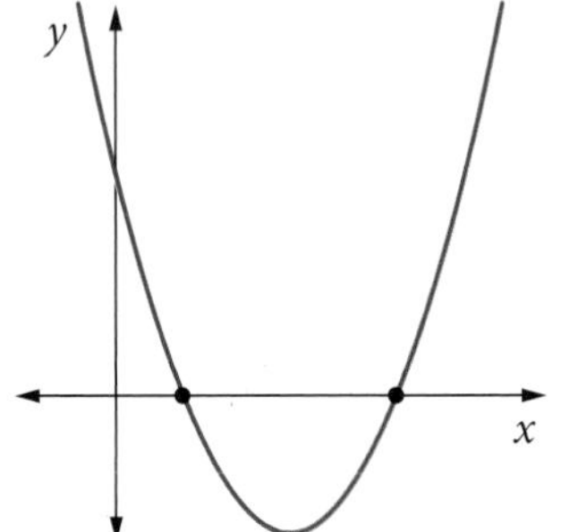

If the graph intersects the x-axis once, then the equation, $f(x) = 0$, has two equal real roots.

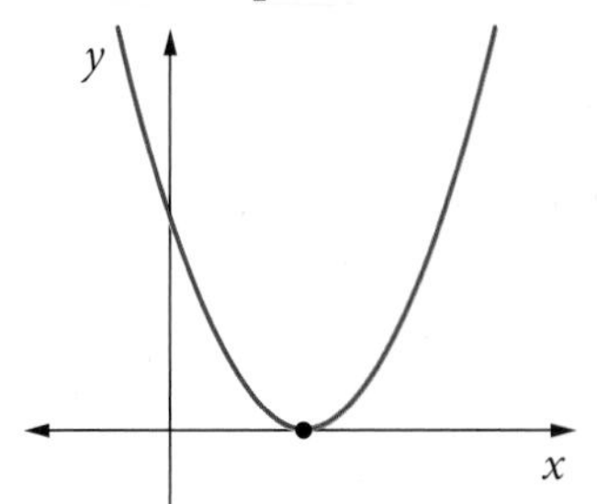

If the graph does not intersect the x-axis at all, then the equation, $f(x) = 0$ has no real roots.

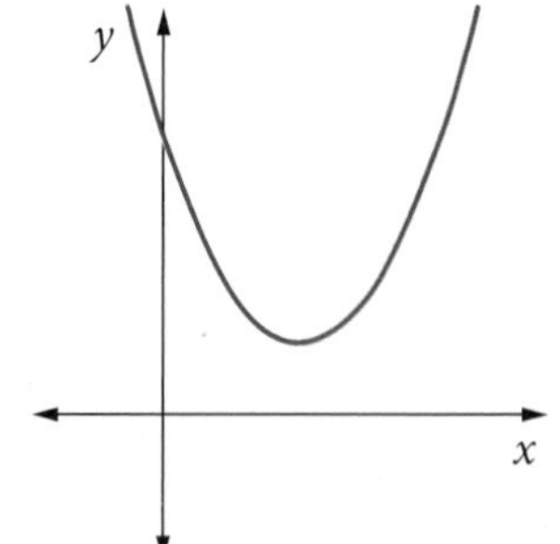

Links across the syllabus

Functions of this type are covered in Chapter 28: Complex Numbers.

EXAMPLE 1

Robbie is playing football in his garden. He kicks the ball from the point A and it lands on the roof of the house, at the point B, as shown in the diagram.

The height of the ball, h metres, x seconds after it has been kicked is given by the function:

$$h(x) = 1 + 12x - 3x^2$$

The line of the roof can be modelled by the function:

$$f(x) = 3x + 1$$

(i) Find the height of the ball after half a second.

(ii) Find the time it takes for the ball to hit the roof, at the point B.

(iii) Find the height of the ball, above the ground, when it hits the roof.

Solution

(i) To find the height of the ball after half a second, find the value of $h(x)$, when $x = 0{\cdot}5$:

$h(x) = 1 + 12x - 3x^2$

$h(0{\cdot}5) = 1 + 12(0{\cdot}5) - 3(0{\cdot}5)^2$ (substitute 0·5 in for x)

$h(0{\cdot}5) = 1 + 6 - 3(0{\cdot}25)$ (simplify)

$h(0{\cdot}5) = 7 - 0{\cdot}75$

$h(0{\cdot}5) = 6{\cdot}25$

Therefore, the ball is at a height of 6·25 m after half a second.

(ii) The point B is where the functions intersect (are equal).

Let $h(x) = f(x)$

$1 + 12x - 3x^2 = 3x + 1$

$1 + 12x - 3x^2 - 3x - 1 = 0$ (subtract $3x + 1$ from both sides)

$-3x^2 + 9x = 0$ (simplify)

$3x(-x + 3) = 0$ (factorise by HCF)

$3x = 0$ or $-x + 3 = 0$ (solve)

$x = 0$ or $3 = x$

$x = 0$ is at the point A, therefore we know that $x = 3$ is at the point B.

This means it takes 3 seconds for the ball to hit the roof.

(iii) To find the height of the ball when it hits the roof, find the value of $h(x)$, when $x = 3$:

$h(x) = 1 + 12x - 3x^2$

$h(3) = 1 + 12(3) - 3(3)^2$ (substitute 3 in for x)

$h(3) = 1 + 36 - 3(9)$ (simplify)

$h(3) = 37 - 27$

$h(3) = 10$

Therefore, the ball is at a height of 10 m when it hits the roof (at the point B).

EXAMPLE 2

The diagram shows the graph of the function $f(x) = -2x^2 + bx + c$, where $b, c \in R$

The function crosses the y-axis at 30.

The equation $f(x) = 0$ has a root at $x = 3$.

Use this information to find:

(i) the values of b and c

(ii) the other root of $f(x) = 0$.

(iii) Explain how you can tell from the graph that $f(x) = 0$ has two distinct real roots.

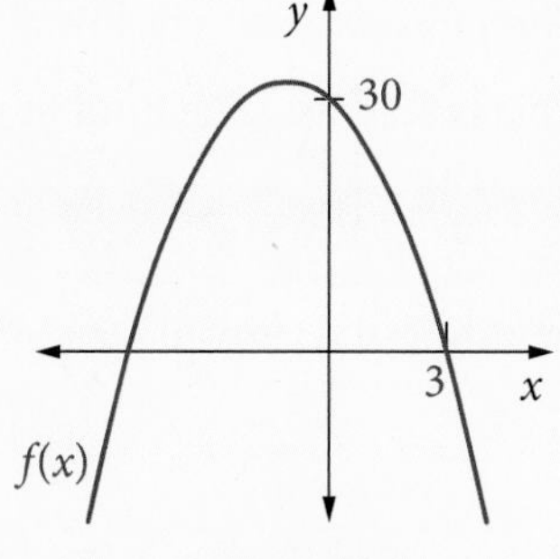

Recall:
Where a graph crosses the x-axis, $y = 0$
Where a graph crosses the y-axis, $x = 0$

Solution

(i) The graph crosses the y-axis at (0, 30):

$x = 0$ and $y = 30$, so $f(x) = 30$:

$f(x) = -2x^2 + bx + c$

Substitute 0 in for x and 30 for $f(x)$:

$30 = -2(0)^2 + b(0) + c$

$30 = -2(0) + 0 + c$

$30 = 0 + 0 + c$

$30 = c$

A quadratic equation in the form $ax^2 + bx + c = 0$ crosses the y-axis at c. Therefore, we could have immediately said $c = 30$

When the graph crosses the x-axis:

$x = 3$ and $y = f(x) = 0$

$f(x) = -2x^2 + bx + 30$

Substitute 3 in for x and 0 for $f(x)$:

$0 = -2(3)^2 + b(3) + 30$

$0 = -2(9) + 3b + 30$

$0 = -18 + 3b + 30$

$0 = 12 + 3b$

$-12 = 3b$

$-4 = b$

(ii) $f(x) = -2x^2 - 4x + 30$ since $b = -4$ and $c = 30$ (from part **(i)**)

Find the roots of $f(x) = 0$: $f(x) = -2x^2 - 4x + 30$

$0 = -2x^2 - 4x + 30$ (substitute 0 in for $f(x)$)

$0 = x^2 + 2x - 15$ (divide both sides by -2)

$0 = (x + 5)(x - 3)$ (factorise)

$x + 5 = 0$ or $x - 3 = 0$ (solve)

$x = -5$ or $x = 3$

Therefore, the second root of $f(x) = 0$ is $x = -5$.

(iii) The graph of $f(x)$ crosses the x-axis at two different points, therefore $f(x) = 0$ has two distinct real roots.

Limit of a function

Limits answer the question 'What does $f(x)$ do as x approaches a given value?'

To find the limit of a function at a certain point, we must approach the x-value from both sides (where possible) and find the corresponding value for $f(x)$ in each case.

We can then use this data to make an educated guess as to what the value of $f(x)$ would be at the given x value.

For the graph shown, we can see that as we get closer and closer to $x = a$, the function gets closer and closer to b.

Therefore, we can say $\lim_{x \to a} f(x) = b$

This is read as: 'The limit of $f(x)$, as x tends to a, equals b'.

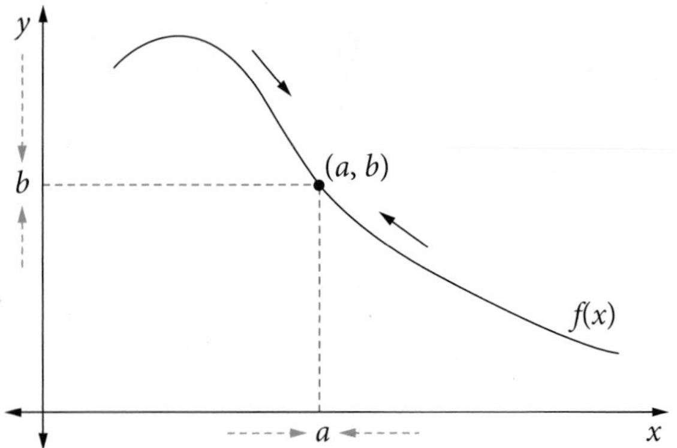

Discussion Time 

Work with a classmate to copy and complete the following table.

x	3·9	3·99	3·999	3·9999	…	4·0001	4·001	4·01	4·1
$f(x) = x + 4$					…				
$g(x) = \dfrac{x^2 - 16}{x - 4}$					…				
$h(x) = \dfrac{x^2 + x - 20}{x - 4}$					…				

1. Hence, write down the value of each of the following:

   (i) $\lim_{x \to 4} f(x)$ (ii) $\lim_{x \to 4} g(x)$ (iii) $\lim_{x \to 4} h(x)$

2. Verify your answers to part **1** by evaluating each function, when $x = 4$.

   Was it possible to evaluate the limit algebraically, in each case?

   If not, can you give a reason why not?

EXAMPLE 3

The diagram shows a section of the graph of the function $f(x) = 2x + 1$.

Complete the following table and hence, find $\lim_{x \to \infty} f(x)$

The symbol ∞ means 'infinity'

x	1	10	100	1,000	10,000	100,000	1,000,000
$f(x) = 2x + 1$							

Solution

Working out the value for $f(x)$ in each case gives the following completed table:

x	1	10	100	1,000	10,000	100,000	1,000,000
$f(x) = 2x + 1$	3	21	201	2001	20,001	200,001	2,000,001

From the table, we can see that as the value for x gets bigger, the value for $f(x)$ also gets bigger.

Therefore, as x gets closer to infinity, the value for $f(x)$ gets closer to infinity.

So, $\lim_{x \to \infty} f(x) = \infty$

Practice Questions 7.2

1. $f(x) = 2x + 7$, where $x \in \mathbb{R}$
Find:
   (i) $f(0)$ **(ii)** $f(3)$ **(iii)** $f(-2)$ **(iv)** $f(1{\cdot}5)$
   (v) the value of x for which $f(x) = 1$.

2. Let $h(x) = 3x - 5$
   (i) Find $h(5)$.
   (ii) Find the value of k for which $h(5) = k[h(0)]$.
   (iii) Find the value of a, for which $h(a) = a - 1$.

3. $g(x) = \frac{1}{4}(x - 5)$
   (i) Evaluate $g(9)$.
   (ii) Find the value of x for which $g(x) = -2$.

4. $h(x) = \dfrac{x+7}{4}$
   (i) Find $h(0)$.
   (ii) Find $h(-2)$.
   (iii) Hence, evaluate $h(0) + h(-2)$.

5. Let $h(x) = 3x^2 - 2x - 8$
Find:
   (i) $h(0)$ **(ii)** $h(1)$ **(iii)** $h(-1)$ **(iv)** $h(-2)$
   (v) The values of x for which $h(x) = 0$.

6. Let $g(x) = x^2 - 2x + 4$
   (i) Simplify $g(x - 5)$.
   (ii) Find the value of x for which $g(x - 5) = g(x) - 5$.

7. A function $g(x)$ is defined as follows: $g: x \rightarrow \dfrac{2x^2 + x - 15}{2x - 5}$
   (i) Copy and complete the following table.

x	2·4	2·49	2·499	2·4999	…	2·5001	2·501	2·51	2·6
$g(x) = \dfrac{2x^2 + x - 15}{2x - 5}$					…				

   (ii) Use the completed table to evaluate $\lim\limits_{x \to 2{\cdot}5} g(x)$

8. The given graph represents the function $f(x) = ax + b$.
The function crosses the x-axis at the point (1·5, 0) and the y-axis at (0, 3).
Find the values of a and b.

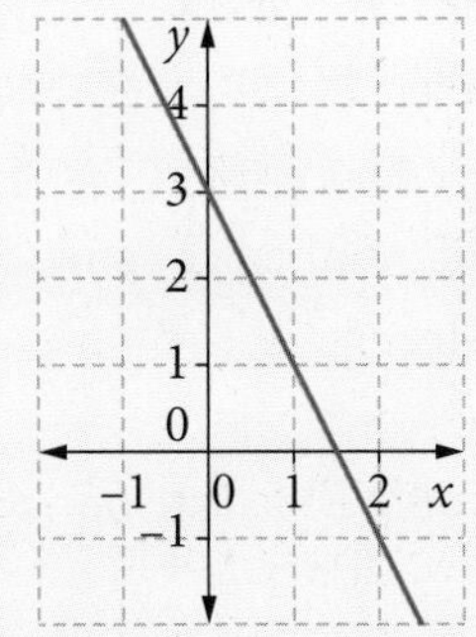

9. The diagram shows the graph of the function $g(x) = x^2 + px + q$, where $p, q, \in \mathbb{R}$
The function crosses the y-axis at 3.
The equation $g(x) = 0$ has a root at $x = 1$
Use this information to find:

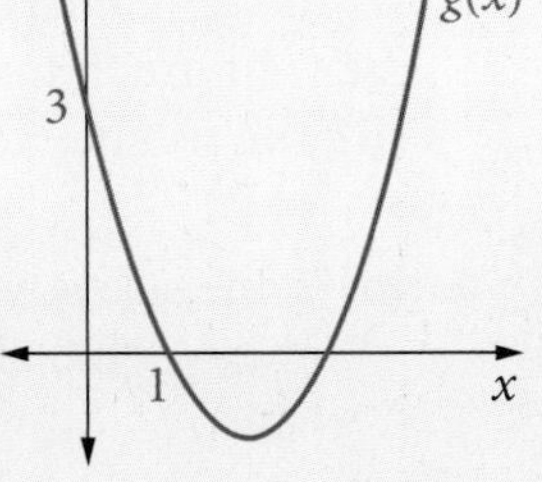

   (i) the values of p and q.
   (ii) the other root of $g(x) = 0$.
   (iii) Explain how you could tell from the diagram that $g(x) = 0$ has two distinct real roots.
   (iv) $\lim\limits_{x \to \infty} g(x)$, based on the diagram.

10. Let $g(x) = x^2 + px + q$, where $p, q, \in \mathbb{R}$
   (i) Find the value of p, given $g(-5) = g(-1)$
   (ii) Given that there is only one value of x for which $g(x) = 0$, find the value of q.

11. Two functions $f(x)$ and $g(x)$ are defined as follows:
$f: x \rightarrow 5 - x - 2x^2$ and $g: x \rightarrow 3 - x$, where $x \in \mathbb{R}$
   (i) Using the same axes and scales, graph the functions in the domain $-3 \leq x \leq 2$.
Use your graph to:
   (ii) estimate the maximum value of $f(x)$
   (iii) estimate the values of x, for which $f(x) = 1$
   (iv) find the values of x, for which $f(x) = g(x)$
   (v) find the range of values of x, for which $f(x) < g(x)$.

12. The diagram shows part of the graph of the function $f: x \to 4x^2 + px + q$, where $x \in \mathbb{R}$ and $p, q, \in \mathbb{Z}$. The points (2, 6) and (−1, 0) lie on the graph of f, as shown in the diagram.

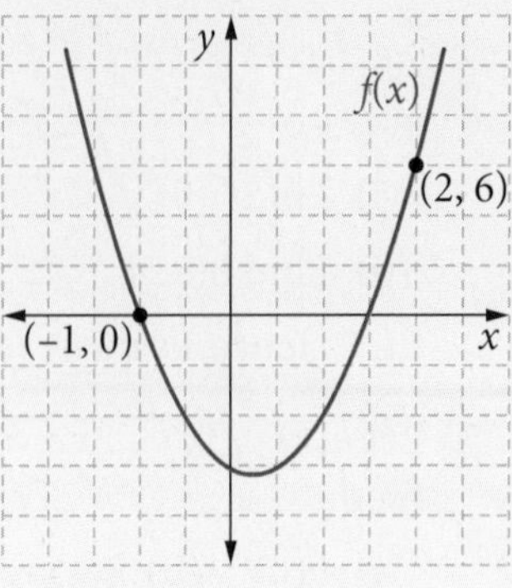

(i) Find the value of p and the value of q.

(ii) Solve $f(x) = -4$

(iii) A second function is defined as $g(x) = -2x - 2$, where $x \in$ R.

Find the points where the $g(x)$ function intersects the $f(x)$ function.

13. The diagram shows part of the graphs of the functions:
$f(x) = x^2 - 8x + 15$ and $g(x) = x + k$

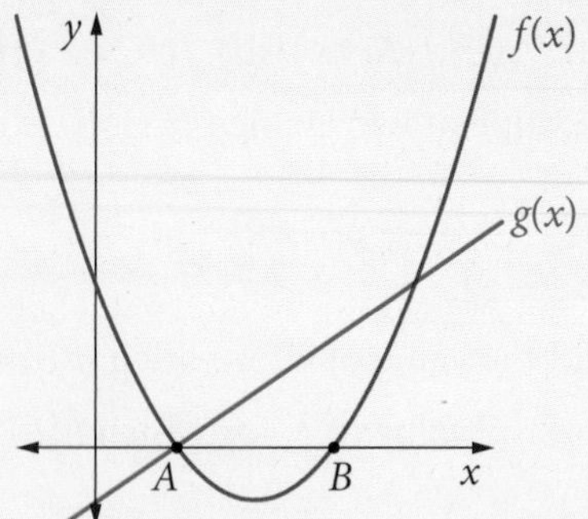

The graph of $f(x)$ cuts the x-axis at A and B.
The graphs of $f(x)$ and $g(x)$ intersect at the point A.

(i) Find the coordinates of the points A and B.

(ii) Find the value of k.

(iii) State the roots of $f(x)$ and $g(x)$.

(iv) Verify that $f(x)$ and $g(x)$ also intersect at the point (6, 3).

14. Petrol costs a certain amount per litre. The table shows the cost of various volumes of petrol.

No. of litres (L)	0	10	20	30	40	50
Cost in euro (C)	0	14·20	28·40	42·60	56·80	71·00

(i) Draw a graph to show the relationship between the number of litres and the cost of the petrol, putting the number of litres on the horizontal axis.

(ii) Use your graph to estimate the cost of 47 litres of petrol.

(iii) In the context of this question, what does the slope of the graph represent?

(iv) Write an equation linking the number of litres of petrol pumped (L) and the cost (C), and use this equation to verify your answer for part **(ii)**.

(v) How much would 82 litres of petrol cost?

(iv) If the cost per litre of petrol was to drop, what effect would this have on your graph? Give a reason for your answer.

15. The revenue for a production by a theatre group is $r(t) = -50t^2 + 300t$, where t is the ticket price in euro.
The cost for the production is $c(t) = 560 - 50t$

(i) Copy and complete the following table:

t	0	1	2	3	4	5	6
$r(t)$							
$c(t)$							

Using the same axes and scale, graph the functions $r(t)$ and $c(t)$ in the domain $0 \leq t \leq 6$.
Use your graph to determine:

(ii) the revenue taken in, if the tickets are priced at €2

(iii) if the tickets were priced at €5, whether the theatre group make a profit or a loss. Justify your answer

(iv) the ticket price that will allow the production to break even.

The group will break even when revenue = cost.

(v) Use algebra to verify your answer for part **(iv)**.

Further Functions

16. The function $f: x \to 9x - 2x^2, 0 \le x \le 5, x \in \mathbb{R}$ represents the height in kilometres reached by an incoming missile launched at 10 am (where $x = 0$) The function $g: x \to 7x - 10 - x^2, 2 \le x \le 5, x \in \mathbb{R}$ represents the height in kilometres reached by an intercepting missile launched from the ground at 10:10 am ($x = 2$).

    (i) Using the same axes and scales, graph the two functions in their given domains.

    Use your graphs to estimate:

    (ii) the maximum height reached by the incoming missile

    (iii) the height at which the two missiles meet

    (iv) the time at which the two missiles meet.

    (v) Use algebra to verify your answer to part **(iv)**.

Section 7.3: Cubic Functions

Learning Outcomes:

You should be able to:

- graph functions in the form $ax^3 + bx^2 + cx + d$, where a, b, c and $d, \in \mathbb{Z}$ and $x \in \mathbb{R}$
- solve problems involving cubic functions

A **cubic function** is a function in the form $f(x) = ax^2 + bx^2 + cx + d$

Graph of a cubic function

- The function crosses the y-axis at the point $(0, d)$.
- A cubic function has two points where it turns and changes direction (i.e. stops increasing and starts decreasing or vice versa).
- Whether the curve starts by increasing or decreasing is determined by the value of a, the coefficient of the x^3 part of the function.

Observing the following:
- Linear function $f(x) = ax + b$
- Quadratic function $f(x) = ax^2 + bx + c$
- Cubic function $f(x) = ax^3 + bx^2 + cx + d$

We can see that each function crosses the y-axis at the constant value (i.e. b, c and d).

If the coefficient of the x^3 part is positive ($\boldsymbol{a > 0}$), the graph ends by increasing:

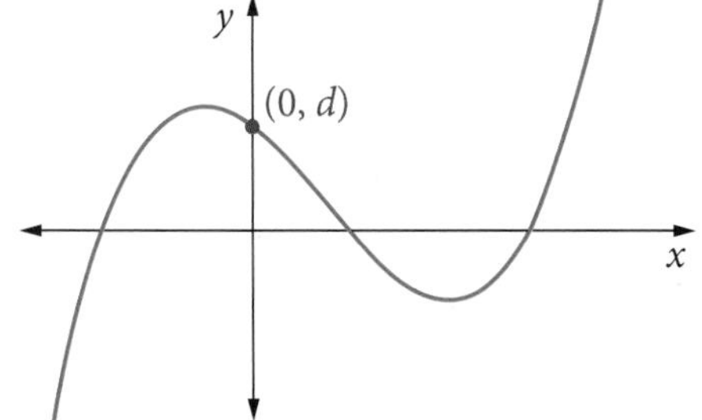

If the coefficient of the x^3 part is negative, ($\boldsymbol{a < 0}$), the graph ends by decreasing:

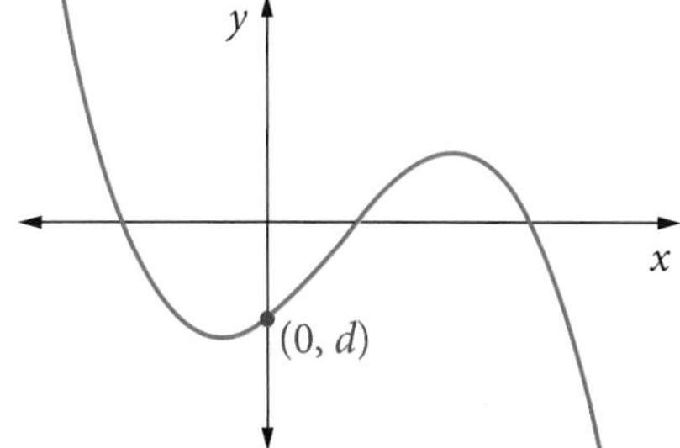

Roots of a cubic equation

For a cubic equation, $f(x) = 0$, the roots are the values which satisfy the equation. These are the points where the graph of the function crosses the x-axis (the x-intercepts). The position of the graph determines how many roots the equation $f(x) = 0$ has.

If the graph intersects the x-axis three times, then the function has three, distinct real roots.

If the graph intersects the x-axis twice, then the function has three real roots, two of which are equal.

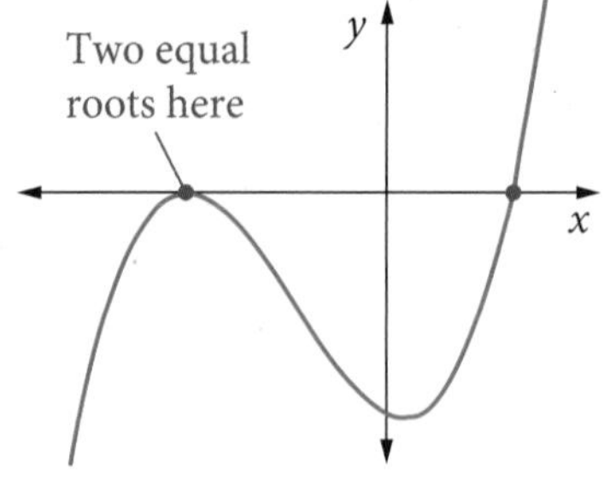

If the graph intersects the x-axis once, then the function has only one real root.

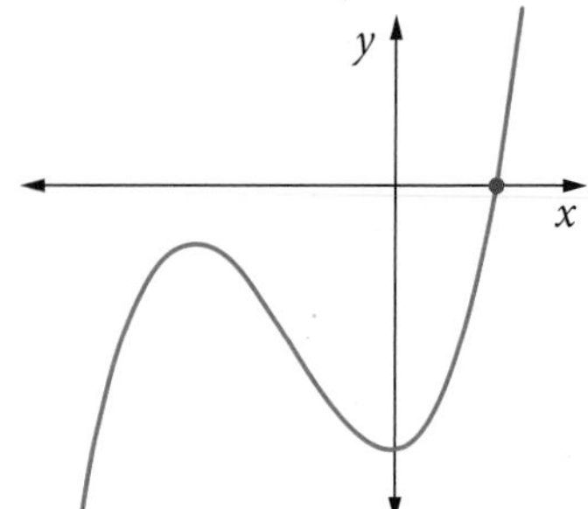

A special case

A function in the form $f(x) = (x + a)^3$, where $a \in \mathbb{R}$, has three equal real roots.

The function crosses the x-axis at one point only, called the saddle point, as shown in the diagram.

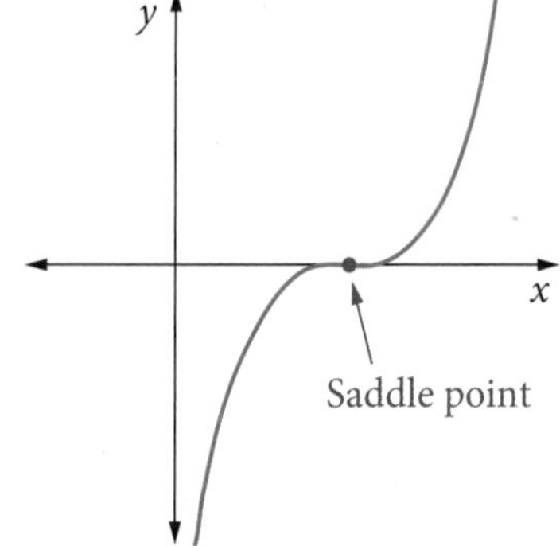

EXAMPLE 1

(i) Graph the function $h(x) = x^3 + 3x^2 - 18x - 40$ in the domain $-6 \leq x \leq 4$.

(ii) Use your graph to identify the roots of the equation $h(x) = 0$.

(iii) Use your graph to estimate the values of x, for which $x^3 + 3x^2 - 18x - 40 = -20$

Recall that you can use the 'function' facility on your calculator to generate the coordinates of the ordered pairs.

Solution

(i) Use a table to find the points along the curve:

x	$x^3 + 3x^2 - 18x - 40$	$h(x) = y$
−6	$(-6)^3 + 3(-6)^2 - 18(-6) - 40$	−40
−5	$(-5)^3 + 3(-5)^2 - 18(-5) - 40$	0
−4	$(-4)^3 + 3(-4)^2 - 18(-4) - 40$	16
−3	$(-3)^3 + 3(-3)^2 - 18(-3) - 40$	14
−2	$(-2)^3 + 3(-2)^2 - 18(-2) - 40$	0
−1	$(-1)^3 + 3(-1)^2 - 18(-1) - 40$	−20
0	$(0)^3 + 3(0)^2 - 18(0) - 40$	−40
1	$(1)^3 + 3(1)^2 - 18(1) - 40$	−54
2	$(2)^3 + 3(2)^2 - 18(2) - 40$	−56
3	$(3)^3 + 3(3)^2 - 18(3) - 40$	−40
4	$(4)^3 + 3(4)^2 - 18(4) - 40$	0

Plot these ordered pairs and draw the curve, through the points as shown below:

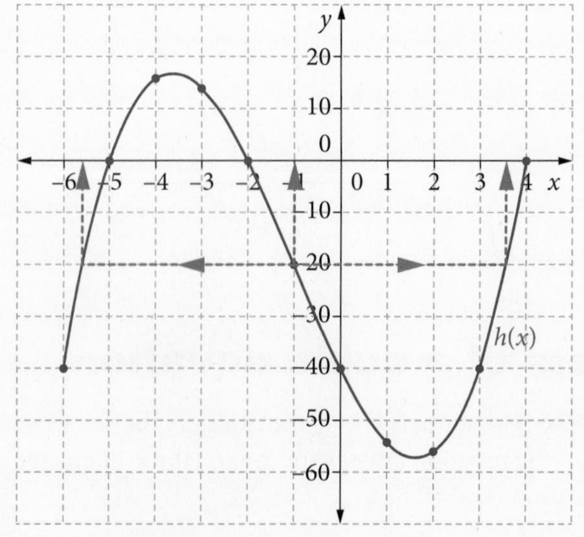

(ii) The roots of the equation $h(x) = 0$ are the values of x where the graph crosses the x–axis. By studying the graph, we can see that the roots of $h(x) = 0$ are $x = -5$, -2 and 4.

(iii) $x^3 + 3x^2 - 18x - 40 = -20$ means $h(x) = -20$, since $h(x) = x^3 + 3x^2 - 18x - 40$

To find the values of x, for which $h(x) = y = -20$:

Draw a horizontal line through -20 on the y–axis (shown in red on the graph).

At the points where this line intersects the graph, draw a vertical line upwards to the x–axis and read the x values.

When $h(x) = -20$, $x = -5{\cdot}6$, -1 and $3{\cdot}6$.
These values for x could also be known as the roots of the equation $h(x) = -20$.

When asked to find values **from the graph**, it is very important that you show the work done on the graph. Use dotted lines, where appropriate.

Practice Questions 7.3

1. For each of the following functions, $f(x)$, state how many real roots the equation $f(x) = 0$ has.

(i)

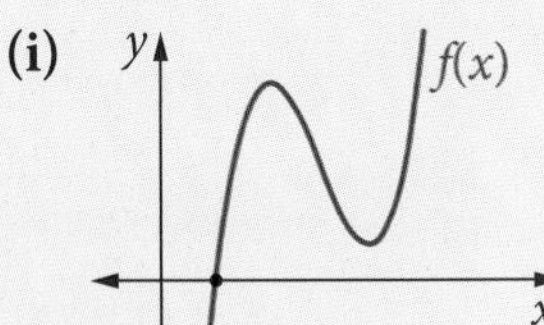

(ii)

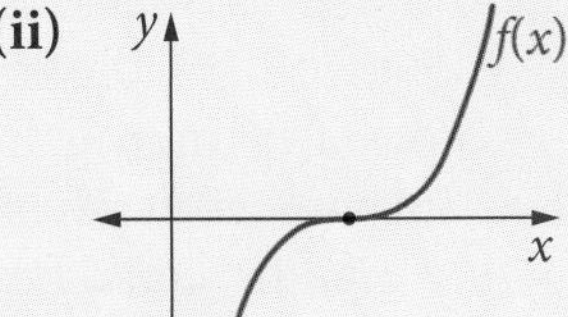

(iii)

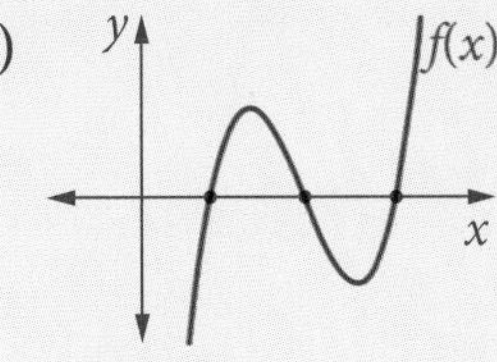

(iv)

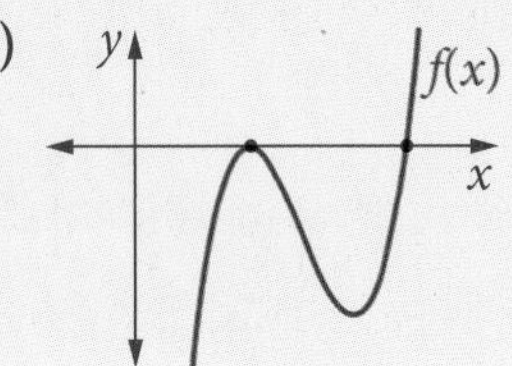

2. The diagram shows part of the graph of the function $f(x) = 2x^3 + 7x^2 - 7x - 12$.

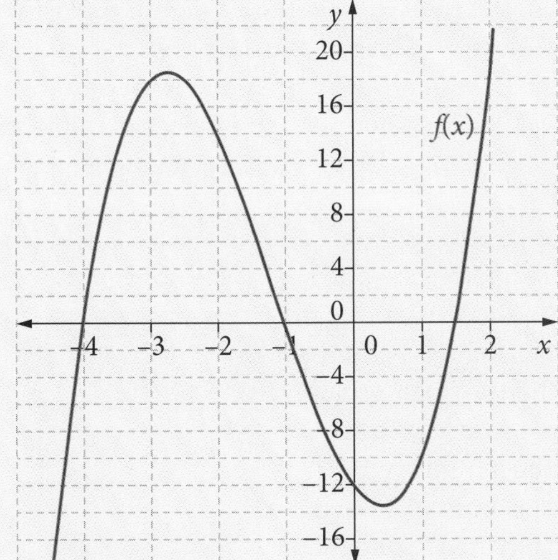

Use the graph to:

(i) estimate the roots of the equation $f(x) = 0$

(ii) find $f(-3)$

(iii) find $f(0)$

(iv) estimate the values of x for which $f(x) = 14$

(v) find the range of values of x for which $f(x) < 0$.

$f(x) < 0$ means that $y < 0$.
This happens below the x-axis.

3. Graph the function $f(x) = x^3 - 2x^2 - 4x + 3$ in the domain $-2 \leq x \leq 3$.
Use your graph to estimate:

(i) the roots of the equation $f(x) = 0$

(ii) the values of x for which $x^3 - 2x^2 - 4x + 3 = -2$

(iii) The range of values of x for which $f(x) > 0$.

4. **(i)** Graph the function $g(x) = 3 + 7x - 2x^2 - x^3$ in the domain $-4 \leq x \leq 3$.

(ii) Use your graph to estimate:

(a) the roots of the equation $g(x) = 0$

(b) the values of x for which $g(x) = 2$

(c) $g(-1{\cdot}5)$

(d) $g(0{\cdot}5)$.

(iii) Check the accuracy of your estimated roots in part **(ii) (a)**, by checking if they satisfy the equation $g(x) = 0$.

5. A cubic function $g(x) = ax^3 + bx^2 + cx + d$, where $a, b, c, d \in \mathbb{R}$.
$g(x)$ crosses the y-axis at the point $(0, 12)$ and the equation $g(x) = 0$ has roots $x = -2$, 1 and 3.

(i) Use the point $(0, 12)$ to find the value of d.

(ii) Draw a sketch of the function $g(x)$.

(iii) Use your sketch to determine whether the variable a is positive or negative. Give a reason for your answer.

6. A cubic function $f(x) = ax^3 + bx^2 + cx + d$, where $a, b, c, d \in \mathbb{R}$. $f(x)$ crosses the x-axis at the point $(0, -9)$ and the equation $f(x) = 0$ has roots $x = -3, -1$ and $1{\cdot}5$.
   (i) Use the point $(0, -9)$ to find the value of d.
   (ii) Draw a sketch of the function $f(x)$.
   (iii) Use your sketch to determine whether the variable a is positive or negative. Give a reason for your answer.

7. The diagram shows part of the graph of the function $f(x) = -x^3 + bx^2 + cx + d$, where $b, c, d, \in \mathbb{Z}$

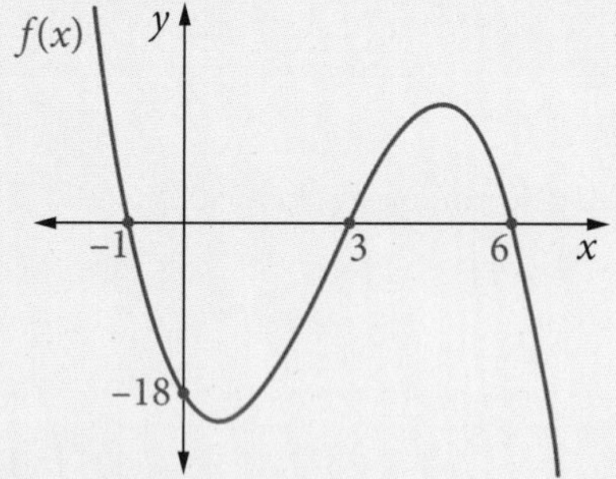

The graph crosses the x-axis at $x = -1$, 3 and 6. The graph crosses the y-axis at $y = -18$
   (i) Substitute the point $(0, -18)$ into the function $f(x)$, and hence find the value of d
   (ii) Form two equations in terms b and c.
   (iii) Hence, solve for b and c and write down the function $f(x)$.

8. Using the same axes and scale, graph the functions: $f(x) = x^3 + 5x^2 - 4x - 20$ and $g(x) = -4 - 2x$ in the domain $-5 \leq x \leq 2$.
   Use your graph to estimate:
   (i) the values of x for which $f(x) = g(x)$
   (ii) the range of values of x for which $f(x) > g(x)$
   (iii) the range of values of x for which $f(x) < g(x)$.

9. Let $f(x) = 2x^3 + px^2 + qx + 14$, where $p, q, \in \mathbb{R}$.
   (i) Given that $f(2) = 0$, form an equation in terms of p and q.
   (ii) If $f(-1) = 0$, find the values of p and q.

10. A farmer's crop becomes infected with blight. After a number of days, the farmer sprays the crop to kill off the blight.

The number of plants, newly infected on day t of the outbreak is given by

$$p(t) = 10t^2 - t^3, \text{ where } t \leq 10$$

   (i) Copy and complete the following table, to find the number of plants newly infected each day, for the first 10 days:

T (days)	0	1	2	3	4	5	6	7	8	9	10
$p(t)$											

   (ii) Hence, graph the function $p(t)$ in the domain $0 \leq t \leq 10$.
   (iii) Use your graph to estimate how long it took for the spray to begin to have an effect on the blight.
   (iv) How long did it take for the spray to fully kill the blight? Justify your answer.

11. In the last year (starting January 1st), the volume of water (in megalitres) in a reservoir, after t months, could be described by the model

$$V(t) = 630 - 247t + 32t^2 - t^3$$

   (i) Draw a graph to illustrate the volume of water in the reservoir for the 12 months of last year. (Note: $t = 0$ represents January 1st)
   The reservoir authority rules that if the volume falls below 125 Ml, water restrictions are put in place.
   (ii) Use your graph to determine during which month(s) water restrictions were put in place.

12. The diagram shows a square sheet of cardboard of side length 18 cm, from which four small squares, each of side length x, have been removed. The sheet can be folded to form an open rectangular box, of height x.

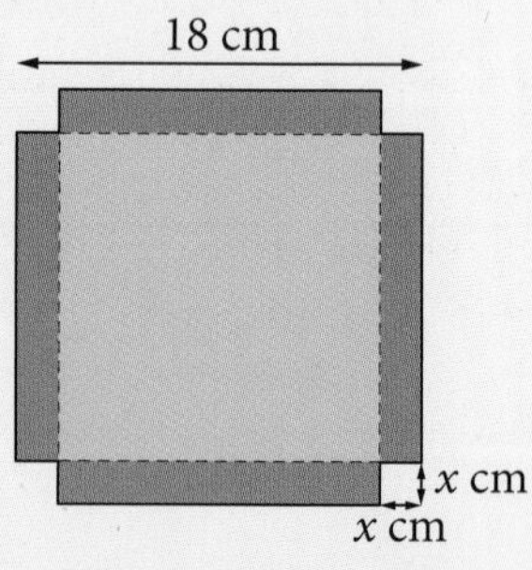

   (i) Write the length and the width of the box in terms of x.
   (ii) Show that the volume of the box, in terms of x, is $4x^3 - 72x^2 + 324x$.
   (iii) Graph the volume of the box in the domain $0 \leq x \leq 9$.
   (iv) Use your graph to estimate the maximum volume of the box.
   (v) Give a reason why the domain for the volume was restricted to $x \leq 9$.

13. A company has calculated that the daily cost (in hundreds of euro) of producing x items is modelled by the cost function:

$$c(x) = 2x^2 + 35x - 100 - 0{\cdot}5x^3$$

The daily income (in hundreds of euro) from the sale of x items is given by the revenue function:

$$r(x) = 6x^2 + 20x$$

   (i) On a given day, the company produces five items and sells five items. Find the production cost and total income for that day.

   (ii) Hence, find the profit made by the company on that day.

   (iii) Find an expression, in terms of x, for the profit, p, made from the production and sale of x items. Give your answer in the form $p(x) = ax^3 + bx^2 + cx + d$, where $a, b, c, d \in \mathbb{R}$.

   (iv) Draw a graph showing the daily profit made from the sale of up to nine items. That is, for $0 \le x \le 9$.

   (v) If the company wishes to make a daily profit of at least €35,000, use your graph to determine how many items they should produce and sell daily.

Section 7.4: Exponential Functions

Learning Outcomes:

You should be able to:

- graph functions in the form ab^x, where $a \in \mathbb{N}$ and $b, x \in \mathbb{R}$
- solve problems involving exponential functions

An **exponential function** is a function in the form $f(x) = ab^x$

Graph of an exponential function

- The curve intersects the y-axis at $(0, a)$. This point is called the focal point.
- An exponential function is constantly increasing or decreasing.
- The value of b determines whether the curve of $f(x) = ab^x$ is increasing or decreasing.
- The bigger the value for b, the sharper the graph will rise (or fall).

If $b = 1$, then $b^x = 1^x = 1$
Therefore, if $b = 1$ $f(x) = ab^x = a$
Hence, if $b = 1$, the graph is neither increasing nor decreasing. It is a horizontal line.

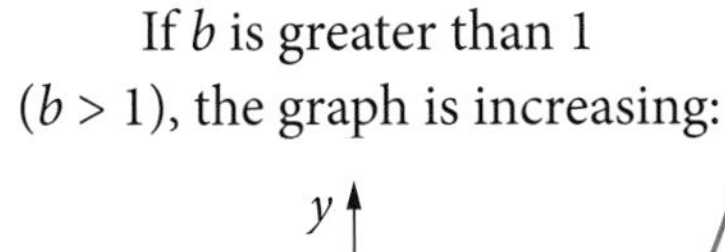

If b is greater than 1 ($b > 1$), the graph is increasing:

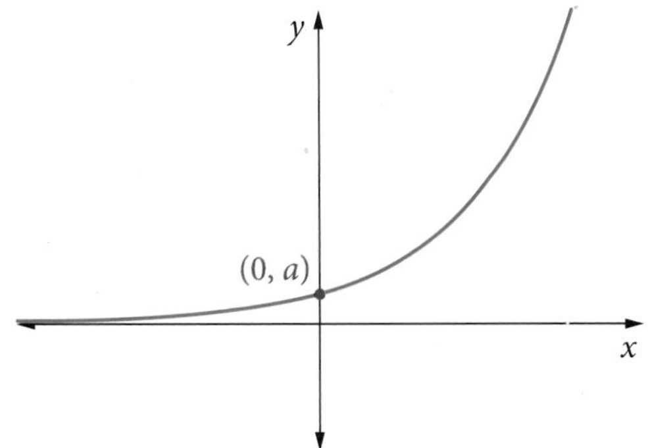

If b is between 0 and 1 ($0 < b < 1$), the graph is decreasing:

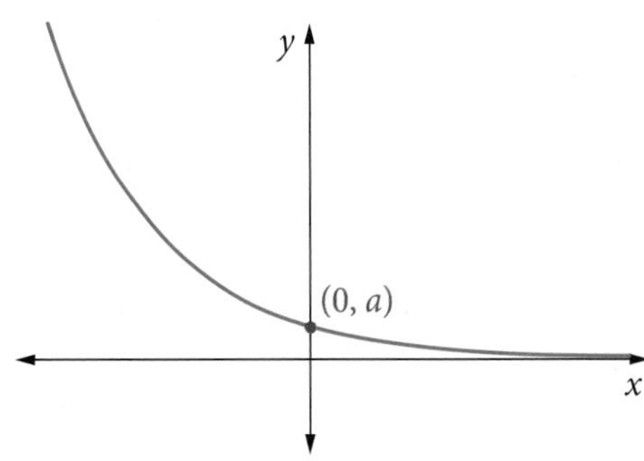

Further Functions

Exponential growth or decline can be modelled by the function:

$$f(x) = \text{initial value}(1 + \text{percentage change})^{\text{time}}$$

This is the same as the exponential function $f(x) = ab^x$, but
a = initial value
b = 1 + percentage change
x = time

In the case of **growth**, the percentage change will be **positive**.

In the case of **decline**, the percentage change will be **negative**.

EXAMPLE 1

(i) Using the same axes and scales, graph the functions $f(x) = \left(\frac{1}{2}\right)^x$ and $g(x) = 2(3)^x$ in the domain $-3 \le x \le 1$.

(ii) From your graph, estimate the point of intersection of f and g.

(iii) Find the range of values of x, for which $f(x) < g(x)$.

Solution

(i) To graph $f(x) = \left(\frac{1}{2}\right)^x$:

x	$\left(\frac{1}{2}\right)^x$	$f(x)$
−3	$\left(\frac{1}{2}\right)^{-3}$	8
−2	$\left(\frac{1}{2}\right)^{-2}$	4
−1	$\left(\frac{1}{2}\right)^{-1}$	2
0	$\left(\frac{1}{2}\right)^{0}$	1
1	$\left(\frac{1}{2}\right)^{1}$	0·5

To graph $g(x) = 2(3^x)$:

x	$2(3^x)$	$g(x)$
−3	$2(3^{-3})$	0·07 = 0·1
−2	$2(3^{-2})$	0·22 = 0·2
−1	$2(3^{-1})$	0·67 = 0·7
0	$2(3^{0})$	2
1	$2(3^{1})$	6

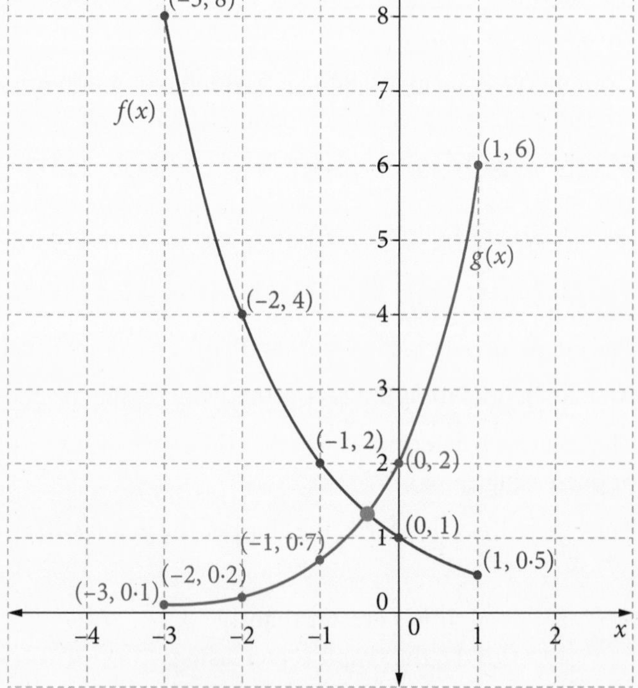

(ii) From the graph, the point of intersection (shown in green on the graph) of $f(x)$ and $g(x)$ is $(-0{\cdot}4, 1{\cdot}3)$.

In practice, when graphs are hand-drawn, the points can be plotted to one decimal place.

(iii) Since the $g(x)$ graph is constantly increasing and the $f(x)$ graph is constantly decreasing, $f(x) < g(x)$ for all values of x greater than $-0{\cdot}4$. Therefore, $f(x) < g(x)$ for $x > -0{\cdot}4$.

EXAMPLE 2

Stacey invested €200 in a special savings account. The money earns 8% compound interest per annum. A function to determine the value, v, of the investment after t years is given by:

$$v(t) = 200(1{\cdot}08)^t$$

(i) Find the value of the investment, to the nearest euro, after four years.

(ii) Draw a graph, showing the value of the investment, at the end of each year, for the first 10 years (i.e. for $0 \le t \le 10$).

(iii) Use your graph to find how long it takes for the investment to double in value.

(iv) If Stacey had invested €500 instead of €200, and the rate of interest was 6% instead of 8%, how would the value function, $v(t)$ change? Write the new function.

Solution

(i) Find $v(t)$ when $t = 4$:

$$v(t) = 200(1{\cdot}08)^t$$
$$v(4) = 200(1{\cdot}08)^4$$
$$v(4) = 272{\cdot}0977$$

Therefore, the value of the investment after four years is €272.

(ii) Complete the table:

t	$200(1{\cdot}08)^t$	$v(t)$
0	$200(1{\cdot}08)^0$	200
1	$200(1{\cdot}08)^1$	216
2	$200(1{\cdot}08)^2$	233
3	$200(1{\cdot}08)^3$	252
4	$200(1{\cdot}08)^4$	272
5	$200(1{\cdot}08)^5$	294
6	$200(1{\cdot}08)^6$	317
7	$200(1{\cdot}08)^7$	343
8	$200(1{\cdot}08)^8$	370
9	$200(1{\cdot}08)^9$	400
10	$200(1{\cdot}08)^{10}$	432

Graph the ordered pairs:

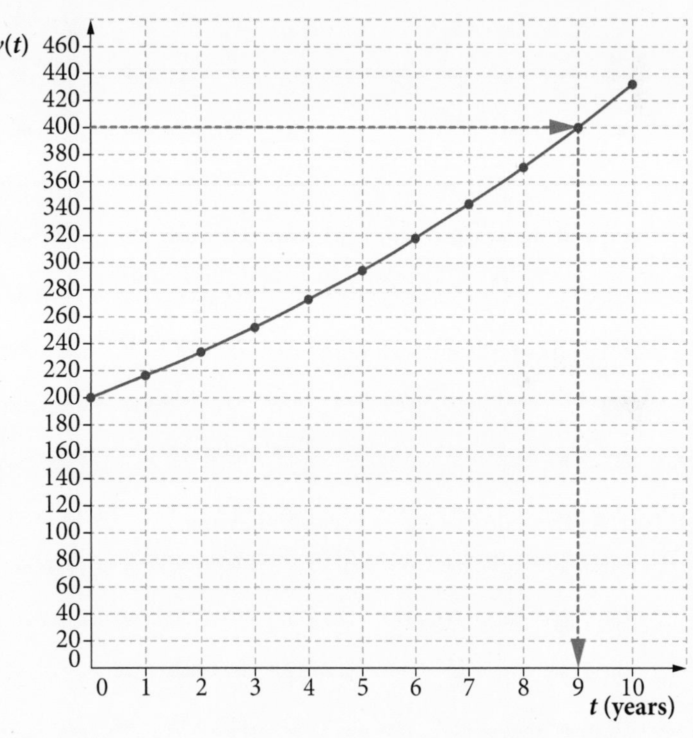

(iii) The value of the investment has doubled when it is worth €400. Reading from the graph, we see that this occurs when $t = 9$ years.

(iv) Studying the first function: $v(t) = 200(1{\cdot}08)^t$. The investment was 200 and the rate was 8%.

And so, if the investment is 500 and the rate is 6%, the function would be: $v(t) = 500(1{\cdot}06)^t$

Practice Questions 7.4

1. Graph each of the following exponential functions, in the domain $-3 \leq x \leq 3$. In each case, state whether the graph is increasing or decreasing.

   (i) 4^x (ii) $3(2^x)$ (iii) $\left(\frac{1}{2}\right)^x$ (iv) $\left(\frac{1}{3}\right)^x$

2. **Without** graphing the following functions, determine:

   (i) the coordinates of the point where each function crosses the y-axis. Give a reason for your answer.

   (ii) whether each graph is increasing or decreasing. Give a reason for your answer.

   (a) $6(2^x)$ (c) $0{\cdot}5^x$ (e) $4(0{\cdot}2)^x$

   (b) $3\left(\frac{1}{4}\right)^x$ (d) 5^x (f) $15(1^x)$

3. The diagram shows a sketch of the graph of function $f(x) = 3(5^x)$.

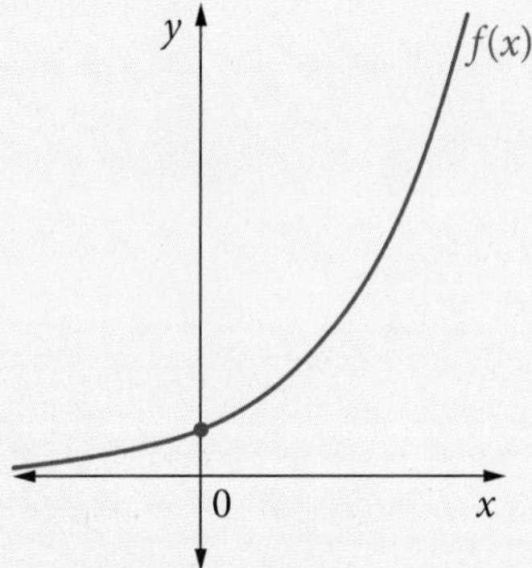

   (i) Find the coordinates of the point where $f(x)$ crosses the y-axis. Give reason for your answer.

   (ii) Is this graph increasing or decreasing?

   (iii) As the value of x gets very large, what happens to the value of $f(x)$? That is, find $\lim_{x \to \infty} f(x)$. Give reason for your answer.

   (iv) As the value of x gets very small, what happens to the value of $f(x)$? That is, find $\lim_{x \to -\infty} f(x)$. Give a reason for your answer.

4. The curve $y = a(5^x)$, where $a \in \mathbb{N}$ passes through the points (2, 75). Find the value of a.

5. The curve $y = 4(b^x)$, where $b \in \mathbb{N}$ passes through the points (3, 108). Find the value of b.

6. The graph of the function $g(x) = a(2^x)$, where $a \in \mathbb{N}$ is shown.

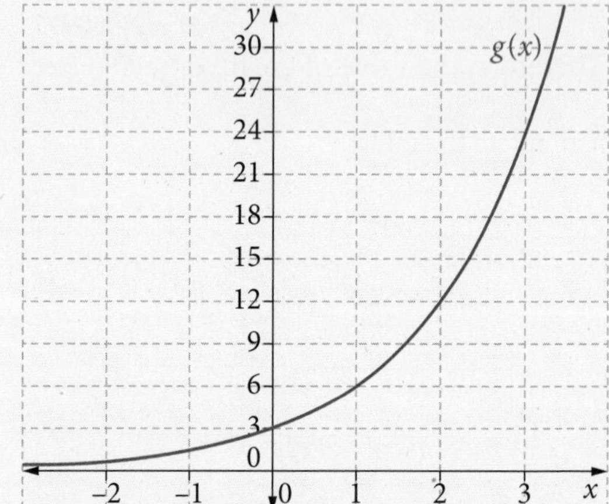

   Use the grid to answer the following questions.

   (i) Write down the value of a.

   (ii) Find the value of $g(x)$ when $x = 3$.

   (iii) Estimate the value of x when $g(x) = 9$.

   (iv) As the value of x gets very large, what happens to the value of $g(x)$? Give a reason for your answer.

7. (i) $f(x) = 5^x$ and $g(x) = 3(0{\cdot}4^x)$ are two functions. Copy and complete the following table.

x	-1	$-0{\cdot}5$	0	$0{\cdot}5$	1
$f(x)$					
$g(x)$					

   (ii) Using the table from part (i), graph the functions $f(x)$ and $g(x)$ using the same axes and scale, in the domain $-1 \leq x \leq 1$.

   (iii) From your graph, estimate the point of intersection of f and g.

   (iv) Find the range of values of x, for which $f(x) > g(x)$.

Further Functions

8. The diagram shows the graph of three functions: $f(x) = 2^x$, $g(x) = 4^x$ and $h(x) = 6^x$
   (i) Match each function to its graph. Give a reason for your answer.
   (ii) Which function is increasing at the quickest rate?

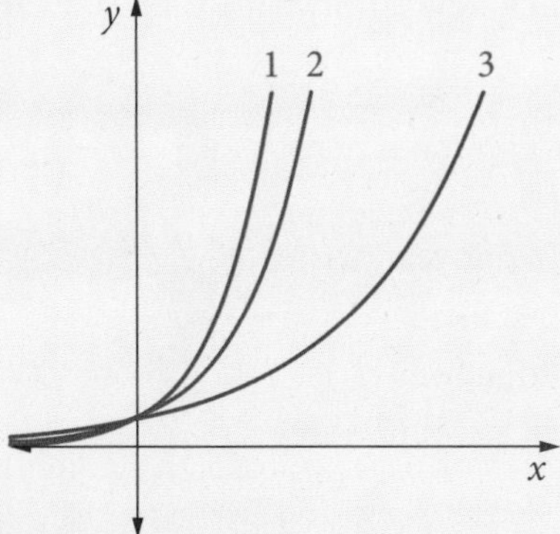

9. The curve $y = ab^x$, where $a, b \in \mathbb{N}$ passes through the points (0, 2) and (3, 54). Find the values of a and b.

10. The curve $y = ab^x$, where $a, b \in \mathbb{N}$ passes through the points (0, 5) and (3, 320). Find the values of a and b.

11. A car purchased for €20,000 is expected to depreciate, at a rate of 8% per year. The situation can be modelled by

$$v(t) = 20{,}000(0{\cdot}92)^t$$

where $v(t)$ is the value of the car, and t is the years since the car was purchased.
   (i) Draw a graph representing the value of the car over the first 12 years after its purchase (i.e. $0 \leq t \leq 12$).
   (ii) Use your graph to estimate the value of the car after seven-and-a-half years.
   (iii) Use your graph to estimate when the car would have halved in value. Give your answer to one decimal place.
   (iv) As the years go on, what would you expect the final value of the car to be? Give a reason for your answer.

Links across the syllabus

Depreciation and other situations of growth and decline are covered in Chapter 9: Arithmetic II.

12. A watch purchased for €250 is expected to increase in value, at a rate of 5% per year. The situation can be modelled by

$$v(t) = 250(1{\cdot}05)^t$$

where $v(t)$ is the value of the watch, t years since the watch was purchased.
   (i) Draw a graph representing the value of the watch over the first 10 years after its purchase (i.e. $0 \leq t \leq 10$).

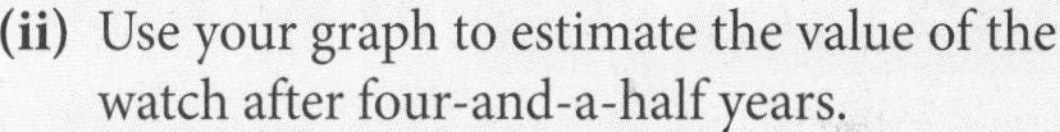

   (ii) Use your graph to estimate the value of the watch after four-and-a-half years.
   (iii) Use your graph to estimate when the value of the watch has increased by €100. Give your answer to one decimal place.

13. A fungus has an initial mass of 10 kg and grows on a daily basis. The mass of the fungus after t days can be approximated by either of the following two functions:

$$A(t) = 10 + 1{\cdot}2t^2$$

$$B(t) = 10(1{\cdot}3)^t$$

   (i) What type of function is $A(t)$?
   (ii) What type of function is $B(t)$?
   (iii) Copy and complete the following table and, hence, graph the functions $A(t)$ and $B(t)$ using the same axes and scale.

T (days)	0	1	2	3	4	5	6	7	8	9	10
$A(t)$											
$B(t)$											

Use your graph to:

(iv) Estimate, to one decimal place, when the two functions approximate the same mass.

(v) Estimate the range of values for t, during which the $B(t)$ function approximates a smaller mass than $A(t)$.

(vi) Harvesting will occur when the mass of the fungus is 80 kg. When should harvesting occur, in order to ensure that the mass is above 80 kg?

14. Liam won some money in the lottery. With his winnings, he bought a new family car for €30,000 and a diamond ring for his wife for €2,900.

(i) Given that the car depreciates at a rate of 12% per year, show that $c(t)=30000(0{\cdot}88)^t$, where $c(t)$ is the value of the car after t years.

(ii) Given that the diamond ring increases in value at a rate of 11% per year, write the function $r(t)$, where r is the value of the ring after t years.

(iii) Copy and complete the following table and, hence, graph the functions $c(t)$ and $r(t)$ using the same axes and scale.

T (years)	0	1	2	3	4	5	6	7	8	9	10	11	12
$c(t)$													
$r(t)$													

Use your graph or otherwise to:

(iv) estimate, to the nearest year, when the car and the ring have the same value

(v) estimate, to the nearest year, when the value of the car is approximately twice the value of the ring.

Section 7.5: Transforming Graphs

Learning Outcome:

You should be able to:

- recognise and apply transformations to functions on a coordinated plane

The graph of a function can be transformed by altering the function itself. The different ways to transform a graph are outlined below.

1. Adding a constant to, or subtracting a constant from, the function, causes the graph of the function to move in the vertical direction.

$$y = f(x) \pm c$$

Adding a constant, $+c$, moves the graph vertically upwards, in the positive y-direction.

Subtracting a constant, $-c$, moves the graph vertically downwards, in the negative y-direction.

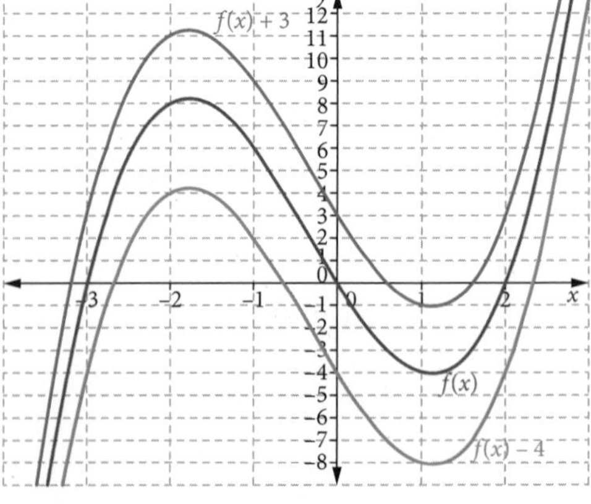

- The function $f(x)$ is shown (in blue).
- The function $f(x) + 3$ represents a translation vertically upwards by 3 units (shown in red).
- The function $f(x) - 4$ represents a translation vertically downwards by 4 units (shown in green).

Adding a constant moves the graph upwards. Subtracting a constant moves the graph downwards.

2. Adding a constant to, or subtracting a constant from, the x part of the function, causes the graph of the function to move in the horizontal direction.

$$y = f(x \pm c)$$

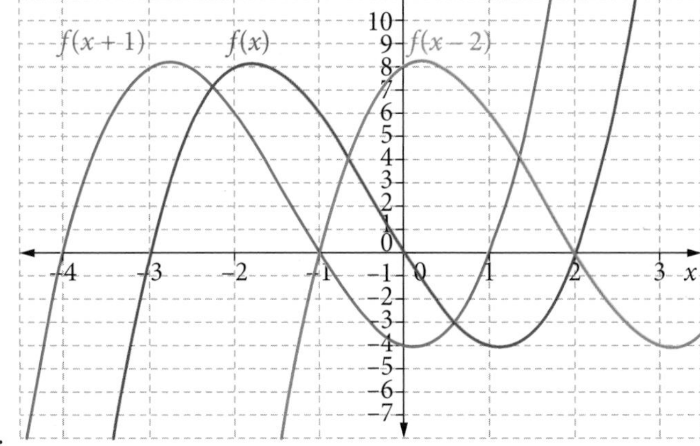

Adding a constant to the x part, $f(x + c)$, moves the graph horizontally, in the negative x-direction.

Subtracting a constant from the x part, $f(x - c)$, moves the graph horizontally, in the positive x-direction.

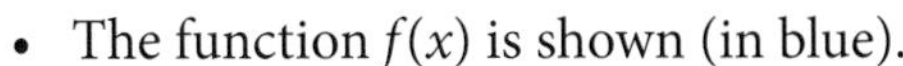

- The function $f(x)$ is shown (in blue).
- The function $f(x + 1)$ represents a translation horizontally to the left by one unit (shown in red).
- The function $f(x - 2)$ represents a translation horizontally to the right by two units (shown in green).

This result of this transformation is opposite to what you might expect.
Adding a constant moves the graph to the left.
Subtracting a constant moves the graph to the right.

3. Multiplying the x part of a function, or the entire function, by a negative, causes the graph of the function to be reflected in the axes.

$$y = -f(x) \text{ and } y = f(-x)$$

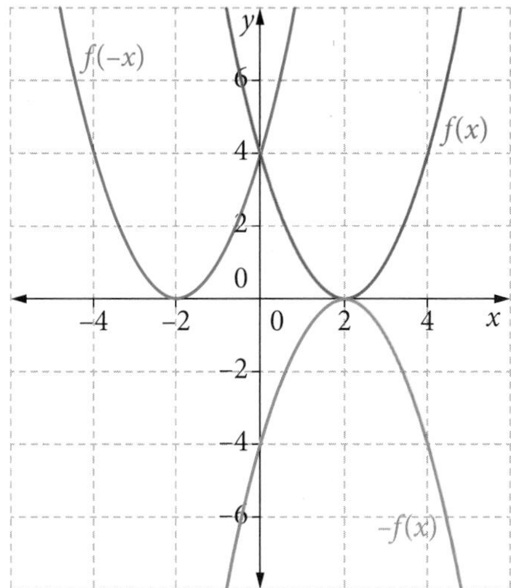

The function $f(x)$ is shown (in blue).

The graph of $y = f(-x)$ is a reflection in the y-axis of the graph of $y = f(x)$ (shown in red).

The graph of $y = -f(x)$ is a reflection in the x-axis of the graph of $y = f(x)$ (shown in green).

4. Multiplying the function by a constant causes the graph of the function to stretch, or compress, in the vertical direction.

$$y = kf(x), \text{ where } k > 0$$

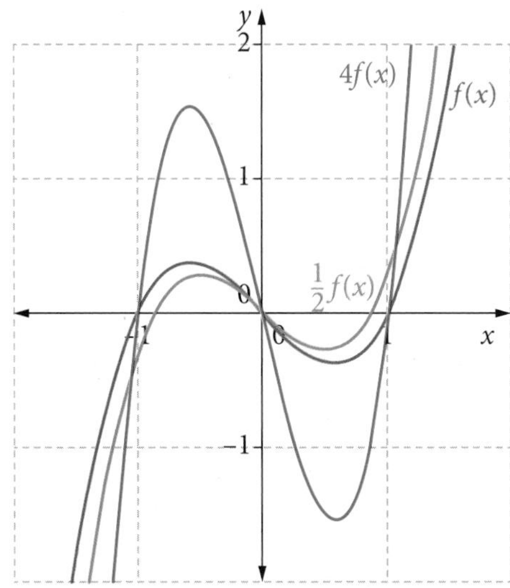

Multiplying a function by a constant will change the height of the function. However, it will not change the points where the function crosses the x-axis, the roots of the function. This means that the roots of $f(x)$ are the same as the roots of $kf(x)$.

If $k > 1$ the curve will appear to stretch (get vertically taller), as shown in red.

If $k < 1$ the curve will appear to compress (get vertically shorter), as shown in green.

These four transformations have the same effect on the graphs of **all** types of functions: linear, quadratic, cubic and exponential.

Further Functions

EXAMPLE 1

The diagram shows the graph of a function $f(x)$.
Using the same axis and scale graph the following:

(i) $f(x) + 3$

(ii) $f(x + 2) - 1$

(iii) $\frac{1}{2}f(x)$

(iv) $-f(x)$

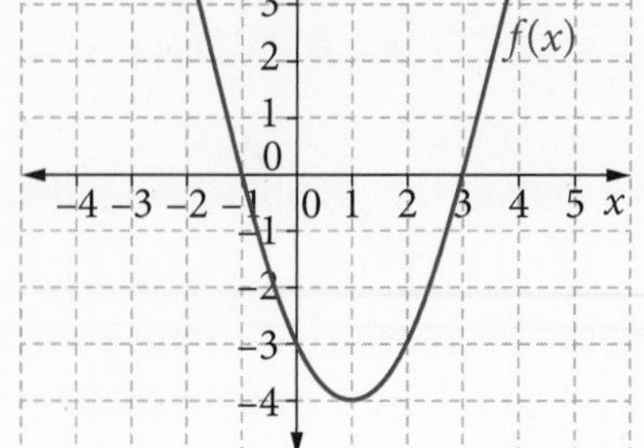

Solution

(i) $f(x) + 3$

Adding 3 units to the $f(x)$ function moves the graph 3 units upwards.

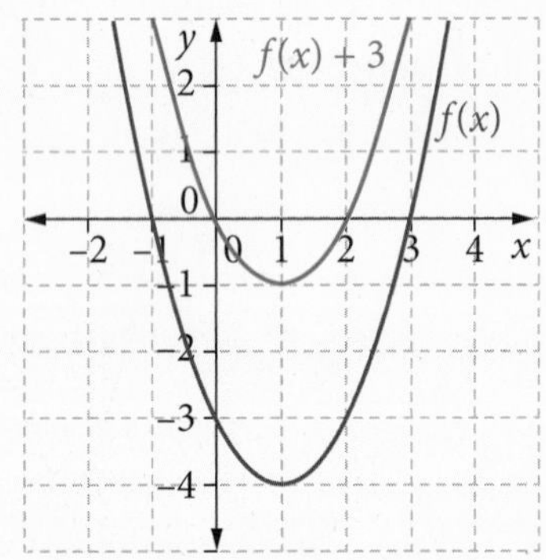

(ii) $f(x + 2) - 1$

Adding 2 units to the x part of the function moves the function 2 units to the left.
Subtracting 1 unit from the function moves the graph 1 unit downwards.

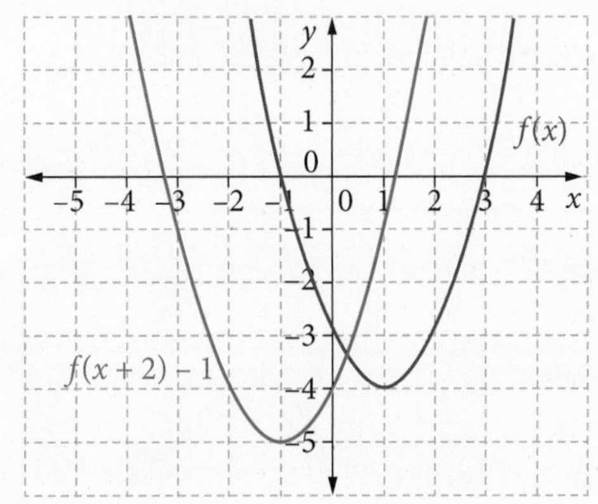

(iii) $\frac{1}{2}f(x)$

A constant in front of the function multiplies all y-values by that constant. Therefore the height of the graph is halved.

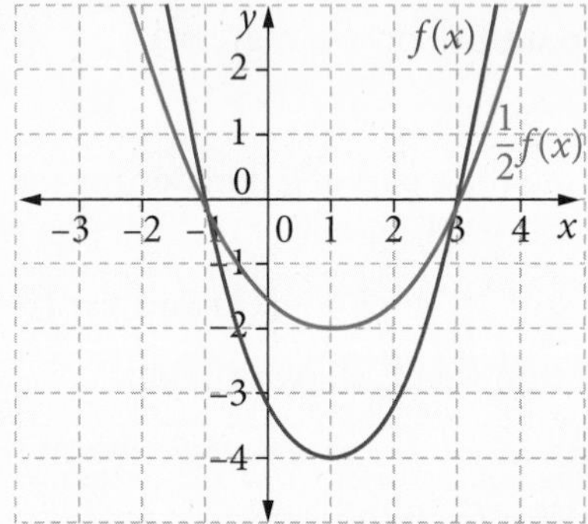

(iv) $-f(x)$

Putting a negative in front of the function reflects the function in the x-axis.

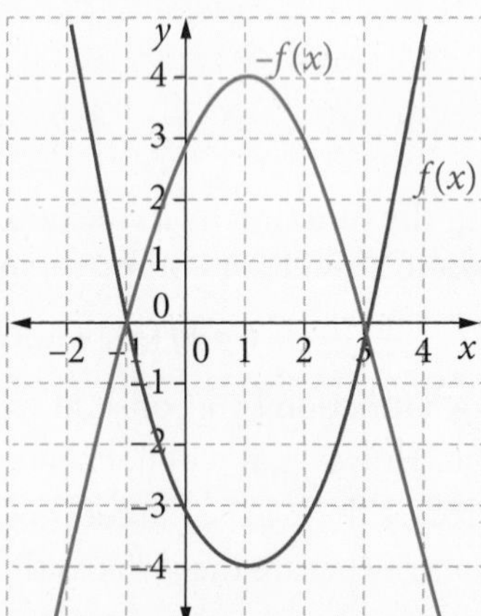

Practice Questions 7.5

1. The diagram shows the graph of a function $k(x)$.

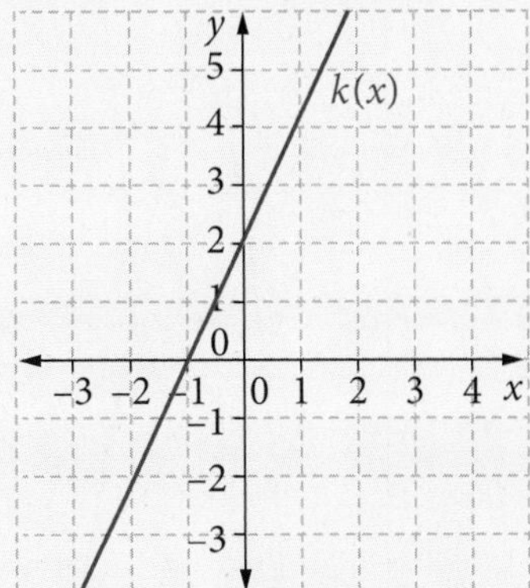

Copy the graph into your copybook.
Using the same axes and scale, graph the following:

(i) $k(x) - 3$ **(ii)** $k(x - 3)$ **(iii)** $k(x + 1)$

2. The diagram shows the graph of a function $g(x)$.

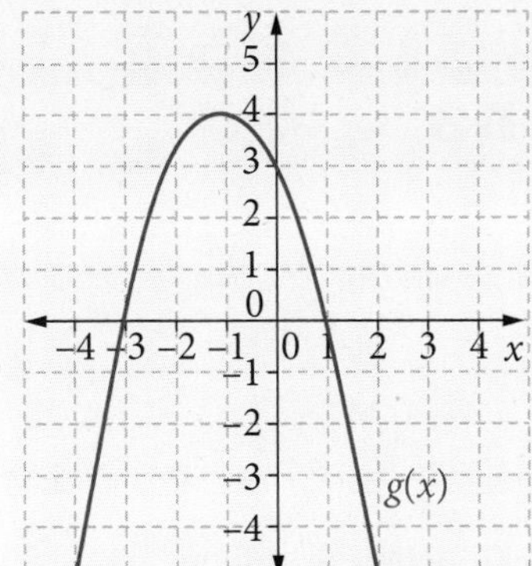

Copy the graph into your copybook.
Using the same axes and scale, graph the following:

(i) $g(x) - 2$ **(iii)** $2g(x)$

(ii) $g(x - 2)$ **(iv)** $-g(x)$

3. The diagram shows the graph of a function $f(x) = x^2 - 4$.

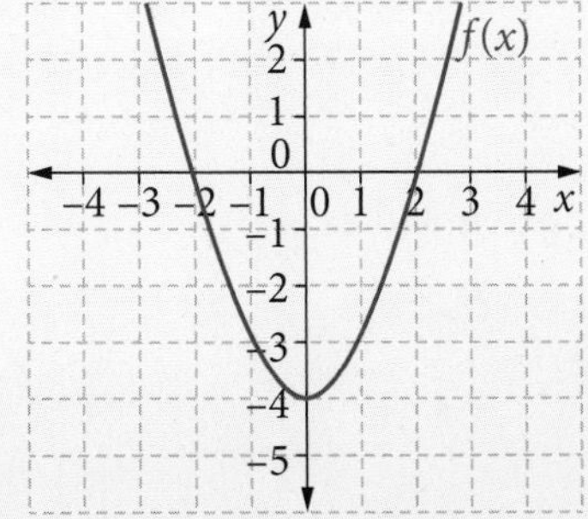

Copy the graph into your copybook. Using the same axes and scale, graph the following:

(i) $g(x) = f(x) + 3$

(ii) $k(x) = f(x + 1) - 3$

(iii) $m(x) = \frac{1}{4}f(x)$

4. The diagram shows the graph of a cubic function.

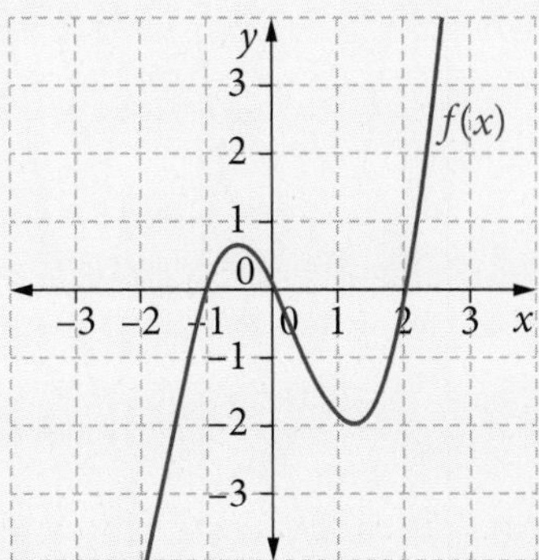

Copy the graph into your copybook. Using the same axis and scale, graph the following:

(i) $f(x) + 2$

(ii) $f(x + 2) - 1$

5. The diagram shows a graph of the function, $f(x) = x^3$.

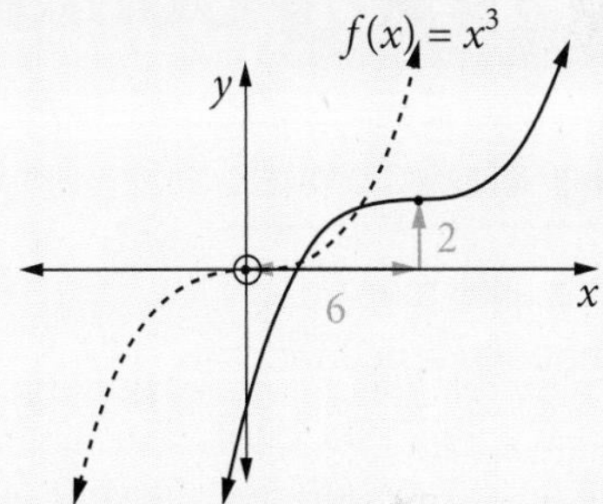

The graph is moved as shown:
6 units horizontally to the right
2 units vertically upwards.
Write the function of the new graph, in terms of x.

6. For each of the following, describe fully the transformation which maps the graph of $f(x)$ onto the graph of $g(x)$.

(i) $f(x) = 3x$ onto $g(x) = 3x + 2$

(ii) $f(x) = x^2$ onto $g(x) = x^2 - 3$

(iii) $f(x) = 4x^3$ onto $g(x) = 4(x + 5)^3$

(iv) $f(x) = 2x^2 + 3x + 7$ onto $g(x) = 2x^2 + 3x + 4$

(v) $f(x) = 6^x$ onto $g(x) = 6^{x-1}$

(vi) $f(x) = 4^x + 3$ onto $g(x) = 4^{x+2} + 2$

7. Function A (blue) is defined by the equation $y = x^2$. By observation, or otherwise, write down the equation of the functions B, C and D.

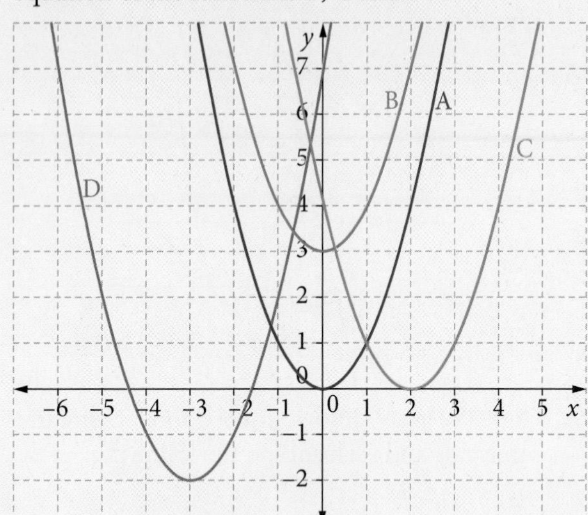

8. The graph of $y = f(x)$ is shown in red. Write down the equations of $g(x)$ and $h(x)$ in terms of $f(x)$.

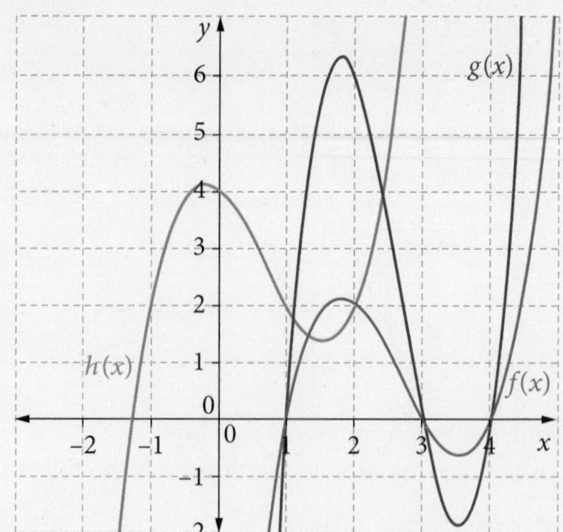

Section 7.6: Composite Functions

Learning Outcome:

You should be able to:

- form composite functions

A **composite function** is formed when one function uses the output of another function as its input.

In the diagram below, a function $g(x)$ takes an input of A and outputs B. Then a second function, $f(x)$, takes the input of B and outputs C.
The effect of the two functions being applied one after the other is to send A to C.

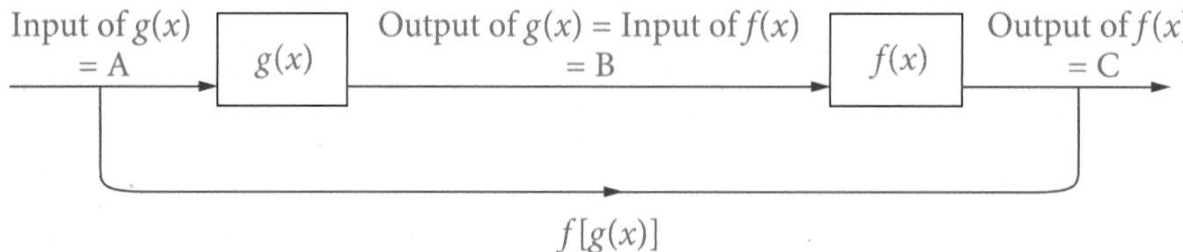

The composite function shown above is called **'f after $g(x)$'** and it could be denoted as:

$$f[g(x)] = fg(x) = (f \circ g)(x)$$

This means the $f(x)$ function is applied after the $g(x)$.

The composite function of 'f after $f(x)$' is denoted as: $f^2(x)$

EXAMPLE 1

$f(x) = 6^x$ and $k(x) = 5 - x$.

(i) Find $f(2)$

(ii) Hence, find $(k \circ f)(2)$

Solution

(i) $f(x) = 6^x$

$f(2) = 6^2$

$f(2) = 36$

(ii) $(k \circ f)(2)$

$k(36) = 5 - (36)$ ($f(2) = 36$, from part **(i)**)

$k(36) = 5 - 36$

$k(36) = -31$

Therefore, $(k \circ f)(2) = -31$

EXAMPLE 2

$h(x) = 3x - 1$ and $g(x) = x^2$. Find:

(i) $hg(2)$

(ii) $(g \circ h)(2)$

(iii) $(g \circ h)(x)$

(iv) $h^2(x)$

Solution

(i) $hg(2)$

Find $g(2)$: $g(2) = (2)^2$

$g(2) = 4$

$hg(2) = h(4) = 3(4) - 1$

$= 12 - 1$

$= 11$

Therefore, $hg(2) = 11$

(ii) $(g \circ h)(2)$

Find $h(2)$: $h(2) = 3(2) - 1$

$h(2) = 5$

$(g \circ h)(2) = g(5) = (5)^2$

$= 25$

Therefore, $(g \circ h)(2) = 25$

(iii) $(g \circ h)(x)$:

$g(3x - 1) = (3x - 1)^2$

$g(3x - 1) = (3x - 1)(3x - 1)$

$g(3x - 1) = 9x^2 - 6x + 1$

Therefore, $(g \circ h)(x) = 9x^2 - 6x + 1$

(iv) $h^2(x)$

$h(h(x)) = 3(3x - 1) - 1$

$h(h(x)) = 9x - 3 - 1$

$h(h(x)) = 9x - 4$

Therefore, $h^2(x) = 9x - 4$

Practice Questions 7.6

1. The diagram shows a pair of functions, whereby the output of the first function f, becomes the input of the second function, g.

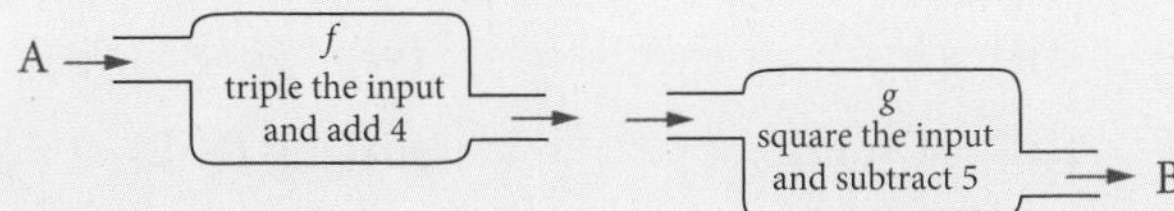

Find the outputs at point B for the following inputs at A:

(i) 1 **(ii)** 3 **(iii)** 0 **(iv)** −2 **(v)** −5

2. $f(x) = 2x + 1$ and $g(x) = 5 - x$ are two functions, where $x \in \mathbb{R}$.
Find:

(i) $f(2)$

(ii) $g(-1)$

(iii) $fg(-1)$

(iv) $(g \circ f)(2)$

(v) $g(f(x))$

(vi) $(f \circ g)(-3)$

(vii) $g^2(5)$

(viii) $f^2(x)$

3. $p(x) = x^2 - 4$ and $q(x) = 7x + 1$ are two functions, where $x \in \mathbb{R}$.
Find:

(i) $p(-3)$	**(v)** $(q \circ p)(-2)$
(ii) $q(5)$	**(vi)** $q^2(-2)$
(iii) $qp(0)$	**(vii)** $q(p(x))$
(iv) $(p \circ q)(-1)$	**(viii)** $p^2(x)$

4. The diagram shows the graphs of two functions, $f(x)$ and $g(x)$. Use the graph to find the value of the following:

(i) $f(1)$	**(v)** $gf(-4))$
(ii) $g(-3)$	**(vi)** $(f \circ g)(0)$
(iii) $f(g(-3))$	**(vii)** $g[g(1)]$
(iv) $(g \circ f)(1)$	**(viii)** $f^2(-2)$

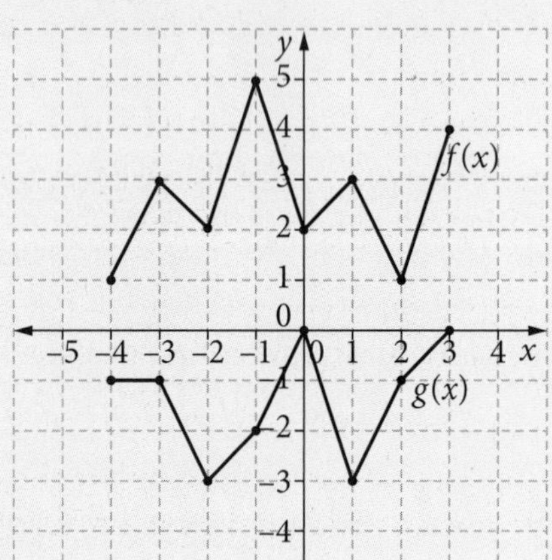

5. The diagram shows the graphs of two functions, $g(x)$ and $h(x)$. Use the graph to find the value of the following:

(i) $h(-1)$	**(v)** $h(h(-4))$
(ii) $g(0)$	**(vi)** $(g \circ h)(2)$
(iii) $g(h(-3))$	**(vii)** $hg(-4)$
(iv) $(h \circ g)(-1)$	**(viii)** $g^2(-2)$

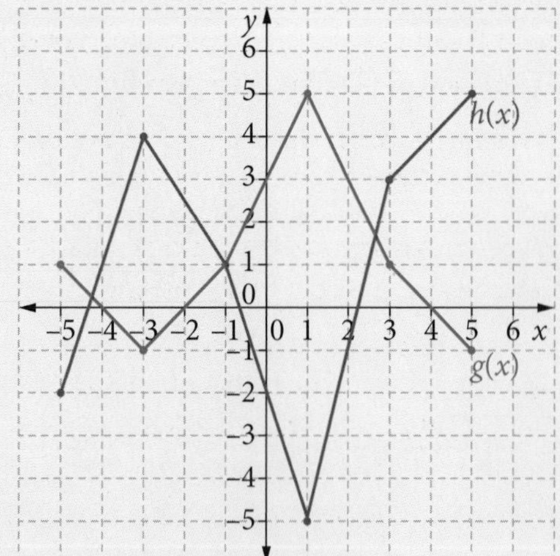

6. The diagram shows the graphs of two functions, $g(x)$ and $f(x)$. Use the graph to find the value of the following:

(i) $g(0)$
(ii) $f(-1)$
(iii) $g(f(-1))$
(iv) $(f \circ g)(3)$
(v) $g(g(3))$
(vi) $(g \circ f)(4)$
(vii) $fg(-2)$
(viii) $f^2(0)$

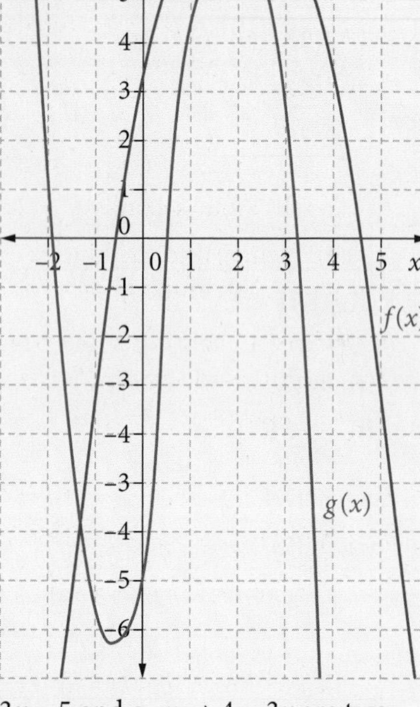

7. $f: x \rightarrow x^3 + x^2 - 3x - 5$ and $g: x \rightarrow 4 - 3x$ are two functions, where $x \in \mathbb{R}$:

(i) $f(2)$	**(iii)** $gf(-2)$
(ii) $fg(0)$	**(iv)** $(f \circ g)(2)$

8. $f(x) = 6 + 2x - x^3$, $g(x) = 3x^2 + x - 4$ and $h(x) = 5x + 2$ are three functions, where $x \in \mathbb{R}$.
Find:

(i) $h(g(2))$	**(v)** $fg(-1)$
(ii) $fh(0)$	**(vi)** $(h \circ f)(-2)$
(iii) $g(f(1))$	**(vii)** $h^2(-3)$
(iv) $(f \circ g)(2)$	**(viii)** $(f \circ (g \circ h))(-1)$

9. $f(x) = 5 + 2x - x^2$, $h(x) = 5x + 2$ and $g(x) = 2^x$ are three functions, where $x \in \mathbb{R}$.
Find

(i) $h(g(1))$	**(v)** $g^2(3)$
(ii) $gh(0)$	**(vi)** $(h \circ f)(-3)$
(iii) $g(f(1))$	**(vii)** $gf(-2)$
(iv) $(f \circ g)(2)$	**(viii)** $(f \circ (h \circ g))(-1)$

10. An object is accelerating along a straight track. After x seconds, its velocity is given by the following function:

$$v(x) = 5 + 3x, \text{ where } x \in \mathbb{N}$$

The amount of kinetic energy, in joules, the object has after x seconds, is given by the function: $k(v) = 200\,v^2$

where v is the velocity of the body at an instant, in metres per second.

(i) Find the velocity of the object after:

(a) two seconds **(c)** 12 seconds

(b) four seconds **(d)** 20 seconds.

(ii) Hence, find the kinetic energy the object has, at each of the times given in part **(i)**.

(iii) Write an expression, in x, for the amount of kinetic energy the object has after x seconds.

11. A shop has reduced the price of all laptops by 30%.

(i) Find the sale price of a laptop, if it was originally priced at €750.

(ii) On a given day, the shop is offering a special discount of 10% off all sale prices. Find the discounted price of the laptop.

(iii) What is the overall percentage discount applied to the laptop?

(iv) If x is the original price of a laptop, write an expression for $s(x)$, the price of the laptop in the 30% off sale.

(v) Write an expression for $d(y)$, the price of the laptop, after the additional 10% discount is applied, where y is the sale price.

(vi) Hence, find the composite function, $ds(x)$, the price of a €x laptop, after **both** discounts have been applied. Use this composite function to verify your answer to part **(iii)**.

Revision and Exam Style Questions – Section A

1. Let $g(x) = 9 + kx$
Given that $g(-2) = 3$, find the value of k.

2. The graph shown represents the flight of a golf ball. The height of the ball, after t seconds, is given by the function

$$h(t) = at - t^2, \text{ where } t \in \mathbb{R}.$$

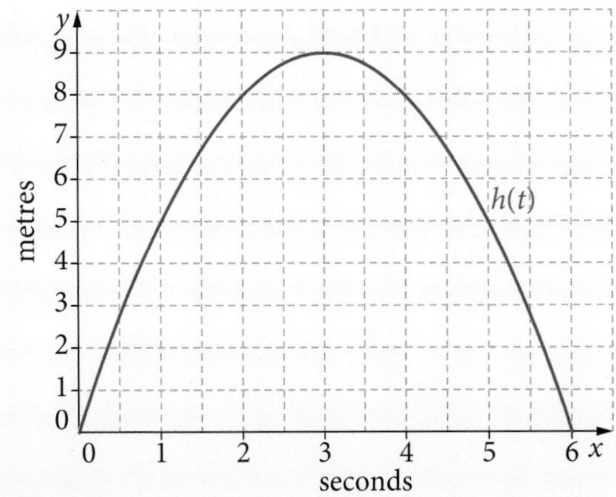

(i) After how many seconds is the ball at a height of 8 m?

(ii) Find the two times when the height of the ball is 5 m.

(iii) Find the value of a.

3. The diagram shows part of the graph of the function $f: x \rightarrow x^2 + 2x - 3$, where $x \in \mathbb{R}$.

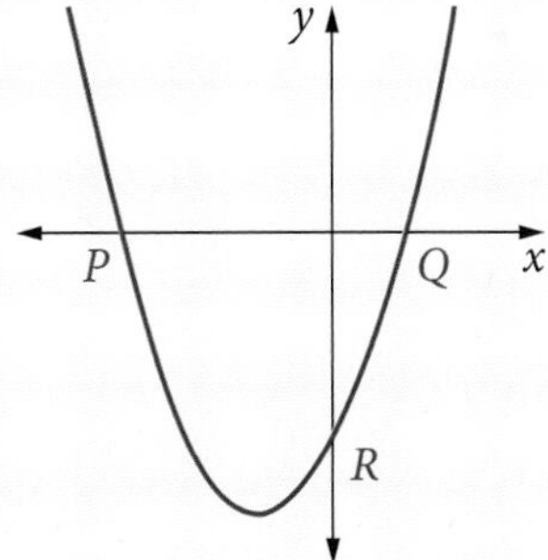

(i) The graph intersects the x-axis at the points P and Q and the y-axis at R. Find the coordinates of the points P, Q and R.

(ii) Hence, write down the range of values of x for which $x^2 + 2x - 3 \leq 0$

4. Which of the following show the graph of a function? Give a reason for your answer.

(a)

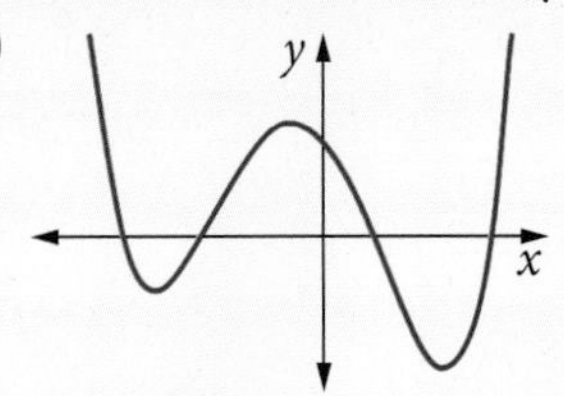

(b) 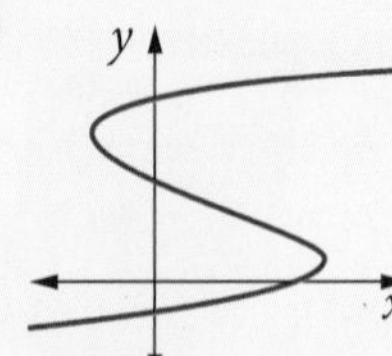

(c) 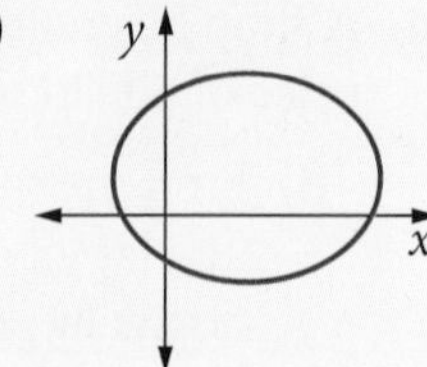

5. $f: x \to 3x^2 - 1$ and $g: x \to 2x - 3$. Find:

(i) $f(2)$

(ii) $fg(0)$

(iii) $gf(-2)$

(iv) $(f \circ g)(x)$

6. $g(x) = x^2 + x + k$ is a function defined on $\mathbb{R}$, where $k \in \mathbb{Z}$.

(i) If $g(1) = -4$, find the value of k.

(ii) Hence, solve the equation $g(x + 5) = 0$

7. (i) Graph the function $g(x) = 2x^3 - 5x^2 - 2x + 5$ in the domain $-1 \le x \le 3$.

(ii) Use your graph to estimate:

(a) the roots of the equation $g(x) = 0$

(b) the values of x for which $g(x) = -1$

(c) $g(0{\cdot}5)$

(d) $g(-0{\cdot}5)$

(iii) Check the accuracy of your estimated roots in part **(ii) (a)**, by checking if they satisfy the equation $g(x) = 0$.

8. A puddle contains 500 litres of water. The water is evaporating at a rate of 6% per hour. The volume of the water remaining in the puddle, after t hours, is given by:

$$v(t) = 500\,(0{\cdot}94)^t$$

(i) Is the value of $v(t)$ increasing or decreasing? Give a reason for your answer.

(ii) If $t = 0$ represents 8 am, find the volume of water remaining at 3 pm. Give your answer to two decimal places.

(iii) Copy and complete the following table and hence graph the function $v(t)$ using the same axes and scale.

t	0	1	2	3	4	5	6	7	8	9	10
$v(t)$											

Use your graph to:

(iv) Estimate, to the nearest hour, when the volume of water is at 350 litres.

(v) Estimate the volume of water remaining in the puddle at 5 pm.

(vi) Estimate, to the nearest hour, when the volume of the water has been **reduced by** 40%.

9. The function $g: x \to 2x^3 - 4x^2 - 5x + 4$ is defined for $x \in \mathbb{R}$.

(i) Find the coordinates of the y-intercept of the graph of $g(x)$. That is, the point where the graph of g cuts the y-axis.

(ii) Verify, using algebra, that the point $(-1, 3)$ is on the graph of g.

10. The graph of $f(x) = -x^2 + 2x + 3$, where $x \in \mathbb{R}$, is shown in the diagram.

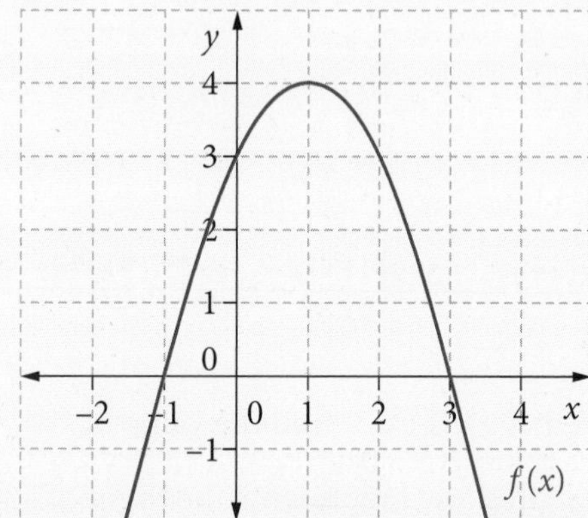

Copy the graph into your copybook. Using the same axes and scale, graph each of the following functions:

(i) $g(x) = f(x) - 2$

(ii) $h(x) = f(x - 2) + 1$

11. Clay pigeon shooting is a sport which involves a clay target, being released from a trap to simulate the flight of a bird. The objective of the sport is to shoot the clay.
The path of the clay is modelled by the function $h(t) = -5t^2 + 32t + 2$, where h represents the height of the clay, in metres, t seconds after the clay is released.

Donald shoots his gun. The path of Donald's bullet is modelled by the function $b(t) = 31{\cdot}5t + 1$, where b represents the height of the bullet, in metres, t seconds after the clay is released.

Find:

(i) the time when the bullet hits the clay

(ii) the height of the clay at this time.

The device releasing the clay is adjusted, and the clay now follows a path modelled by the function $h(t) = -5t^2 + 44t + 2$.

If the path of the bullet remains the same, find:

(iii) after how many seconds the bullet will hit the clay

(iv) the height of the clay, at this time.

Revision and Exam Style Questions – Section B

More challenging problems

1. Let $g(x) = ax + b$, where a, b, and $x \in \mathbb{R}$
Given that $g(0) = -2$ and $g(2) = 4$, find the value of a and the value of b.

2. $h : x \rightarrow 2x + p$ and $g : x \rightarrow q - 5x$ are two functions defined on $\mathbb{R}$, where p and q are real numbers.
   (i) If $h(1) = -5$ and $g(-1) = 4$, find the value of p and the value of q.
   (ii) Find, in terms of x, an expression for $(h \circ g)(x)$.
   (iii) Find the values of x, for which $(h \circ g)(x) = x^2$.

3. Let f be the function $f : x \rightarrow x^2 - 3x$, where $x \in \mathbb{R}$.
   (i) Express $f(k)$ and $f(2k + 1)$ in terms of k.
   (ii) Hence, find the values of k for which $f(k) = f(2k + 1)$.

4. The graphs of two functions, f and g, are shown on the coordinate grid.
The functions are:
$$f(x) = (x - 4)^2 - 4$$
$$g(x) = (x + 1)^2 - 4$$

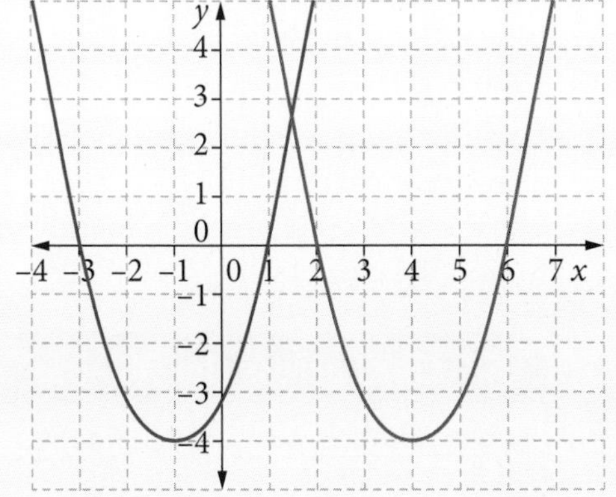

   (i) Identify which graph is f and which graph is g.
   (ii) Write down the roots of $f(x) = 0$ and the roots of $g(x) = 0$.
   (iii) The function $h(x) = (x - 2)^2 - 4$ is later plotted on the coordinate grid. What are the roots of the equation $h(x) = 0$.

5. A toddler has an ear infection. The doctor said there are approximately 50,000,000 bacteria in his left ear. The penicillin the doctor prescribed will kill 8% of the bacteria every hour.
   (i) Write the function $b(t)$ where b is the number of bacteria, t hours after the toddler starts taking the penicillin.

> Recall:
> $f(x)$ = initial value (1 + percentage change)^{time}

Use your expression for $b(t)$ to find the number of bacteria in the toddler's left ear after:
   (ii) four hours
   (iii) two days
   (iv) one week.

6. $f : x \rightarrow 3x - 1$ and $g : x \rightarrow 3x^2 + 2$ are two functions defined on $\mathbb{R}$.
   (i) Find an expression for $(f \circ g)(x)$, in terms of x.
   (ii) Find an expression for $(g \circ f)(x)$, in terms of x.
   (iii) Find the two values of x for which $(f \circ g)(x) = (g \circ f)(x)$.

7. Rhod needs to hire an electrician. He contacts two different companies for their prices.
Company A charge €45 for each hour onsite and no flat fee.
Company B charge a call out fee of €75 plus €25 for each hour onsite.

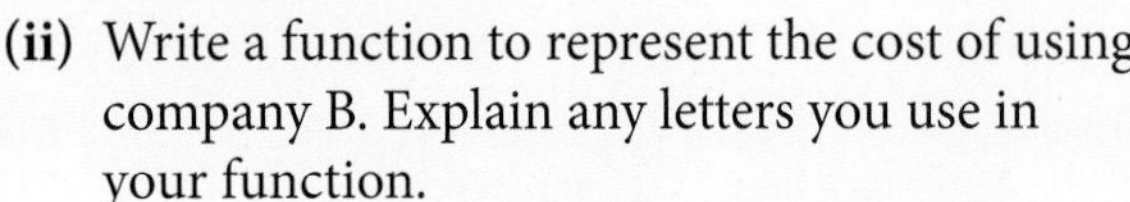

(i) Write a function to represent the cost of using company A. Explain any letters you use in your function.

(ii) Write a function to represent the cost of using company B. Explain any letters you use in your function.

(iii) Using the same axes and scales, graph each function to show the cost of having an electrician onsite for up to six hours. Clearly indicate which graph represents which company.

(iv) If Rhod thinks the job will take two hours, which company should he use? Justify your answer.

(v) If Rhod thinks the job will take five hours, which company should he use? Justify your answer.

(vi) Using the graphs, or otherwise, find how many hours Rhod could hire an electrician such that the cost incurred would be the same from both companies.

8. An investor is looking to invest in a start-up company. His advisor presents him with two options: company A and company B.

The annual projected profits of the two companies, A and B, (in thousands of euro) are modelled using two functions: $A: t \rightarrow 3t + 5$ and $B: t \rightarrow 3(1{\cdot}5^t)$ respectively, where t is in years.

(i) Using the same axes and scales, graph both functions in the domain $0 \leq t \leq 5$. Clearly label each graph.

(ii) Describe the growth pattern of the profits of each company. Make reference to the function type.

Use your graph to estimate:

(iii) The projected profit for each company after 2·5 years.

(iv) After how many years will the projected profit of both companies be the same? Give your answer to one decimal place.

(v) How many years will it take each company to make a profit of €12,000?
Give your answers to one decimal place.

(vi) After a number of years the investor plans to cash out his investment for 10% of the annual projected profit at that time. Determine which company he should invest in, if he plans to cash out after:

(a) three years. Justify your answer.

(b) six years. Justify your answer.

9. An electricity meter indicates the number of units of energy, u, used by a consumer. The number of joules of energy, x, is converted into units using the following function:

$$u(x) = \frac{x}{3{\cdot}6 \times 10^6}$$

An energy company's monthly charge (in euro) for u units, is given by the function:

$$c(u) = 22{\cdot}5 + 0{\cdot}07u$$

(i) How many units of energy are equivalent to $5{\cdot}4 \times 10^8$ joules?

(ii) Find the cost of using 520 units of energy.

(iii) Find the cost of using the following amounts of electricity, from this energy company:

(a) $6{\cdot}48 \times 10^8\ J$

(b) $1{\cdot}44 \times 10^9\ J$

(c) $1{\cdot}98 \times 10^9\ J$

(iv) Find the composite function, $(c \circ u)(x)$, for the total cost of using x joules of energy.

Use this composite function to verify your answer for part **(iii) (a)**.

(v) Use the composite function, found in part **(iv)**, to find the cost of using $2{\cdot}97 \times 10^9\ j$ of energy.

Links across the syllabus

Index notation is covered in Chapter 5: Indices and Index Notation.

Now that you have completed the chapter, revisit the 'Something to think about...' question.

Arithmetic I

CHAPTER 08

Sections covered within this chapter:

KEY WORDS

- Ratio
- Inverse proportion
- Accumulated Error
- Proportion
- Mark-up
- Tolerance interval
- Direct proportion
- Margin
- Exchange rate

SOMETHING TO THINK ABOUT...

Fergus estimates that he can run 1 km in 6 minutes.

(i) Find this estimated speed in km/hr.

Fergus runs a half marathon, a distance of 13·1 miles, in 2 hours 15 minutes.

(ii) Given that 1 km = 0·621 miles, find Fergus' true speed in km/hr.

(iii) Hence, find the percentage error in Fergus' estimate.

Section 8.1: Ratio and Proportion

Learning Outcome:

You should be able to:

- solve problems using ratio and proportion

Ratio

> A **ratio** is a relationship between two quantities.

Ratios are used to show how quantities are divided or shared. A ratio in the form 3 : 5 means that a quantity is divided into 8 parts (3 + 5) and then shared in such a way that the first portion is $\frac{3}{8}$ of the total and the second share is $\frac{5}{8}$ of the total. Ratios are normally expressed in whole numbers. A ratio can be simplified by multiplying or dividing all parts by the same value. For example, to simplify $\frac{1}{2} : \frac{3}{5}$, we multiply both sides of the ratio by the LCM of the denominators, which is 10: $10\left(\frac{1}{2}\right) : 10\left(\frac{3}{5}\right) = 5 : 6$

To solve questions involving ratios, follow these steps:

Step 1: Add the parts to find the total number of parts.

Step 2: Divide, to find one part.

Step 3: Multiply to find the required share.

EXAMPLE 1

Isabelle and James share a punnet of 55 strawberries in the ratio of 4 : 7.

(i) How many strawberries does Isabelle get?

(ii) How many strawberries does James get?

Solution

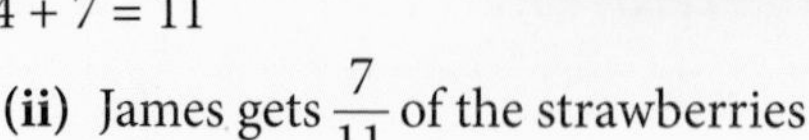

Step 1: Add the ratios: 4 + 7 = 11

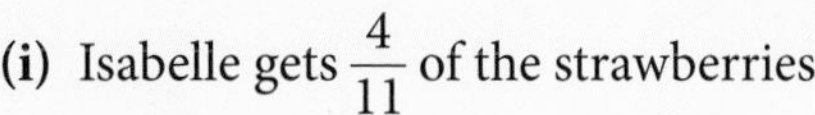

(i) Isabelle gets $\frac{4}{11}$ of the strawberries

Step 2: $\frac{1}{11}$ of 55 = 5

Step 3: $\frac{4}{11}$ of 55 = 20 (multiply by 4)

Therefore, Isabelle gets 20 strawberries.

(ii) James gets $\frac{7}{11}$ of the strawberries

Step 2: $\frac{1}{11}$ of 55 = 5

Step 3: $\frac{7}{11}$ of 55 = 35 (multiply by 7)

Therefore, James gets 35 strawberries.

James' share could also be found by subtracting Isabelle's share from the total: James share = 55 – 20 = 35

EXAMPLE 2

The ratio of boys to girls in a class is 4 : 5. If there are 16 boys in the class, find:

(i) The number of girls in the class

(ii) The total number of students in the class.

In this question, we weren't given the total amount, but the value of one share. However, the steps are still applied in the same way.

Solution

(i) *Step 1:* Add the ratios: 4 + 5 = 9

Therefore the boys make up $\frac{4}{9}$ of the class.

$\frac{4}{9} = 16$

Step 2: $\frac{1}{9} = 4$ (divide by 4)

Step 3: $\frac{5}{9} = 20$ (multiply by 5)

Therefore, there are 20 girls in the class.

(ii) Total in the class = Boys + Girls

= 16 + 20

= 36

EXAMPLE 3

A prize fund of €270 is divided between three people, Paula, Quentin and Rachel, such that Rachel gets three times Paula's share and Quentin gets half of Paula's share.

(i) Find the ratio into which the prize is divided between the three winners.

(ii) Hence, find how much each person receives.

Solution

(i) Let Paula's share be one part

Rachel's share = 3(Paula) = 3(1) = 3

Quentin's share = $\frac{1}{2}$ (Paula) = $\frac{1}{2}$ (1) = $\frac{1}{2}$

Therefore, ratio: P : Q : R

$1 : \frac{1}{2} : 3$ (multiply all parts by 2)

$2 : 1 : 6$

When ratios involve fractions, it is best practice to multiply all ratios by the LCM of the denominators, to express the ratios as whole numbers.

(ii) ***Step 1:*** Add the ratios: 2 + 1 + 6 = 9

Step 2: One part = $\frac{1}{9}$ of €270 = €30

Step 3: Paula = $\frac{2}{9}$ = 2 × €30 = €60

Quentin = $\frac{1}{9}$ = €30

Rachel = $\frac{6}{9}$ = 6 × €30 = €180

Proportion

A **proportion** compares part of a quantity to the total quantity.

For example, on a shelf of 12 books, four of them are non-fiction and the rest are fiction. We can say that the proportion of the books which are non-fiction is $\frac{4}{12} = \frac{1}{3}$ of the total.

Direct proportion relates to two variables, whereby as one increases the other increases.

For example, if a waiter is working in a restaurant and is paid an hourly rate, then the more hours he works, the more pay he will get. In this case the time worked is directly proportional to the money earned.

Inverse proportion relates to two variables, whereby as one increases the other decreases.

For example, if we increase the number of people working on a task, then the task will be completed in less time. In this case the time to complete the task would be inversely proportional to the number of people working on it.

EXAMPLE 4

A science teacher is ordering new test tubes for the school laboratory.
If 12 test tubes cost €30, find the cost of buying a class set of 33 test tubes.

€30

Solution

12 test tubes = €30

1 test tube = $\frac{€30}{12}$ = €2·50 (divide by 12)

33 test tubes = €2·50 × 33 = €82·50 (multiply by 33)

Therefore, 33 test tubes cost €82·50.

The total cost is directly proportional to the number of items bought.

EXAMPLE 5

35 workers can build a house in 16 days. How many days will 14 workers, working at the same rate, take to build the same house?

Solution

35 workers take 16 days

1 worker takes 35 × 16 = 560 days (As the number of workers decreases, the number of days increases)

14 workers take 560 ÷ 14 = 40 days (As the number of workers increases, the number of days decreases)

Therefore, 14 workers will take 40 days to build the house.

Practice Questions 8.1

1. Mike and Nat share the €1,170 rent on a house in the ratio 4 : 5. How much does each pay towards the rent?

2. One piece of pipe 210 centimetres long is to be cut into two pieces, with the lengths of the pieces being in a 3 : 4 ratio. What are the lengths of the pieces?

3. Alan and Barbara share a prize fund in the ratio 4 : 7. Alan gets €32.
   (i) How much does Barbara get?
   (ii) Find the total prize fund.

4. The instructions for mixing a certain type of concrete call for one part cement, two parts sand, and three parts gravel. You have 80,000 cubic centimetres of sand. How much cement and gravel should you mix with this sand?

5. A prize fund is divided between Ron, Sam and Maria in the ratio 2 : 3 : 5. If Maria got €150, find the total amount of the prize and the money received by Ron and Sam.

6. A sum of money is to be distributed among A, B, C and D in the proportion of 5 : 2 : 4 : 3. Given that C gets €120 more than D,
   (i) what is B's share?
   (ii) what is the total sum of money, which was divided up?

7. (i) Express the ratio $\frac{1}{2}:\frac{1}{3}:\frac{1}{4}$ as a ratio of natural number.
   (ii) Divide 416 in the ratio $\frac{1}{2}:\frac{1}{3}:\frac{1}{4}$.

8. When Caoimhe had travelled 48 km, she had completed $\frac{3}{8}$ of her journey. Find the length of her journey.

9. The diagram shows the ingredients needed to make 12 scones.

   (i) How much dried fruit is needed to make three scones?
   (ii) How much sugar is needed to make 54 scones?
   (iii) How much milk is needed to make 40 scones?

10. The tax on a property is directly proportional to the value of the property. Tax on a property with an assessed value of €451,000 is €1,100. What is the assessed value of a property if the tax is €1,400?

11. If twelve inches correspond to 30·48 centimetres, how many centimetres are there in forty inches?

12. If eight pounds are equal to 3·64 kilograms, how many kilograms would be equal to 12·5 pounds?

13. €370 is divided into three parts such that the second part is $\frac{1}{4}$ of the third part and the ratio between the first and the third part is 3 : 5.
   (i) Write the triple ratio in simplest form.
   (ii) Find the amount of each part.

14. Biologists want to know roughly how many fish live in a certain lake, but they don't want to upset or otherwise harm the fish by draining the lake. They let down small nets in a few different spots around the lake, catching, tagging and releasing 102 fish.

   A week later, after the tagged fish have had a chance to mix thoroughly with the general population of fish, the biologists come back and let down their nets again. They catch 72 fish, of which 6 are tagged. Assuming that the catch is representative, how many fish live in the lake?

15. A farmer has enough food to feed 300 cows for 18 days. If he buys 100 more cows, how long would the same amount of food feed the total number of cows?

16. In a circuit, the resistance, R ohms, is inversely proportional to the current, I amps. When the resistance is 12 ohms, the current in the circuit is 7 amps. Find the current when the resistance in the circuit is 2·4 ohms.

17. When playing a string instrument, the frequency of the note produced is inversely proportional to the length of the string. A string of length 76 cm has a frequency of 278 Hz.
   (i) Find the frequency of a string of length 120 cm.
   (ii) Find the length of a string of frequency 1 Hz.
   (iii) Hence, find the length of a string of frequency 350 Hz.

18. It takes a water heater 10 minutes to boil 250 kg of water.
   (i) How long would it take to boil 325 kg of water?
   (ii) Find the mass of water in the heater, if it takes 17 minutes to boil.

   The time it takes to boil a fixed mass of water in the heater is inversely proportional to the power rating of the heater. If a 1400 W heater can boil 100 kg of water in 6 minutes, find:
   (iii) how long an 800 W heater will take to boil 100 kg of water
   (iv) the power of the boiler which can boil 100 kg of water in 4·5 minutes.

Section 8.2: Decimals, Fractions and Percentages

Learning Outcome:

You should be able to:

- solve everyday problems involving percentages – including VAT and percentage profit and loss

Decimals, fractions and percentages are just different ways of showing the same value.

For example: a half can be written as a decimal as 0·5, as a fraction as $\frac{1}{2}$, or as a percentage as 50%.

Three-quarters can be written as a decimal as 0·75, as a fraction as $\frac{3}{4}$, or as a percentage as 75%.

To convert from a decimal or fraction to a percentage: multiply by 100 and include the % sign.

To convert from a percentage to a decimal or fraction: divide by 100 and remove the % sign.

EXAMPLE 1

Convert the following to a percentage:

(i) 0·28 **(ii)** $\frac{2}{5}$ **(iii)** 0·875 **(iv)** $\frac{3}{8}$

Solution

Multiply all values by 100:

(i) $0{\cdot}28 \times 100 = 28\%$ | **(ii)** $\frac{2}{5} \times 100 = 40\%$ | **(iii)** $0{\cdot}875 \times 100 = 87{\cdot}5\%$ | **(iv)** $\frac{3}{8} \times 100 = 37{\cdot}5\%$

EXAMPLE 2

Convert the following to a fraction, in simplest form.

(i) 30% **(ii)** 22% **(iii)** 65% **(iv)** 62·5%

Solution

Divide all percentages by 100:

(i) $\frac{30}{100} = \frac{3}{10}$ | **(ii)** $\frac{22}{100} = \frac{11}{50}$ | **(iii)** $\frac{65}{100} = \frac{13}{20}$ | **(iv)** $\frac{62{\cdot}5}{100} = \frac{625}{1000} = \frac{5}{8}$

EXAMPLE 3

Find 15% of €400.

Solution

Convert the percentage to a fraction:

$15\% \text{ of } €400 = \frac{15}{100} \times €400 = €60$

alternatively

Convert the percentage to a decimal:

$15\% \text{ of } €400 = 0{\cdot}15 \times €400 = €60$

Percentages in real-world contexts

You can use the % button on your calculator, when doing calculations involving percentages.

Percentages are often used in the world around us. For example, valued added tax (VAT) is a tax which is added to goods or services. It is a percentage of the price of the goods or the charge for the service.

When goods are sold for a price different to what was paid for them (the cost price), the seller will either make a profit, if the selling price is greater than the cost price, or a loss, if the selling price is less than the cost price.

We can find the **percentage profit or loss** using the following formulae:

Mark-up is the profit as a percentage of the cost price.

$$\text{Mark-up} = \frac{\text{Profit}}{\text{Cost price}} \times 100$$

Margin is the profit as a percentage of the selling price.

$$\text{Margin} = \frac{\text{Profit}}{\text{Selling price}} \times 100$$

where selling price = cost price + profit

$$\text{Percentage loss} = \frac{\text{Loss}}{\text{Cost price}} \times 100$$

EXAMPLE 4

A laptop is sold for €1,028·50, which includes VAT of 21%.

(i) Find the cost of the laptop before the VAT was added.

(ii) Find the cost of the laptop if the rate of VAT was 17%.

Solution

(i) €1,028·50 includes the 21% VAT, and so the figure of €1,028·50 is made up of the selling price of 100% and the VAT of 21%.

Therefore,

€1,028·50 = 121%

€8·50 = 1% (divide by 121)

€850 = 100% (multiply by 100)

(ii) Find 17% of €850 and add it on or find 117% of €850

117% of €850

$= 1{\cdot}17 \times €850$

$= €994{\cdot}50$

EXAMPLE 5

An electrical retailer sells a consignment of televisions at a 15% margin. If the retailer bought the televisions for €425 each, find their selling price.

Solution

Selling price = cost price + profit

$$\text{Margin} = \frac{\text{Profit}}{\text{Selling price}} \times 100$$

$$15\% = \frac{\text{Profit}}{\text{Cost price} + \text{Profit}} \times 100$$

$$0{\cdot}15 = \frac{P}{425 + P} \quad \text{(divide both sides by 100)}$$

$$0{\cdot}15(425 + P) = P \quad \text{(multiply both sides by } (425 + P))$$

$$63{\cdot}75 + 0{\cdot}15P = P$$

$$63{\cdot}75 = P - 0{\cdot}15P \quad \text{(subtract } 0{\cdot}15P \text{ from both sides)}$$

$$63{\cdot}75 = 0{\cdot}85P$$

$$75 = P \quad \text{(divide both sides by } 0{\cdot}85)$$

Therefore, the profit on each television was €75.

Thus the selling price = €425 + €75 = €500

Practice Questions 8.2

1. Find 23% of €650.
2. There are 320 eggs in a box. Given that 3·5% of the eggs are broken, how many eggs were unbroken?
3. A dealer is selling a car for €18,500. She offers a 7% discount if the buyer can pay with cash. How much would the car cost after the discount?
4. James and Melanie are buying a house for €380,000. Their solicitor charges fees as follows: €350 plus $1\frac{1}{2}$% of the purchase price. The solicitor also charges VAT at the rate of 23% on his fees. Calculate the total fee, including VAT, that James and Melanie have to pay to their solicitor.
5. Express $\frac{2}{3}$ of 0·69 as a percentage of 9·20.
6. Ian earns €371 a week after a 6% rise. What was his pay before the rise?
7. The population of birds on an island decreased by 2·5% in one year to 6,630. What was the population before the decrease?
8. The price of a litre of petrol on 1st April was €1·20. The price on 1st September was €1·12. Calculate the percentage decrease over this period.
9. A music shop has a sale: all items are reduced by 20%. The sale price of a CD is €6·24. What was the original price?
10. Faye invests some money at a rate of 6% per annum. After one year there is €2,703 in the account. How much did she invest?

    Per annum means annually or yearly.
11. Shirley bought a smartphone and sold it a year later for €306, making a loss of 32%. Calculate how much Shirley paid for the smartphone originally.
12. A restaurant buys three cases of drinks for €28 each. There are 12 bottles in each case. They sell all the bottles for €3·20 each. Do they make a profit or loss? What is this as a percentage of the original amount they spent?
13. 10% of a number is 18. Find 42% of the same number.
14. A raffle to raise money for a charity is being held. The first prize is €120, the second is €90, the third is €60 and the fourth is €30. The cost of printing tickets is €45 for the first 500 tickets and €7·50 for each additional 50 tickets. The smallest number of tickets that can be printed is 500. Tickets are sold at €2·50 each.

    (i) What is the minimum possible cost of holding the raffle?

Arithmetic I

(ii) If 500 tickets are printed, how many tickets must be sold in order to avoid a loss?

(iii) If 1,000 tickets are printed and 68% of the tickets are sold, how much money will be raised for the charity?

15. Two shops are selling the same DVD. In shop A the DVD costs €11·49. In shop B the same DVD costs €13·99. Shop B have an offer of '20% off all DVDs'. Which shop should you buy the DVD from?

16. The price of a new dishwasher is €376. This price includes VAT at a rate of 17·5%. What was the price before VAT was added?

17. Dmitri buys a car for €9,760, which includes VAT at 22%. In the budget, the VAT rate was dropped to 18%. If Dmitri had waited until after the budget to buy the car, find the difference in price he would have paid.

18. A grocer bought 15 boxes of tinned fruit at €15 per box, each box containing 24 tins. He sold 320 tins at 84c each, but the remaining tins were damaged and unfit for sale. Find his percentage margin on the entire transaction.

19. Places for Biology, Physics and Chemistry in a school are in the ratio 8 : 7 : 5. There is a proposal to increase these places by 40%, 50% and 75% respectively. What will be the ratio of increased places?

20. The present reading on the electricity meter in John's house is 63,852 units. The previous reading was 62,942 units.

(i) How many units of electricity were used since the previous reading?

(ii) What is the cost of the electricity used, if electricity costs 11·14c per unit?

(iii) A standing charge of €11·25 is added and VAT is then charged on the full amount. If John's total bill is €134, find the rate of VAT, correct to one decimal place.

21. A retailer buys calculators at €7·50 and sells them for €10. Find:

(i) the percentage mark-up on the sale

(ii) the percentage margin on the sale.

22. A retailer bought a laptop for €800 and sold it for €950. Calculate:

(i) the percentage mark-up on the sale

(ii) the percentage margin on the sale.

23. A retailer bought a suite of garden furniture for €850.

(i) If they sold it for a 40% mark-up, find the sale price.

(ii) If they sold it for a 40% margin, find the sale price to the nearest cent.

24. A shopkeeper sells dresses at a 25% margin. If she bought the dresses for €21 each, find their selling price.

25. A retailer bought a consignment of tablets for €12,000. He sold half of them at a 14% mark-up and the other half at a 20% margin. Calculate the total revenue taken in and hence the total profit made.

26. A retailer bought a shipment of MP3 players for €8,500. He sold a quarter of them at a 16% mark-up and the remaining three quarters at a 36·25% margin. Calculate the total revenue taken in and hence the total profit made.

Section 8.3: Percentage Error and Tolerance

Learning Outcome:

You should be able to:

- calculate percentage error and tolerance

Relative error and percentage error

When calculations are being made, errors can occur; especially calculations which involve estimations or rounding. The error amount is the difference between the estimate and the true value.

For example, Mary guessed her shopping would come to €120. It actually came to €114·50.
The error in her estimate is €120 – €114·50 = €5·50

Error is an absolute value, so it is always positive. The notation $|x|$ means 'take the absolute (positive) value of x'.

$$\text{Error} = |\text{True value} - \text{Estimate value}|$$

$$\text{Relative error} = \frac{\text{Error}}{\text{True value}}$$

$$\text{Percentage error} = \frac{\text{Error}}{\text{True value}} \times 100\%$$

Accumulated error is the collected inaccuracy that can occur when multiple errors are added up.

Tolerance

When measurements are being made, errors can occur. Tolerance is the amount of error we will accept or allow in a particular measurement. For example, a plumber may have a tolerance of +0·5 mm or –0·5 mm when he is fitting pipes in a hot press to ensure there will be no leaks. A coffee company allow a tolerance of +1 g or –1 g of coffee when filling the containers.

The range of variation tolerated is known as the tolerance interval and this gives a lower bound and an upper bound to the tolerance.

A tolerance interval is a range of acceptable values, within a given situation.

EXAMPLE 1

A packet of biscuits states that it weighs 400 g ± 2·2%.
Find the range of possible weights you would expect one of these packets of biscuits to weigh.

Solution

2·2% of 400 g $= \frac{2\cdot2}{100} \times 400 = 8\cdot8$ g

Therefore each packet should weigh 400 g ± 8·8 g

Lower bound: 400 g – 8·8 g = 391·2 g

Upper bound: 400 g + 8·8 g = 408·8 g

Hence, the tolerance interval is 391·2 g to 408·8 g.

EXAMPLE 2

When using a calculator to add 2·6 and 4·2, a student strikes the multiplication key instead of the addition key. Calculate the percentage error in the result, correct to one decimal place.

Solution

True value = 2·6 + 4·2 = 6·8

Incorrect value = (2·6) × (4·2) = 10·92

Error = |True value – Incorrect value|

Error = |6·8 – 10·92|

Error = |–4·12|

Error = 4·12 (This is the absolute value of –4·12)

$$\text{Percentage error} = \frac{\text{Error}}{\text{True value}} \times 100\%$$

$$\text{Percentage error} = \frac{4\cdot12}{6\cdot8} \times 100\%$$

Percentage error = 60·588%

Percentage error = 60·6%

Practice Questions 8.3

1. A box of toothpicks states that it holds 250 toothpicks ±6%.
   - (i) What's the smallest number of toothpicks you would expect in the box?
   - (ii) What's the greatest number of toothpicks you would expect in the box?
2. A builder estimates that he will take 27 days to complete a project. In fact, it takes him 30 days. Find the relative error and hence the percentage error in his prediction.
3. Which of the following has the greatest percentage error:
   - (i) 42 rounded to 40
   - (ii) 62·6 rounded to 65
   - (iii) 126 rounded to 130
   - (iv) 1·12 rounded to 1
4. Let $p = 7{\cdot}2$ and let $q = 13{\cdot}65$. Find the percentage error in each of the following approximate values:
   - (i) $p = 7$
   - (ii) $p + q = 20$
   - (iii) $q = 14$
   - (iv) $q - p = 6$
5. The length of a car and a trailer is measured using a tape measure and the measurement is given to the nearest metre. Their combined length is recorded as 12 m. If the true length of the car and trailer is 12 m 36 cm, find the percentage error in the measurement. Give your answer to one decimal place.
6. Flour is sold in 1 kg bags. The quality control department will accept a tolerance of 20 grams.
   - (i) Find the tolerance interval for the bags of flour.
   - (ii) Four bags of flour are checked at random and found to weigh:
     A: 985 g B: 1,018 g C: 978 g D: 1,006 g
     Which, if any, of these bags of flour would be rejected?
7. At the top of Pat's English exam paper is written 78%, but when he adds up the marks he finds that he should have gotten 84%.
   - (i) Find the error in the teacher's marking.
   - (ii) Hence, find the percentage error.
8. Ruth is trying to work out $\sqrt{76{\cdot}2}$ but she miscopies it and calculates $\sqrt{72{\cdot}6}$ instead. Find her percentage error correct to two significant figures.
9. A regular hexagon has sides 3·2 cm long. Sylvester measures one side and says it is 3·1 cm long. Find:
   - (i) the actual perimeter of the hexagon
   - (ii) the perimeter, using Sylvester's measurement
   - (iii) the percentage error in Sylvester's calculation, correct to one decimal place.
10. Four items in a supermarket cost €3·12, €9·82, €4·27 and €16·63.
    - (i) Orla estimates the total cost of the groceries by rounding the cost of each item to the nearest euro. Calculate the percentage error in her estimate.
    - (ii) Brendan estimates the total cost of the groceries by ignoring the cent part of the cost of each item. Calculate the percentage error in his estimate.
11. Chris is measuring a room that he hopes to convert into a new kitchen. Chris measures the length of the room to be 88·5 inches and the width to be 76 inches.
    - (i) Using 2·5 cm per inch, Chris finds the dimensions of the room in metres. What dimensions does Chris get?
    - (ii) The precise conversion should be 2·54 cm per inch. What are the actual dimensions of the room, in metres?
    - (iii) Chris calculates the floor area of the room, using his values. Find the percentage error in Chris's measurement of the area.

12. Throughout the 19th century various mathematicians attempted to find the true and exact value of π. These estimates of π, to five decimal places, are listed in the table below and shown in the graph.

Year	Estimate	Year	Estimate	Year	Estimate	Year	Estimate	Year	Estimate
1826	3·20000	**1844**	3.17778	**1855**	3·15532	**1869**	3·12500	**1876**	3·14283
1832	3·06250	**1846**	3.17480	**1859**	3·14159	**1871**	3·15470	**1876**	3·13397
1833	3·20222	**1848**	3.20000	**1860**	3·12500	**1871**	3·15544	**1878**	3·20000
1833	3·16483	**1848**	3.12500	**1862**	3·14214	**1872**	3·16667	**1878**	3·13514
1835	3·20000	**1850**	3.14159	**1862**	3·20000	**1873**	3·14286	**1879**	3·14286
1836	3·12500	**1851**	3·14286	**1863**	3·14063	**1874**	3·15208	**1879**	3·14158
1837	3·23077	**1853**	3.12381	**1865**	3·16049	**1874**	3·14270	**1881**	3·14159
1841	3·12019	**1854**	3·16667	**1866**	3·24000	**1874**	3·15300	**1885**	3·14187
1842	3·14162	**1854**	3·17124	**1868**	3·14214	**1875**	3·14270	**1885**	3·14286
1843	3·04862	**1854**	3·20000	**1868**	3·14159	**1875**	3·15333	**1885**	3·15625

Given that the actual value for π is 3·141592653589793…, use the table or the graph given, to find:

(i) the lowest estimate for π

(ii) the highest estimate for π

(iii) the range of estimates for π

(iv) which year(s) gave the best estimate for π

(v) which year(s) gave the worst estimate for π

(vi) the percentage error for the worst estimate, by rounding the true value of π to five decimal places.

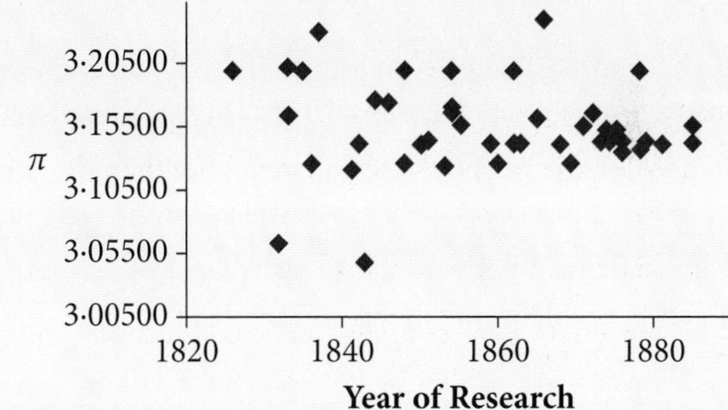

13. A faulty petrol pump actually delivers 1·04 litres of petrol for every 1 litre that the pump registers. During one day the pump registers 2,650 litres.

(i) What was the actual volume of petrol delivered?

(ii) Customers paid €1·35 for every litre of petrol registered. Find the total amount paid for the petrol.

(iii) If the pump had registered the correct volume delivered, how much more would have been paid?

14. Annika buys a cylindrical sand pit for her children to play in. She needs to know the internal volume (capacity) of the pit, so that she can order sand to fill it.
Using a measuring tape, Annika measures the height of the pit to be 80 cm and width (diameter of the top) to be 2·2 m.

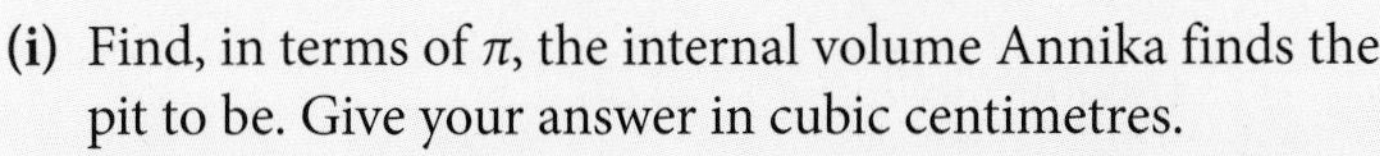

(i) Find, in terms of π, the internal volume Annika finds the pit to be. Give your answer in cubic centimetres.

Vol of cylinder = $\pi r^2 h$

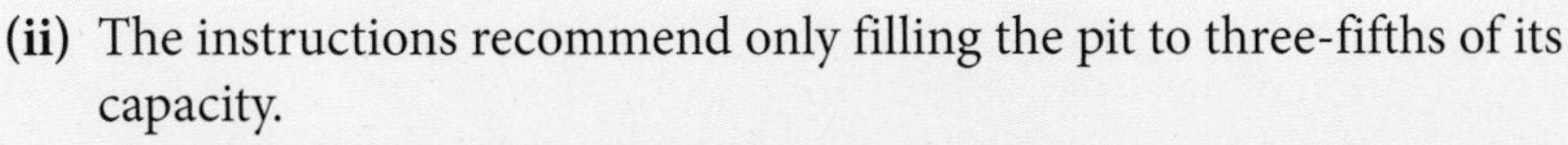

(ii) The instructions recommend only filling the pit to three-fifths of its capacity.

How much sand should Annika order, correct to the nearest cm^3?

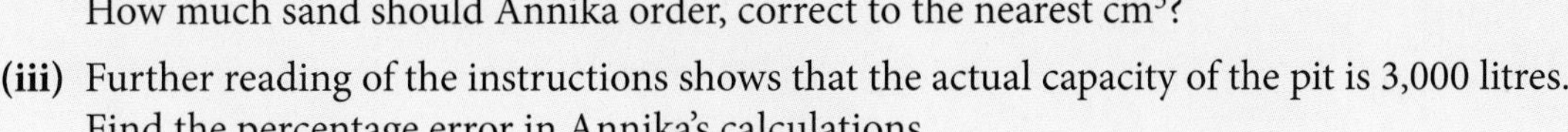

(iii) Further reading of the instructions shows that the actual capacity of the pit is 3,000 litres. Find the percentage error in Annika's calculations.

Section 8.4: Currency Transactions

Learning Outcome:

You should be able to:

- handle currency transactions

Different countries use different currencies. When a person is travelling between countries, they will need to convert, or exchange, their money from one currency to another.

> An **exchange rate** is the rate at which one currency may be converted into another.

Currency can be exchanged in banks, credit unions, post offices and bureaux de change offices. Each of these institutions will have exchange rate tables, showing two rates: one called 'we buy' and one called 'we sell', as seen in the graphic.

	We Buy	We Sell
USA	1.4280	1.2507
JAPAN	173.204	154.358
UK	0.7205	0.6520
SWITZERLAND	1.7160	1.5587
AUSTRALIA	1.7596	1.5681
CANADA	1.6028	1.4292
DENMARK	7.7532	7.1170
NORWAY	8.4145	7.7207

If you want to change a different currency into euro, the institution will **buy** the foreign currency from you at the 'we buy' rate.

If you want to change euro into a different currency, the institution will **sell** you this currency at the 'we sell' rate.

In general, the 'we buy' rate will be higher than the 'we sell' rate. Take care to use the correct rate when answering a question where you are given two rates.

To solve problems involving currency exchange, follow these steps:

Step 1: Write the given exchange rate such that the required currency is on the right side.

Step 2: Divide both sides to get 1 on the left side.

Step 3: Multiply both sides to get the value required.

EXAMPLE 1

Given an exchange rate of €1 = 7·44 Danish krone:

(i) How many Danish krone would you get for €275?

(ii) How many euro would you get for 4,836 Danish krone?

Solution

(i) *Step 1:* €1 = 7·44 Danish krone (we want krone, so put krone on the right side)

Step 2: Not required since left side is already 1

Step 3: €275 = 7·44 × 275 (multiply both sides by 275)

€275 = 2046 Danish krone

(ii) *Step 1:* 7·44 DK = €1 (we want euro, so put euro on the right side)

Step 2: $1 \text{ DK} = €\frac{1}{7{\cdot}44}$ (divide both sides by 7·44)

Step 3: $4{,}836 \text{ DK} = €\frac{1}{7{\cdot}44} \times 4836$ (multiply both sides by 4,836)

4,836 DK = €650

EXAMPLE 2

Josh is travelling to Canada on holidays. He goes to the post office and sees the following on the exchange rate board:

	We buy	We sell
Canadian dollars	1·51	1·39

(i) Josh changes €1,200 into Canadian dollars. How many dollars does he receive?

(ii) At the end of his holiday, Josh has $94 left. If he changes these dollars in the post office, with the same rates as shown above, how many euro will he receive? Give your answer to the nearest cent.

Solution

(i) Since the post office is selling dollars to Josh, we use the 'we sell' rate:

Step 1: €1 = $1·39 (we want dollars, so put dollars on the right side)

Step 2: Not required since left side is already 1

Step 3: €1,200 = 1·39 × 1,200 (multiply both sides by 1200)

€1,200 = $1,668

(ii) Since the post office is buying dollars from Josh, we use the 'we buy' rate.

Step 1: $1·51 = €1 (we want euro, so put euro on the right side)

Step 2: $\$1 = €\frac{1}{1{\cdot}51}$ (divide both sides by 1·51)

Step 3: $\$94 = €\frac{1}{1{\cdot}51} \times 94$ (multiply both sides by 94)

$94 = $62·25 to the nearest cent

EXAMPLE 3

Linda returns to Ireland, from a holiday in New Zealand, with $204·60. The bank offers Linda an exchange rate of €1 = NZD $1·65. They also charge a percentage commission on the transaction. If Linda receives €120·28, find the percentage commission charged by the bank.

Solution

Step 1: $1·65 = €1 (we want euro, so put euro on the right side)

Step 2: $\$1 = €\frac{1}{1{\cdot}65}$ (divide both sides by 1·65)

Step 3: $\$204{\cdot}60 = €\frac{1}{1{\cdot}65} \times 204{\cdot}60$ (multiply both sides by 204·60)

$204·60 = €124

Charge = €124 − €120·28 = €3·72

$$\text{Percentage charge} = \frac{\text{charge}}{\text{original sum}} \times 100$$

$$\text{Percentage charge} = \frac{3{\cdot}72}{124} \times 100 = 3\%$$

Percentage charge = 3%

Discussion Time

Financial institutions show two different rates for currency exchange.

On a given day, the exchange rates from Euro of US dollars at a particular bank are as shown in the table.

	We buy	We sell
US dollars	1·24	1·12

Work with a classmate to answer the following questions:

1. Jake has received a gift of $100 from his aunt in America. If he exchanges it in this bank, on this day, find how many euro he will receive. Give your answer to the nearest cent.
2. Susan wishes to get $100 to send to her niece in New York as a gift. If she goes to this bank, on this day, how much will she have to pay, in euro, for the $100? Give your answer to the nearest cent.
3. Comment on your answers to questions **1.** and **2.** Consider the transactions from the bank's point of view.
4. Hence, why do you think that financial institutions have two different exchange rates?

Practice Questions 8.4

1. A train ticket costs €30. How much would the ticket cost in Australian dollars, given €1 = $1·52.
2. A hotel room costs 125 Swiss francs. How much would the hotel room cost in Canadian dollars, given 1 Swiss franc = $1·32.
3. Given AUS $1 = 4·8 Chinese yuan, find:
   (i) the number of Chinese yuan, equivalent to AUS $32
   (ii) the number of Australian dollars, equivalent to 624 Chinese yuan.
4. Whilst on holiday in London, Ciara bought a handbag for £64 sterling. In Dublin, an identical handbag costs €87·99.
   The exchange rate is £1 = €1·40. In which city was the handbag cheapest and by how much? Give your answer in euro, correct to the nearest cent.
5. A part for a machine costs €450 in France and the same part costs R 1,050 in South Africa.
   If €1 = R 2·35, in which country is it cheaper, and by how much (in euro)?
6. Todd buys a pair of shoes in Switzerland. He can pay either 81 Swiss francs or 72 euro.
   The exchange rates are USD $1 = 0·98 Swiss francs and USD $1 = €0·89.
   Which currency should he choose to pay in to get the best price, and how much would he save? Give your answer in US dollars.
7. Given US$1 = 110 Japanese yen and US$1 = 66 Russian ruble. Find the exchange rate between the Japanese yen and the Russian ruble.
8. Pawel is planning a trip from Dublin to Poland to visit some friends and family. He goes to the post office to exchange some euro into Polish zloty. The exchange rate board is as follows and there is 0% commission on the transactions.

	We buy	We sell
Polish zloty	4·45	4·21

   (i) Pawel exchanges €300 into zloty. How many zloty does he receive?
   (ii) That evening Pawel realises that he has mixed up his work schedule and is not in fact able to make the trip. He returns to the post office the next day to exchange the zloty back into euro. Given that the rates have not changed, how many euro does Pawel receive? Give your answer to the nearest cent.
   (iii) Find the overall profit made by the post office on Pawel's transactions. Give your answer to the nearest cent.
9. Iman is travelling to Egypt from France. She goes to a bank and sees the following on the exchange rate board:

	We buy	We sell
Egyptian pounds	10·25	9·89

   (i) How many Egyptian pounds will Iman get for €800?
   (ii) On her return to France, Iman has £580 Egyptian pounds.
   How many euro will she receive for these pounds?

10. A bank in New York is offering foreign exchange rates, as shown in the table.

Currency	We buy	We sell
British pound	0·73	0·68
Euro	0·96	0·90
Canadian dollar	1·42	1·30
Mexican peso	19·8	18·49
Japanese yen	115	111

Use this table to answer the following questions:

(i) How many Japanese yen would you get for US$150?

(ii) How many US dollars would you get for 2,370 Mexican peso? Give your answer to the nearest cent.

(iii) How many euro would you get for US$720?

(iv) How many US dollars would you get for 23,000 Japanese yen? Give your answer to the nearest cent.

(v) Diane is given $300 Canadian dollars as a gift. She is planning a trip to Japan. How many Japanese yen can she get, at this bank, for the CD $300?

Change the first currency into US dollars and then into the second currency.

(vi) Matthew is travelling from Cancun, Mexico to London. He stops off in New York for a few hours and goes into this bank to change 32,500 Mexican peso into British pounds. How many British pounds does he get? Give your answer to the nearest penny.

11. When the exchange rate is €1 = $1·22, a person buys $2,013 from a bank. If the bank charges a commission of 4%, calculate the total cost in euro.

12. Chan wants to change some Hong Kong dollars (HKD) into US dollars (USD). The exchange rate is 1 HKD = 0·13 USD. The bank charges 2% commission. How many US dollars will Chan receive if he pays 2,448 HKD, including the commission?

13. Toby is travelling from Mexico to Canada. The bureau de change at the airport is selling Canadian dollars at a rate of 1 peso = $0·071 Canadian dollars. Toby needs $935. If he pays 13,564 pesos for the complete transaction, find the percentage commission he paid to the bureau de change. Give your answer to the nearest percent.

14. Ken returns to Australia, from a holiday in Thailand, with 2,496 Thai baht. The bank offers an exchange rate of $1 = 26 Thai baht. They also charge a percentage commission on the transaction. If Ken receives $93·60, find the percentage commission charged by the bank.

15. (i) Chris owns a music shop. He imports 100 drum sets from America for US$69,000 in total. Given the current exchange rate is €1 = US$1·15, find the price at which he must sell each drum set in Ireland, if he is to apply a 24% mark-up.

(ii) Four months later, the exchange rate is €1 = US$1·20. If Chris buys some more drums for the same price of US$690 each and sells them for the same price as in part **(i)**, what is the percentage mark-up on the sales? Give your answer to one decimal place.

Section 8.5: Distance, Speed and Time

Learning Outcome:

You should be able to:

- solve problems which involve calculating average speed, distance and time

There are three formulae which connect distance, speed and time. When using these formulae, speed means the average speed for the journey.

When doing calculations, it is important that the units are consistent. i.e. if the speed is in kilometres per hour, then the distance must be in kilometres and the time must be in hours.

$$\text{Speed} = \frac{\text{Distance}}{\text{Time}} \qquad \text{Time} = \frac{\text{Distance}}{\text{Speed}} \qquad \text{Distance} = \text{Speed} \times \text{Time}$$

To help you remember these formulae, consider the triangle on the right. By covering the quantity required, distance, speed or time, any of the three formulae above can be found by inspection.

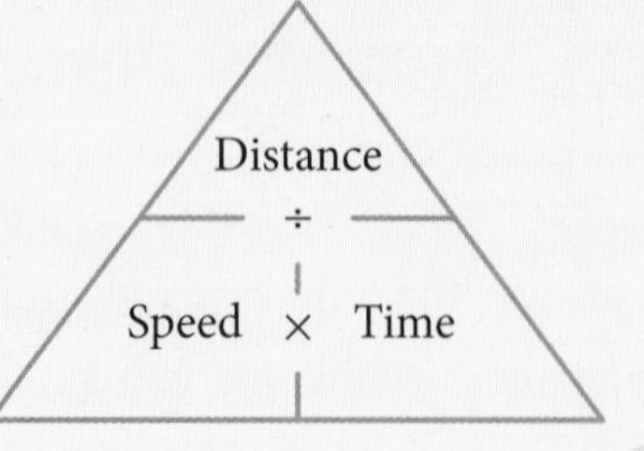

Graphical method

The formula Distance = Speed × Time is a linear equation. Comparing this formula with the equation of a line $y = mx + c$, gives the following:

Distance = Speed × Time

$$y = mx + c$$

Therefore, the slope of the graph = speed = rate of change.

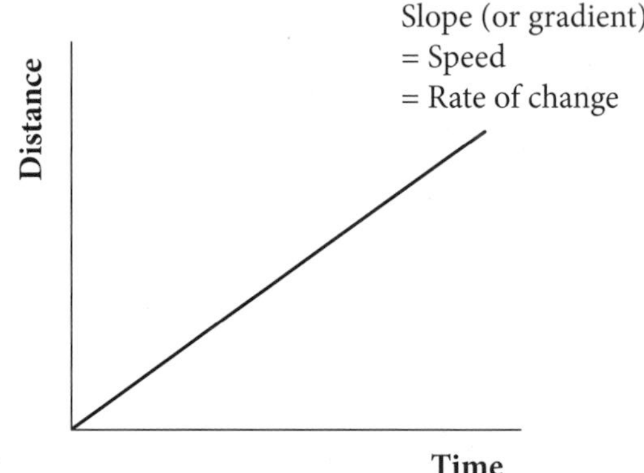

The steeper the line, the greater the speed.
A horizontal line means the speed is zero and so, the object is at rest.

Links across the syllabus

Linear functions and their graphs are covered in Chapter 3: Algebra II.

EXAMPLE 1

A train leaves Belfast at 08:40 and arrives in Dublin at 10:25.
The distance from Belfast to Dublin is 168 km.
Find the average speed of the train in kilometres per hour (km/h)

Solution

Method 1 – Mathematical method

Distance = 168 km

Time: 10:25 – 08:40 = 1 hour 45 minutes

We need the time all in hours, therefore we need to convert 45 minutes into hours.
We do this by dividing by 60:

$$\frac{45}{60} = 0{\cdot}75 \text{ hours}$$

Therefore, time = 1·75 hours.

$$\text{Speed} = \frac{\text{Distance}}{\text{Time}} = \frac{168}{1{\cdot}75} = 96 \text{ km/h}$$

To convert minutes to hours, divide by 60.
To convert hours to minutes, multiply by 60.

Method 2 – Graphical method

Draw a distance/time graph

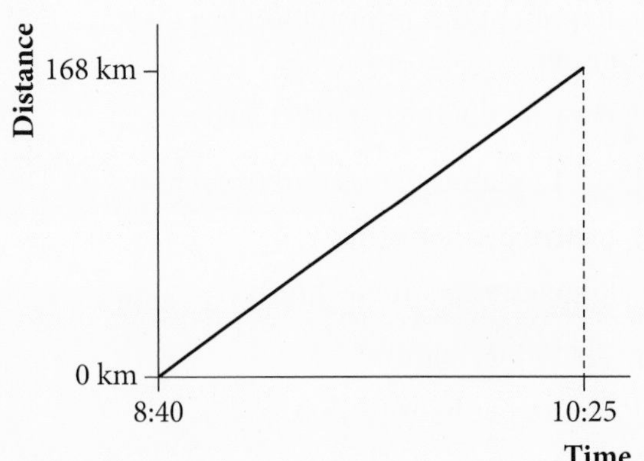

Speed = Rate of change = Slope

$$\text{Slope} = \frac{\text{Change in distance}}{\text{Change in time}}$$

$$\text{Slope} = \frac{168 - 0}{10{:}25 - 8{:}40}$$

$$\text{Slope} = \frac{168}{1 \text{ hr } 45 \text{ mins}}$$

$$\text{Slope} = \frac{168}{1{\cdot}75} = 96$$

Therefore, the speed of the car = 96 km/h

EXAMPLE 2

Two cyclists, Dominic and Josh, are 972 m apart and heading towards each other.
Dominic is cycling at a constant speed of 27 km/h and Josh is cycling at a constant speed of 6 m/s.

(i) How long does it take until they meet?

(ii) How far has each cyclist travelled, when they meet?

Solution

Before starting a question, you must make sure that all units are the same. Make conversions as required.

(i) Dominic's speed:

Convert 27 km/h into m/s:

27 km/h (× 1000)

27,000 m/h (÷ 3600)

$\frac{27000}{3600}$ m/s

$\frac{15}{2} = 7{\cdot}5$ m/s

7·5 m/s → ← 6 m/s

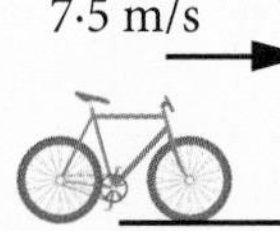

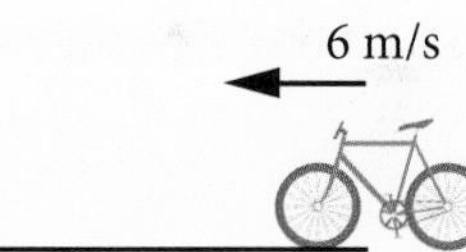

Dominic 972 m **Josh**

Use the formula to find the distance travelled by each cyclist in T seconds:

Dominic:

Distance = Speed × Time

Distance = 7·5 × T

Distance = 7·5T

Josh:

Distance = Speed × Time

Distance = 6 × T

Distance = 6T

The total distance travelled by both cyclists before they meet is 972 m.

Distance travelled by Dominic + distance travelled by Josh = 972 m

$$7{\cdot}5T + 6T = 972 \text{ m}$$

$$13{\cdot}5T = 972 \text{ m}$$

$$T = \frac{972}{13{\cdot}5} = 72 \text{ seconds}$$

Therefore, Dominic and Josh will meet after 72 seconds.

(ii) Distance travelled by Dominic = 7·5(72) = 540 m

Distance travelled by Josh = 6(72) = 432 m

Practice Questions 8.5

1. Find the speed of a bullet, which travels a distance of 30 metres in 2·5 seconds.

2. Bill jogs a distance of 300 m. His motion is shown in the graph.

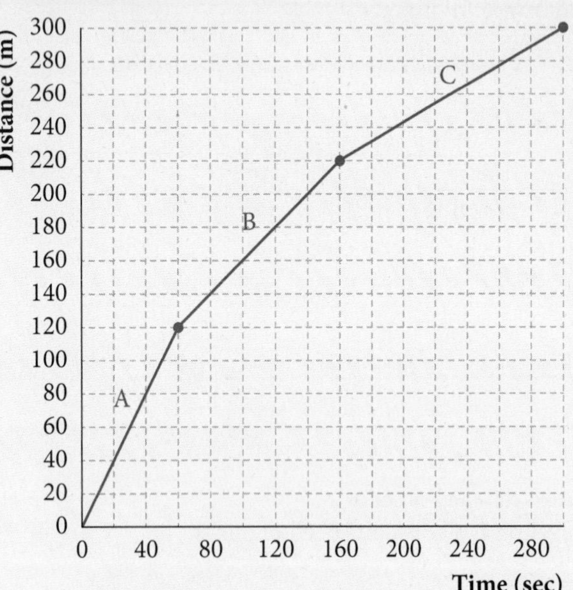

(i) Use the graph to find the speed at which Bill travelled during each of the three sections A, B and C.

(ii) Can you suggest a reason why Bill's speed would have changed during the 300 m?

(iii) Find the average speed that Bill jogged at, over the full 300 m.

$$\text{Average speed} = \frac{\text{Total distance}}{\text{Total time}}$$

3. An airplane leaves New York and travels 3,930 km to Los Angeles. The journey takes 4 hours 22 minutes.

(i) Draw a distance/time graph to represent this information.

(ii) Hence, or otherwise, find the speed of the airplane.

4. A train leaves Waterford at 10:25 and travels 165 km at an average speed of 75 km/h to Dublin. At what time does it arrive in Dublin?

You can use the DMS or the degree button on your calculator to convert time in decimal form to hours, minutes and seconds.

5. A person is travelling at 20 m/s for 4 hours and 20 minutes.

(i) Represent this information in a distance/time graph.

(ii) How far did the person travel?

6. Convert 12 metres per second (m/s) into:

(i) metres per hour (m/hr)

(ii) kilometres per hour (km/hr).

7. Convert 72 km/h into:

(i) metres per hour (m/hr)

(ii) metres per second (m/s).

8. Light travels at a speed of approximately $2{\cdot}9 \times 10^8$ m/s. How many kilometres will light travel in 12 minutes? Express your answer in the form $a \times 10^n$, where $n \in \mathbb{N}$ and $1 \leq a < 10$.

Links across the syllabus

Index notation is covered in Chapter 5: Indices and Index Notation.

9. The time taken by Edel to travel from Derry to Waterford, a distance of 378 km, is six hours. Her return journey from Waterford to Derry, by the same route, takes an extra 45 minutes.

(i) Draw two distance/time graphs to represent Edel's journeys.

(ii) By how many km/h is her average speed slower on the return journey?

10. How many miles per hour is equivalent to a speed of 22 metres per second, given that 1 mile is equal to 1·6 km?

11. A motorist drove 60 km on a motorway in 40 minutes. He drove the next 25 km on a side road in 35 minutes.

(i) Draw a distance/time graph to represent the motorist's journey.

(ii) Find his average speed in km/h.

12. A train travelled the first 120 km of a journey in 1 hour and 12 minutes. It then travels the remaining 60 km in 48 minutes.

(i) Draw a distance/time graph to represent the train's journey.

(ii) Find the average speed of the train for the whole journey.

13. George frequently travels from his home to Galway, a distance of 119 km. The journey usually takes 1 hour 45 minutes.
   (i) Find his average speed in kilometres per hour for the journey.
   (ii) On a day of very heavy rain, his average speed on a 28 km section of the journey was reduced to 35 km/h. How long did this section of the journey take on that day?
   (iii) How much longer did the total journey take on that day, if he completed the rest of the journey at his usual average speed? Give your answer correct to the nearest minute.

14. Two athletes running towards each other at 4 m/s and 6 m/s are 750 m apart. How long will it take them to meet?

15. A car travelling at 85 km/h is 550 m behind another car travelling at 60 km/h in the same direction. How long will it take the first car to catch up with the second car?

16. A train of length 110 metres approaches a tunnel of length 425 metres. If the train is travelling at 72 km/h, how long will it take it to pass **completely** through the tunnel? Give your answer correct to the nearest second.

17. The distance from town A to town B is half the distance from town B to town C. The total journey from town A to town C, through town B, is 120 km. A car travels at x km/h from town A to town B. It increases its speed by 20 km/h on the journey from town B to town C.
The total time for the journey is 1 hr 18 minutes.
   (i) Find the distance from town A to town B.
   (ii) Find the time taken for the car to travel from town A to town B, in terms of x.
   (iii) Find the value of x.

Links across the syllabus

Solving equations involving fractions is covered in Chapter 3: Algebra II.

18. Dublin's port tunnel has a length of 4·5 km and runs from Dublin port to the M50 motorway. The speed limit inside the tunnel is 80 km/h.
A traffic management system records the time a vehicle enters and exits the tunnel. It then uses these times to determine whether the vehicle has broken the speed limit.
The entry and exit times for three vehicles A, B and C are recorded in the following table. Note that each record gives the time in hours, minutes and seconds, to the nearest second.

Vehicle	Time of entry	Time of exit
A	09:12:22	09:16:05
B	11:58:42	12:01:47
C	17:08:23	17:11:42

   (i) Did any of these vehicles break the speed limit? If yes, which one(s)? Justify your answer. Where appropriate, give calculations to two decimal places.
   (ii) To allow for variations in speedometers, the roads authority allows a tolerance of 2·5% to the 80 km/h speed limit. This means that a vehicle will not receive a speeding fine unless its speed is outside of the tolerance.
   Taking the tolerance into account, will any of these vehicles get a speeding fine?
   If yes, which one(s)? Justify your answer.

Revision and Exam Style Questions – Section A

1. Enda pays a fixed monthly charge of €11 for his mobile phone. This charge includes 100 free text messages and 50 minutes free call time each month. Further call time costs 12 cent per minute and additional text messages cost 3 cent each. In one month, Enda sends 162 text messages and his call time is 2 hours 12 minutes.
   (i) Find the total cost of his fixed charge, text messages and call time.
   (ii) VAT is added to this cost at the rate of 23%. Find the amount paid, including VAT.

2. €320 is $\frac{4}{13}$ of a prize fund. Find the total prize fund.

3. Convert 164 miles into kilometres, taking 5 miles to be equal to 8 kilometres.

4. Yellow brass is made of copper and zinc, mixed in the ratio 13 : 7.
   (i) Find the mass of zinc used to make a sample of brass of mass 740 g.
   (ii) A sample of brass contains 481 g of copper. Find the mass of this sample of brass.

5. (i) Hannah changed €900 into US dollars, when the rate of exchange was €1 = $1·55. How many dollars did she get?
   (ii) After her holiday Hannah had $132 left. She changed these dollars back into euro and received €105·60. What was the exchange rate when Hannah changed her money back into euro?

6. A picture measuring 35 cm high by 50 cm wide is to be enlarged so that the width is now 90 cm. How tall will the picture be?

7. A greengrocer buys apples at €12 for a box of 96 and sells them in bags of 6 for €2. Find:
   (i) his percentage mark-up, to the nearest percent
   (ii) his percentage margin, to one decimal place.

8. Yvonne and Stuart are planning a holiday. The expenses for the trip as are follows: Flights are €732·45, car rental is €304·72, villa rental is €875 and travel insurance is €82.
   (i) Yvonne estimates the cost of the holiday by rounding each figure to the nearest €10. Find the percentage error in her estimate. Give your answer to two decimal places.
   (ii) Stuart estimates the cost of the holiday by rounding each figure to the nearest €50. Find the percentage error in his estimate. Give your answer to one decimal place.

9. A die is rolled. Find the probability of getting a 4. Give your answer in the following forms:
   (i) a fraction
   (ii) a decimal, to two decimal places
   (iii) a percentage, to the nearest whole number.

10. The cost of staying for three nights in a hotel in Wales is £285·12 sterling.
    (i) Find the cost in euro, given that €1 = £0·88.
    (ii) This cost is 8% more than the cost a year ago. Find, in euro, the cost a year ago.

11. Agatha goes for a run. Her motion is shown in the graph.

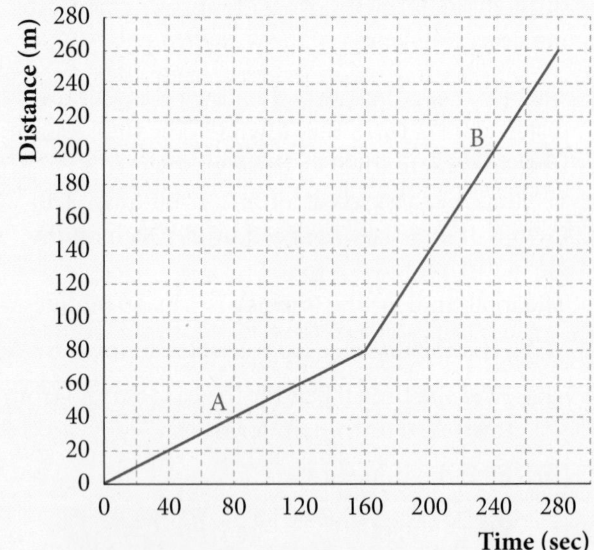

    (i) Use the graph to find Agatha's speed in sections A and B.
    (ii) Find Agatha's average speed over the whole journey. Give your answer to two decimal places.

12. The teacher writes $(a + b)^2$ on the board. Janice miscopies this as $(a - b)^2$.
If $a = 5$ and $b = 1$, find:
    (i) the value of $(a + b)^2$
    (ii) the value Janice calculates
    (iii) the percentage error in Janice's calculation. Give your answer to one decimal place.

13. A motorist travelled the first 63 km of his journey at an average speed of 84 km/h. The next part of his journey took 1 hour 15 minutes. If the total distance travelled in the two parts was 220 km, calculate his average speed for the whole journey.

Revision and Exam Style Questions – Section B

More challenging problems

1. While on holidays in London, Jemma went to the bank to change €120 into pounds sterling. The exchange rate was £1 = €1·27. By mistake, the cashier gave her the equivalent of US$120. The exchange rate for this was £1 = US$1·44. Calculate the percentage error in the transaction, correct to one decimal place.

2. Christian bought a tablet computer for €514·50, including value added tax (VAT) of 22·5%.
    (i) What was the cost of the tablet, before the VAT was added?
    (ii) How much VAT was paid?

    Eighteen months later, Christian sold the tablet online for £300. Given that the exchange rate on that day was €1 = £0·72, find:
    (iii) the selling price, in euro. Give your answer to the nearest cent.
    (iv) the percentage loss made by Christian.

3. The salaries of Paul, Quentin and Robert are in the ratio 2 : 3 : 5. If they get salary increases of 15%, 10% and 20% respectively, what will be the ratio of their new salaries?

4. A shop owner buys an item for €115. She wants to apply a mark-up of 40% of the cost price of the item. She must then add VAT at 21% to this amount, to find the price that she would need to charge the customer.
    (i) Find the selling price, correct to the nearest cent.

    The shop owner adjusts the price charged to the customer so that the euro value is a multiple of 10, whilst keeping the mark-up as close as possible to 40%.
    (ii) Using this adjusted price, calculate the actual percentage mark-up achieved, correct to the nearest percent.

5. The following table shows the comparison of metric to imperial units. Use this table to answer the following questions. Where appropriate, give your answer to two decimal places.

Metric	Imperial
1 kg	2·205 pounds
28 g	1 ounce
1 litre	1·76 pints
1 km	0·621 miles
1 cm	0·394 inches

    (i) Jane needs 3·5 kg of sugar. How many pounds of sugar does she need?
    (ii) The distance from Galway to Cork is 123 miles. Find this distance in kilometres.
    (iii) Jake is on a diet. In one week, he loses four pounds. Find his weight loss, for that week, in kilograms.
    (iv) A furniture catalogue says that a table is 90 cm long and 60 cm wide. Find the dimensions of the table in inches.
    (v) Michelle has found a recipe for a cake on an American website. Among other things, the recipe calls for eight ounces of flour, six ounces of sugar and one pint of milk. It also says the cake has to be cooked in an eight inch tin. Convert all given measurements to metric.

6 A metal alloy is produced by mixing two metals, A and B, in the ratio 4 : 7 respectively. A costs €96 per kilogram and B costs €50 per kilogram. Calculate the cost of a kilogram of the alloy, correct to the nearest cent.

7. Miguel cycled from Wicklow to Bray, a distance of 30 km.
He left Wicklow at 9:30 and arrived in Bray at 11:20, having stopped in Greystones for 20 minutes.
Greystones is 22 km from Wicklow.
Miguel's average speed between Wicklow and Greystones was x km/h. His average speed for the second part of the journey, between Greystones and Bray, was 6 km/h slower than his speed between Wicklow and Greystones.
   (i) Write an expression in x to represent the above information.
   (ii) Solve the equation to find Miguel's speed for each part of the journey.
   (iii) If Miguel hadn't stopped for a break in Greystones, and assuming that he still cycled at the same speeds as you found in part **(ii)**, find the average speed for the entire journey.

8. A retailer bought 60 toys at €18·75 each.
He sold 35 of the toys at €32·95 each and sold the remainder at a discounted price.
His total sales amounted to €1,886·20. Find:
   (i) his overall profit
   (ii) his percentage margin, to one decimal place
   (iii) the reduced selling price that he charged and hence the percentage discount he applied to the remaining toys.

9. If 40% of a number is equal to two thirds of another number, what is the ratio of the first number to the second number?

10. **(i)** A merchant buys tea for €3·29 per kg and then sells it at a profit of 60% of the cost price to a customer in England. The exchange rate is £1 (sterling) = €1·45. Calculate the selling price of the tea in £ sterling, correct to two decimal places.
   (ii) The exchange rate changes to £1 (sterling) = €1·51. The selling price, in sterling, remains the same. Calculate the merchant's mark-up in this case, correct to the nearest whole number.

11. The speedometer in a car is faulty. When the car is actually travelling at 57 km/h, the speedometer reads 60 km/h.
   (i) Calculate the percentage error, correct to one decimal place.
   (ii) If the percentage error is the same at all speeds, at what speed is the car actually travelling when the speedometer reads 110 km/h? Give your answer correct to one decimal place.

   The driver is not aware of the fault. He calculates that if he travels at an average speed of 80 km/h as shown on the speedometer, he will reach his destination in four hours.
   (iii) How long, correct to the nearest minute, will it actually take him to reach his destination?

Now that you have completed the chapter, revisit the 'Something to think about…' questions.

CHAPTER 09

Arithmetic II

Sections covered within this chapter:

KEY WORDS

- Statutory
- Compound interest
- Principal
- Depreciation
- Interest
- Appreciate

SOMETHING TO THINK ABOUT... 

At the start of the year 2015, the population of a particular town was P.

During the year 2015, the population of the town increased by 10%.

During the year 2016, the population of the town increased by 5%.

During the year 2017, the population again increased by 5%.

(i) Find the total percentage increase in the population of the town over the three years.

Hint: The answer is not 20%

(ii) If the actual increase in the population was 15,318, find the value of P, the population of the town at the start of 2016.

Section 9.1: Income Tax

Learning Outcome:

You should be able to:

- calculate income tax and know how to handle tax credits

Income tax is a tax which a person pays on money they earn. In Ireland income tax is paid at two different rates. A lower rate on money up to a certain point, called the **standard rate cut-off point**, and then a higher rate on any money earned above the standard cut-off point.

Tax credits are used to reduce the tax calculated on gross pay. People are entitled to tax credits depending on their personal circumstances, e.g. married person or civil partner tax credit, home carer tax credit, employee (PAYE) tax credit, etc. You can think of tax credits as being the amount of tax which you can keep.

To find the tax which is due (tax payable) we calculate the gross tax and then subtract the tax credits.

The following is called the **income tax equation**:

Gross tax – Tax credits = Tax payable

Gross tax is calculated as follows:

Standard rate on all income up to the standard rate cut-off point + A higher rate on all income above the standard rate cut-off point

If a person earns less than the standard rate cut-off point, then they pay tax only at the standard rate on all their income.

Deductions on income

A deduction is an amount of money taken from your income.
All deductions can be divided into two categories:

Statutory means required by law.

Statutory deductions:	**Non-statutory deductions:**
Compulsory deductions, which must be paid. These are calculated on gross income.	Voluntary deductions, which the worker can choose to pay or not pay.
Examples:	Examples:
Income tax	Pension contributions
Pay-Related Social Insurance (PRSI)	Trade union subscriptions
Universal Social Charge (USC)	Health insurance payments

Pay-Related Social Insurance (PRSI)

PRSI is made up of social insurance and health contributions. The social insurance part goes to funds to pay for social welfare and benefits in Ireland. The health contribution part goes to the Department of Health to help fund health services in Ireland. The amount of PRSI an employee pays depends on how much they earn and is calculated as a percentage of their gross earnings (earnings before tax has been deducted). The employer will also pay a contribution to the employee's PRSI payment.

Universal Social Charge (USC)

The Universal Social Charge is a tax payable on gross income. USC is charged at different rates, which increase as the level of income increases. The rates for USC can be changed annually in the budget and so, when a question involves USC, you will be told the rates to use.

EXAMPLE 1

Katie has a gross yearly income of €54,250. She has a standard rate cut-off point of €31,500 and a tax credit of €3,955. The standard rate of tax is 20% on income up to the standard rate cut-off point and 41% on all income above the standard rate cut-off point.

Calculate:

(i) Katie's gross income tax for the year

(ii) the amount of income tax Katie paid for the year

(iii) the USC paid by Katie, given that the rates of USC are as follows:

1% on the first €12,000
3% on the next €6,500
5·5% on the next €51,000
6% on all income above €69,500

(iv) Katie's net income.

Solution

(i) Gross tax = Tax of 20% on income up to standard cut-off point of €31,500

+

Tax of 41% on income above standard cut-off point

Gross tax = 20% of €31,500 + 41% of €22,750

= €31,500 × 0·2 + €22,750 × 0·41

= €6,300 + €9,327·50

= €15,627·50

Income above the standard rate cut-off point

= €54,250 − €31,500

= €22,750

(ii) Income tax equation:

Gross tax − tax credit = tax payable

€15,627·50 − €3,955 = €11,672·50

Therefore she paid €11,672·50 in tax.

(iii) Since Katie's income does not go above €69,500, we do not need to apply the 6% rate.

Therefore, the USC payable on an income of €54,250 is as follows:

1% on €12,000 = €120

3% on €6,500 = €195

5·5% on €35,750 = €1,966·25 (€54,250 − €12,000 − €6,500 = €35,750)

Total USC = €2,281·25

(iv) Net income = Gross income − Tax payable − USC

Net income = €54,250 − €11,672·50 − €2,281·25

Net income = €40,296·25

EXAMPLE 2

A man paid €11,060 in tax for the year. He had a tax credit of €4,140 and a standard rate cut-off point of €26,000. The standard rate of tax is 19% of income up to the standard rate cut-off point and 38% on all income above the standard rate cut-off point.

Calculate:

(i) the amount of income taxed at the rate of 38% **(ii)** the man's gross income for the year.

Solution

(i) Gross tax = 19% of (income below cut-off point) + 38% of (income above cut-off point)

Gross tax = 19% of €26,000 + 38% of (income above cut-off point)

Gross tax = €4,940 + 38% of (income above cut-off point)

Tax payable = Gross tax − tax credit

Tax payable = [€4,940 + 38% of (income above cut-off point)] − €4,140

Tax payable = €4,940 + 38% of (income above cut-off point) − €4,140

Tax payable = €800 + 38% of (income above cut-off point)

€11,060 = €800 + 38% of (income above cut-off point)

€10,260 = 38% of (income above cut-off point) (€800 subtracted from both sides)

€270 = 1% of (income above cut-off point) (both sides divided by 38)

€27,000 = 100% of (income above cut-off point) (both sides multiplied by 100)

Therefore, the amount of income taxed at the higher rate of 38% was €27,000.

(ii) Gross income = standard rate cut-off point + income above the standard rate cut-off point

= €26,000 + €27,000 = €53,000

Practice Questions 9.1

1. Sam has a gross yearly income of €20,700. He has a standard rate cut-off point of €22,500 and a tax credit of €2,200. The standard rate of tax is 18%. Calculate:
   (i) the amount of gross tax for the year
   (ii) the amount of tax paid for the year.

2. Tanya has a gross yearly income of €41,500. She has a standard rate cut-off point of €22,750 and a tax credit of €3,950. The standard rate of tax is 20% of income up to the standard rate cut-off point and 41% on all income above the standard rate cut-off point. Calculate:
   (i) the amount of gross tax for the year
   (ii) the amount of tax paid for the year.

3. John has a gross income per fortnight of €1,750. The standard rate of income tax is 20% and the higher rate is 42%. He has tax credits of €105 per fortnight and his standard rate cut-off point is €1,295 per fortnight. After tax is paid, what is John's net income per fortnight?

4. Asal pays income tax, a Universal Social Charge (USC) and Pay-Related Social Insurance (PRSI) on her gross wages. Her gross weekly wages are €625.
   (i) Asal pays income tax at a rate of 21%. She has weekly tax credits of €72. How much income tax does she pay?
   (ii) Asal pays USC at the rate of 1·6% on the first €195, 3% on the next €112 and 5% on the balance. Calculate the amount of USC Asal pays.
   (iii) Asal also pays PRSI. Her total weekly deductions of income tax, USC and PRSI amount to €136·63 How much PRSI does Asal pay?
   (iv) Hence, find the rate of PRSI that Asal pays on her gross earnings.

5. Howard has a gross weekly income of €925. He has a standard rate cut-off point of €588 and a tax credit of €75. The standard rate of tax is 17% of income up to the standard rate cut-off point and 39% on all income above the standard rate cut-off point.
   (i) Calculate the amount of gross tax for the year.
   (ii) Howard pays a Universal Social Charge (USC) of 1% on the first €300, then 3% on the next €140 and 6% on all remaining income. Calculate how much USC he owes.
   (iii) Calculate Howard's net salary after tax and USC have been deducted.

6. Valerio has a gross yearly income of €73,150. He has a standard rate cut-off point of €32,500 and a tax credit of €4,850. The standard rate of tax is 21% of income up to the standard rate cut-off point and 42% on all income above the standard rate cut-off point.
   (i) Calculate the amount of gross tax for the year.
   (ii) Valerio pays Universal Social Charge (USC) of 1% on the first €12,300, then 3% on the next €8,400 and 6% on all remaining income. Calculate how much USC he owes.
   (iii) Calculate Valerio's net salary after tax and USC have been deducted.

7. Gustav earned €51,000 last year. The standard rate cut-off point was €29,200. The standard rate of income tax was 18% and the higher rate was 43%. Gustav has tax credits of €4,300.
   (i) Calculate the tax paid by Gustav on his income.

   Gustav also has to pay a 2% income levy on his gross income, USC of 2·5% on the first €10,000 of his salary and 4% on the next €5,500, 6% on the next €8,000 and 8% on all remaining income, a weekly PRSI contribution of €35, a monthly health insurance payment of €65, a monthly pension contribution of €340 and a weekly trade union subscription of €7·50.

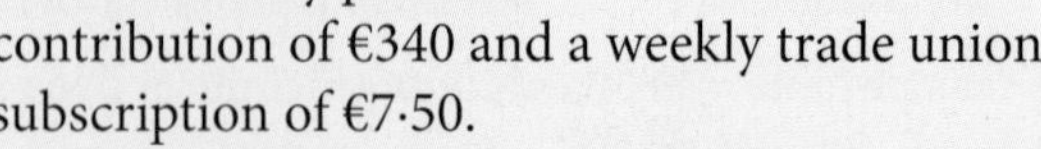

   (ii) Calculate Gustav's **monthly** net income after all deductions have been made.

There are 12 months in one year.
There are 52 weeks in one year.

Arithmetic II

8. The table shows the hours Tony worked over five days.

Day	Wednesday	Thursday	Friday	Saturday	Sunday
Hours worked	6	7	7·5	6	h

Tony's basic rate of pay is €13·50 per hour.

He is paid one and a half times the basic rate for work on Saturday and Sunday.

(i) Calculate Tony's total pay for Wednesday, Thursday, Friday and Saturday.

(ii) Tony was paid a total of €540 for the five days' work. Find h, the number of hours Tony worked on Sunday.

(iii) Tony pays income tax at the rate of 20%. He has weekly tax credits of €63. How much income tax does he pay?

(iv) Tony pays the USC at the rate of 2% on the first €193, 4% on the next €115 and 7% on the balance. Calculate the amount of USC Tony pays.

(v) Tony also pays PRSI. His total weekly deductions amount to €76·92. How much PRSI does Tony pay?

9. Siofra has a gross income of €72,300. Her standard rate cut-off point is €29,700. The standard rate of tax is 19% and the higher rate is 41%. She has a tax credit of €3,750. Siofra pays USC at the following rates: 1% on the first €12,000, 3% on the next €6,500, 5% on the next €46,500 and 8% on any income above €65,000. Siofra is in PRSI class A1, which means that she does not pay PRSI on the first €127 earned per week, but she pays it at a rate of 4% on all income above that amount (assume a 52-week year). Siofra pays trade union subscriptions of €17 every two weeks, health insurance of €99 per month and a pension contribution of €375 per month.

(i) Calculate the total amount of income tax Siofra must pay for the year.

(ii) Calculate her USC payment for the year.

(iii) Calculate her PRSI contribution per week, to the nearest cent.

(iv) What is Siofra's weekly net income, after all deductions?

10. Josiah has a gross yearly income of €26,500. He has a standard rate cut-off point of €28,000 and a tax credit of €1,550. If he pays tax of €4,015, calculate the standard rate of tax.

11. Lily has a gross income of €50,000. Her total income tax payable amounts to €10,460. The standard rate cut-off point is €32,000. The standard rate of tax is 20% and the higher rate is 42%. What are Lily's tax credits for the year?

12. Fiona has a gross income of €62,000, tax credits of €3,210 and a standard rate cut-off point of €31,500. Fiona pays €15,280 tax for the year.

(i) Given the standard rate of tax is 19%, find the higher rate of tax.

(ii) The following year, Fiona gets a pay increase. She now pays €16,551 in tax. If all rates, tax credits and standard cut-off point stay the same, find the amount that Fiona's salary increased by.

(iii) Find the percentage increase in Fiona's salary going from the first year to the second year.

Section 9.2: Compound Interest

Learning Outcome:

You should be able to:

- calculate compound interest on investments and loans

Principal is a sum of money borrowed or invested.

Interest is the sum of money that you pay for borrowing or that is paid to you for investing.

Compound interest is interest which is calculated not only on the initial principal, but also the accumulated interest of previous years.

When a sum of money earns interest, this interest is then added to the principal to form a bigger principal. The following year, this new principal (original principal plus interest) earns more interest, and so on. This is called compound interest.

Rates of interest

There are two main rates of interest, which we will be dealing with. These are:

- **Annual Equivalent Rate (AER)**, which is the rate of interest earned on an **investment**, in a year.
- **Annual Percentage Rate (APR)**, which is the rate of interest charged on a **loan**, in a year.

To solve questions involving compound interest, do the following:

Method 1:

Take one year at a time. Calculate the interest for the first year and add this to the principal to form the new principal for the second year. Calculate the interest earned during the second year and add it on to form the principal for the third year, and so on.

This method will always work; however, it may not be the most practical method to use if the question involves a large number of years.

Multiplying the principal by $(1 + i)$ will give the new principal for the following year, where i is the annual interest rate as a decimal.

Method 2:

Using the compound interest formula $F = P(1 + i)^t$

Where,

P = the principal: the sum of money borrowed or invested at the beginning of the period.
t = time: the number of **years** for which the sum of money is borrowed or invested.
i = the interest rate: the percentage **rate per year** at which interest is charged, expressed as a decimal (for example, $i = 0{\cdot}08$ represents a rate of 8%)
F = the final amount: the sum of money, including interest, at the end of the period.

The formula for compound interest appears on page 30 of the booklet of *formulae and tables* as shown:

$$F = P(1+i)^t$$

Compound interest
F = final value, P = principal

If the interest rate is an annual rate, then time must be in years.

You cannot use the formula if either of the following is the case:

1) The interest rate, i, changes during the period.
2) Money is added or subtracted during the period.

EXAMPLE 1

€20,000 was invested for three years at compound interest. The rate for the first year was 3%, the rate for the second year was 4·2%, and the rate for the third year was 4·8%.

Calculate the amount after three years, to the nearest cent.

Solution

The annual rate is changing, therefore we must use Method 1:

Year 1: $P = 20{,}000,\ i = 0{\cdot}03,\ t = 1$

$F = P(1 + i)$

$F = 20{,}000(1 + 0{\cdot}03)$

$F = 20{,}000(1{\cdot}03)$

$F = 20{,}600$

Year 2: $P = 20{,}600,\ i = 0{\cdot}042,\ t = 1$

$F = 20{,}600(1 + 0{\cdot}042)$

$F = 20{,}600(1{\cdot}042)$

$F = 21{,}465{\cdot}20$

Year 3: $P = 21{,}465{\cdot}20,\ i = 0{\cdot}048,\ t = 1$

$F = 21{,}465{\cdot}20(1 + 0{\cdot}048)$

$F = 21{,}465{\cdot}20(1{\cdot}048)$

$F = 22{,}495{\cdot}5296$

Therefore the amount at the end of the third year is €22,495·53

> The final amount at the end of each year is the principal amount for the next year.

EXAMPLE 2

€9,000 is invested in a savings account where the interest is compounded annually at a rate of 2·3%.

(i) Calculate the future value of this investment in four and a half years.

(ii) Calculate the total interest earned in the four and a half years.

Solution

(i) Since the rate is not changing, we can use the formula, where $P = 9{,}000$, $i = 0{\cdot}023$, $t = 4{\cdot}5$

$F = P(1 + i)^t$

$F = 9{,}000(1 + 0{\cdot}023)^{4{\cdot}5}$

$F = 9{,}000(1{\cdot}023)^{4{\cdot}5}$

$F = 9{,}969{\cdot}7177$

> Use the x^y or $x^{\square}$ button on your calculator to evaluate $(1{\cdot}023)^{4{\cdot}5}$

Therefore, €9,000 amounts to €9,969·72 at the end of the four and a half years.

(ii) Interest earned = Final amount − Initial amount

Interest earned = €9,969·72 − €9,000

Interest earned = €969·72

EXAMPLE 3

€P was invested at a rate of 3·4% per annum. If the future value of the investment, in seven years' time, was €20,219, calculate the value of P, correct to the nearest euro.

Solution

$F = P(1 + i)^t$

$20{,}219 = P(1 + 0{\cdot}034)^7$ $F = €20{,}219,\ i = 0{\cdot}034,\ t = 7$

$20{,}219 = P(1{\cdot}034)^7$

$\dfrac{20{,}219}{(1{\cdot}034)^7} = P$ (divide both sides by $(1{\cdot}034)^7$)

$15{,}999{\cdot}849625 = P$

$€16{,}000 = P$ to the nearest euro

EXAMPLE 4

An investment bond gives 18% interest at the end of nine years. Calculate the AER for this bond. Give your answer to two decimal places.

Solution

If €1 is invested, then at the end of the nine years, it will be worth €1 + (18% of €1) = €1·18

If the interest had been compounded annually:

$F = P(1 + i)^t$

$1{\cdot}18 = 1(1 + i)^9$ $P = €1, F = €1{\cdot}18, t = 9, i = ?$

$\sqrt[9]{1{\cdot}18} = 1 + i$ (get 9th root of both sides)

$1{\cdot}01856 = 1 + i$

$0{\cdot}01856 = i$ (subtract 1 from both sides, to get i on its own)

$1{\cdot}856\% = \text{AER}$ (Multiply by 100 to get into percentage form)

$1{\cdot}86\% = \text{AER}$

Use the $\boxed{\sqrt[x]{\ }}$ or $\boxed{\sqrt{x}}$ button on your calculator to evaluate $\sqrt[9]{1{\cdot}18}$

Discussion Time

Work with a classmate to discuss the following problem:

A married couple are looking to invest a sum of €10,000 for a year. They find two savings accounts:

Savings account type *A*, which advertises that it applies interest at a rate of 1% at the end of every month.

Savings account type *B*, which advertises that it applies interest at a rate of 12% at the end of every year.

The couple think that these two accounts will give the same return. Do you agree?

Decide which account, if either, would deliver a better return on the invested €10,000.

Practice Questions 9.2

1. Calculate the compound interest earned on each of the following. Give all answers correct to the nearest cent.
   - **(i)** €800 invested for three years at 4% per annum.
   - **(ii)** €1,200 invested for five years at 3% per annum.
   - **(iii)** €9,000 invested for four years at 2·5% per annum.
   - **(iv)** €5,250 invested for seven years at 3·8% per annum.
2. A sum of €6,000 is invested with an annual equivalent rate (AER) of 4·6%. Find the value of the investment when it matures in eight years' time. Give your answer to the nearest cent.
3. Which will earn more interest: €5,000 invested for two years at 3% per annum or €5,000 invested for three years at 2% per annum? Give your answer to the nearest cent.
4. €8,500 is invested in a savings account where the interest is compounded annually with a rate of 2·8%. Calculate the future value of this investment in three and a half years. Give your answer to the nearest cent.
5. €4,600 is borrowed at a rate of 7% per annum. Find the value of the loan after 36 months. Give your answer to the nearest cent.

   Convert the months into years by dividing by 12.
6. €15,000 is invested in a savings account where the interest is compounded annually with an AER of 3·5%. Calculate the future value of this investment in 51 months. Give your answer to the nearest cent.

7. €11,500 was invested for three years at compound interest. The rate for the first year was 1·5%, the rate for the second year was 2·2%, and the rate for the third year was 3%.
Calculate the final amount after three years, to the nearest cent.

8. €22,000 was invested for four years at compound interest. The rate for the first year was 2·4%, the rate for the second year was 3%, and the rate for the third and fourth years was 4·6%.
Calculate the final amount after four years, to the nearest cent.

9. A woman borrowed €34,000 at 8% per annum compound interest. She agreed to repay €8,000 at the end of the first year, €10,000 at the end of the second year and to clear the debt at the end of the third year. How much must be paid to clear the debt? Give your answer to the nearest cent.

10. A man borrowed €15,000. He agreed to repay €2,500 after one year, €3,500 after two years and the balance at the end of the third year. If the interest was charged at 7·3% in the first year, 5% in the second year and 4·5% in the third year, how much was paid to clear the debt? Give your answer to the nearest cent.

11. What sum of money, to the nearest euro, will have a future value of €88,578·05 in six years at 10% per annum compound interest?

12. What sum of money, to the nearest euro, will have a future value of €4,116·69 in four years at 6·5% per annum compound interest?

13. What sum of money, to the nearest euro, will have a future value of €2,036·53 in five years at 2·5% AER?

14. How much should I invest, to the nearest euro, at 5% compound interest per annum, to have €8,000 in my account in five years' time?

15. €15,500 was invested at a rate of r% per annum. If the future value of the investment in five years' time was €21,236·34, calculate the value of r, correct to one decimal place.

16. €8,000 was invested at a rate of r% per annum. If the future value of the investment in three years' time was €8,741·82, calculate the value of r.

17. An investment bond gives 25% interest at the end of 10 years. Calculate the AER for this bond. Give your answer to two decimal places.

18. A savings account gives 21% interest at the end of eight years. Calculate the AER for this savings account. Give your answer to two decimal places.

19. Annette invests €P at r% compound interest per annum. After a year it amounts to €2,438. After two more years it amounts to €2,739·33. Find the values of r and P.

20. €75,000 was invested for three years at compound interest. The rate for the first year was 3%. The rate for the second year was $2\frac{1}{2}$%. At the end of the second year €10,681·25 was withdrawn.
    (i) Find the principal for the third year.
    (ii) The rate for the third year was r%. The total investment at the end of the third year was €70,897·50. Calculate the value of r correct to one decimal place.

21. A person invested €30,000 for three years at 5% AER.
    (i) Calculate the amount after two years.
    (ii) After two years a sum of money was withdrawn. The money which remained amounted to €26,250 at the end of the third year. Calculate the amount of money withdrawn after two years.

22. €45,000 was invested for three years at compound interest. The AER for the first year was 6%, the AER for the second year was 4% and the AER for the third year was 3%. At the end of the first year €7,700 was withdrawn. At the end of the second year €W was withdrawn. At the end of the third year the investment was worth €37,080. Find the value of W.

23. €7,500 was invested for two years at r% per annum compound interest.
    (i) The amount of the investment at the end of the first year was €7,860. Find the value of r.
    (ii) At the start of the second year €W was withdrawn from the account. The interest earned during the second year was €252. Find the value of W, to the nearest cent.

Section 9.3: Depreciation and other Situations of Growth and Decline

Learning Outcome:

You should be able to:
- solve problems involving depreciation and other situations of growth and decline

Over time material goods (e.g. machinery, vehicles, etc.) lose value as a result of wear and tear and age. This loss of value is known as **depreciation**.

Reducing balance method

Using the reducing balance method, the cost of the asset is depreciated at a constant rate each year. This method is based on the principle that an asset is more useful in its initial years than in its later years. The depreciated value of an asset can be found by calculating the value at the end of each year, known as the net book value, or by using the depreciation formula.

Depreciation formula

$$F = P(1 - i)^t$$

Where, F = final value (Net book value, NBV)

P = original value at the start of the period

i = rate, in decimal form

t = number of years

The depreciation formula is similar to the compound interest formula, except that because the value is decreasing, rather than increasing, there is a negative sign in front of i.

The formula for depreciation appears on page 30 of the booklet of *formulae and tables* as shown:

$F = P(1-i)^t$ **Depreciation – reducing balance method** F = later value, P = initial value

The methods used for calculating compound interest apply here also. That is, take one year at a time or use the formula.

EXAMPLE 1

A company buys a machine for €12,000. They estimate that it will depreciate at a rate of 9% per annum. Find the value of the machine, to the nearest euro, after four years by:

(i) calculating the net book value at the end of each year.

(ii) using the depreciation formula.

Solution

(i)

Year	Value at the start of the year	Depreciation	Value at the end of the year
1	12,000	12,000 × 9% = 1,080	12,000 − 1,080 = 10,920
2	10,920	10,920 × 9% = 982·80	10,920 − 982·80 = 9,937·20
3	9,937·20	9,937·20 × 9% = 894·348	9,937·20 − 894·348 = 9,042·852
4	9,042·852	9,042·852 × 9% = 813·85668	9,042·852 − 813·85668 = 8,228·99532

So the value at the end of the fourth year is: 8,228·995 = €8,229

(ii) $P = 12{,}000$, Rate = 9%, so $i = \frac{9}{100} = 0{\cdot}09$, $t = 4$ years.

$F = P(1 - i)^t$

$F = 12{,}000(1 - 0{\cdot}09)^4$

$F = 12{,}000(0{\cdot}91)^4$

$F = 8{,}228{\cdot}995$

Thus, after four years, the machine is worth €8,229.

Other situations of growth or decline

The compound formula does not only apply to financial situations; it can be used in any situation where the value is increasing or decreasing at a steady rate (e.g. population growth, bacteria growth, radioactive decay).

EXAMPLE 2

There are 160 bacteria at 0 hours, and the number of bacteria increase at a rate of 8% per hour.

(i) How many bacteria will there be after 12 hours, to the nearest whole number?

(ii) If the growth continues at this rate, how many bacteria will be present in one week? Give your answer to the nearest whole number.

> In this question, t is in hours, not years.

Solution

(i) $F = P(1 + i)^t$

$P = 160, \quad i = 8\% = 0{\cdot}08, \quad t = 12$

$F = 160(1 + 0{\cdot}08)^{12}$

$F = 160(1{\cdot}08)^{12}$

$F = 402{\cdot}9072$

Therefore, after 12 hours, there are 403 bacteria, to the nearest whole number.

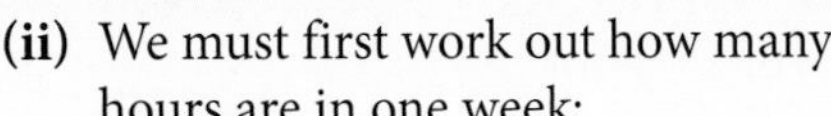

(ii) We must first work out how many hours are in one week:

1 week = 7 days × 24 hours = 168 hours

$F = P(1 + i)^t$

$P = 160, \quad i = 8\% = 0{\cdot}08, \quad t = 168$

$F = 160(1 + 0{\cdot}08)^{168}$

$F = 160(1{\cdot}08)^{168}$

$F = 65{,}964{,}595{\cdot}62$

Therefore, after one week, there are 65,964,596 bacteria, to the nearest whole number.

Practice Questions 9.3

1. A car which was bought for €49,000 depreciates at 8% per annum.
   (i) Use a table to calculate the value of the car at the end of each year, over a three-year period.
   (ii) Use the formula for depreciation to check your answer for the net book value (NBV) of the car at the end of the third year.

2. A car depreciates at 15% per annum. If it was bought for €30,000, find its value after six full years.

3. A painting was purchased for €33,000. If it appreciates in value by 4·5% per annum, what would be its value in five years' time, correct to the nearest euro?

> **Appreciate** means to increase in value.

4. A machine costs €120,000 when new. In the first year it depreciates by 15%. In the second year it depreciates by 8% of its value at the end of the first year. In the third year it depreciates by 5% of its value at the end of the second year.

New Price	€120,000
Value after 1 year	
Value after 2 years	
Value after 3 years	

   (i) Copy and complete the table, to calculate the machine's value after three years.
   (ii) Calculate its total depreciation after three years.

5. Robert bought a new car for €28,000. If the rate of depreciation on the car is 8·5% the first year and then 4·2% for every year after that, what would be the value of the car after five years?

6. A company buys a photocopier for €4,400 and four new computers at €1,150 each. After four years the company runs into financial difficulty and so must sell off its assets. The photocopier depreciated at a rate of 4% per annum and the computers depreciated at a rate of 9% the first year and then 7·5% per annum after that.
   - **(i)** Calculate how much money the company can sell these items for after the four years.
   - **(ii)** What was the total percentage loss that the company experienced on these goods? Give your answer to one decimal place.

7. A house was bought at the start of 1978 for the equivalent of €4,250. If the average annual rate of appreciation of the house was 12·5%, find the value of the house at the start of 2018, correct to the nearest euro.

8. Sarah's car depreciated at the rate of 16% per annum. If she sold it for €4,500, how much did she pay for the car when she bought it seven years ago? Give your answer to the nearest euro.

9. A diamond ring was bought at the start of 1905 for the equivalent of €120. At the start of 2010 the ring is worth €4,445.

   - **(i)** How old is the ring?
   - **(ii)** Find the annual rate of appreciation of the ring, to the nearest percent. Give your answer to one decimal place.

10. A tractor is bought for €27,500. It depreciates at an annual rate of r%. If its net book value after four years is €19,700, calculate the rate of depreciation.

11. A car was bought for €24,000 in January 2015 and depreciates at a rate of r% per annum. If the NBV of the car at the end of 2018 was €18,738, calculate the value of r.

12. A car has lost 55% of its original value by the end of six years. Calculate the average annual rate of depreciation for this car. Give your answer to two decimal places.

13. An asset is worth 65% of its original value at the end of four years. Calculate the average annual rate of depreciation for this asset. Give your answer to two decimal places.

14. The present population of a country is 13·7 million people. If this is expected to increase by 1·6% per annum over the next decade, find the population of the country in 10 years' time. Give your answer in millions, correct to one decimal place.

15. A farmer has 9,000 cows in his herd. During a three-month drought, 4% of the herd dies each month. How many cows remain in the herd at the end of the drought period?

16. After four years, the NBV of an asset is €93,690. If the original cost was €120,000, find the rate of depreciation to the nearest percent.

17. A fleet of trucks were purchased at the start of January 2006 for €1·2 million. The NBV of the fleet was €425,000 at the end of December 2016.
   - **(i)** Find the annual rate of depreciation.
   - **(ii)** Hence, find the value of the fleet at the end of 2010, correct to the nearest €10,000.

18. A town had a population of 45,000 people. 53% of the population were men and the remainder were women. During the black plague, 12% of the men and 8% of the women died each month.
   - **(i)** After the first year of the plague, what was the population of the town?
   - **(ii)** At the end of the first year of the plague, what percentage of the population was male? Give your answer to the nearest whole number.

Revision and Exam Style Questions – Section A

1. A sum of €12,000 is invested in a ten-year government bond with an annual equivalent rate (AER) of 1·5%. Find the value of the investment when it matures in ten years.

2. **(i)** A deposit account will earn 3% interest in the first year and 6% interest in the second year. The interest is added to the account at the end of each year. If €12,000 is invested in this account, how much will it amount to at the end of two years?

   (ii) Show that, to the nearest euro, the same amount of interest is earned by investing the money for two years in an account that pays compound interest at 4·49% AER.

3. Jose earns €27,500 per annum and has a tax credit of €1,120. The standard rate cut-off point is €22,000. The standard rate of tax was 27% and the higher rate was 38%.

   (i) Calculate Jose's annual net income.

   (ii) By how much would Jose's net income be increased if the 27% rate of tax is reduced to 25%?

4. A savings account gives 4% at the end of the first year, 5% at the end of the second year and 6·5% at the end of the third year. Find:

   (i) the final value of €2,000, invested for three full years

   (ii) the equivalent AER for this savings account. Give your answer to one decimal place.

5. **(i)** A house valued at €750,000 in 2006 has depreciated by a **total** of 20% in 6 years. Find the value of the house in 2012.

   (ii) The contents of the house (furniture, electrical goods, valuables) were valued at €30,000 in 2006. The contents depreciated by 6% every year, by the reducing balance method.

   Find the value of the contents in 2012. Give your answer to the nearest euro.

   (iii) House insurance is charged at a rate of 0·1% of the value of the house and its contents. Find the difference in cost of the insurance policy, to the nearest euro, for house insurance in 2006 and 2012.

6. Frank is married and earned €46,800 last year. The standard rate cut-off point for a married person was €35,300. The standard rate of income tax was 21% and the higher rate was 42%. Frank has tax credits of €3,600.

   (i) Calculate the tax paid by Frank on his income.

   Frank also has to pay a 3% income levy on his gross income, USC of 2% on the first €12,500 of his salary, 4% on the next €6,200 and 6% on all remaining income. Frank also pays a monthly health insurance payment of €90, a weekly pension contribution of €85 and a weekly trade union subscription of €8.

   (ii) Calculate Frank's annual net income after all deductions have been made.

7. Pat has a credit card with a €1,500 limit. Interest is charged on the balance due at the end of each month, at a rate of 1·8% per month.

   (i) At the **start** of April, Pat owes €1,200 on the card. Given that he makes no payments on what is owed, and does not use the card further, find the total amount he owes at the start of November.

   (ii) During November, Pat purchases an item online, costing \$170. Given the exchange rate is €1 = \$1·12, find, to the nearest euro, the sum which will be charged to Pat's credit card.

   (iii) The credit card company reject this payment and Pat's order is cancelled.
   Give a reason why this might be the case.
   What advice would you give Pat?

   (iv) Find the annual percentage rate (APR) charged on Pat's credit card, to two decimal places.

8. €8,500 was invested for two years at compound interest.

   (i) The rate of interest for the first year was 4%. Find the amount of the investment at the end of the first year.

   (ii) The amount of the investment at the end of the second year was €9,237·80. Find the rate of interest for the second year, to one decimal place.

9. On a Wednesday night in winter, 12 cm of snow fell in a town. On Thursday morning, from 8 am onwards, the snow started to melt at a steady rate of 8% per hour.
   (i) Find how many centimetres of snow remained at 3 pm. Give your answer to two decimal places.
   (ii) Show that by 10 pm, over half of the snow had melted.
   (iii) From 10 pm Thursday night until 8 am on Friday morning, the melting rate reduced to 5% per hour. Find the depth of the snow at 8 am the following morning. Give your answer to one decimal place.
   (iv) If the rate of snow melting continues in this way (8% per hour from 8 am to 10 pm and 5% per hour from 10 pm to 8 am), use **trial and improvement** to estimate the day and time when there will be 0·5 cm of snow remaining.

Revision and Exam Style Questions – Section B

More challenging problems

1. A savings account will earn 2% interest in the first year, 3·5% interest in the second year and 5% in the third year. The interest is added to the account at the end of each year.
   (i) If a person invested €8,000 in this account, how much will they have in the account at the end of the three years? Give your answer to the nearest cent.
   (ii) Show that, to the nearest euro, the same amount of interest is earned by investing the money for three years in an account that pays compound interest at 3·49% AER.

2. The standard rate of income tax is 20% and the higher rate is 41%.
   The standard rate cut-off point is €36,500.
   Alex has a gross income of €47,500 and total tax credits of €1,830.
   (i) Calculate Alex's net income.
   (ii) The following year Alex's gross income increases.
   The tax rates, cut-off point and tax credits remain unchanged.
   His net tax now amounts to €15,105.
   What is his new gross income?

3. A government bond gives 25% interest after 12 years. Find the AER for this bond, correct to two decimal places.

4. What sum of money invested at 6% per annum compound interest will amount to €4,000 in five years? Give your answer correct to the nearest euro.

5. (i) In city A, house prices have increased by 3% each year for the last three years. If a house cost €180,000 three years ago, calculate, to the nearest euro, its value today.
   (ii) In city B, a house worth €100,000 three years ago is now valued at €119,102. Calculate the yearly percentage increase in the value of this house.

6. David bought a car for €10,000. The car depreciations at a constant annual rate. If after nine and a half years the value of the car is halved, find the annual rate of depreciation, correct to the nearest percent.

7. At the start of each academic year, Jane took out a student loan of €P at an APR of 8% per annum.

   (i) At the start of year 1, Jane borrows €P for 3 years at 8% per annum compound interest.
   Find, in terms of P, the value of this loan at the end of the three years.
   (ii) At the start of year 2, Jane borrows €P for 2 years at 8% per annum compound interest. Find, in terms of P, the value of this loan at the end of the two years.
   (iii) At the start of year 3, Jane borrow €P for 1 year at 8% per annum compound interest. Find, in terms of P, the value of this loan at the end of the year.
   (iv) At the end of the three years, Jane owes a total of €8,765·28. Calculate P.

8. A scientist is running an experiment. Under certain conditions, the number of bacteria in a particular culture increase by 40% every hour. If there are 500 bacteria in the sample at the start of the experiment, find:

   (i) the number of bacteria present after three hours

   (ii) the number of bacteria present after five hours.

   (iii) After five hours of testing, the scientist introduces a chemical which reduces the rate of growth of the bacteria from 40% to a new value. Seven hours later, there are 7,153 bacteria present in the sample. Find the new rate of growth after the chemical has been added.

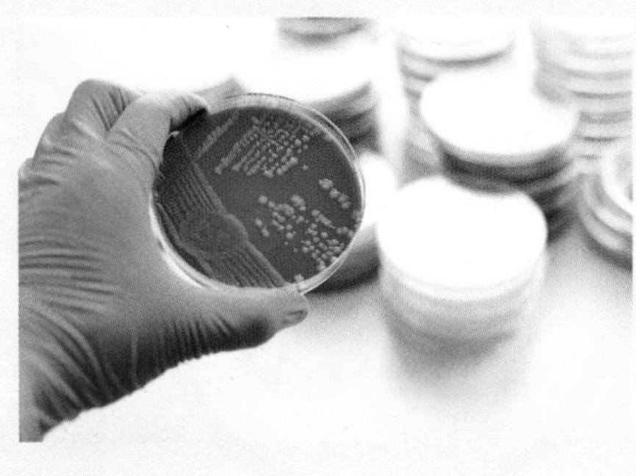

9. €600 is invested at r% per annum. The interest earned is subject to tax at 35%. After one year, tax of €8·40 was paid on the interest earned.

   (i) Find the total amount of interest earned.

   (ii) Hence, calculate r.

10. A savings bond earns an interest rate of 1·25% for each year the bond is kept. The interest is compounded annually. The interest earned is taxed at 20% when the bond is redeemed.

   (i) €15,000 is invested in this bond for four years. What is the net amount payable (after tax is deducted) at the end of the four years?

   (ii) If the investor keeps the bond for eight years, a bonus of 15% is paid on the interest earned, before tax is deducted.
   What is the amount payable on an investment of €10,000 invested in this bond for eight years?

Now that you have completed the chapter, revisit the 'Something to think about…' question.

CHAPTER 10

Geometry I – Introduction to Theorems

Sections covered within this chapter:

KEY WORDS

- Axiom
- Implies
- Theorem
- Converse
- Proof
- Ray
- Corollary
- Transversal

SOMETHING TO THINK ABOUT…

The picture shows a piece of road with a train track crossing it.

Find the value of x. Explain your reasoning fully.

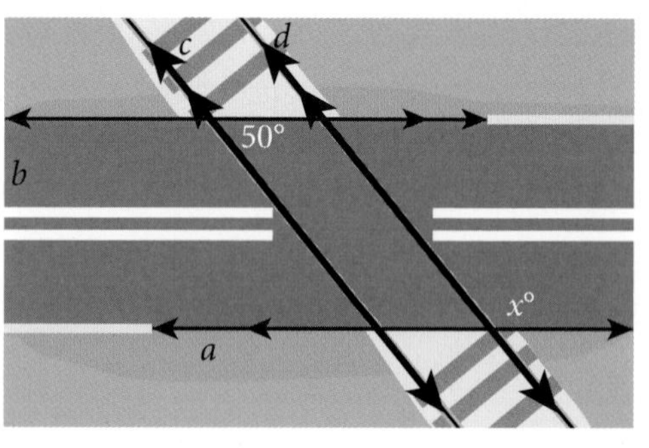

Geometry is one of the oldest branches of Maths. It is the study of the properties of lines and shapes. Geometry is used in many everyday applications such as architecture, engineering, construction, animation and navigation to name but a few.

Section 10.1: Theorem Language

Learning Outcome:

You should be able to:

- define the terms axiom, theorem, proof, corollary, implies and converse

In geometry there are a number of commonly used terms that we must be able to define.

An **axiom** is a statement that is taken to be true without the need for a proof.

A **theorem** is a statement that can be proven from the axioms and other theorems by logical argument.

A **proof** is a step-by-step explanation that uses axioms and previously proven theorems to show another theorem is correct.

A **corollary** is a statement that follows readily from a previous theorem.

Implies is used in a proof when we can write a fact we have proved by our previous statements.
The symbol for implies is $\Rightarrow$

The **converse** of a theorem is the reverse of a theorem.

Section 10.2: Axioms

Learning Outcome:

You should be able to:

- recall and apply axioms 1 – 5

Axiom 1

Given any two points, you can draw exactly one straight line between them.

Axiom 2

The properties of the distance between any two points.

The following properties exist for the distance between two points:

1. The distance between two points is never negative.
   Distance between A and B is written as $|AB|$, since $|\ |$ means the absolute value, i.e. take the positive value.
2. The distance from A to B is equal to the distance from B to A. $|AB| = |BA|$
3. If a point C lies between A and B, then $|AB| = |AC| + |CB|$
4. Given a ray from the point A and a distance d such that $d > 0$, there is only one point, B on the ray where $|AB| = d$.

A **ray** is a line with a single endpoint that extends infinitely in one direction.

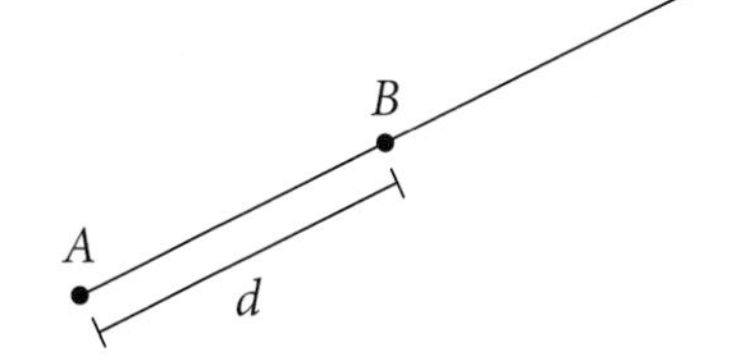

Axiom 3

The properties of the measure of an angle.

The following properties exist for the measure of an angle:

1. The number of degrees in any angle is always between 0° and 360°.
2. A straight angle is 180°. Any two angles that sum up to 180° are called **supplementary angles.**
3. An ordinary angle measures less than 180°.
4. Given a line AB, there is exactly one ray from A on each side of the line AB that makes an angle of d, where d is between 0° and 180°.

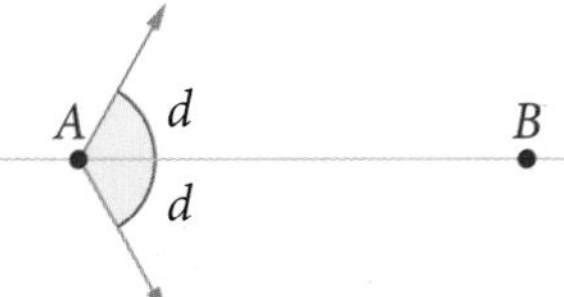

Geometry I

5. When an angle is divided into smaller angles, then the sum of the smaller angles is equal to the original angle.

$|\angle ABC| = |\angle ABD| + |\angle DBC|$

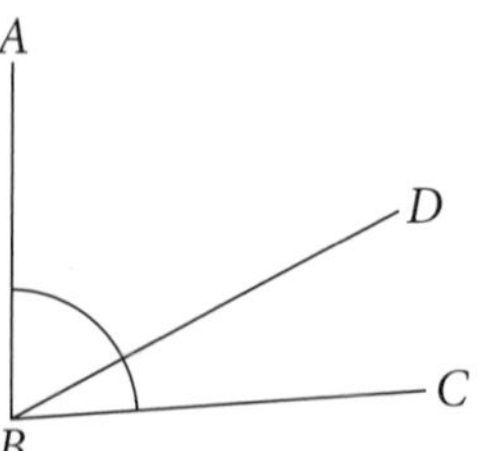

Axiom 4

The conditions for congruency.

The conditions for congruency are dealt with in Chapter 11: Geometry II.

Axiom 5

Given any line l and a point P, there is exactly one line through P that is parallel to l.

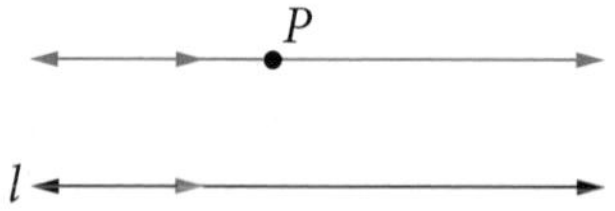

Practice Questions 10.1

1. Define each of the following terms:
   - (i) Axiom
   - (ii) Theorem
   - (iii) Proof
   - (iv) Corollary
   - (v) Implies
   - (vi) Converse

2. For each of the following statements,
   - (a) state the converse statement:
     - (i) If two lines are perpendicular, then they intersect at right angles.
     - (ii) If $x = 12$ then $x < 20$.
     - (iii) If two lines are parallel, then they never meet.
     - (iv) If a triangle has two sides of equal length, then the triangle is isosceles.
   - (b) Determine which of the converse statements, if any, are true.

3. If a point F lies between two points, D and E, such that $|DF| = |EF|$, then which of the following is true?
   - (i) $|DF| = |DE|$
   - (ii) $|DF| = \frac{1}{2}|DE|$
   - (iii) $|DE| = \frac{1}{2}|DF|$
   - (iv) $|DF| = \frac{1}{3}|DE|$

4. Two distinct lines, r and s, cannot have which of the following?
   - (i) Any point in common.
   - (ii) One point in common.
   - (iii) Two points in common.

5. Given two points, which of the following is true?
   - (i) No line can be drawn through them.
   - (ii) One unique line can be drawn through them.
   - (iii) More than one line can be drawn through them.
   - (iv) None of these.

6.

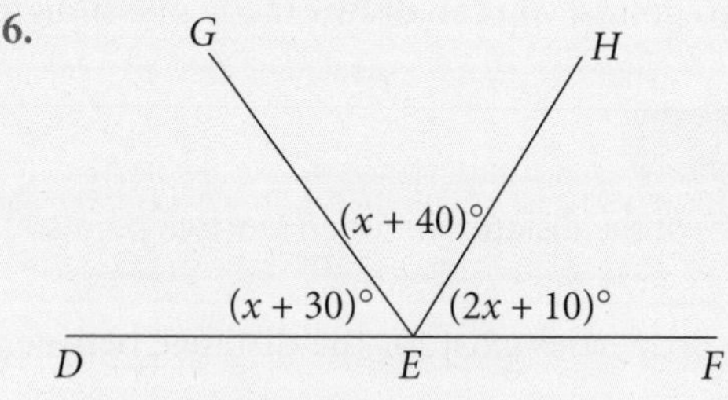

   - (i) Find the value of x.
   - (ii) Find the measure of $\angle HEF$.

7. Find the measure of:

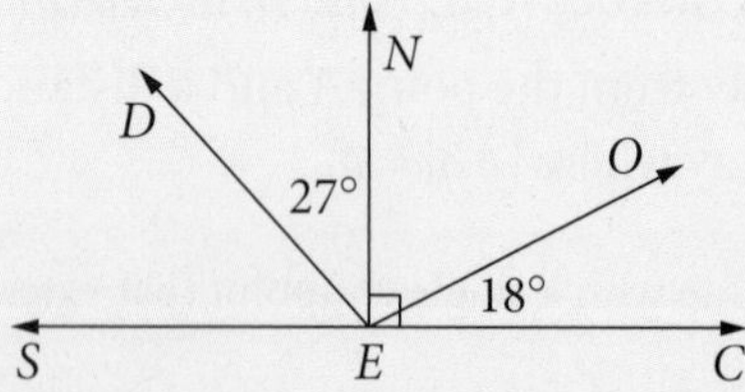

   (i) $\angle NEO$ (ii) $\angle DES$ (iii) $\angle DEO$ (iv) $\angle SEO$

8. Find the value of f, g, h and i shown below.

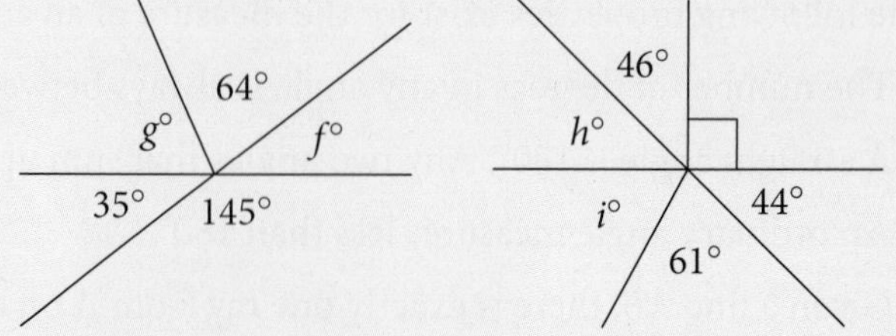

Section 10.3: Line Theorems

Learning Outcome:

You should be able to:

- understand and use line theorems to solve problems

In the syllabus the theorems are numbered in a logical order, but you are not required to know which number relates to which theorem. In this chapter and Chapter 11: Geometry II, theorems are grouped into sections based on the shape they relate to. Theorem numbers are also provided for easy reference to the syllabus.

1. Vertically opposite angles are equal. (Theorem 1)

You are not required to prove any of the theorems for this course.

When two straight lines AB and CD intersect as shown,
$\angle AEC$ and $\angle BED$ are called vertically opposite angles.
$\angle AED$ and $\angle BEC$ are also vertically opposite.

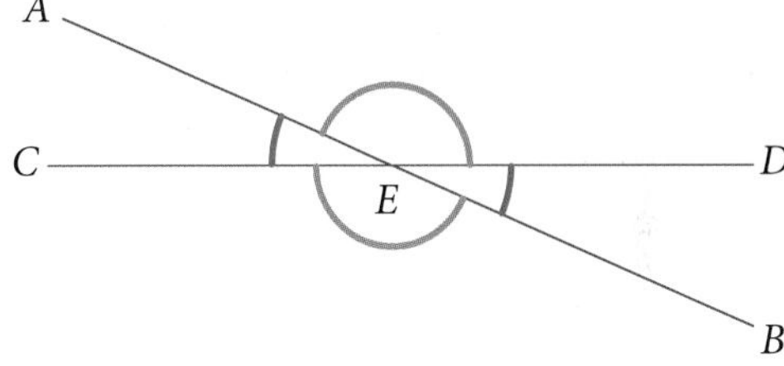

To identify vertically opposite angles, look out for an '**X**' shape.

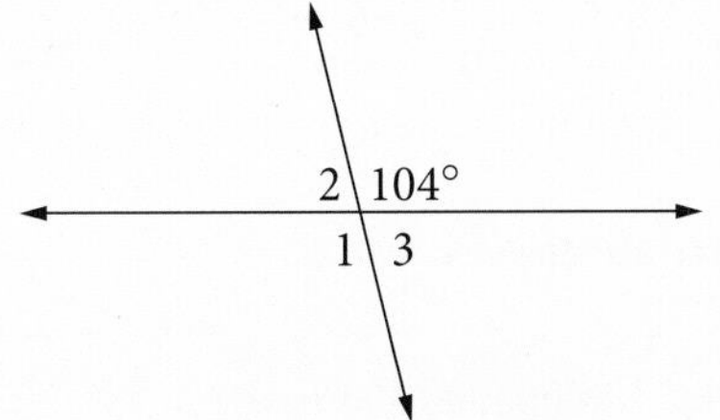

EXAMPLE 1

Find $|\angle 1|$, $|\angle 2|$, and $|\angle 3|$.

Solution

Identify the **X** as shown in red.

$\angle 1$ is vertically opposite 104°.

$\angle 2$ is vertically opposite $\angle 3$.

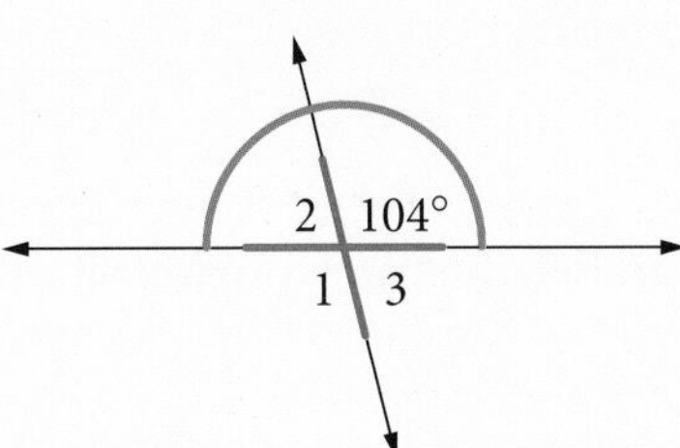

$|\angle 1| = 104°$ vertically opposite

$|\angle 2| + 104° = 180°$ straight line shown in green

$|\angle 2| = 180° - 104°$

$|\angle 2| = 76°$

$|\angle 3| = 76°$ vertically opposite $\angle 2$

EXAMPLE 2

Find the value of x, and hence find the measure of the four angles shown:

Solution:

$|\angle LAP| = |\angle OAT|$ vertically opposite

$5x - 15 = 3x + 1$

$5x - 3x = 1 + 15$

$2x = 16$

$x = 8$

$|\angle LAP| = 5x - 15$
$= 5(8) - 15$
$= 40 - 15$
$= 25°$

$|\angle OAT| = 3x + 1$
$= 3(8) + 1$
$= 24 + 1$
$= 25°$

$|\angle LAT| = 20x - 5$
$= 20(8) - 5$
$= 160 - 5$
$= 155°$

$|\angle PAO| = 155°$

The angles LAT and PAO are vertically opposite and so must be equal.

2. If a transversal makes equal alternate angles on two lines, then the lines are parallel. (Theorem 3)

A **transversal** is a line that cuts across two or more lines.

Parallel lines are shown on a diagram using an arrow on both lines.

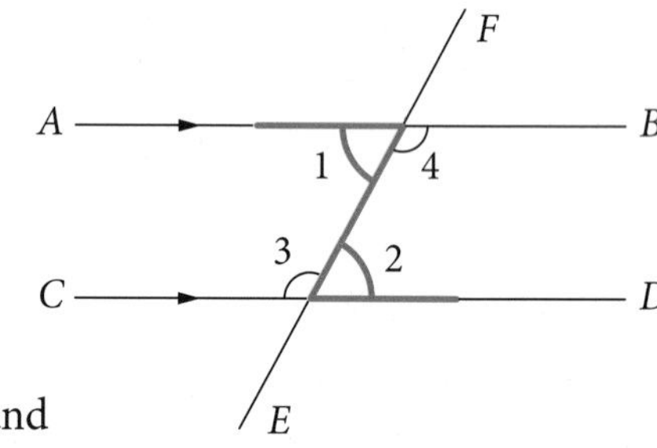

If a transveral, EF, cuts two lines AB and CD such that $|\angle 1| = |\angle 2|$, then AB and CD are parallel. $\angle 1$ and $\angle 2$ are called alternate angles.

Similarly, $|\angle 3| = |\angle 4|$ and are also alternate angles.

Alternate angles are on opposite (alternate) sides of the transversal.

To identify alternate angles, look out for an '**Z**' shape.

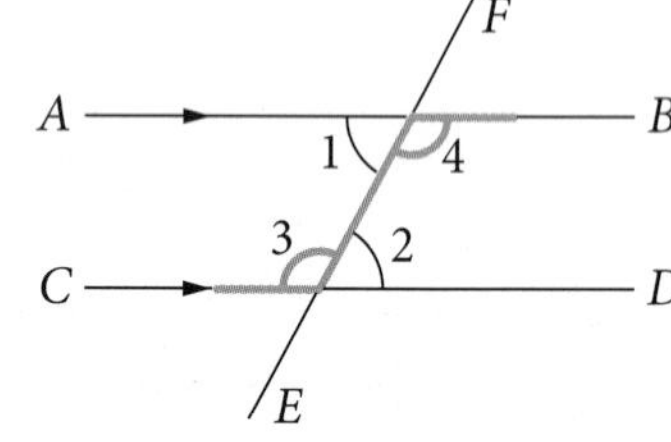

Converse: If two lines are parallel, then any transversal will make equal alternate angles with them.

If two lines l and k are parallel, as shown in the diagram, then $|\angle 1| = |\angle 2|$ and $\angle 1$ and $\angle 2$ are called alternate angles.

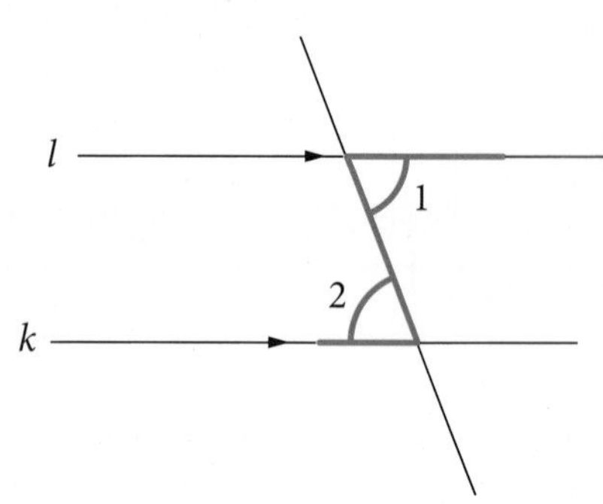

Geometry I

EXAMPLE 3

If the line r is parallel to the line s, find all the labelled angles. Explain your reasoning.

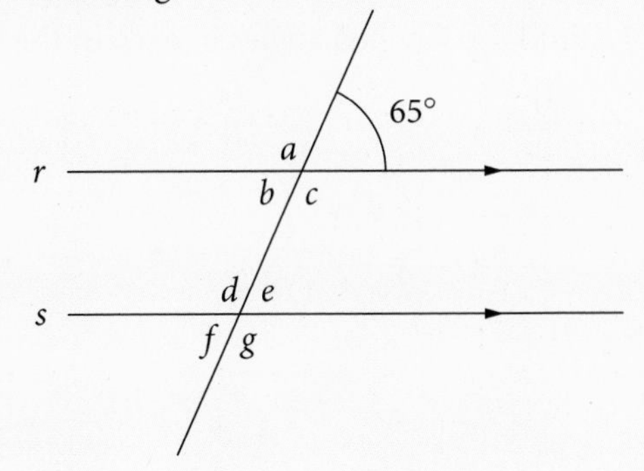

Solution

$\lvert\angle a\rvert = 180° - 65° = 115°$	straight line
$\lvert\angle b\rvert = 65°$	vertically opposite 65°
$\lvert\angle c\rvert = 115°$	vertically opposite a
$\lvert\angle d\rvert = 115°$	alternate to c
$\lvert\angle e\rvert = 65°$	alternate to b
$\lvert\angle f\rvert = 65°$	vertically opposite e
$\lvert\angle g\rvert = 115°$	vertically opposite d

3. Two lines are parallel if and only if for any transversal, corresponding angles are equal. (Theorem 5)

If a transversal, XY, cuts two lines d and e producing corresponding angles, $\angle 1$ and $\angle 2$ that are equal, as shown, then the two lines are parallel.

Corresponding angles are in the same (corresponding) positions on the parallel lines.

To identify corresponding angles, look out for the '**F**' shape.

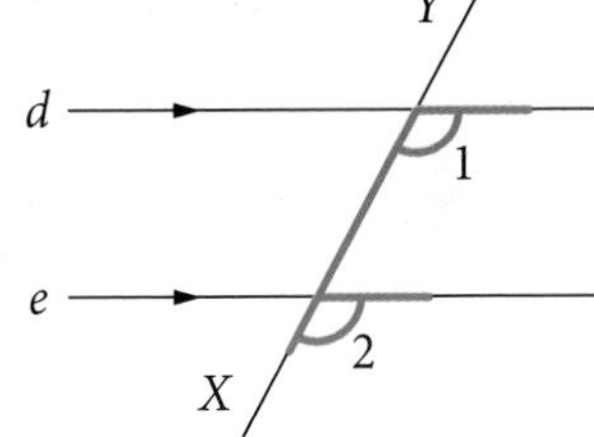

EXAMPLE 4

Investigate if the lines g and h are parallel. Justify your answer.

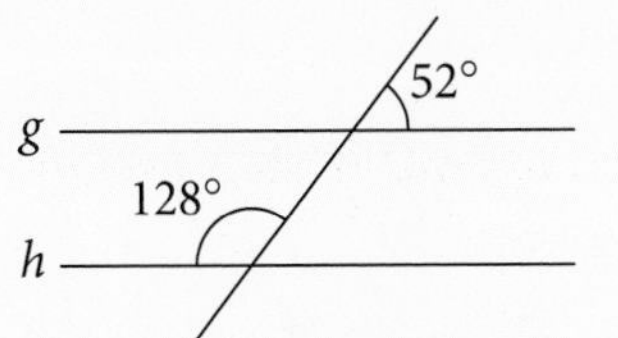

Solution

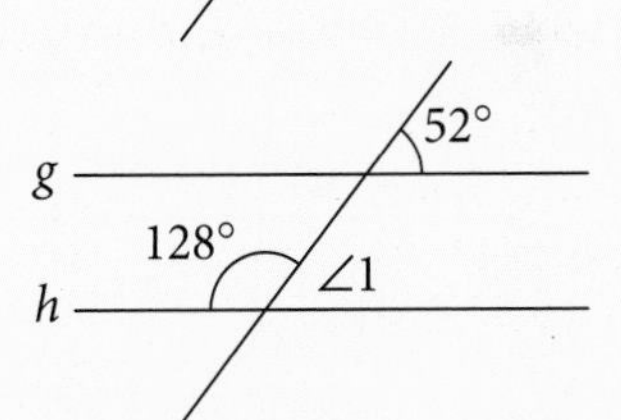

$|\angle 1| = 180° - 128°$ straight line

$|\angle 1| = 52°$

Since, $|\angle 1| = 52°$ we can say that it corresponds to the 52° angle above it.
Hence, the lines g and h are parallel.

4. If three parallel lines cut off equal segments on some transversal line, then they will cut off equal segments on any other transversal. (Theorem 11)

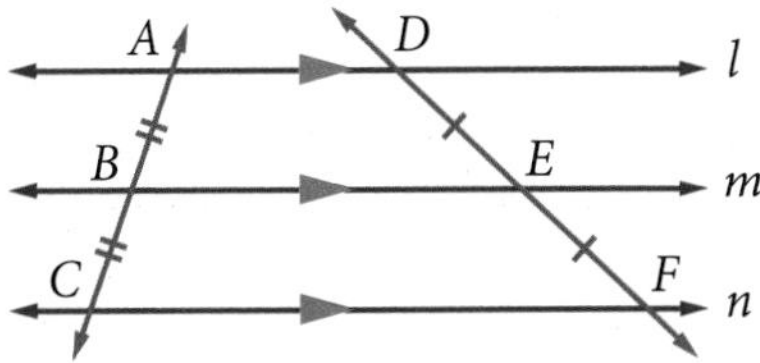

If l, m and n are parallel and $|AB| = |BC|$ then $|DE| = |EF|$.

EXAMPLE 5

In the diagram shown, $|AB| = |BC| = 8$ cm, and $|DE| = 10$ cm
Find the value of $|EF|$.

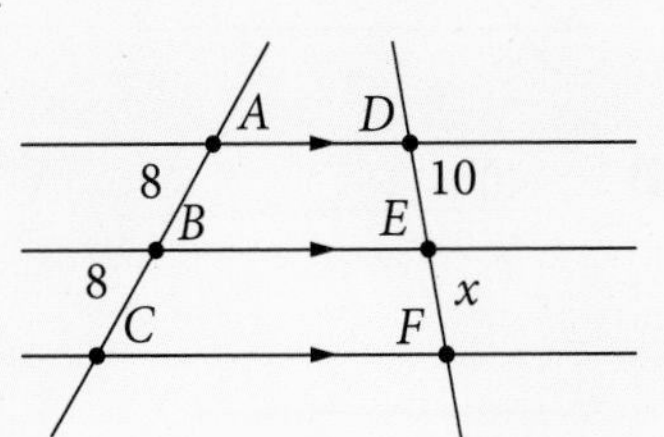

Solution

If $|AB| = |BC|$, then $|DE| = |EF|$ (Theorem 11)

Filling in the values we get:

$|EF| = |DE|$

$x = 10$ cm

Practice Questions 10.2

It is good practice to state your reasons for any statements made.

1. Find the labelled angles in each of the following. State reasons in each case.

(i)

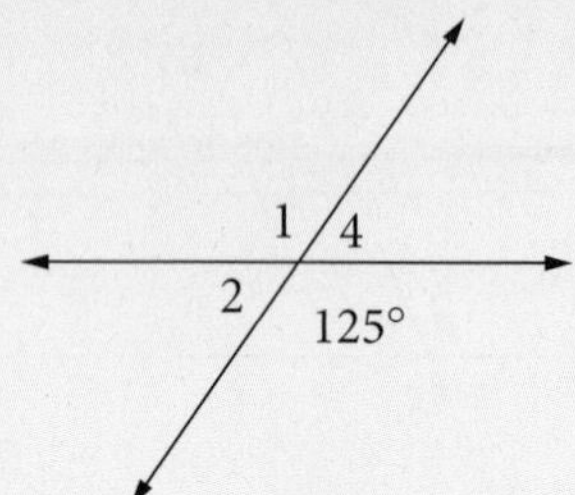

(iii)

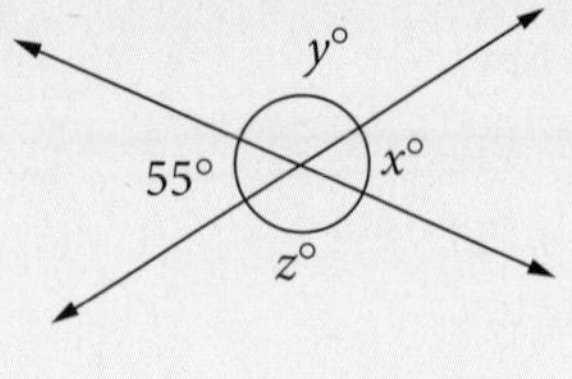

(v)

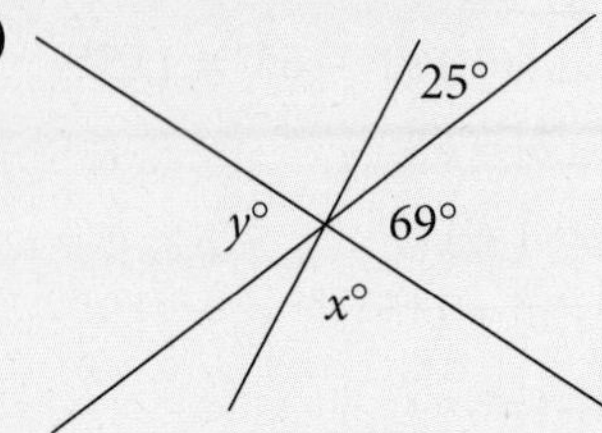

(ii)

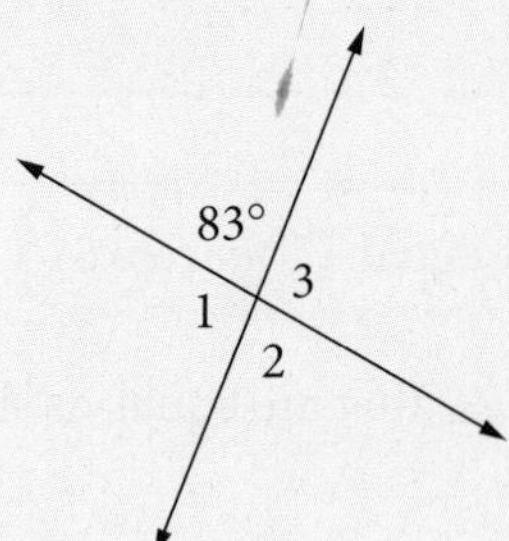

(iv)

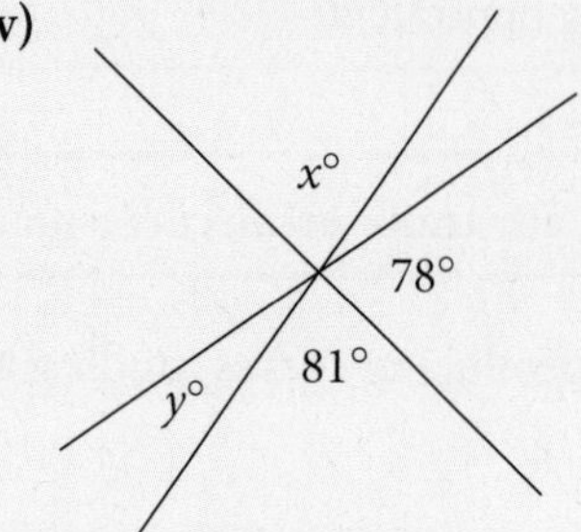

(vi)

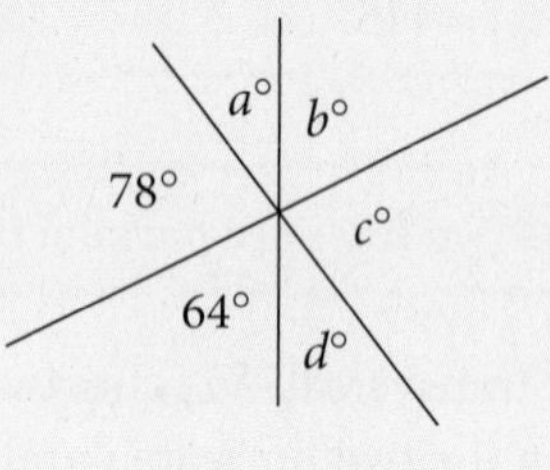

2. Find the values of a and b in each of the following:

(i)

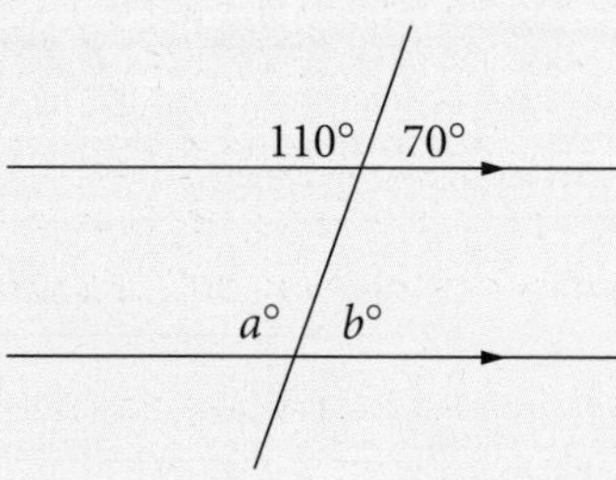

(iii)

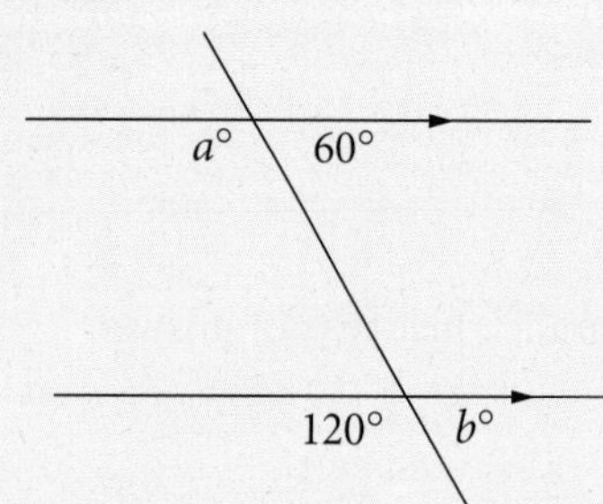

(v)

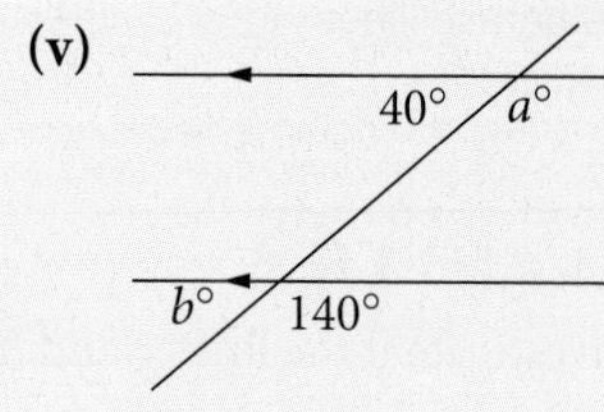

(ii)

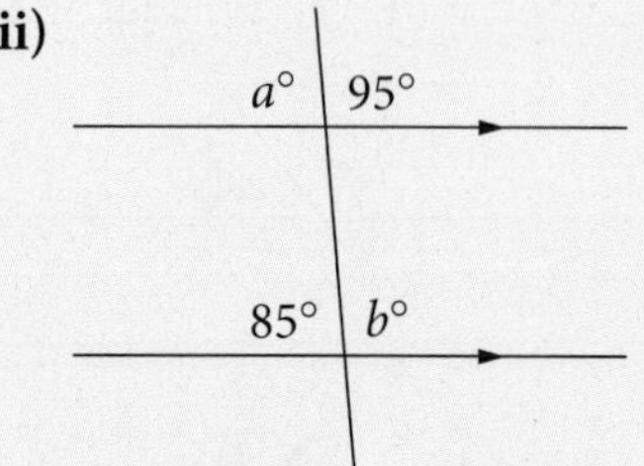

(iv)

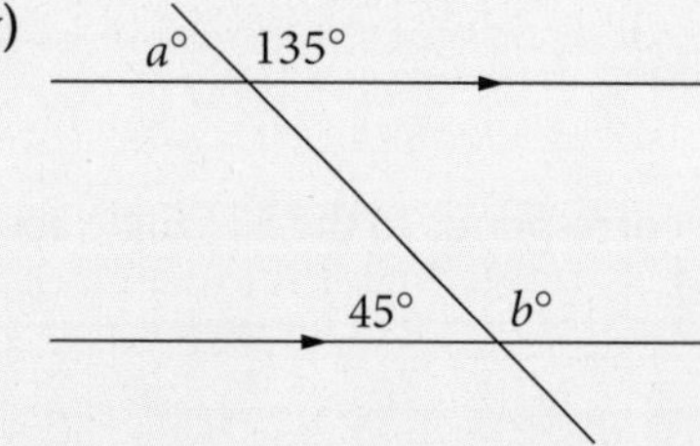

(vi)

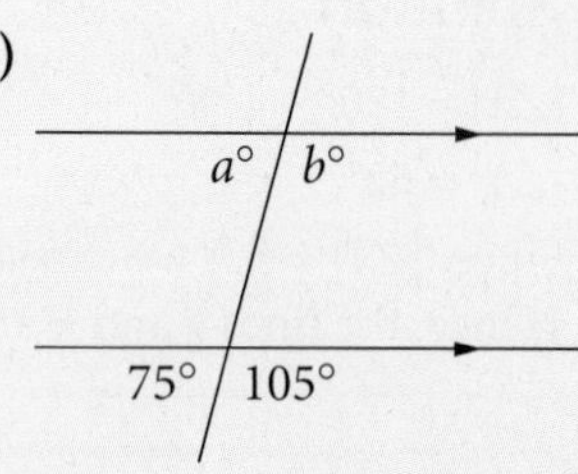

3. Find the value of x in each of the following:

(i)

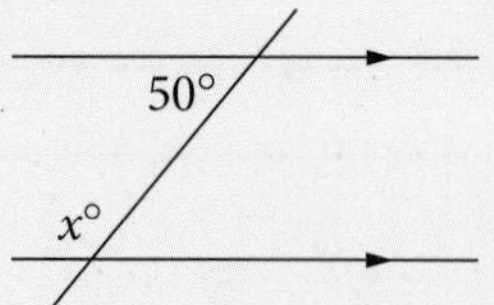

(iii)

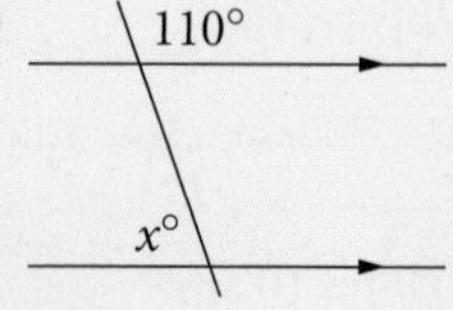

(v)

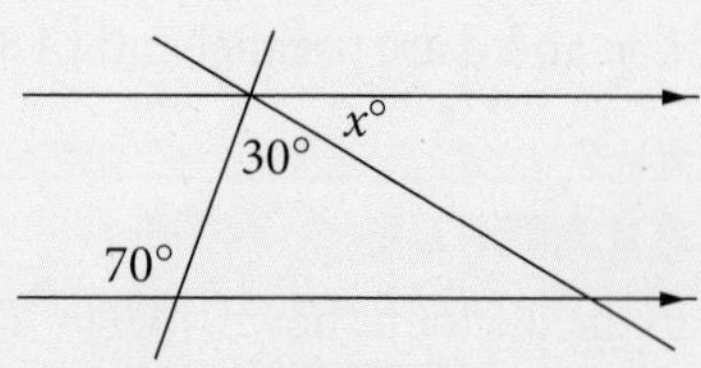

(ii)

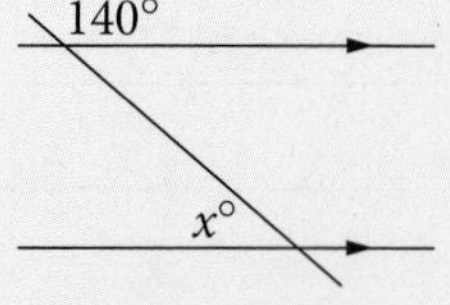

(iv)

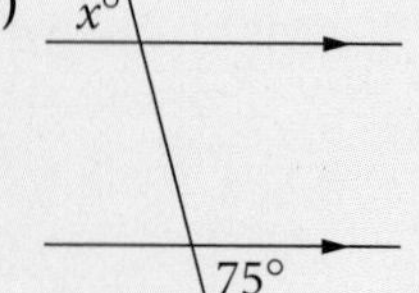

(vi)

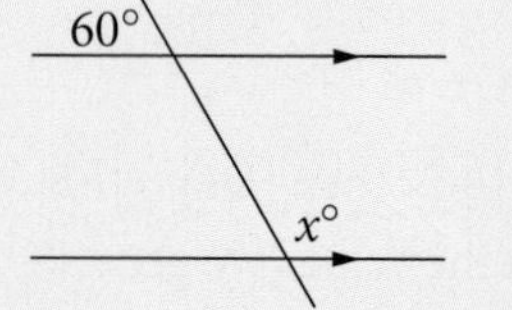

4. Given $|\angle 1| = 115°$ and $|\angle 12| = 110°$, find the measure of all the angles shown. Explain your reasoning in each case.

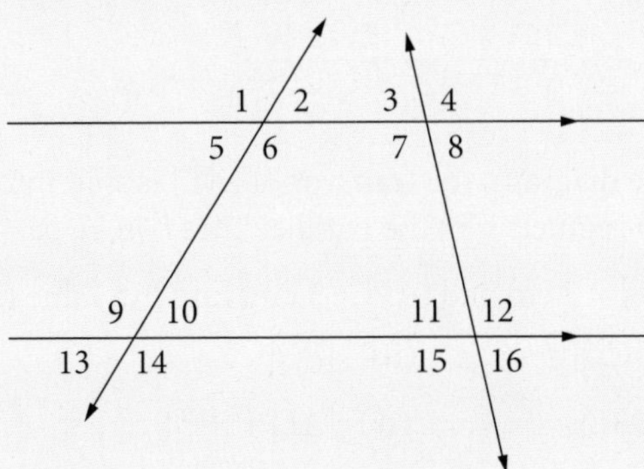

5. Find the value of x, y and z. Justify your answers.

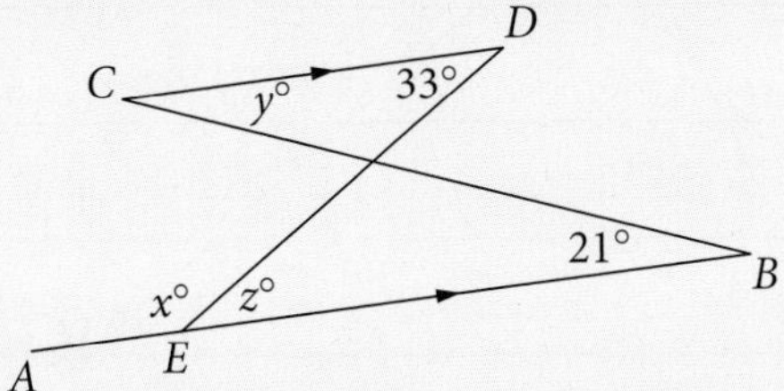

6. Investigate whether the lines a and b are parallel in each of the following. Justify your answer in each case.

(i)

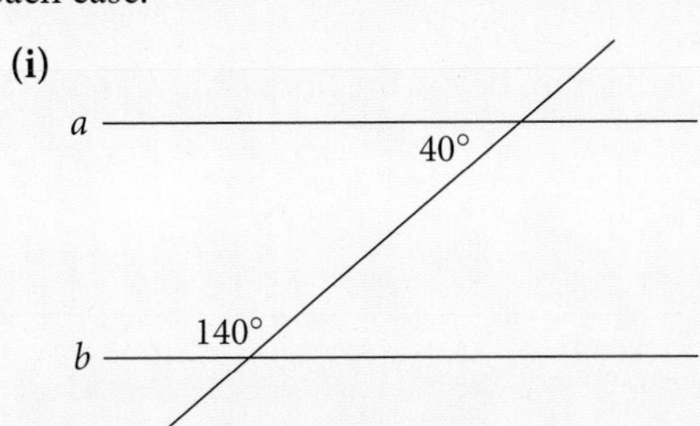

(ii)

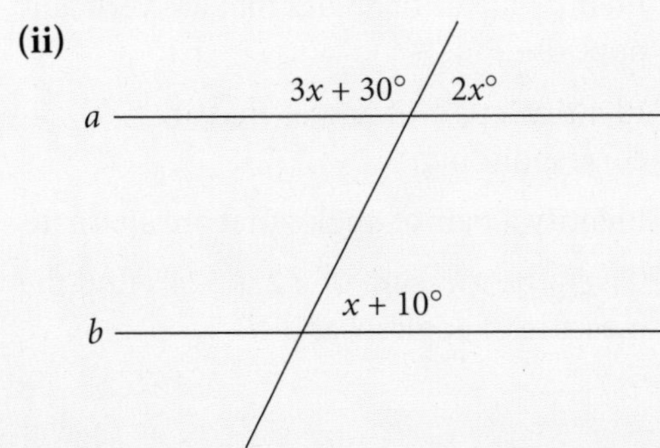

7. A shop owner uses pieces of tape to paint a window advertisement as shown.

Assuming the tape lines are parallel and the letters are slanted at an 80° angle, what is the measure of $\angle 1$? Justify your answer.

8. 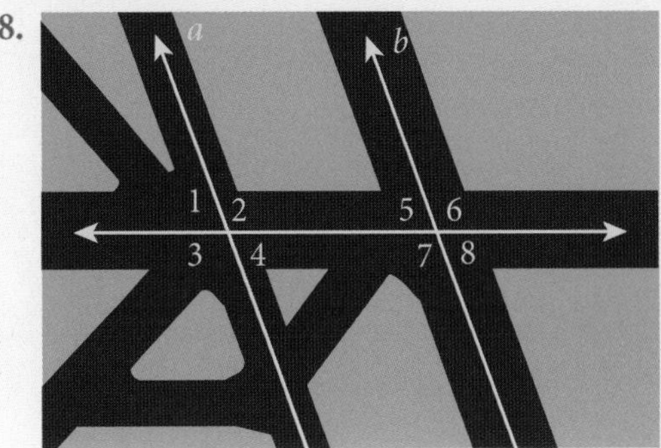

The photograph shows a network of roads. Assuming a and b are parallel, explain the relationship between the following pairs of angles:

(i) $\angle 5$ and $\angle 8$

(ii) $\angle 2$ and $\angle 7$

(iii) $\angle 4$ and $\angle 7$

9. From the diagram:

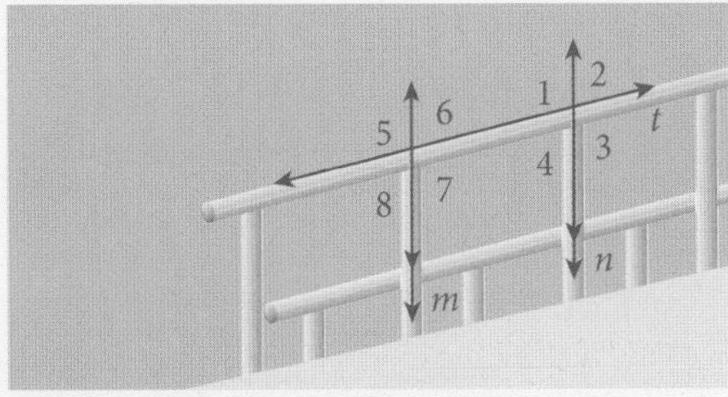

(i) Identify the parallel lines.

(ii) Identify the transversal.

(iii) How many angles are formed by the transversal?

(iv) Which of the angles are equal? Justify your answer.

10. The painted lines that separate parking spaces are parallel.
The measure of $\angle 1$ is 68°.
What is the measure of $\angle 2$? Explain.

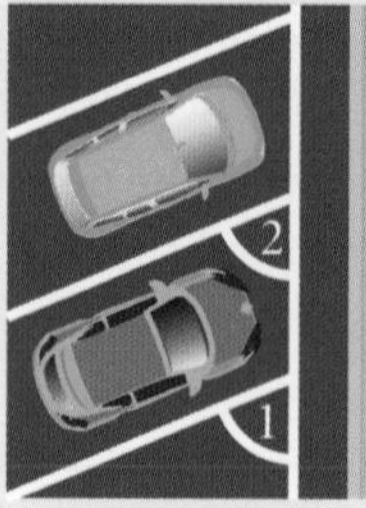

11. Find the value of x in each of the following:

(i)

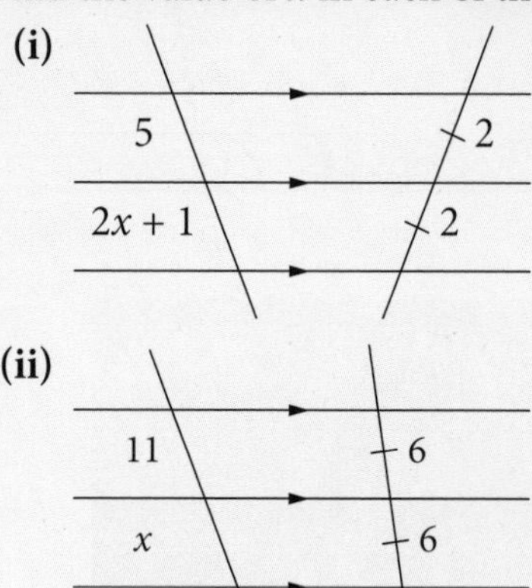

(ii)

(iii)

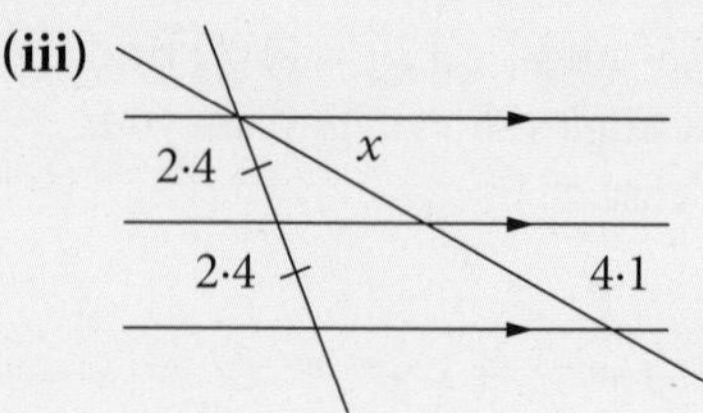

12. In the diagram, the transversal $[AE]$ is split into equal segments by the parallel lines l, m, n, p.
If $|AB| = 2$ cm and $|AP| = 5$ cm, find the value of:
(i) $|CD|$
(ii) $|BE|$
(iii) $|PQ|$
(iv) $|AE| + |PQ|$

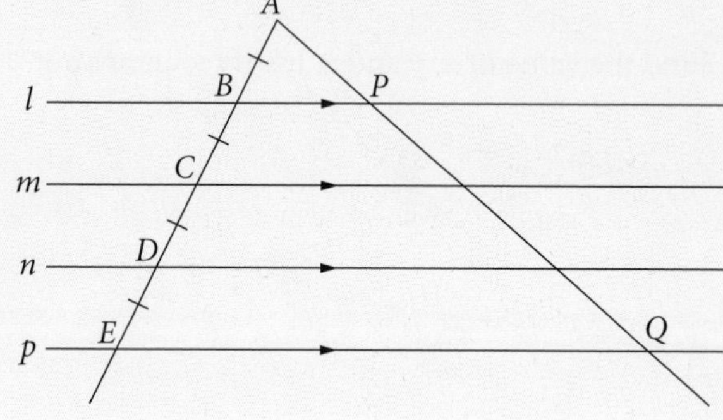

Revision and Exam Style Questions

1. Explain the following terms:
(i) Axiom
(ii) Theorem
(iii) Converse
(iv) Proof
(v) Corollary
(vi) Implies

2. Explain the difference between an axiom and a theorem.

3. ABC is a straight line.

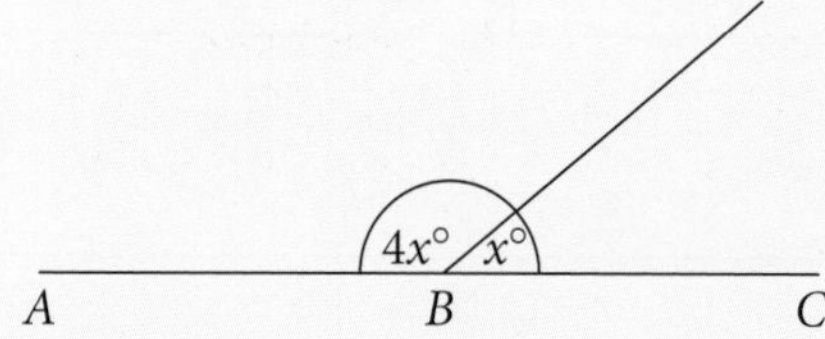

(i) Find the value of x.
(ii) Hence, find the measure of each angle shown.
(iii) What axiom did you use to find the value of x?

4. In the diagram below the lines l and k are parallel.

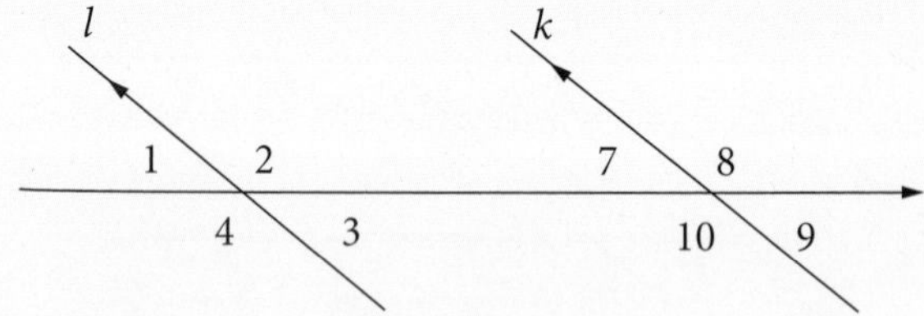

(i) Identify a pair of angles that are vertically opposite.
(ii) Identify a pair of angles that are corresponding.
(iii) Identify a pair of angles that are alternate.
(iv) Given the measure of $\angle 2$ is 124°, find the measure of angles 9 and 10.

5. In the diagram the lines r and s are parallel.

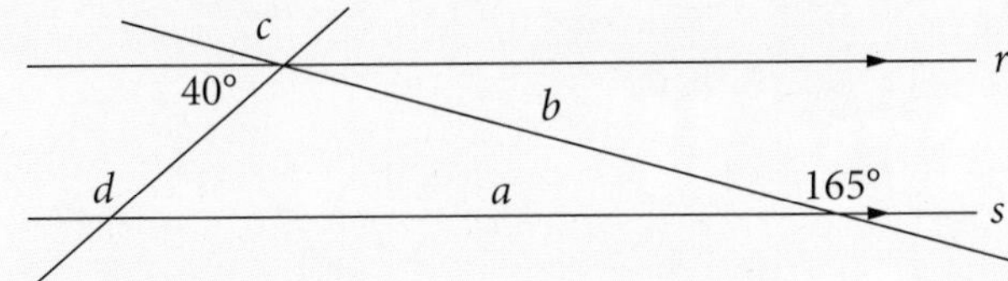

Find the measure of:

(i) angle a (iii) angle c

(ii) angle b (iv) angle d.

6. You reflect the beam of light from a desk lamp off a mirror lying flat on a desk, as shown.
If $|\angle 1| = |\angle 3|$, determine whether $|\angle DBA| = |\angle EBC|$.
Justify your answer.

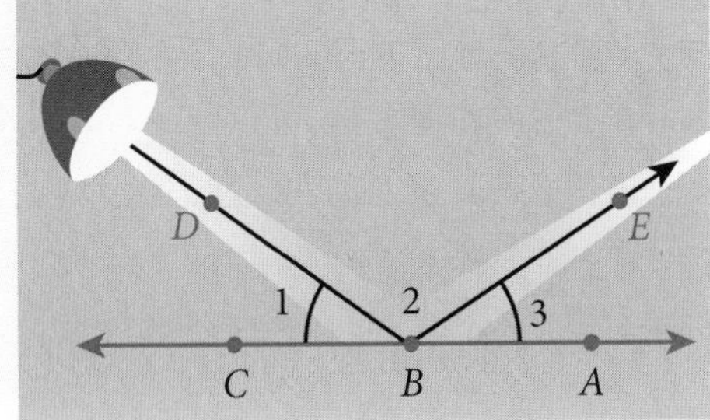

7. In the diagram below l, m and n are parallel.
Find the value of x and y.

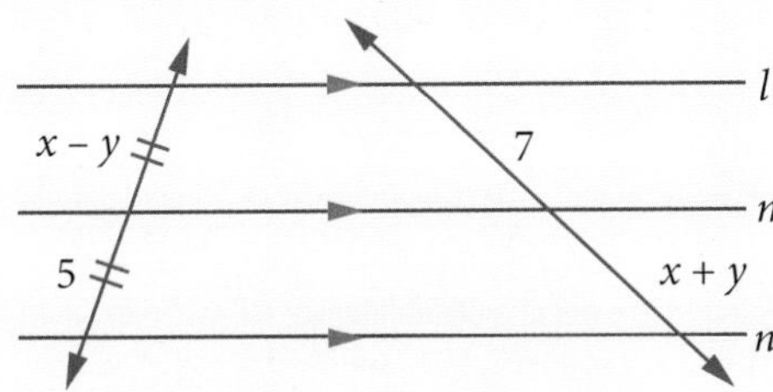

8. Find the measure of the angles:

(i) a (v) e

(ii) b (vi) f

(iii) c (vii) g

(iv) d (viii) h

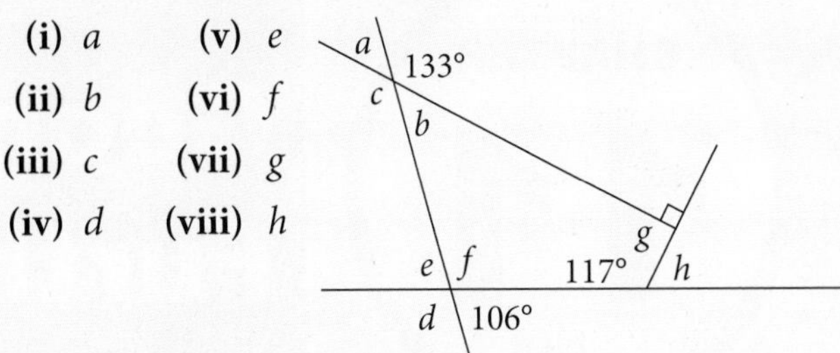

9. The diagram shows three parallel lines and two transversals.

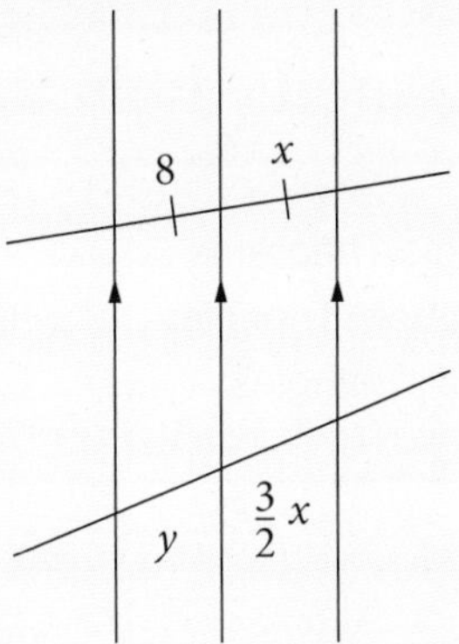

(i) Find the value of x and y.

(ii) State the theorem used to solve for x and y.

10. (i) Find the values of each of the unknown angles shown in the diagram.

(ii) State the theorem or axiom you use to find each of the unknown angles.

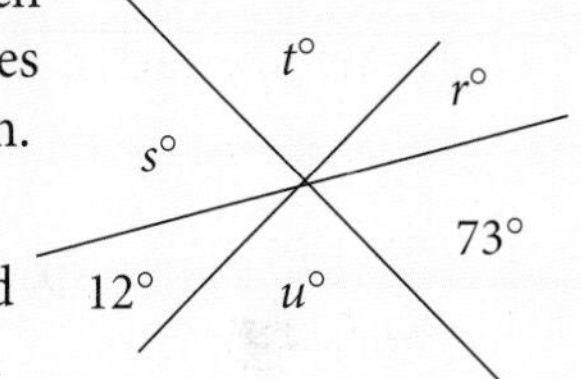

Now that you have completed the chapter, revisit the 'Something to think about…' question.

Geometry I

CHAPTER 11 Geometry II – Further Theorems

Sections covered within this chapter:

KEY WORDS

- Congruent
- Arc
- Similar triangles
- Tangent
- Radius
- Chord
- Diameter
- Cyclic quadrilateral

SOMETHING TO THINK ABOUT... 

You are standing on the edge of the sea and you want to work out how deep it is 50 metres from the shore. You know the depth 10 metres from the shore is 3 metres.

Assuming the depth increases at a constant rate, calculate the depth at 50 metres.

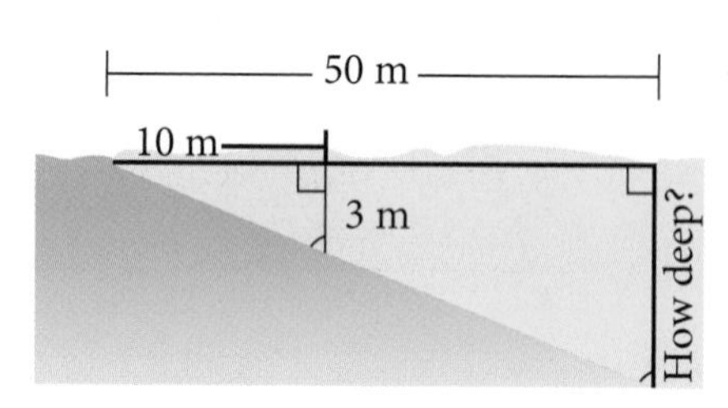

Section 11.1: Triangle Theorems

Learning Outcome:

You should be able to:

- understand and use the triangle theorems to solve problems

In the Leaving Certificate exam, you can be asked to use the theorems to find the value of unknowns or solve other geometrical problems.

When using theorems, it is accepted practice to state the theorem's name as reason to justify a particular step in the solution.

1. In an isosceles triangle, the angles opposite the equal sides are equal. (Theorem 2)

If $|AB| = |AC|$ as shown, then $|\angle ABC| = |\angle ACB|$.

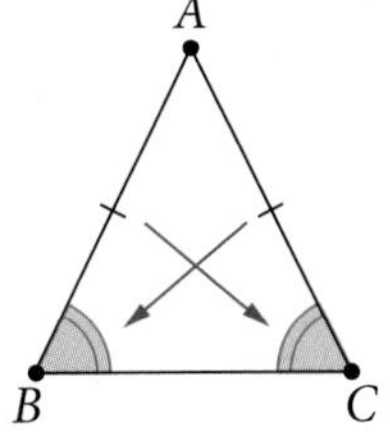

Conversely, if two angles are equal, then the triangle is isosceles.

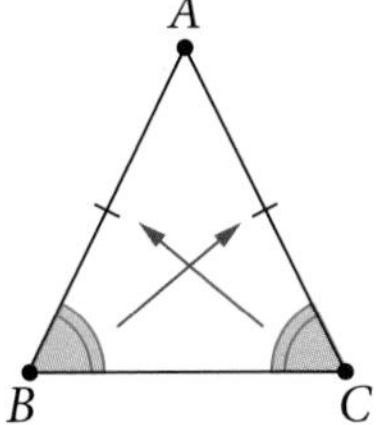

2. The angles in any triangle add up 180°. (Theorem 4)

$|\angle A| + |\angle B| + |\angle C| = 180^\circ$

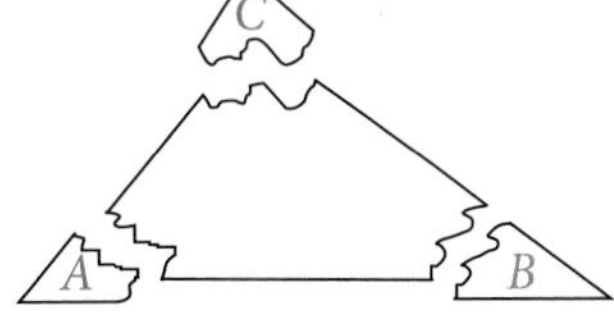

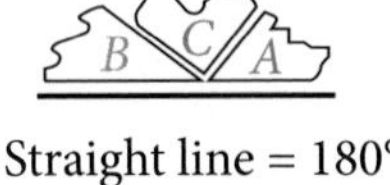

Straight line = 180°

EXAMPLE 1

Find the measure of each of the angles shown in the diagram. Justify your answers.

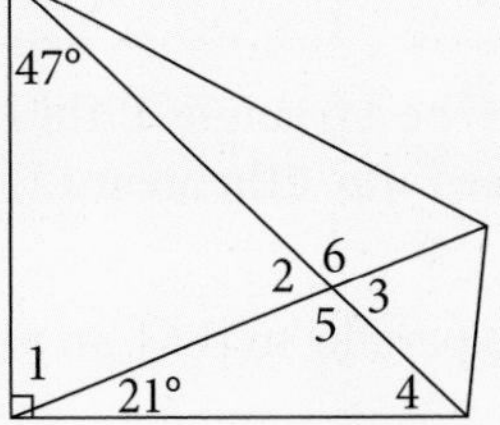

Solution

$|\angle 1| + 21^\circ = 90^\circ$ right angle

$|\angle 1| = 90^\circ - 21^\circ$

$|\angle 1| = 69^\circ$

$47^\circ + 69^\circ + |\angle 2| = 180^\circ$ 3 angles of triangle = 180°

$116^\circ + |\angle 2| = 180^\circ$

$|\angle 2| = 180^\circ - 116^\circ$

$|\angle 2| = 64^\circ$

$|\angle 2| = |\angle 3|$ vertically opposite angles

$|\angle 3| = 64^\circ$

$|\angle 5| + |\angle 2| = 180^\circ$ straight line 180°

$|\angle 5| + 64^\circ = 180^\circ$

$|\angle 5| = 180^\circ - 64^\circ$

$|\angle 5| = 116^\circ$

$|\angle 5| = |\angle 6|$ vertically opposite angles

$|\angle 6| = 116^\circ$

$|\angle 4| + |\angle 5| + 21^\circ = 180^\circ$ 3 angles of triangle

$|\angle 4| + 116^\circ + 21^\circ = 180^\circ$

$|\angle 4| + 137^\circ = 180^\circ$

$|\angle 4| = 180^\circ - 137^\circ$

$|\angle 4| = 43^\circ$

3. Each exterior angle in a triangle is equal to the sum of the interior opposite angles. (Theorem 6)

The exterior angle is formed by extending any of the three sides of the triangle.

In the diagram, $\angle 1$ is the exterior angle in each case.

$|\angle 1| = |\angle 2| + |\angle 3|$

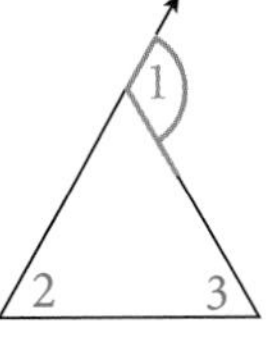

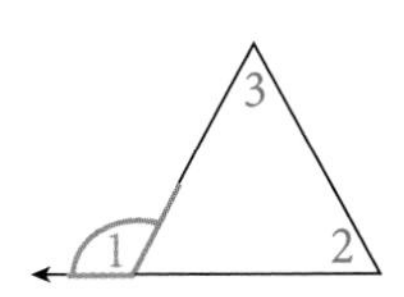

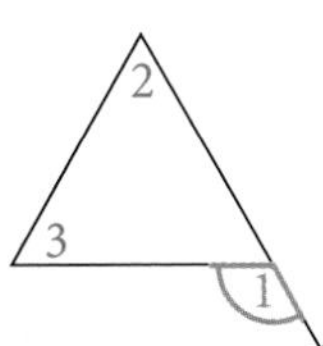

4. The angle opposite the greater of two sides is greater than the angle opposite the lesser side.(Theorem 7)

The biggest angle is always opposite the longest side, and the smallest angle is always opposite the shortest side.

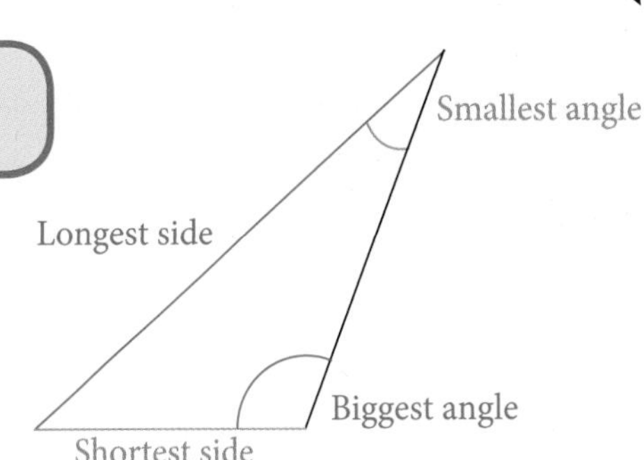

Conversely, the side opposite the greater of two angles is greater than the side opposite the lesser angle.

5. Two sides of a triangle are together greater than the third. (Theorem 8)

This theorem is sometimes known as the **triangle inequality**.

If any two sides added together are not greater than the other side, then a triangle cannot be formed.

$|AB| + |BC| > |AC|$

$|AB| + |AC| > |BC|$

$|AC| + |BC| > |AB|$

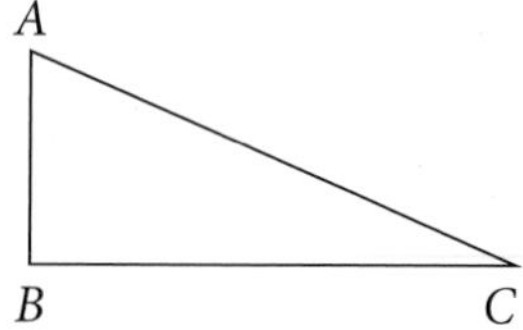

For example, a triangle with sides 3, 4 and 9 cannot be formed because:

$3 + 4 \not> 9$

$7 \not> 9$

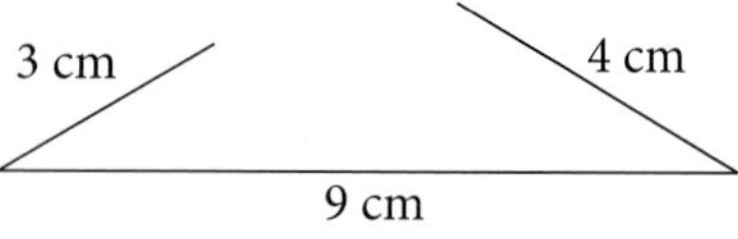

6. Let *ABC* be a triangle. If the line *t* is parallel to *BC* and cuts [*AB*] in the ratio m : n, then it also cuts [*AC*] in the same ratio. (Theorem 12)

The line t is parallel to $|BC|$, so $m : n = |AD| : |DB| = |AE| : |EC|$

This means that the ratios of sides of this triangle are the same.

Therefore, $\dfrac{|AD|}{|DB|} = \dfrac{|AE|}{|EC|}$

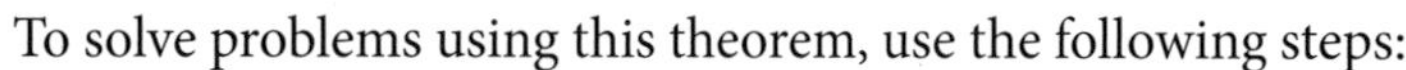

To solve problems using this theorem, use the following steps:

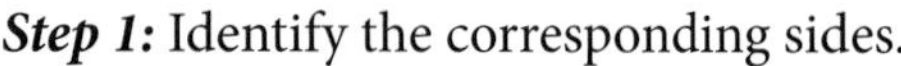

Step 1: Identify the corresponding sides.

Step 2: Write the ratio with the unknown side on the top left.

Step 3: Fill in the values for the given sides.

Step 4: Solve for the unknown side.

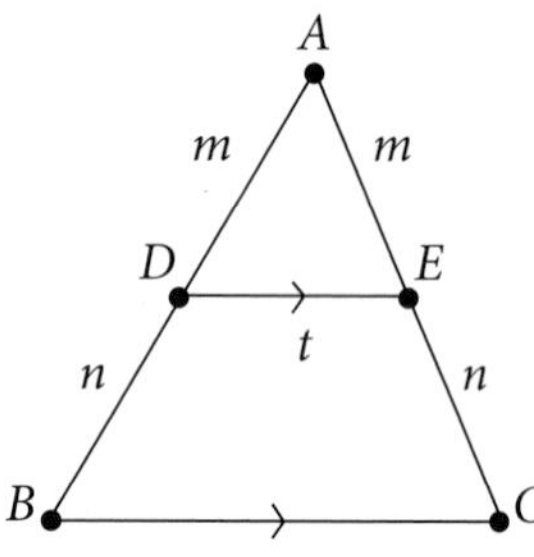

EXAMPLE 2

Find $|RT|$.

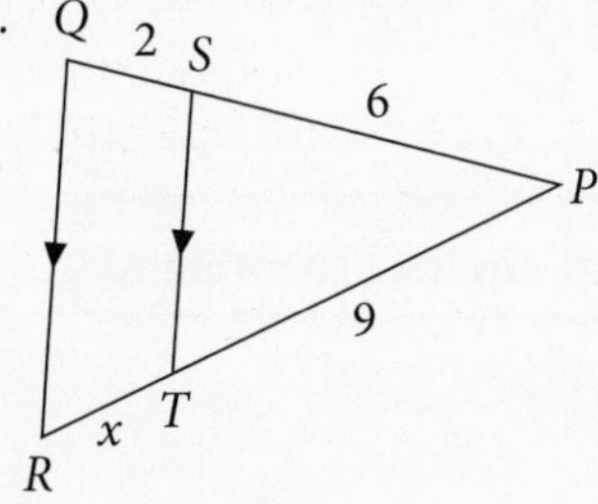

Solution

Step 1: Identify the corresponding sides.

$|RT|$ corresponds to $|QS|$ and $|TP|$ corresponds to $|SP|$.

Step 2: Write the ratio with the unknown side on the top left

$\dfrac{|RT|}{|TP|} = \dfrac{|QS|}{|SP|}$.

Both top values are corresponding lengths in the triangle.

Step 3: Fill in the values $\dfrac{x}{9} = \dfrac{2}{6}$

Step 4: Solve for the unknown side

$$\frac{x}{9} = \frac{2}{6}$$

$$9\left(\frac{x}{9}\right) = 9\left(\frac{2}{6}\right) \quad \text{multiply both sides by 9}$$

$$x = \frac{18}{6}$$

$$x = 3$$

EXAMPLE 3

Find x.

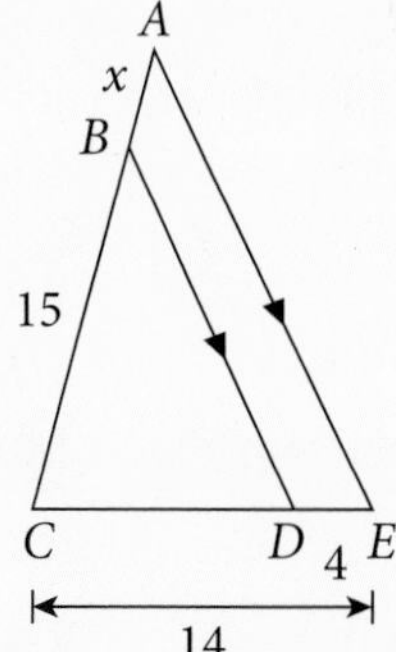

Solution

Step 1: x corresponds to 4 and 15 corresponds to 10 (14 – 4)

Step 2: $\frac{|AB|}{|BC|} = \frac{|DE|}{|CD|}$

Step 3: $\frac{x}{15} = \frac{4}{10}$

Corresponding sides are put on top of the fractions.

Step 4: $\frac{x}{15} = \frac{4}{10}$

$15\left(\frac{x}{15}\right) = 15\left(\frac{4}{10}\right)$ multiply both sides by 15

$x = \frac{60}{10}$

$x = 6$

7. For a triangle, base times height does not depend on the choice of base. (Theorem 16)

The height, (h), of a triangle is a perpendicular line segment drawn from a vertex to its opposite side.

The opposite side, which forms a right angle with the height, is called the base, (b), of the triangle. Any triangle has three heights and three bases.

Links across the syllabus

Area of triangle is covered in Chapter 16: Area and Perimeter.

The diagrams below show the three heights and bases for the triangle ABC.

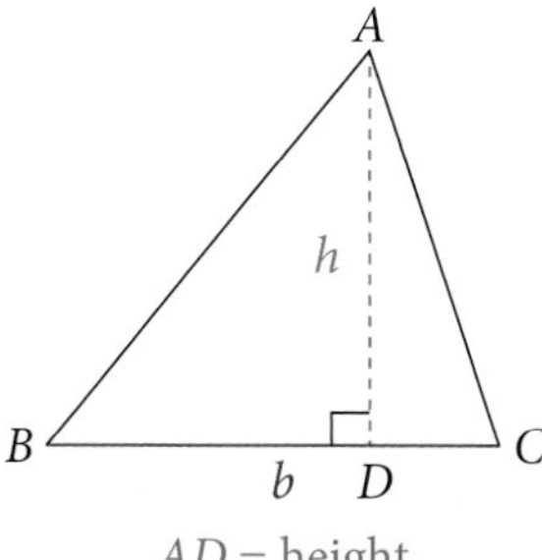

AD = height
BC = base

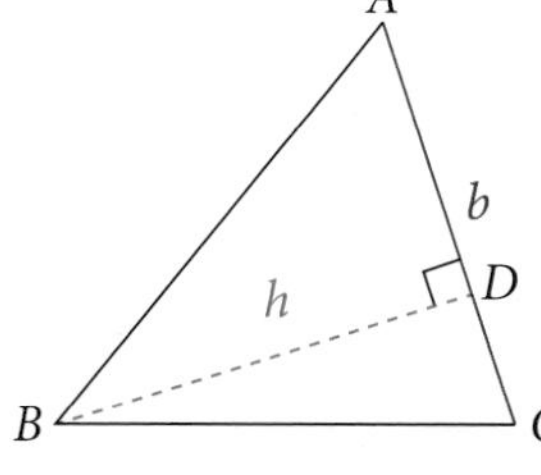

BD = height
AC = base

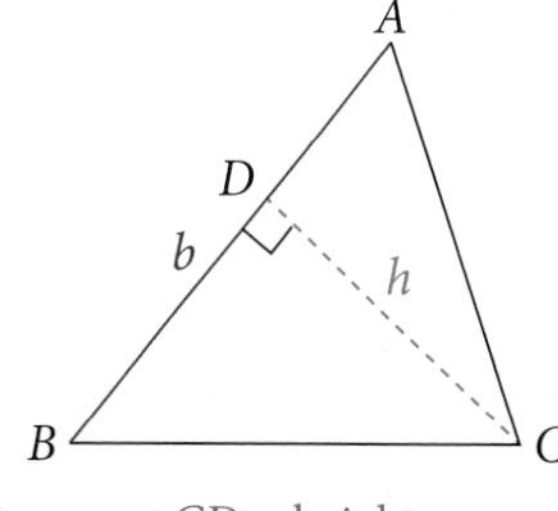

CD = height
AB = base

Practice Questions 11.1

1. Find the value of x and y in each of the following triangles:

(i)

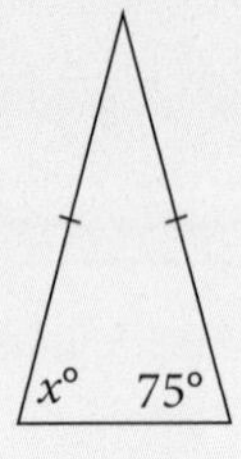

(iii)

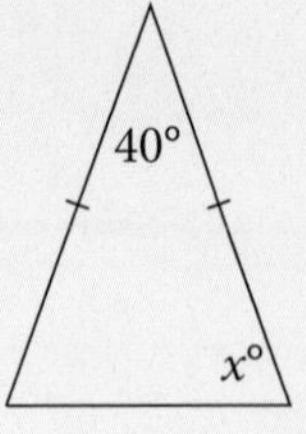

(v)

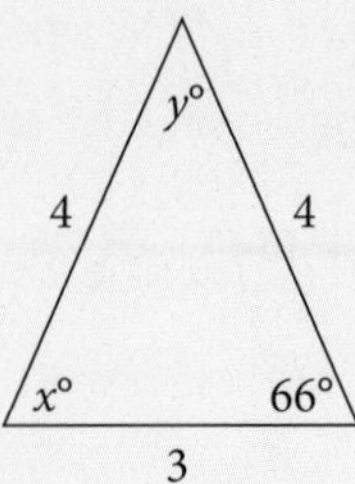

(ii)

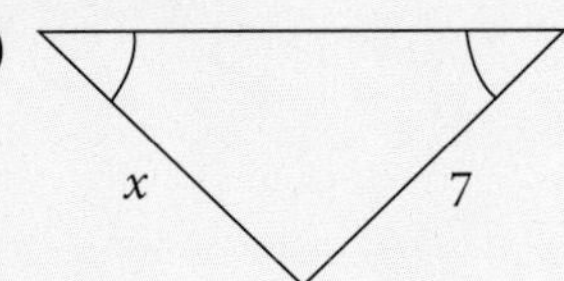

(iv)

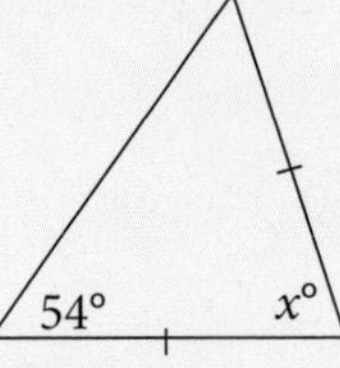

(vi)

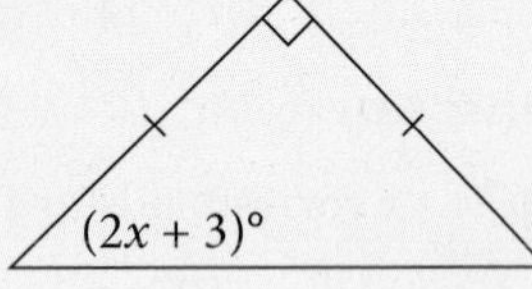

2. Find the labelled angle in each of the following:

(i)

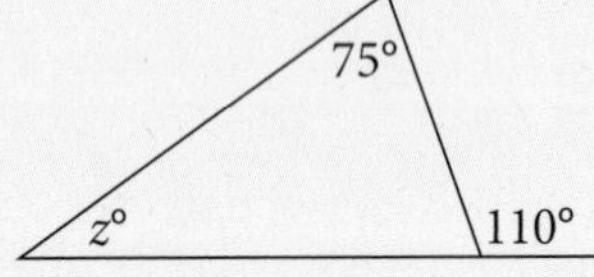

(iii)

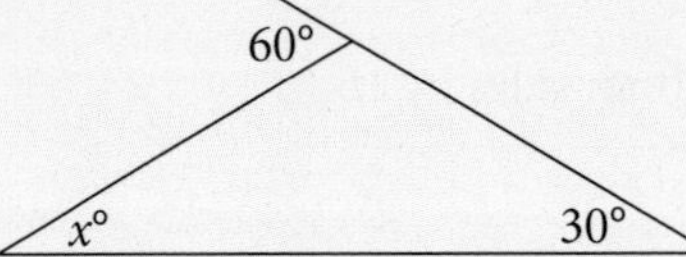

(v)

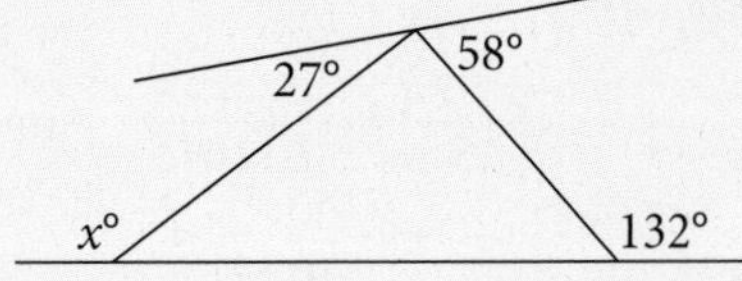

(ii)

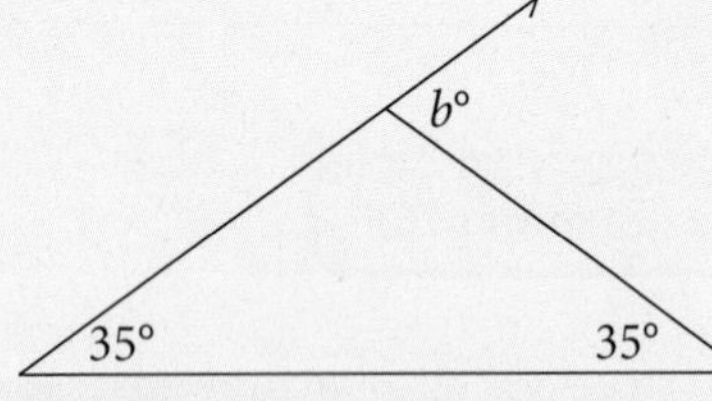

(iv)

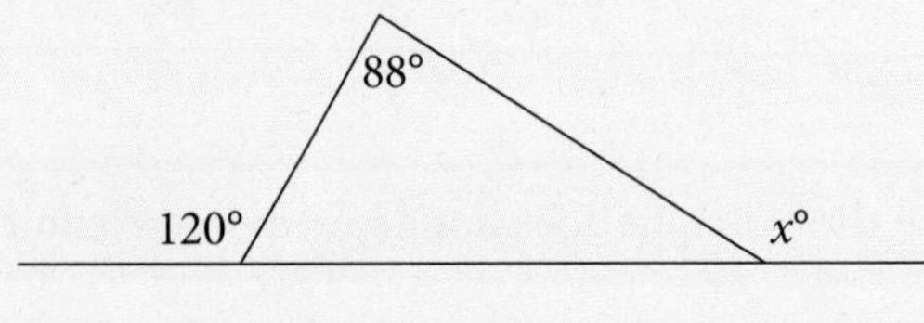

3. Identify the smallest and largest angle in each of the following triangles:

(i)

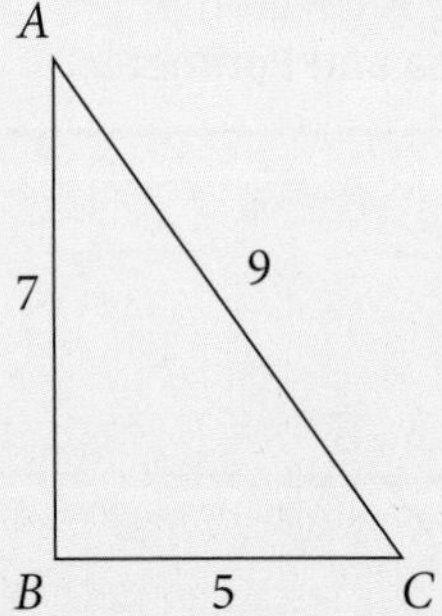

(ii)

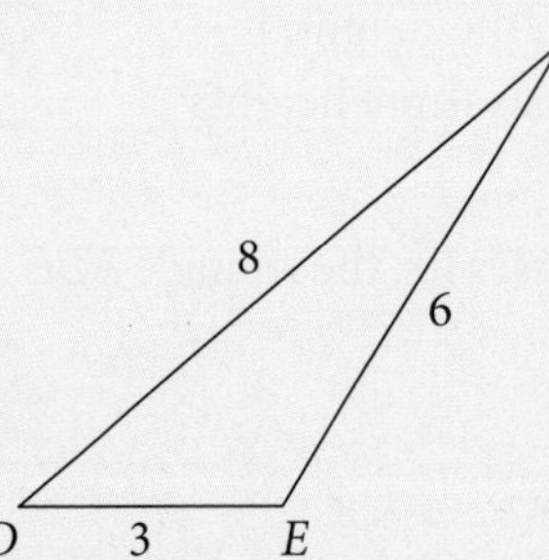

(iii)

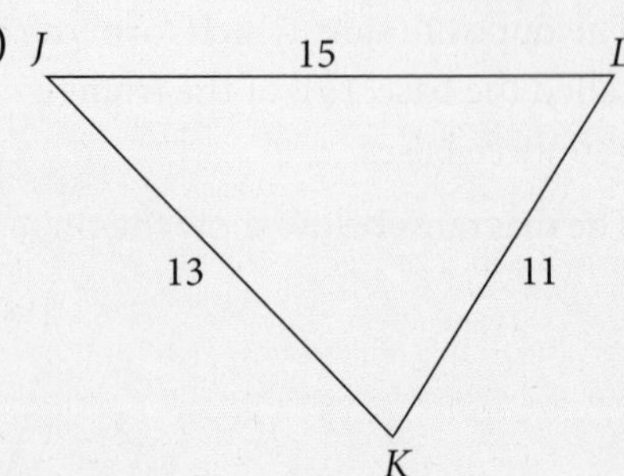

4. Identify the shortest and longest side for each of the following triangles:

(i)

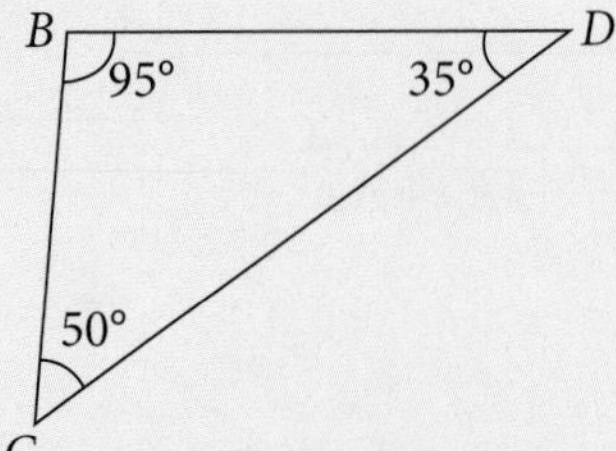

(ii)

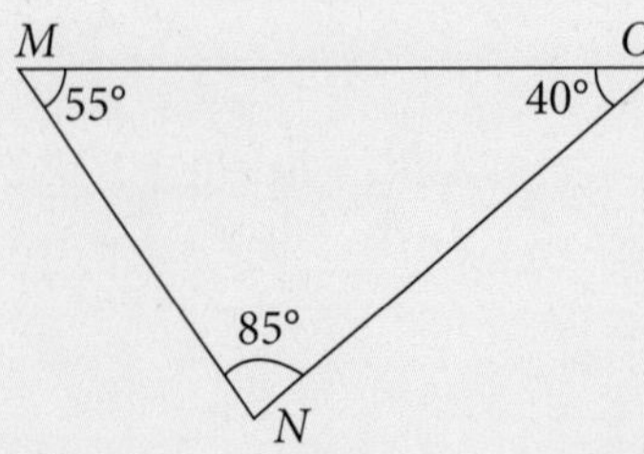

(iii)

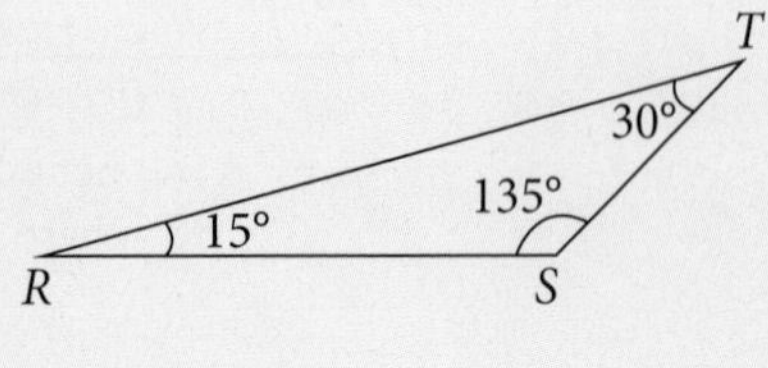

5. The following are six triangles. Some of the measurements on the sides of the triangles are wrong. Identify which triangles have incorrect measurements. Justify your answers.

(i)

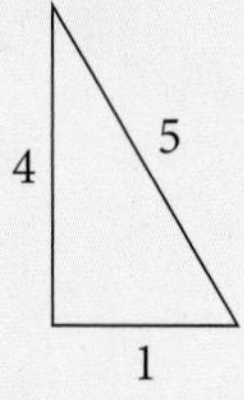

(iii)

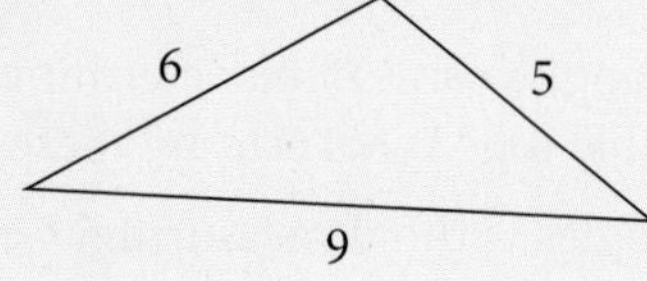

(v)

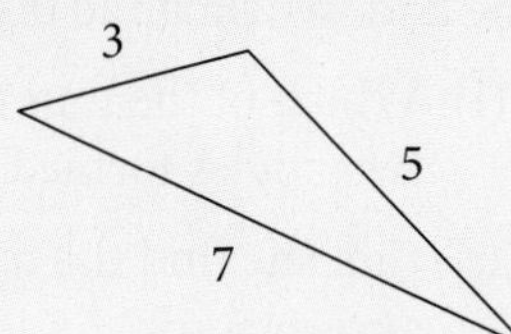

(ii)

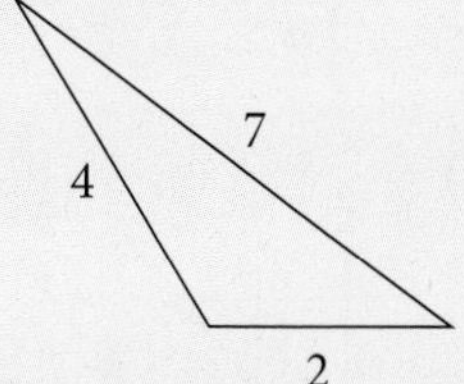

(iv)

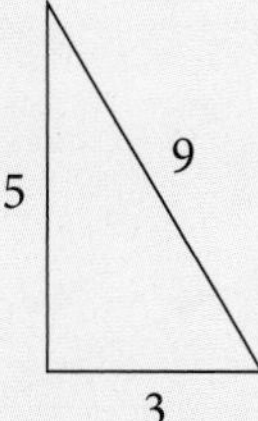

(vi)

6. Find the labelled angles in each of the following. Justify your answers.

(i)

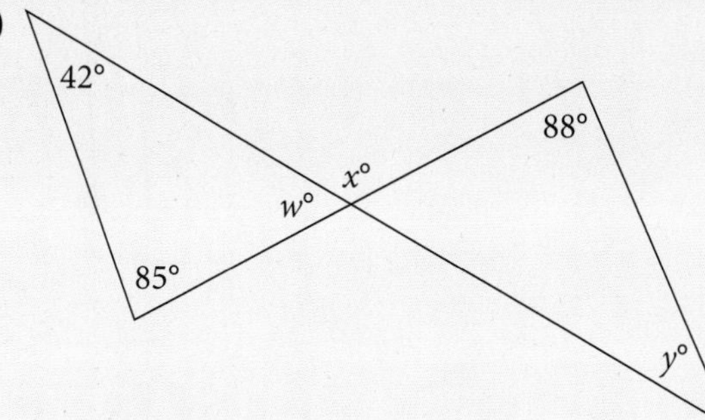

(iii)

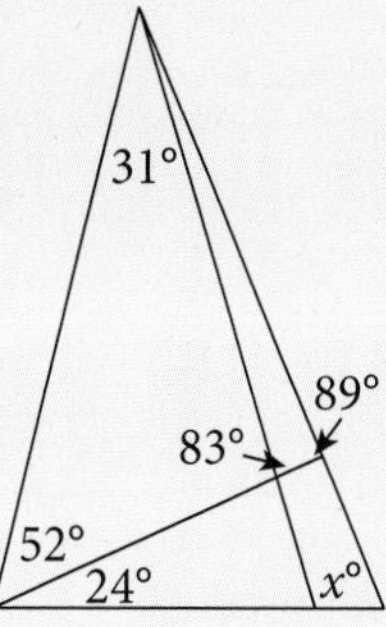

(ii)

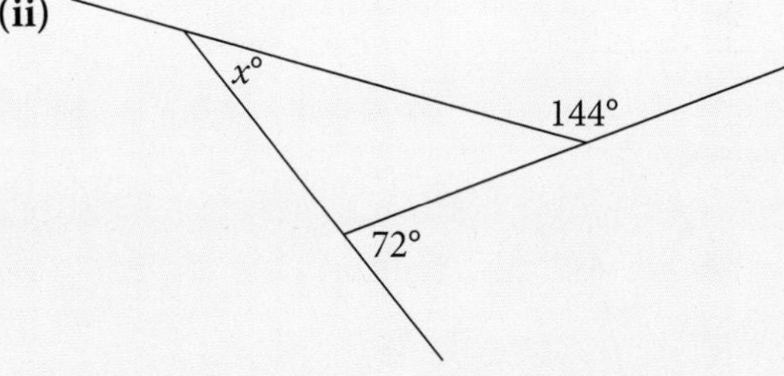

(iv)

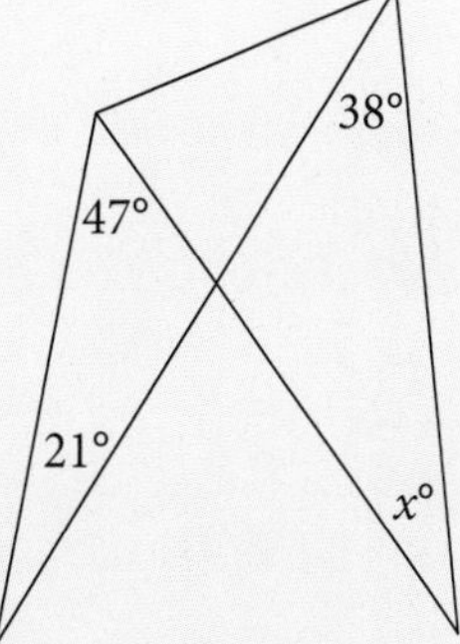

7. Find the value of x and y in the diagram and, hence, calculate each of the angles shown.

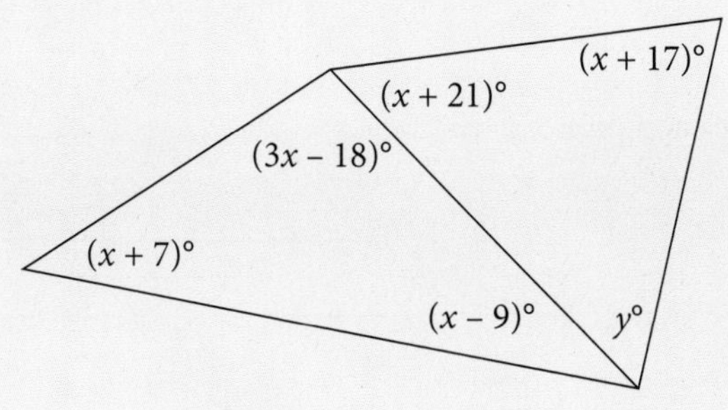

8. The picture shows a piece of bunting on sale during the World Cup. Calculate the value of x.

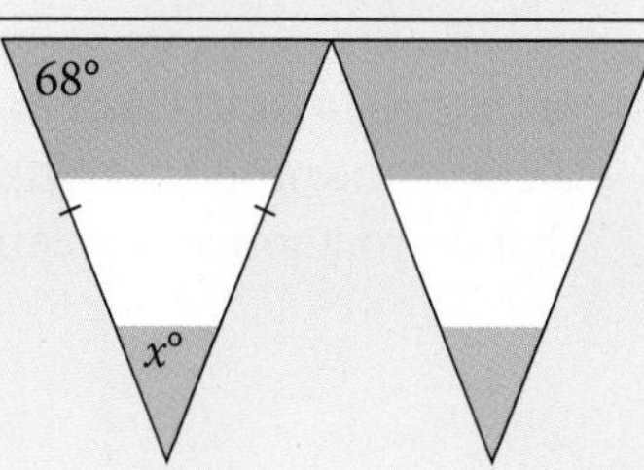

9. Celine bought a drafting table and set it up so that she can draw comfortably from her stool. She measured the two angles created by the legs and the table top in case she had to dismantle the table.

   (i) Which of the four numbered angles can Celine determine by knowing the two angles formed with the table top? What size are these angles?

   (ii) Can she find the remaining angles without measuring? Give a reason for your answer.

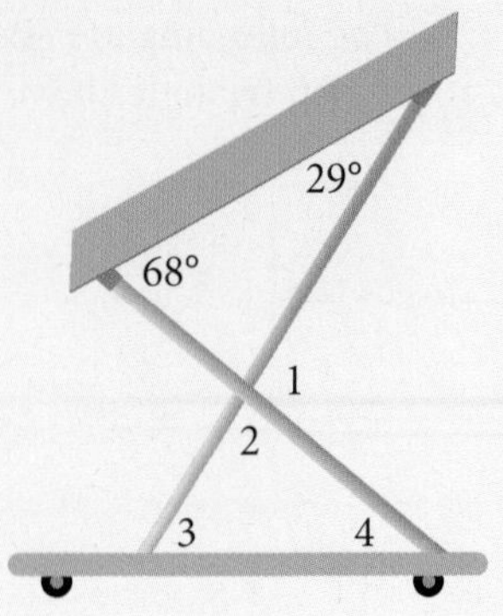

10. Find x in each of the following:

(i)

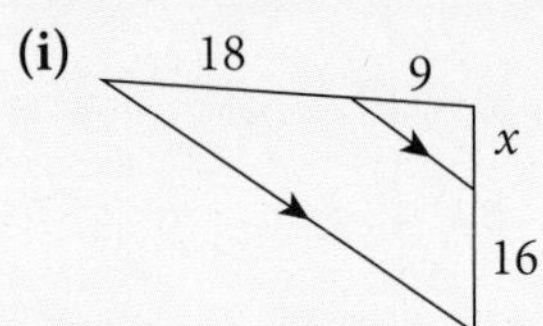

(iii)

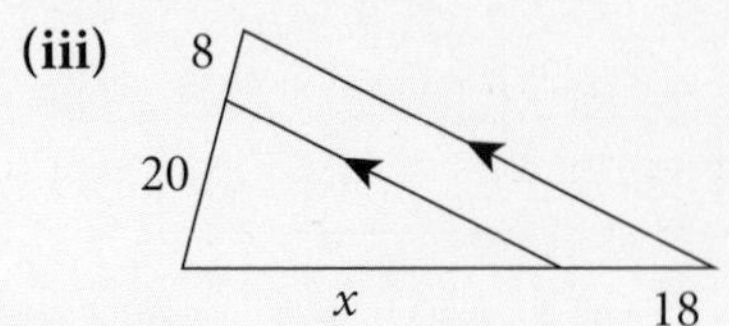

(v)

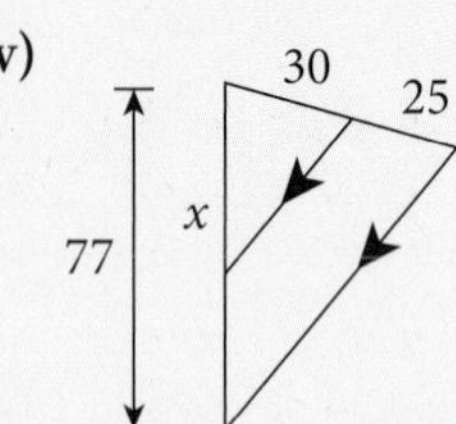

(ii)

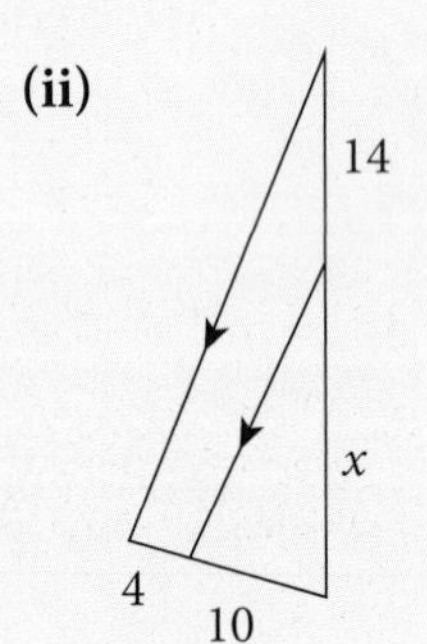

(iv)

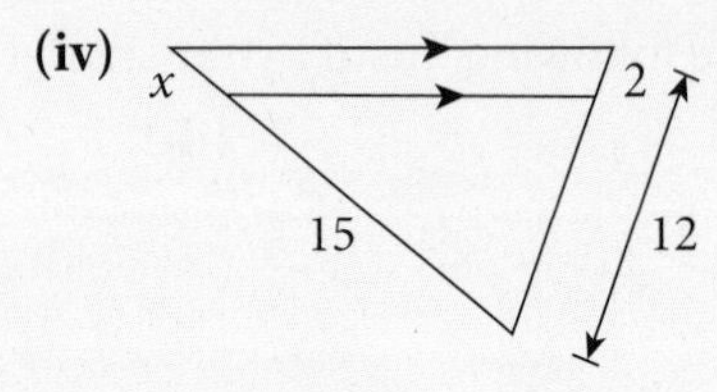

(vi)

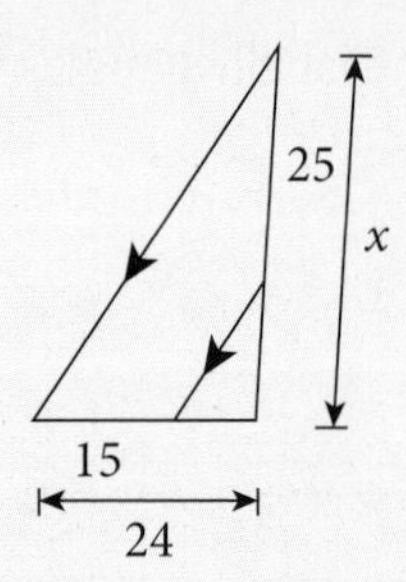

11. Solve for x in each of the following:

(i)

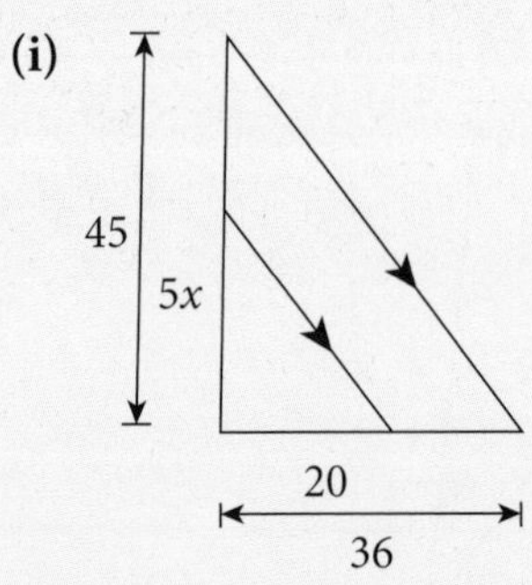

(ii)

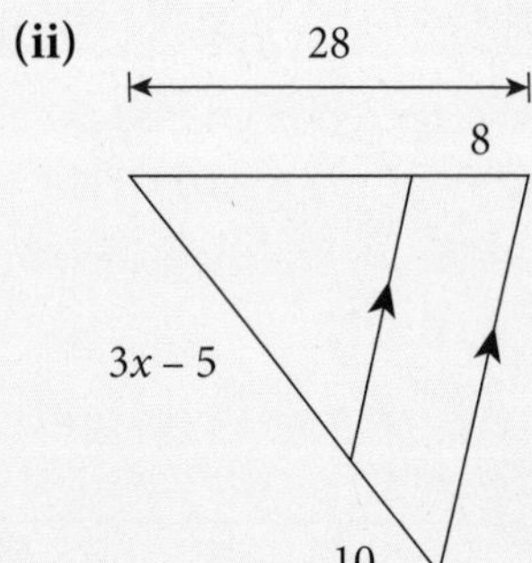

12. (a) Identify the base of the ΔABC when given:

   (i) height = $|CX|$
   (ii) height = $|AY|$
   (iii) height = $|BZ|$

   (b) Measure the heights and bases to one decimal place.

   (i) Calculate the product of the base by the height for each pair.
   (ii) What do you notice? Explain your answer.

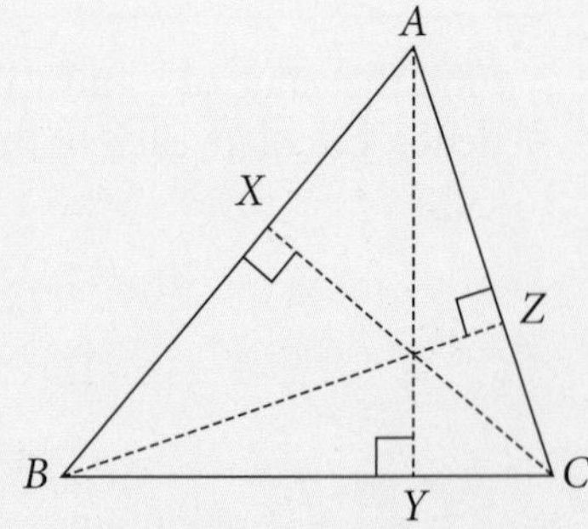

Geometry II

Section 11.2: Congruent Triangles

Learning Outcome:

You should be able to:

- understand the conditions necessary for congruence and use them to prove congruence

Congruent objects are identical. They are the same shape and size. The symbol for congruent is ≡ i.e. $\Delta ABC \equiv \Delta PQR$ means ΔABC is congruent to ΔPQR.

Axiom 4 lists the conditions needed for triangles to be described as congruent. To prove two triangles are congruent, one of the following conditions must be satisfied:

The symbol for congruent is ≡
i.e. $\Delta ABC \equiv \Delta PQR$

Side side side (SSS)

When the sides are the same, then the triangles are congruent.

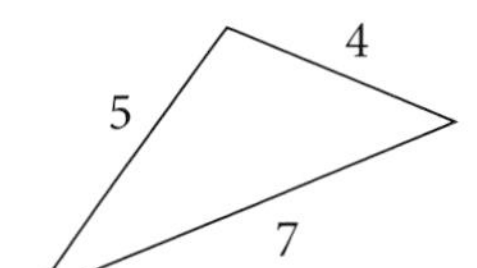

is congruent to:

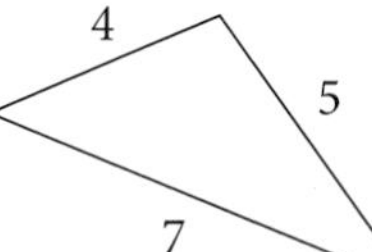

Side angle side (SAS)

When two sides and the angle **between** them are **equal**, then the triangles are congruent.

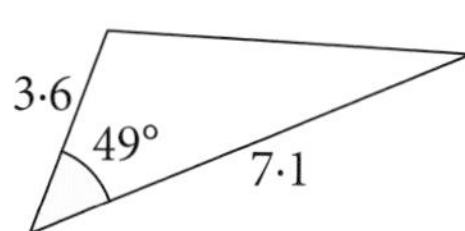

is congruent to: 3·6 49° 7·1

Angle side angle (ASA)

When two angles and the **included** side are **equal**, then the triangles are congruent.

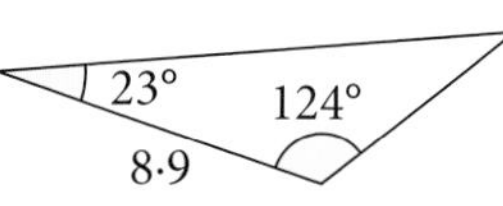

is congruent to:

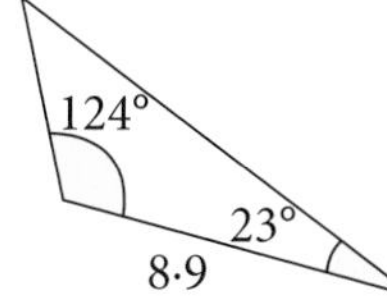

Right angle, hypotenuse and any other side (RHS)

If two triangles are right-angled, have equal hypotenuses and another equal side, the triangles are congruent.

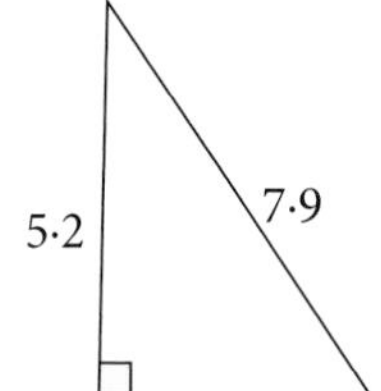

is congruent to:

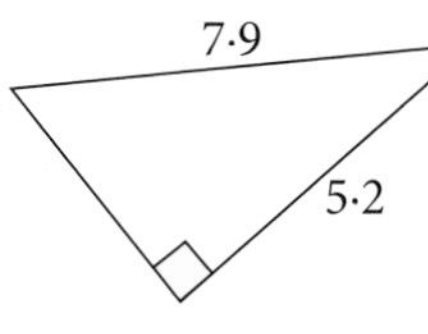

EXAMPLE

Given E is the midpoint of $[BD]$, prove $\Delta EAB \equiv \Delta ECD$.
Explain your answer fully.

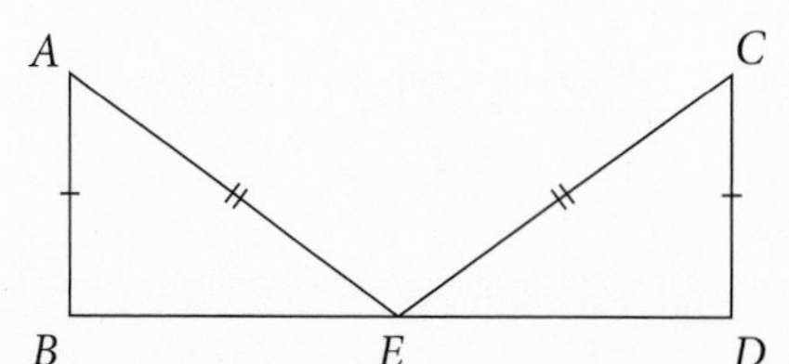

Solution

When answering questions in geometry, it is important that we give a reason for any statement we make.

Statements	**Reason**
$\lvert AB\rvert = \lvert CD\rvert$	Given in diagram.
$\lvert AE\rvert = \lvert CE\rvert$	Given in diagram.
$\lvert BE\rvert = \lvert ED\rvert$	E is the midpoint $\lvert BD\rvert$.

$\therefore \Delta EAB \equiv \Delta ECD$ by SSS (side side side).

Practice Questions 11.2

1. What more do you need to know in the diagram on the right in order to prove congruency by:
   (i) *ASA*?
   (ii) *SAS*?

2. From the information in the diagram, can you prove $\Delta FDG \equiv \Delta FDE$? Explain your answer.

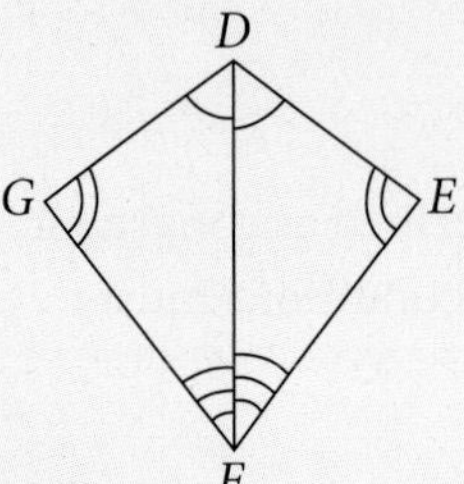

3. State whether ΔABC and ΔAED are congruent. Justify your answer.

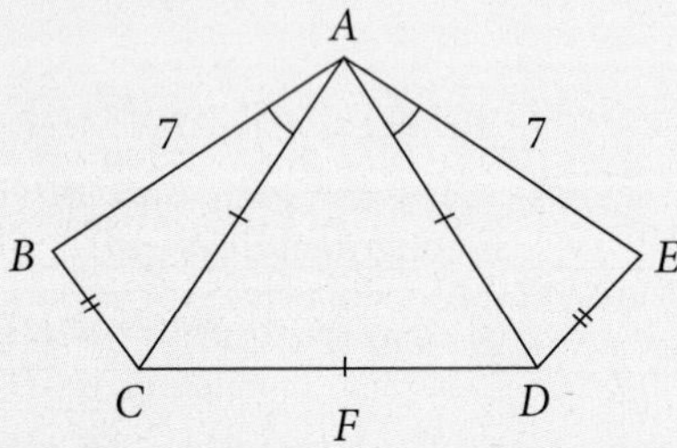

4. Is there enough information to prove the two triangles are congruent in each of the following? If so, write down the method that would be used. If not, explain why not.

   (i)

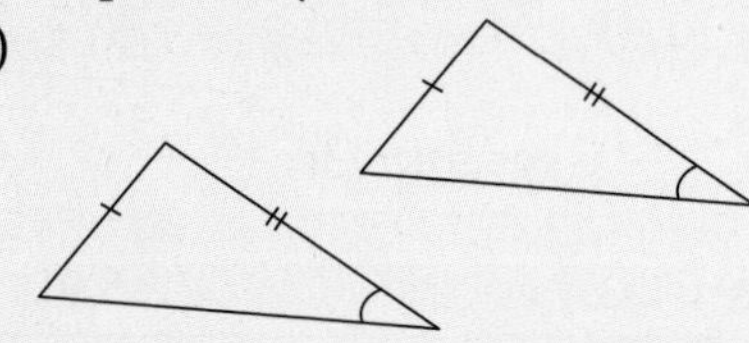

   (ii)

   (iii)

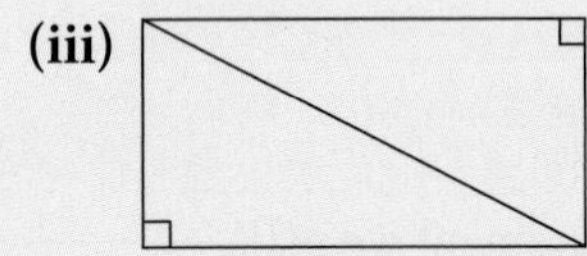

   (iv)

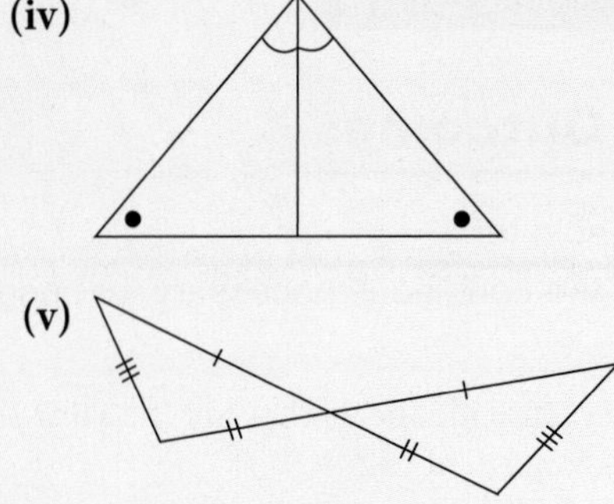

   (v)

   (vi)

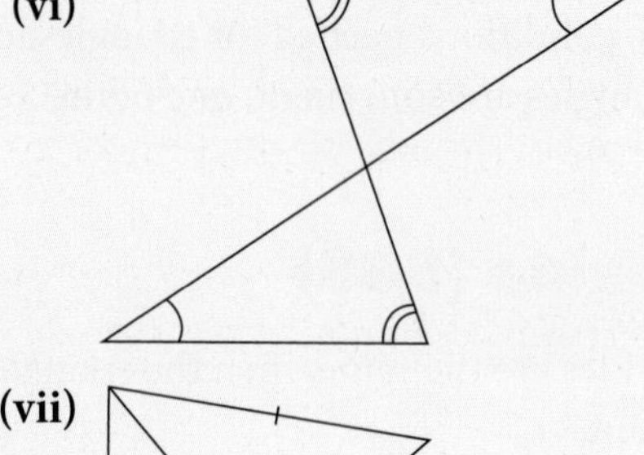

   (vii)

   (viii)

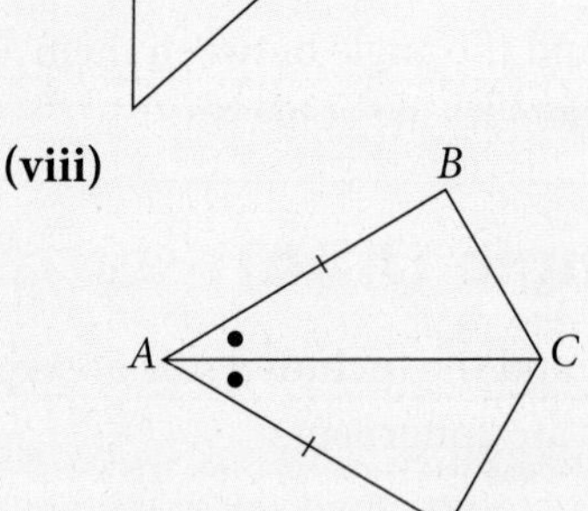

5. An architect is designing a window in a house as shown in the picture. He wants to make ΔXYT congruent to ΔZYT. He designs the window so that $|XY| = |YZ|$ and $|\angle XYT| = |\angle ZYT|$. Prove that ΔXYT is congruent to ΔZYT.

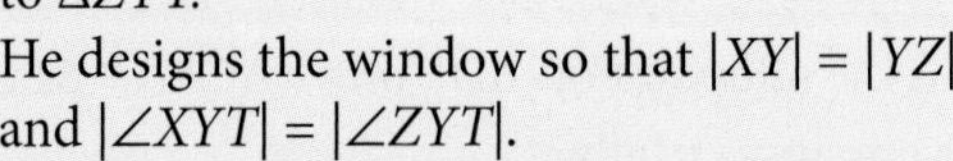

Section 11.3: Similar Triangles

Learning Outcome:

You should be able to:

- understand and use similar triangles to solve problems

Similar triangles have the same angles. (Equiangular)

The word similar suggests a comparison between objects that are alike but not the same.

Similar triangles have the same shape but not necessarily the same size. A similar triangle results when a triangle undergoes an enlargement or reduction.

To prove that two triangles are similar we must prove that two of the angles in the triangles are the same.

8. If two triangles are similar then their sides are proportional, in order. (Theorem 13)

If ΔABC is similar to ΔDEF, then $\frac{|AB|}{|DE|} = \frac{|AC|}{|DF|} = \frac{|BC|}{|EF|}$

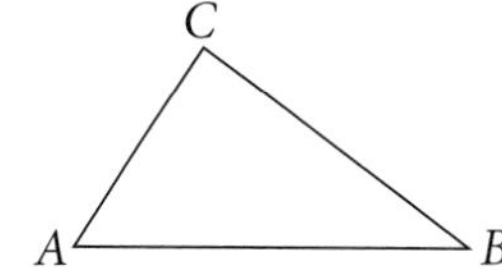

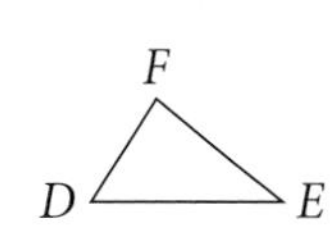

To use this theorem, we must firstly prove that the two triangles in question are similar.

Discussion Time 

Working with a classmate, solve the following:

1. Given that $[AE] \parallel [BD]$, use theorem 12 to find the value of x.
2. Identify an angle that corresponds to $\angle AEC$.
3. Identify an angle that corresponds to $\angle EAC$.
4. What can you say about the angles in ΔAEC and ΔBDC?
5. Investigate whether: $\frac{|AC|}{|BC|} = \frac{|EC|}{|DC|}$

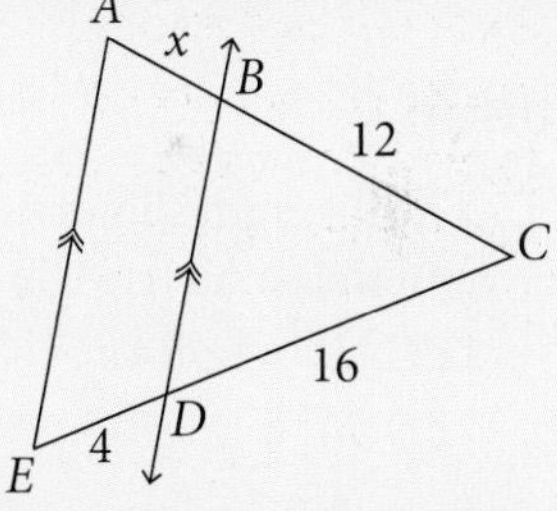

When using this theorem to find unknown sides, the following steps should be followed:

Step 1: Prove the triangles are similar, unless told in the question.

Step 2: Identify the corresponding sides.

Step 3: Write the ratio with the unknown side on the top left.

Step 4: Fill in the relevant values.

Step 5: Solve for the unknown.

EXAMPLE 1

Show that ΔACE and ΔBCD are similar triangles and list the corresponding sides.

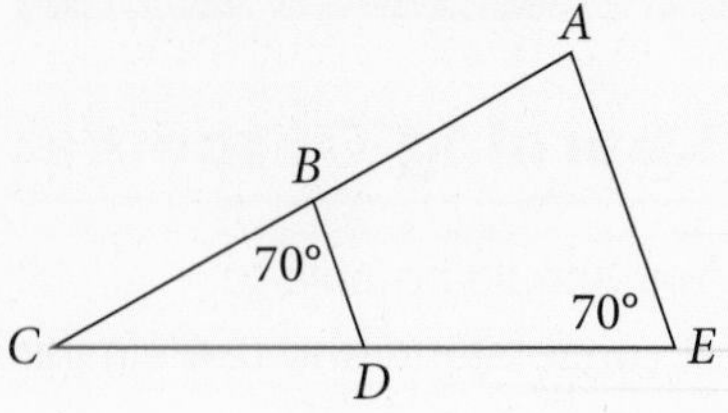

Solution

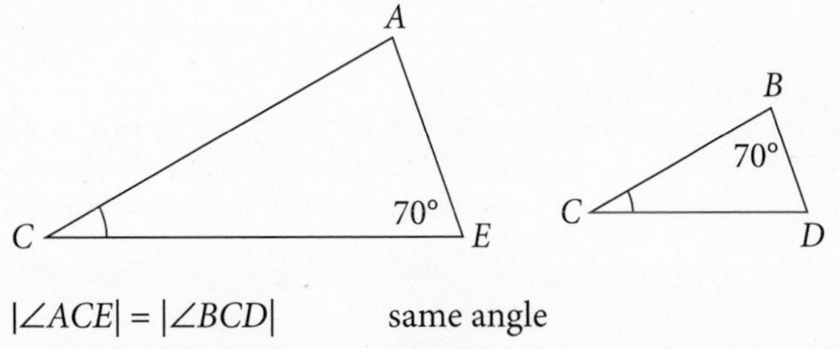

$|\angle ACE| = |\angle BCD|$ same angle

$|\angle AEC| = |\angle DBC|$ given

Two angles are equal, therefore the triangles are similar.

Corresponding sides are opposite the equal angles, so:

$|AC|$ corresponds to $|CD|$,

$|AE|$ corresponds to $|BD|$

$|CE|$ corresponds to $|CB|$.

EXAMPLE 2

Find the value of x.

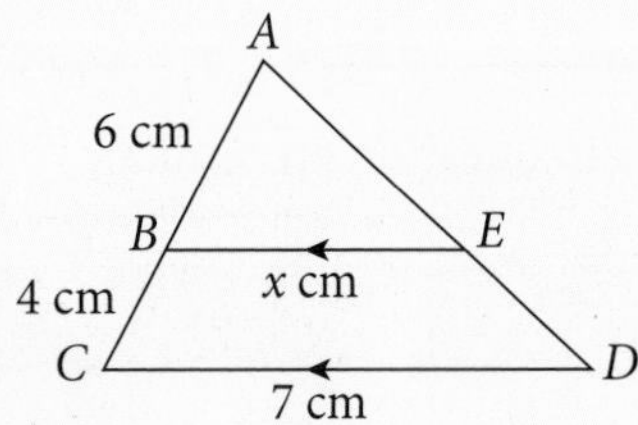

Solution

Step 1: The diagram shows two triangles, the large triangle ΔACD and the small triangle ΔABE.

$|\angle CAD| = |\angle BAE|$ same angle

$|\angle DCA| = |\angle EBA|$ corresponding angles because $[BE] \parallel [CD]$

$|\angle CDA| = |\angle BEA|$ corresponding angles

ΔCAD is equiangular to ΔBAE and therefore the triangles are similar.

Step 2: $|CA|$ corresponds to $|BA|$, $|CD|$ corresponds to $|BE|$ and $|AD|$ corresponds to $|AE|$.

Step 3: We are looking for $|BE|$, therefore the ratio is $\dfrac{|BE|}{|CD|} = \dfrac{|AB|}{|AC|}$

Step 4: $\dfrac{x}{7} = \dfrac{6}{10}$

Step 5: $\dfrac{x}{7} = \dfrac{6}{10}$ multiply both sides by 7

$$7\left(\frac{x}{7}\right) = 7\left(\frac{6}{10}\right)$$

$$x = \frac{42}{10}$$

$$x = 4{\cdot}2 \text{ cm}$$

EXAMPLE 3

Tara is 1·3 m tall. She stands 7 m in front of a tree and casts a shadow 1·8 m long. Her shadow ends at the same point where the shadow of the tree ends. How tall is the tree, to the nearest metre?

We assume that vertical trees, buildings, people, etc. form a right angle with the horizontal ground unless otherwise told.

Solution

In these types of word problems, it is useful to sketch the situation first.

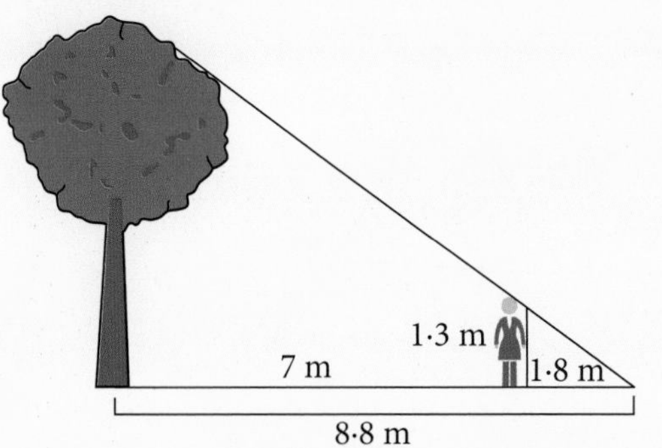

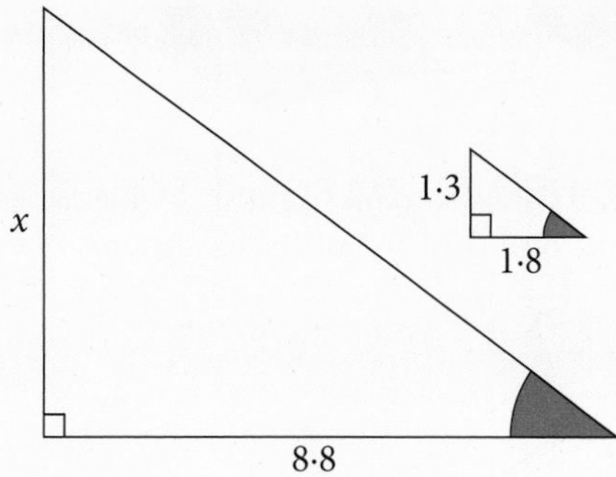

The two triangles are similar as they have a common angle, shown in red, and both contain a right angle.

x corresponds with 1·3 and 8·8 corresponds with 1·8. So the ratio we use is:

$$\frac{x}{1 \cdot 3} = \frac{8 \cdot 8}{1 \cdot 8} \qquad \text{multiply both sides by } 1 \cdot 3$$

$$1 \cdot 3\left(\frac{x}{1 \cdot 3}\right) = 1 \cdot 3\left(\frac{8 \cdot 8}{1 \cdot 8}\right)$$

$$x = 6 \cdot 3\dot{5}$$

The height of the tree to the nearest metre is 6 m.

Practice Questions 11.3

1. Show that the two triangles are similar in each of the following:

(i)

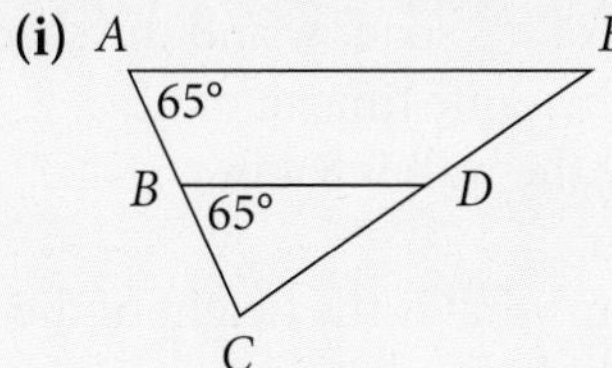

(ii)

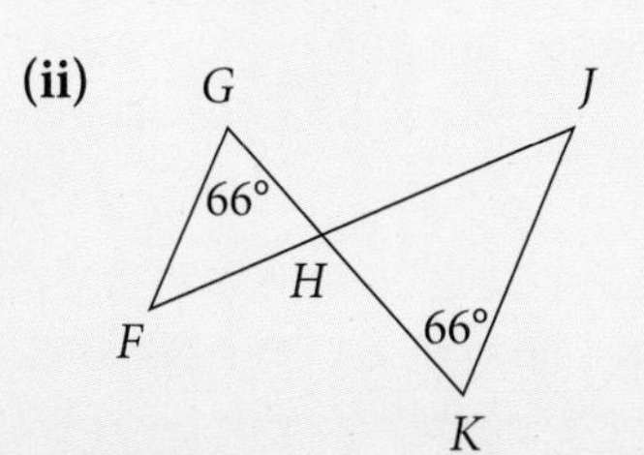

(iii)

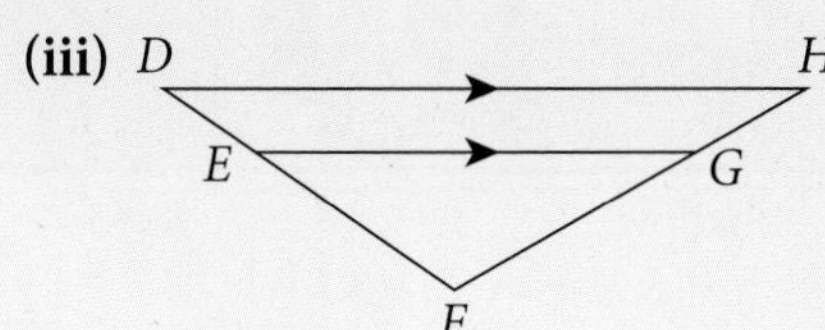

(iv)

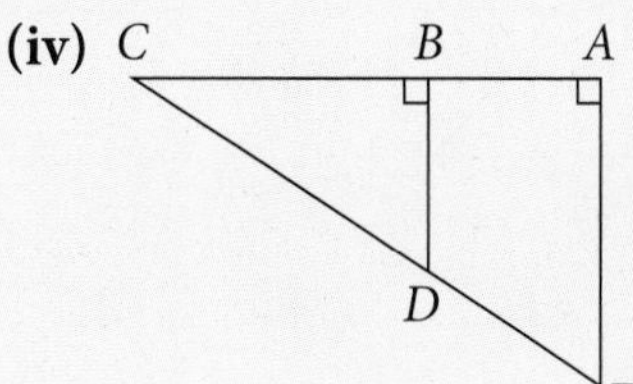

(v)

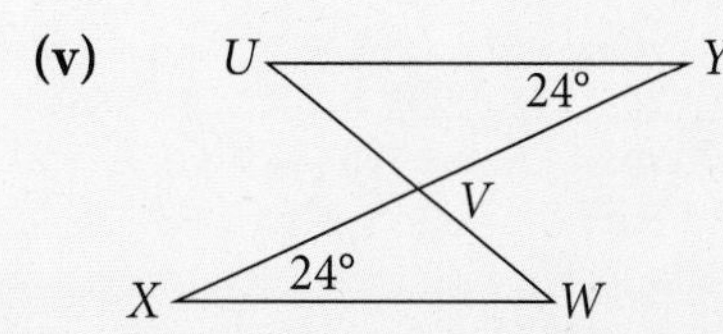

(vi)

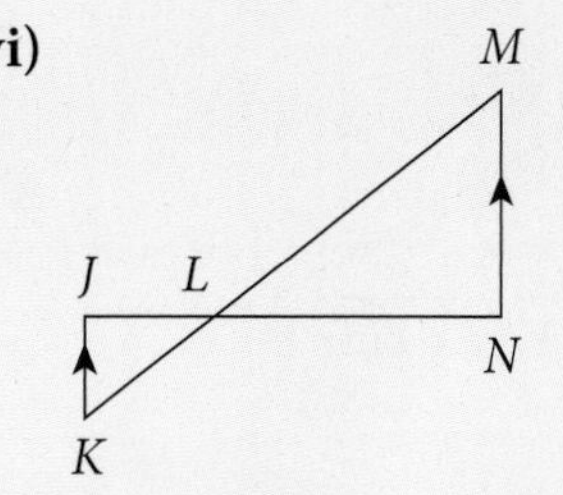

2. A company makes tents of different sizes and colours. Use the information shown in the diagrams to decide whether the triangular faces of these tents are similar. Justify your answer.

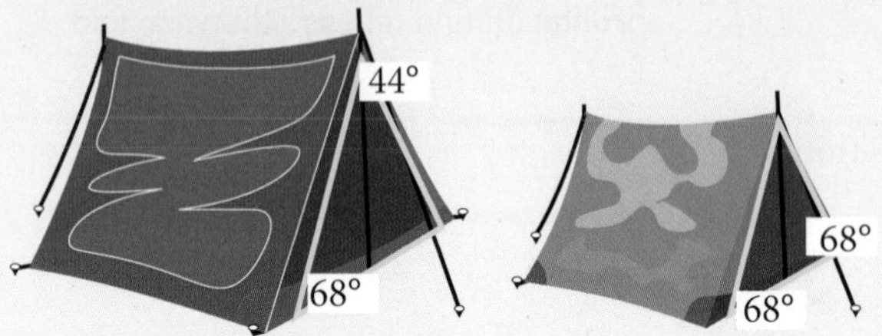

3. In the shape $ABCD$, $AB \parallel DC$, $AD \parallel BC$ and $|EC|$ is 5 units. $|AE| = 4$ units and $|EB| = 2$ units, as shown.

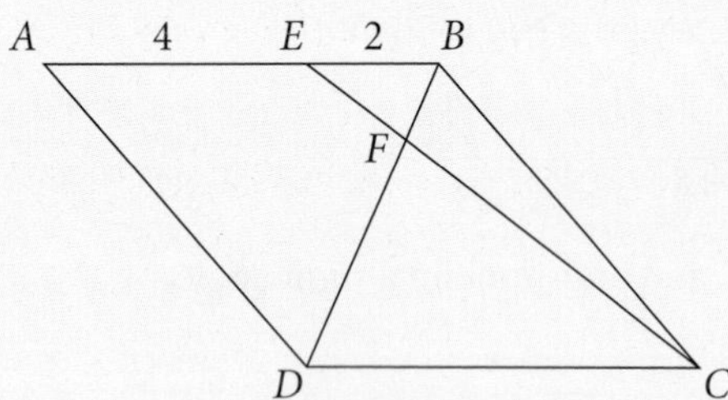

(i) Identify a pair of similar triangles in the diagram.

(ii) Explain why the triangles you named are similar

(iii) Find the length of $|FC|$.

4. By firstly showing the triangles are similar, find x in each of the following:

(i)

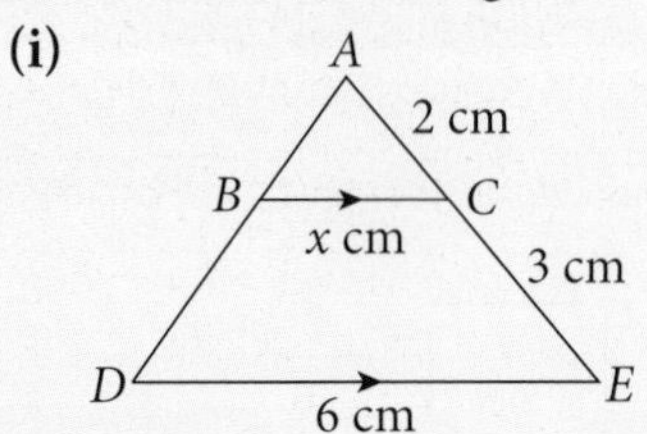

(ii)

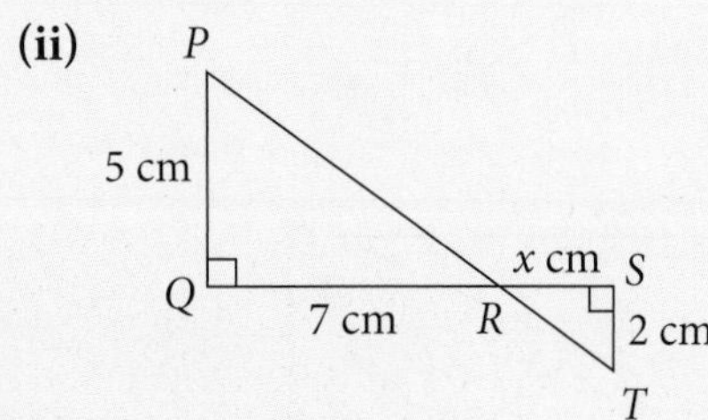

(iii)

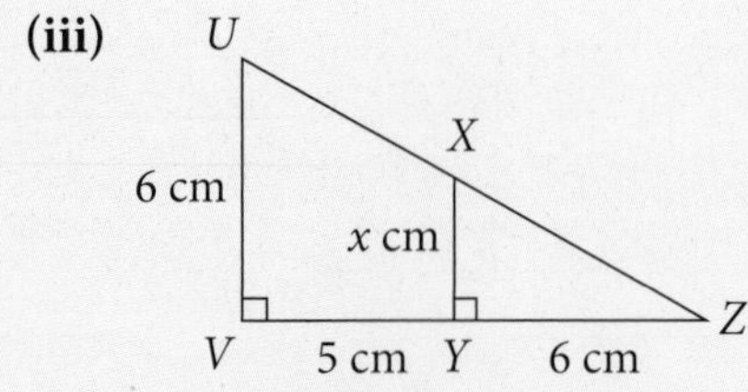

(iv)

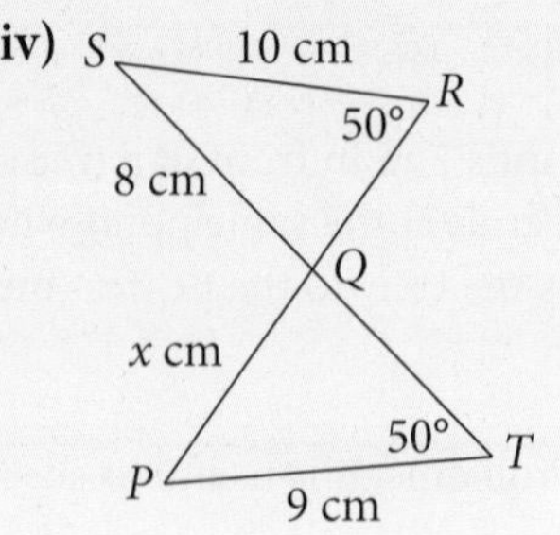

(v)

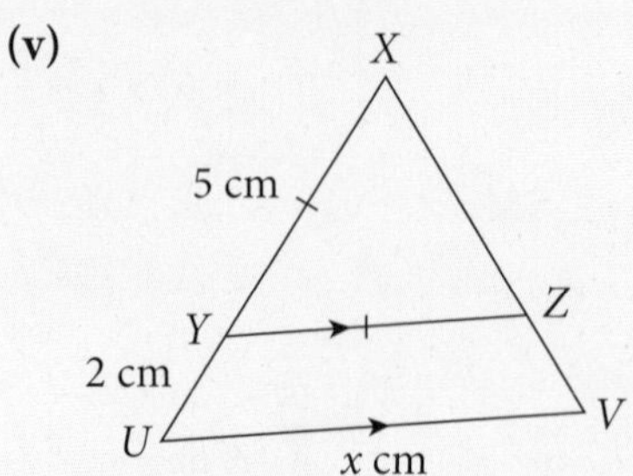

(vi)

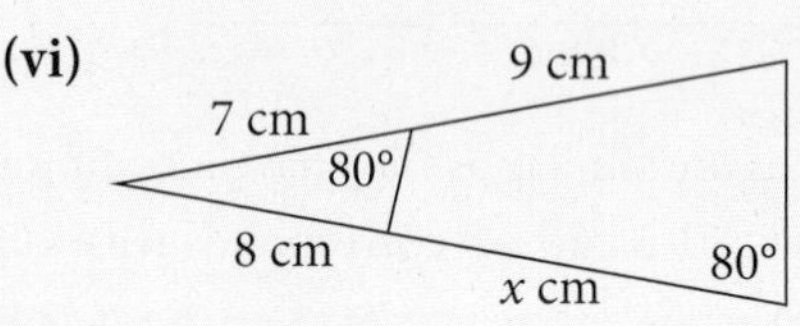

5. On the shoe rack shown, $|BA| = 33$ cm, $|CB| = 27$ cm, $|CD| = 44$ cm, and $|DE| = 25$ cm. Investigate whether the shelf $[BD]$ is parallel to the floor $[AE]$.

C B D A E

Use the converse of the theorem.

6. Sam wants to measure the height of a vertical climbing wall in his local park. He decides to measure the length of his shadow and the shadow cast by the wall at the same time of day.
The shadow cast by the wall is 8·4 m.
His shadow is 3·1 m.
If his height is 1·7 m, what is the height of the wall?

Since the sun's rays are parallel, these triangles are similar.

Geometry II

7. The height of the net in tennis is 0·9 m and the service line is 6 m from the net.
From what height will a player serve the ball so that it will just pass over the net and land 2 m from the net?

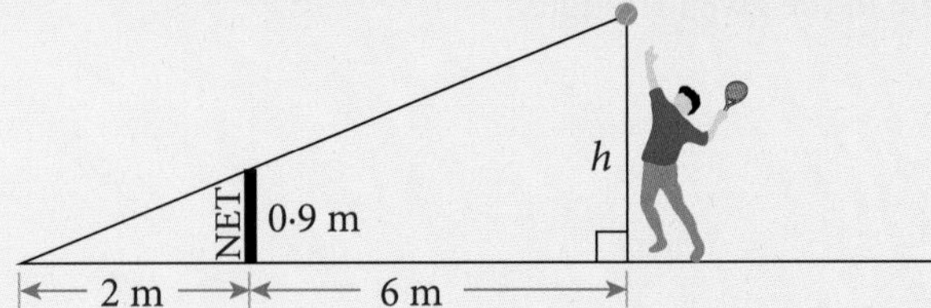

8. Chloe is 1·5 m tall. Her shadow is 3·5 m long. She notices that the end of her shadow, the top of her head, and the top of a building are in a straight line. The building is 28 m tall.
   (i) Draw a sketch to represent this situation.
   (ii) Use your sketch to work out how far she is from the building.

9. A father and son are standing side by side. How tall is the son if the father is 1·8 m tall and casts a shadow 3·2 m long, while his son's shadow is 2·4 m long?

10. Two extension ladders are leaning at the same angle against a vertical wall. The 3 m ladder reaches 2·4 m up the wall.
How much farther up the wall does the 8 m ladder reach?

Section 11.4: Pythagoras' Theorem

Learning Outcome:

You should be able to:
- understand and use Pythagoras' theorem to solve problems

9. In a right-angled triangle the square of the hypotenuse is equal to the sum of the squares of the other two sides. (Theorem 14)

Links across the syllabus

Pythagoras' theorem is covered in Chapter 20: Trigonometry I.

Remember, the hypotenuse is the side opposite the right angle (90°) and is the longest side.

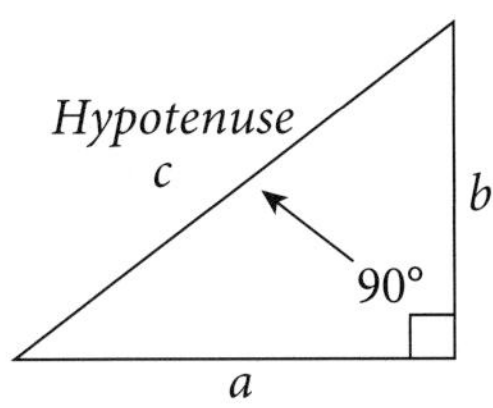

Pythagoras' theorem is in the booklet of *formulae and tables* on page 16, as shown.

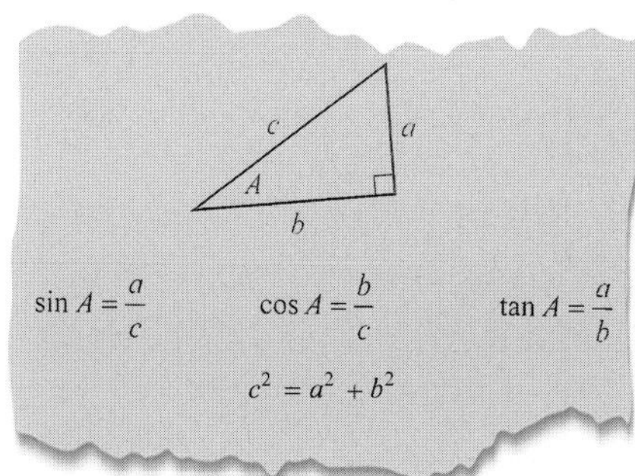

10. Converse of Pythagoras: If the square of one side of a triangle is the sum of the squares of the other two, then the angle opposite the first side is a right angle. (Theorem 15)

EXAMPLE

Find the length of the missing side in the given triangle.
Give your answer in surd form.

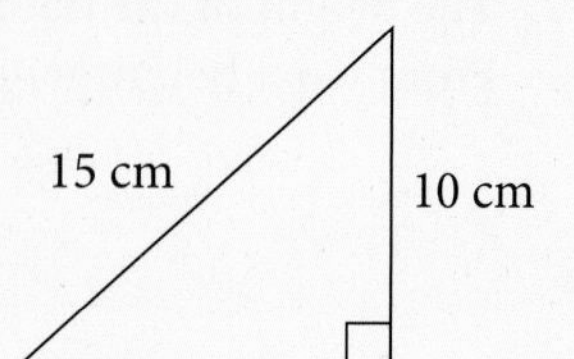

Solution

Identify the hypotenuse as 15 cm.

Formula: $c^2 = a^2 + b^2$

$15^2 = 10^2 + b^2$ (hypotenuse = 15)

$225 = 100 + b^2$

$225 - 100 = b^2$ (subtract 100 from both sides)

$125 = b^2$

$\sqrt{125} = b$ (square root both sides)

$5\sqrt{5}$ cm $= b$

Links across the syllabus

Breaking down surds is covered in Chapter 1: Number Systems.

Practice Questions 11.4

1. Find the length of the third side to one decimal place in each of the following triangles:

(i)

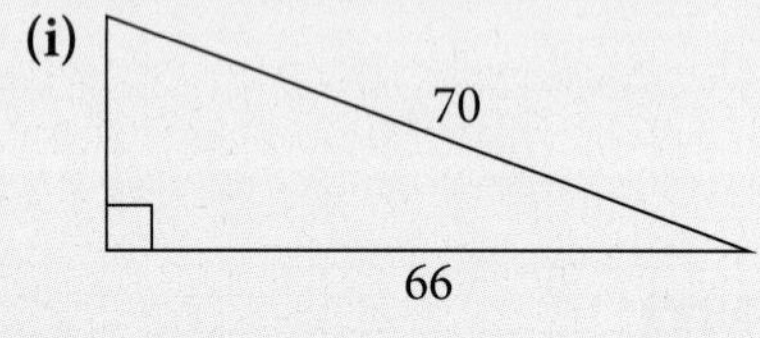

(ii)

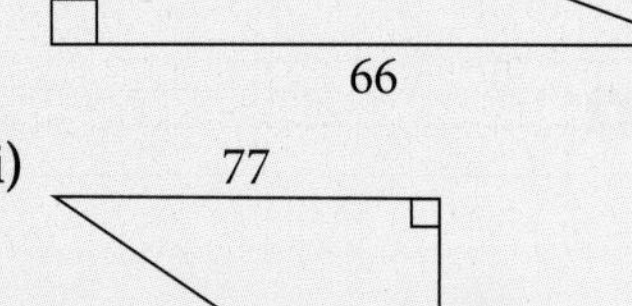

(iii)

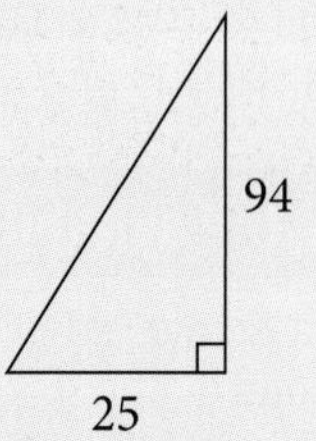

(iv)

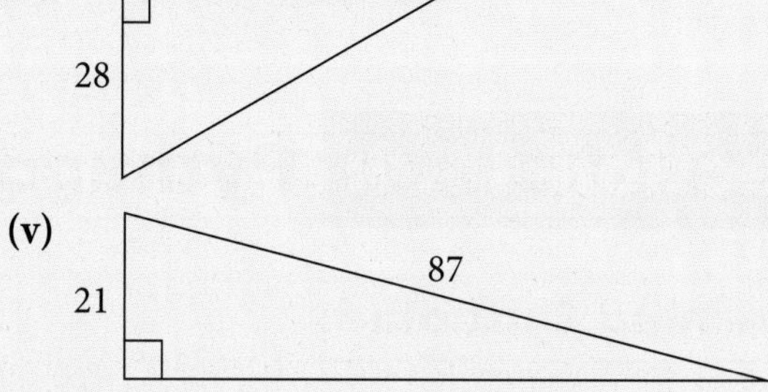

(v)

(vi)

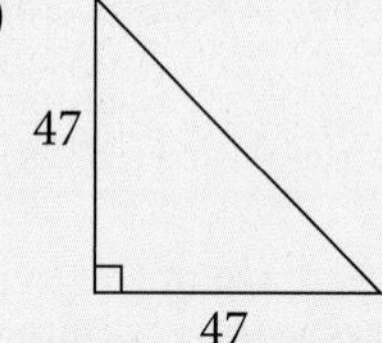

2. Are the following triangles right-angled triangles? Justify your answers.

(i)

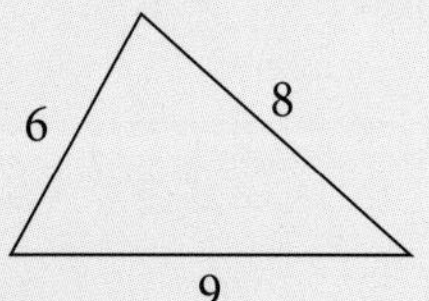

(ii)

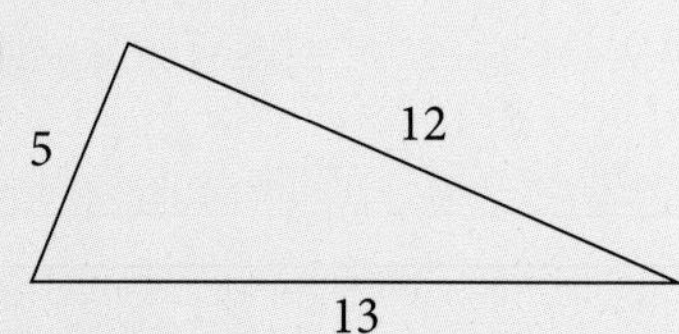

(iii)

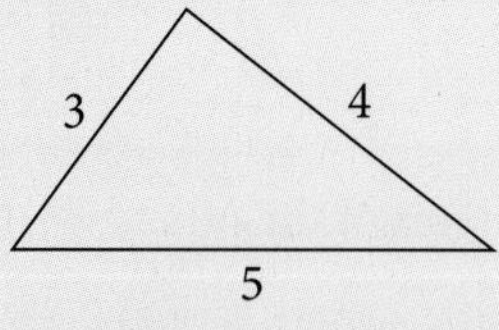

(iv)

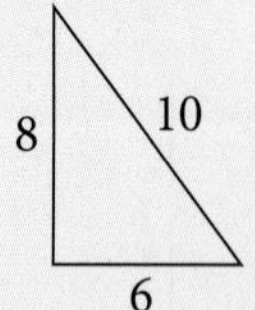

(v)

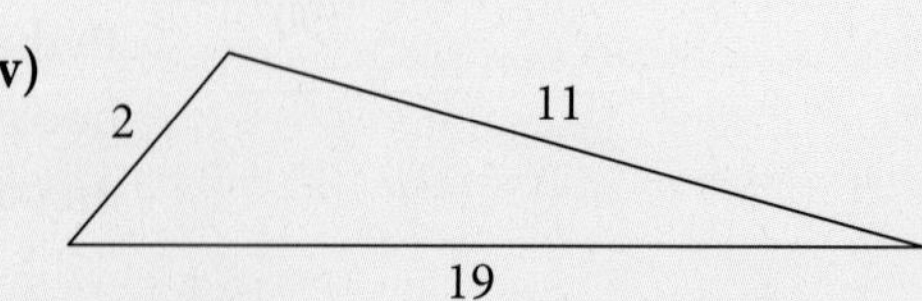

(vi)

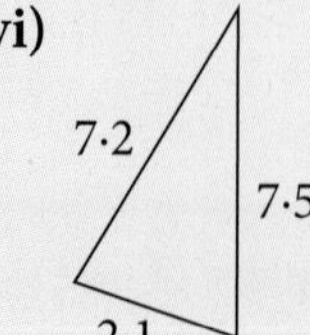

Geometry II

3. Triangle ABC is a right-angled triangle. Calculate $|AC|$, correct to three significant figures.

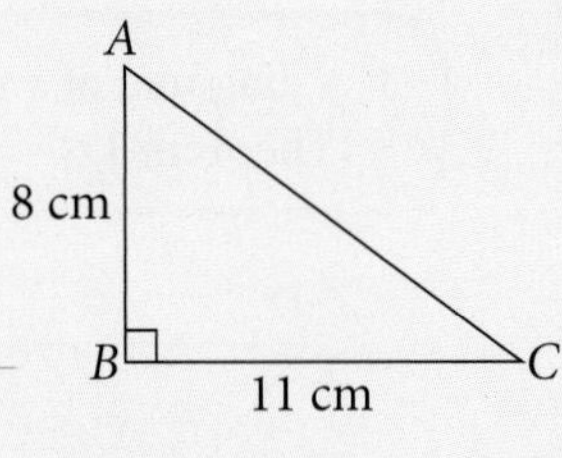

4. $ABCD$ is a rectangle. Calculate $|DC|$, correct to one decimal place.

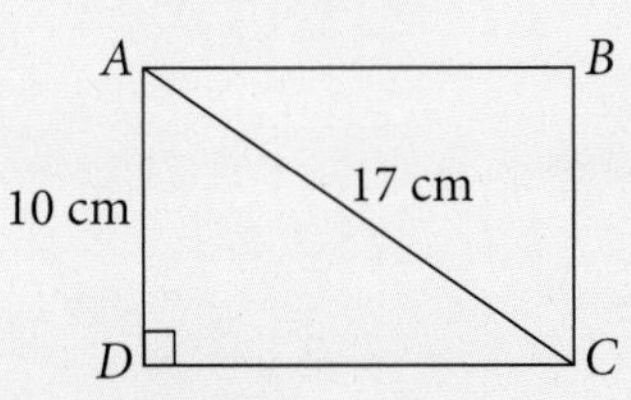

5. Televisions are sold by the length of the diagonal of the screen.

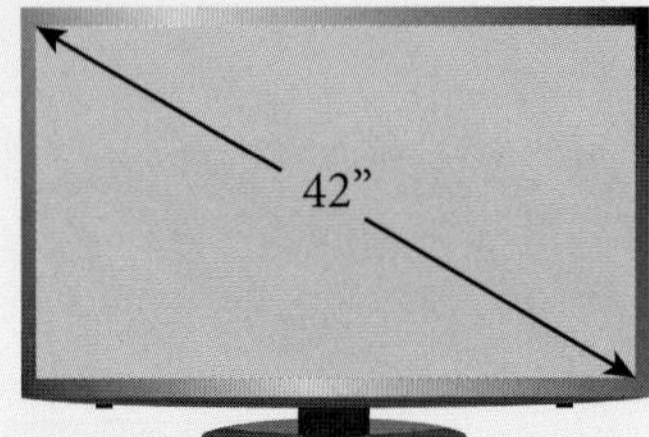

(i) If the height of the screen on a 42 inch television is 20·6 inches, what is its width?

(ii) What is the aspect ratio (height:width) of the television?

6. A ladder is 6 m long. The ladder is placed on horizontal ground, resting against a vertical wall. The instructions for using the ladder say that the bottom of the ladder must not be closer than 1·5 m from the bottom of the wall.
How far up the wall can the ladder reach? Give your answer correct to one decimal place.

7. Steve made a small rectangular table for his bedroom. The sides of the table are 3·6 m and 1·8 m. If the diagonal of the table measures 4·3 m, is the table square?

A table which is ‘square’ has right angles at the corners.

Section 11.5: Parallelogram Theorems

Learning Outcome:

You should be able to:

- understand and use parallelogram theorems and corollary to solve problems

A parallelogram is a four-sided figure in which opposite sides are parallel. All squares, rectangles and rhombuses are parallelograms.

1. In a parallelogram, opposite sides are equal and opposite angles are equal. (Theorem 9)

$$|AB| = |DC| \quad \text{and} \quad |AD| = |BC|$$
$$|\angle ADC| = |\angle ABC| \text{ and } |\angle BAD| = |\angle BCD|$$

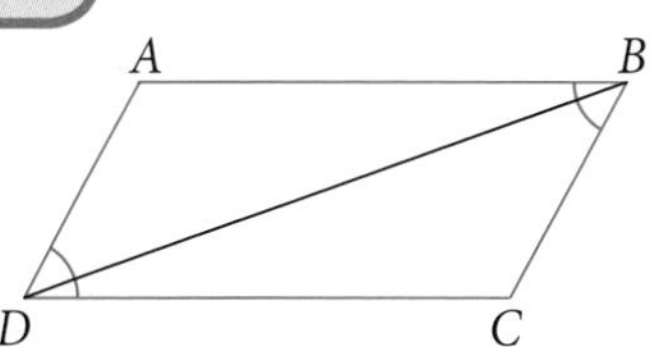

Converse 1: If the opposite angles of a quadrilateral are equal, it is a parallelogram.

Converse 2: If the opposite sides of a quadrilateral are equal, it is a parallelogram.

Corollary: A diagonal divides a parallelogram into two congruent triangles.

Discussion Time

Working with a classmate, prove that in the parallelogram shown, ΔABD is congruent to ΔCBD.

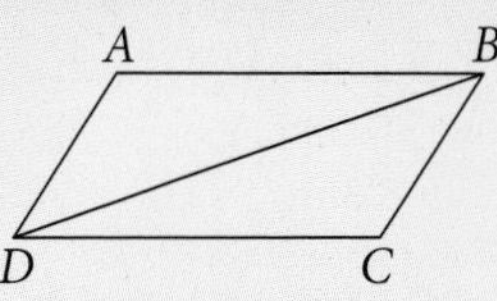

2. The diagonals of a parallelogram bisect each other. (Theorem 10)

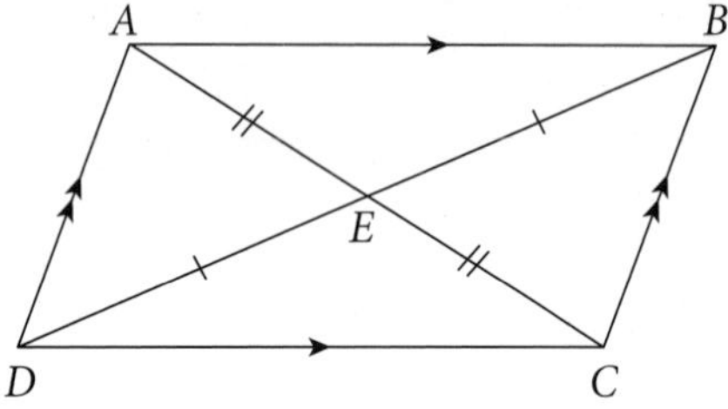

$|AE| = |EC|$ and $|DE| = |EB|$

3. A diagonal of a parallelogram bisects its area. (Theorem 17)

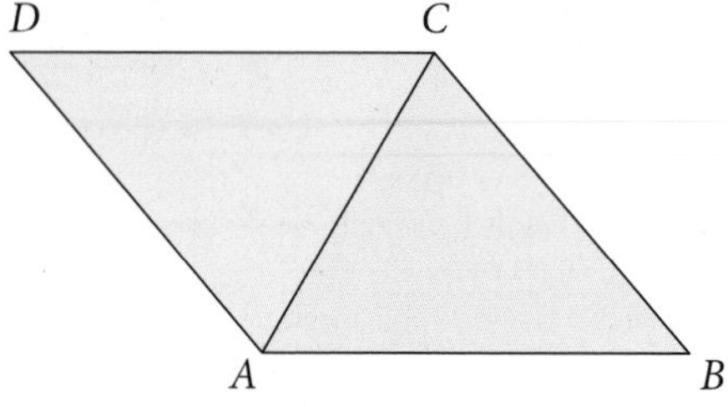

Area ΔABC = Area ΔADC

4. The area of a parallelogram is the base by the height. (Theorem 18)

Area of a parallelogram = (base) × (height)

Links across the syllabus

The area of a parallelogram is also covered in Chapter 16: Area and Perimeter.

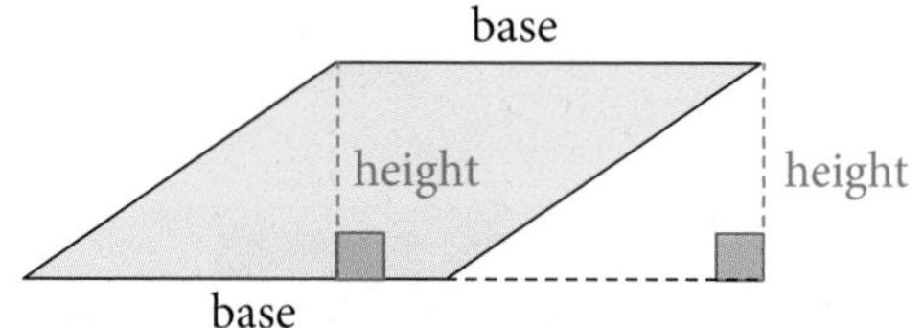

Practice Questions 11.5

1. Find the value of x in each parallelogram.

(i)
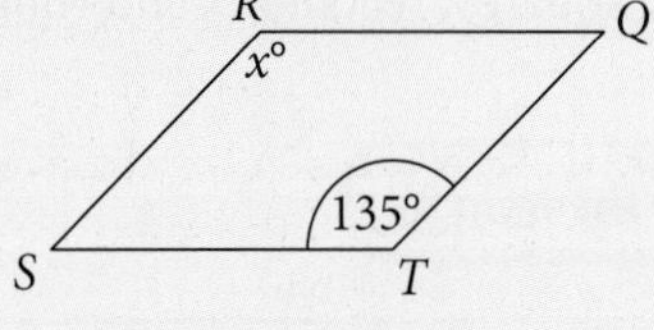

(ii)
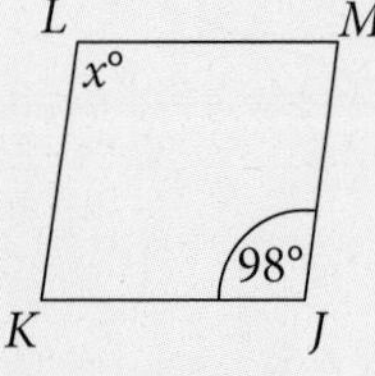

(iii)
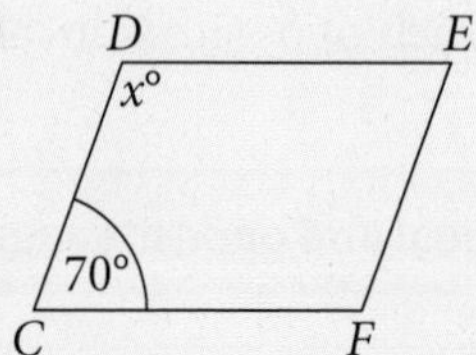

(iv)
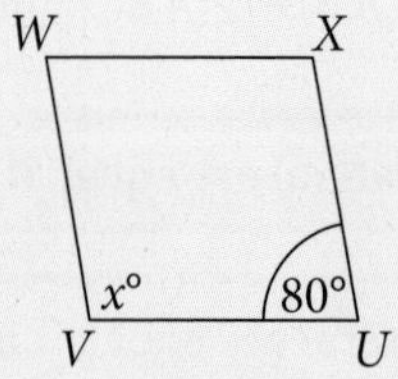

(v)
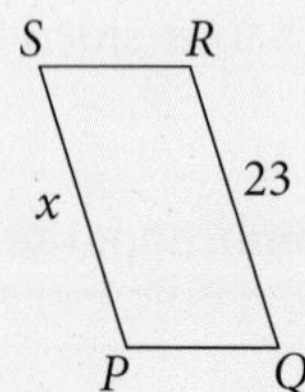

(vi)
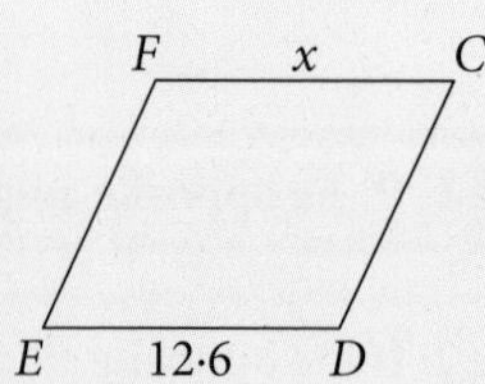

2. Find the area of the following parallelograms:

(i)
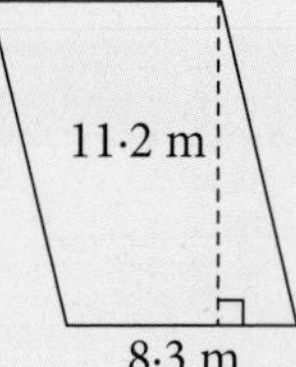

(ii)
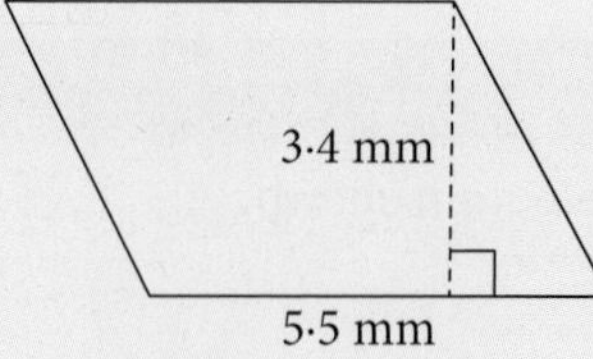

(iii)
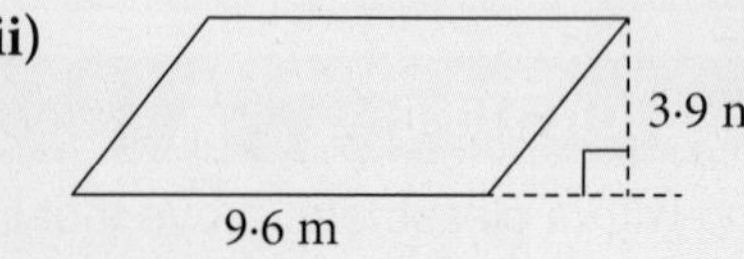

3. Answer the following questions based on the paralleogram shown:

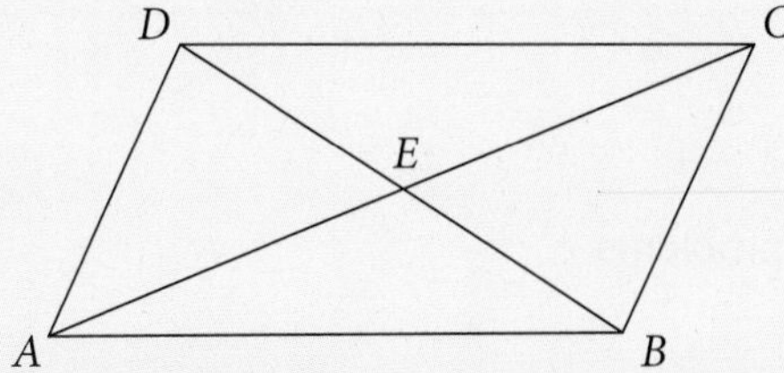

(i) If $|AD|$ is 15 cm, what length is $|CB|$?

(ii) If $|DC|$ is 24 cm, what length is $|AB|$?

(iii) If $|AC|$ is 32 cm, what length is $|AE|$?

(iv) If $|DE|$ is 13 cm, what length is $|DB|$?

(v) If $|\angle DAB|$ is 100°, what size is $\angle ADC$?

4. Find the length of each of the sides of the parallelogram shown.

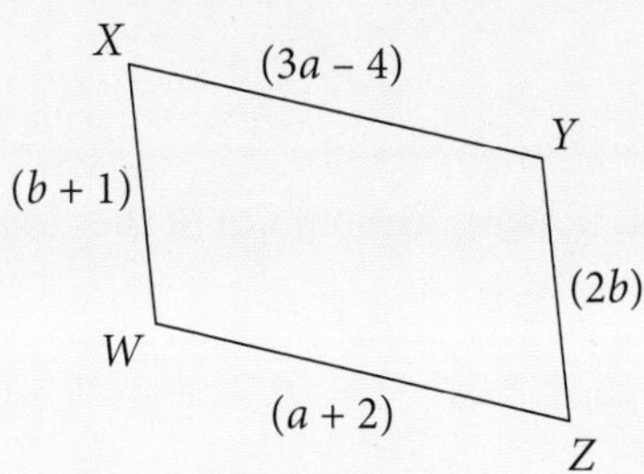

5. Calculate the size of each of the angles in the parallelogram shown here.

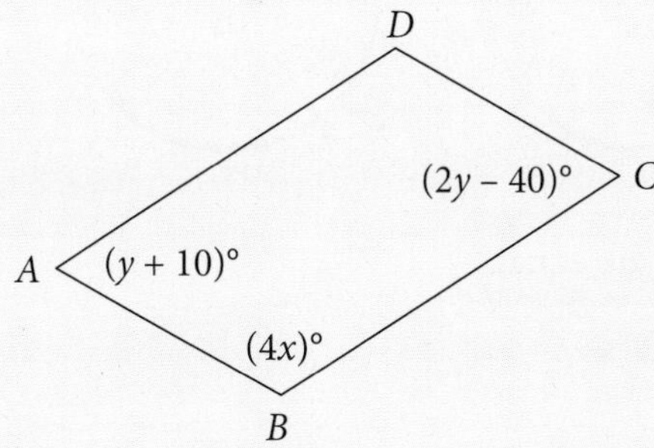

6. $ABCD$ is a parallelogram.

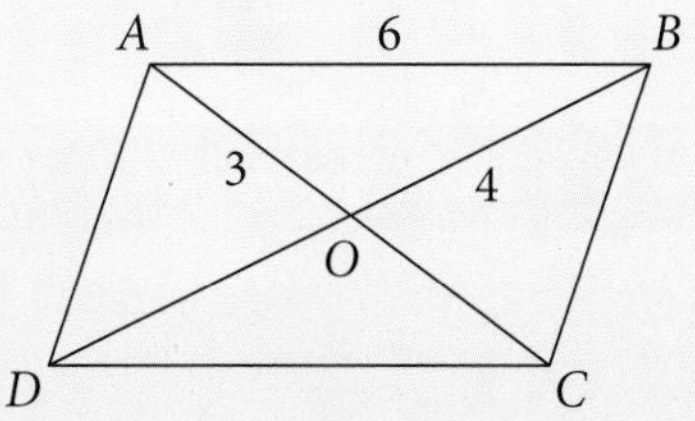

$|AO| = 3$, $|BO| = 4$ and $|AB| = 6$

(i) Find $|AC| + |BD|$.

(ii) Investigate whether ΔDOC is right-angled.

7. $ABCD$ is a parallelogram. The diagonals intersect at the point O.

$|AO| = x + 4$, $|BO| = 2y - 6$, $|CO| = 3x - 4$, and $|DO| = y + 2$

(i) Draw $ABCD$. (ii) Solve for x and y.

8. In a parallelogram, $PQRS$, the ratio of $|PQ|$ to $|QR|$ is 4 : 3.
Find $|PQ|$ when the perimeter of $PQRS$ is 28.
Hence, draw a sketch of $PQRS$.

9. $ABCD$ is a parallelogram.

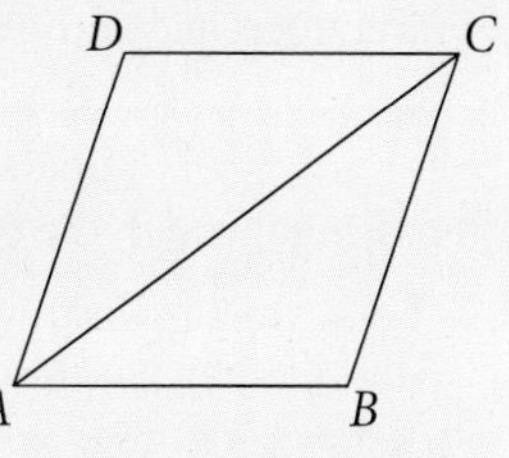

(i) Show that ΔABC is congruent to ΔADC.

(ii) If the area of ΔABC is 58 cm^2, find the area of $ABCD$. Justify your answer.

10. The light shown is attached to the wall by an arm that can extend away from the wall. In the figure, points D, E, F, and G are the vertices of a parallelogram. This parallelogram is one of several that change shape as the light is extended.

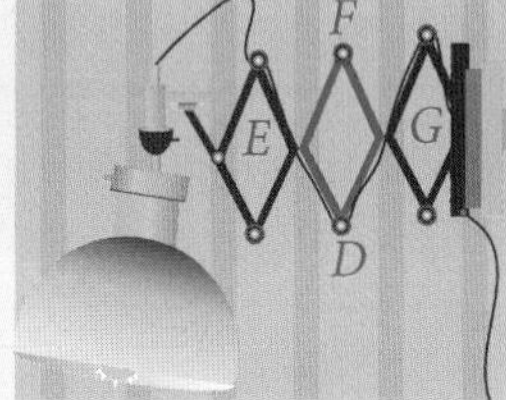

(i) What happens to $\angle E$ as $\angle F$ increases? Explain.

(ii) What happens to $|FD|$ as $\angle F$ decreases? Explain.

(iii) What happens to the overall distance between the light and the wall as $\angle F$ decreases? Explain.

11. A snooker player shoots a cue ball, and it rolls back to where it started, as shown in the diagram. The ball bounces off each edge at the same angle at which it hits the edge.

The ball hits the first edge at an angle of 63°.
So, $|\angle AEF| = |\angle BEH| = 63°$.

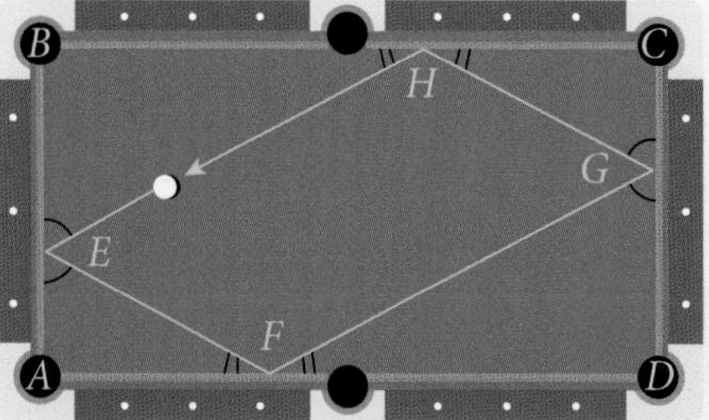

(i) What is the measure of $\angle AFE$? Explain.

(ii) Explain why $|\angle FGD| = 63°$.

(iii) What is the measure of $\angle GHC$ and $\angle EHB$?

(iv) Is $EFGH$ a parallelogram? Explain your reasoning.

Section 11.6: Circle Theorems

Learning Outcome:

You should be able to:

- understand and use the circle theorems and corollary to solve problems

Circle terms

A **radius** is the distance from the centre of a circle to any point on the circumference of the circle.

A **diameter** is a line-segment from one side of the circle to the other, passing through the centre.

An **arc** is any part of the circumference.

A **tangent** is a line which touches a circle at only one point.

A **chord** is a line-segment joining the two ends of an arc.

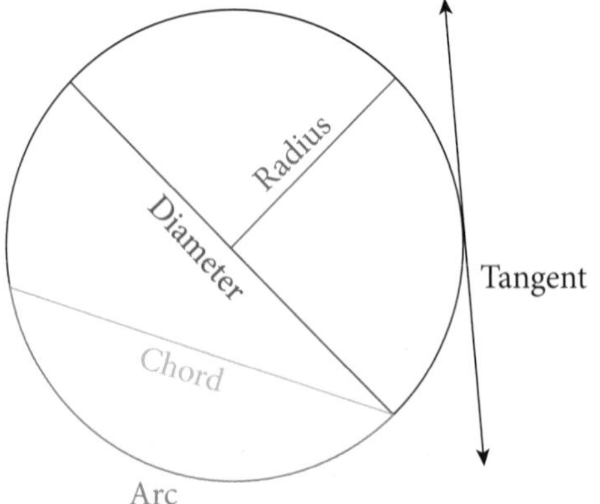

1. The angle at the centre of a circle standing on a given arc is twice the angle at any given point of the circle standing on the same arc. (Theorem 19)

$|\angle BOC| = 2|\angle BAC|$

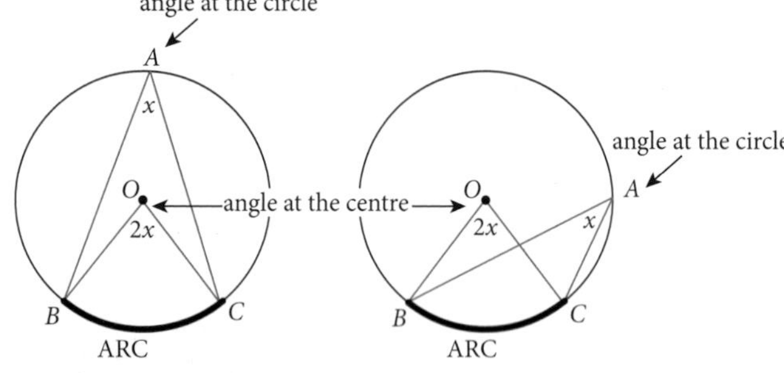

Corollary: All angles at points of the circle, standing on the same arc, are equal.

$\angle AOB$ and $\angle ACB$ are both standing on the arc AB.

The measure of $\angle AOB$ and $\angle ACB$ are equal.

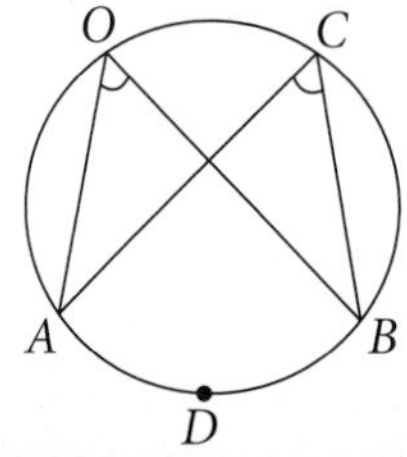

Discussion Time 

Work with a classmate to answer the following questions.

Consider the diagram.

1. What do we call the line *AB*?
2. What is the measure of ∠*AOB*?
3. Name the arc ∠*AOB* is standing on.
4. Name the arc ∠*APB* is standing on.
5. What is the measure of ∠*APB*? Justify your answer.
6. What shape is formed in the circle by the line *AB*?

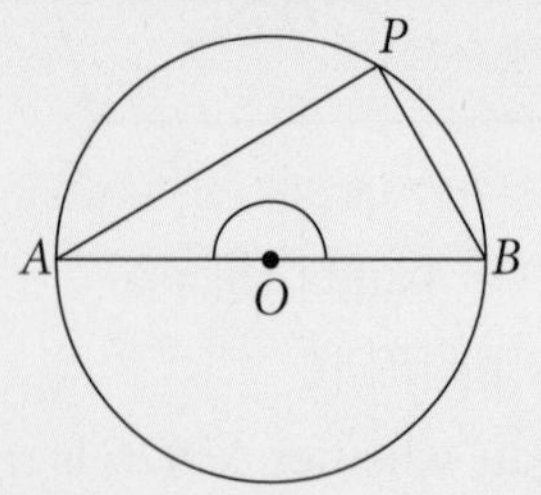

Corollary: Each angle in a semicircle is a right angle.

Corollary: If the angle standing on a chord [*AB*] at some point of the circle is a right angle, then [*AB*] is a diameter.

A cyclic quadrilateral is a four-sided figure in which all the vertices are on the circumference of a circle.

Corollary: If *ABCD* is a cyclic quadrilateral, then opposite angles sum to 180°.

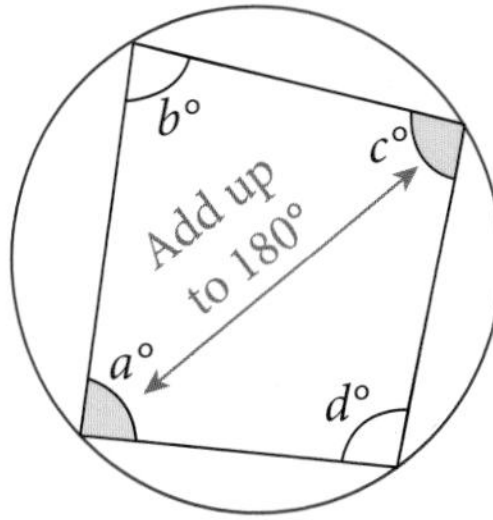

$a + c = 180°$

$b + d = 180°$

2. Each tangent is perpendicular to the radius that goes to the point of contact. (Theorem 20)

The line ℓ is a tangent to the circle s as it only touches the circle at one point.
P is the point where ℓ touches s and is called the point of contact, or point of tangency.
The line ℓ is perpendicular to the radius.

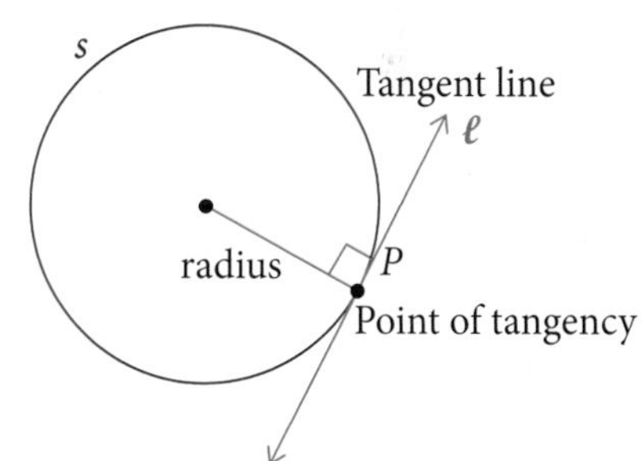

Converse: If *P* lies on the circle, *s* and a line ℓ through *P* is perpendicular to the radius to *P*, then ℓ is tangent to *s*.

Corollary: If two circles share a common tangent line at one point, then the two centres and that point are all on the one line (collinear).

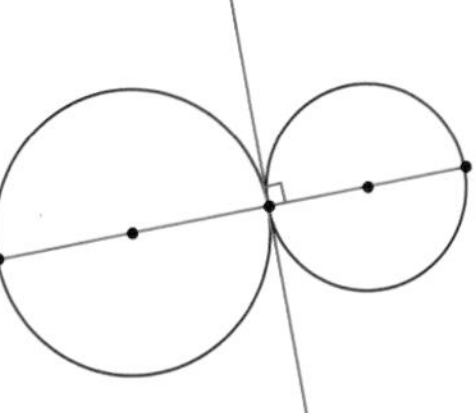

3. (i) The perpendicular from the centre of a circle to a chord bisects the chord.
(ii) The perpendicular bisector of a chord passes through the centre. (Theorem 21)

O is the centre, AB is a chord and OC is the perpendicular bisector.

(i) $|AC| = |CB|$

(ii) $[OC]$ passes through the centre.

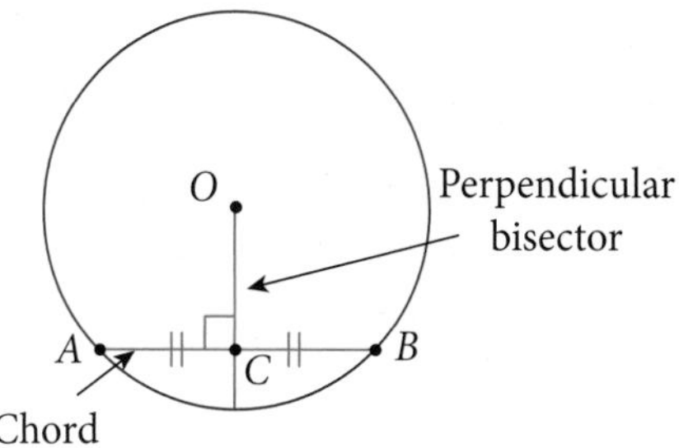

EXAMPLE 1

Find the labelled angles in the diagram.

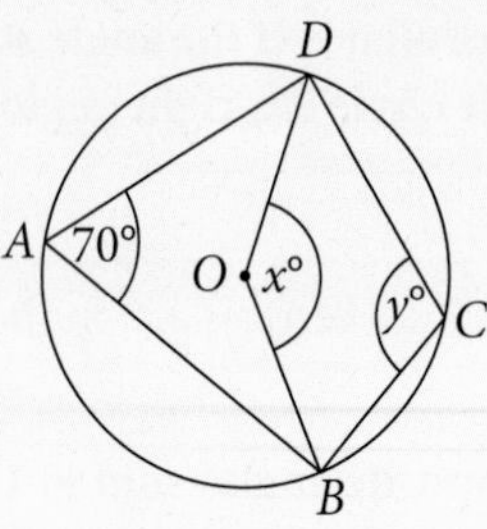

Solution

$x° = 70° \times 2$ angle at the centre is twice the angle at the circle

$x° = 140°$

$ABCD$ is a cyclic quadrilateral.

$y° + 70° = 180°$ opposite angles in a cyclic quadrilateral sum to 180°

$y° = 180° - 70°$

$y° = 110°$

EXAMPLE 2

In the diagram $|OA| = 5$ cm and $|OB| = 13$ cm.

(i) What is the measure of angle OAB? Explain your answer.

(ii) Find $|AB|$.

(iii) Find the area of ΔOAB.

(iv) Using the area of the triangle, find $|AC|$.

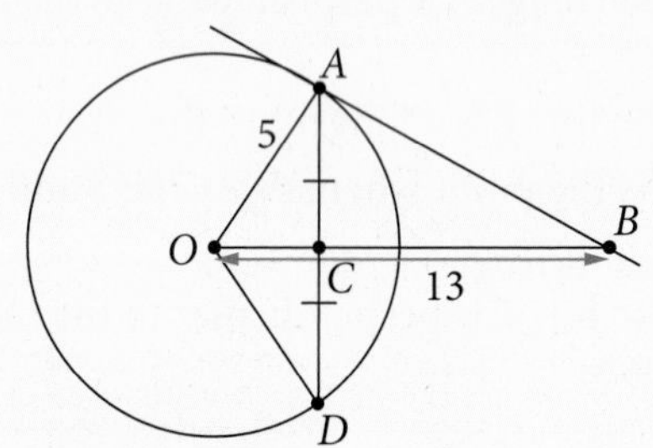

Solution

(i) $|\angle OAB| = 90°$ a tangent is perpendicular to the radius at the point of tangency.

(ii)

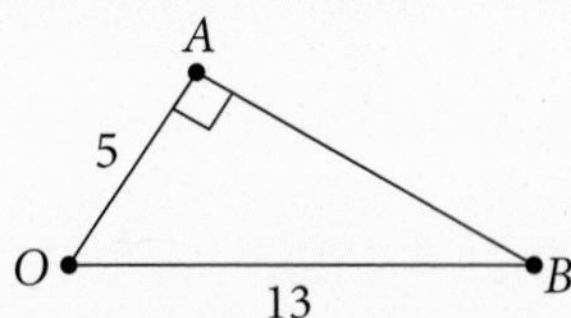

$$|OB|^2 = |OA|^2 + |AB|^2$$
$$13^2 = 5^2 + |AB|^2$$
$$169 = 25 + |AB|^2$$
$$169 - 25 = |AB|^2$$
$$144 = |AB|^2$$
$$\sqrt{144} = |AB|$$
$$12 \text{ cm} = |AB|$$

(iii) Since $|\angle OAB| = 90°$

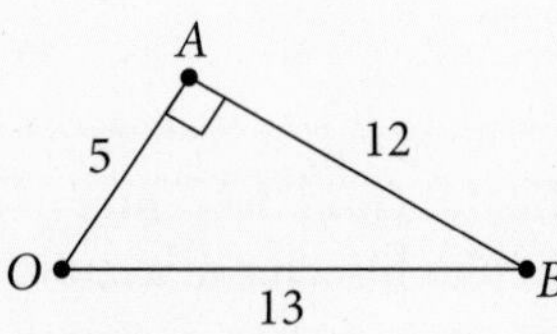

$[AB]$ is the perpendicular height and $[OA]$ is the base

$$\text{area} = \frac{1}{2}(\text{base})(\text{perpendicular height})$$
$$= \frac{1}{2}(5)(12) = 30 \text{ cm}^2$$

(iv) We can use the area of ΔOAB to find $|AC|$.

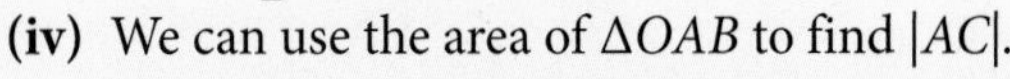

Since $[OB]$ bisects the chord AD, $|\angle ACB| = 90°$.

$[AC]$ is the perpendicular height of ΔOAB, when $[OB]$ is the base. [Theorem 16]

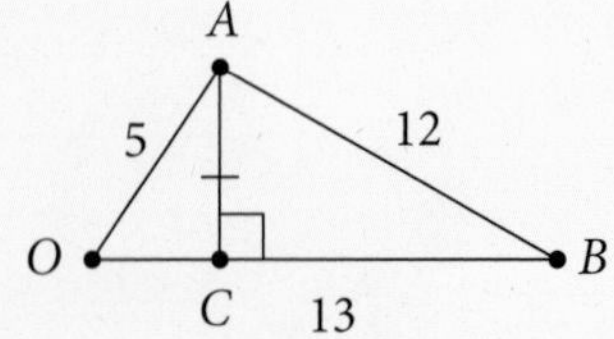

$$\text{area} = \frac{1}{2}(\text{base})(\text{perpendicular height})$$
$$30 = \frac{1}{2}(13)(|AC|)$$

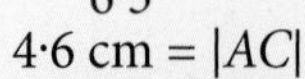

$$30 = 6{\cdot}5\,|AC|$$
$$\frac{30}{6{\cdot}5} = |AC|$$
$$4{\cdot}6 \text{ cm} = |AC|$$

Practice Questions 11.6

1. Find the labelled angle in each of the following circles. Give a reason.

(i)

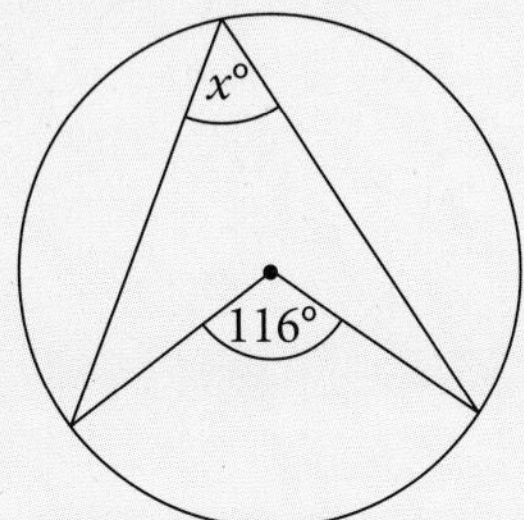

(iii)

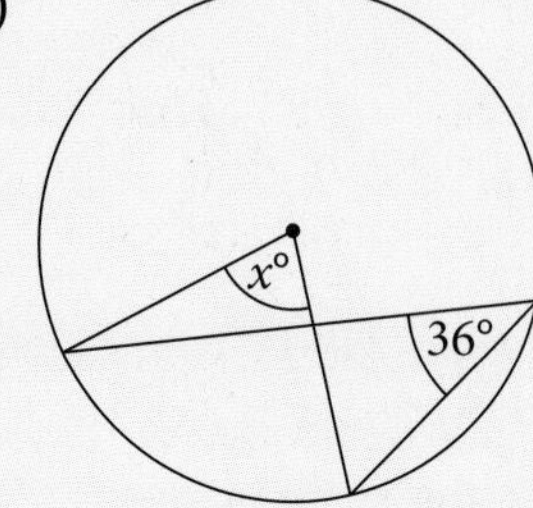

(v)

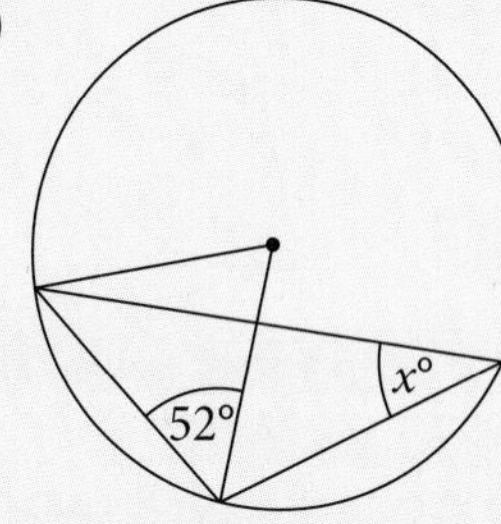

(ii)

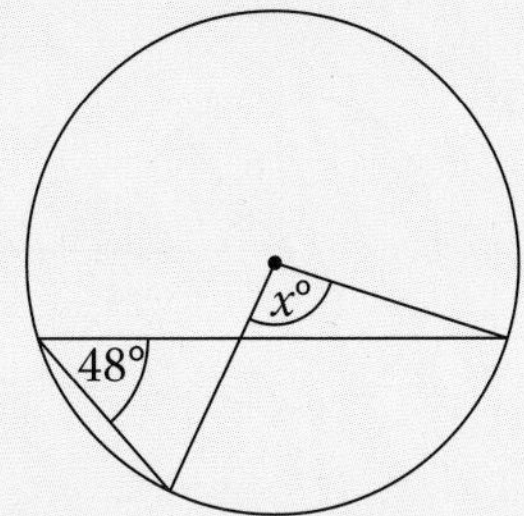

(iv)

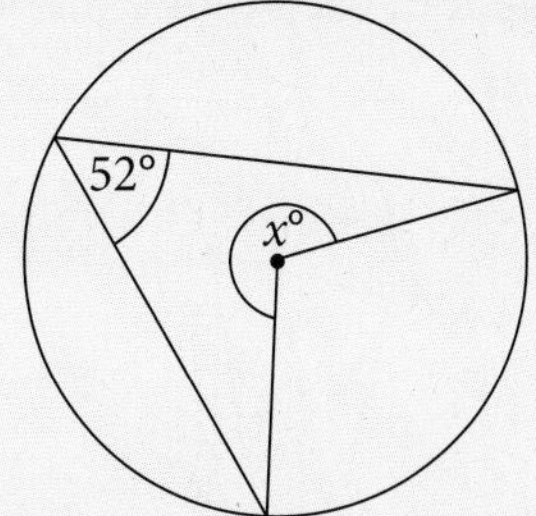

(vi)

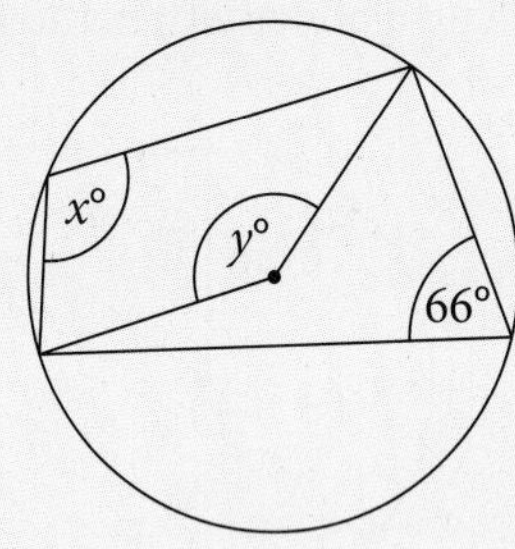

2. Find the labelled angle in each of the following circles. Give a reason.

(i)

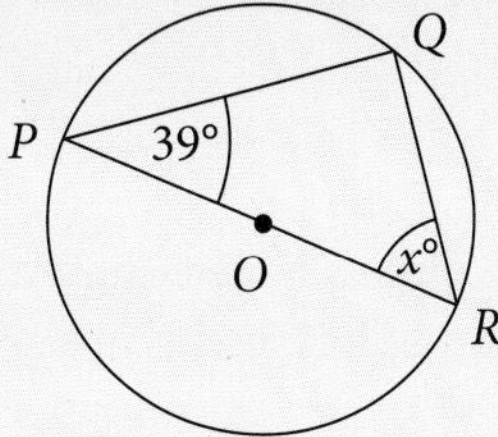

(ii)

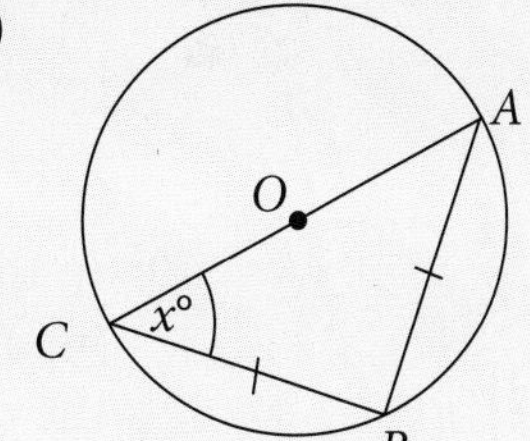

(iii)

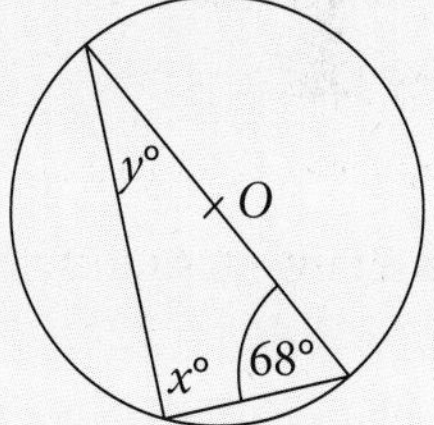

3. Explain why ΔAOC is equilateral.

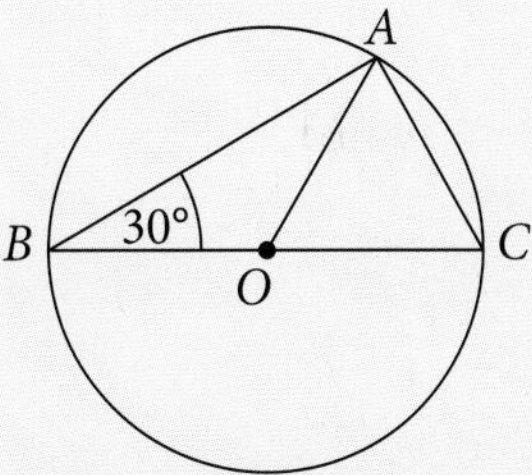

4. Find the labelled angles in each of the following circles. Give a reason.

(i)

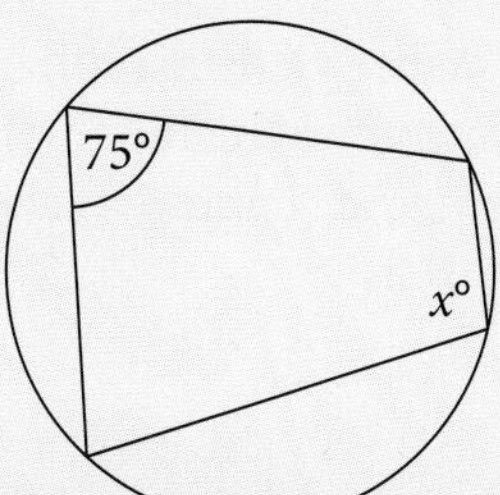

(iii)

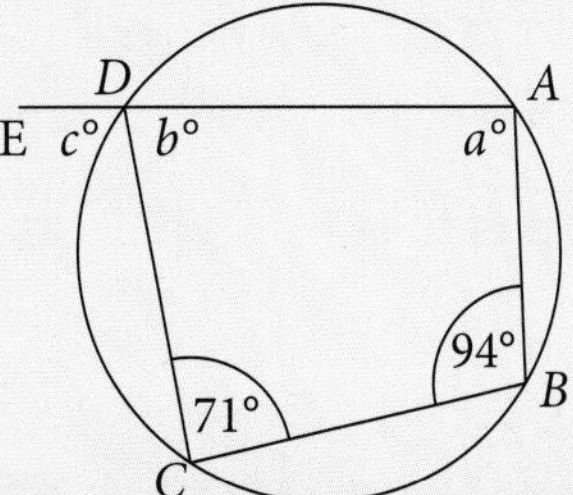

(v)

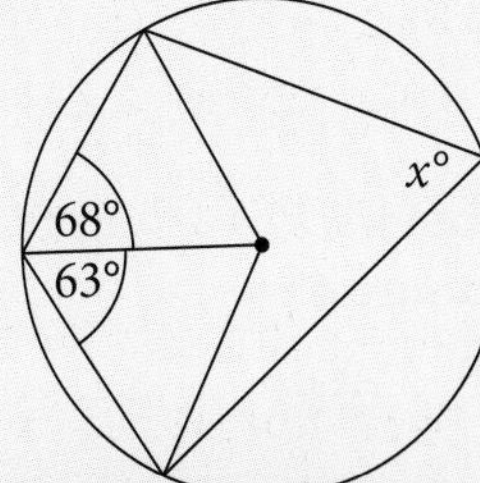

(ii)

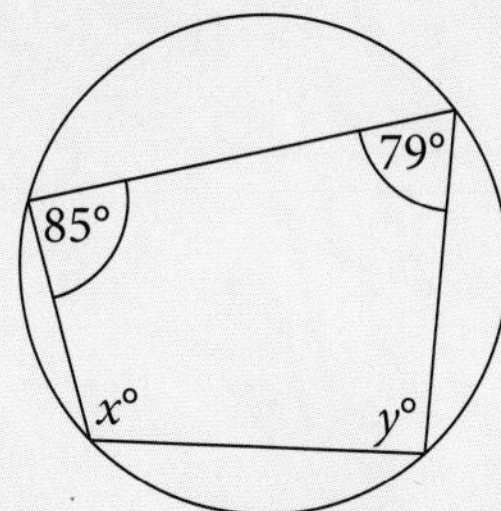

(iv)

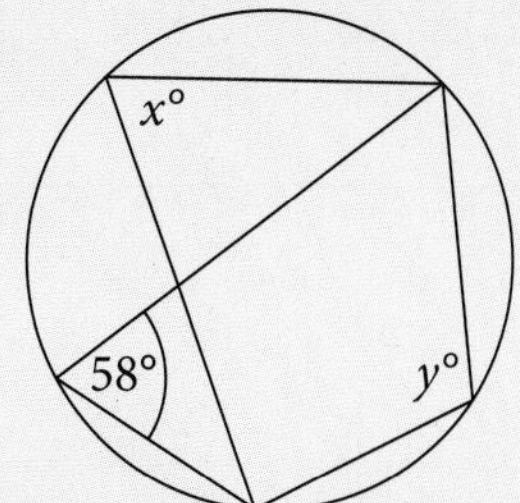

(vi)

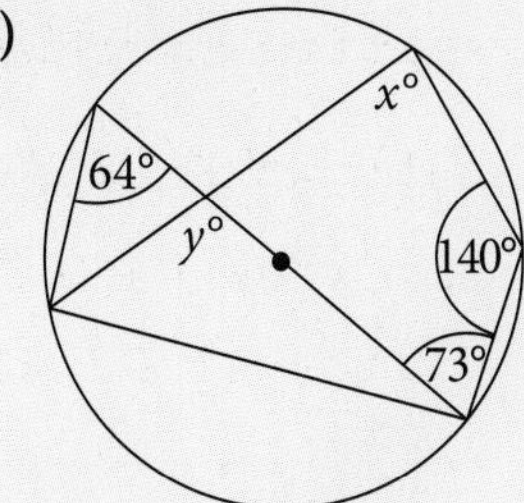

5. If AD is a tangent in each of the following circles find the missing angles.

(i)

(ii)

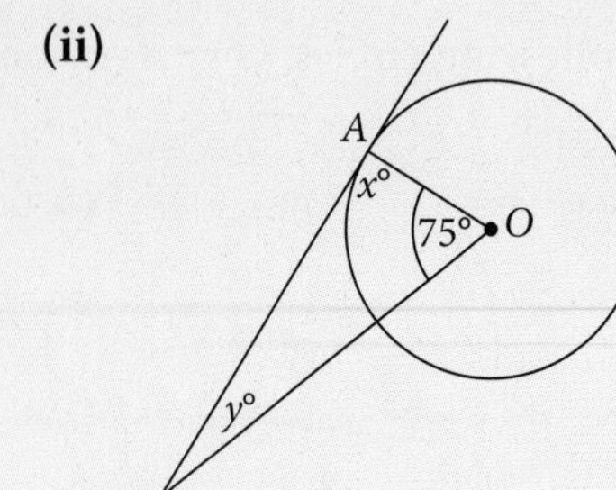

(iii)

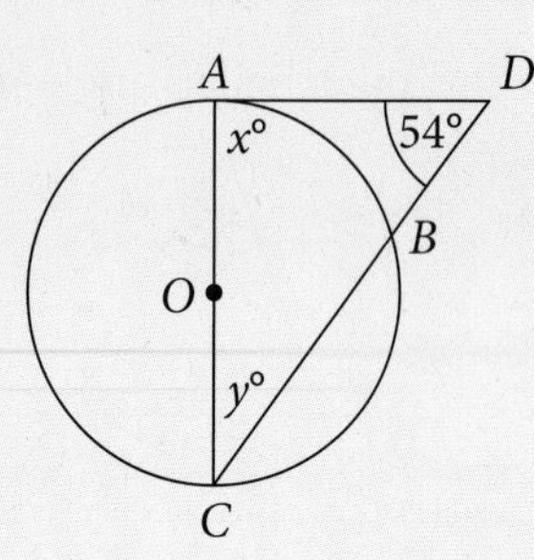

6. Investigate whether the line AB is a tangent in each of the following:

(i) A 8 cm B, 6 cm, 10 cm, O

(ii)

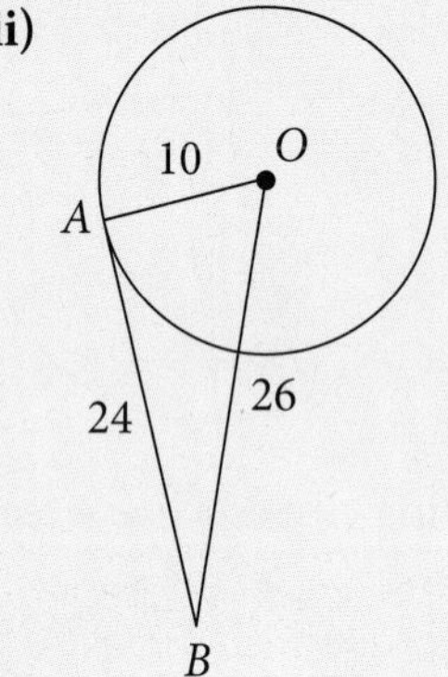

(iii)

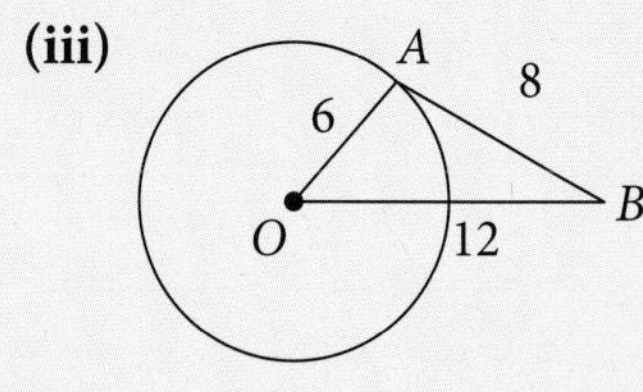

7. PQ is a tangent to the circle at A.
Angle $|\angle BAQ| = 72°$

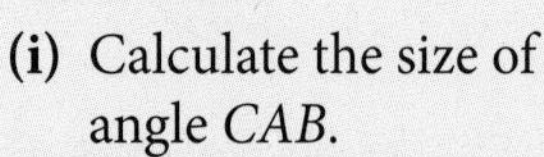
(i) Calculate the size of angle CAB.

(ii) Calculate the size of angle BCA.

Give reasons for your answers.

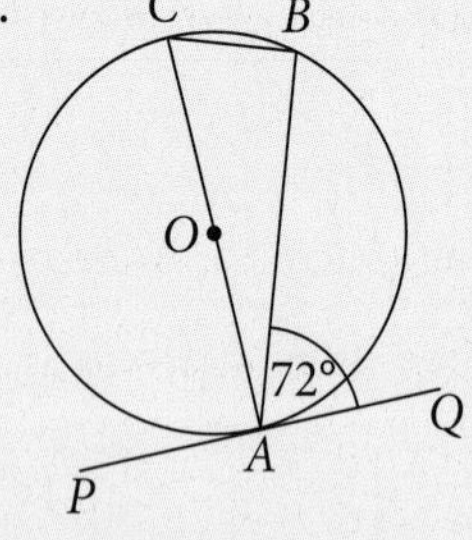

8. In the diagram,
$BD \perp AC$, $|AC| = 16$ cm and $|AB| = 10$ cm.
Find $|BD|$.
Explain your work.

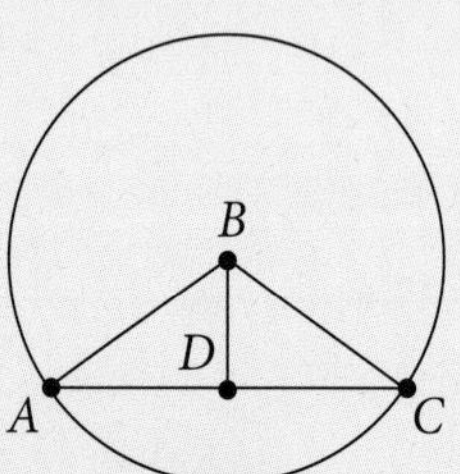

9. Given $[AD]$ is a tangent to the circle, find the measure of:

(i) $\angle AOD$

(ii) $\angle ABC$

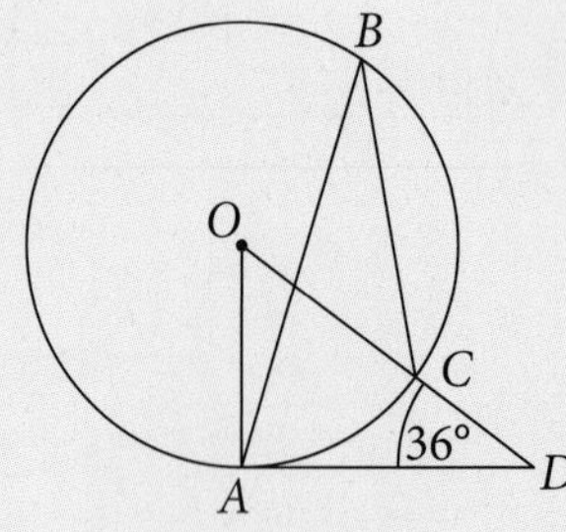

10. In the figure, the two circles have equal radii and intersect at points B and D. A and C are centres of the circles.
$|AC| = 8$, and the radius of each circle is 5. $BD \perp AC$.
Find $|BD|$. Explain your work.

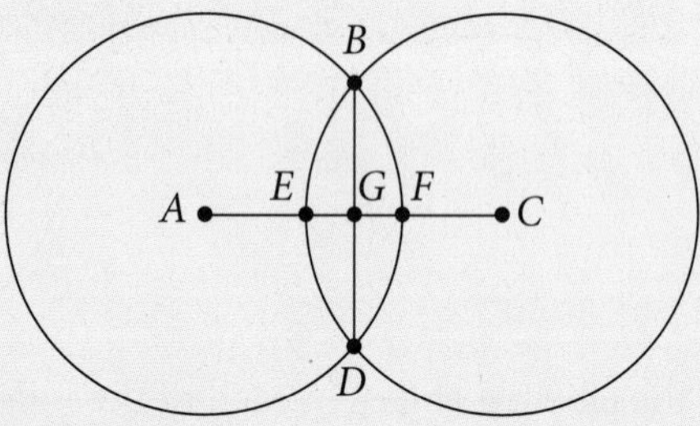

11. Two cirlces with the centre O, have radii of 5 cm and 13 cm. AB is a tangent to the inner circle and intersects the outer circle at A and B as shown.
Find the length of $[AB]$.

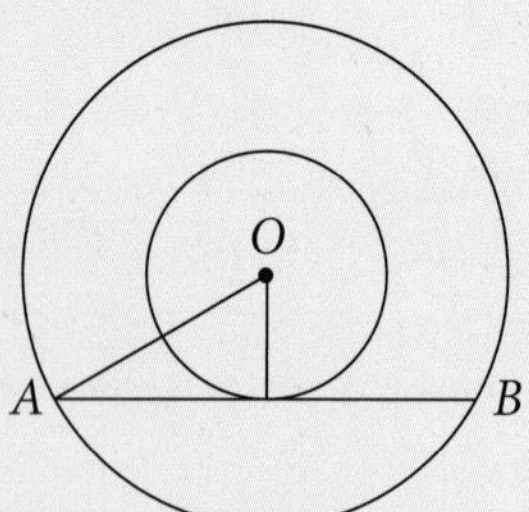

12. In the diagram, O is the centre of the circle and AT is a tangent.
Find the measure of $\angle OTQ$. Explain your work.

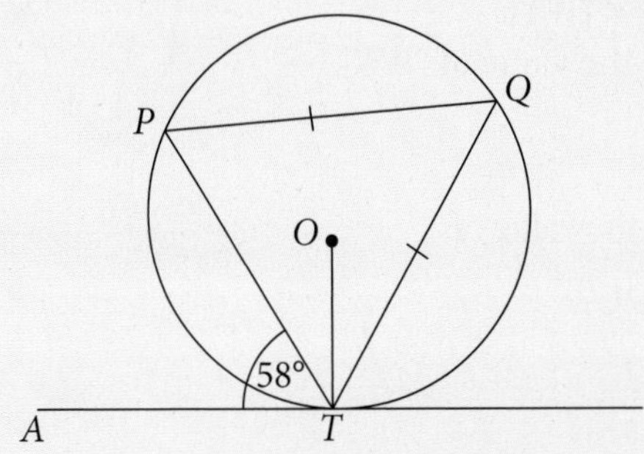

13. PQ and QR are tangents to the circle with centre Y. $[QY]$ intersects the chord $[PR]$ at the point X.

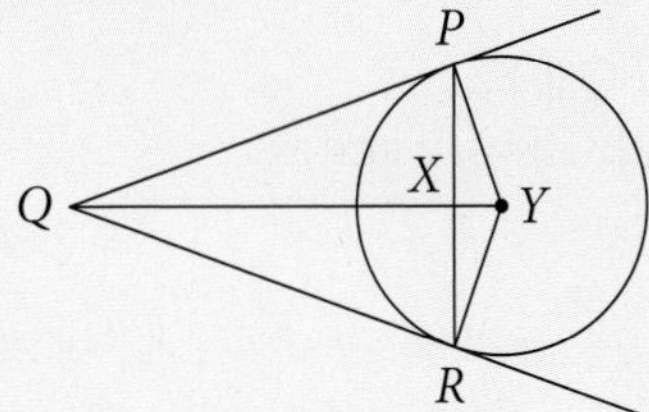

(i) Prove that the triangles PQY and RQY are congruent.

(ii) Hence, prove that $[QY]$ bisects the chord $[PR]$.

14. PQ is a tangent to the circle at A. $|PQ|$ is parallel to $|BC|$.
$|AB| = |AC|$; $|AD| = |DC|$; $|\angle BAP| = 74°$.
Calculate the measure of:
(i) $\angle BCA$ (ii) $\angle BAC$ (iii) $\angle DCA$

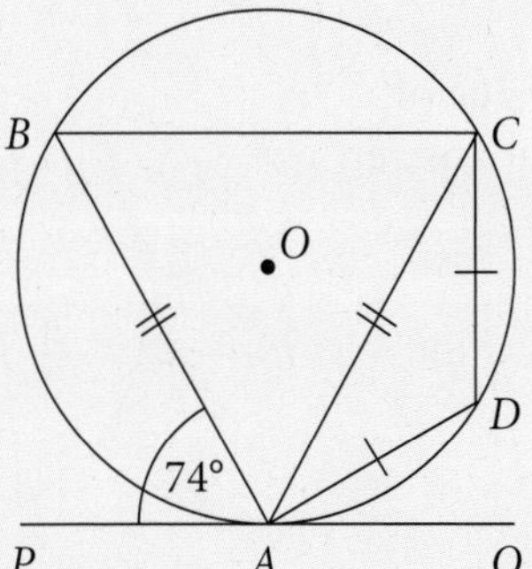

Revision and Exam Style Questions – Section A

1. Find the the values of a, b, c, and d.
Explain your answers.

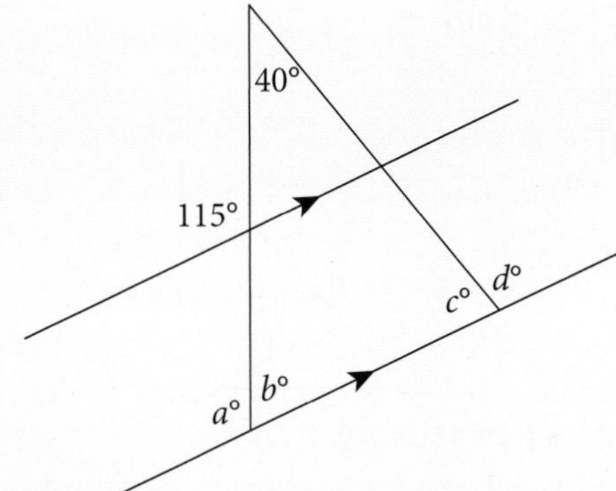

2. $ABCD$ is a parallelogram.
$|\angle DAC| = 87°$ and $|\angle ACD| = 44°$.
Calculate $|\angle ABC|$, giving reasons for your answer.

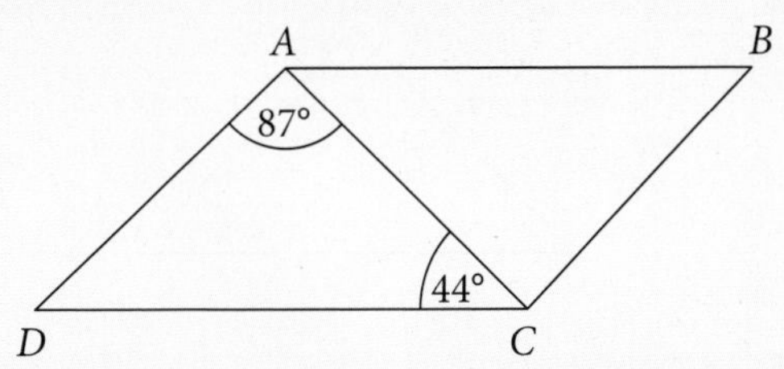

3. The diagram shows a car jack. $ABCD$ is a parallelogram.
When diagonal $|AC| = 48$ cm, diagonal $|BD| = 20$ cm and the angle where they intersect is 90°, calculate $|AB|$.

4. ΔABC is a right-angled triangle. $|BC|$ is the diameter of the circle.
$|AB| = 3$ cm, $|AC| = 4$ cm.

(i) Find $|BC|$.

(ii) What is the length of $|OA|$?

(iii) Identify two isosceles triangles in the diagram.

(iv) If $|\angle AOC| = 103°$, calculate the measure of $\angle AOB$ and $\angle OBA$.

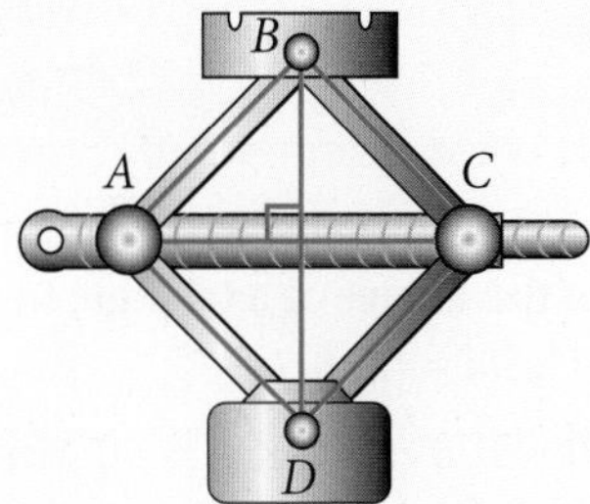

5. ABC is a right triangle $|\angle ACB|$ equal to 74°. The lengths of the sides AM, MQ and QP are all equal. Find $|\angle QPB|$.

6. Find the value of x. Justify your answer.

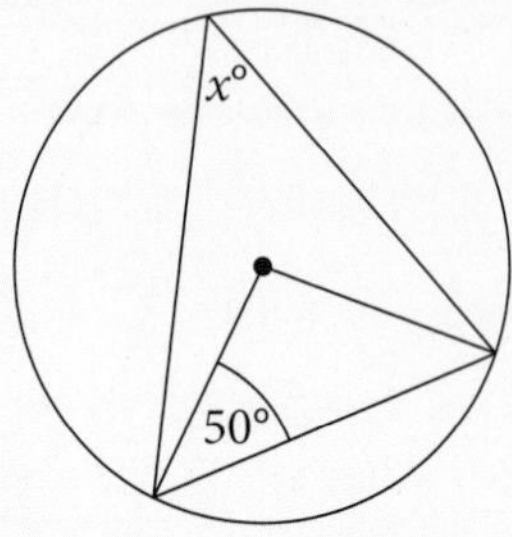

7. Find

(i) $|\angle PQR|$ (ii) $|\angle PSR|$

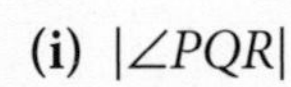

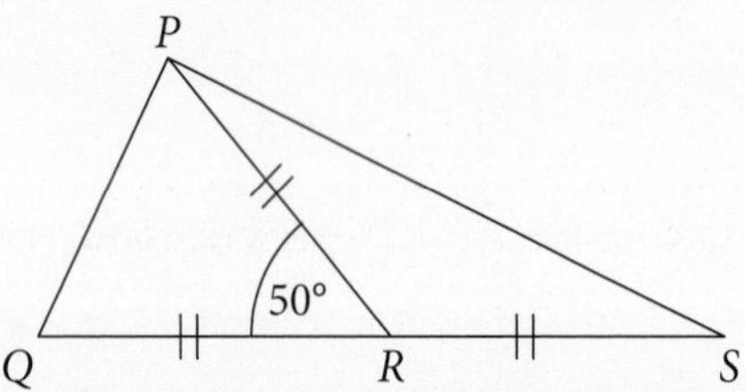

8. The length of the diameter of the circle with centre O, shown in the diagram, is $5\sqrt{2}$ cm and $|WX| = |WY|$. Find the value of $|WX|$.

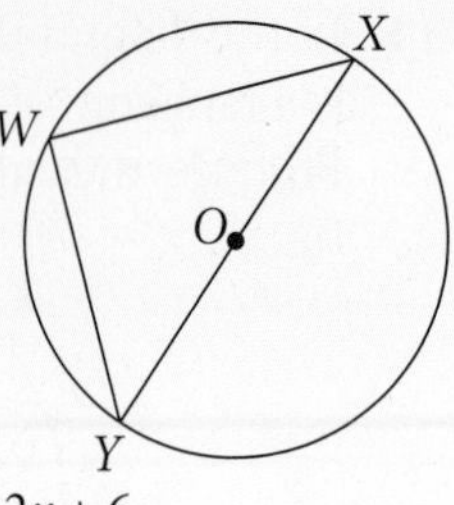

9. Find the value of:

(i) x

(ii) y

(iii) s

(iv) t

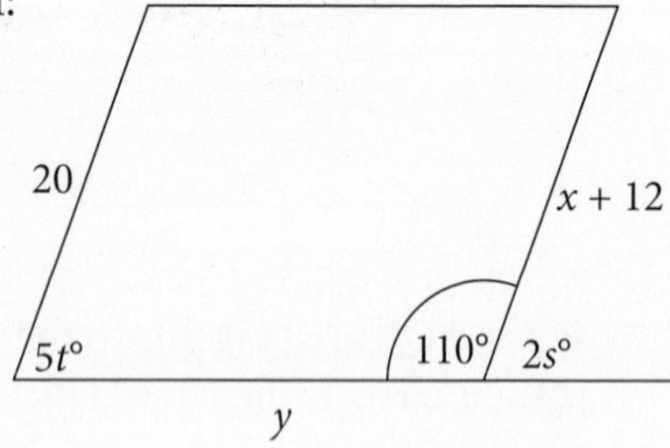

10. In ΔXYZ $PQ \parallel YZ$. $|XY| = 14$, $|XZ| = 10$ and $|XQ| = 2$. Find $|PY|$.

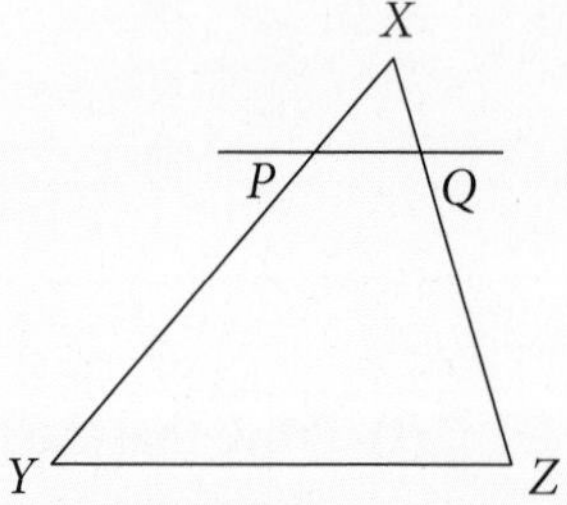

Revision and Exam Style Questions – Section B

More challenging problems

1. (i) Using the angles shown in the diagram below, state at least two theorems.

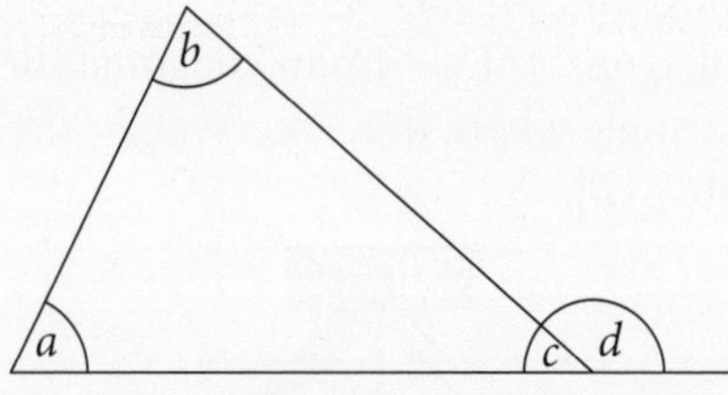

(ii) Use the diagram and what you know about the sum of the angles of a triangle to explain why $|\angle a| + |\angle b| = |\angle d|$.

(iii) If $|\angle d| = 100°$ and $|\angle a| = 40°$, find the measure of $\angle b$ and $\angle c$.

2. QS bisects both of the angles PSR and PQR. Prove that QS is the diameter of the circle.

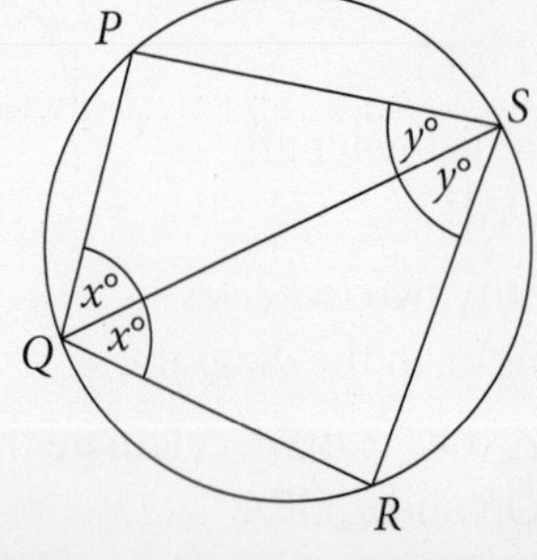

3. $|BE| \parallel |CD|$.
ABC and AED are straight lines.
$|AB| = 4$ cm, $|BC| = 6$ cm, $|BE| = 5$ cm, $|AE| = 4{\cdot}8$ cm.

(i) Calculate $|CD|$.

(ii) Calculate $|ED|$.

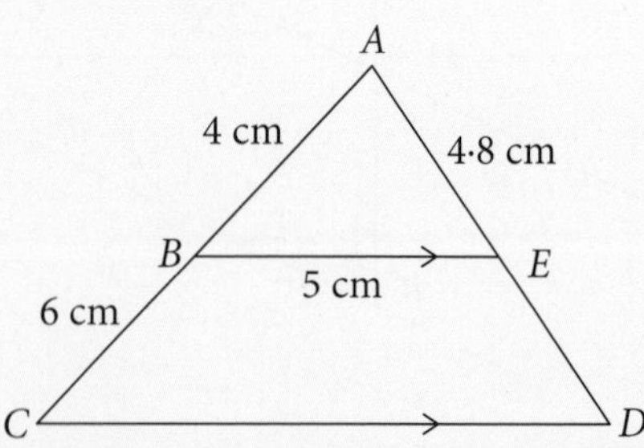

4. If n must be a whole number, what is the smallest possible value of n?

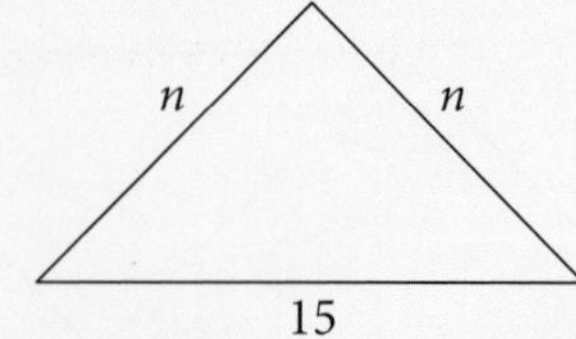

5. The Jamaican flag is a parallelogram in which the yellow lines form the diagonals, as shown.
Prove that the green triangles are congruent.
Justify your answer.

6. In the circle shown, O is the centre and BC is a diameter.
$|\angle ACP| = 40°$ and QP is a tangent at C.
   (i) Find $|\angle ACO|$.
   (ii) Find $|\angle OAB|$.
Justify your answers.

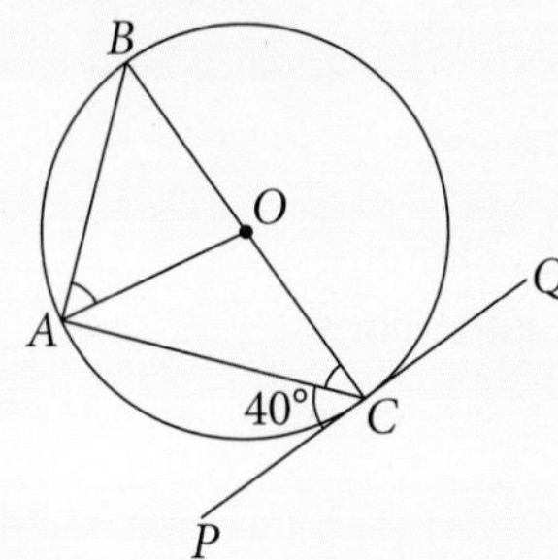

7. In the triangles PQR and TSQ, $|\angle QRP| = |\angle QST|$.
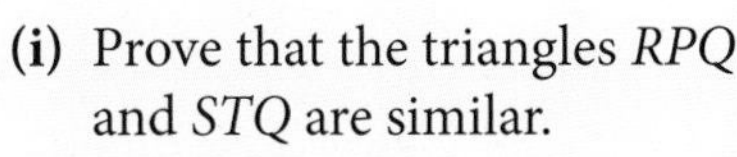
   (i) Prove that the triangles RPQ and STQ are similar.
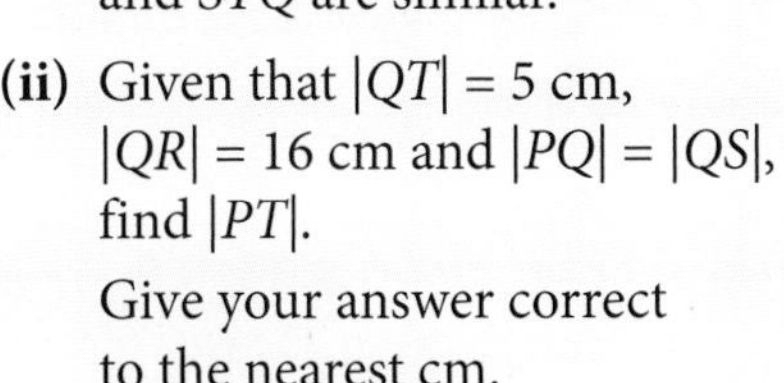
   (ii) Given that $|QT| = 5$ cm, $|QR| = 16$ cm and $|PQ| = |QS|$, find $|PT|$.
   Give your answer correct to the nearest cm.

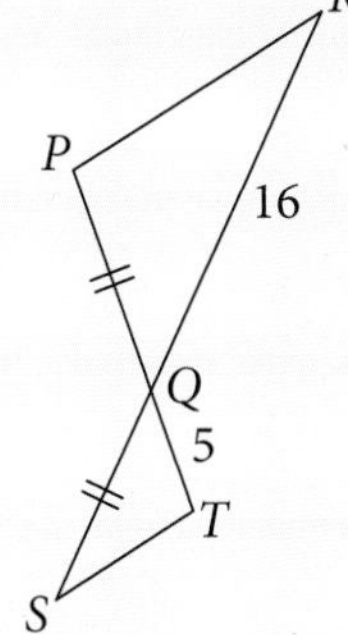

8. (i) What is the specific name for the shape $ABCD$?
   (ii) Give one property of the shape $ABCD$.
   (iii) Find the value of x.

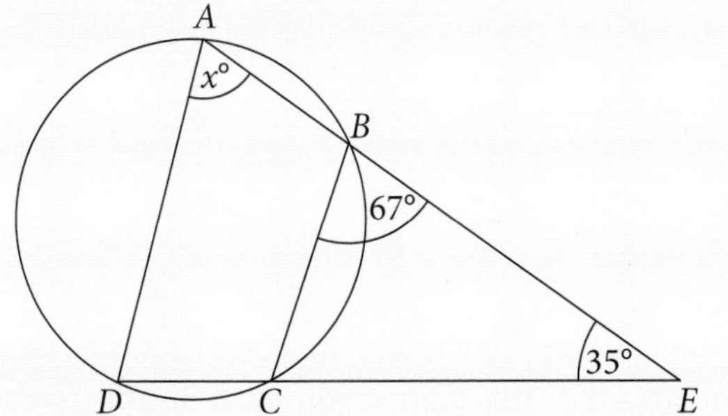

9. A circle has chord of length 10 cm.
The shortest distance from the circle's centre to the chord is 4 cm.
Find the radius of the circle correct to one decimal place.

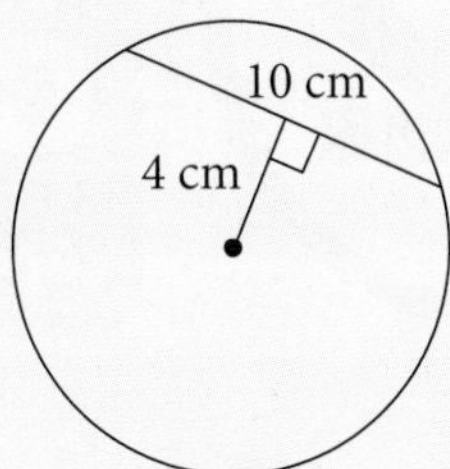

10. During a total eclipse of the sun, the moon is directly in line with the sun and blocks the sun's rays. The distance DA between the centre of the Earth and the centre of the sun is 149,600,000 km. The distance DE between the centre of Earth and the centre of the moon is 384,400 km. The radius AB of the sun is 696,300 km.
Use the diagram and the given measurements to estimate the radius EC of the moon, to the nearest kilometre.

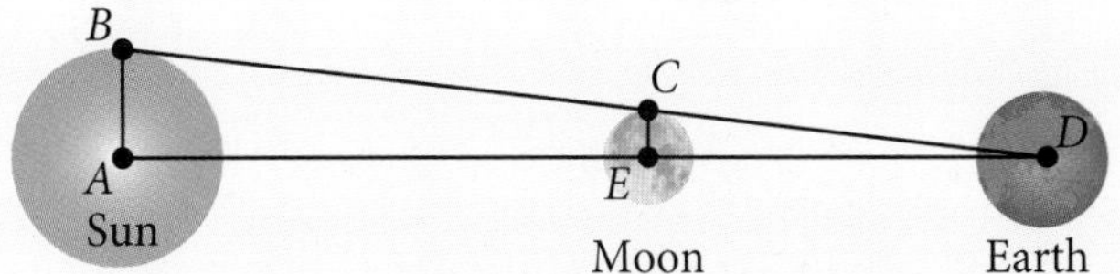

11. In the diagram, AB is parallel to CD.
$[AD]$ bisects $\angle CDB$ and $[BC]$ bisects $\angle ABD$.
Show that ΔBOD and ΔAOB are congruent.

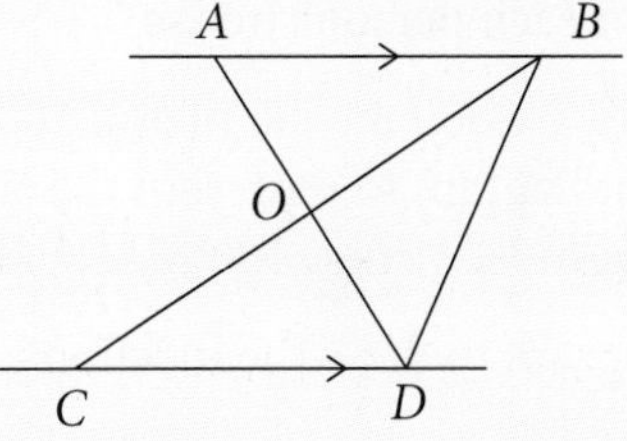

Now that you have completed the chapter, revisit the 'Something to think about…' question.

CHAPTER 12

Geometry III – Constructions

Sections covered within this chapter:

KEY WORDS

- Bisector
- Incircle
- Median
- Circumcircle
- Incentre
- Circumcentre
- Centroid

SOMETHING TO THINK ABOUT…

You and two friends plan to meet to walk to school together.

You want the meeting place to be the same distance from each person's house.

If your houses are 800 m, 600 m and 500 m apart, draw a diagram to represent the situation. In your diagram let 1 cm = 100 m.

Use your diagram to draw the location of the meeting place.

Your house

Friend's house

Friend's house

Introduction

Construction in geometry means drawing shapes, angles or lines accurately. To draw these constructions, we can use a pencil, compass, straight edge (ruler), protractor and set-squares. For this course you must be able to carry out 19 constructions. You have already met 13 of these constructions in your Junior Certificate.

Section 12.1: Revision of Basic Junior Certificate Constructions

Learning Outcome:

You should be able to:

- recall the basic Junior Certificate constructions and use them to solve problems

Line segment of a given length on a given ray

Step 1: Draw a ray, AB, as shown.

Step 2: With the point of the compass at 0 cm on a ruler, adjust the width of the compass until it is the width of the required line segment.

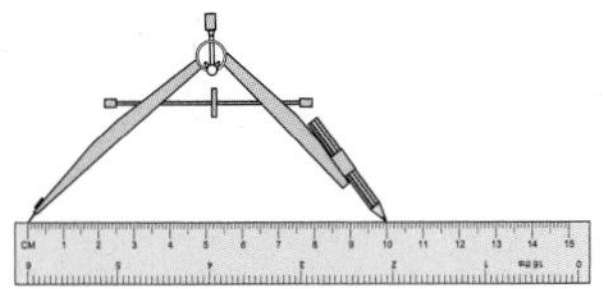

Step 3: With the compass set at the required width and the point of the compass on A, draw an arc on AB.

Label the point of intersection C. $[AC]$ is the required line segment.

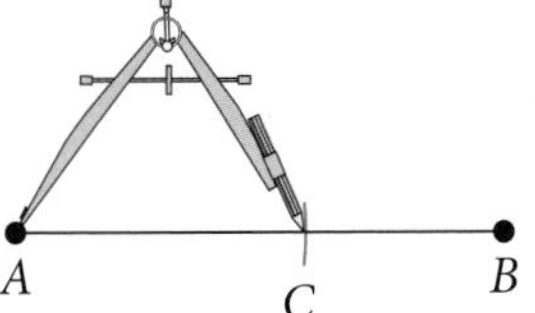

Angle of a given number of degrees with a given ray as one arm

Step 1: Draw a ray, AB, as shown.

Step 2: With the centre of the protractor on the point A and in line with AB, measure the required angle.
Mark the point C as shown.

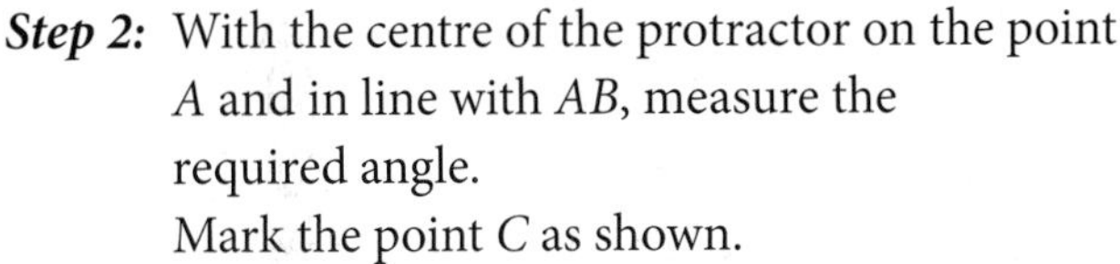

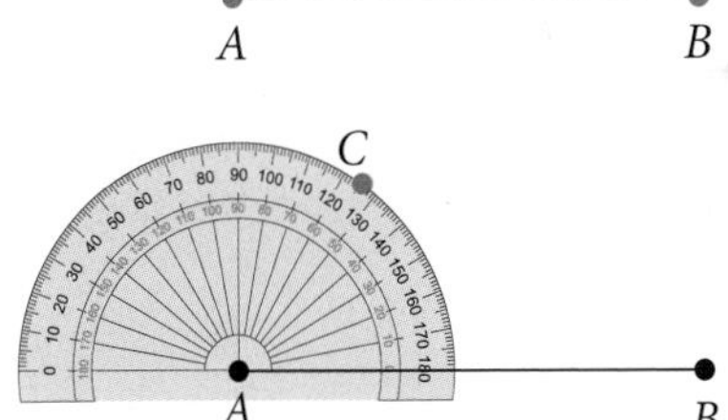

Step 3: Draw a line from A through the point C.
$\angle CAB$ is the required angle.

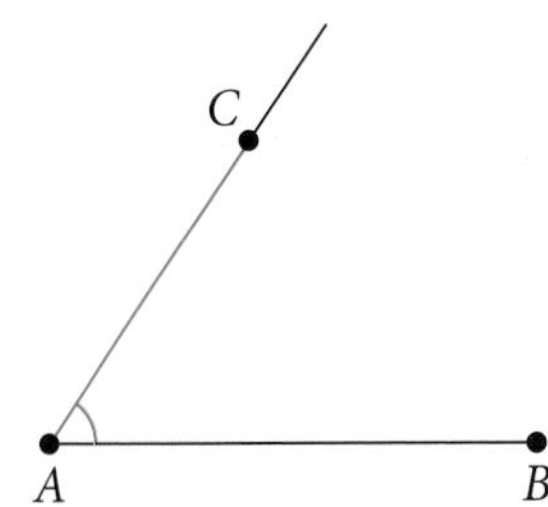

Bisector of an angle

A **bisector** divides something into two equal parts.

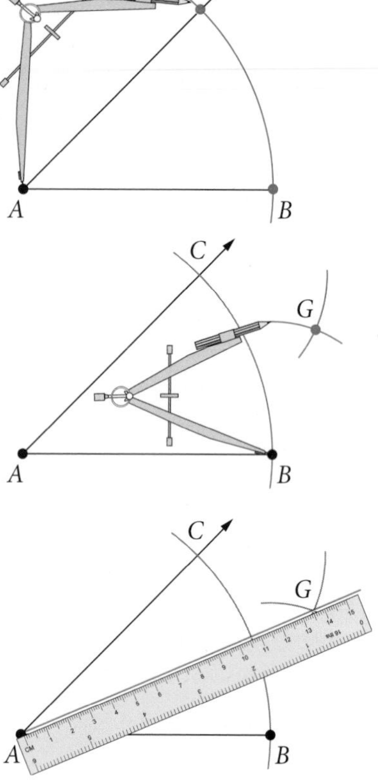

Step 1: Draw $\angle A$, as shown. Place the compass at A. Draw an arc that intersects both arms of the angle. Label the intersections B and C.

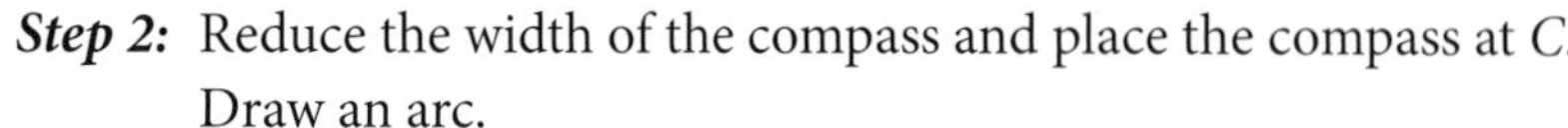

Step 2: Reduce the width of the compass and place the compass at C. Draw an arc.

Step 3: Keep the same compass setting. Place the compass at B. Draw an arc such that it intersects the arc drawn in step 2. Label the intersection of the two arcs G.

Step 4: Use a straight edge to draw a line through A and G.

$[AG]$ bisects $\angle A$.

Therefore, $\angle GAC$ is equal to $\angle GAB$.

Perpendicular bisector of a line

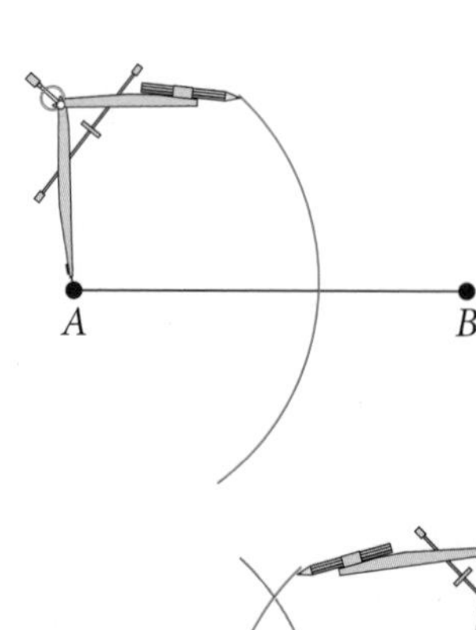

Step 1: Draw a line segment $[AB]$. Place the compass at A. Use a compass setting that is greater than half the length of $[AB]$. Draw an arc.

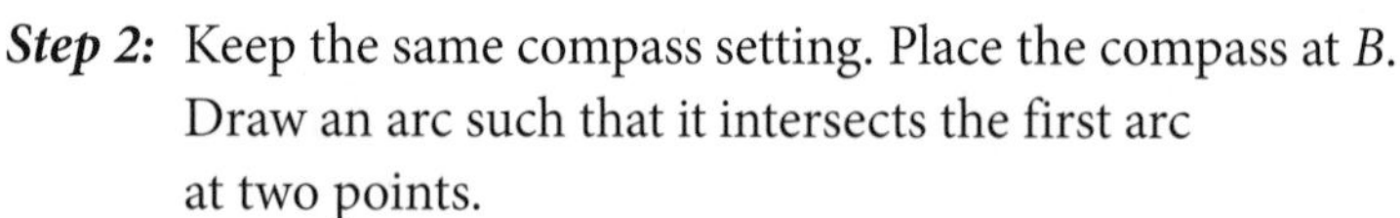

Step 2: Keep the same compass setting. Place the compass at B. Draw an arc such that it intersects the first arc at two points.

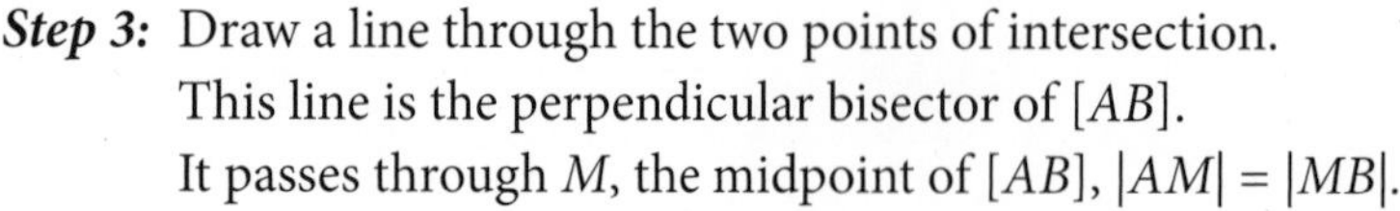

Step 3: Draw a line through the two points of intersection. This line is the perpendicular bisector of $[AB]$. It passes through M, the midpoint of $[AB]$, $|AM| = |MB|$.

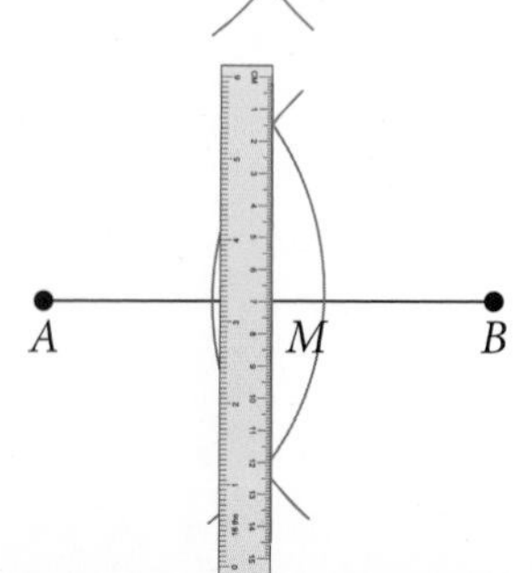

Line perpendicular to a given line *l*, passing through a given point on *l*

Step 1: Draw a line, *l*, and mark a point *P* on *l*.

l
P

Step 2: Place your compass point on *P*.
Keeping the compass width fixed, draw two arcs on *l* either side of *P*.

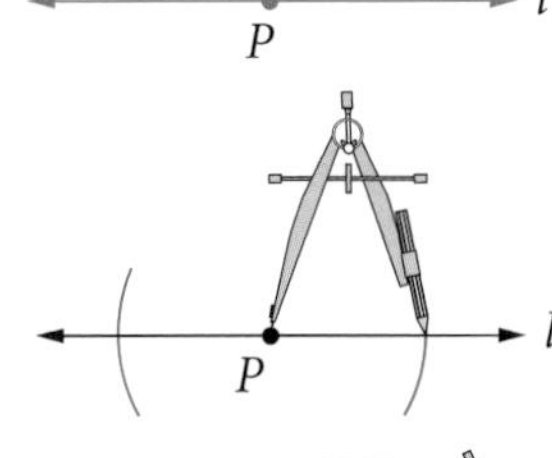

Step 3: Increase the width of the compass.
Place the compass point where the arc crossed the line on the right side of *P*, as shown and make a small arc above the line *l*.

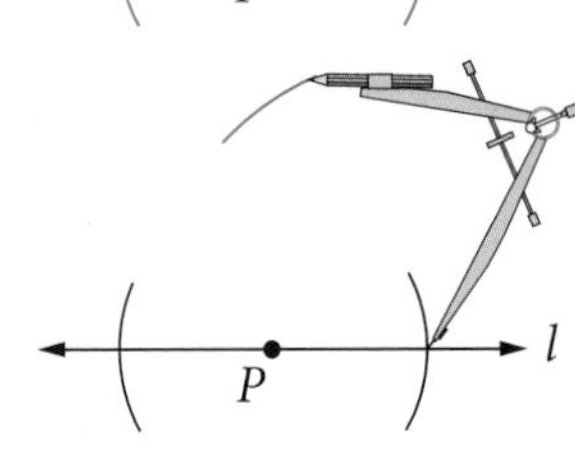

Step 4: Without changing the width of the compass, place the compass point where the arc crossed the line on the left side of *P*.
Draw another arc such that the two arcs above the line intersect.

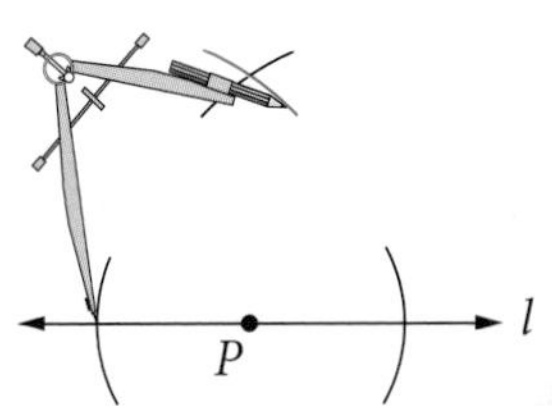

Step 5: With your straight edge, connect the intersection of the two small arcs to point *P*.

This new line is perpendicular to the given line and passes through the point *P*.

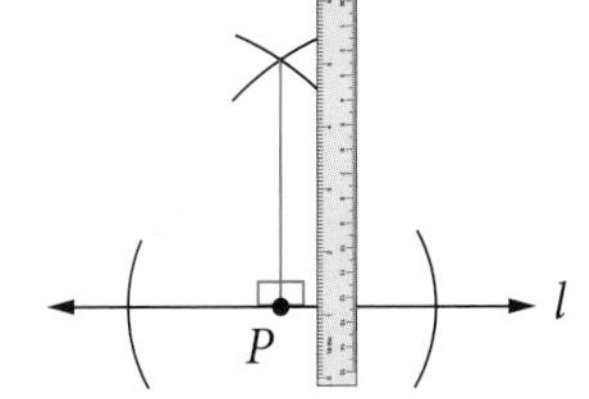

These steps can also be used if the point is not on the line.

Line parallel to a given line, through a given point

Method 1: Using a straight edge and a set square

Step 1: Draw a line, *m,* and a point, *P,* not on *m*.

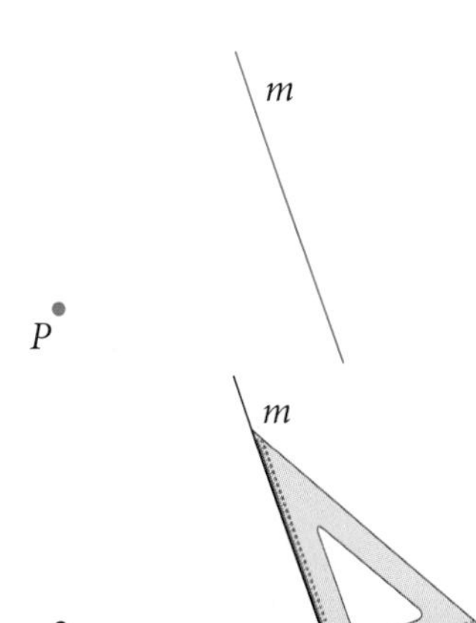

Step 2: Place an edge of the set square along the given line, *m*.

m

P

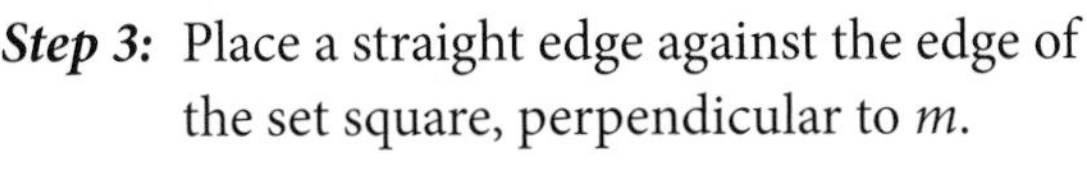
Step 3: Place a straight edge against the edge of the set square, perpendicular to *m*.

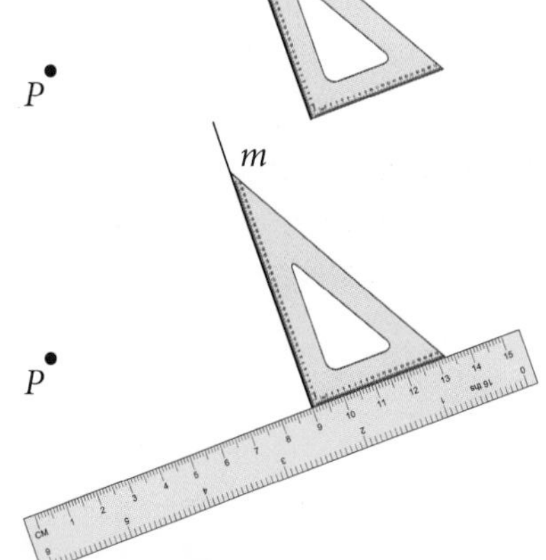

Step 4: Slide the set square along the straight edge until the edge used in step 2 passes through the given point P.

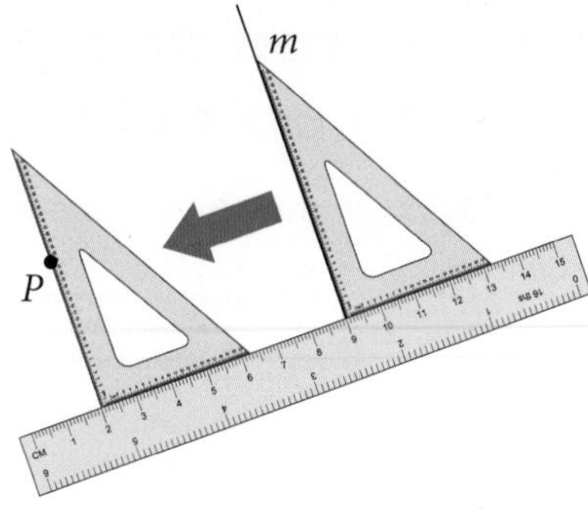

Step 5: Without moving the set square, draw a line through P.

This line is the required parallel line.

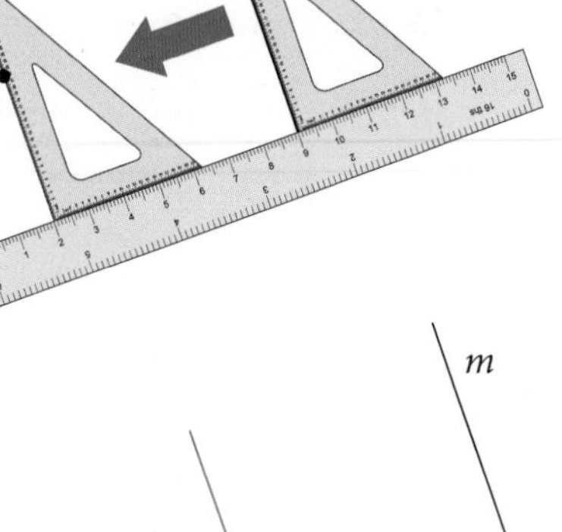

Method 2: Using a compass and a ruler

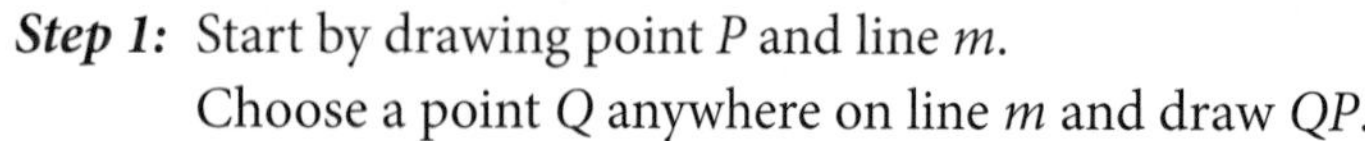

Step 1: Start by drawing point P and line m.
Choose a point Q anywhere on line m and draw QP.

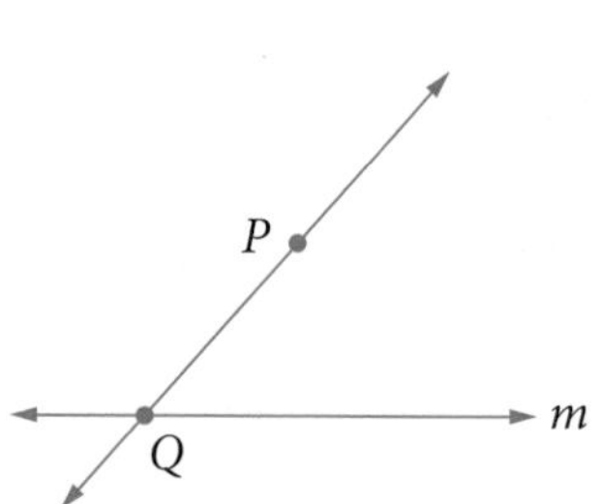

Step 2: Place the compass point on Q and draw an arc that crosses QP and line m. Label points A and B.
Using the same compass setting, place the compass point on P and draw an arc. Label point C, as shown.

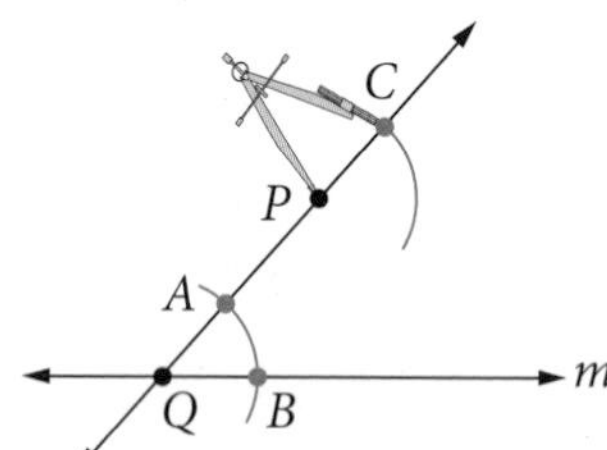

Step 3: With a compass width $|AB|$, place the compass point on C and draw an arc such that it intersects the arc through C, as shown.
Label the intersection of these arcs D.

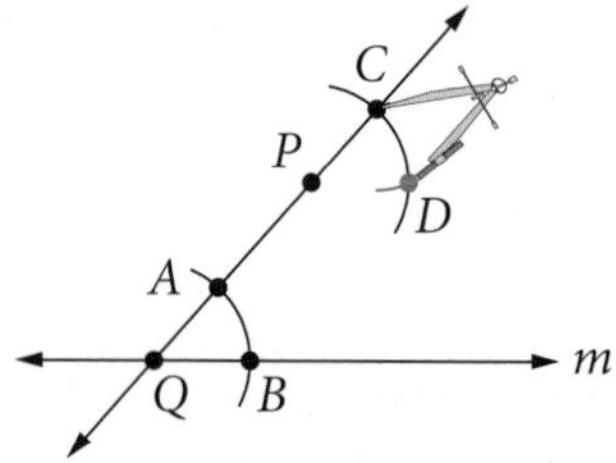

Step 4: Draw PD. This line is parallel to line m.

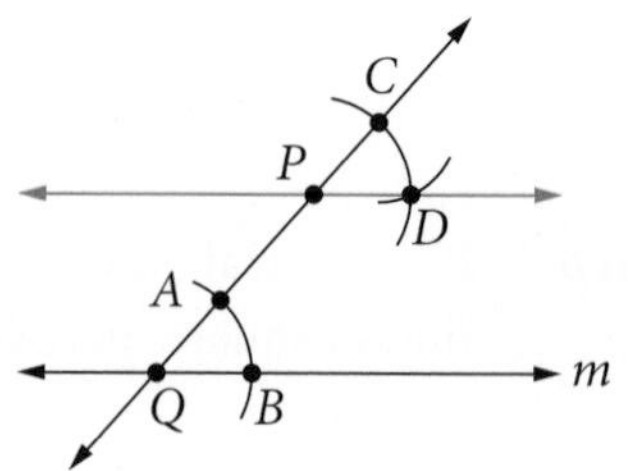

Division of a segment into two or three equal segments without measuring it

Step 1: Draw a line AB of any length.
Choose any point C not on AB.
Draw $[AC$.

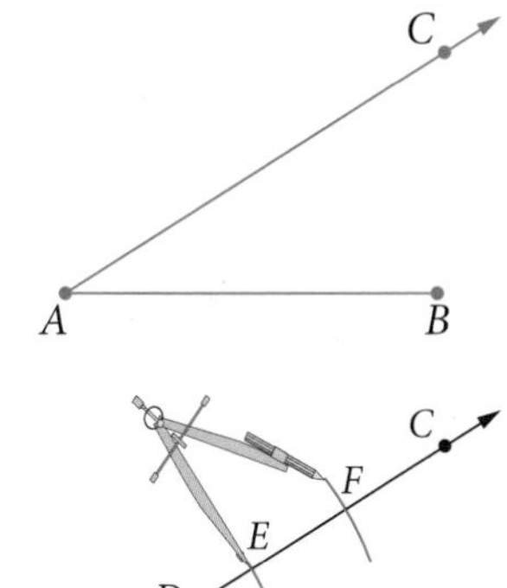

Step 2: Place the point of a compass at A and make an arc of any radius intersecting AC. Label the point of intersection D.
Using the same compass setting, make two more arcs on AC, as shown.
Label the points of intersection E and F and note that $|AD| = |DE| = |EF|$.

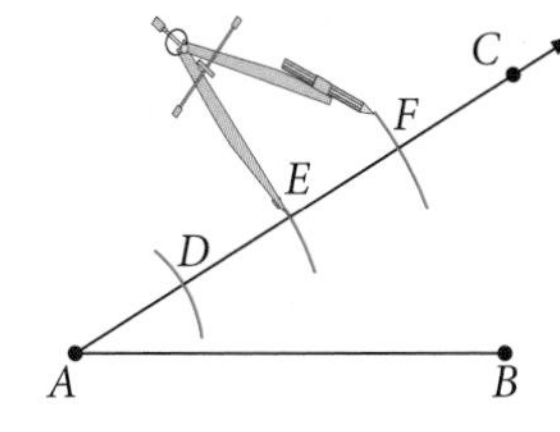

Step 3: Join F to B.

Step 4: Using a set square, draw a line from E, parallel to FB, to a new point, K, on $[AB]$.

Step 5: Using a set square, draw a line from D, parallel to FB, to a new point, J, on $[AB]$.

Recall how to construct parallel lines using a set square

Lines DJ, EK and FB are all parallel, and they divide AB equally. So, that $|AJ| = |JK| = |KB|$.

Rectangle, given side lengths

Step 1: Draw line segment $[AB]$ of length equal to one of the lengths given.

Step 2: Draw a ray at A perpendicular to the line segment $[AB]$.

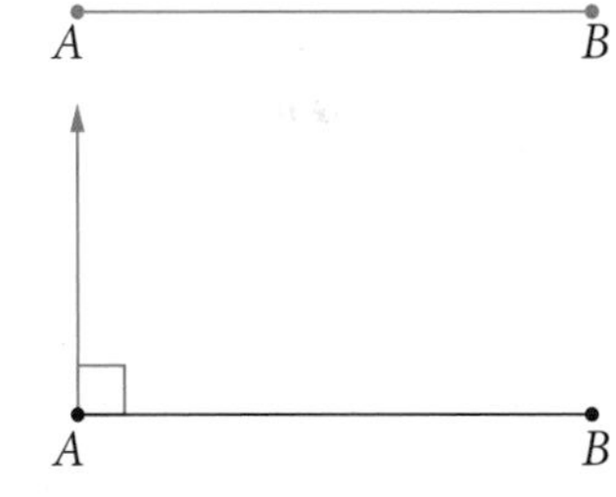

Step 3: With the point of the compass on A and compass width equal to the other given length, draw an arc on the ray drawn in step 2.

Label this point D.

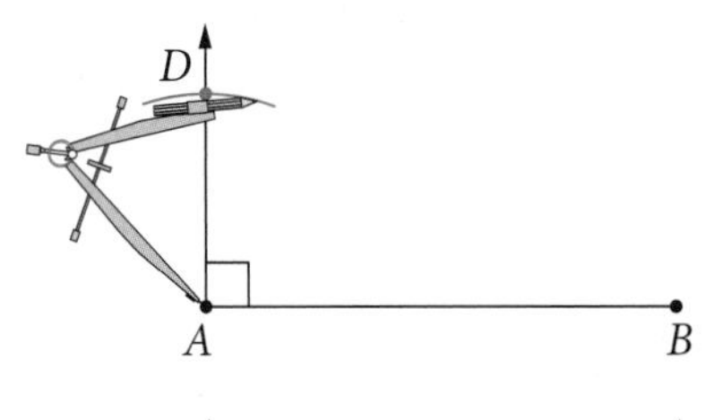

Step 4: Repeat steps 2 and 3 at B.

Step 5: Join C to D to produce the required rectangle.

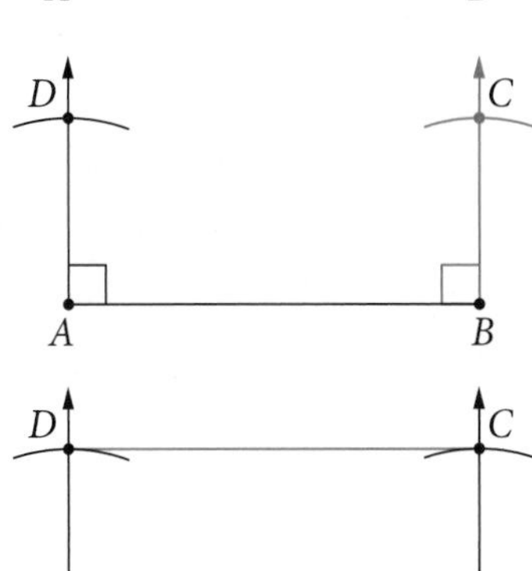

Geometry III

Practice Questions 12.1

Don't erase your construction lines – the examiners are looking to see these.

1. (i) Construct the following angles:
   (a) 70° (b) 100° (c) 130° (d) 124°
   (ii) Construct the bisector of each of the angles in (i) above.

2. In the diagram, [BC] bisects the angle ABD.
   (i) If $|\angle ABC| = 54°$, find $|\angle ABD|$.
   (ii) If $|\angle ABD| = 112°$, find $|\angle ABC|$.
   (iii) If $|\angle ABC| = (3x + 1)°$ and $|\angle ABD| = (5x + 19)°$, find the value of x.
   (iv) If $|\angle ABC| = (5x - 3)°$ and $|\angle CBD| = (2x + 15)°$, find x.

3. Draw the following line segments and construct the perpendicular bisector of each one. Measure each side to verify the line segment has been bisected.
   (i) 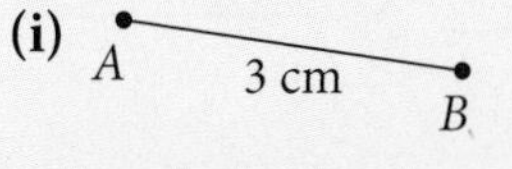 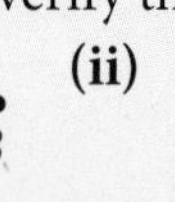
   (ii) 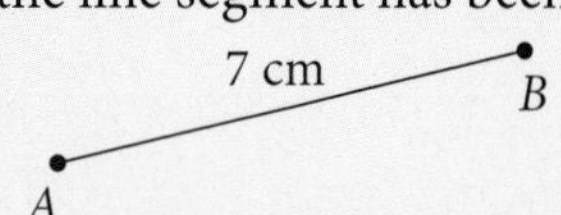 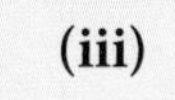
   (iii) 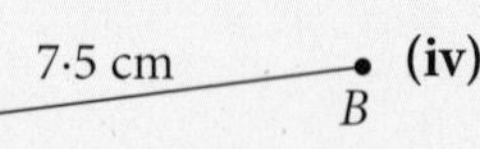 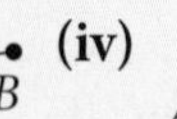
   (iv) 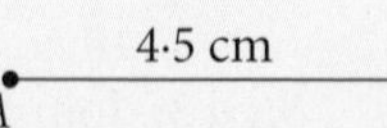

4. Copy the line segment [AB] and the point C shown in each case below. Construct the line segment through C that is:
   (i) perpendicular to [AB]
   (ii) parallel to [AB].
   (a) 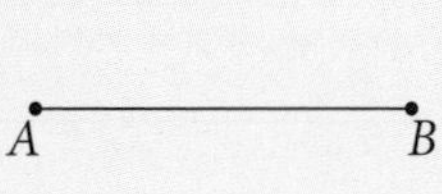 (b) 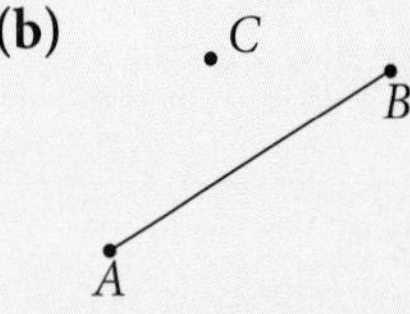 (c) 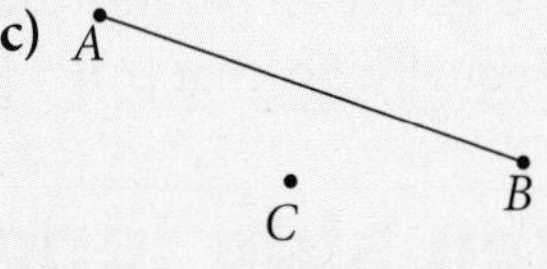 (d) 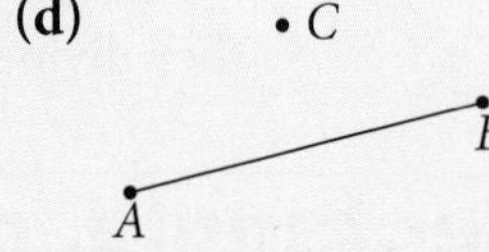

5. Draw the line segment [AB] of length given in each part below and then divide each line segment into three equal parts. Verify your result by measuring.
   (i) 12 cm (iii) 15 cm (v) 7·5 cm
   (ii) 9 cm (iv) 6 cm (vi) 13·5 cm

6. Construct a rectangle, ABCD, using the following measurements:
   (i) $|AB| = 12$ cm, $|CD| = 4$ cm
   (ii) $|AB| = 6$ cm, $|CD| = 3{\cdot}5$ cm
   (iii) $|AB| = 2{\cdot}8$ cm, $|CD| = 6{\cdot}6$ cm
   (iv) $|AB| = 1{\cdot}9$ cm, $|CD| = 3{\cdot}1$ cm

7. The penalty spot on a soccer pitch is located on the perpendicular bisector of the goal line. The width of the goal line is 7·3 m and the penalty spot is 11 m from the goal line.

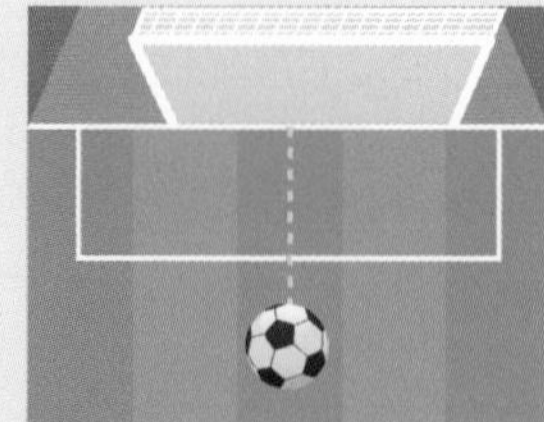

Taking a scale of 1 m = 1 cm, show the location of the penalty spot on a scale diagram.

8. The diagram shows one of the constructions you have studied.

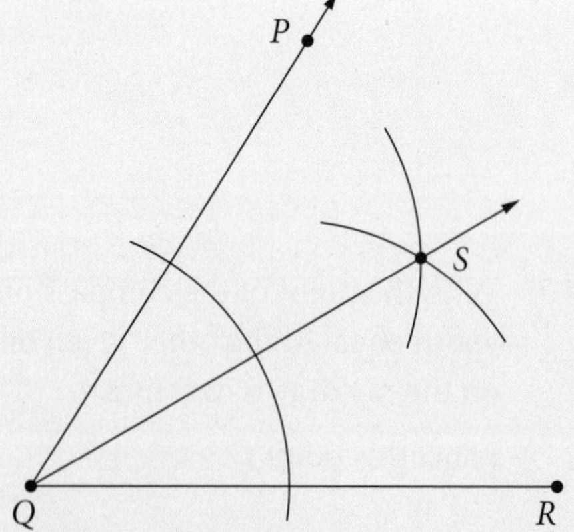

   (i) Based on this construction, which of the following statements are true?
   (a) $|\angle PQR| = |\angle RQS|$
   (b) $|\angle RQS| = |\angle PQS|$
   (c) $|\angle PQS| = \frac{1}{2}|\angle PQR|$
   (d) $2|\angle PQR| = |\angle PQS|$
   (ii) Change each of the untrue statements to make them true.

Geometry III

9. Which of the following diagrams represents the construction of the perpendicular bisector of a line?

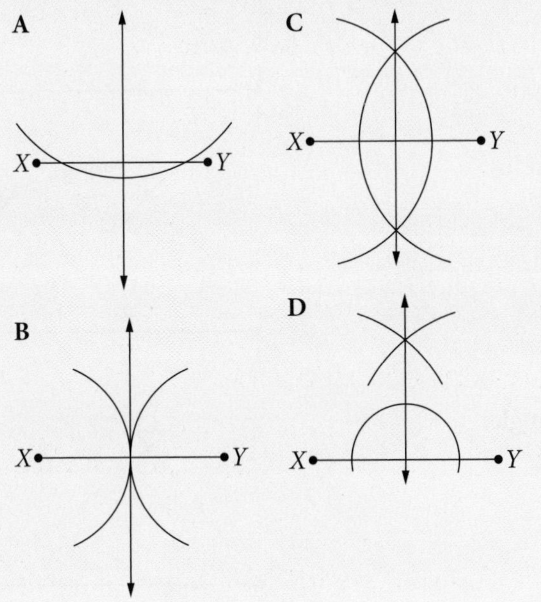

10. As part of a construction studies project for his Leaving Certificate, Jack must build a frame using the four pieces of wood shown in the diagram.

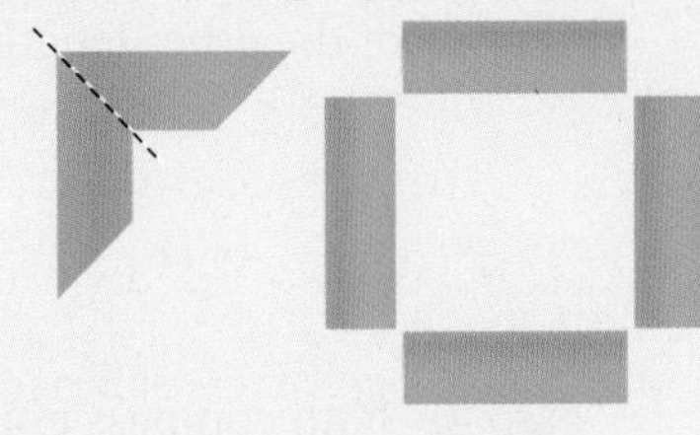

To join the corners neatly, he decides to cut each corner along the bisector of the angle as shown.

Using your compass and ruler, show how Jack bisected the corner angles of the four wooden pieces shown above to create the finished corner pieces.

Section 12.2: Revision of Junior Certificate Triangle Constructions

Learning Outcome:

You should be able to:

- recall the following Junior Certificate triangle constructions and use them to solve problems

For each of the following constructions, it is good practice to draw a rough sketch first. You should include all given measurements on your rough sketch.

Triangle, given lengths of three sides (SSS data)

Step 1: Draw a rough sketch of the triangle to be constructed. Include all given information on your sketch.

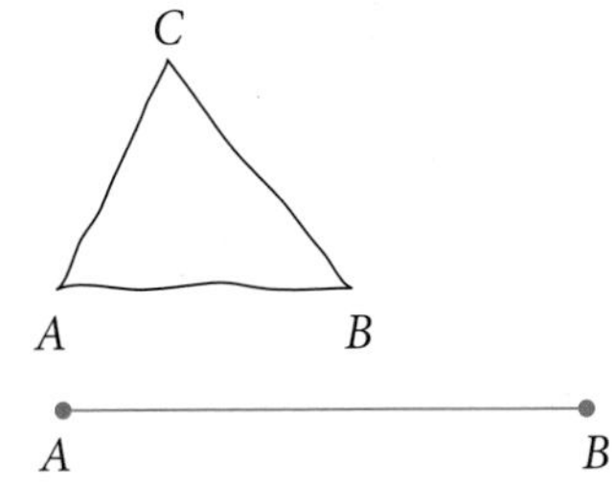

Step 2: Draw a line segment, $[AB]$, which has a length equal to the longest length given.

Step 3: With compass point on A and compass width equal to one of the other lengths given, draw an arc as shown.

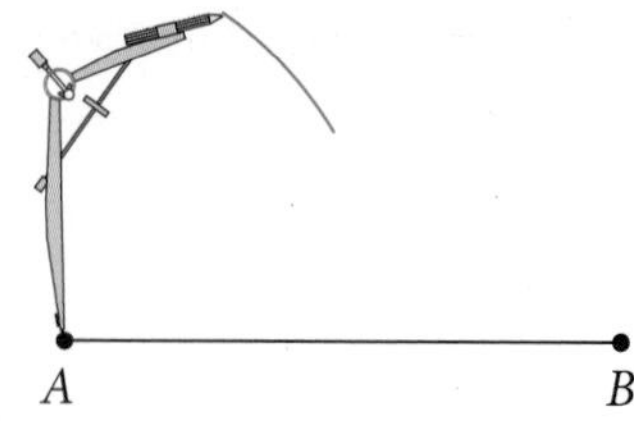

Step 4: With compass point on B and compass width equal to the third length given, draw an arc that intersects the arc from step 3.
Label the intersection point C.

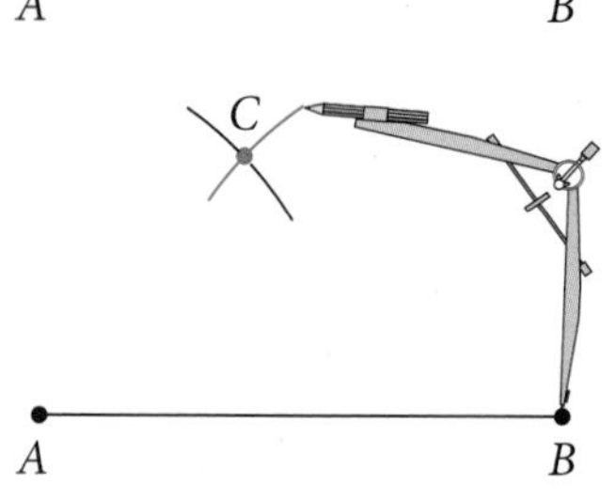

Step 5: Join A to C and B to C to produce the required triangle.

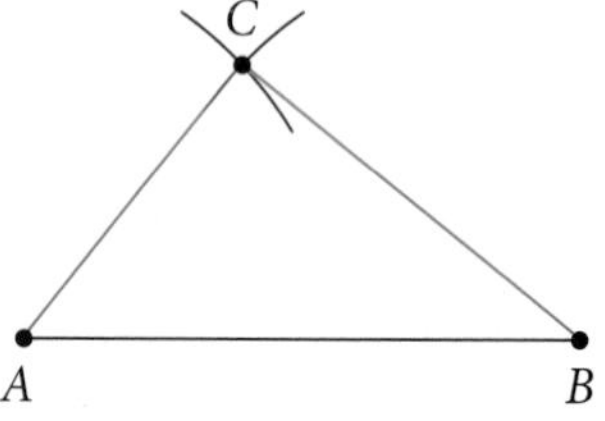

Triangle, given two sides and the angle in between (SAS data)

Step 1: Draw a rough sketch of the triangle to be constructed.
Include the given information on your sketch.

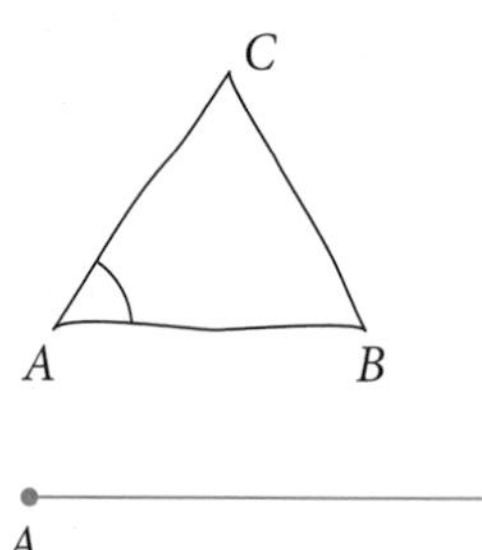

Step 2: Draw a line segment, $[AB]$, which has a length equal to one of the lengths given.

A B

Step 3: With the centre of the protractor on the point A and in line with AB, measure the required angle.
Mark the point X as shown. Draw a ray from A through X.

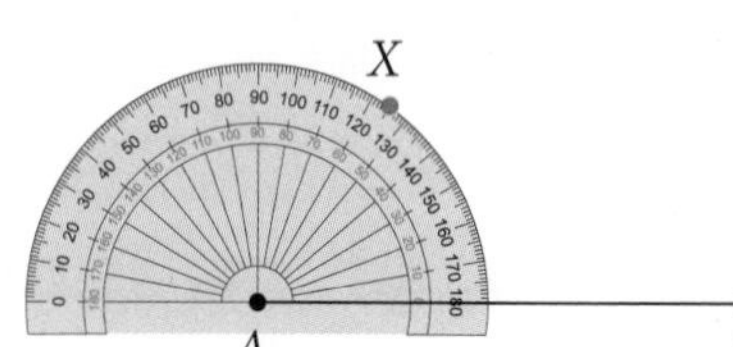

It is extremely important to make sure you construct the angle at the correct point.

Step 4: With compass point on A and compass width equal to the second length given, draw an arc on the ray $[AX$, as shown.
Label the point of intersection of the arc C.

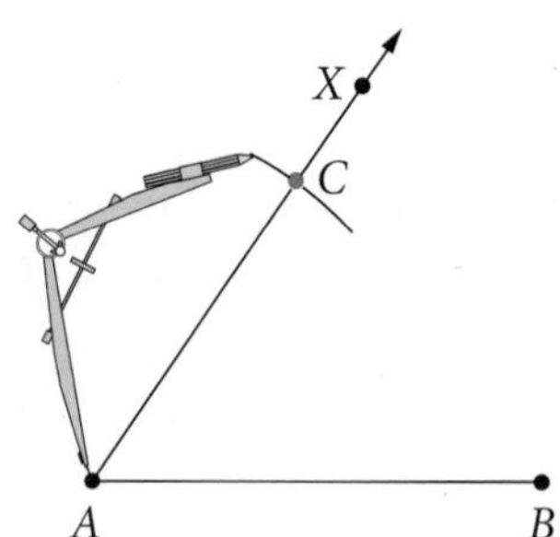

Step 5: Join B to C to produce the required triangle.

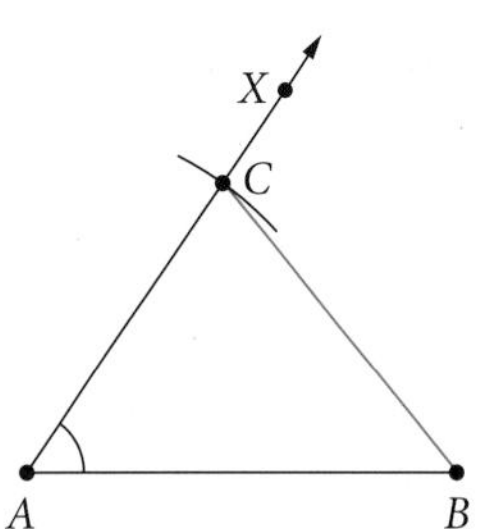

Triangle, given two angles and the side between (ASA data)

Step 1: Draw a rough sketch of the triangle to be constructed. Include the given information on your sketch.

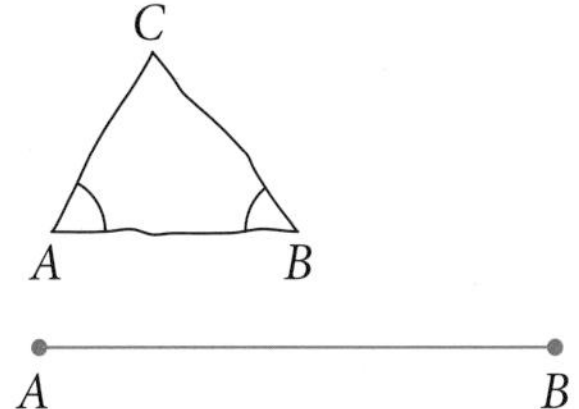

Step 2: Draw a line segment, $[AB]$, which has a length equal to the length given.

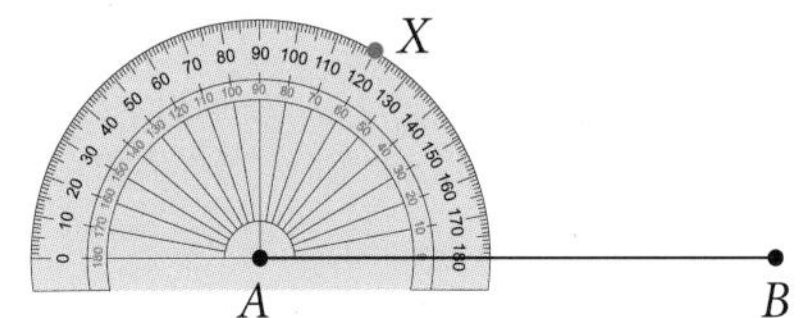

Step 3: With the centre of the protractor on the point A and in line with AB, measure one of the given angles. Mark the point X as shown.

Draw a ray from A through X.

Step 4: With the centre of the protractor on the point B and in line with AB, measure the other given angle. Mark the point Y as shown.

Draw a ray from B through Y.

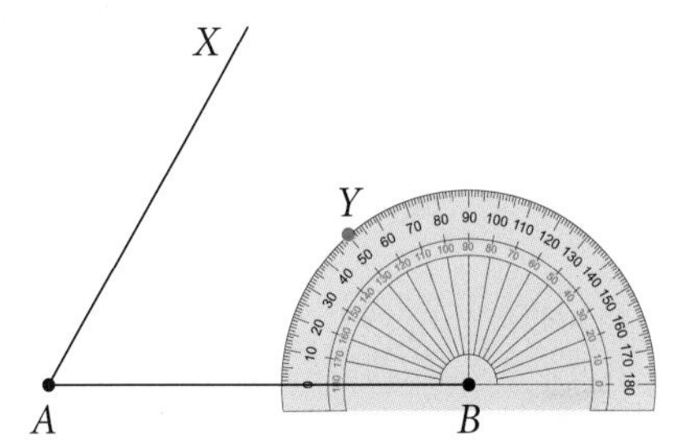

Step 5: Label the intersection of the rays $[AX$ and $[BY$ that you constructed in steps 3 and 4 as C to produce the required triangle.

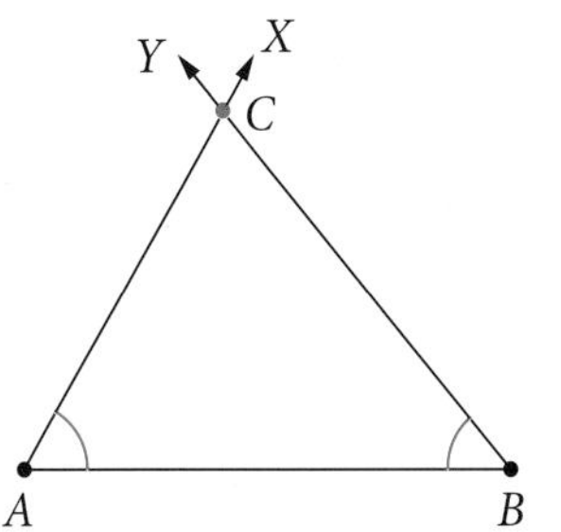

Right-angled triangle, given the length of the hypotenuse and one other side (RHS)

Step 1: Draw a rough sketch of the triangle to be constructed. Include the given information on your sketch.

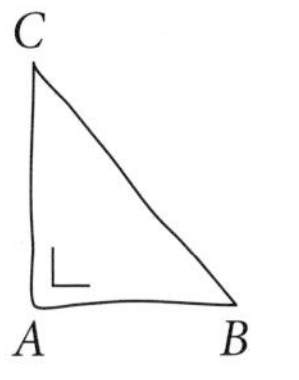

Step 2: Draw a line segment $[AB]$, which has a length equal to the side given that is not the hypotenuse.

Step 3: With the centre of the protractor on the point A and in line with AB, measure an angle of 90°.
Mark the point X as shown.
Draw a ray from A through X.

Step 4: With compass point on B and compass width equal to the length of the given hypotenuse, draw an arc on the ray $[AX$.
Label the intersection of the arc C.

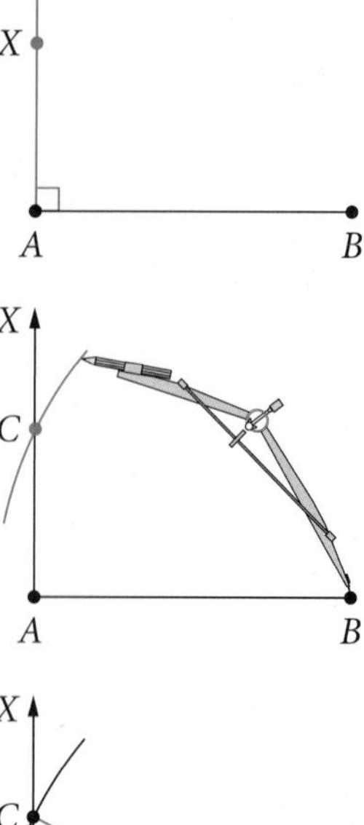

Step 5: Join B to C to produce the required triangle.

Right-angled triangle, given hypotenuse and one of the acute angles (several cases)

Step 1: Draw a rough sketch of the triangle to be constructed.
Include the given information on your sketch.

Step 2: Draw a line segment $[AB]$, which has a length equal to the given hypotenuse.

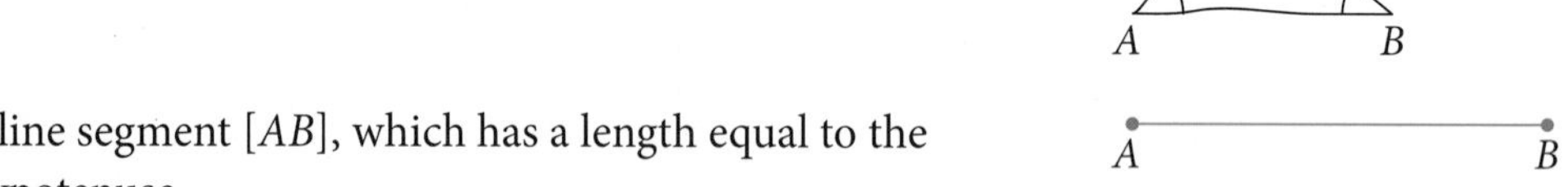

Step 3: Using a protractor, construct the acute angle given at A.
Mark the point X, as shown.
Draw a ray from A through X.

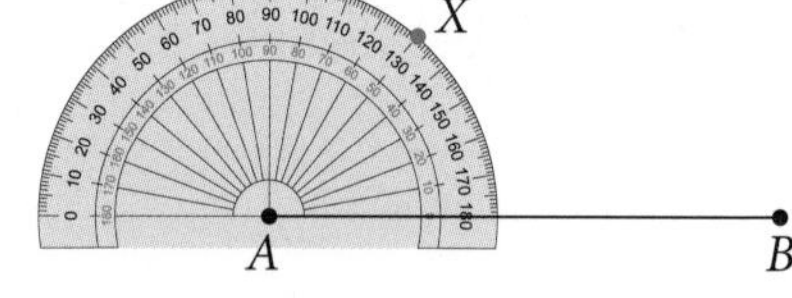

Step 4: Work out the other acute angle (remember, the three angles in a triangle add up to 180°). Using a protractor, construct this acute angle at B. Mark the point Y as shown.
Draw a ray from A through Y.

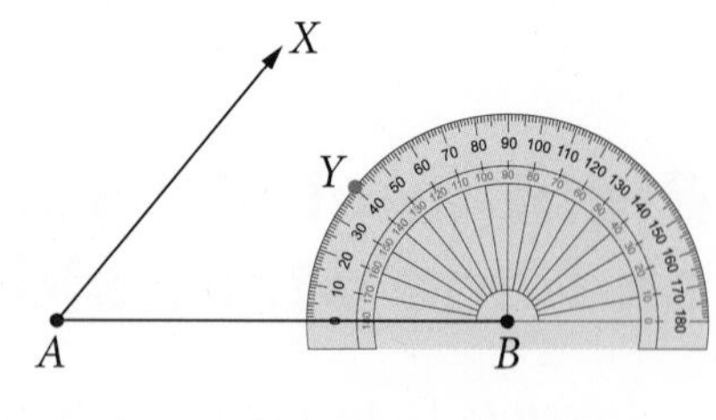

Step 5: Mark the point where the rays $[AX$ and $[BY$ intersect as C.
This is the required triangle.

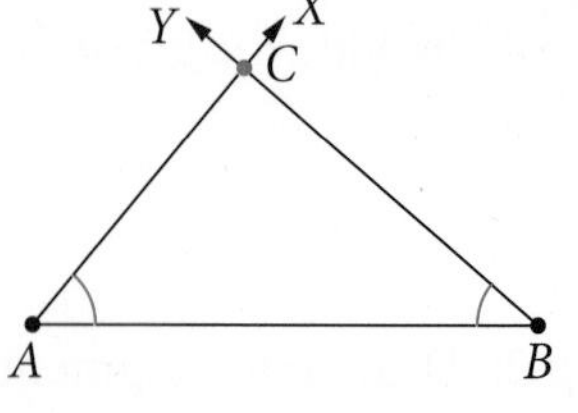

Practice Questions 12.2

It is good practice to draw a rough sketch first.

1. Construct the triangle ABC where:
   (i) $|AB| = 6$ cm, $|BC| = 5$ cm and $|AC| = 4$ cm
   (ii) $|AB| = 10$ cm, $|AC| = 4$ cm and $|BC| = 9$ cm
   (iii) $|AB| = 9{\cdot}5$ cm, $|BC| = 7$ cm and $|AC| = 4$ cm
   (iv) $|BC| = 6{\cdot}3$ cm, $|AB| = 8{\cdot}2$ cm and $|AC| = 4{\cdot}1$ cm
2. Construct the triangle ABC where:
   (i) $|AB| = 5$ cm, $|\angle BAC| = 50°$ and $|AC| = 7$ cm
   (ii) $|AB| = 7$ cm, $|\angle CAB| = 110°$ and $|AC| = 3$ cm
   (iii) $|AC| = 5$ cm, $|AB| = 3$ cm and $|\angle BAC| = 30°$
   (iv) $|AB| = 3{\cdot}5$ cm, $|\angle BAC| = 140°$ and $|AC| = 3{\cdot}5$ cm
3. Construct the following triangles when given the information below:
   (i) $|\angle QPR| = 60°$, $|PQ| = 7{\cdot}5$ cm and $|\angle PQR| = 70°$
   (ii) $|\angle BAC| = 20°$, $|AB| = 6$ cm and $|\angle ABC| = 140°$
   (iii) $|\angle YXZ| = 60°$, $|YX| = 9$ cm and $|\angle XYZ| = 60°$
   (iv) $|\angle BAC| = 72°$, $|AB| = 8$ cm and $|\angle ABC| = 63°$
4. Construct the following right-angled triangles ABC when $|AB|$ is the hypotenuse.
   (i) $|AB| = 7$cm, $|BC| = 5$ cm
   (ii) $|AB| = 5{\cdot}8$ cm, $|BC| = 4{\cdot}5$ cm
   (iii) $|AB| = 11$ cm, $|BC| = 6{\cdot}8$ cm
   (iv) $|AB| = 12$ cm, $|BC| = 5{\cdot}2$ cm
5. Construct the following right-angled triangles ABC when $|AB|$ is the hypotenuse.
   (i) $|AB| = 8$ cm and $|\angle CAB| = 45°$
   (ii) $|AB| = 7$ cm and $|\angle BAC| = 38°$
   (iii) $|AB| = 6$ cm and $|\angle CAB| = 56°$
   (iv) $|AB| = 4{\cdot}8$ cm and $|\angle BAC| = 34°$
6. (i) Construct ΔRST where $|RS| = 9$ cm, $|\angle RST| = 60°$ and $|\angle SRT| = 60°$.
   (ii) What is the measure of angle $|\angle RTS|$?
   (iii) What type of triangle is ΔRST?
   (iv) State how long the other sides of the triangle are without measuring them.

Section 12.3: Leaving Certificate Constructions

Learning Outcome:

You should be able to:

- complete the Leaving Certificate constructions and use them to solve problems

Circumcentre and circumcircle of a given triangle, using only straight edge and compass

The **circumcircle** is a circle that passes through the three vertices of a triangle.

The **circumcentre** is the centre of the circumcircle. It is the point at which the perpendicular bisectors of the sides of the triangle intersect.

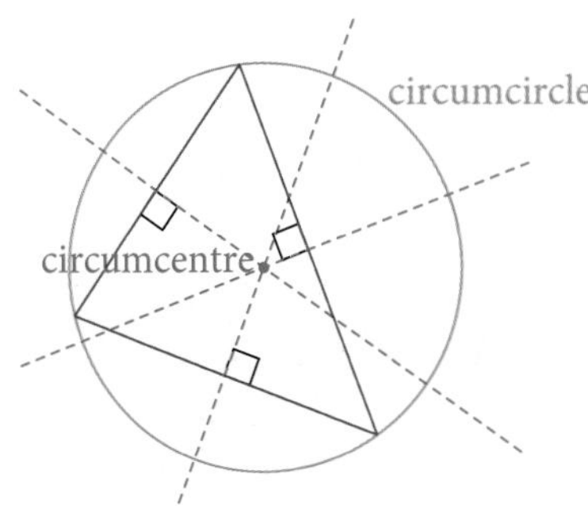

In practice it is sufficient to find the point of intersection of the perpendicular bisectors of two of the sides of the triangle.
The third would confirm your answer.

Step 1: Draw the perpendicular bisector of AB.

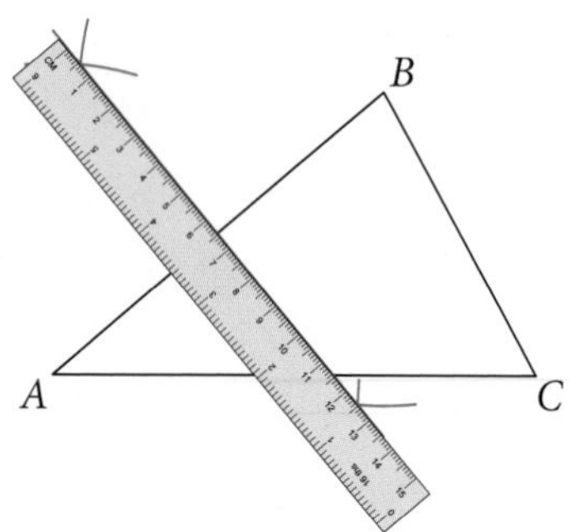

Step 2: Draw the perpendicular bisector of BC.
Label the intersection of the bisectors D.
This is the circumcentre.

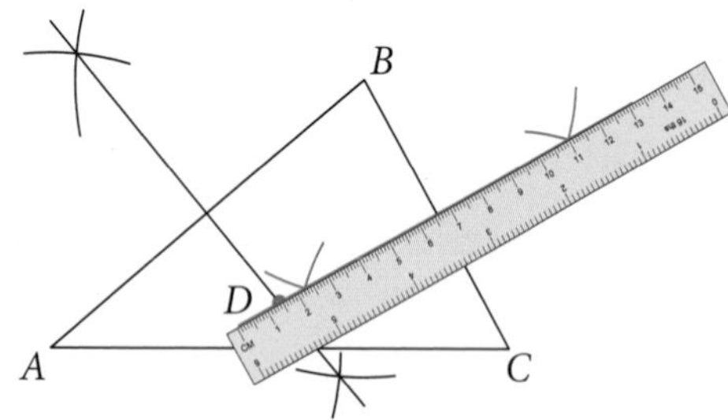

Step 3: Place the compass at D.
Set the width by using any vertex of the triangle.
This is the radius of the circumcircle.
Draw the circle. It should pass through all three vertices A, B, and C.

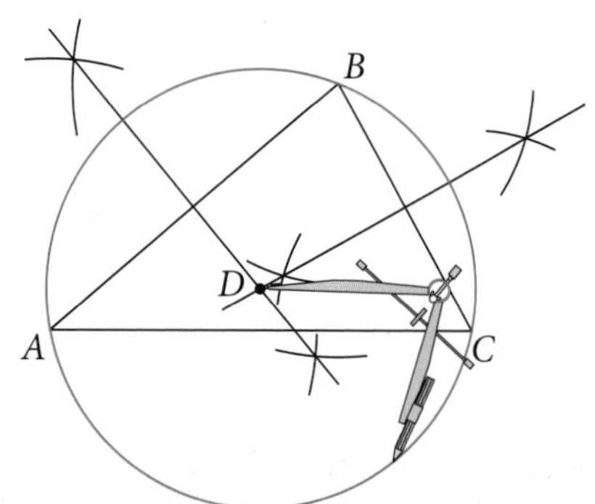

The circumcentre is the same distance from each of the vertices of the triangle.

Discussion Time 

Work with a classmate to construct triangles with the following side lengths:

1. 4 cm, 3 cm, 3 cm **2.** 5 cm, 4 cm, 3 cm **3.** 6 cm, 4 cm, 3 cm

A triangle can be described as acute (all the angles are less than 90°), obtuse (one of the angles is greater than 90°) or right-angled (one of the angles is 90°).

(i) Identify the type of triangle constructed in **1** – **3** above.

(ii) Construct the circumcentre of each of the triangles constructed above.

(iii) Investigate the relationship between the position of the circumcentre and the type of triangle.

Incentre and incircle of a given triangle, using only straight edge and compass

The **incircle** is a circle inscribed in (drawn inside) a triangle so as to touch (but not cross) each side of the triangle.

The **incentre** is the centre of the incircle. It is the point at which the bisectors of the angles of the triangle intersect.

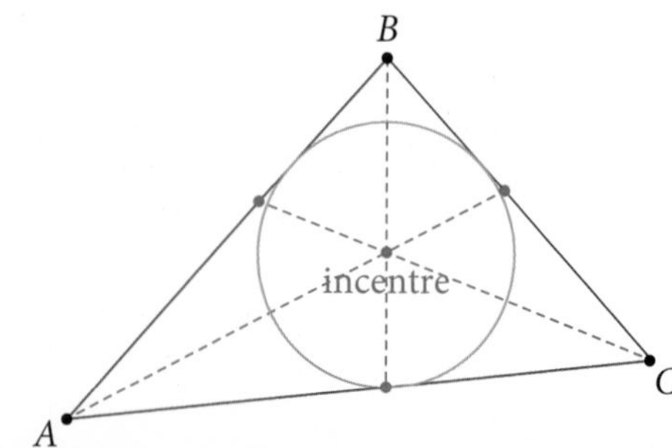

Step 1: Draw the bisector of $\angle A$.

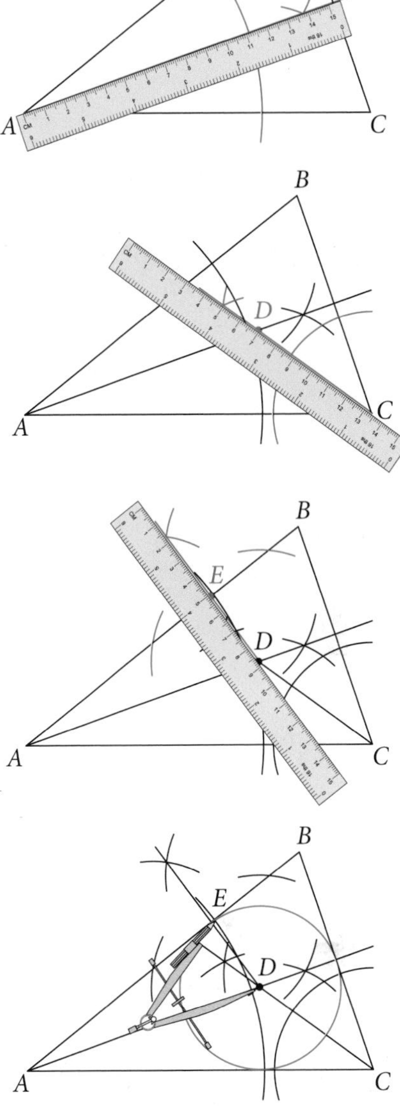

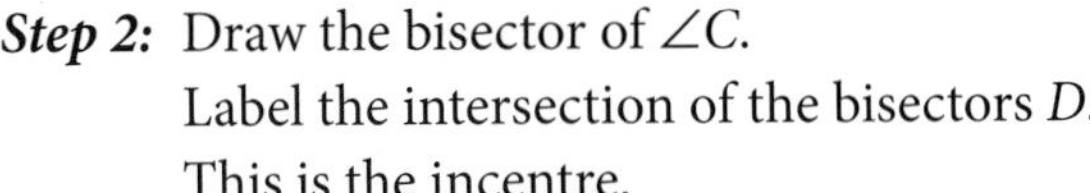
Step 2: Draw the bisector of $\angle C$.
Label the intersection of the bisectors D.
This is the incentre.

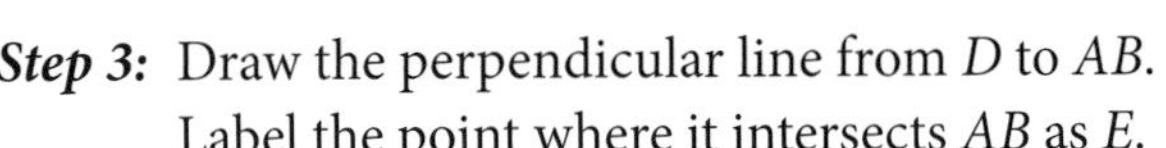
Step 3: Draw the perpendicular line from D to AB.
Label the point where it intersects AB as E.

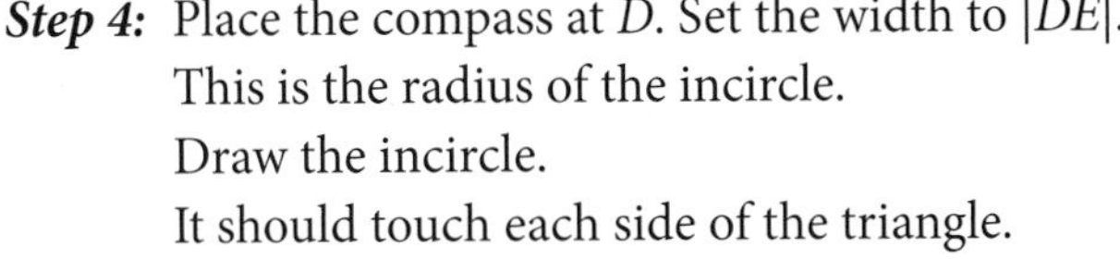
Step 4: Place the compass at D. Set the width to $|DE|$.
This is the radius of the incircle.
Draw the incircle.
It should touch each side of the triangle.

Angle of 60°, without using a protractor or set square

Step 1: Draw a line segment $[AB]$ of any length.

Step 2: With the compass point on A, draw a large arc that passes through B.

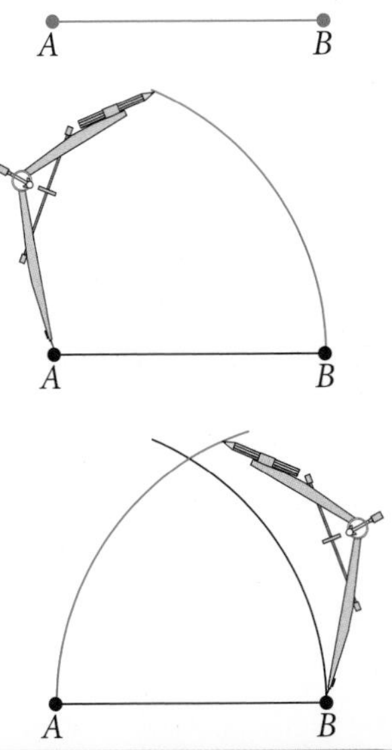

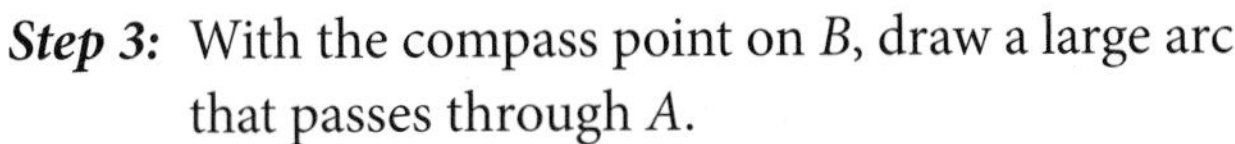
Step 3: With the compass point on B, draw a large arc that passes through A.

Step 4: Mark the point of intersection of these two arcs as C.
Join A to C to produce the required angle of 60°.

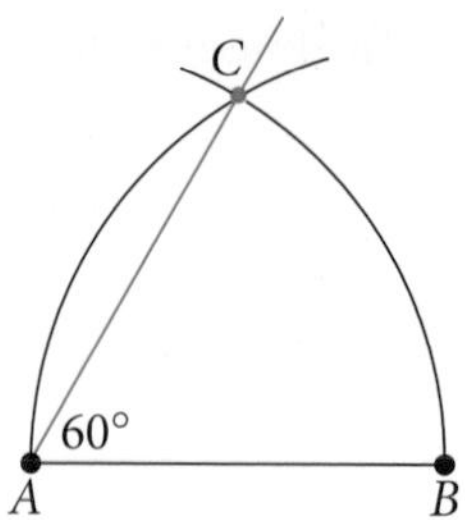

Tangent to a given circle at a given point on it

Step 1: Draw a circle, c, with centre, O, and point on the circle, P, as shown.

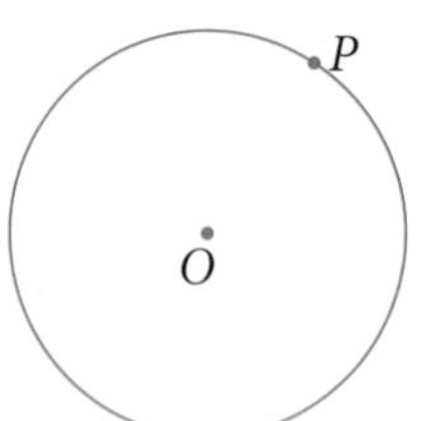

Step 2: Draw a ray from O through P.

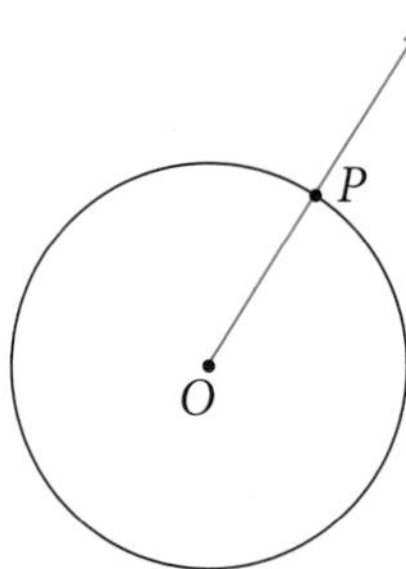

Step 3: Draw a line perpendicular to the ray $[OP$ through the point P.
This line is the required tangent.

Recall how to construct a line perpendicular to a given line.

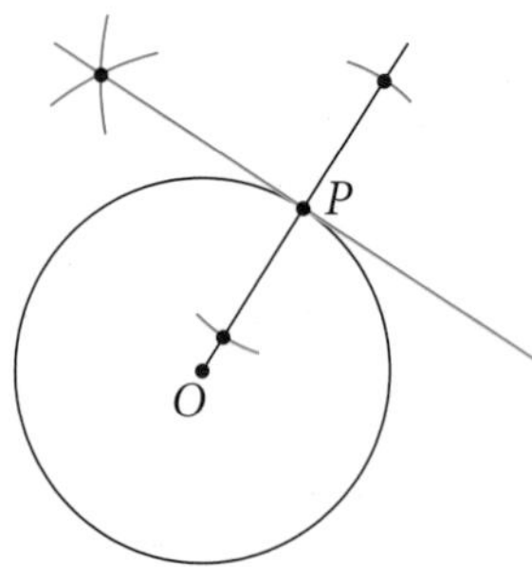

Parallelogram, given the length of the sides and the measure of the angles

Constructing a rectangle is a special case of this construction, where the angles at the corners are 90°.

Step 1: Draw a line segment $[AB]$, which has a length equal to one of the lengths given.

Step 2: At A, construct the given angle and draw a ray.

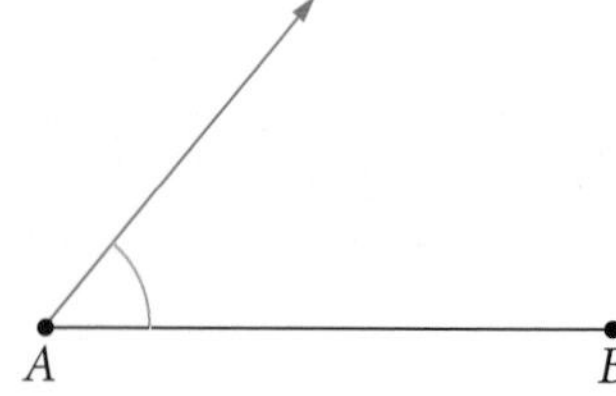

Geometry III

Step 3: With the compass point on A and the compass width equal to the other length given, draw an arc on the ray $[A$. Mark the point where the arc intersects the ray D.

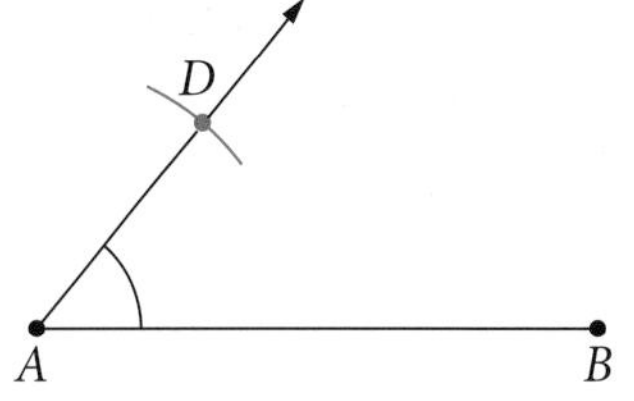

Step 4: At the point B, draw a ray parallel to the line segment $[AD]$.

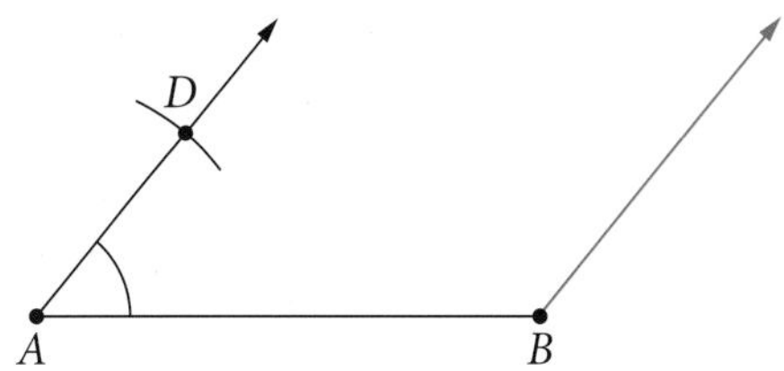

Step 5: With the compass point on B and the compass width equal to $|AD|$, draw an arc on the ray $[B$. Mark the point where the arc intersects the ray C. Join D to C to produce the required parallelogram.

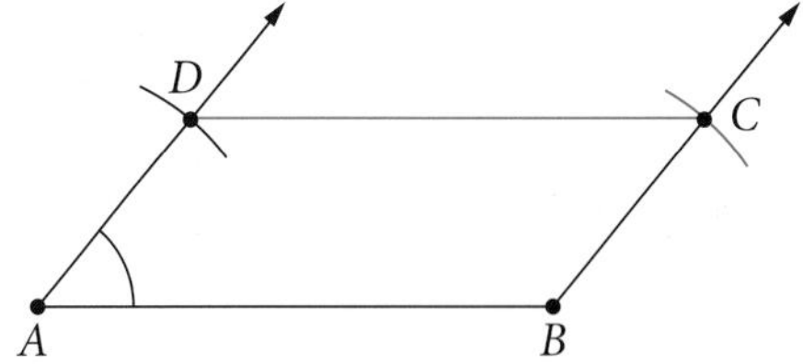

Centroid of a triangle

The **centroid** of a triangle is the centre of gravity (balance point) of the triangle. It is the point of intersection of the medians of the triangle.

The **median** of a triangle is a line that joins a vertex to the midpoint of the opposite side.

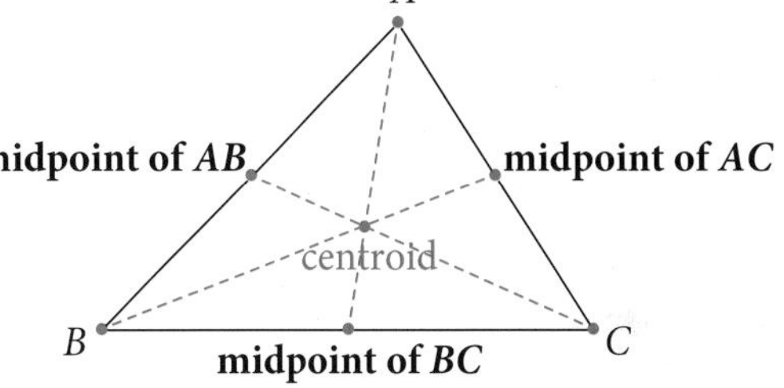

In the diagram, the median through A is the line joining A to the midpoint of BC.

Step 1: Draw the perpendicular bisector of $[AB]$. Label the midpoint of $[AB]$ X.

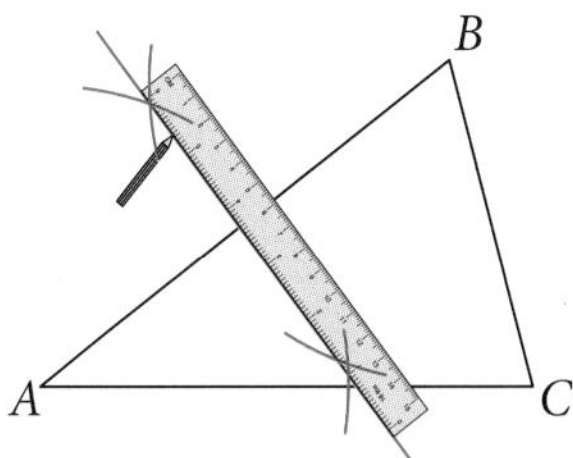

Step 2: Draw the median from the midpoint X to the opposite vertex C.

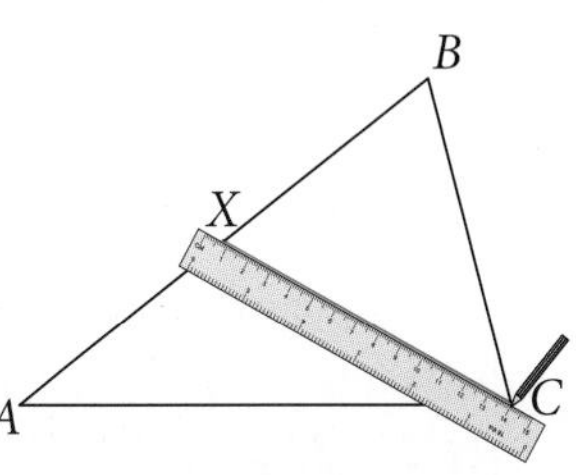

Step 3: Repeat steps 1 and 2 to draw the median through A.

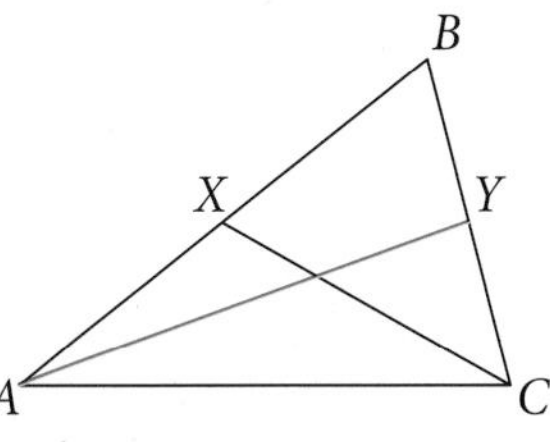

Step 4: Label the point where the medians intersect P.
This is the required centroid of the triangle.

The centroid divides the median in a 2 : 1 ratio.

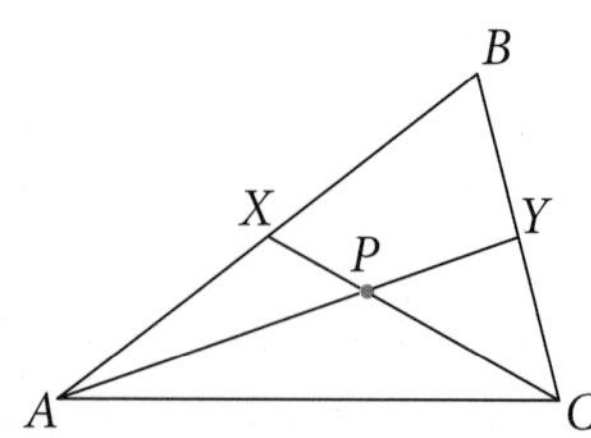

Discussion Time

Work with a classmate to:

1. Construct an equilateral triangle of side length 8 cm.
2. Construct the circumcentre of the triangle.
3. Construct the incentre of the triangle.
4. Construct the centroid of the triangle.

What do you notice?

Practice Questions 12.3

1. Define fully each of the following and describe them as the point of intersection of something:
   (i) Circumcentre **(ii)** Incentre **(iii)** Centroid
2. Construct the following triangles XYZ and hence construct the circumcircle of each.
   (i) $|XY| = 5$ cm, $|YZ| = 6$ cm and $|XZ| = 7$ cm
   (ii) $|XY| = 6$ cm, $|YZ| = 7$ cm and $|XZ| = 9$ cm
   (iii) $|\angle XYZ| = 50°$, $|\angle YZX| = 70°$ and $|YZ| = 4$ cm
   (iv) $|XY| = 10$ cm, $|YZ| = 5$ cm and $|\angle XYZ| = 20°$
3. Contruct the following triangles PQR and, hence, construct the incircle of each.
   (i) $|PQ| = 10$ cm, $|PR| = 6$ cm, $|QR| = 8$ cm
   (ii) $|PQ| = 9$ cm, $|PR| = 6$ cm, $|\angle PQR| = 35°$
   (iii) $|PQ| = 11$ cm, $|\angle PQR| = 70°$, $|PR| = 8{\cdot}5$ cm
   (iv) $|\angle QPR| = 95°$, $|\angle PQR| = 50°$ and $|PQ|$ 6 cm
4. Construct the following triangles ABC and, hence, construct the centroid of each.
   (i) $|AB| = 4{\cdot}5$ cm, $|AC| = 3{\cdot}5$ cm and $|BC| = 3$ cm
   (ii) $|\angle ABC| = 60°$, $|\angle BAC| = 42°$ and $|AB| = 7$ cm
   (iii) $|AB| = 2{\cdot}5$ cm, $|BC| = 4$ cm and $|\angle ABC| = 121°$
   (iv) $|\angle ABC| = 65°$, $|\angle BAC| = 55°$ and $|AB| = 5$ cm
5. A local council wants to position a street light so that it is the same distance from each of the streets shown in the diagram.
   Jane says that they should use the circumcentre of the triangle created by the three streets. Jack says this won't work.
   Which person do you agree with? Justify your answer.

6. Stephen wants to put the largest possible circular fish pond in his triangle shaped garden, shown on the right.
   (i) Stephen measures the lengths of the garden and finds that $|QR| = 10{\cdot}5$ m, $|PR| = 9{\cdot}9$ m and $|PQ| = 8{\cdot}4$ m.
   Using a scale of 1 m = 1 cm, show the construction required to produce the largest possible pond.
   (ii) Stephen decides to leave a path of width one metre around the pond.
   Will the centre of the pond be in the same position as in part **(i)**? Justify your answer.

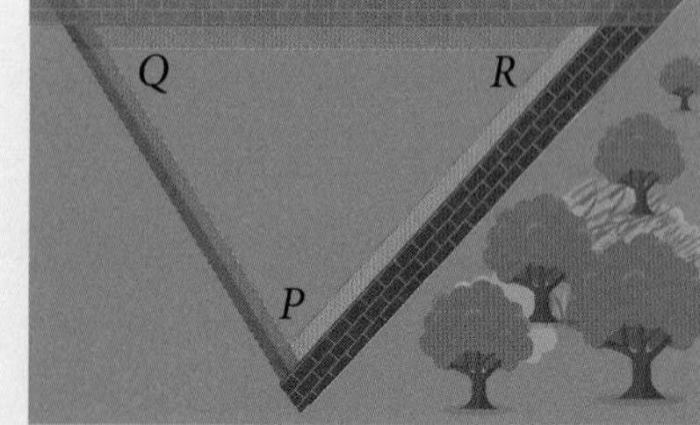

7. Your friend says that the circumcentre of an equilateral triangle is also the incentre of the triangle. Is your friend correct? Explain your reasoning.

8. Construct the following triangles and hence construct the centre of gravity of each.
   (i) Sides 8 cm, 10 cm and 18 cm
   (ii) Sides 7·3 cm and 8 cm, angle 38°
   (iii) Angles 40° and 65°, side 7 cm

9. The residents of the area around the park shown in the scaled diagram want paths built through the park. They suggest the paths should run from the midpoint of each side to its opposite corner.
   (i) What is the mathematical term to describe each path?
   (ii) The paths intersect at the point P. What is the mathematical term for the point P?
   (iii) Copy the diagram and construct the location of P.

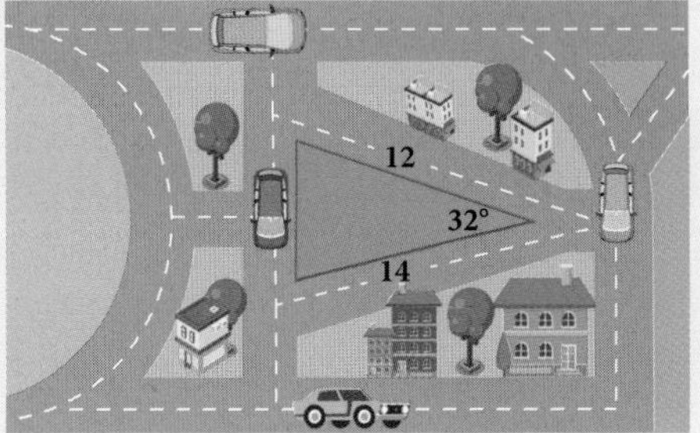

10. Construct the circles below and, using a protractor, mark the point P on the circle at the given angle from a horizontal radius (diagram for (i) is shown). Hence, construct the tangent to the circle at P.
   (i) radius 4 cm, angle 15°
   (ii) radius 6 cm, angle 28°
   (iii) radius 3 cm, angle 55°
   (iv) radius 5 cm, angle 75°
   (v) radius 3·5 cm, angle 120°
   (vi) radius 7 cm, angle 135°

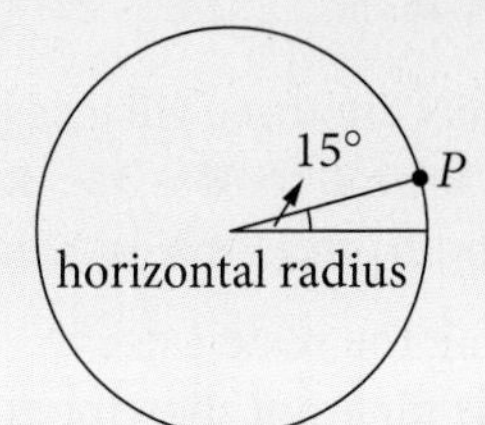

Revision and Exam Style Questions – Section A

1. Construct a triangle ABC with $|AC| = 10$ cm, $|BC| = 8$ cm and $|AB| = 6$ cm. What is the measure of the angle ABC?

2. Construct a line segment $[RS]$ of 7 cm. Construct the perpendicular bisector of $[RS]$.

3. Construct a rectangle, $ABCD$, where $|AB| = 7$ cm and $|BC| = 4$ cm.

4. ABC is a triangle. $|\angle ABC| = 78°$, $|AC| = 7$ cm and $|\angle BAC| = 43°$. Construct this triangle.

5. Construct an equilateral triangle with sides of length 6 cm.

6. (i) Construct a parallelogram, $ABCD$, with sides $|AB| = 5$ cm and $|BC| = 7$ cm and $|\angle ABC| = 80°$.
   (ii) What is the measure of $\angle BAD$?

7. (i) Construct a triangle XYZ in which $|XY| = 10$ cm, $|XZ| = 6$ cm and $|\angle ZXY| = 50°$. All construction lines must be clearly shown.
   (ii) Show how to bisect $\angle XYZ$ without using a protractor.

8. Construct a right-angled triangle PQR, where $|\angle QPR| = 42°$, $|PQ| = 8$ cm and $|\angle RQP| = 90°$.

9. Construct, without using a protractor or set square, an angle of 60°. Hence, construct, on the same diagram, and using a compass and straight edge only, an angle of 30°.

10. (i) Construct ΔDEF such that, $|DE| = 6{\cdot}5$ cm, $|\angle DEF| = 50°$ and $|\angle DFE| = 30°$.
   (ii) Construct the point M on $[EF]$ such that $[DM]$ is perpendicular to $[EF]$.
   (iii) Measure the length of $[DM]$.

Revision and Exam Style Questions – Section B

More challenging problems

1. (i) Construct the triangle DEF, such that $|DE| = 8$ cm, $|EF| = 6$ cm and $|DF| = 12$ cm.
   (ii) Construct the circumcircle of the triangle. Show all construction lines clearly.
   (iii) Under what condition(s) does the circumcentre of a triangle lie inside the triangle? Justify your answers.

2. (i) Show how to construct the triangle ABC, with sides $|AB| = 10$ cm, $|BC| = 9$ cm and $|AC| = 7$ cm.
   (ii) Explain what is meant by the incentre.
   (iii) Show how to construct the incircle of triangle ABC. All construction lines must be clearly shown.

3. L, M and N are three villages in an area. The distance from L to M is 32·5 km, from M to N is 30 km and from L to N is 20 km.
   (i) Using the scale 1 cm = 2·5 km, construct a scale diagram showing the locations of the three villages.

Links across the syllabus

Scale diagrams are covered in Chapter 16: Area and Perimeter.

   (ii) A new sports centre is to be built equidistant from each of the three villages. Indicate the location of the sports centre on your diagram. Show all construction lines clearly.
   (iii) What is the geometric name for this point?

4. (i) Draw a circle of radius 4·5 cm.
   (ii) Construct the tangent to the circle at a point P at any position on the circle.
   (iii) What theorem is used in the construction of the tangent?
   (iv) On the same diagram, construct $|\angle POB| = 60°$, where B is another point on the circle and O is the centre, without using a protractor or set square.
   (v) What type of triangle is OPB? Give a reason for your answer.

5. (i) Complete each of the following statements.
   (a) The circumcentre of a triangle is the point of intersection of ....
   (b) The incentre of a triangle is the point of intersection of ....
   (c) The centroid of a triangle is the point of intersection of ....
   (ii) In an equilateral triangle, the circumcentre, the incentre and the centroid are all in the same place. Explain why this is the case.

6. Given a line segment $[AB]$, 8 cm in length:
   (i) construct the perpendicular bisector of $[AB]$
   (ii) construct an equilateral triangle with side $[AB]$.
   (iii) For a given point P not on AB, construct a line segment PQ parallel to AB such that $|AB| = |PQ|$.

7. Copy the diagram on the right onto graph paper. The points A, B, and C represent the circumcentre, centroid and incentre.

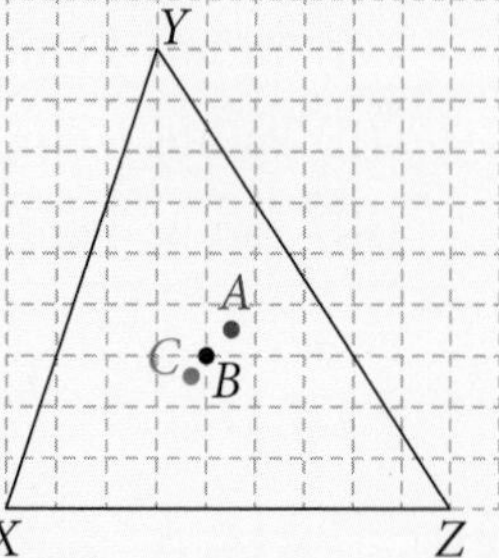

   (i) Identify which point is the circumcentre, incentre and centroid.

   Imagine the points X, Y and Z are three rural villages that share a fire station.
   (ii) Where would be the fairest location for the fire station? Justify your answer.

8. A platform at a busy train station is in the shape of a triangle, shown in red in the diagram.

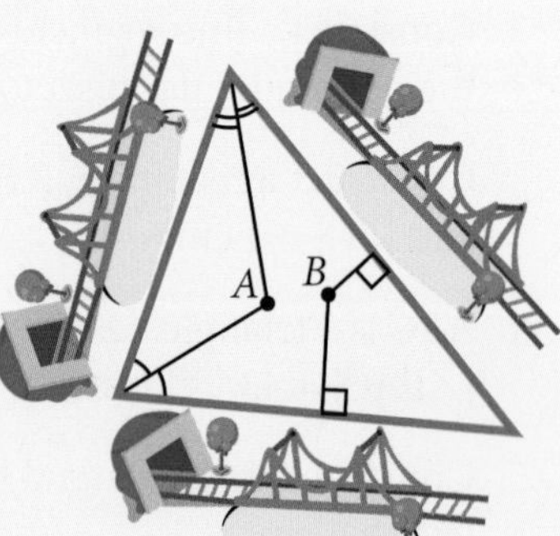

You are trying to talk to your friend on the phone while standing on this platform. The trains are very loud and you can barely hear.
In order to hear better, you should stand at the point which is as far away as possible from **all** three tracks. Should you stand at A or B? Explain your choice.

9. A circus performer wants to balance a triangular piece of wood on the end of a stick as part of his act. He wants to mark the point where the piece will be balanced. The piece of wood has side lengths 0·75 m, 1 m and 1·25 m.
   (i) Construct a scale diagram of the piece of wood, such that 1 m = 6 cm.
   (ii) On your diagram, mark the point the performer is looking for.

10. As part of a marketing campaign for foreign tourists, Bórd Fáilte are promoting 'The Viking Triangle', formed by joining the cities of Kilkenny and Waterford and the town of Wexford, as shown on the map below.
    Frank is asked to find a site for a visitor centre in this region. He proposes the site marked with a blue dot on the map.
    (i) How did he construct the position of the site?
    (ii) What is the mathematical term for this proposed site?
    (iii) Why, do you think, did Frank choose this site?
    (iv) In your opinion, is this a good location for the visitor centre?
    Give a reason for your answer.

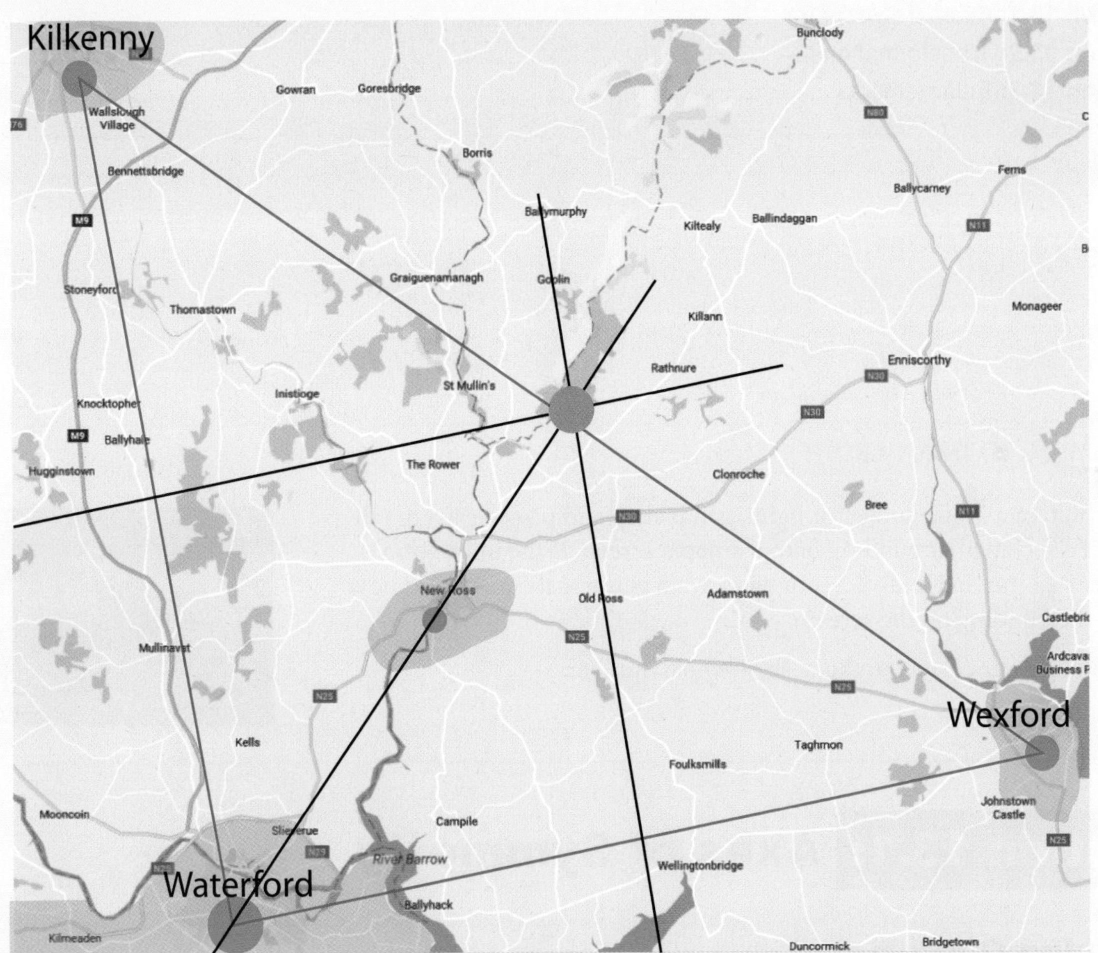

Now that you have completed the chapter, revisit the 'Something to think about…' question.

CHAPTER 13 Geometry IV – Transformation Geometry and Enlargements

Sections covered within this chapter:

KEY WORDS

- Axis of symmetry
- Translation
- Rotation
- Centre of enlargement
- Object
- Central symmetry
- Enlargement
- Image
- Axial symmetry
- Scale factor

SOMETHING TO THINK ABOUT... 

A light bulb in a movie projector lights a film strip and projects a 6 m tall image of a rectangular building onto a cinema screen. If the image on the film is 23 mm tall and 14·2 mm wide, what is the scale factor and how wide is the building on the screen?

Give your answer correct to the nearest whole number.

Section 13.1: Axes of Symmetry

Learning Outcome:

You should be able to:

- locate axes of symmetry in simple shapes

An **axis of symmetry** is a line that divides a shape into two parts in such a way that each side is the mirror image of the other.

An axis of symmetry can be vertical, horizontal or slanted in any direction.

It is possible for a shape to have no axis of symmetry or more than one axis of symmetry.

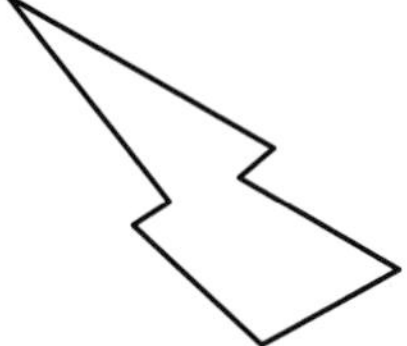
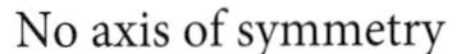
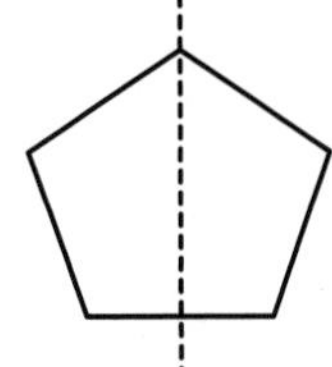
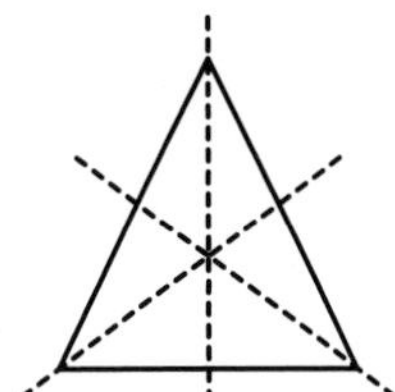

No axis of symmetry One axis of symmetry Three axes of symmetry

You can also be asked to identify the axis of symmetry of a graph. An example of this is shown below.

The dotted red line is the axis of symmetry, since it divides the graph into two identical halves.

All quadratic functions are symmetrical about the turning point.

The equation of this axis of symmetry is $x = 3$, since it passes through 3 on the x-axis.

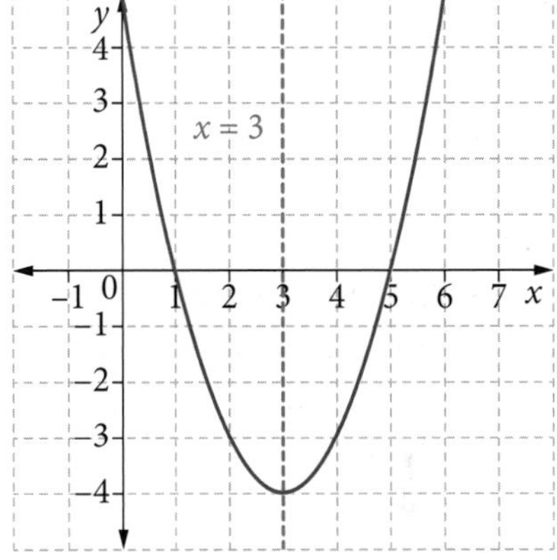

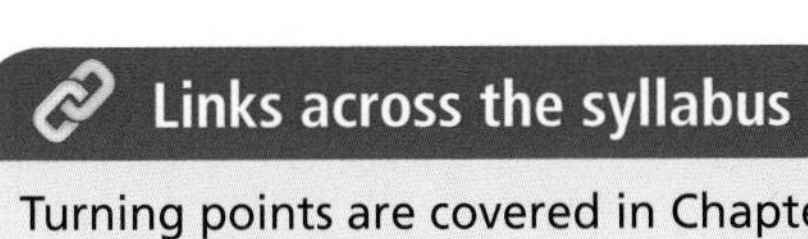

Turning points are covered in Chapter 26: Differential Calculus I.

Practice Questions 13.1

1. Is the dotted line on each shape an axis of symmetry?

(i) (ii) (iii) (iv)

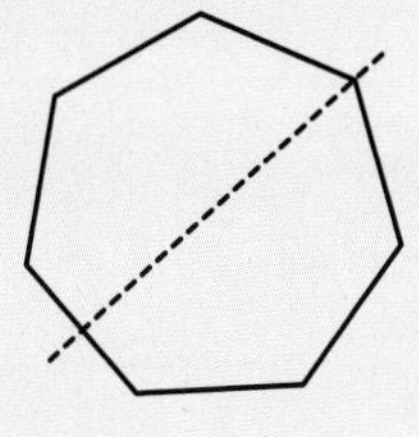
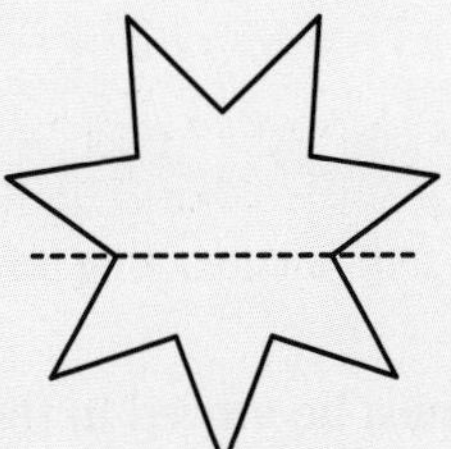
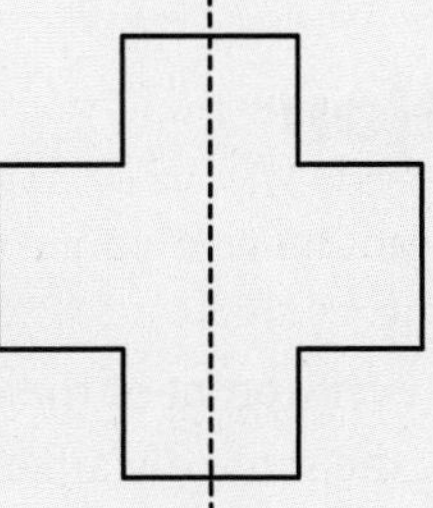

2. How many axes of symmetry, if any, does each of the following shapes have?

(i) (ii) (iii) (iv)

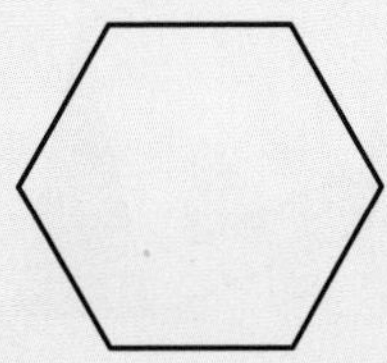
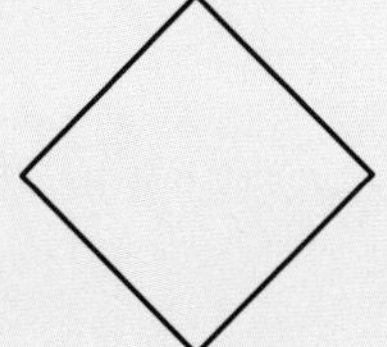
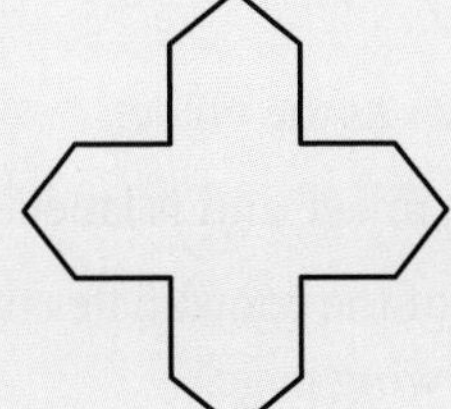

3. Draw a shape that has the number of lines of symmetry specified below:

   (i) Three lines **(ii)** One line **(iii)** No lines **(iv)** Four lines

4. Write the equation for the axis of symmetry of each of the following graphs:

(i)

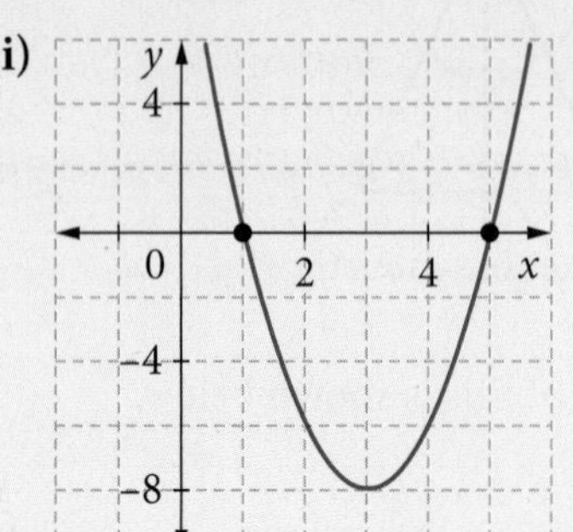

(ii)

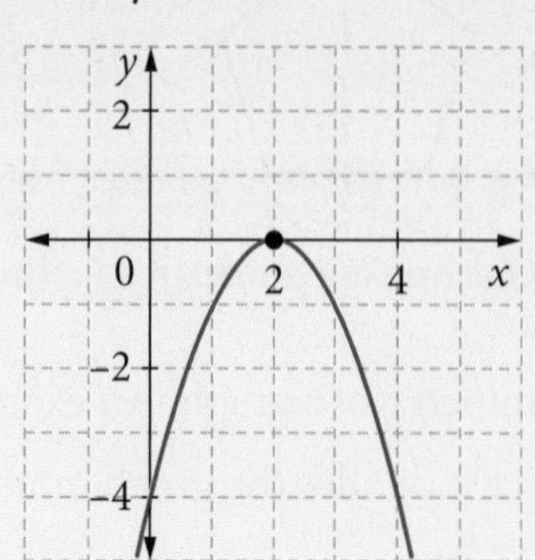

(iii)

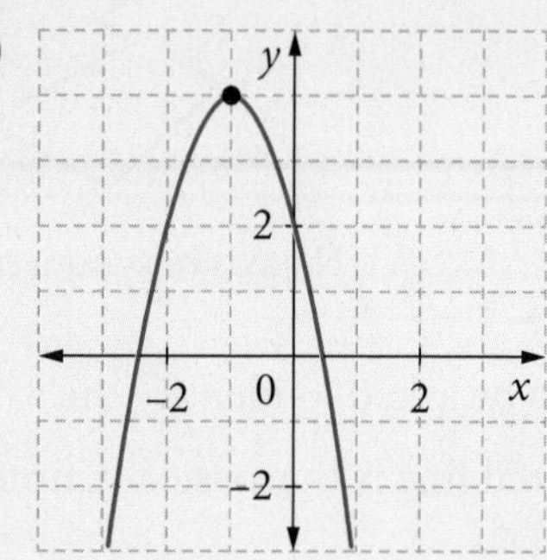

Section 13.2: Transformations

Learning Outcome:

You should be able to:

- recognise images of points and objects under translation, central symmetry, axial symmetry and rotation

A transformation is a process which changes the position (and possibly the size and orientation) of a shape. In this section we will look at four types of transformations: translation, central symmetry, axial symmetry and rotation.

The original shape is known as the **object.**

The shape that is formed following a transformation is known as the **image.**

Translation

Translation means moving a point or shape without changing it in any other way.

In a translation, every point of the object must be moved in the same direction and by the same distance.

In the example shown, the points A, B and C are moved parallel to the line PQ, in the direction P to Q and by the length of PQ. (Each black dotted line is parallel to PQ and the same length as PQ.)

The translation is given the notation $\overrightarrow{PQ}$.

The original (red) triangle ABC is known as the object.

The new (blue) triangle is known as the image and is labelled $A'B'C'$.

Translations can also be given in terms of the coordinates of two points. Look at the example on the following page.

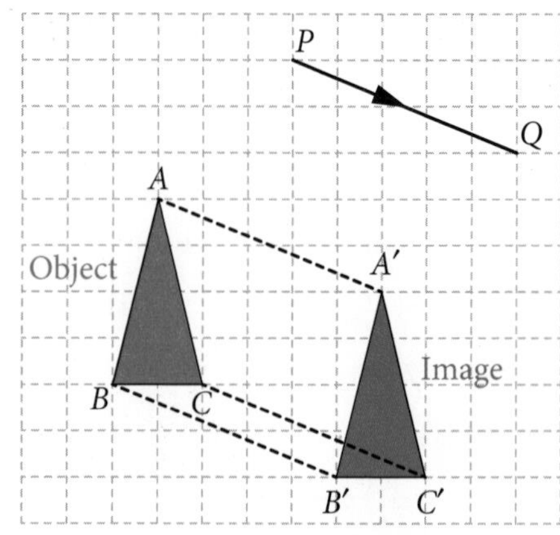

Geometry IV

EXAMPLE

Move the point $P(2, -3)$ under $\overrightarrow{AB}$, where $A = (1, 0)$ and $B = (-2, 4)$.

Solution

To answer this type of translation question we work out what happens to each coordinate in the translation and apply this to our given point.

$$A(1, 0) \xrightarrow{\text{subtract 3 from } x\text{, add 4 to } y} B(-2, 4)$$

$$P(2, -3) \xrightarrow{\text{subtract 3 from } x\text{, add 4 to } y} P'(-1, 1)$$

Subtracting from the x-coordinate moves the image to the **left;** **adding** to the x-coordinate moves the image to the **right**.

Subtracting from the y-coordinate moves the image **down;** **adding** to the y-coordinate moves the image **up**.

Links across the syllabus

The coordinates of a point may need to be translated when using the coordinate geometry formula for the area of a triangle, which is covered in Chapter 14: Coordinate Geometry I.

Central symmetry

Central symmetry involves finding the image of an object through a point.

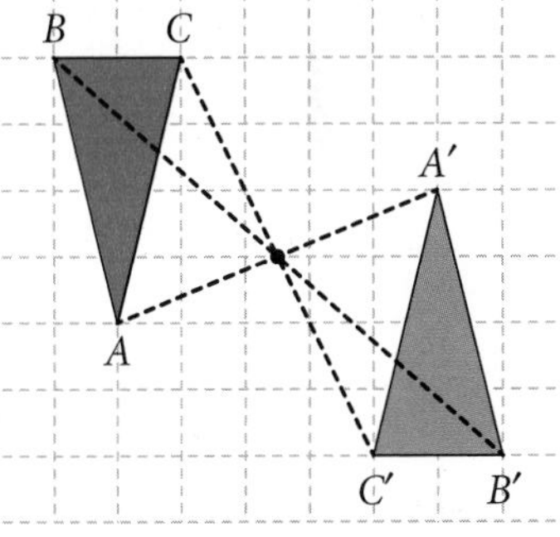

To find the image of an object under central symmetry, each point on the object is joined to the point of symmetry and then the line is extended the same distance out the other side of the point of symmetry, i.e. the point of symmetry is the midpoint of the line joining any point to its image.

The image under central symmetry is the same size and shape but is upside down and facing the opposite direction.

The effect of central symmetry in the origin (0, 0) on coordinates of a point is that the sign of both coordinates changes.

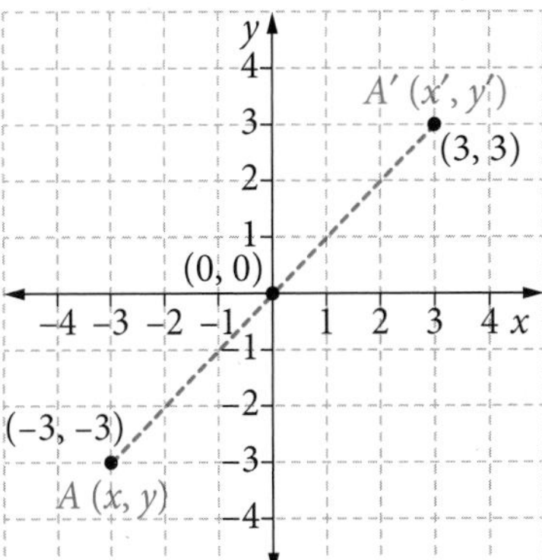

The image of $A(-3, -3)$ under central symmetry in (0, 0) is $A'(3, 3)$ as shown in the diagram.

Axial symmetry

Axial symmetry involves finding the image of an object through a line. It creates a mirror image of the object. Axial symmetry is sometimes called reflection in a line.

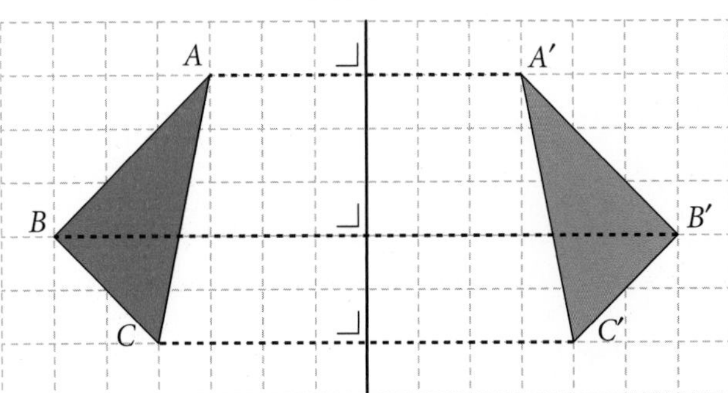

To find the image of an object under axial symmetry, each point on the object is joined perpendicularly to the line of symmetry and extended the same distance out the other side of the line of symmetry.

The effect of axial symmetry on the coordinated plane is as follows:

Under axial symmetry in the x-axis, the sign of the x-coordinate stays the same and the sign of the y-coordinate changes.

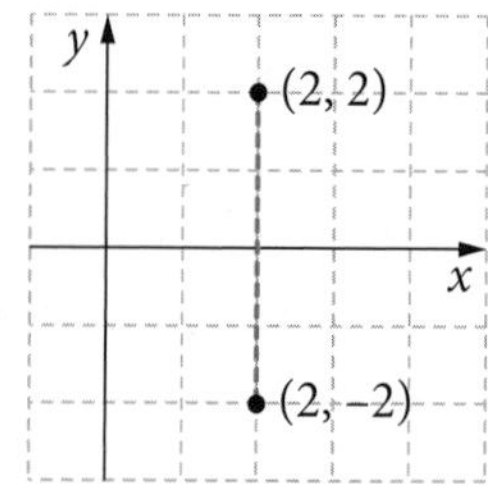

Under axial symmetry in the y-axis, the sign of the x-coordinate changes and the sign of the y-coordinate stays the same.

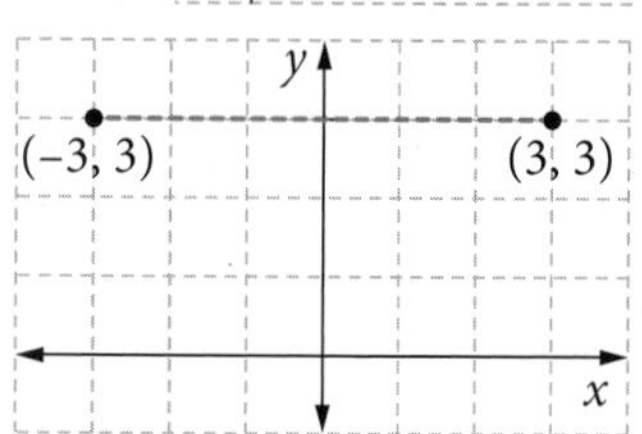

Rotation

Rotation involves finding the image of an object by moving the object by a certain angle around a point called the point of rotation. Rotation creates an image that is the same shape and size but has moved along a circular path.

To find the image of an object under rotation, each point on the object is turned by the number of degrees specified.

The image under rotation is the same size and shape as the object but may be turned in different directions depending on the angle of rotation.

A rotation of 90° clockwise about the origin has the following effect on the coordinates of a point: $(x, y) \rightarrow (y, -x)$

The x- and y-coordinates are swapped and the sign of the **new** y-coordinate is changed.

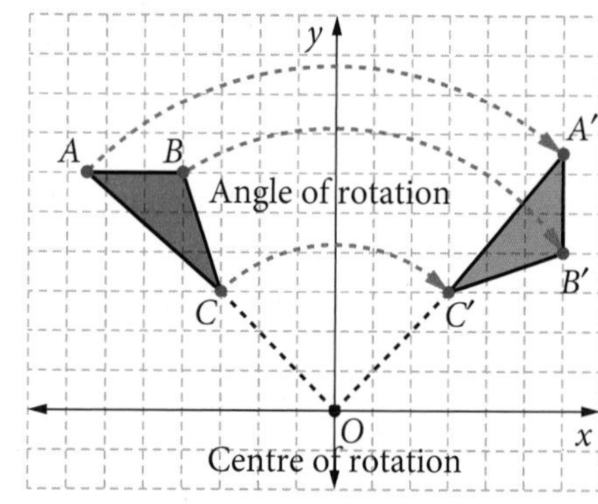

A rotation of 180° is the same as central symmetry in (0, 0).

EXAMPLE 1

(i) Construct the image of the quadrilateral $ABCD$ under translation $\overrightarrow{BD}$.

(ii) Compare the coordinates of the object point and its image under the translation and comment on the effect of the translation on the coordinates.

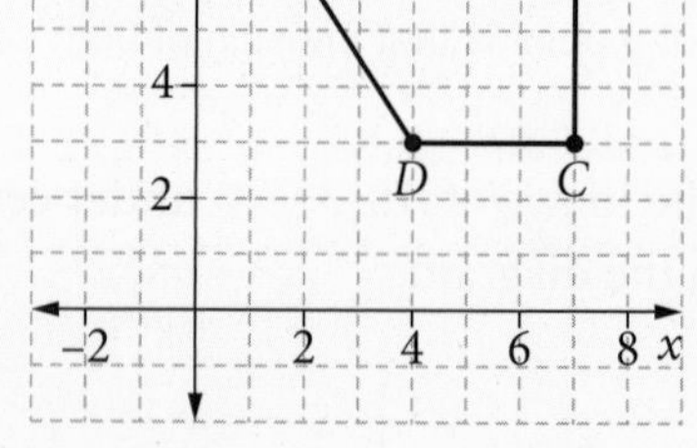

Solution

(i) Copy the distance and direction of the translation $\overrightarrow{BD}$.

Move each point on $ABCD$ the same distance as the length of BD and parallel to BD. Join the translated points to form $A'B'C'D'$.

In the diagram $|AA'| = |BD|$, $|BB'| = |BD|$, $|CC'| = |BD|$ and $|DD'| = |BD|$, and the lines joining each point to its image are parallel to BD.

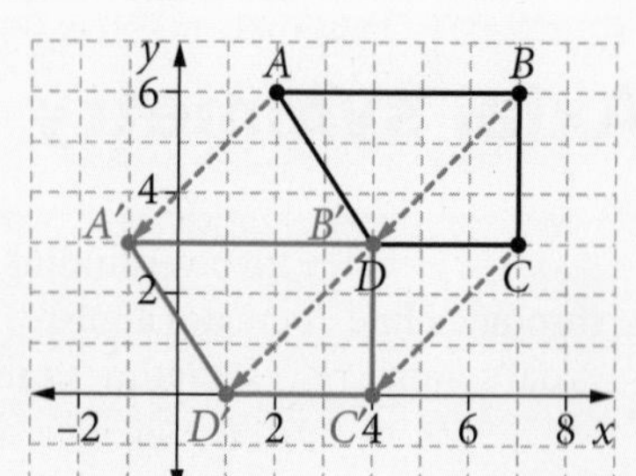

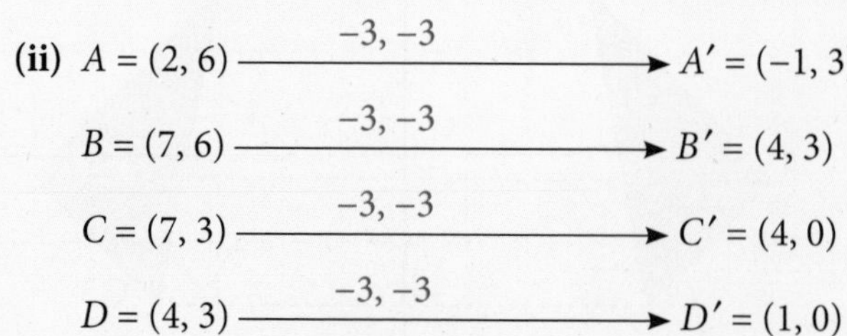

(ii) $A = (2, 6) \xrightarrow{-3,\,-3} A' = (-1, 3)$

$B = (7, 6) \xrightarrow{-3,\,-3} B' = (4, 3)$

$C = (7, 3) \xrightarrow{-3,\,-3} C' = (4, 0)$

$D = (4, 3) \xrightarrow{-3,\,-3} D' = (1, 0)$

The translation $\overrightarrow{BD}$ subtracts 3 from the x-coordinate and subtracts 3 from the y-coordinate.

In words, this translation moves the image three units left and three units down.

EXAMPLE 2

(i) Construct the image of the quadrilateral $ABCD$ under central symmetry in the origin.

(ii) Compare the coordinates of the object point and its image under central symmetry in the origin, and comment on its effect on the coordinates.

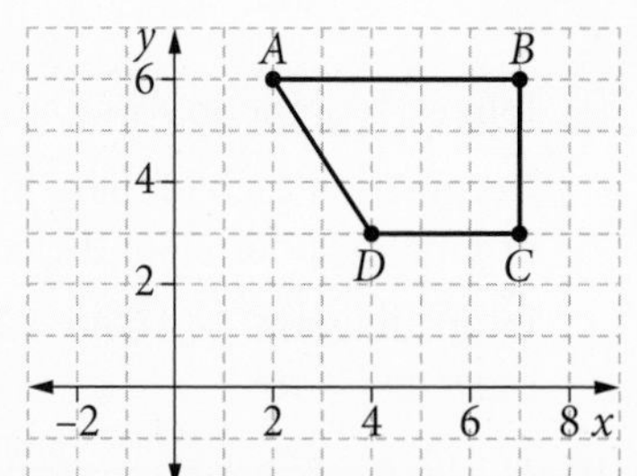

Solution

(i) Join each point on $ABCD$ to the origin (0, 0) and continue the line the same distance on the other side. Join the endpoints of these lines to form $A'B'C'D'$.

In the diagram, the distance between each point on $ABCD$ and (0, 0) is equal to the distance between its image and (0, 0).

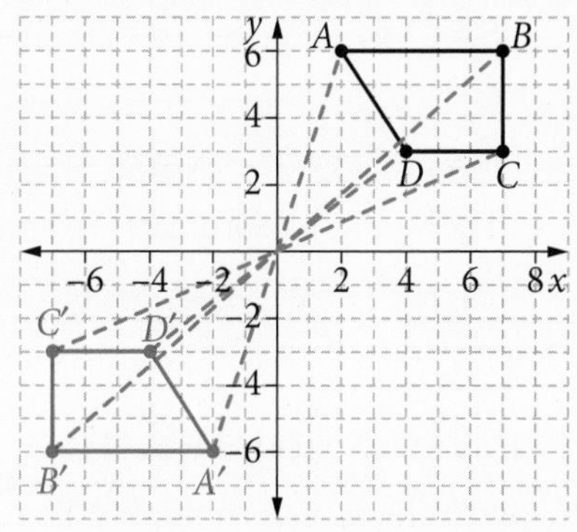

(ii) $A = (2, 6) \longrightarrow A' = (-2, -6)$

$B = (7, 6) \longrightarrow B' = (-7, -6)$

$C = (7, 3) \longrightarrow C' = (-7, -3)$

$D = (4, 3) \longrightarrow D' = (-4, -3)$

Central symmetry in the origin changes the sign of both the x- and the y-coordinates.

EXAMPLE 3

(i) Construct the image of the quadrilateral $ABCD$ under axial symmetry in the y-axis.

(ii) Compare the coordinates of the object point and its image under axial symmetry in the y-axis, and comment on its effect on the coordinates.

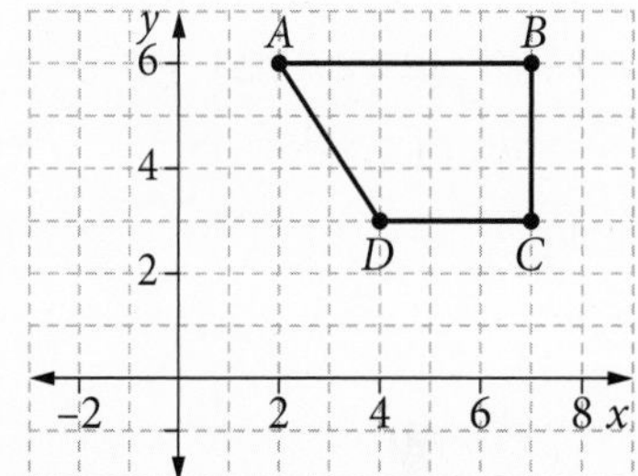

Solution

(i) Join each point perpendicularly to the y-axis and continue the line the same distance beyond the y-axis. Join the endpoints of these lines to form $A'B'C'D'$.

In the diagram, the distance between each point and the y-axis is equal to the distance between its image and the y-axis.

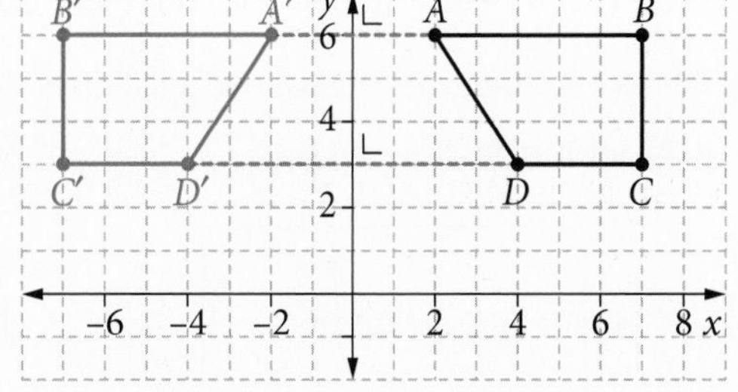

(ii) $A = (2, 6) \longrightarrow A' = (-2, 6)$

$B = (7, 6) \longrightarrow B' = (-7, 6)$

$C = (7, 3) \longrightarrow C' = (-7, 3)$

$D = (4, 3) \longrightarrow D' = (-4, 3)$

Axial symmetry in the y-axis changes the sign of the x-coordinate.

EXAMPLE 4

(i) Construct the image of the quadrilateral $ABCD$ under a rotation of 90° clockwise about the origin.

(ii) Compare the coordinates of the object point and its image under the rotation of 90° about the origin, and comment on its effect on the coordinates.

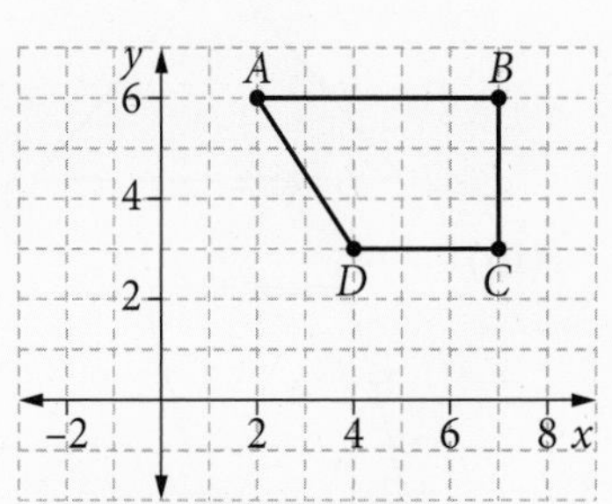

Solution

(i) Join each point on $ABCD$ to $(0, 0)$.

Reconstruct each of these line segments at a position 90° clockwise from their original position. Join the endpoints of these lines to form $A'B'C'D'$.

In the diagram, $|\angle AOA'| = 90°$, $|\angle BOB'| = 90°$, $|\angle COC'| = 90°$ and $|\angle DOD'| = 90°$.

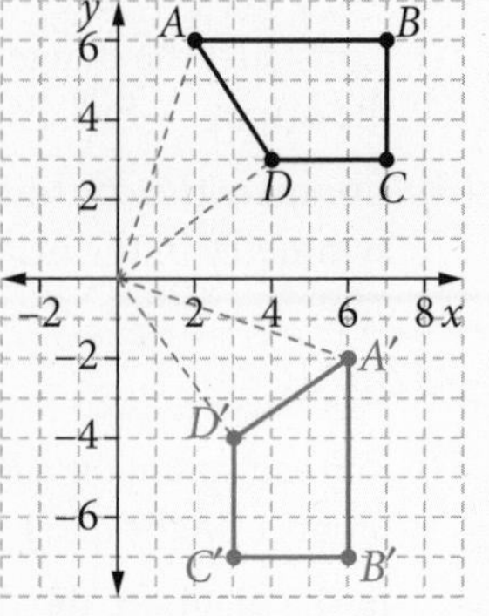

(ii) $A = (2, 6) \longrightarrow A' = (6, -2)$

$B = (7, 6) \longrightarrow B' = (6, -7)$

$C = (7, 3) \longrightarrow C' = (3, -7)$

$D = (4, 3) \longrightarrow D' = (3, -4)$

The x- and y-coordinates swapped position and the sign of the new y-coordinate changed.

Practice Questions 13.2

1. Given the transformation $\Delta XYZ \rightarrow \Delta X'Y'Z'$, identify which triangle is the object and which triangle is the image.

2. Determine whether each of the following transformations is a translation. Justify your answers.

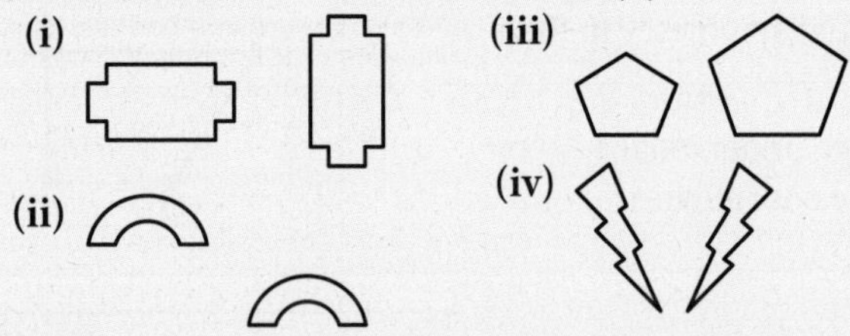

3. Move the origin (0, 0) under the following translations:
   - (i) $(5, 2) \rightarrow (-2, 1)$
   - (ii) $(-3, 7) \rightarrow (-5, 3)$
   - (iii) $(8, -3) \rightarrow (5, -3)$
   - (iv) $(-5, -1) \rightarrow (3, 4)$

4. Draw the image of the following shapes under the translation $\overrightarrow{AC}$:

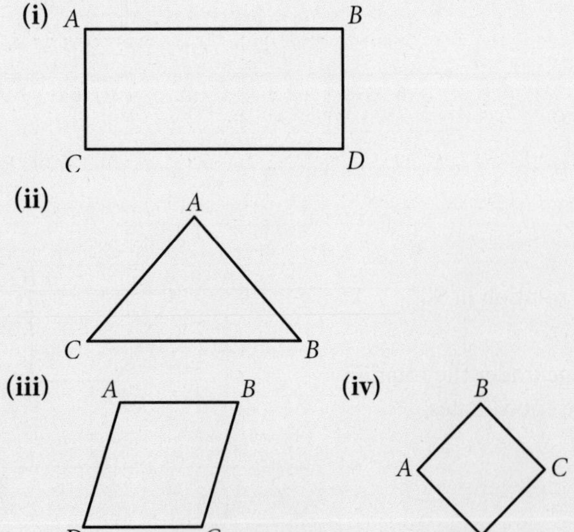

5. Copy each letter shown in the diagram onto a separate piece of graph paper.

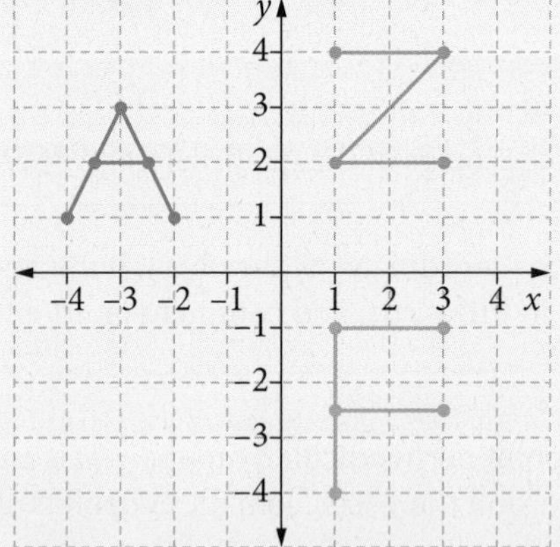

Find the images of each letter under:
   - (i) central symmetry in the origin
   - (ii) axial symmetry in the x-axis
   - (iii) axial symmetry in the y-axis.

6. The coordinates of the triangle QRS are as follows: $Q(-6, 12)$, $R(-1, -3)$, and $S(5, 9)$.
   From your knowledge of the effect of transformations on the coordinates of a point, write the coordinates of $Q'R'S'$, the image of QRS, under:
   - (i) axial symmetry in the x-axis
   - (ii) central symmetry in $(0, 0)$
   - (iii) axial symmetry in the y-axis
   - (iv) rotation of 90° clockwise about the origin.

7. Copy the following shapes on to graph paper and then draw the image under the rotation given:

(i) Rotation: 90° clockwise about the origin

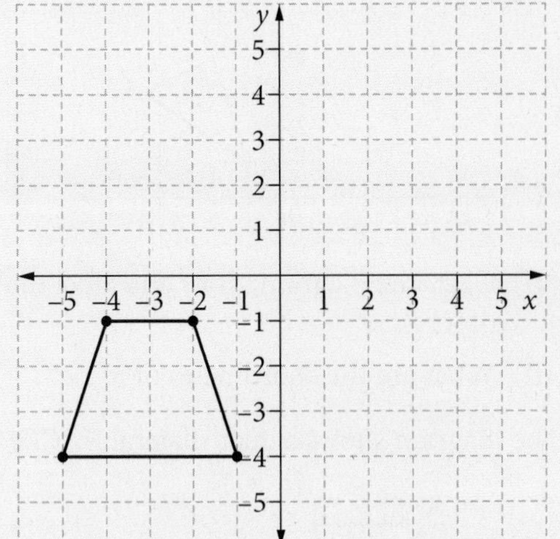

(ii) Rotation: 270° anticlockwise about the origin

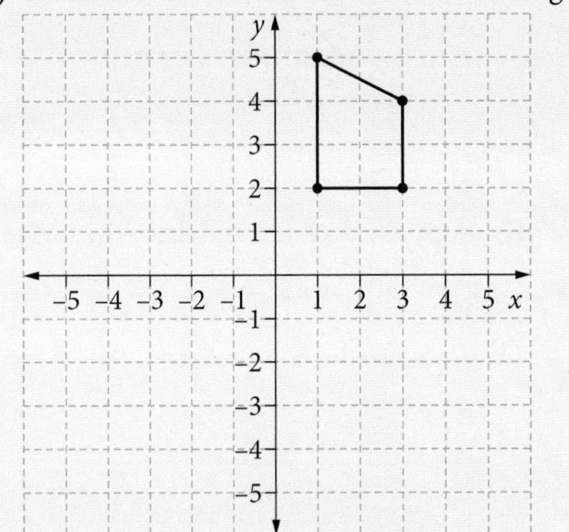

(iii) Rotation: 180° about the origin

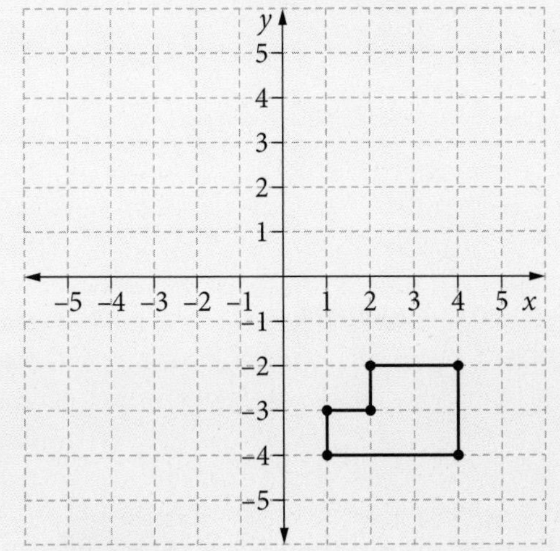

When the rotation is 180°, direction doesn't matter.

8. Identify the type of transformation that has taken place in each of the following:

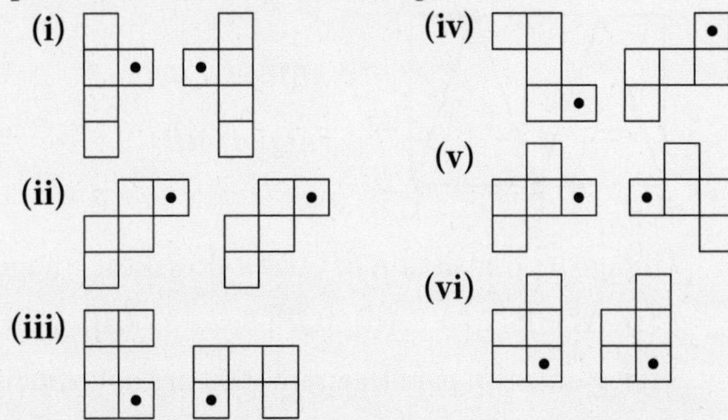

9. Each of the pictures labelled *A*, *B* and *C* shown below are the image of the figure shown in the box on the right, under a transformation.

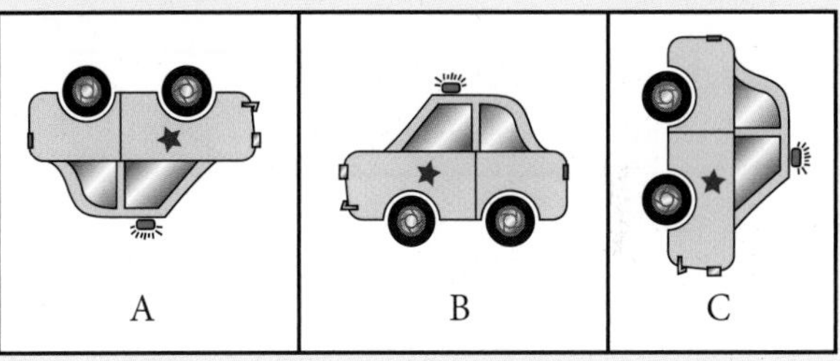

For each of *A*, *B* and *C*, state what the transformation is (translation, central symmetry, axial symmetry or rotation) and in the case of a rotation, state the angle.

10. The diagram shows two parallelograms, *CDEG* and *CEFG*.

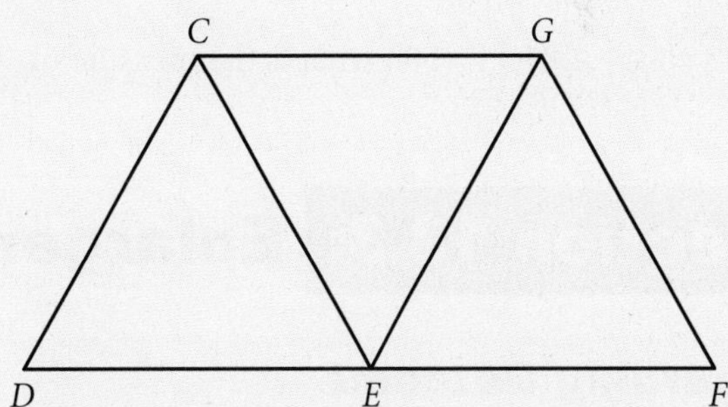

(i) Name two translations equal to $\overrightarrow{CG}$.

(ii) Find the image of *F* under the translation $\overrightarrow{EC}$.

Under the translation $\overrightarrow{CG}$, find the image of:

(iii) ΔCDE

(iv) $[DE]$

(v) $\angle DEC$

11. *ABCD* is a rectangle. *P* is the midpoint of [*BC*].

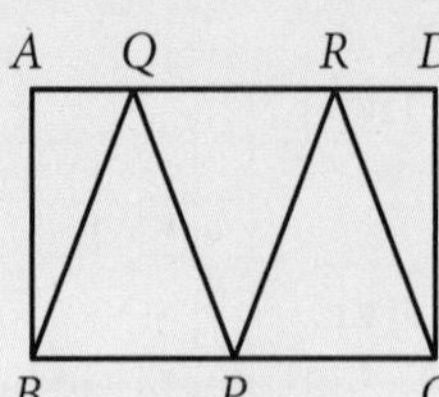

$|BP| = |QR|$ and

$|AQ| = |RD|$

Under the translation $\overrightarrow{BP}$, write down the image of:

(i) ΔQBP (ii) $[QP]$ (iii) $\angle BQP$

(iv) Name two parallelograms that are not rectangles.

(v) Name two angles equal to $\angle QBP$.

(vi) If $|AB| = 6$ cm and $|AQ| = 3$ cm, calculate the area of the rectangle *ABCD*.

12. *PQRS* is a rectangle. *PAQS* and *SQRB* are parallelograms.

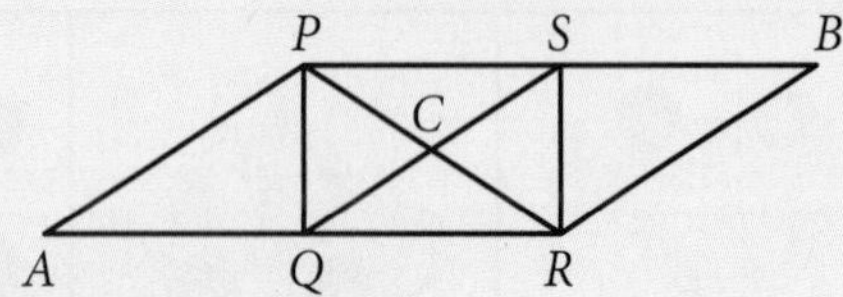

(i) Name three line segments equal in length to [*QR*].

(ii) What is the image of ΔSRB under central symmetry in *C*?

(iii) What is the image of ΔPAQ under axial symmetry in the line *PQ*?

(iv) What is the image of [*PA*] under the translation $\overrightarrow{SB}$?

(v) If $|\angle PAQ| = 50°$, what is the measure of $|\angle PQC|$?

13. The triangle *XYZ*, shown in the diagram, undergoes axial symmetry in the *y*-axis.

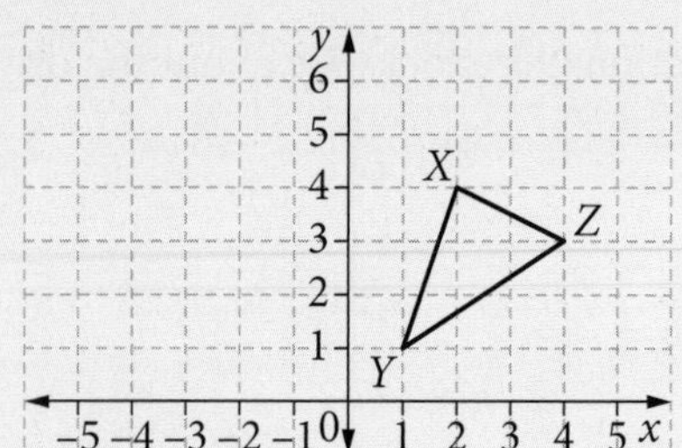

(i) Copy the diagram, draw and label the image of *XYZ*.

(ii) What are the coordinates of *X′Y′Z′*?

14. The diagram shows a quadrilateral *ABCD*.

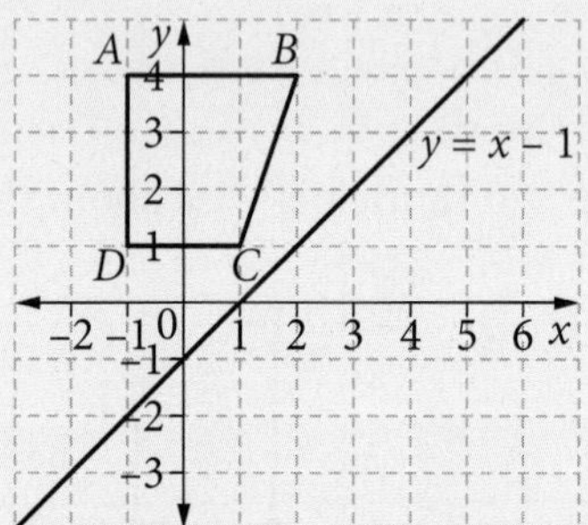

(i) Copy the diagram and draw the image of *ABCD* under axial symmetry in the line $y = x - 1$.

(ii) What are the coordinates of *A′B′C′D′*?

Section 13.3: Enlargements

Learning Outcomes:

You should be able to:

- construct an enlargement
- find the centre of an enlargement and the scale factor for a given enlargement
- understand the effect of an enlargement on the area of an object

Constructing enlargements

An **enlargement** is a transformation that produces an image that is the same shape as the original, but is a different size (bigger or smaller).

Under an enlargement, the object and its image are said to be similar.

When performing an enlargement we must use a scale factor (k).

> The **scale factor** is how many times bigger or smaller the image is than the object.

- If $k > 1$, then the image is larger than the object.
- If $k = 1$, then the image and the object are the same size.
- If $0 < k < 1$, then the image is smaller than the object.

To perform the enlargement we also need to know the centre of enlargement.

> The **centre of enlargement** is the point from which the enlargement is constructed.

Steps to carry out an enlargement

Step 1: Find the distance from the centre of enlargement to a point on the object.

Step 2: Multiply the distance from step 1 by the scale factor.

Step 3: Draw a line from the centre of enlargement towards or through the point on the object such that the length of the line is equal to the answer to step 2.

Step 4: Mark the end of the line as the image point.

Step 5: Repeat for all points on the object.

Step 6: Join the image points to form the enlarged image.

EXAMPLE

Construct the image of ΔABC under an enlargement with a scale factor 3 and a centre O. Investigate the effect of the enlargement on the coordinates of the vertices.

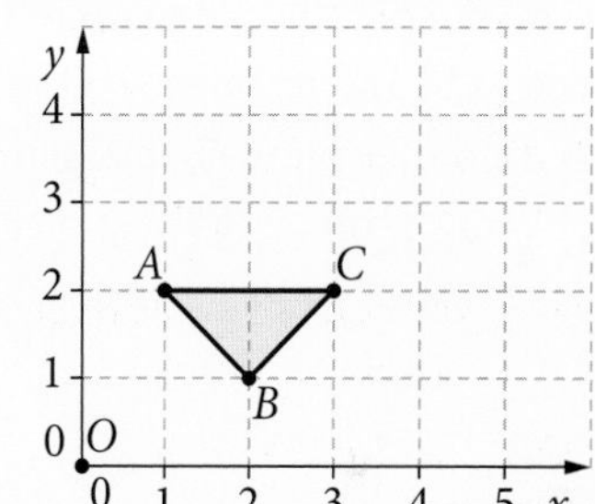

Solution

Step 1: Measure $|OA|$, $|OB|$ and $|OC|$.

Step 2: Multiply $|OA|$ by 3, $|OB|$ by 3 and $|OC|$ by 3.

Step 3: Starting from O, draw a line through A that is $3|OA|$ long.

Step 4: Mark this point A'.

Step 5: Starting from O, draw a line through B that is $3|OB|$ long. Mark this point as B'.

Starting from O, draw a line through C that is $3|OC|$ long. Mark this point as C'.

Step 6: Join the image points to form the image $A'B'C'$, shown in green.

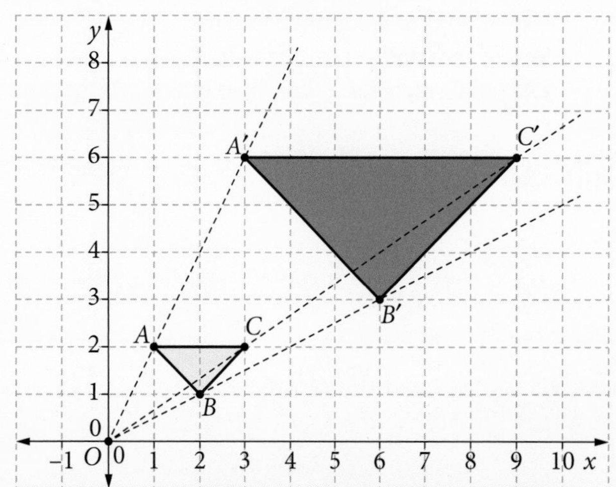

In the diagram,

$$|OA'| = 3|OA|$$
$$|OB'| = 3|OB|$$
$$|OC'| = 3|OC|$$

To investigate the effect of the enlargement on the coordinates of the points we will compare the coordinates of each point to those of its image:

$A(1, 2) \longrightarrow A'(3, 6)$

$B(2, 1) \longrightarrow B'(6, 3)$

$C(3, 2) \longrightarrow C'(9, 6)$

As you can see the coordinates of the image points are three times those of the object.

> When an object is enlarged through (0, 0) the coordinates of the image points can be found by multiplying the coordinates of the object points by the scale factor.

Finding the centre of enlargement

Sometimes you will be given the object and its image and asked to find the centre of enlargement.

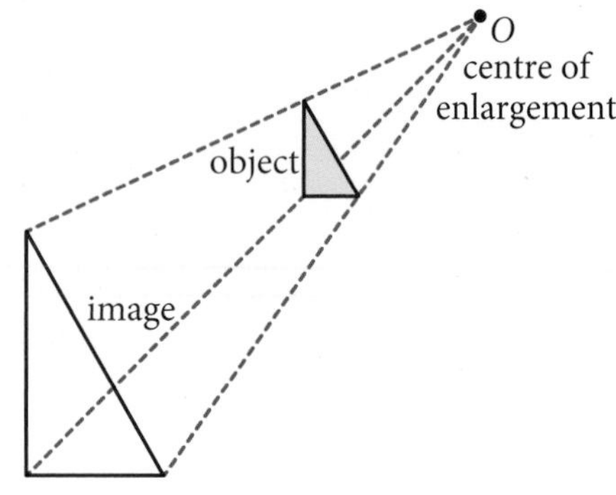

To find the centre of enlargement

Step 1: Draw a dashed line through each point on the object and its corresponding point on the image.

Step 2: Extend these lines until they meet.

Step 3: Where the lines meet is the centre of enlargement.

Finding the scale factor

We can also be asked to find the scale factor when given the object and its image.

To find the scale factor we simply divide the length of one of the sides of the image by the length of the corresponding side of the object.

$$\text{Scale factor } (k) = \frac{\text{image length}}{\text{object length}}$$

EXAMPLE

Given PQR and its image $P'Q'R'$ as shown:

(i) find the centre of enlargement.

(ii) given $|QR| = 1{\cdot}8$ cm and $Q'R' = 3{\cdot}6$ cm; find k, the scale factor.

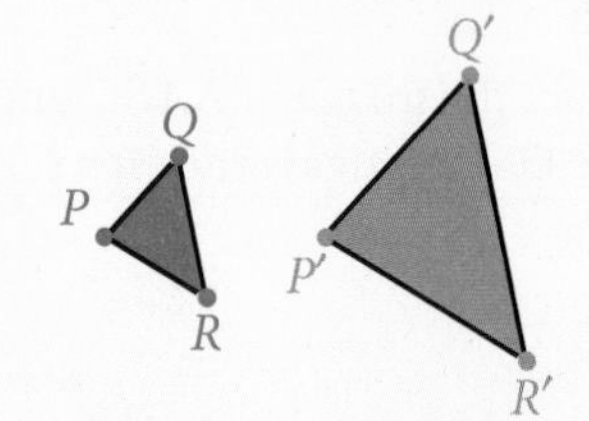

Solution

(i) Join P' to P and continue the line
Join Q' to Q and continue the line
Join R' to R and continue the line
The point where these three lines intersect is the centre of enlargement, O.

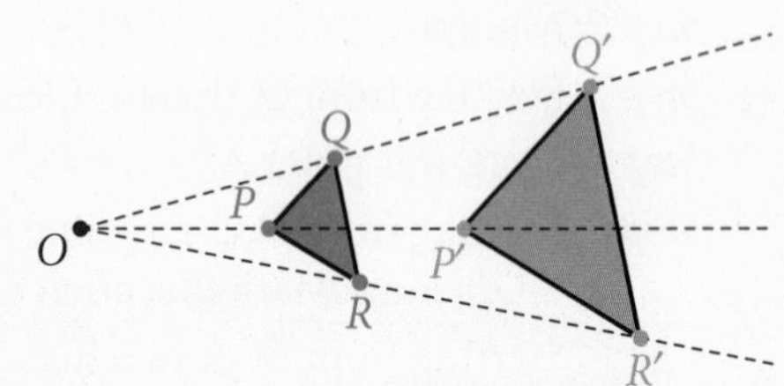

(ii) $\text{Scale factor } (k) = \frac{\text{image length}}{\text{object length}}$

$$k = \frac{3{\cdot}6}{1{\cdot}8}$$

$$k = 2$$

Effect of enlargement on the area of an object

Discussion Time

Work with a classmate to answer the following questions.

1. A rectangle has length 6 cm and width 2 cm. What is the area of this rectangle?
2. This rectangle undergoes an enlargement with a scale factor of 2. Draw the enlarged object.
3. The original rectangle undergoes enlargement with a scale factor of $\frac{1}{2}$. Draw the enlarged object.
4. Fill in the following table:

	Rectangle length	Rectangle width	Rectangle area
Scale factor $k = 2$			
Scale factor $k = \frac{1}{2}$			

5. Describe the relationship between the area of the original rectangle and the area the new rectangle in each case.
6. Can you form a general equation, in terms of k, for the relationship between the area of an object and the area of its enlargement, based on the answers to question 5?

When an object is enlarged by a scale factor k, its area is increased by k^2.

$$\text{image area} = k^2 \text{ (object area)}$$

or

$$\frac{\text{image area}}{\text{object area}} = k^2$$

EXAMPLE

Triangle OMJ is the image of triangle OLK under an enlargement with centre O.
$|OM| = 2$ and $|ML| = 3$.

(i) Find the scale factor of enlargement.

(ii) If $|OJ| = 1{\cdot}8$, find $|JK|$.

(iii) If the area of triangle OLK is 12·5 cm², find the area of triangle OMJ.

K, J, 1·8, O, M, L, 2, 3

Solution

(i) $|OM| = 2 = \text{image length}$

$|OL| = 5 = \text{object length}$

$$\text{Scale factor} = \frac{\text{image length}}{\text{object length}} = \frac{2}{5}$$

(ii) $\frac{|OJ|}{|OK|} = k$

$\frac{1{\cdot}8}{|OK|} = \frac{2}{5}$ multiply both sides by $|OK|$

$$(|OK|)\left(\frac{1{\cdot}8}{|OK|}\right) = (|OK|)\left(\frac{2}{5}\right)$$

$1{\cdot}8 = \frac{2|OK|}{5}$ multiply both sides by 5

$$5(1{\cdot}8) = (5)\left(\frac{2|OK|}{5}\right)$$

$9 = 2|OK|$ divide both sides by 2

$4{\cdot}5 = |OK|$

$|JK| = |OK| - |OJ|$

$|JK| = 4{\cdot}5 - 1{\cdot}8 = 2{\cdot}7$ cm

(iii) image area $= k^2$ (object area)

$$\text{Area of } OMJ = \left(\frac{2}{5}\right)^2 (12{\cdot}5)$$
$$= \left(\frac{4}{25}\right)(12{\cdot}5)$$
$$= 2 \text{ cm}^2$$

Practice Questions 13.3

1. Copy the following shapes on to graph paper and complete the enlargement with centre O and the given scale factor.

   (i) Scale factor 2

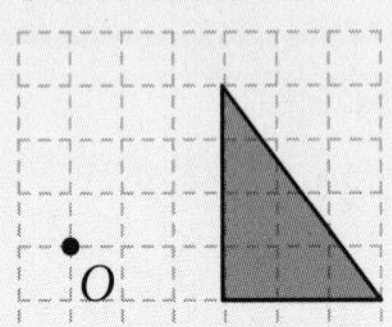

   (iv) Scale factor 4

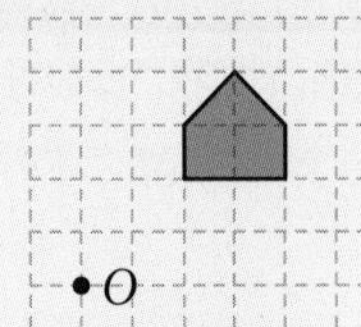

   (ii) Scale factor 4

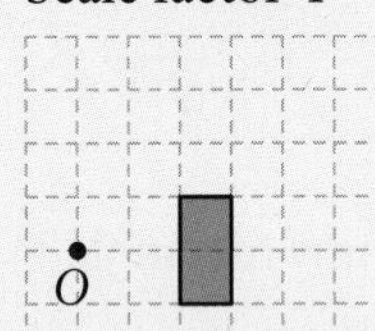

   (v) Scale factor 2

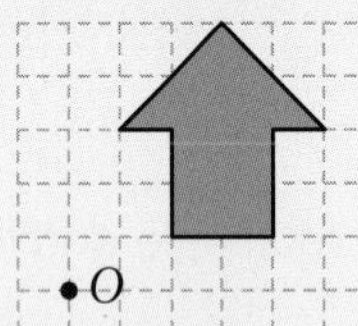

   (iii) Scale factor 3

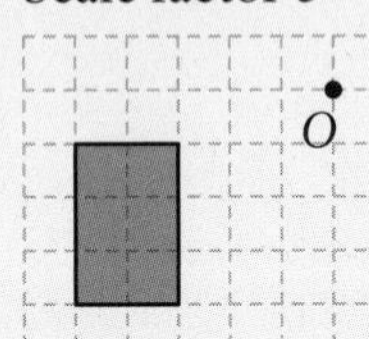

   (vi) Scale factor 3

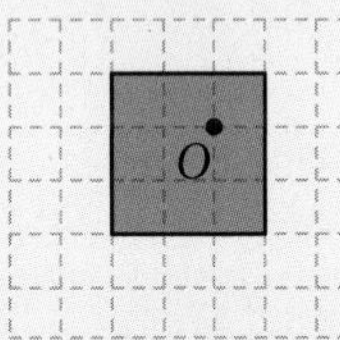

2. Copy the following shapes on to graph paper and complete the enlargement with centre of enlargement shown and scale factor given.

   (i) Scale factor $\frac{1}{2}$

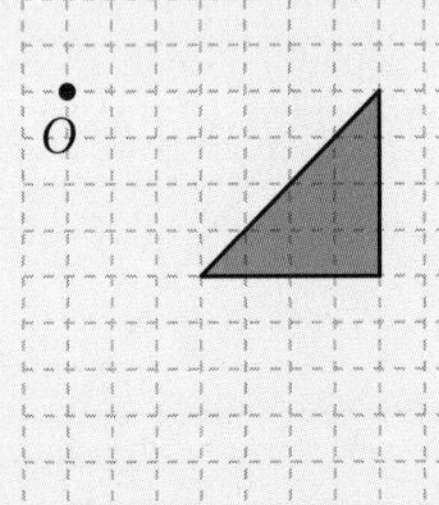

   (iii) Scale factor $\frac{1}{4}$

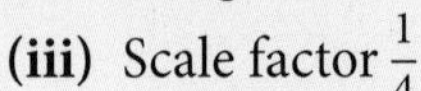

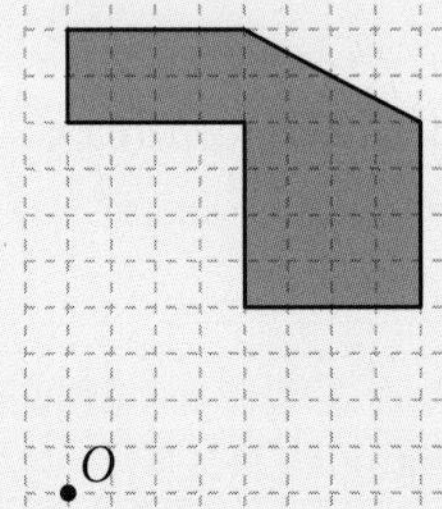

   (ii) Scale factor $\frac{1}{3}$ (iv) Scale factor $\frac{3}{4}$

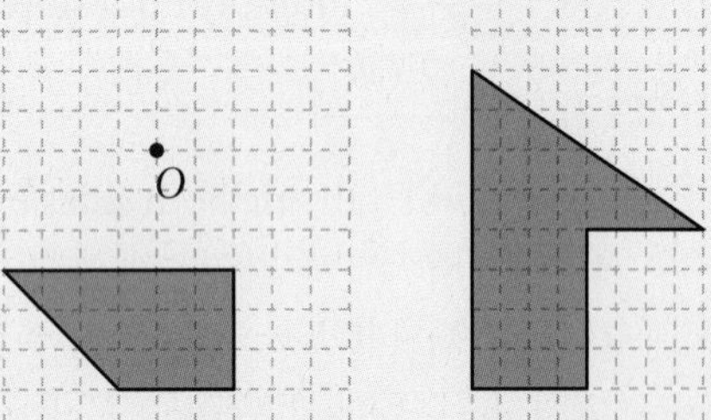

3. Copy the following shape on to graph paper and complete the enlargement with centre of enlargement at the origin (0, 0) and given scale factor.

   (i) Scale factor 2

   (ii) Scale factor $\frac{1}{3}$

   (iii) Comment on the size difference between the object and its image under each of the enlargements above.

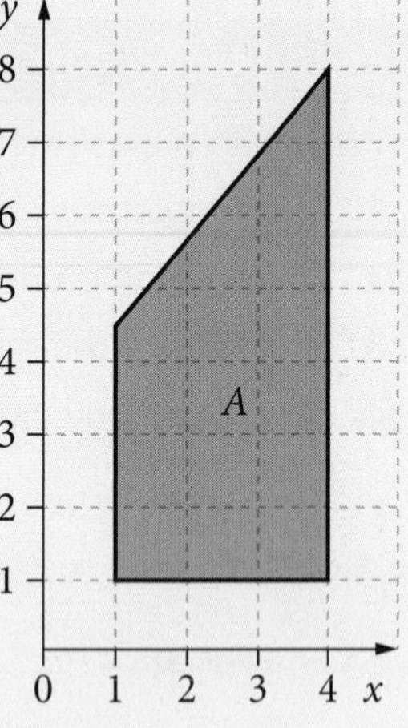

4. Copy the following diagrams on to graph paper and find the centre of enlargement for each:

   (i)

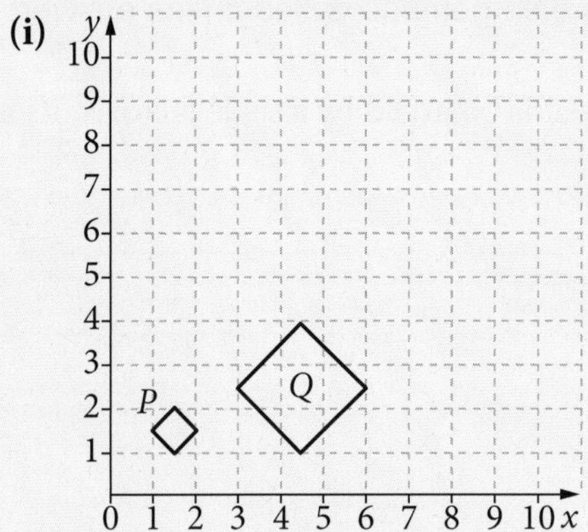

   (ii)

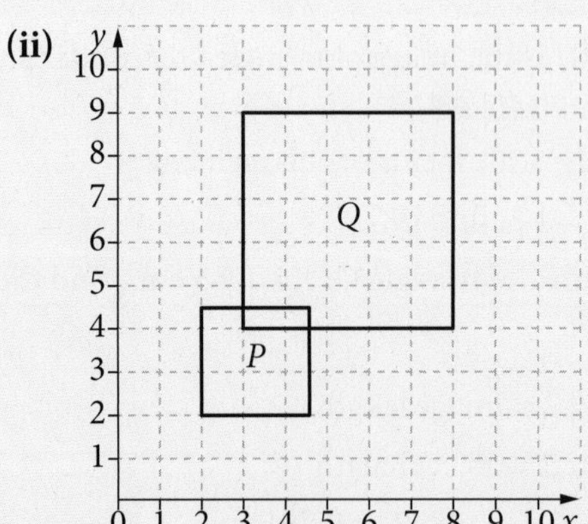

   (iii)

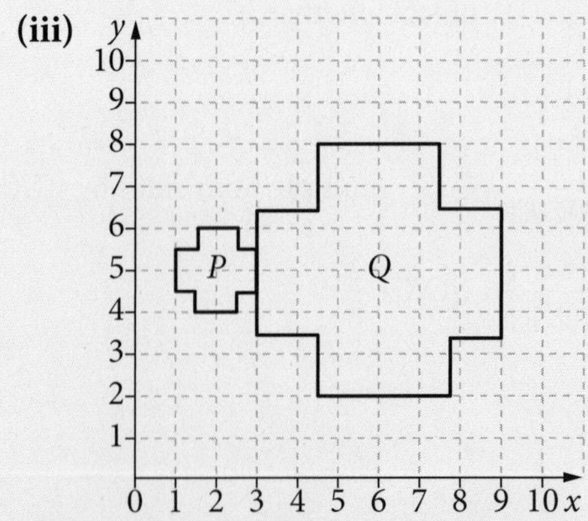

(iv)

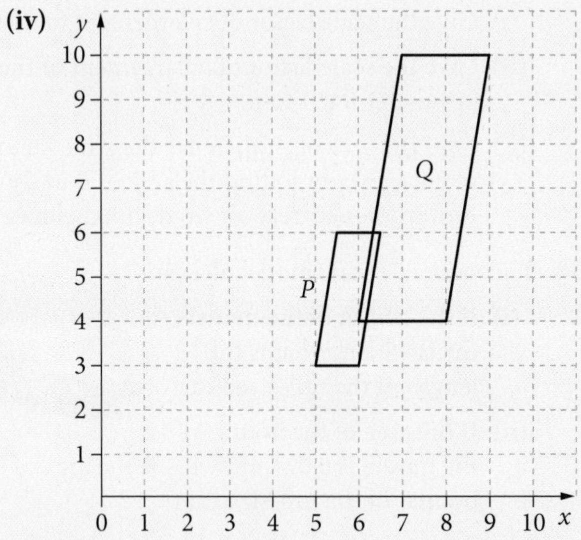

(v)

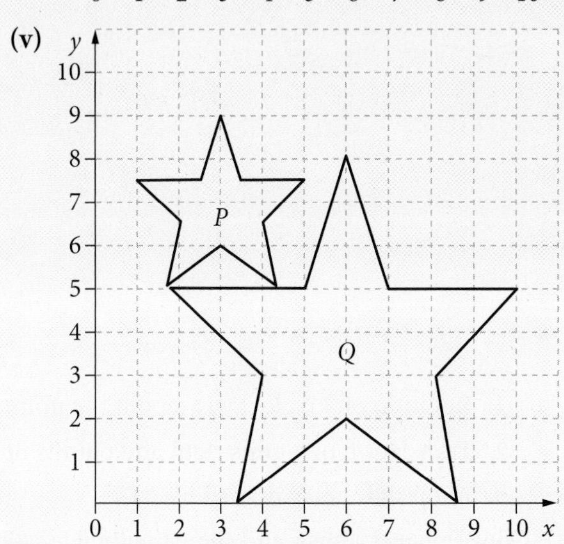

(vi)

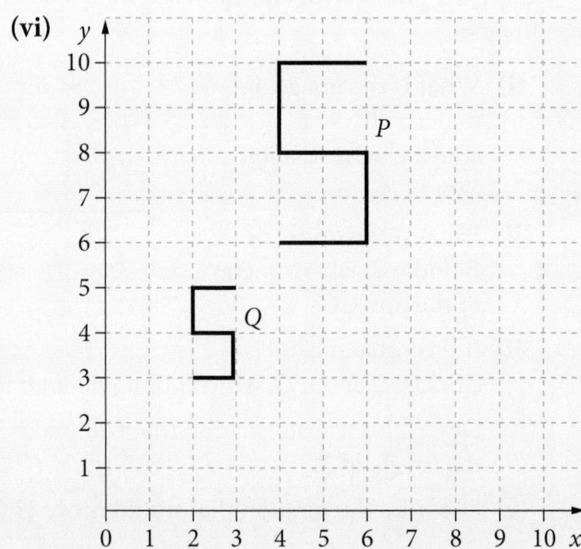

5. Use the grid to find the scale factor of enlargement from *A* to *B* in each of the following:

(i)

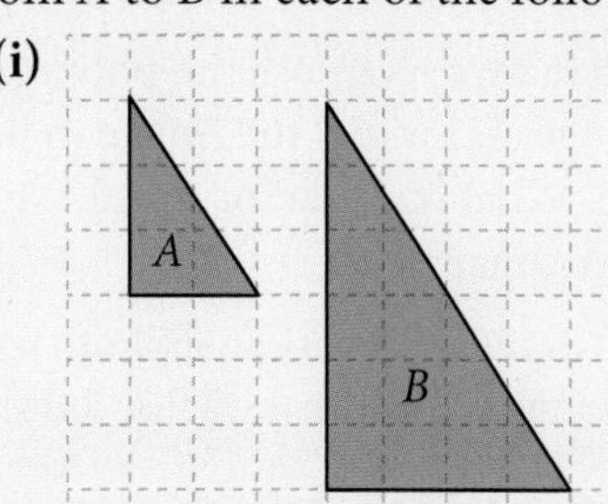

(ii)

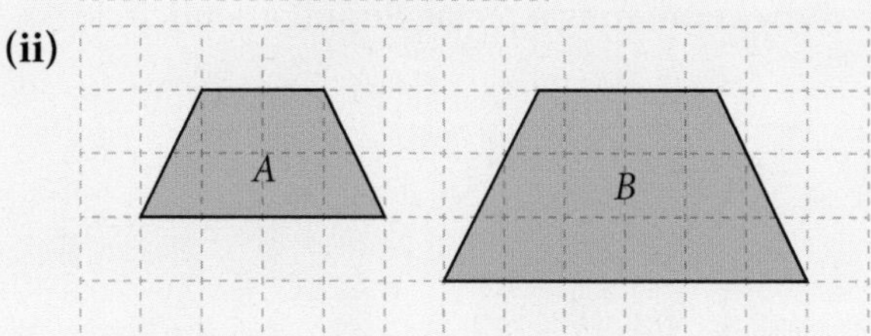

(iii)

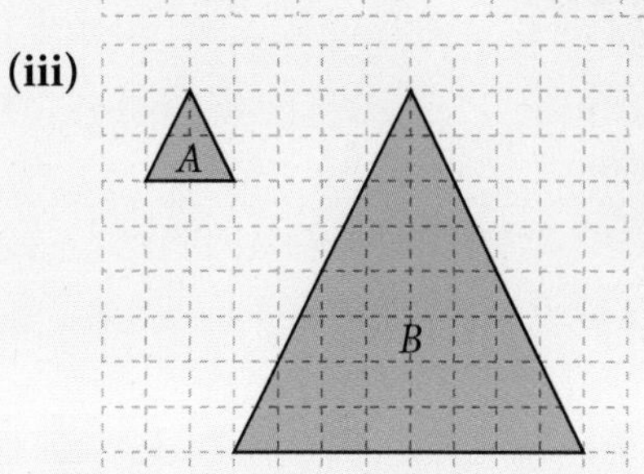

(iv)

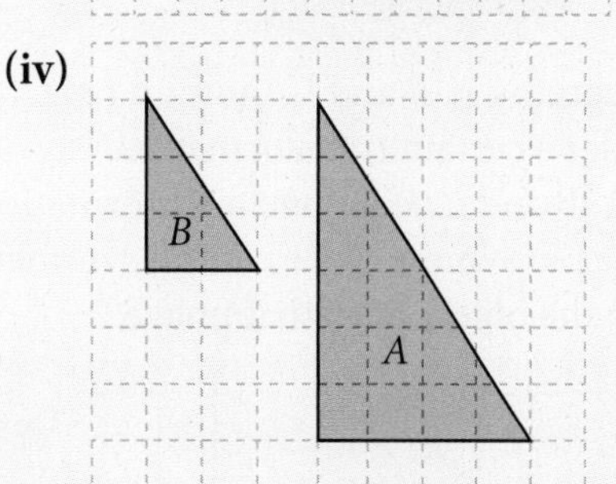

(v)

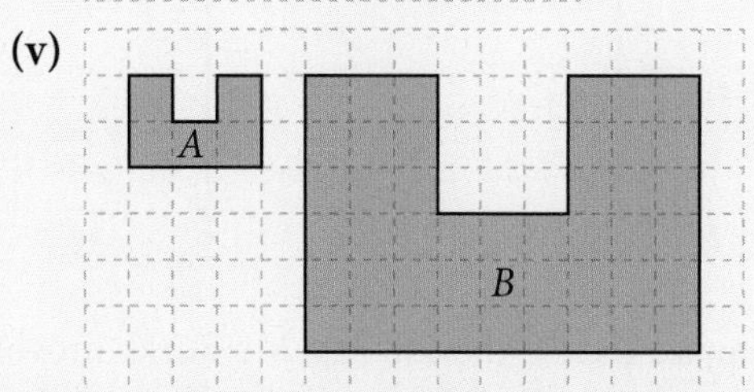

6. A photograph is 8 cm long. It is enlarged by a scale factor of three. How long will the enlarged photo be?

7. Alex made a scale diagram of the plan for his garden. The garden measures 18 m by 12 m. On the scaled diagram the longer side measures 8 cm. What is the length of the shorter side in the diagram?

8. Diana is editing a digital photo that is 640 pixels wide and 480 pixels high on her computer screen.
   (i) Suppose Diana wants to use the photograph on a web page and wants the image to be 32 pixels wide. What scale factor should she use to reduce the image?
   (ii) She decides to resize the original photo so that it is 600 pixels high. What scale factor did she use?

9. Two window frames (shown below) are designed by combining a rectangle and a semicircle.

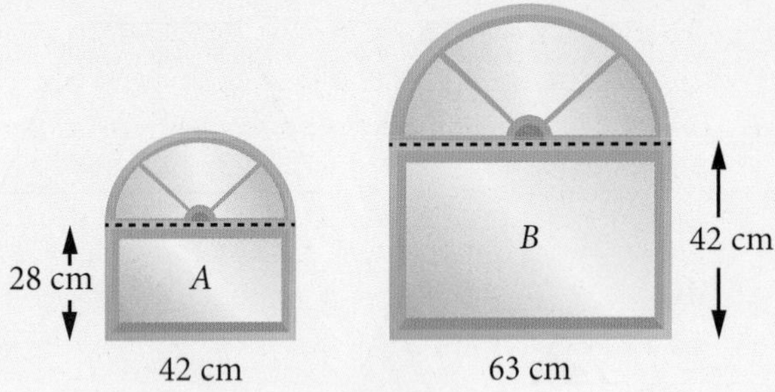

   (i) Give the scale factor of enlargement for A to B.
   (ii) Give the scale factor of enlargement of the perimeter for A to B.
   (iii) Find the area of A, then use the scale factor of enlargement to find the area of B in square centimetres correct to two decimal places.

10. Theo has a $\frac{1}{10}$ scale model of a car.
   (i) If the length of the model car is 45 cm, what is the length of the full-sized car?

   (ii) If the area of the bonnet of the model is 0·021 m^2, what is the area of the bonnet of the full-sized car?

Revision and Exam Style Questions – Section A

1. The three diagrams A, B and C show an object and its image under a certain transformation. For each of A, B and C, state one transformation (translation, axial symmetry or central symmetry) that will map the object onto that image.

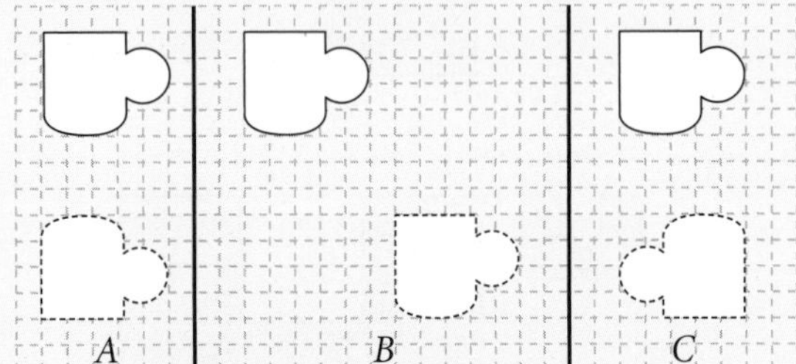

2. During a PE class the teacher, Mr Burke moves a gym mat using the following transformations one after another:

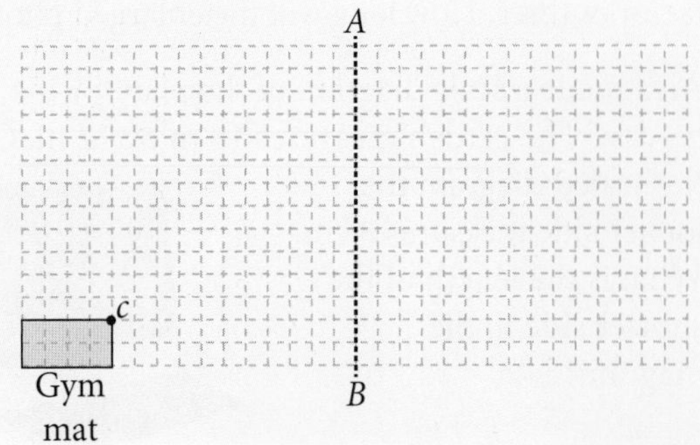

   1. Rotation of 90° clockwise about the point C.
   2. Translation of 8 units right and 6 units up.
   3. Axial symmetry in the line AB.

   Copy the grid shown and show the final location of the mat.

3. (i) What is the image of G under a 90° anticlockwise rotation about O?
   (ii) What is the image of E under axial symmetry in the line GC?
   (iii) If F is rotated 270° clockwise about O, which point will it go to?
   (iv) Describe a transformation that will make F the image of B.
   (v) Describe the rotation that would move H to F.

4. Copy the diagram and enlarge the triangle ABC using a scale factor of 3·5 and a centre of enlargement O.

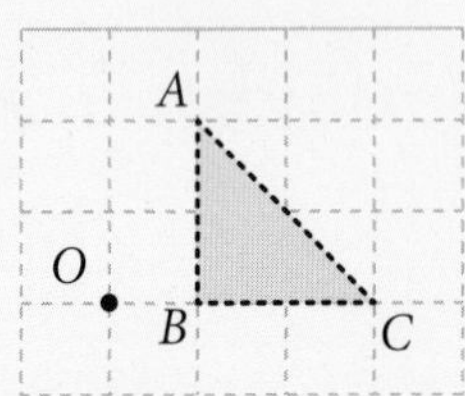

5. The diagram shows a regular hexagon.

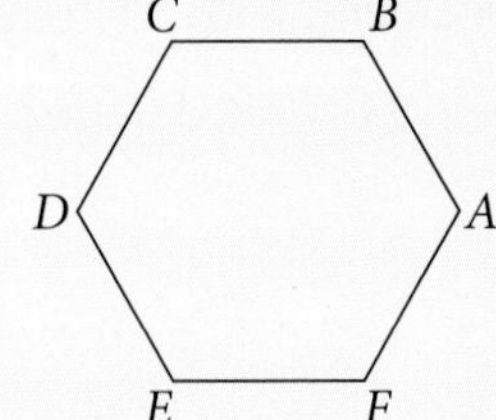

(i) How many axes of symmetry has the hexagon?

(ii) Copy the diagram into your copy and draw in the axes of symmetry.

(iii) [AD] and [CF] intersect at O. What is the measure of the angle of the rotation, about O, which maps A onto C?

(iv) Describe one transformation which maps [AF] to [CD].

6. Each of the pictures labelled A, B and C shown below is the image of the figure shown on the right, under a transformation. For each of A, B and C, state what the transformation is (translation, central symmetry, axial symmetry or rotation) and in the case of a rotation, state the angle.

7. Describe the transformation shown in A, B, C and D below.

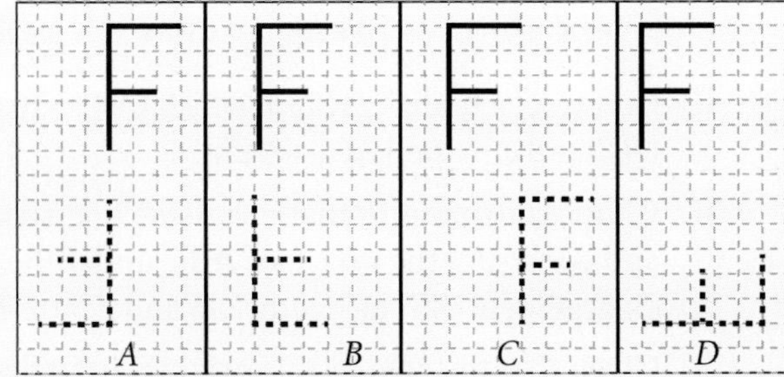

8. A ferris wheel is an example of a rotation. The ferris wheel shown has 20 cars.

(i) What is the measure of the angle of rotation if seat 1 of this ferris wheel is moved to the seat 5 position.

(ii) If seat 1 in the diagram is rotated 144°, find the seat position in the diagram that it now occupies.

9. $EFGH$ is a square and $EFHX$ is a parallelogram.

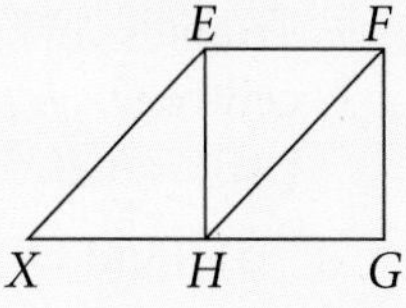

Under the translation $\overrightarrow{XH}$, what is the image of:

(i) ΔEXH **(ii)** $[EH]$ **(iii)** $\angle EXH$

Under the translation $\overrightarrow{FE}$, what is the image of:

(iv) ΔFHG **(v)** $[FH]$ **(vi)** $\angle GFH$

Name a translation equal to:

(vii) $\overrightarrow{XE}$ **(viii)** $\overrightarrow{EH}$ **(ix)** $\overrightarrow{HG}$

10. The diagram shows a quadrilateral, A, and its image under different transformations. Write down the coordinates of the vertices of A under:

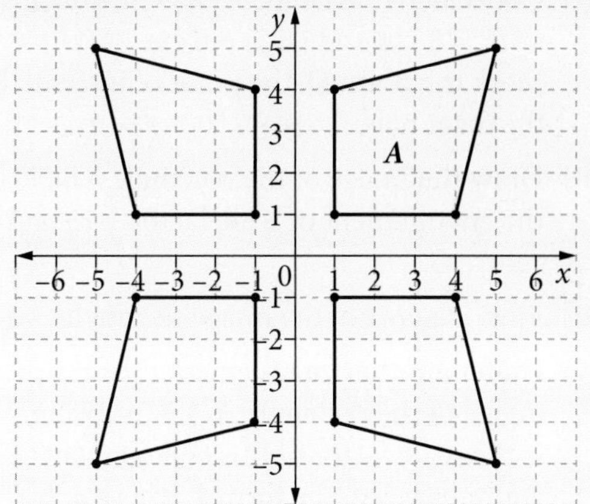

(i) axial symmetry in the y-axis.

(ii) central symmetry in the point (0, 0).

(iii) axial symmetry in the x-axis.

11. The diagram shows a shape that has undergone several transformations. Describe the single transformation that maps:

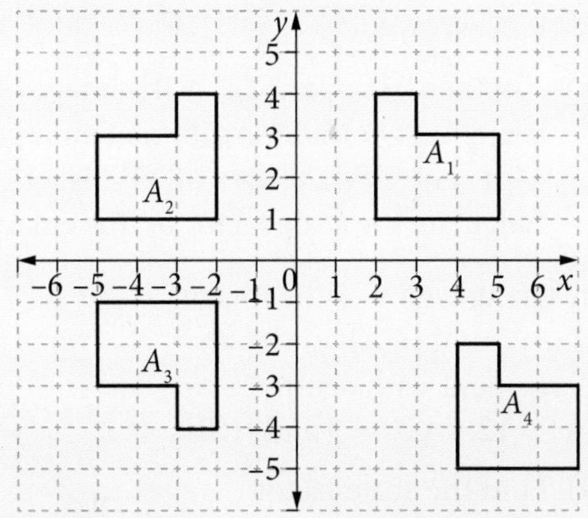

(i) A_1 to A_2 **(iii)** A_1 to A_4

(ii) A_1 to A_3 **(iv)** A_2 to A_3

Geometry IV

12. Triangle XYZ is the image of triangle ABC under enlargement, with centre O.
$|AB| = 6$ and $|XZ| = 18$. The scale factor is 1·5.

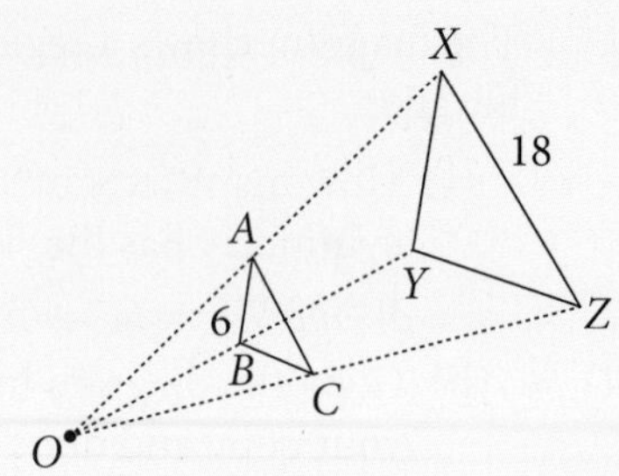

(i) Find $|XY|$.

(ii) Find $|AC|$.

(iii) If the area of triangle ABC is 31·2 square units, calculate the area of triangle XYZ.

Revision and Exam Style Questions – Section B

More challenging questions

1. (i) Construct a rectangle $ABCD$ in which $|AB| = 8$ cm and $|BC| = 6$ cm.
Mark the point O, the point of intersection of the diagonals.

(ii) Draw the image of the rectangle $ABCD$ under the enlargement of scale factor 1·75 and centre O.

(iii) Find the area of the image rectangle.

(iv) Under another enlargement the area of the image of the rectangle $ABCD$ is 27 cm^2. What is the scale factor of this enlargement? Give your answer in the form $\frac{a}{b}$, where $a, b \in \mathbb{N}$.

2. (i) Construct an equilateral triangle, PQR, of side 8 cm.

(ii) Construct the image of the triangle PQR under enlargement with centre P and scale factor 2.

(iii) Given that the height of PQR is $4\sqrt{3}$ cm, find the area of the image triangle, correct to the nearest cm^2.

(iv) Another triangle, XYZ, is the image of triangle PQR under a different enlargement with centre P. The area of XYZ is $3\sqrt{3}$ cm^2. Calculate the scale factor of this enlargement.

3. The triangle CDE is the image of the triangle CAB under an enlargement with centre C.
$|CA| = 12$, $|AD| = 9$ and $|CB| = 8$.

(i) Find the scale factor of the enlargement.

(ii) Find $|BE|$.

(iii) The area of the triangle CDE is 98 square units. Find the area of the triangle CAB.

4. The triangle $A'B'C'$ is the image of the triangle ABC under an enlargement.

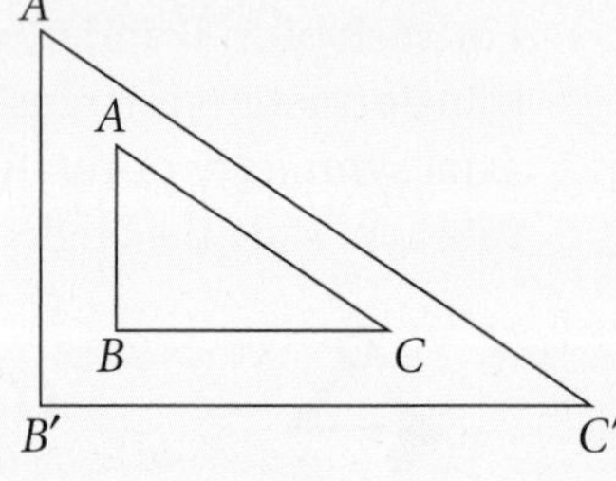

(i) Find, by measurement, the scale factor of the enlargement.

(ii) Copy the diagram and show how to find the centre of the enlargement.

(iii) Units are chosen so that $|BC| = 10$ units. How many of these units is $B'C'$?

(iv) Find the area of triangle ABC, given that the area of $A'B'C'$ is 104 square units.

5. (i) Construct a triangle ABC in which $|AB| = 10$ cm, $|BC| = 8$ cm and $|AC| = 6$ cm.

(ii) Choose any point P that is outside the triangle and construct the image of ABC under the enlargement of scale factor 0·6 and centre P.

(iii) Given that the area of this original triangle is 24 cm^2, calculate the area of the image triangle.

6. (i) Draw a square, $OPQR$, with sides 12 cm.

(ii) Draw the image of this square under the enlargement with centre O and scale factor 0·5.

(iii) Calculate the area of this image square.

(iv) Under another enlargement the area of the image of the square $OPQR$ is 120 cm^2. What is the scale factor of this enlargement?

7. The diagram shows two identical squares $ABCD$ and $DCEF$. Their diagonals intersect at X and Y.

   (i) Under the translation $\overrightarrow{BC}$, what is the image of:

   (a) D **(d)** $[AX]$

   (b) $[DC]$ **(e)** $[XD]$

   (c) ΔBXC **(f)** $\angle XBA$

   (ii) Name another square.

   (iii) If the area of ΔABX is 6 cm^2, find the area of

   (a) ΔABD **(c)** the rectangle $ABEF$

   (b) ΔACF

8. The diagram shows four equilateral triangles.

   (i) Under the translation $\overrightarrow{VU}$, what is the image of:

   (a) R

   (b) $[QV]$

   (c) ΔRUV

   (d) $\angle VQR$

   (ii) Name a translation that maps ΔQRV onto ΔRSU.

   (iii) If the area of the parallelogram $QSTV$ is 20 cm^2, what is the area of $RSUV$?

   (iv) What is the measure of $\angle RUT$?

9. A triangle, A, is drawn on graph paper as shown.

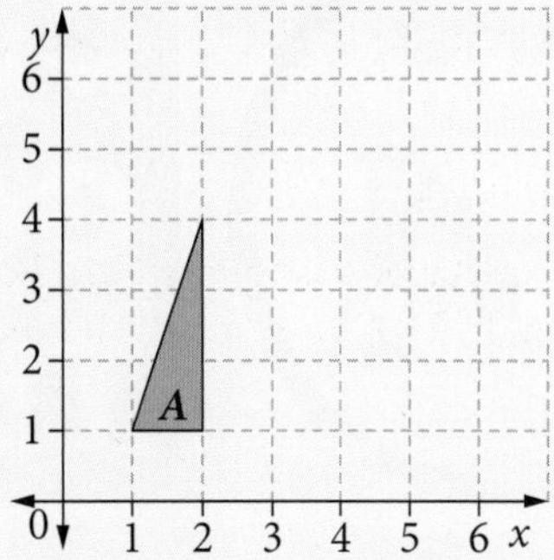

   (i) Calculate the area of triangle A.

   (ii) Copy the triangle A and enlarge it by a scale factor of 3 with centre of enlargement (0, 0). Call this triangle B.

   (iii) Find the area of triangle B.

   (iv) Find the ratio of the area of triangle B to triangle A.

   (v) Comment on the significance of your answer to part **(iv)**.

10. The 2 litre and 500 ml bottles of cola shown in the diagram are similar. The height of the label on bottle A is 8 cm. The curved surface area of the label on bottle A is 60 cm^2. The curved surface area of the label on bottle B is 375 cm^2. Find the height of the label on bottle B.

Now that you have completed the chapter, revisit the 'Something to think about…' question.

CHAPTER 14 Coordinate Geometry I: The Line

Sections covered within this chapter:

KEY WORDS

- Cartesian plane
- Slope
- y-intercept
- Intersection
- Origin
- Rate of change
- Collinear
- Quadrants
- Linear relationship
- Coefficient

SOMETHING TO THINK ABOUT... 

A ship leaves a port, P, and travels in the direction shown in the diagram. A lighthouse is situated 20 km east of the port P, at the point L. On its journey, the ship passes a buoy at the point B, which is 4 km east and 2 km north of the port, P.

If the ship continues on this straight path, use coordinate geometry to determine the shortest distance between the ship and the lighthouse?

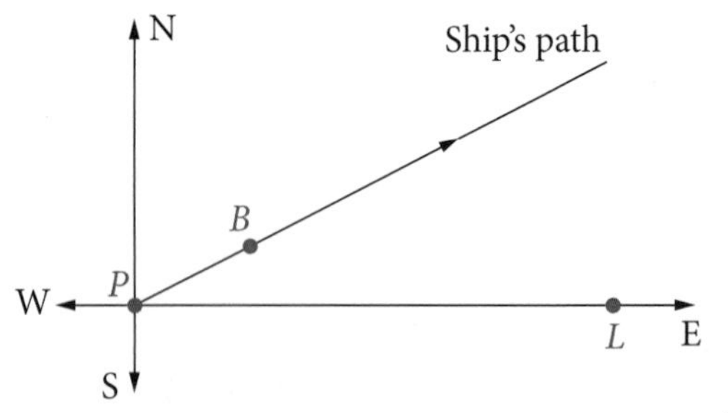

Introduction

The topic of geometry deals with points, lines, shapes and their properties. Coordinate geometry is an extension of geometry, where the objects and shapes are plotted onto a coordinated plane. Plotting points and shapes onto a coordinated plane allows us to apply algebraic functions to the shapes.

Links across the syllabus

Coordinate geometry provides a connection between algebra and geometry, through graphs of lines and circles.

It is very important that you are familiar with the elements of the geometry section of your course when working on coordinated geometry problems. You will need to be able to work with line segments and points. You will also need to be familiar with various shapes and their properties.

Section 14.1: Coordinating the Plane

Learning Outcome:

You should be able to:
- plot points on a coordinated plane

The **Cartesian plane** is a coordinated flat plane onto which we can plot points. It is formed by two intersecting number lines.

The horizontal number line is called the x-axis.

The vertical number line is called the y-axis.

The coordinates of a point are given as (x, y).

Origin is the point (0, 0). This is the point where the two axes intersect. It is labelled O.

The plane is divided into four sections, called **quadrants,** as show in the diagram.

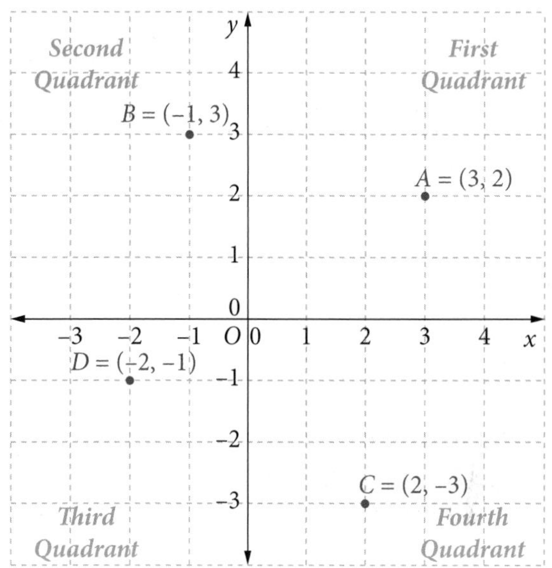

EXAMPLE

Plot the points $A(4, 1)$, $B(-2, 3)$, $C(-2, -1)$ and $D(4, -3)$ on a coordinated plane. Use your diagram to answer the following questions.

(i) What shape is the quadrilateral $ABCD$?

(ii) Find the length of the line segment $[BC]$.

(iii) Find the point in the middle of the line segment $[AC]$.

Solution

(i) $ABCD$ is parallelogram

(ii) By counting the boxes vertically downwards from the point B to the point C, we find that $|BC| = 4$ units

(iii) Using a ruler or the grid lines, join the point A to the point C, and find that the point in the middle of $[AC] = (1, 0)$

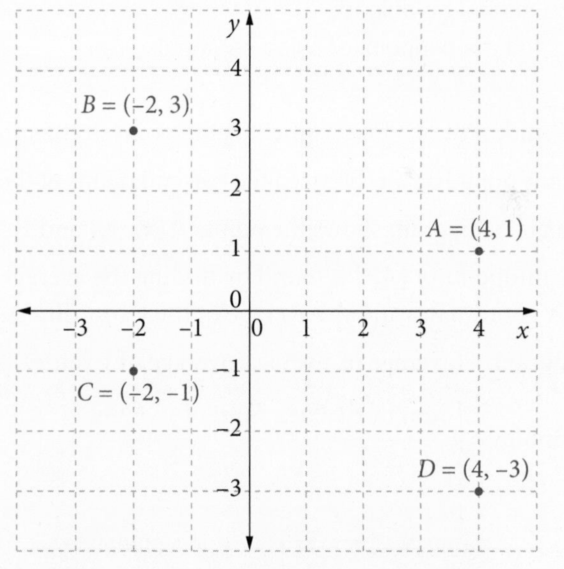

Practice Questions 14.1

1. Draw a coordinated plane from −6 to 6 on each axis and plot the following points. In each case state which quadrant the point lies in.
   (i) (−3, 5)
   (ii) (2, −6)
   (iii) (−4, −3)
   (iv) (5, 4)
   (v) (1, −4)

2. Draw a coordinated plane from −4 to 4 in each direction. Then plot and label each of the following points. In each case state which axis the point lies on.
   (i) (0, 3)
   (ii) (−1, 0)
   (iii) (4, 0)
   (iv) (0, −3)

3. **(i)** From the given diagram, write down the coordinates of the points A, B, C, D, E, F and G.

   (ii) Explain why it is easier to find $|FB|$ than $|DB|$.

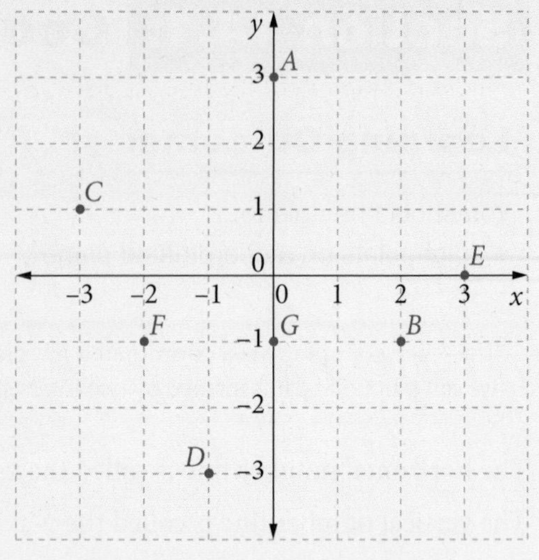

4. Plot the points $A(2, 4)$ and $B(-2, 3)$ on a Cartesian plane. Plot two appropriate points C and D, such that $ABCD$ is a parallelogram.

Section 14.2: Midpoint of a Line Segment

Learning Outcome:

You should be able to:

- find the midpoint of a line segment

The midpoint of a line segment is the point in the middle of the line segment.

It is the point halfway between the two end points of the line segment.

The given diagram shows the points $A(x_1, y_1)$ and $B(x_2, y_2)$.

The midpoint of $[AB]$ is found by finding the average of the x coordinates and the average of the y coordinates.

Midpoint = (average of x values, average of y values)

$$\text{Midpoint} = \left(\frac{\text{Sum of } x \text{ values}}{2}, \frac{\text{Sum of } y \text{ values}}{2}\right)$$

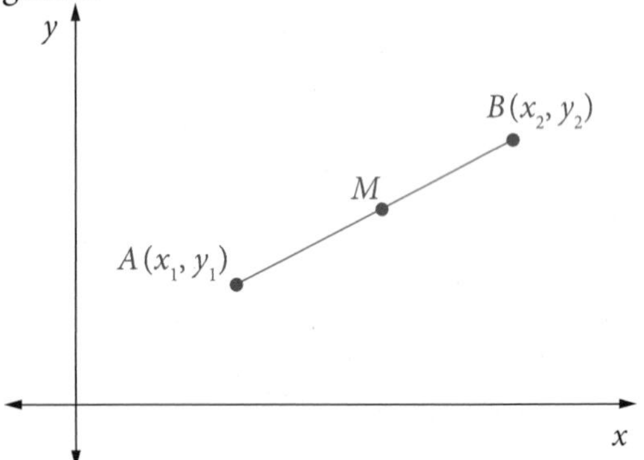

> Midpoint of a line segment joining the points (x_1, y_1) and (x_2, y_2) is
>
> $$\text{Midpoint} = \left(\frac{x_1 + x_2}{2}, \frac{y_1 + y_2}{2}\right)$$

The formula for the **midpoint** of a line segment appears on page 18 of the booklet of *formulae and tables* as shown:

$$\left(\frac{x_1 + x_2}{2}, \frac{y_1 + y_2}{2}\right) \qquad \text{midpoint of } [PQ]$$

EXAMPLE 1

Find the midpoint of the line segment joining the following pairs of points.

(i) (1, −2) and (5, 4) **(ii)** (−6, 2) and (3, −8)

Solution

(i) (1, −2) and (5, 4)

$(x_1, y_1) \quad (x_2, y_2)$

$$\text{Midpoint} = \left(\frac{1+5}{2}, \frac{-2+4}{2}\right)$$
$$= \left(\frac{6}{2}, \frac{2}{2}\right)$$
$$= (3, 1)$$

(ii) (−6, 2) and (3, −8)

$(x_1, y_1) \quad (x_2, y_2)$

$$\text{Midpoint} = \left(\frac{-6+3}{2}, \frac{2+(-8)}{2}\right)$$
$$= \left(\frac{-3}{2}, \frac{2-8}{2}\right)$$
$$= \left(-\frac{3}{2}, -\frac{6}{2}\right)$$
$$= (-1{\cdot}5, -3)$$

EXAMPLE 2

R is the midpoint of *PQ*. The coordinates of *P* are (6, −1) and the coordinates of *R* are (4, 3). Find the coordinates of *Q*.

Links across the syllabus

Use your knowledge of translations, from transformation geometry covered in Chapter 13: Geometry IV, to move the points.

Solution

Drawing a diagram of the line segment:

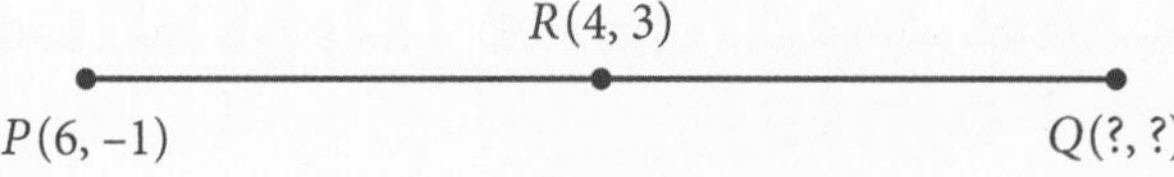

The translation needed to go from *P* to *R* is: subtract 2 from the *x* and add 4 to the *y*.

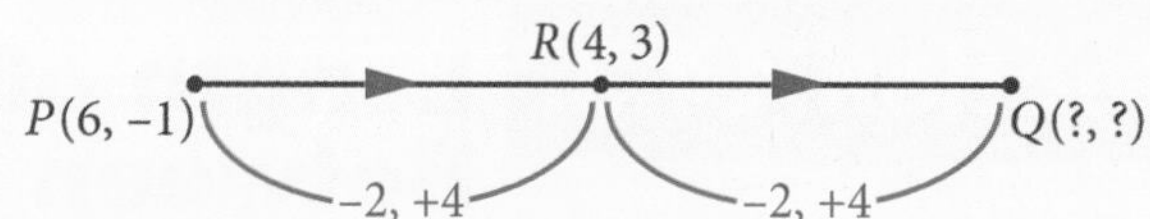

Apply this same translation to the point *R*:

$R(4, 3) \Rightarrow (4-2, 3+4) \Rightarrow Q(2, 7)$

Therefore, $Q = (2, 7)$

Practice Questions 14.2

1. Find the midpoint of the line segment joining the following pairs of points.
   - **(i)** (3, 1) and (5, 3)
   - **(ii)** (−2, 4) and (6, −2)
   - **(iii)** (0, 5) and (−4, −7)
   - **(iv)** (−2, 4) and (−5, −4)
   - **(v)** (1, −5) and (4, −3)
   - **(vi)** (6, −2) and (−1, 3)

2. **(i)** Plot the points *P*(−5, 3) and *Q*(−4, −5) on a Cartesian plane.

   (ii) Hence, or otherwise, find the midpoint of the line segment [*PQ*].

3. The points (−1, 8) and (5, 2) are two ends of a diameter of a circle. Find the coordinates of the point *C*, the centre of the circle.

4. *M* is the midpoint of *LN*. The coordinates of *N* are (0, −13) and the coordinates of *M* are (−2, −3). Find the coordinates of *L*.

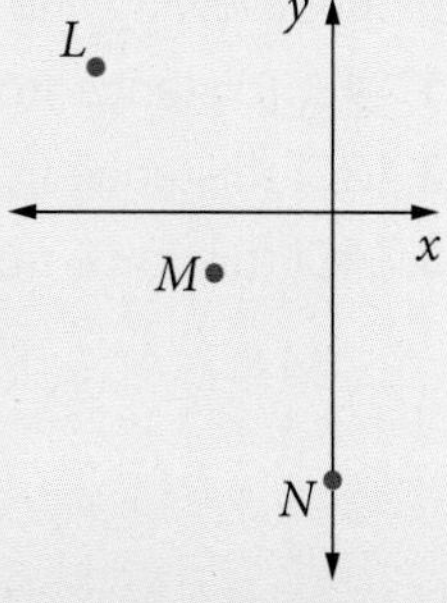

5. An air traffic controller is looking at his display and notices that at a given instant three airplanes are positioned in a straight line. Airplane *A* is at position (−6, 2) and airplane *B* is at position (−1, −1).

   (i) Plot the positions of airplanes *A* and *B* on a coordinated plane.

   (ii) If airplane *B* is halfway between airplane *A* and another airplane, *C*, find the coordinates of *C*'s position.

6. $A(-4, 5)$, $B(-1, 2)$, $C(6, 3)$ and $D(3, 6)$ are the vertices of a parallelogram.
   (i) Plot these points and hence sketch the parallelogram.
   (ii) Find the midpoint of $[BD]$.
   (iii) Show that the midpoint of $[AC]$ is also the midpoint of $[BD]$.

7. The coordinates of a quadrilateral $DEFG$ are $D(-3, -5)$, $E(-4, 3)$, $F(2, 6)$, and $G(3, -2)$. Verify that the diagonals bisect each other and hence that $DEFG$ is a parallelogram.

8. The coordinates of a quadrilateral $STUV$ are $S(-4, -3)$, $T(-6, 7)$, $U(6, 5)$ and $V(7, -3)$.
   (i) Investigate whether the diagonals bisect each other.
   (ii) What does your answer to part **(i)** tell you about the quadrilateral $STUV$?

9. AB is the diameter of a circle whose centre is the point $(3, 4)$. If the coordinates of A are $(1, 2)$, find the coordinates of B.

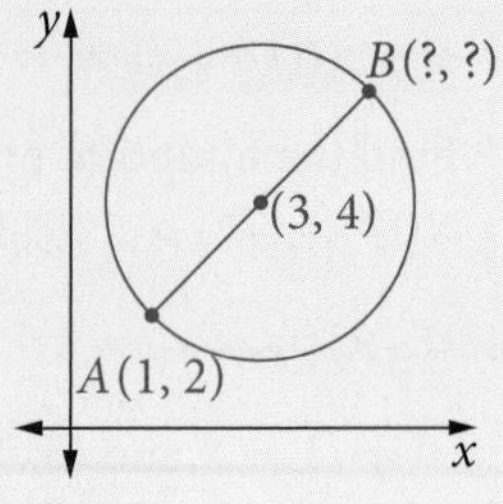

10. If the midpoint of $(0, 7)$ and $(2, 3)$ is the same as the midpoint of (a, b) and $(5, 5)$, find the value of a and b.

11. A parallelogram $ABCD$ is plotted as shown. $A = (-1, 4)$ and $B = (-3, -1)$. The centre point of the parallelogram is $(0{\cdot}5, 2)$. Find the coordinates of the points C and D.

Section 14.3: Length of a Line Segment (Distance Between Two Points)

Learning Outcome:

You should be able to:

- find the length of a line segment

Discussion Time 

Work with a classmate to find the length of the following line segments:

1. $|AB|$ (distance from A to B)

2. $|BC|$ (distance from B to C)

3. $|AC|$ (distance from A to C)

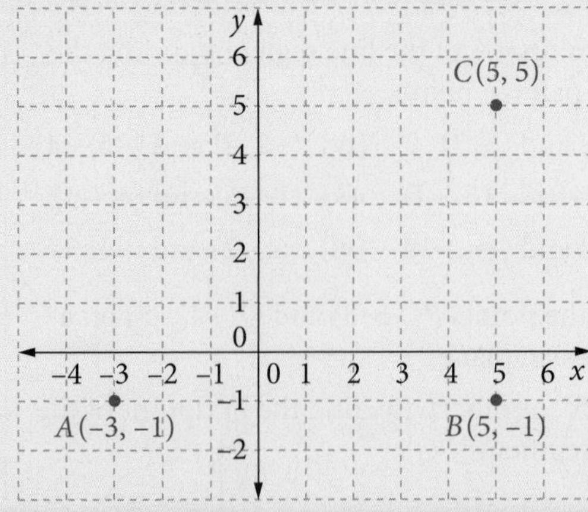

The given diagram shows the points $A(x_1, y_1)$ and $B(x_2, y_2)$

We can see that $|AC| = x_2 - x_1$ and $|BC| = y_2 - y_1$

$|AB|$ can now be found using Pythagoras' Theorem.

$|AB|^2 = |AC|^2 + |BC|^2$

$|AB|^2 = (x_2 - x_1)^2 + (y_2 - y_1)^2$

$|AB| = \sqrt{(x_2 - x_1)^2 + (y_2 - y_1)^2}$

Links across the syllabus

Pythagoras' Theorem is covered in Chapter 11: Geometry II and Chapter 20: Trigonometry I.

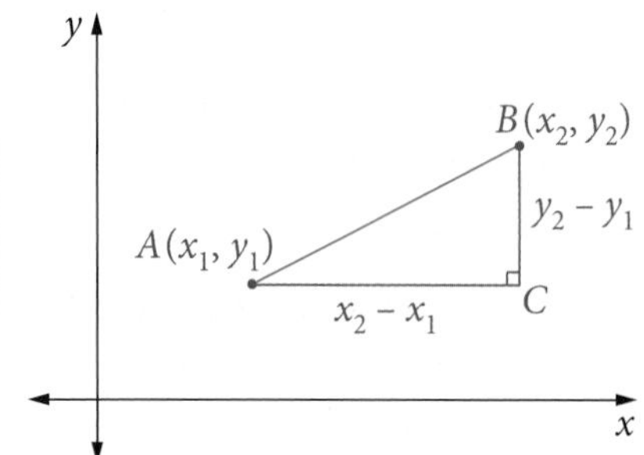

Distance between two points (x_1, y_1) and (x_2, y_2) is

$$D = \sqrt{(x_2 - x_1)^2 + (y_2 - y_1)^2}$$

The formula for the **length** of a line segment appears on page 18 of the booklet of *formulae and tables* as shown:

$$|PQ| = \sqrt{(x_2 - x_1)^2 + (y_2 - y_1)^2}$$ length of $[PQ]$

To find the length of a line segment, we use one of the following methods:

Method 1:

Step 1: Label the points as (x_1, y_1) and (x_2, y_2).

Step 2: Substitute the coordinates into the formula.

Step 3: Simplify.

Method 2:

Step 1: Plot the points.

Step 2: Form a right-angled triangle.

Step 3: Use Pythagoras' Theorem to find the length of the required line segment.

EXAMPLE 1

Find the distance between the points (4, −2) and (−2, 5).

Solution

Method 1:

Step 1: (4, −2) and (−2, 5)

(x_1, y_1) (x_2, y_2)

$D = \sqrt{(x_2 - x_1)^2 + (y_2 - y_1)^2}$

Step 2: $D = \sqrt{(-2 - 4)^2 + (5 - (-2))^2}$

Step 3: $D = \sqrt{(-6)^2 + (5 + 2)^2}$

$D = \sqrt{(-6)^2 + (7)^2}$

$D = \sqrt{36 + 49}$

$D = \sqrt{85}$

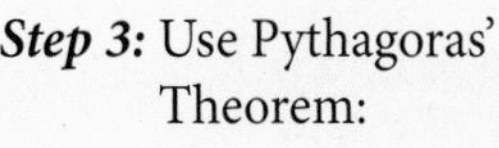

Method 2:

Step 1: Plot the points (4, −2) and (−2, 5).

Step 2: Form a right-angled triangle, with the required line segment as the hypotenuse as shown in the graph:

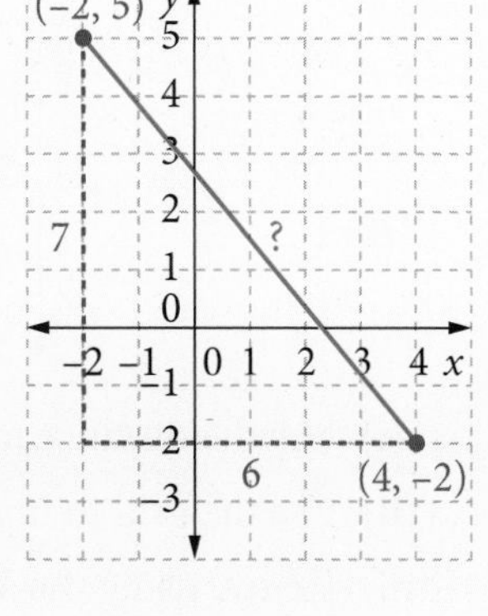

Step 3: Use Pythagoras' Theorem:

$D^2 = (6)^2 + (7)^2$

$D^2 = 36 + 49$

$D = \sqrt{36 + 49}$

$D = \sqrt{85}$

Coordinate Geometry I

EXAMPLE 2

$P(-3, 0)$ and $Q(k, 3)$ are two points.
Given $|PQ| = \sqrt{45}$, find two possible values for k.

Solution

Step 1: $(-3, 0)$ and $(k, 3)$
$(x_1, y_1) \quad (x_2, y_2)$

$$|PQ| = \sqrt{(x_2 - x_1)^2 + (y_2 - y_1)^2}$$

Step 2: $= \sqrt{(k - (-3))^2 + (3 - 0)^2}$

Step 3: $= \sqrt{(k + 3)^2 + (3)^2}$

$= \sqrt{k^2 + 6k + 9 + 9}$

$= \sqrt{k^2 + 6k + 18}$

$|PQ| = \sqrt{45}$

$\sqrt{k^2 + 6k + 18} = \sqrt{45}$

$k^2 + 6k + 18 = 45$ (square both sides)

$k^2 + 6k - 27 = 0$

$(k + 9)(k - 3) = 0$ (factorise)

$k = -9$ or $k = 3$

Practice Questions 14.3

1. Find the distance between each of the following pairs of points. Give your answer in surd form, where appropriate.
   (i) $(2, 4)$ and $(6, 7)$
   (ii) $(3, -4)$ and $(2, 1)$
   (iii) $(-5, 4)$ and $(-2, 7)$
   (iv) $(-2, 1)$ and $(1, 5)$
   (v) $(-4, 4)$ and $(-2, -3)$
   (vi) $(-1, -2)$ and $(2, -3)$

2. The diagram shows the points A, B and C on a coordinated plane.

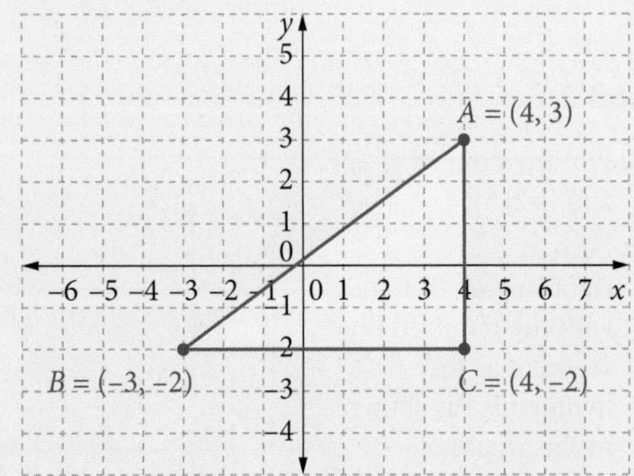

   (i) Use the distance formula to find $|AB|$.
   (ii) Use the grid to find $|BC|$ and $|AC|$.
   (iii) Hence, using the Theorem of Pythagoras, verify your answer for (i).

3. **(i)** Find the point M, the midpoint of $A(-1, -3)$ and $B(7, 3)$.
   (ii) Hence show that $|AM| = |BM|$.

4. $A(2, 5)$, $B(-1, 2)$ and $C(2, -1)$ are the vertices of a triangle. Prove that ΔABC is isosceles.

5. $P(2, 3)$, $Q(1, -2)$ and $R(12, 1)$ are the vertices of a triangle, which is right-angled at the point P.
   Find $|PQ|$ and $|PR|$ and hence find the area of the triangle.

6. A ship, A, is anchored at the point $(6, 1)$. Its radar detects another ship, S. At a given instant ship S is at position $(13, -10)$.
   (i) Find the distance between the two ships at this time.
   (ii) Ship S moves along a straight path. Two hours later S is at position $(20, 21)$.
   Calculate the speed of ship S to one decimal place.
   (Take all lengths to be kilometres.)

7. **(i)** Given $|AB| = \sqrt{41}$, where $A(p, 2)$ and $B(2, 6)$, find two possible values for p.
   (ii) Hence, plot B and the two possible points for A on a Cartesian plane.

8. $P(-4, -1)$ and $Q(3, k)$ are two points. If $|PQ| = \sqrt{74}$, find two possible values for k.

9. (i) $A(0, -3)$, $B(-3, k)$ and $C(3, 3)$ are three points on the coordinated plane. Given $|AC| = |BC|$, find two possible values for k.

(ii) Hence plot the two possible triangles ABC, on a coordinated plane.

10. The diagram shows a scale map of a town. The proposed route for a charity run is marked by pink dashes along the roads. There are three key points $A(12, 42)$, $B(30, 12)$ and $C(58, 36)$ along the route. The run starts and ends at point B.

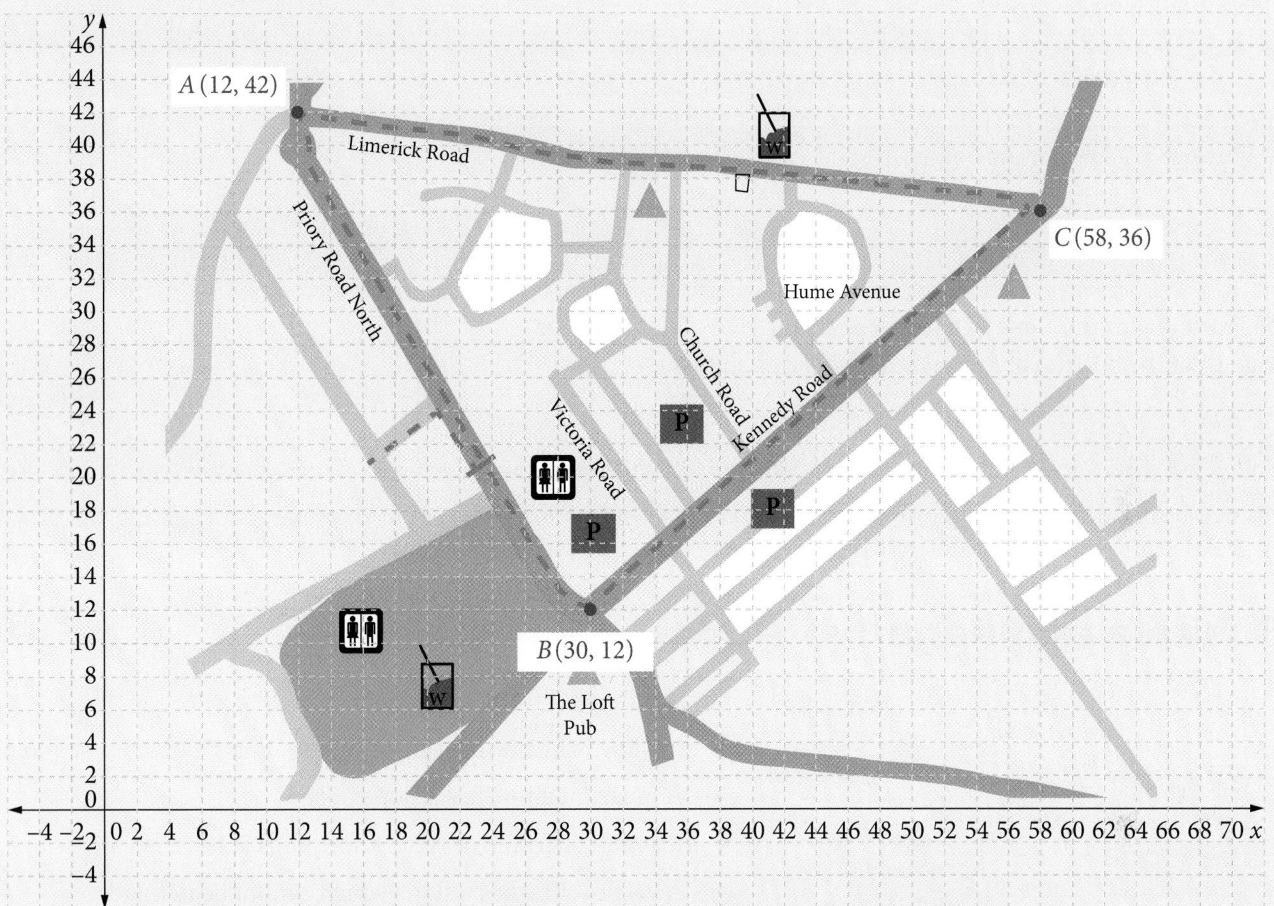

(i) If the map is drawn with a 1 unit = 100 m scale, find the total length of the run. Give your answer to the nearest metre.

(ii) Hazel completed the run in 88 minutes. Find her average speed in kilometres per hour. Give your answer to one decimal place.

(iii) Richard completed the run seven minutes before Hazel crossed the finish line. Find his average speed in kilometres per hour. Give your answer to one decimal place.

Section 14.4: Slope of a Line Segment

Learning Outcome:

You should be able to:

- find the slope of a line

The **slope** or gradient of a line is a value that describes both the direction and the steepness of the line.

The given diagram shows the points $A(x_1, y_1)$ and $B(x_2, y_2)$

$$\text{Slope} = \frac{\text{Rise}}{\text{Run}}$$

$$\text{Slope} = \frac{\text{Vertical change}}{\text{Horizontal change}}$$

Vertical change $= y_2 - y_1$

Horizontal change $= x_2 - x_1$

$$\text{Slope} = \frac{y_2 - y_1}{x_2 - x_1}$$

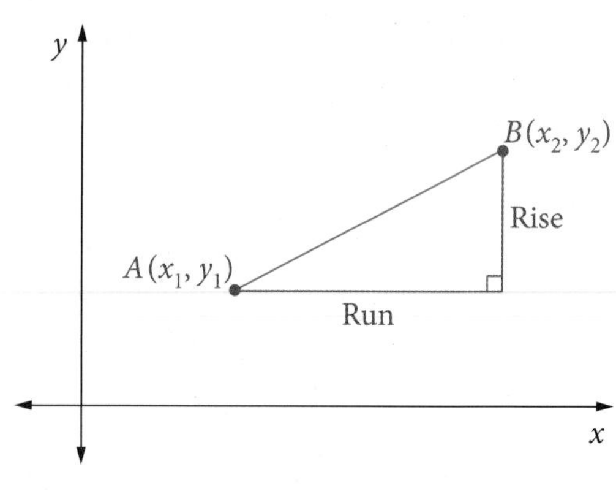

The slope of a line can also be known as the **rate of change** of the line.

The slope, m, of the line passing through the points (x_1, y_1) and (x_2, y_2) is Slope $= m = \frac{y_2 - y_1}{x_2 - x_1}$

The formula for the **slope** of a line appears on page 18 of the booklet of *formulae and tables* as shown:

$m = \frac{y_2 - y_1}{x_2 - x_1}$ slope of PQ

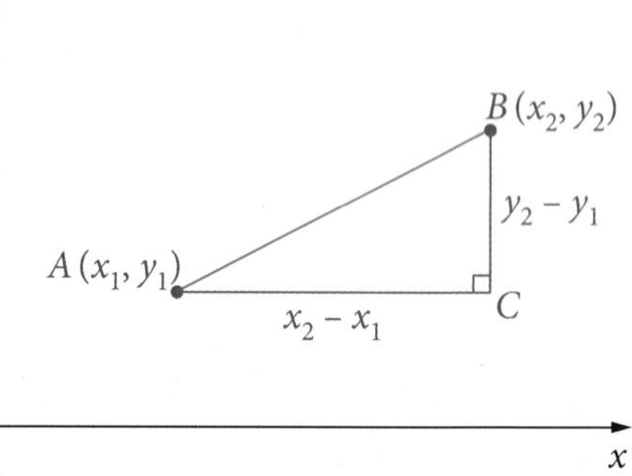

Positive and negative slopes

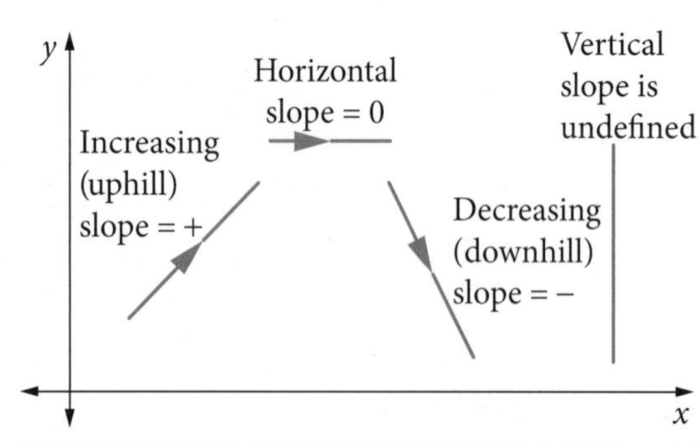

Graphs are read from left to right.

- If a line is increasing (going uphill), it has a positive slope.
- A horizontal line has a slope of zero.
- If a line is decreasing (going downhill), it has a negative slope.
- A vertical line has a slope which cannot be defined.

The size of the number represents the steepness of the line. For example, a line with slope -2 is steeper than a line with slope $-\frac{1}{2}$.

EXAMPLE

(i) Use the formula Slope $= \frac{\text{Rise}}{\text{Run}}$ to find the slope of each of the following line segments.

(ii) Use the formula Slope $= \frac{y_2 - y_1}{x_2 - x_1}$ to verify your answer in each case.

(a)

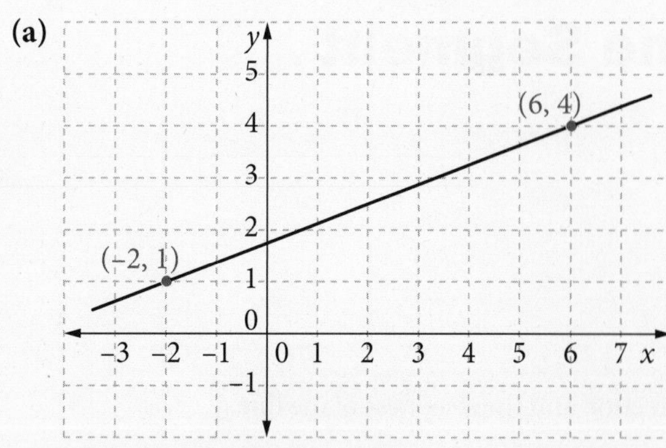

(b)

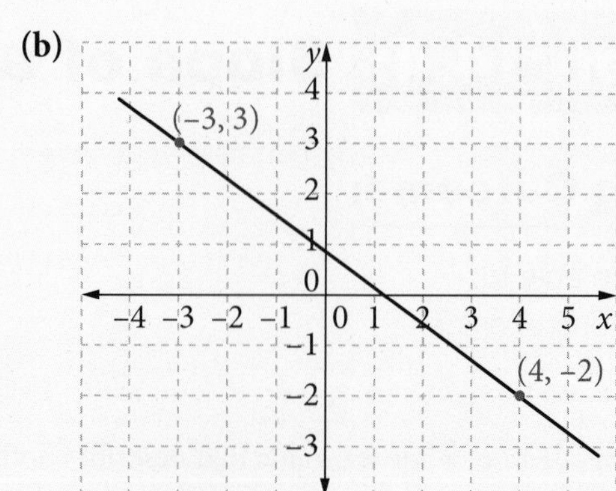

Solution

(a) (i)

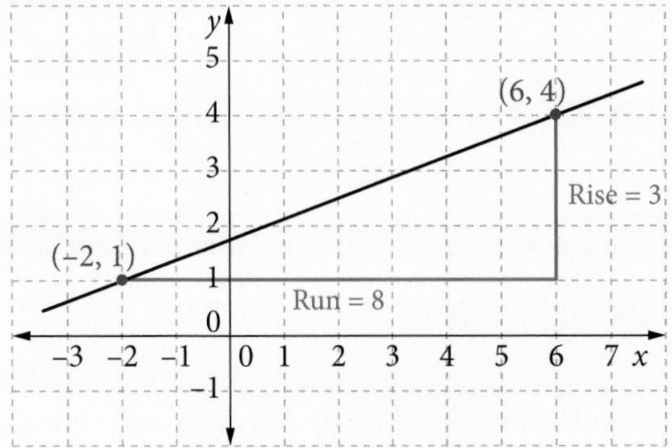

$$\text{Slope} = \frac{\text{Rise}}{\text{Run}} = \frac{3}{8}$$

(ii) $(-2, 1) = (x_1, y_1)$ $(6, 4) = (x_2, y_2)$

$$\text{Slope} = \frac{y_2 - y_1}{x_2 - x_1}$$

$$\text{Slope} = \frac{4 - 1}{6 - (-2)}$$

$$\text{Slope} = \frac{4 - 1}{6 + 2} = \frac{3}{8}$$

(b) (i)

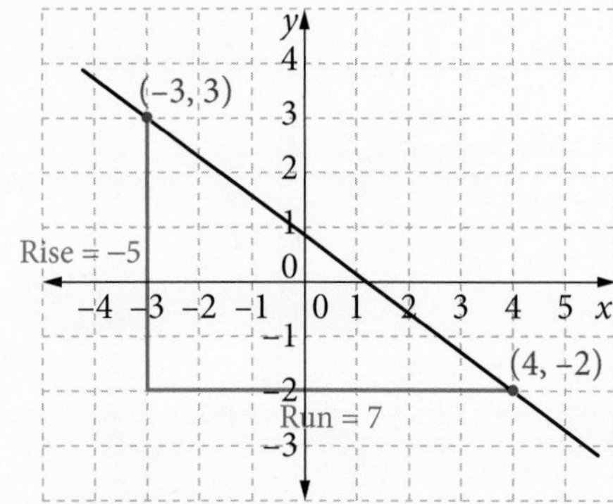

$$\text{Slope} = \frac{\text{Rise}}{\text{Run}} = \frac{-5}{7} = -\frac{5}{7}$$

(ii) $(-3, 3) = (x_1, y_1)$ $(4, -2) = (x_2, y_2)$

$$\text{Slope} = \frac{y_2 - y_1}{x_2 - x_1}$$

$$\text{Slope} = \frac{-2 - 3}{4 - (-3)}$$

$$\text{Slope} = \frac{-2 - 3}{4 + 3} = \frac{-5}{7} = -\frac{5}{7}$$

Remember, the direction of the line shows that the slope is negative.

Practice Questions 14.4

1. (i) Use the formula $\text{Slope} = \frac{\text{Rise}}{\text{Run}}$ to find the slope of each of the following line segments.

   (ii) Use the formula $\text{Slope} = \frac{y_2 - y_1}{x_2 - x_1}$ to verify your answer in each case.

(a)

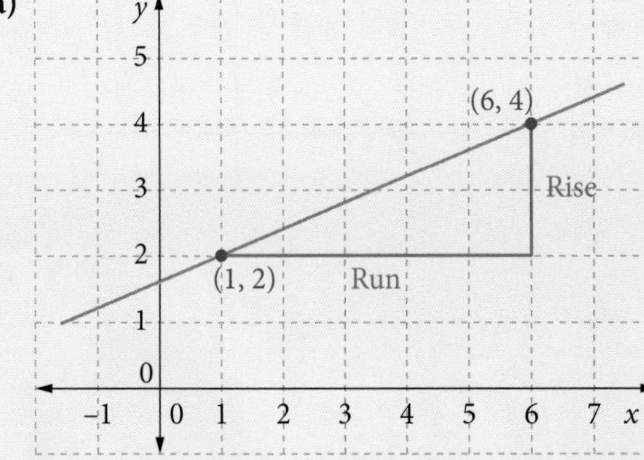

(b)

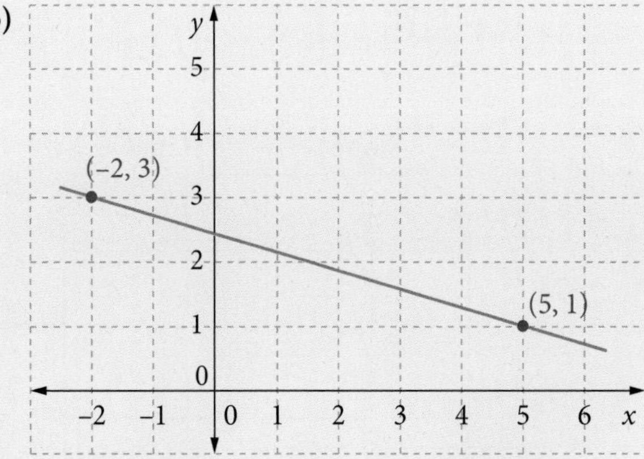

(c)

(d)

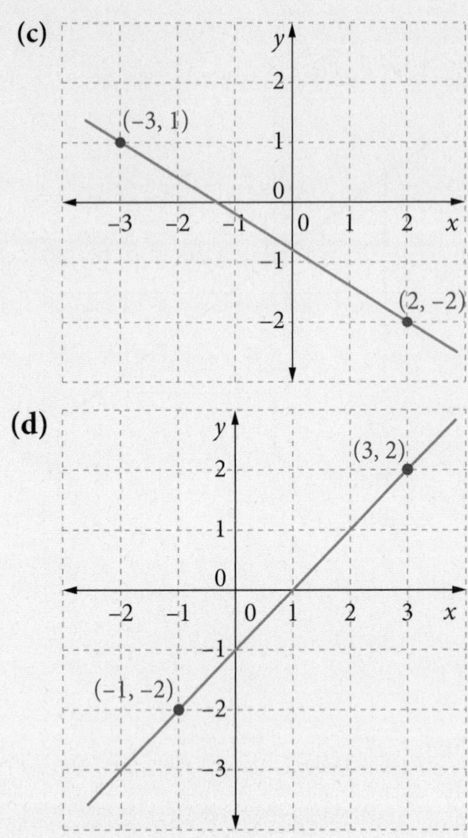

2. The diagram shows six line segments, labelled a, b, c, d, e and f.
Match each slope to its respective line.

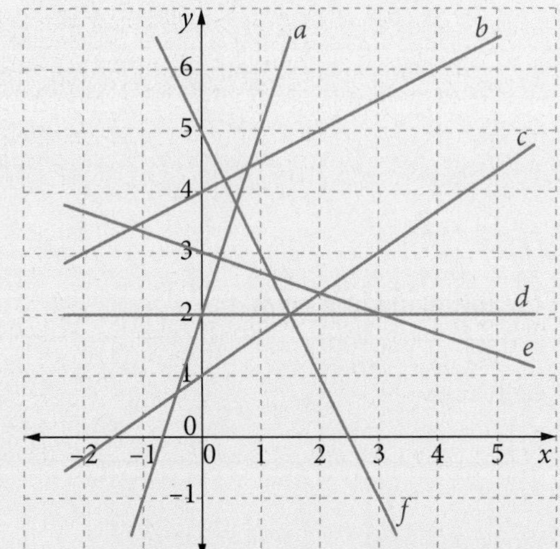

Slope	Line
$\frac{2}{3}$	
0	
−2	
$\frac{1}{2}$	
3	
$-\frac{1}{3}$	

3. On a coordinated plane, draw a line which passes through the point (1, 4) and has a slope of 2.

4. On a Cartesian plane, draw a line which passes through the point (−2, 6) and has a slope of −3.

5. On a coordinated plane, draw a line which passes through the point (2, 1) and has a slope of $\frac{2}{3}$.

6. On a coordinated plane, draw a line which passes through the point (−3, 5) and has a slope of $-\frac{1}{4}$.

7. Find the slope of the line segment joining the points (−5, 4) and (3, 4). What can you conclude about this line segment?

8. Find the slope of the line which passes through each of the following pairs of points. Hence determine whether each line is increasing (going uphill), decreasing (going downhill) or horizontal.
   (i) (4, 2) and (5, 7)
   (ii) (−3, 8) and (−1, −2)
   (iii) (0, −4) and (−6, 0)
   (iv) (−2, −7) and (−1, 6)

9. The line which passes through the points (4, −1) and (7, k) has a slope of 2. Find the value of k.

10. The line which passes through the points (1, 2) and (k, 5) has a slope of $\frac{3}{7}$. Find the value of k.

11. The line which passes through the points (2, k) and (6, −1) has a slope of $-\frac{3}{2}$. Find the value of k.

12. The line k makes equal intercepts on the axes at A and B, as shown. Find the slope of k.

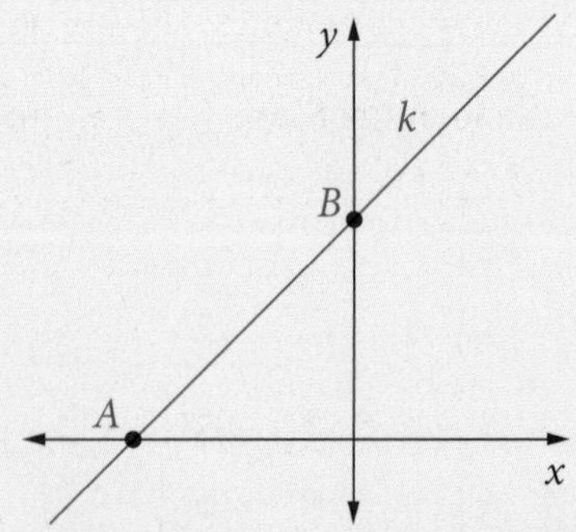

Slope = $\frac{\text{Rise}}{\text{Run}}$

Section 14.5: Parallel and Perpendicular Lines

Learning Outcome:

You should be able to:
- work with parallel and perpendicular lines

Parallel lines

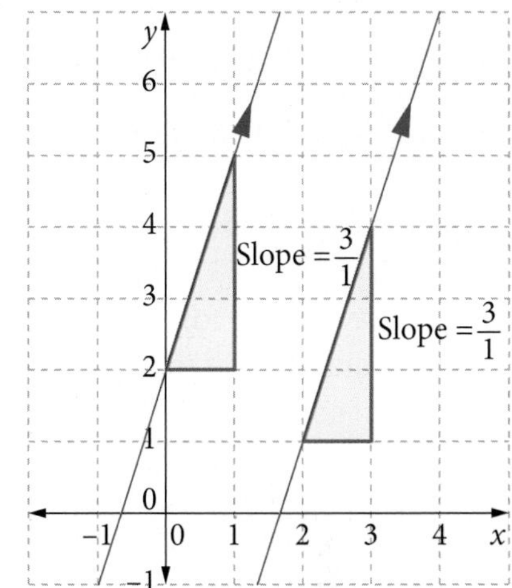

If two lines are parallel, their slopes are equal.

$$\text{If } l_1 \parallel l_2 \text{ then } m_1 = m_2$$

In the given diagram, the two lines are parallel, therefore their slopes are equal:

$$\frac{3}{1} = \frac{3}{1}$$

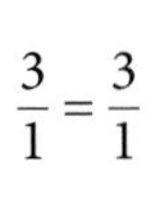

Perpendicular lines

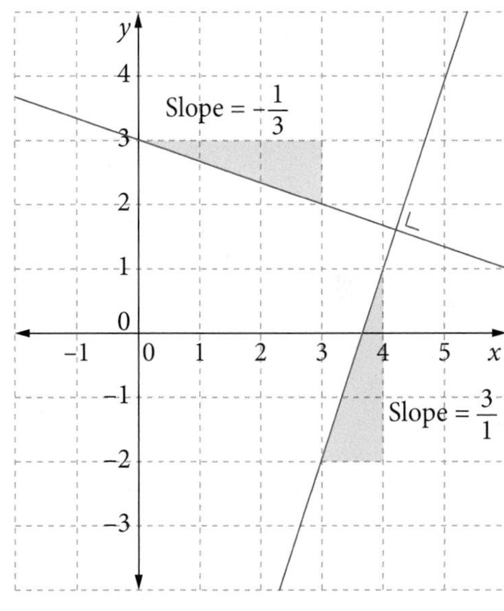

If two lines are perpendicular, when we multiply their slopes, we get −1.
Therefore, the product of their slopes is −1.

$$\text{If } l_1 \perp l_2 \text{ then } m_1 \times m_2 = -1$$

In the given diagram, the two lines are perpendicular, therefore the product of the slopes is:

$$-\frac{1}{3} \times \frac{3}{1} = -\frac{3}{3} = -1$$

If we know the slope of a line and we need to find the slope of a line perpendicular to it, we turn the given slope upside down and change the sign. This is known as the **negative reciprocal**.

For example, if given slope = $\frac{3}{2}$, then the perpendicular slope = $-\frac{2}{3}$

Practice Questions 14.5

1. The line d contains the points (1, −2) and (6, 2), the line e contains the points (4, −3) and (7, 0) and the line f contains the points (−3, −1) and (2, 3). Investigate the following:
   - **(i)** Is $d \parallel e$?
   - **(ii)** Is $d \parallel f$?
   - **(iii)** Is $e \parallel f$?

2. The line a contains the points (−3, −1) and (−2, −4), the line b contains the points (−3, −2) and (6, 1) and the line c contains the points (2, 3) and (4, −3). Investigate the following:
   - **(i)** Is $a \perp b$?
   - **(ii)** Is $a \perp c$?
   - **(iii)** Is $b \perp c$?
   - **(iv)** Is $a \parallel b$?
   - **(v)** Is $a \parallel c$?
   - **(vi)** Is $b \parallel c$?

3. The line r has a slope of $\frac{2}{3}$.
   (i) Find the slope of the line s, where $r \parallel s$.
   (ii) Find the slope of the line t, where $r \perp t$.
4. The line a has a slope of $-\frac{4}{7}$.
   (i) Find the slope of the line b, where $a \parallel b$.
   (ii) Find the slope of the line c, where $a \perp c$.
5. The slopes of six lines are given below. Write down the slope of a line which is perpendicular to each of these lines:
   (i) $\frac{1}{2}$ (iii) 4 (v) $-\frac{1}{4}$
   (ii) $\frac{3}{5}$ (iv) $-\frac{5}{2}$ (vi) -3

Section 14.6: Linear Relationships

Learning Outcomes:

You should be able to:
- understand linear relations and their graphs
- recognise that a relationship in the form $ax + by + c = 0$ is a linear relationship

 Links across the syllabus

Linear relationships are covered in Chapter 3: Algebra II, Chapter 6: Pattern and Chapter 7: Further Functions.

A **linear relationship** is one where increasing or decreasing one variable will cause a corresponding increase or decrease in the other variable.

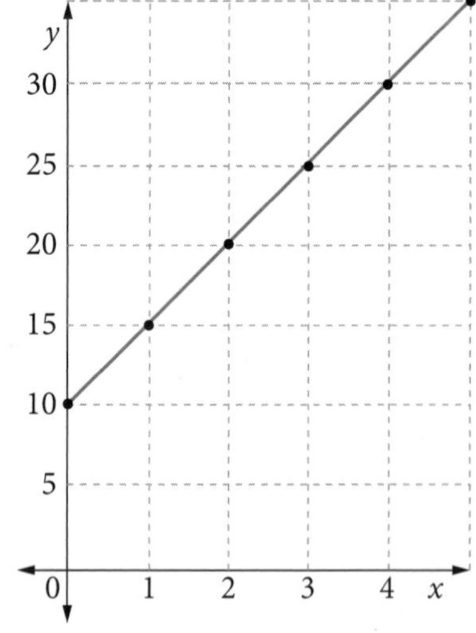

The graph of a linear relationship is a straight line.

The equation of this line can be described as follows:

$$y = \text{Starting value} + (\text{growth rate})x$$

For the given diagram, the line starts at 10 and rises by 5 for every one unit across, so the growth rate is 5.

Therefore, the equation of the line would be: $y = 10 + 5(x)$

In general, any linear relationship can be expressed by an equation in the form:

$$y = mx + c$$

Where, c = Starting value = y-intercept

m = Growth rate = slope of the graph

The **y-intercept** is the point where the line crosses the y-axis.

The formula for the **equation** of a line appears on page 18 of the booklet of *formulae and tables* as shown:

$y = mx + c$	equation of PQ

EXAMPLE

A taxi has a base starting charge of €4. The passenger is then charged an additional €1·50 for every kilometre travelled.

(i) Write a function for the cost of a trip in terms of k, where k is the number of kilometres travelled.

(ii) Graph the function in the domain from 0 km to 16 km.

(iii) Use your graph to find the cost of a trip which lasted 12 km.

(iv) Use your graph to find the distance covered during a trip which cost €13.

Solution

(i) Cost of a trip = base charge of €4 + €1·50 per kilometre

$$c = €4 + €1{\cdot}50(k)$$

$$c = 4 + 1{\cdot}5(k)$$

Equation for a linear relationship:
y = Starting value + (growth rate)x

(ii) Find the start and end points.

When $k = 0$ km:

$$c = 4 + 1{\cdot}5(k)$$
$$c = 4 + 1{\cdot}5(0)$$
$$c = 4 + 0$$
$$c = 4$$

Start point: (0, 4)

When $k = 16$ km:

$$c = 4 + 1{\cdot}5(k)$$
$$c = 4 + 1{\cdot}5(16)$$
$$c = 4 + 24$$
$$c = 28$$

End point: (16, 28)

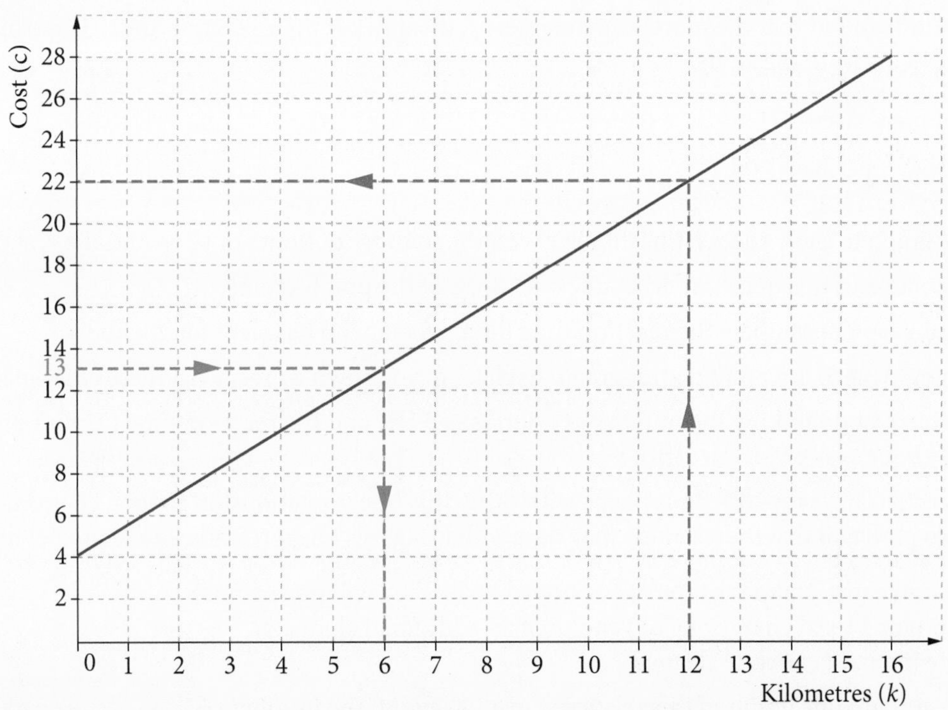

(iii) From the graph above, when the number of kilometres, $k = 12$, the cost equals €22 (illustrated by the red line on the graph).

(iv) From the graph above, when the cost equals €13, the number of kilometres equals 6 (illustrated by the green line on the graph).

Coordinate Geometry I

Practice Questions 14.6

1. A linear relationship starts at −3 on the y-axis and increases at a rate of 4 units for every 1 unit across.
   (i) Sketch this linear relationship on a Cartesian plane.
   (ii) Write an equation which represents this linear relationship.

2. A linear relationship starts at 7 on the y-axis and decreases at a rate of 3 units for every 2 unit across.
   (i) Sketch this linear relationship on a coordinated plane.
   (ii) Write an equation which represents this linear relationship.

3. Joe is a scuba diver. He starts at the surface of the water and descends below the surface at a constant rate. The table shows the depth of the diver over 5 minutes.

No. of minutes (M)	0	1	2	3	4	5
Depth in metres (D)	0	4·8	9·6	14·4	19·2	24·0

   (i) Draw a graph to show the relationship between the number of minutes passed and the depth of the diver.
   (ii) Use your graph to estimate what depth Joe is at, after 3 minutes 15 seconds.
   (iii) Write an equation linking the number of minutes passed (M) and the depth of the diver (D) and use this equation to verify your answer for part **(ii)**.
   (iv) At what depth will Joe be after 45 minutes?
   (v) Do you think this graph is an accurate representation of the diver's motion, as time goes on? Give a reason for your answer.

4. A scientific study found that the more someone sleeps, the quicker their reaction time. The table below shows some of the results from the study.

No. of hours' sleep (H)	0	1	2	3	4	5
Reaction time in seconds (T)	6	5·7	5·4	5·1	4·8	4·5

   (i) Draw a graph to show the relationship between the number of hours of sleep and the reaction time.
   (ii) In the context of this question, what does the slope of the graph represent?
   (iii) Use your graph to estimate the reaction time for a person who has slept for 2·5 hours.
   (iv) The point (3·34, 5) is a point on this graph. Explain, in your own words, what these coordinates represent.
   (v) Write an equation linking the number of hours' sleep (H) and the reaction time (T) and use this equation to verify your answer for part **(iii)**.
   (vi) The scientists have identified problems with using this linear relationship as time goes on. Give two problems that the scientists may have with using this linear relationship to predict reaction times.

5. A garden maintenance company offers a service whereby they will power-hose a concrete patio for a fixed charge of €120 and then an additional charge of €8 per square metre of concrete cleaned.
   (i) Draw a straight line graph of this relationship, plotting M, the number of square metres, on the horizontal axis for $0 \leq M \leq 130$.
   (ii) The point (55, 560) is a point on this graph. Explain in your own words what these coordinates represent.
   (iii) Write an equation linking the cost of the cleaning (C) and the number of square metres cleaned (M).
   (iv) Use your equation to find the cost of cleaning a 65 m^2 patio.
   (v) Find the area of a patio which costs €345 to clean.

6. Siobhán makes homemade jams and sells them at a local farmers' market. In preparation for the summer season, she spends €125 on ingredients for the jams and materials. Siobhán sells each jar of jam for €2·80.

   (i) Write an equation to represent the profit (P) which Siobhán will make, if she sells x number of jars.

   (ii) Draw a straight line graph of the relationship between the profit made (P) and the number of jars sold (x), plotting x on the horizontal axis for $0 \leq x \leq 150$.

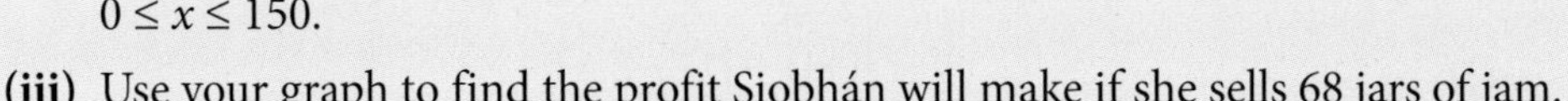

   (iii) Use your graph to find the profit Siobhán will make if she sells 68 jars of jam.

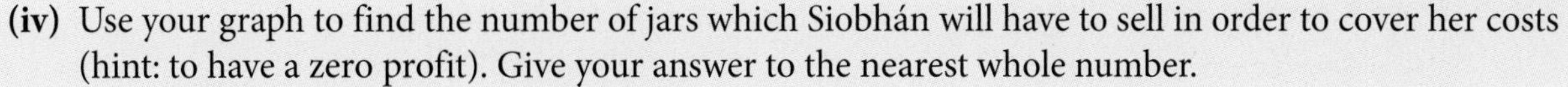

   (iv) Use your graph to find the number of jars which Siobhán will have to sell in order to cover her costs (hint: to have a zero profit). Give your answer to the nearest whole number.

Section 14.7: Equation of a Line

Learning Outcomes:

You should be able to:

- find the equation of a line
- recognise that a relationship in the form $ax + by + c = 0$ is a linear relationship

If we are not given the value for the y-intercept of a line, but instead we are given the coordinates of any point (x_1, y_1) on the line, then it is difficult to use the formula $y = mx + c$ to form the equation of the line.

In this case, the equation of the line can be found by using the formula: $y - y_1 = m(x - x_1)$

It is good practice to write the completed equation of the line in the form $ax + by + c = 0$, where $a, b, c \in \mathbb{R}$.

The formula for the **equation** of a line appears on page 18 of the booklet of *formulae and tables* as shown:

$y - y_1 = m(x - x_1)$ equation of PQ

To investigate if a point is on a line

Substitute the coordinates of the point in for x and y in the equation of the line.

If the equation then balances, the point is on the line.

EXAMPLE 1

(i) Find the equation of the line, which passes through the points (–2, 4) and has a slope of –3.

(ii) Investigate if the point (–1, 1) is on this line.

Solution

(i) Slope, $m = -3$ Point $(-2, 4) = (x_1, y_1)$

$$y - y_1 = m(x - x_1)$$
$$y - 4 = -3(x - (-2))$$
$$y - 4 = -3(x + 2)$$
$$y - 4 = -3x - 6$$
$$3x + y - 4 + 6 = 0$$
$$3x + y + 2 = 0$$

(ii) Substitute the point (–1, 1) into the equation:

$$3x + y + 2 = 0 \quad (x = -1, y = 1)$$
$$3(-1) + (1) + 2 = 0$$
$$-3 + 1 + 2 = 0$$
$$0 = 0$$

The equation balances, since the left side equals the right side; therefore the point (–1, 1) is on the line.

EXAMPLE 2

(i) Find the equation of the line k, which passes through the points (–3, –1) and (6, 5).

(ii) Investigate if the point (3, 2) is on the line k.

If we are not given the slope, we can use two points on the line to find the slope.

Solution

(i) Use the two given points to find the slope of the line:

$(-3, -1) = (x_1, y_1)$ $\quad (6, 5) = (x_2, y_2)$

$$\text{Slope} = \frac{y_2 - y_1}{x_2 - x_1}$$
$$\text{Slope} = \frac{5 - (-1)}{6 - (-3)}$$
$$\text{Slope} = \frac{5 + 1}{6 + 3}$$
$$\text{Slope} = \frac{6}{9}$$
$$\text{Slope} = \frac{2}{3} = m$$

Slope, $m = \frac{2}{3}$ Point $(-3, -1) = (x_1, y_1)$

$$y - y_1 = m(x - x_1)$$
$$y - (-1) = \frac{2}{3}(x - (-3))$$
$$y + 1 = \frac{2}{3}(x + 3)$$
$$3(y + 1) = 3\left[\frac{2}{3}(x + 3)\right]$$
$$3(y + 1) = 2(x + 3)$$
$$3y + 3 = 2x + 6$$
$$-2x + 3y + 3 - 6 = 0$$
$$-2x + 3y - 3 = 0$$

$2x - 3y + 3 = 0$ is the equation of k

(ii) Substitute the point (3, 2) into the equation:

$$2x - 3y + 3 = 0$$
$$2(3) - 3(2) + 3 = 0$$
$$6 - 6 + 3 = 0$$
$$3 \neq 0$$

The equation does not balance since the left side does not equal the right side.

Therefore the point (3, 2) is not on the line k: $2x - 3y + 3 = 0$.

Practice Questions 14.7

1. Find the equation of each of the following lines:
   - **(i)** Containing (2, 1) with slope 3
   - **(ii)** Containing (0, 3) with slope −2
   - **(iii)** Containing (−3, 5) with slope −4
   - **(iv)** Containing (7, 0) with slope $\frac{1}{2}$
   - **(v)** Containing (−2, −4) with slope $\frac{5}{2}$
   - **(vi)** Containing (6, −1) with slope $-\frac{3}{2}$
   - **(vii)** Containing (0, 0) with slope 5
   - **(viii)** Containing (3, −3) with slope $-\frac{5}{7}$

2. **(i)** Find the equation of the line containing the point (−2, 4) and has a slope of $\frac{3}{4}$.
   (ii) Investigate if the point (−6, 1) is on this line.
   (iii) Graph this line on a coordinated plane.

3. The graph shows a line passing through the point (3, 3).

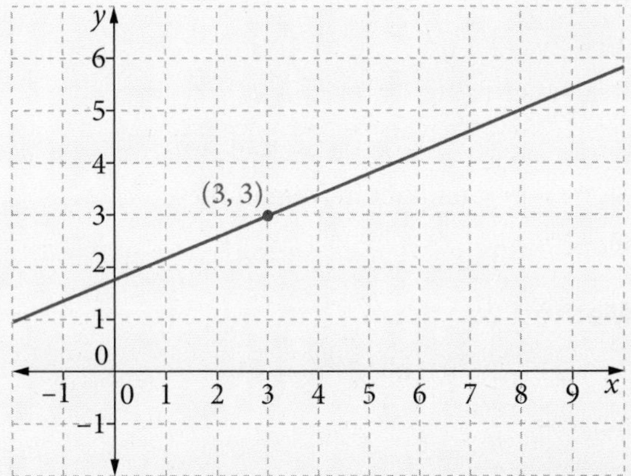

   (i) Use the grid to find the slope of the line.
   (ii) Hence, find the equation of the line.

4. **(i)** Find the equation of the line containing the point (0, 0) with a slope of 3.
   (ii) Investigate if the point (−1, −5) is on this line.
   (iii) Graph this line on a Cartesian plane.

5. **(i)** Find the equation of the line k, containing the point (−4, 4) with a slope of $-\frac{1}{3}$.
   (ii) Find the equation of the line n, also containing the point (−4, 4) and perpendicular to k.
   (iii) Graph these lines on a Cartesian plane.

6. The diagram shows four points A, B, C and D, plotted on a coordinated plane.

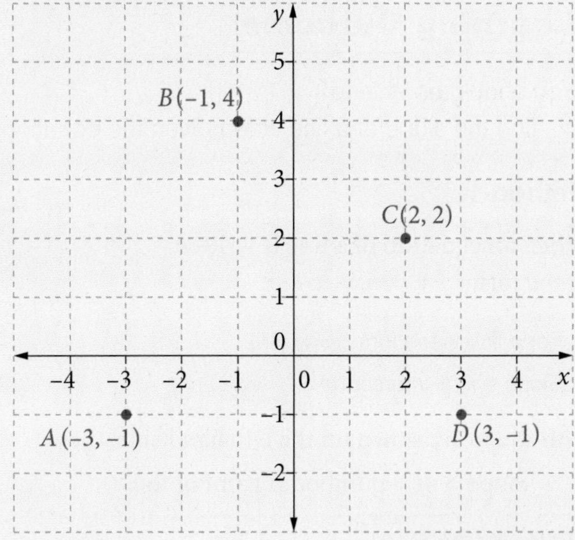

   Using the graph, or otherwise, find the equation of the following lines:

(i) AC	**(iii)** AB	**(v)** CD
(ii) BC	**(iv)** BD	**(vi)** AD

7. Find the equation of the line of each of the following, containing the given pair of points.
   - **(i)** (1, −2) and (5, 2)
   - **(ii)** (1, −2) and (3, −8)
   - **(iii)** (2, −2) and (4, 3)
   - **(iv)** (−4, 8) and (3, −6)
   - **(v)** (0, 3) and (5, 0)
   - **(vi)** (6, −3) and (−6, 7)

8. **(i)** Find the equation of the line which passes through the points (2, 4) and (−3, −1).
   (ii) Investigate if the point (−1, 1) is on this line.
   (iii) Using your answer to part **(ii)**, state whether these three points are collinear.

   Collinear means all on the same line.

9. Find the equation of the line which passes through the point (−2, 2) and the midpoint of the line segment joining the points (4, 3) and (−2, 5).

Section 14.8: Finding the Slope when Given the Equation of the Line

Learning Outcome:

You should be able to:

- find the slope of a line when given the equation

Method 1:

When an equation of a line is written in the form: $y = mx + c$

For a line in the form $y = mx + c$
Slope = m, y-intercept = c

with the y on its own on the left-hand side, then:

Slope = m = number in front of the x

Method 2:

When an equation of a line is written in the form: $ax + by + c = 0$

with all terms on the left-hand side, then:

$$\text{Slope} = -\frac{\text{coefficient of } x}{\text{coefficient of } y} = -\frac{a}{b}$$

The **coefficient** is the number in front of a variable.

EXAMPLE 1

Find the slope of each of the following lines: **(i)** $2x - y + 6 = 0$ **(ii)** $3x + 2y - 2 = 0$

Solution

(i) Method 1:

$2x - y + 6 = 0$

Rearrange to get: $-y = -2x - 6$

Multiplying by -1 gives: $y = 2x + 6$

Slope = m = number in front of the x

Slope = 2

Method 2:

$2x - y + 6 = 0 \quad a = 2 \quad b = -1$

Slope $= -\frac{a}{b}$

Slope $= -\frac{2}{-1}$

Slope $= \frac{2}{1}$

Slope = 2

(ii) Method 1:

$3x + 2y - 2 = 0$

Rearrange to get: $2y = -3x + 2$

$y = -\frac{3}{2}x + 1$

Slope = m = number in front of the x

Slope $= -\frac{3}{2}$

Method 2:

$3x + 2y - 2 = 0 \quad a = 3 \quad b = 2$

Slope $= -\frac{a}{b}$

Slope $= -\frac{3}{2}$

EXAMPLE 2

Given the lines l: $2x + 5y - 3 = 0$ and k: $5x - 2y + 4 = 0$, investigate if $l \perp k$.

Solution

Find the slope of each line:

$2x + 5y - 3 = 0 \quad a = 2 \quad b = 5$

Slope $= -\frac{a}{b}$

Slope $= -\frac{2}{5}$

$5x - 2y + 4 = 0 \quad a = 5 \quad b = -2$

Slope $= -\frac{a}{b}$

Slope $= -\frac{5}{-2} = \frac{5}{2}$

$$\text{Product of the slopes} = \left(-\frac{2}{5}\right)\left(\frac{5}{2}\right) = -\frac{10}{10} = -1$$

Since the product of the slopes $= -1$, $l \perp k$.

Parallel and perpendicular lines

To find the equation of a line parallel or perpendicular to a given line:

Step 1: Find the slope of the given line.

Step 2: Find the slope of the required parallel or perpendicular line.

Step 3: Use the given point and the new slope to find the equation of the required line.

EXAMPLE 3

The equation of the line s is $3x - 4y + 8 = 0$.

Find the equation of the line which passes through the point (4, 2) and is

(i) Parallel to s **(ii)** Perpendicular to s

Parallel lines have equal slopes.

The product of the slopes of perpendicular lines equals −1.

Solution

Find the slope of s: $3x - 4y + 8 = 0 \quad a = 3 \quad b = -4$

Slope $= -\frac{a}{b} = -\frac{3}{-4} = \frac{3}{4}$

(i) Parallel to s, therefore the slope $= \frac{3}{4}$

$$\text{Point} = (4, 2) = (x_1, y_1)$$
$$y - y_1 = m(x - x_1)$$
$$y - 2 = \frac{3}{4}(x - 4)$$
$$4(y - 2) = 3(x - 4)$$
$$4y - 8 = 3x - 12$$
$$-3x + 4y - 8 + 12 = 0$$
$$-3x + 4y + 4 = 0$$
$$3x - 4y - 4 = 0$$

(ii) Perpendicular to s, therefore the slope $= -\frac{4}{3}$

$$\text{Point} = (4, 2) = (x_1, y_1)$$
$$y - y_1 = m(x - x_1)$$
$$y - 2 = -\frac{4}{3}(x - 4)$$
$$3(y - 2) = -4(x - 4)$$
$$3y - 6 = -4x + 16$$
$$4x + 3y - 6 - 16 = 0$$
$$4x + 3y - 22 = 0$$

To find the perpendicular slope, turn the given slope upside-down and change the sign.

Practice Questions 14.8

1. Find the slope of each of the following lines:
   - **(i)** $2x + y - 3 = 0$
   - **(ii)** $5x - y + 2 = 0$
   - **(iii)** $6x + 2y = 9$
   - **(iv)** $3x - 7y = -4$
   - **(v)** $x = 2y + 3$
   - **(vi)** $2y = 7 - 2x$
2. The equation of a line is $3x - y + 5 = 0$. Write this equation in the form $y = mx + c$ and hence find:
   - **(i)** the slope of the line
   - **(ii)** the point at which the line crosses the y-axis.
3. Which of the following lines are parallel to the line $6x - 2y + 5 = 0$
   - **(i)** $3y = 9x - 2$
   - **(ii)** $3x - y - 3 = 0$
   - **(iii)** $x + 3y + 1 = 0$
   - **(iv)** $4y = 12x - 7$
4. Show that the lines $x + 2y - 3 = 0$ and $2x + 4y + 5 = 0$ are parallel.
5. Show that the lines $3x - y + 7 = 0$ and $x + 3y + 2 = 0$ are perpendicular.
6. If the line $5x - 3y + 7 = 0$ is parallel to the line $10x + ky - 1 = 0$, find the value of k.

7. If the line $x + 2y - 2 = 0$ is perpendicular to the line $kx + y + 3 = 0$, find the value of k.

8. Find the equation of the line through $(-3, 1)$, which is parallel to the line $7x + 2y - 5 = 0$.

9. Find the equation of the line through $(3, 2)$, which is perpendicular to the line $4x - y + 2 = 0$.

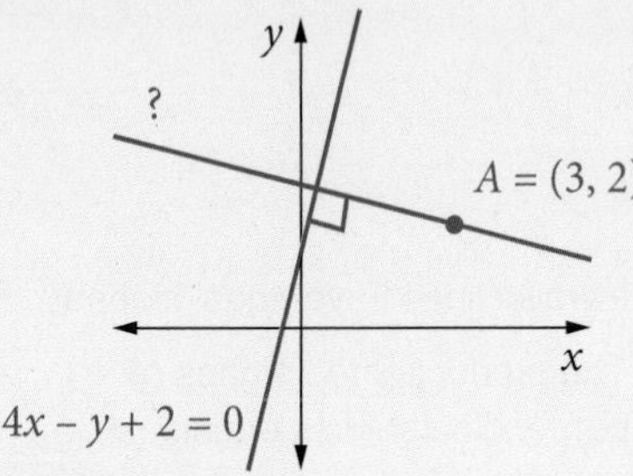

10. l is the line $2x - 5y + 7 = 0$. Find the equation of the line which is:
    (i) parallel to the line l and passing through the point $(2, -1)$
    (ii) perpendicular to the line l and passing through the point $(2, -1)$.

11. n is the line $3x + y - 8 = 0$. Find the equation of the line which is:
    (i) parallel to the line n and passing through the point $(-3, 1)$
    (ii) perpendicular to the line n and passing through the point $(-3, 1)$.

Section 14.9: Graphing Lines when Given the Equation of the Line

Learning Outcome:

You should be able to:

- graph a line, when given its equation

We have already seen how we can use the y-intercept and the slope of a line to graph the line. Another method for graphing a line is to find any two points on the line, plot these and then draw the line passing through these points.

The two methods for graphing a line are outlined below.

Method 1:

Rearrange the equation of the line into the form $y = mx + c$

Then c = y-intercept value

m = slope of the line

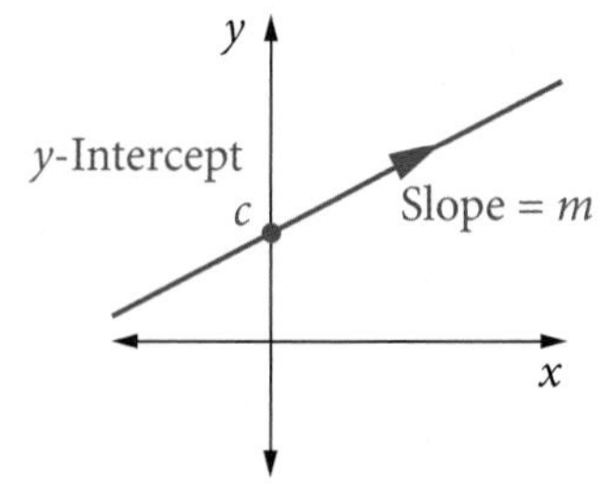

Method 2:

To graph a line, two points on the line are needed.

The easiest two points to find are the points where the line crosses the axes. These are known as the intercepts.

To graph a line, follow these steps:

Step 1: Find the x-intercept by letting $y = 0$ and finding x.

Step 2: Find the y-intercept by letting $x = 0$ and finding y.

Step 3: Plot these two points.

Step 4: Draw a line which passes through these two points.

On the x-axis, $y = 0$
On the y-axis, $x = 0$

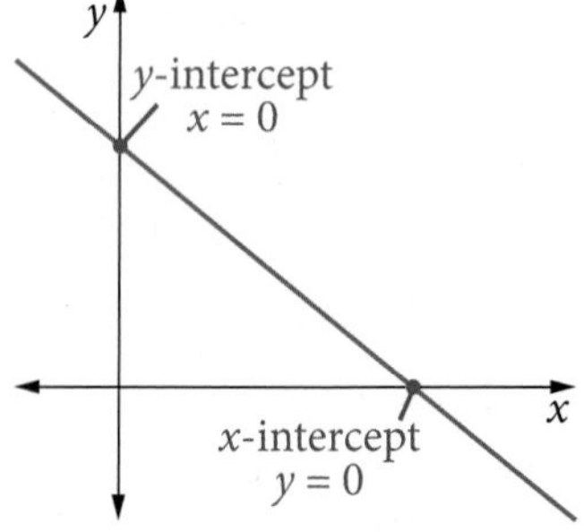

Lines which pass through the origin

If the constant in the equation is equal to zero, so that the equation is in the form $ax + by = 0$, then the line passes through the origin (0, 0), and so the intercept method will not work. In this case, we must find a different point which is on the line.

To graph this line, follow these steps:

Step 1: Let x equal the number in front of the y (or any suitable number) and solve for y.

Step 2: Plot this point.

Step 3: Draw a line which passes through the origin and this point.

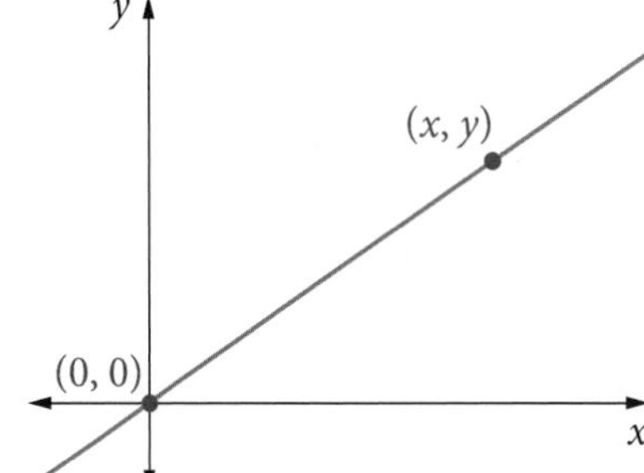

Lines which are parallel to the axes

Some lines are parallel to the x-axis (horizontal) and some lines are parallel to the y-axis (vertical).

The line $x = a$ is vertical and passes through the value a on the x-axis. Its slope is undefined.

The line $y = b$ is horizontal and passes through the value b on the y-axis. Its slope is zero.

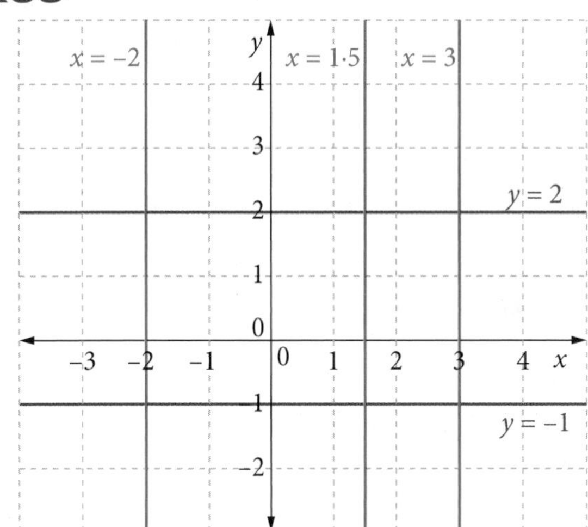

$x = 0$ is the equation of the y-axis.
$y = 0$ is the equation of the x-axis.

EXAMPLE 1

Graph the line $2x - 3y - 12 = 0$

Solution

Method 1:

$$2x - 3y - 12 = 0$$
$$-3y = -2x + 12$$
$$3y = 2x - 12$$
$$y = \frac{2}{3}x - 4$$

y-intercept $= -4$ and slope $= \frac{2}{3}$

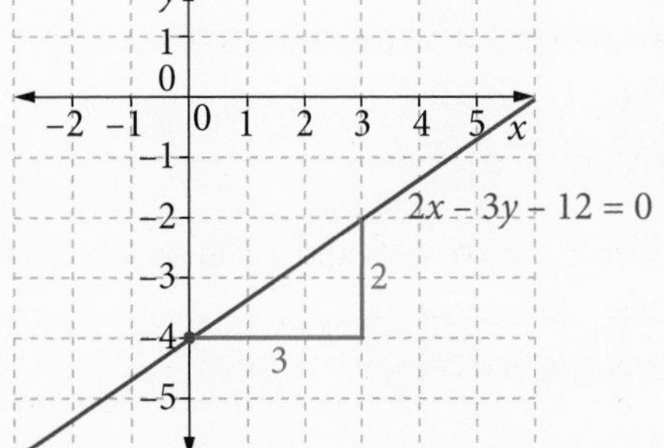

Method 2:

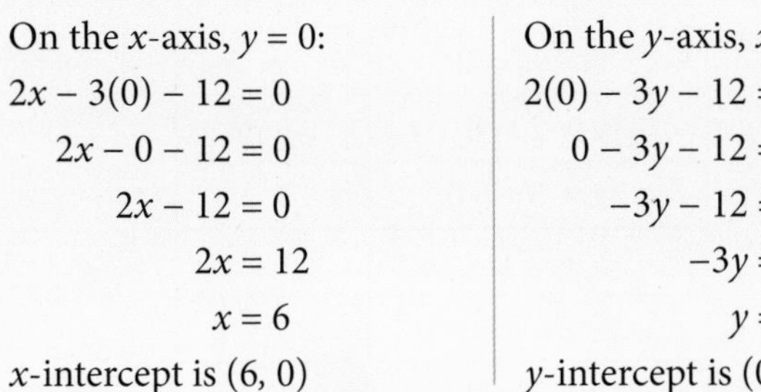

On the x-axis, $y = 0$:

$$2x - 3(0) - 12 = 0$$
$$2x - 0 - 12 = 0$$
$$2x - 12 = 0$$
$$2x = 12$$
$$x = 6$$

x-intercept is (6, 0)

On the y-axis, $x = 0$:

$$2(0) - 3y - 12 = 0$$
$$0 - 3y - 12 = 0$$
$$-3y - 12 = 0$$
$$-3y = 12$$
$$y = -4$$

y-intercept is (0, −4)

Plot these intercepts and draw a line which passes through both points.

EXAMPLE 2

Using the same axes and scale, graph the following three lines:

k: $y = 1$ s: $3x + 4y = 0$ t: $x = -3$

Solution

k: $y = 1$ This is a horizontal line, passing through the value 1 on the y-axis.

s: $3x + 4y = 0$ Since the constant is zero, we know this line passes through (0, 0).

Let $x = 4$ and find y:

$$3(4) + 4y = 0$$
$$12 + 4y = 0$$
$$4y = -12$$
$$y = -3$$

Therefore the line passes through the points (4, −3) and (0, 0).

t: $x = -3$ This is a vertical line, passing through the value −3 on the x-axis.

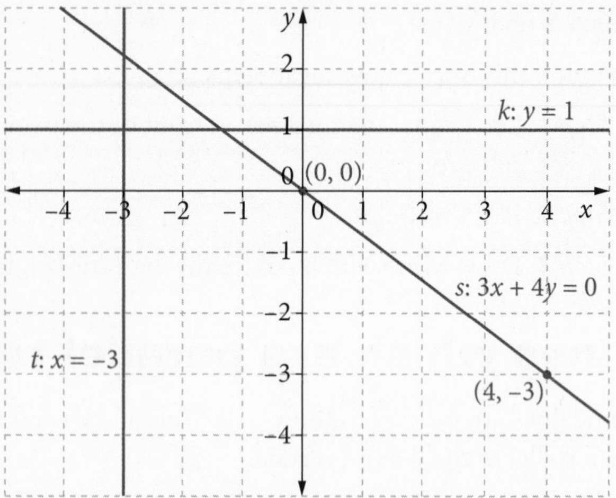

Practice Questions 14.9

1. Sketch, on separate diagrams, the following lines.
   (i) $x + y - 2 = 0$
   (ii) $2x - 3y + 6 = 0$
   (iii) $3x + 2y - 12 = 0$
   (iv) $5x - 3y + 15 = 0$
   (v) $4x - y = 6$
   (vi) $3x + y = 0$
   (vii) $3x + y - 2 = 0$
   (viii) $4x - 5y = 0$
   (ix) $2x + 7y = 0$

2. Using the same axes and scale, sketch the following lines.
   (i) $x = 2$
   (ii) $y = -1$
   (iii) $x = -3$
   (iv) $x - 4 = 0$
   (v) $y - 3 = 0$
   (vi) $2x + 7 = 0$

3. Using the same axes and scale, sketch the lines l: $x - 2y + 5 = 0$ and m: $x + y - 4 = 0$ and hence find the point P, where the lines l and m cross.

4. Using the same axes and scale, sketch the lines $2x - y + 8 = 0$, $3x - y + 11 = 0$ and $5x - y + 17 = 0$ and hence show that they are concurrent (i.e. that they all intersect at the same point).

5. The diagram shows seven lines, labelled a, b, c, d, e, f and g.
   Match each equation to its respective line.

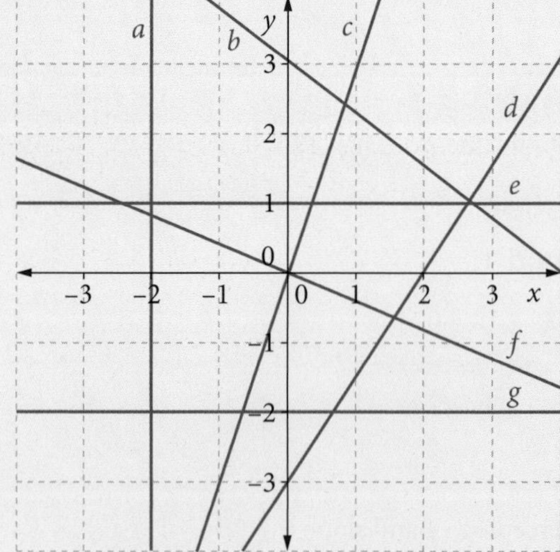

Equation	Line
$3x - y = 0$	
$y + 2 = 0$	
$2x + 5y = 0$	
$y = 1$	
$3x - 2y - 6 = 0$	
$x + 2 = 0$	
$3x + 4y - 12 = 0$	

Section 14.10: Point of Intersection of Two Lines

Learning Outcome:

You should be able to:

- find the point of intersection of two lines

The point of **intersection** is the point where two lines cross over each other.

To find the point of intersection of two lines you could graph the lines on the coordinated plane and read off the point of intersection.

However, it can sometimes be quicker and possibly more accurate to find the point of intersection using algebra.

To do this, write the equation of each line in the form $ax + by = c$, where $a, b, c \in \mathbb{R}$. Solve these two equations simultaneously, to find a value for x and a value for y. The point of intersection is then (x, y).

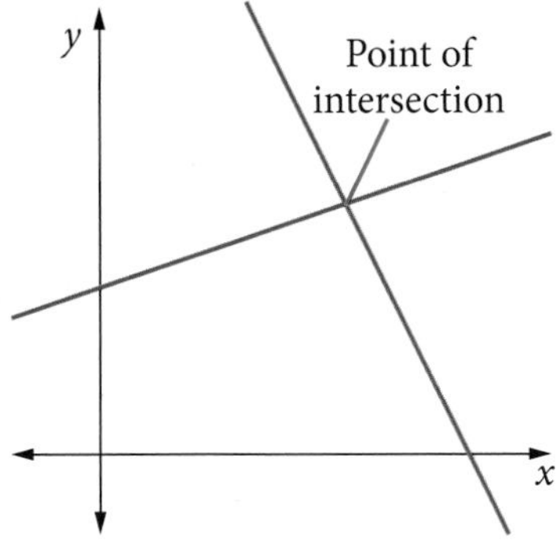

Links across the syllabus

Remember that there are three methods for solving simultaneous equations:

Method 1: Graph the two lines and read the point of intersection of the lines off the graph

Method 2: Elimination method

Method 3: Substitution method

These three methods are covered in Chapter 3: Algebra II and the substitution method is also covered in Chapter 15: Coordinate Geometry II.

EXAMPLE

Given the lines k: $2x + y - 8 = 0$ and n: $x - 3y + 3 = 0$. Find the point P, such that $k \cap n = \{P\}$.

Remember that the symbol $\cap$ means intersection.

Solution

Rewrite the equations:	$2x + y = 8$	Substitute $x = 3$:
	$\underline{x - 3y = -3}$	$2x + y = 8$
Multiply the first equation by 3, to eliminate the ys:	$6x + 3y = 24$	$2(3) + y = 8$
	$\underline{x - 3y = -3}$	$6 + y = 8$
Add the two rows:	$7x = 21$	$y = 8 - 6$
Divide both sides by 7:	$x = 3$	$y = 2$

Therefore, the point of intersection, $P = (3, 2)$

Practice Questions 14.10

1. Diagram shows the lines $x - 2y + 5 = 0$ and $2x + y - 5 = 0$.
   (i) Use the graph to find the point of intersection of the two lines.
   (ii) Use algebra to verify your answer to part **(i)**.

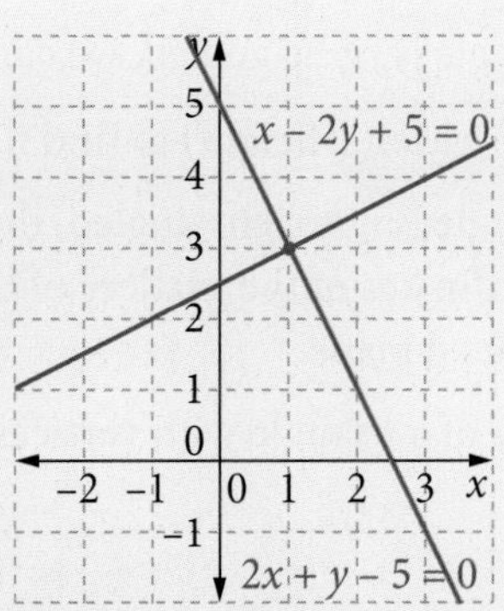

2. Graph the lines $l: 2x + y - 2 = 0$ and $k: x - y + 5 = 0$ on a coordinated plane.
   (i) Use your graph to find the point of intersection of l and k.
   (ii) Use simultaneous equations to verify your answer to part (i).
3. Graph the lines $m: x + y - 3 = 0$ and $n: x + 2y - 8 = 0$ on a coordinated plane.
   (i) Use your graph to find the point P, such that $m \cap n = \{P\}$.
   (ii) Use simultaneous equations to verify your answer to part (i).
4. Find the point of intersection of the following pairs of lines:
   (i) $x + y - 5 = 0$
   $x - y + 1 = 0$
   (ii) $x + 3y - 7 = 0$
   $2x - y + 7 = 0$
   (iii) $3x + y - 9 = 0$
   $x + 2y + 2 = 0$
   (iv) $5x - 4y - 6 = 0$
   $2x - 3y - 8 = 0$
   (v) $2x + 3y - 8 = 0$
   $3x + 2y - 2 = 0$
   (vi) $5x + 3y - 32 = 0$
   $x + 2y - 12 = 0$
5. Two taxi companies operate in a town. Each company charges fares in a different way.
   Company A: sit-in charge of €3·20 and €0·95 per kilometre travelled.
   Company B: sit-in charge of €4·50 and €0·80 per kilometre travelled

   (i) Complete the following table.

Distance (km)	0	1	2	3	4	5	6	7	8	9	10
Company A											
Company B											

   (ii) Using the same axes and scale, draw a graph to represent the relationship between distance travelled and cost for each of the taxi companies.
   (iii) Conor is planning on taking a 5·5 km journey. Which company should he use? Give a reason for your answer.
   (iv) Conor is planning on taking an 9·5 km journey. Which company should he use? Give a reason for your answer.
   (v) Use your graph to estimate the journey length, which will cost the same with both companies.
   (vi) Write down an equation to represent the cost of a journey with each of the taxi companies.
   (vii) Hence, use these equations to verify your answer for part (v).

Section 14.11: Area of a Triangle

Learning Outcome:

You should be able to:

- find the area of a triangle when given the coordinates of its vertices

If a triangle is right-angled, we can use the formula

Area $= \frac{1}{2}$(base)($\perp$height) to find its area.

If a triangle is not right-angled, then we can find its area by using the coordinates of the vertices of the triangle, when plotted on a coordinated plane.

The area of a triangle with vertices $(0, 0)$, (x_1, y_1) and (x_2, y_2) is:

$$\text{Area} = \frac{1}{2}|x_1y_2 - x_2y_1|$$

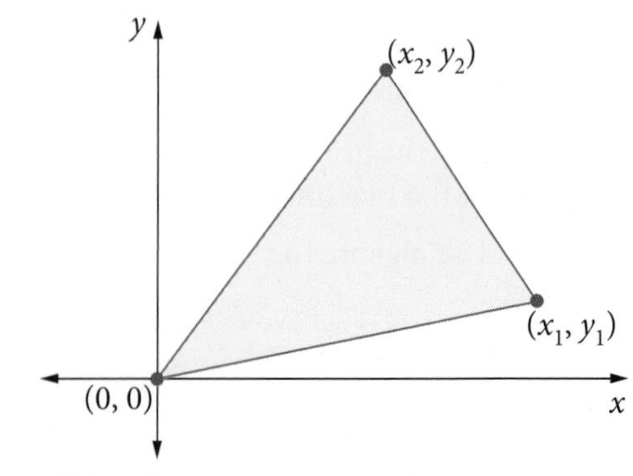

Be aware that before using this formula,
one of the vertices of the triangle **must** be (0, 0).

The formula for the **area of a triangle** appears on page 18 of the booklet of *formulae and tables* as shown:

$\frac{1}{2}|x_1y_2 - x_2y_1|$ area of triangle *OPQ*

EXAMPLE 1

Find the area of the triangle *ABC*, where *A* (0, 0), *B* (3, 2) and *C* (2, −4).

Solution

It is not essential to plot the points, but it may help you to get an idea of the situation.

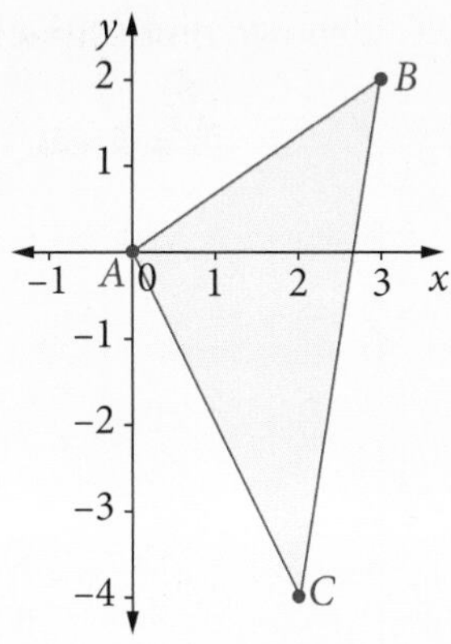

Label the points: $(3, 2) = (x_1, y_1)$
$(2, -4) = (x_2, y_2)$

$$\text{Area} = \frac{1}{2}|x_1y_2 - x_2y_1|$$
$$= \frac{1}{2}|(3)(-4) - (2)(2)|$$
$$= \frac{1}{2}|-12 - 4|$$
$$= \frac{1}{2}|-16|$$
$$= \frac{1}{2}(16)$$
$$= 8 \text{ square units}$$

Since area cannot have a negative value, the notation, | |, means that we must take the absolute value of the answer.

Translating the triangle to the origin

If none of the vertices are (0, 0), then we must move the triangle so that one of the vertices is at the origin. To do this, we find an appropriate translation, which will move one of the vertices to (0, 0) and then move the other vertices by the same translation.

EXAMPLE 2

Find the area of the triangle whose vertices are (−4, −1), (1, −3) and (−3, 3).

Solution

To move (−4, −1) to (0, 0) we add 4 to the *x*-value and add 1 to the *y*-value.
Apply this translation to each of the vertices:
$(-4, -1) \rightarrow +4, +1 \rightarrow (0, 0)$

$(1, -3) \rightarrow +4, +1 \rightarrow (5, -2) = (x_1, y_1)$

$(-3, 3) \rightarrow +4, +1 \rightarrow (1, 4) = (x_2, y_2)$

You can choose to move any of the three vertices to the origin, so long as you then move the other two vertices by the same translation.

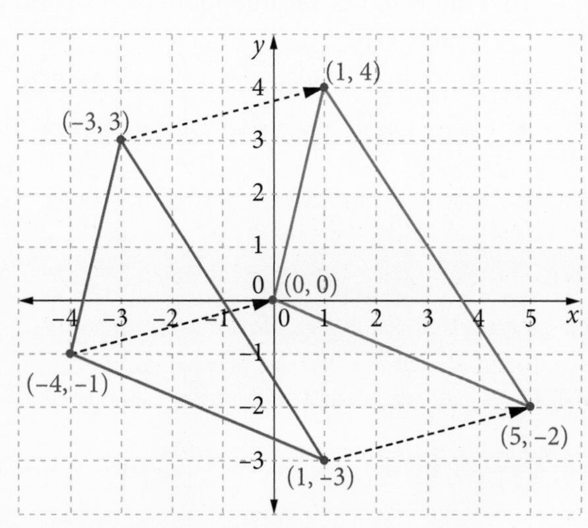

$$\text{Area} = \frac{1}{2}|x_1y_2 - x_2y_1|$$
$$= \frac{1}{2}|(5)(4) - (1)(-2)|$$
$$= \frac{1}{2}|20 + 2|$$
$$= \frac{1}{2}|22|$$
$$= 11 \text{ square units}$$

Links across the syllabus

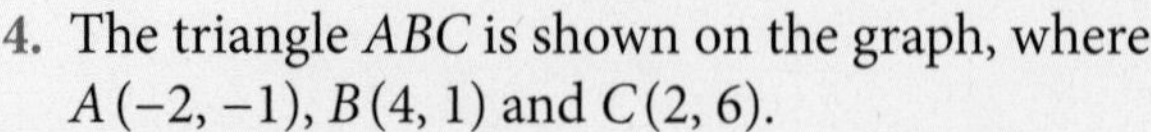

Translations are covered in Chapter 13: Geometry IV.

Practice Questions 14.11

1. Find the area of the triangle whose vertices are:
   (i) (0, 0), (3, 1), (6, 4)
   (ii) (2, –3), (–4, 2), (0, 0)
   (iii) (–2, –2), (0, 0), (3, –1)
   (iv) (–3, –4), (5, 2), (0, 0)

2. The triangle PQR has vertices $P(0, 0)$, $Q(5, 0)$ and $R(5, 4)$.
   (i) Plot the points PQR and hence construct the triangle.
   (ii) Find $|PQ|$, the length of the base of the triangle.
   (iii) Find $|QR|$, the length of the perpendicular height of the triangle.
   (iv) Find the area of ΔPQR, using the formula Area $= \frac{1}{2}$(Base)($\perp$ Height).
   (v) Use the formula Area $= \frac{1}{2}|x_1y_2 - x_2y_1|$, to verify your answer for part **(iv)**.

3. $A(4, 8)$, $B(0, 0)$, $C(6, 2)$
   (i) Find P and Q, the midpoints of $[AB]$ and $[BC]$ respectively.
   (ii) Verify that Area $\Delta BPQ = \frac{1}{4}$(Area ΔABC).

4. The triangle ABC is shown on the graph, where $A(-2, -1)$, $B(4, 1)$ and $C(2, 6)$.

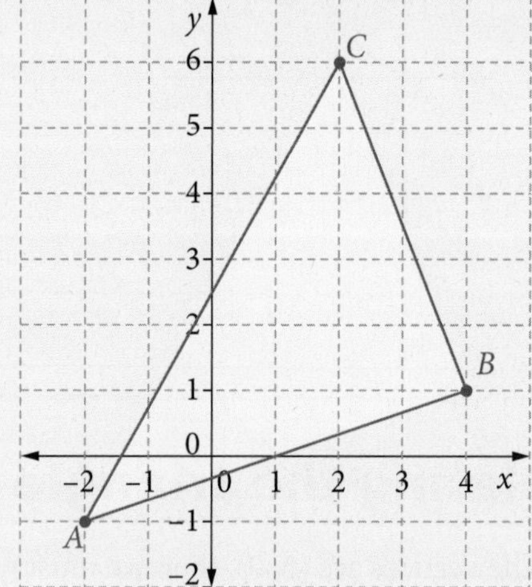

   (i) We can translate the point A to the origin by adding 2 to the x-value and 1 to the y-value. Move the point B and C using this same translation.
   (ii) Hence, using the translated points, find the area of the triangle ABC.

5. By translating one of the vertices to (0, 0), find the area of each of the triangles whose vertices are:
   (i) (–1, 2), (2, 4), (4, –2)
   (ii) (2, 0), (5, 3), (4, –2)
   (iii) (–3, –1), (–1, 4), (2, 3)
   (iv) (–2, –6), (1, 4), (4, –1)

6. By showing that the area of the triangle whose vertices are (–1, –1), (0, 0) and (4, 4) equals zero, prove that these points are collinear.

7. $P(-5, 1)$, $Q(1, 3)$, and $R(7, 5)$ are three points. By finding the area of ΔPQR, investigate if the points P, Q and R are collinear.

8. $A(0, 0)$, $B(-1, 4)$, $C(2, 5)$ and $D(4, -1)$ are the vertices of a quadrilateral, as shown in the diagram.

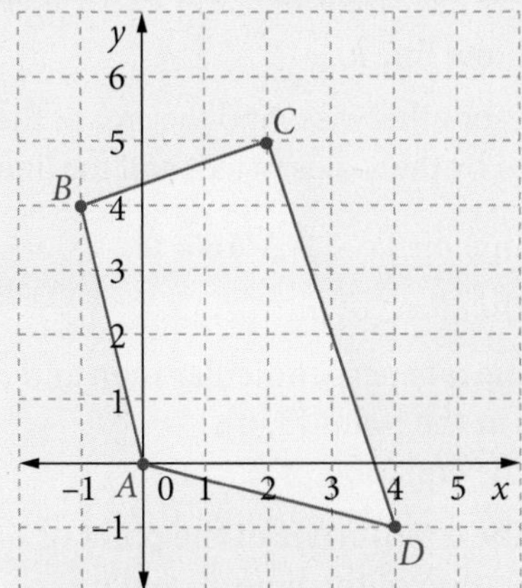

(i) Find the area of triangle ABC.

(ii) Find the area of triangle ACD.

(iii) Hence find the area of the quadrilateral $ABCD$.

9. Find the area of the quadrilateral whose vertices are:

(i) $(0, 0), (-3, 1), (-1, 5), (3, 2)$

(ii) $(0, 0), (-2, 4), (1, 5), (4, -2)$

Plot the vertices and then, using a diagonal from $(0, 0)$, divide the quadrilateral into two triangles.

10. Find the area of the quadrilateral whose vertices are:

(i) $(-2, 7), (4, 0), (6, -9), (-10, -4)$

(ii) $(0, 8), (2, 5), (5, -4), (-3, -3)$

11. $A(-3, 2)$, $B(2, 4)$ and $C(5, -2)$ are three points on the coordinated plane.

(i) Find the coordinates of the point D, such that $ABCD$ is a parallelogram.

(ii) Find the area of the parallelogram $ABCD$.

Revision and Exam Style Questions – Section A

1. The point $(t, 2t)$ lies on the line $4x - 3y + 6 = 0$. Find the value of t.

2. Investigate whether the lines l: $2x - 3y + 7 = 0$ and m: $6x + 4y - 5 = 0$ are perpendicular.

3. Find the equation of the line k, which passes through the point $(3, -2)$ and is perpendicular to the line passing through $(3, 3)$ and $(5, 7)$.

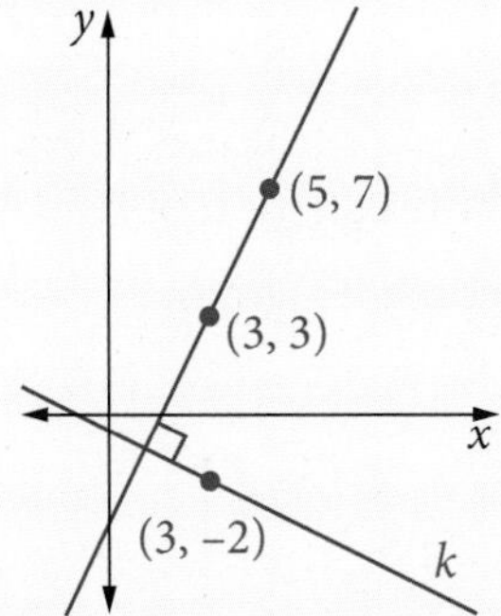

4. $A(-2, 3)$ and $B(2, 6)$ are two points.

(i) Plot the points A and B on a coordinate diagram.

(ii) Find the equation of AB.

(iii) k is the line $3x + 2y - 9 = 0$. Show that k passes through the midpoint of $[AB]$.

(iv) Investigate if k is perpendicular to AB.

5. The point $(3, 2)$ is on the line k: $ax + y - 8 = 0$.

(i) Find the value of a.

(ii) Find the points where the line k intersects the x and y axes.

(iii) Hence sketch the line k.

6. $A(0, 0)$, $B(-4, 1)$ and $C(2, 8)$ are the vertices of a triangle.

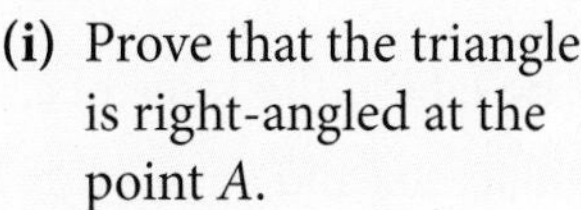

(i) Prove that the triangle is right-angled at the point A.

(ii) Find the area of the triangle ABC.

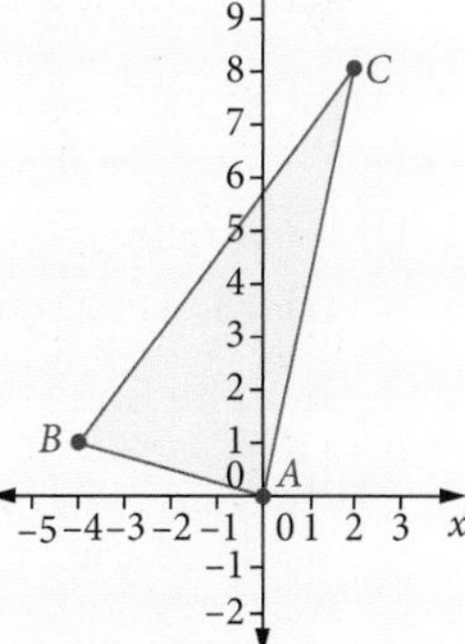

7. $A(-3, 4)$, $B(5, 6)$ and $C(1, -2)$ are three points. P is the midpoint of $[AB]$ and Q is the midpoint of $[AC]$.

(i) Find the coordinates of P and the coordinates of Q.

(ii) Plot A, B, C, P and Q on a coordinate diagram and show the line segments $[BC]$ and $[PQ]$ on your diagram.

(iii) Investigate whether PQ is parallel to BC.

8. $A(2, 3)$, $B(1, -2)$ and $C(12, 1)$ are the vertices of a triangle ABC.
   (i) Investigate if the triangle is right-angled.
   (ii) The point $(3, k)$ is on the line AB. Find the value of k.

9. The line l intersects the x-axis at $(-4, 0)$ and the y-axis at $(0, 3)$.
   (i) Find the slope of l.
   (ii) Find the equation of l.

   The line m passes through $(0, 0)$ and is perpendicular to l.
   (iii) Show the lines l and m on a coordinate diagram.
   (iv) Find the equation of m.
   (v) The point $(t, 4)$ is on the line m. Find the value of t.

10. The line k: $3x + 2y - 12 = 0$ intersects the x-axis at the point P and the y-axis at the point Q.
    (i) Find the coordinates of the points P and Q.
    (ii) Graph the line k.
    (iii) Hence, or otherwise, find the area of the triangle formed by the x-axis, y-axis and the line k.

11. Given the line m: $3x - 4y + 16 = 0$:
    (i) Find the slope of m.
    (ii) The line n is perpendicular to m and cuts the x-axis at the point $(3, 0)$. Find the equation of n.
    (iii) Find the coordinates of the point of intersection of the lines m and n.

12. Given the line l: $2x - 5y + 16 = 0$, find:
    (i) the coordinates of A, where l intersects the x-axis
    (ii) the equation of the line k, of slope 2 and passing through $B(0, -4)$
    (iii) the point C, where $l \cap k = \{C\}$.

Revision and Exam Style Questions – Section B

More challenging problems

1. The coordinates of P and Q are $(1, 5)$ and $(9, -3)$ respectively, find
   (i) the equation of the line PQ
   (ii) the equation of the line k, which passes through the origin O and is perpendicular to PQ
   (iii) the coordinates of the point A, where $PQ \cap k = \{A\}$
   (iv) the coordinates of R, where $QOPR$ is a parallelogram.

2. l is the line $5x - 2y + c = 0$
   (i) $(3, 4)$ is a point on l. Find the value of c.
   (ii) The line k is parallel to l and passes through the point $(-2, 0)$. Find the equation of k.
   (iii) The lines l and k together with the line $x = 2$ and the y-axis, form a parallelogram. Find the coordinates of the vertices of the parallelogram.

3. $A(6, 4)$ and $B(4, 3)$ are two points on the coordinated plane.
   (i) Find the equation of the line AB.
   (ii) The line AB crosses the y-axis at the point C. Find the coordinates of C.
   (iii) Find the ratio $\frac{|AB|}{|BC|}$, giving your answer in the form $\frac{p}{q}$, where $p, q \in \mathbb{N}$.

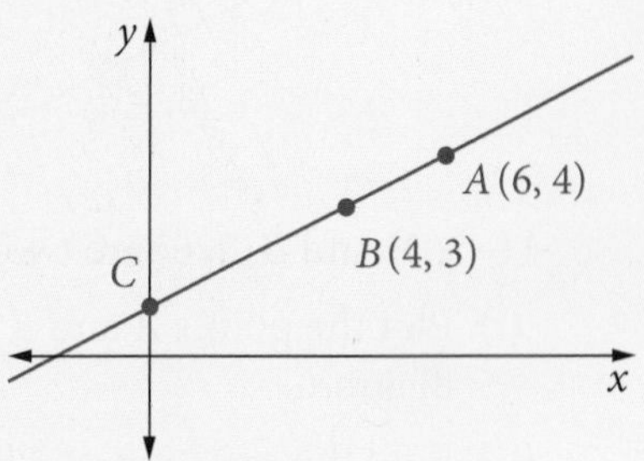

4. The line l has equation $2x - 3y + 12 = 0$.
$A(0, 4)$ and $B(-6, 0)$ are two points.
   (i) Verify that A and B lie on l.
   (ii) Find the slope of l.
   (iii) The line k is perpendicular to l and it contains the point B. Find the equation of k.
   (iv) k intersects the y-axis at the point C. Find the coordinates of C.
   (v) Using the same axis and scale, plot the points A, B and C and graph the lines l and k.
   (vi) D is another point such that $ABCD$ is a rectangle. Find the coordinates of D.
   (vii) Calculate the area of $ABCD$.

5. An electrician charges a call-out fee of €45 and then an additional €1·20 for every minute that he is working on a repair job in a house.
   (i) Write an equation to show the relationship between the total fee which the electrician will charge (F) and the number of minutes he is working on the job (T).
   (ii) Graph this linear relationship for $0 \leq T \leq 120$.
   (iii) Use your graph to find the cost of a 40-minute repair job.
   (iv) Use your graph to find how long the electrician was working on a job, for which he charged €135.
   (v) The point (60, 117) is on this graph. Write a sentence that describes the meaning of these coordinates.
   (vi) If the electrician changed his rate per minute to €1·50, what effect would this have on the graph?
   (vii) If the electrician changed his call-out fee to €20, what effect would this have on the graph?

6. $A(2, 3)$, $B(-4, 1)$ and $C(-2, 5)$ are three points.
   (i) Prove that $AC \perp BC$.
   (ii) Prove that $|AC| = |BC|$
   (iii) Calculate the area of the triangle BAC.
   (iv) The diagonals of the square $BAHG$ intersect at C. Find the coordinates of H and the coordinates of G.
   (v) Find the equation of the line BC and show that H lies on this line.

7. The line k makes equal intercepts on the axes at the points P and Q, as shown.

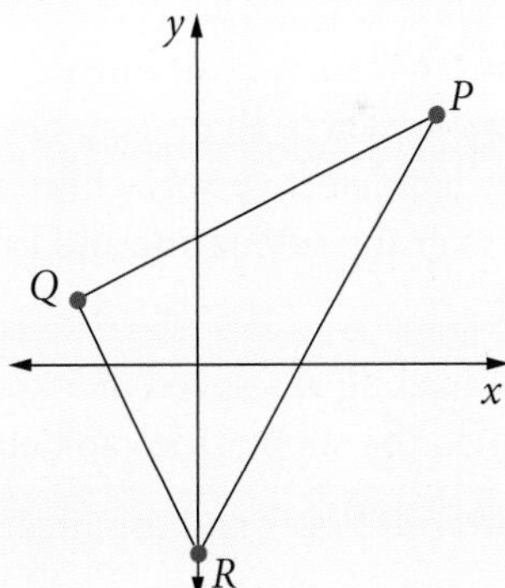

   (i) Write down the slope of k.
   (ii) The point (2, 7) is on k. Find the equation of k.
   (iii) The line n is perpendicular to k and contains the point (2, 1). Find the equation of n.
   (iv) Find the coordinates of the point R, such that $k \cap n = \{R\}$.

8. The points P, Q and R are the vertices of a triangle, as shown.
QR is the line $2x + y + 3 = 0$.
P in the point (4, 4) and Q is the point (−2, 1).

y
P
Q
x
R

   (i) Find the slope of the line PQ.
   (ii) State whether or not PQ and QR are perpendicular to each other. Give a reason for your answer.
   (iii) QR intersects the y-axis at the point R. Find the coordinates of the point R.
   (iv) Find the area of the triangle PQR.

Now that you have completed the chapter, revisit the 'Something to think about…' question.

CHAPTER 15

Coordinate Geometry II: The Circle

Sections covered within this chapter:

KEY WORDS

- Concentric

SOMETHING TO THINK ABOUT… 

A stationary submarine is positioned at the point (0, 0) on a coordinated plane, where all units are in kilometres. The radar of the submarine can detect vessels within the circle $x^2 + y^2 = 50$. A ship passes over the submarine and follows the path $2x - y + 5 = 0$.

If the ship is travelling at a speed of 5 km per hour, find the length of time for which the submarine can detect the ship.

Give your answer in hours and minutes, correct to the nearest minute.

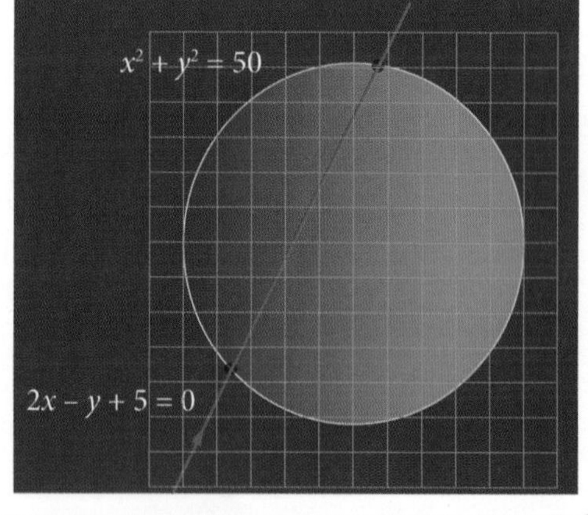

Introduction

Many of the formulae and skills which were covered in the previous chapter, Coordinate Geometry I: The Line, are essential when working through problems in this chapter. You will need to be well practised in how to find the midpoint of a line segment, the length of a line segment, the slope of a line and the equation of a line, in order to solve some of the problems in this chapter.

Section 15.1: Circle with Centre (*h*, *k*) and Radius *r*

Learning Outcomes:

You should be able to:
- form the equation of a circle, when given its centre and radius
- find the centre and radius of a circle, when given its equation

To find the equation of a circle we need the centre and the radius of the circle.

The diagram shows a circle of centre (h, k) and radius r.

The point (x, y) is on the circle.

The radius, r, can be found using the formula for the distance between two points:

(h, k)	and	(x, y)
(x_1, y_1)		(x_2, y_2)

$$\text{Distance} = \sqrt{(x_2 - x_1)^2 + (y_2 - y_1)^2}$$

$$\text{Radius} = \sqrt{(x - h)^2 + (y - k)^2}$$

$$\text{Radius}^2 = (x - h)^2 + (y - k)^2$$

This expression is known as the equation of the circle.

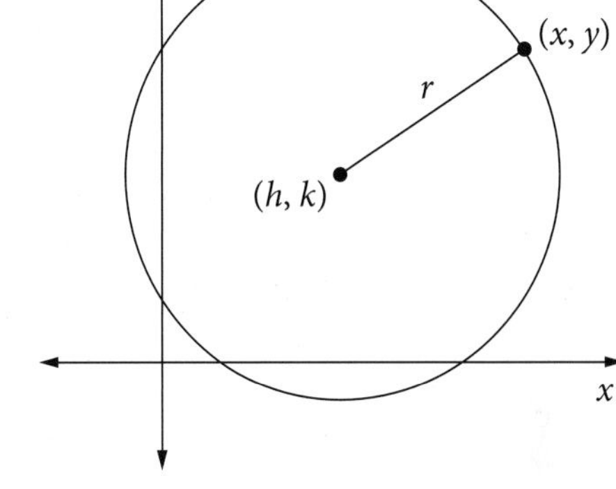

Equation of a circle of centre (h, k) and radius r:

$$(x - h)^2 + (y - k)^2 = r^2$$

The formula for the **equation** of a circle appears on page 19 of the booklet of *formulae and tables* as shown:

$(x-h)^2+(y-k)^2=r^2$	given centre (h,k) and radius r equation

A circle has centre (0, 0) and radius *r*.

The equation of the circle with centre (0, 0) and radius r becomes:

$$(x - 0)^2 + (y - 0)^2 = r^2$$

$$x^2 + y^2 = r^2$$

This formula is not given in the booklet of *formulae and tables*, as it is purely a simplified version of the formula given above.

Equation of a circle of centre (0, 0) and radius r:

$$x^2 + y^2 = r^2$$

EXAMPLE 1

Find the equations of the following circles, given their centre and radius length.

(i) Centre (4, 2), radius = 6

(ii) Centre (0, 0), radius = $\sqrt{3}$

(iii) Centre (0, 7), radius = $3\frac{1}{2}$

(iv) Centre (−1, 7), radius = $\sqrt{11}$

Solution

(i) Centre: (4, 2) and radius = 6

(h, k)

$$(x-h)^2 + (y-k)^2 = r^2$$
$$(x-4)^2 + (y-2)^2 = 6^2$$
$$(x-4)^2 + (y-2)^2 = 36$$

You are not required to multiply out the brackets.

(ii) Centre: (0, 0) and radius = $\sqrt{3}$

(h, k)

$$(x-h)^2 + (y-k)^2 = r^2$$
$$(x-0)^2 + (y-0)^2 = (\sqrt{3})^2$$
$$x^2 + y^2 = 3$$

$(\sqrt{3})^2 = \sqrt{3}\sqrt{3} = \sqrt{9} = 3$

$(\sqrt{a})^2 = \sqrt{a}\sqrt{a} = \sqrt{a^2} = a$

(iii) Centre: (0, 7) and radius = $3\frac{1}{2} = \frac{7}{2}$

(h, k)

$$(x-h)^2 + (y-k)^2 = r^2$$
$$(x-0)^2 + (y-7)^2 = \left(\frac{7}{2}\right)^2$$
$$x^2 + (y-7)^2 = \frac{49}{4} \quad \text{(multiply by 4)}$$
$$4x^2 + 4(y-7)^2 = 49$$

(iv) Centre: (−1, 7) and radius = $\sqrt{11}$

(h, k)

$$(x-h)^2 + (y-k)^2 = r^2$$
$$(x-(-1))^2 + (y-7)^2 = (\sqrt{11})^2$$
$$(x+1)^2 + (y-7)^2 = 11$$

EXAMPLE 2

(i) Find the equation of the circle which has centre (3, 2) and passes through the point (6, 1).

(ii) Find the equation of the image of this circle, under axial symmetry in the x-axis.

Solution

(i) Sketch the circle using the information given:

Centre = (3, 2)

Passing through the point (6, 1)

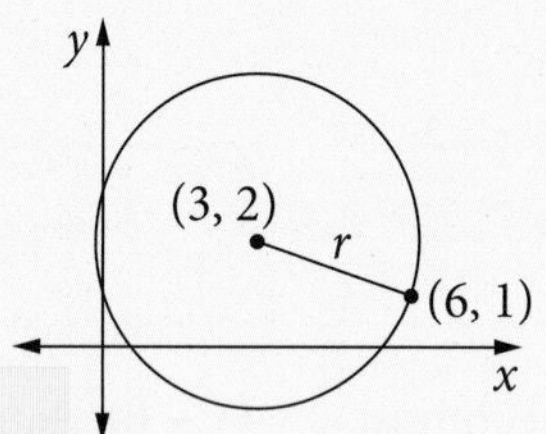

Sketching the circle gives us a clearer picture of the problem and how we can go about solving it.

Find the length of the radius:

Radius = Distance between the points (3, 2) and (6, 1)

$\underset{(x_1, y_1)}{(3, 2)}$ and $\underset{(x_2, y_2)}{(6, 1)}$

$$\text{Distance} = \sqrt{(x_2 - x_1)^2 + (y_2 - y_1)^2}$$
$$\text{Radius} = \sqrt{(6-3)^2 + (1-2)^2}$$
$$r = \sqrt{(3)^2 + (-1)^2}$$
$$r = \sqrt{9+1} = \sqrt{10}$$

Centre: (3, 2) and radius = $\sqrt{10}$

(h, k)

Equation: $(x-h)^2 + (y-k)^2 = r^2$

$$(x-3)^2 + (y-2)^2 = (\sqrt{10})^2$$
$$(x-3)^2 + (y-2)^2 = 10$$

(ii) The image of the circle, under axial symmetry in the x-axis, will have the same radius as the original circle, but its centre will be at (3, −2).

Equation: $(x-h)^2 + (y-k)^2 = r^2$

$$(x-3)^2 + (y-(-2))^2 = (\sqrt{10})^2$$
$$(x-3)^2 + (y+2)^2 = 10$$

Links across the syllabus

Transformations under axial symmetry are covered in Chapter 13: Geometry IV.

EXAMPLE 3

$A(-8, 5)$ and $B(2, -1)$ are points on the coordinated plane.
Find the equation of the circle which has $[AB]$ as a diameter.

Solution

Sketch the circle using the information given:
$A(-8, 5)$ and $B(2, -1)$ are two ends of a diameter.

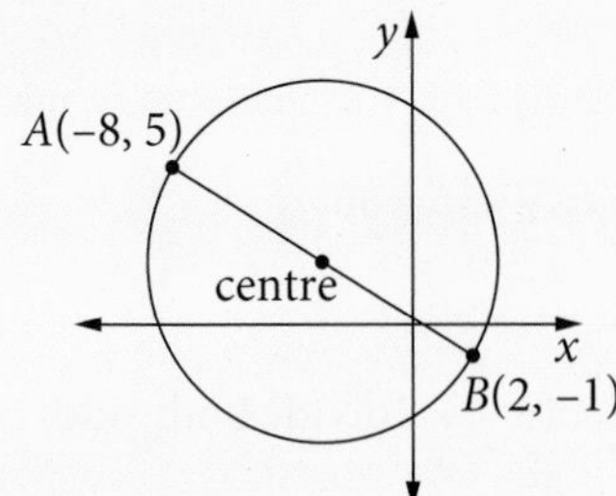

Find the centre of the circle:
Centre = Midpoint of the points $(-8, 5)$ and $(2, -1)$

$(-8, 5)$ and $(2, -1)$
(x_1, y_1) and (x_2, y_2)

$$\text{Midpoint} = \left(\frac{x_1 + x_2}{2}, \frac{y_1 + y_2}{2}\right)$$

$$\text{Centre} = \left(\frac{-8 + 2}{2}, \frac{5 + (-1)}{2}\right) = \left(\frac{-6}{2}, \frac{4}{2}\right) = (-3, 2)$$

Find the radius of the circle:
Radius = Distance between $(-3, 2)$ and $(2, -1)$

$(-3, 2)$ and $(2, -1)$
(x_1, y_1) and (x_2, y_2)

$$\text{Distance} = \sqrt{(x_2 - x_1)^2 + (y_2 - y_1)^2}$$
$$\text{Radius} = \sqrt{(2 - (-3))^2 + (-1 - 2)^2}$$
$$r = \sqrt{(5)^2 + (-3)^2}$$
$$r = \sqrt{25 + 9}$$
$$r = \sqrt{34}$$

Now find the equation of the circle:

Centre: $(-3, 2)$ and radius $= \sqrt{34}$
(h, k)

Equation: $(x - h)^2 + (y - k)^2 = r^2$
$$(x - (-3))^2 + (y - 2)^2 = (\sqrt{34})^2$$
$$(x + 3)^2 + (y - 2)^2 = 34$$

EXAMPLE 4

A circle with centre $(0, -3)$ has a chord of length 12 units at a distance of four units from its centre.
Find the equation of the circle.

Solution

Sketch the circle using the information given:
Centre = $(0, -3)$
Chord of length 12 units, bisected by a radius, coming from the centre, which is 4 units away.

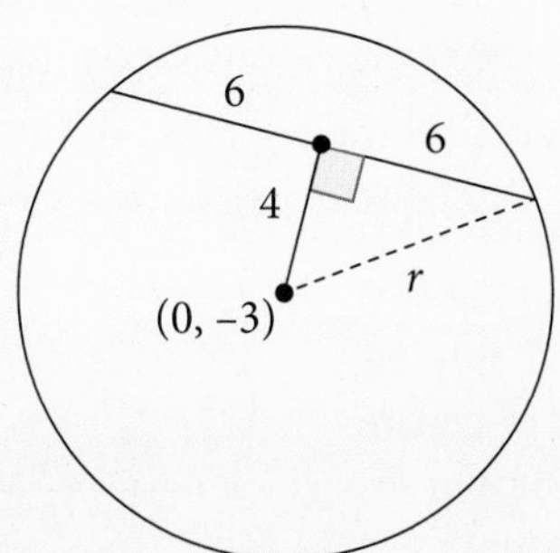

Use Pythagoras' Theorem to find the radius, r:
$r^2 = (4)^2 + (6)^2$
$r^2 = 16 + 36 \Rightarrow r^2 = 52 \Rightarrow r = \sqrt{52}$
Equation: $(x - h)^2 + (y - k)^2 = r^2$
$$(x - 0)^2 + (y - (-3))^2 = (\sqrt{52})^2$$
$$x^2 + (y + 3)^2 = 52$$

Links across the syllabus

Pythagoras' Theorem and the theorem linking a radius and chord of a circle are both covered in Chapter 11: Geometry II.

Find the centre and the radius when given the equation of the circle

When given the equation of a circle and asked to find its centre and radius, rearrange the equation into the form of $(x - h)^2 + (y - k)^2 = r^2$ and then the centre $= (h, k)$ and radius $= r$.

EXAMPLE 5

Find the centre and the radius of the following circles:

(i) $(x - 3)^2 + (y + 7)^2 = 225$

(ii) $x^2 + y^2 = 48$

(iii) $9x^2 + 9y^2 = 49$

(iv) $(x + 1)^2 + (y - 4)^2 = 80$

Solution

(i) $(x - 3)^2 + (y + 7)^2 = 225$

$(x - 3)^2 + (y - (-7))^2 = 225$

Centre $= (3, -7)$

$(\text{Radius})^2 = 225$

$r = \sqrt{225} = 15$

(ii) $x^2 + y^2 = 48$

Centre $= (0, 0)$

$(\text{Radius})^2 = 48$

$r = \sqrt{48}$

$r = \sqrt{16}\sqrt{3}$

$r = 4\sqrt{3}$

Notice that the coordinates of the centre are the same numbers as given in the equation, but with the signs changed.

(iii) $9x^2 + 9y^2 = 49$ (divide both sides by 9)

$x^2 + y^2 = \frac{49}{9}$

Centre $= (0, 0)$

$(\text{Radius})^2 = \frac{49}{9}$

$r = \sqrt{\frac{49}{9}} = \frac{\sqrt{49}}{\sqrt{9}}$

$r = \frac{7}{3}$

For an equation in the form $ax^2 + ay^2 = k$, divide all terms by a, to get the equation into the form $x^2 + y^2 = r^2$.

(iv) $(x + 1)^2 + (y - 4)^2 = 80$

$(x - (-1))^2 + (y - 4)^2 = (\sqrt{80})^2$

Centre $= (-1, 4)$

$(\text{Radius})^2 = 80$

$r = \sqrt{80}$

$r = 4\sqrt{5}$

Practice Questions 15.1

1. Write down the equation of each of the following circles, with given centre and radius.
   (i) Centre $= (2, 5)$ radius $= 4$
   (ii) Centre $= (0, 0)$ radius $= 2{\cdot}5$
   (iii) Centre $= (0, 0)$ radius $= 2\sqrt{5}$
   (iv) Centre $= (-4, 0)$ radius $= 9$
   (v) Centre $= (0, 0)$ radius $= 2\frac{2}{5}$
   (vi) Centre $= (-6, -4)$ radius $= \sqrt{5}$
   (vii) Centre $= (-2, -5)$ radius $= \sqrt{7}$
   (viii) Centre $= (0, 0)$ radius $= 4\sqrt{6}$
   (ix) Centre $= (-3, 7)$ radius $= 6$
   (x) Centre $= (6, -1)$ radius $= \sqrt{10}$

2. A circle has centre $(0, 0)$ and it passes through the point $(-4, -2)$.
   (i) Find the radius of the circle, in surd form.
   (ii) Hence, find the equation of the circle.

3. The points $(-3, 1)$ and $(3, -1)$ are two ends of a diameter of a circle of centre $(0, 0)$, as shown in the diagram.

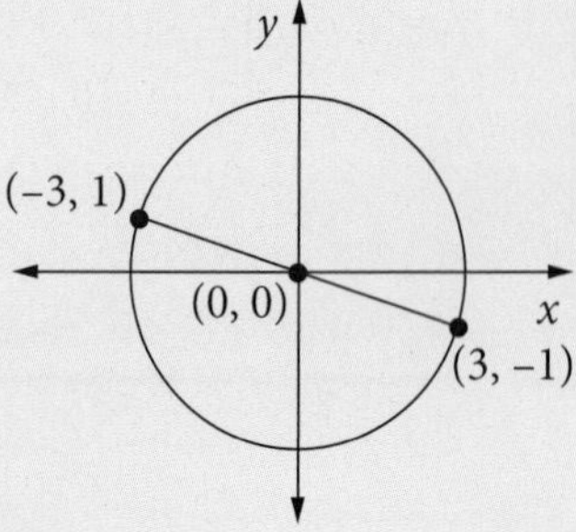

   (i) Find the radius of the circle, in surd form.
   (ii) Hence, find the equation of the circle.

4. Using the diagrams, write down the equation of each of the following circles. Each square on the grid = 1 unit.

(i)

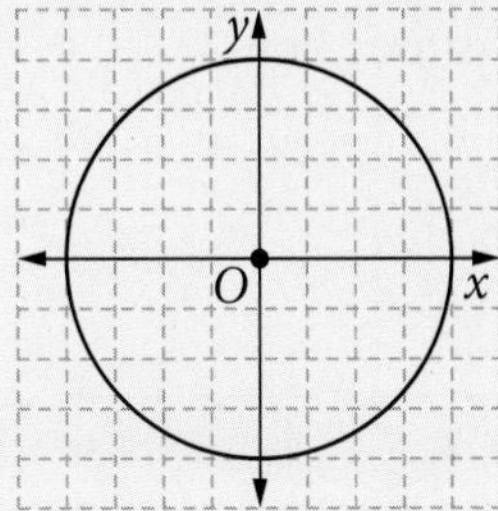

(iv)

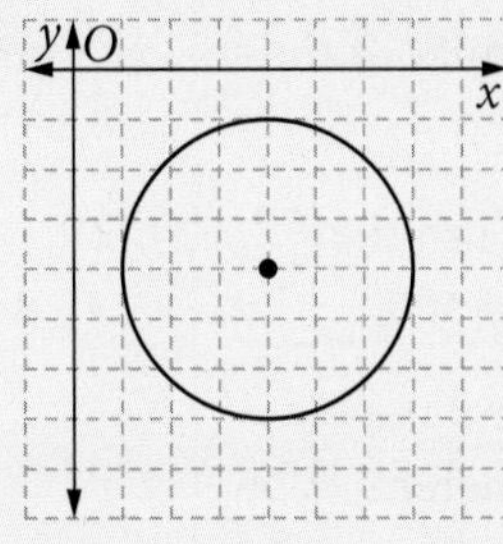

(vii)

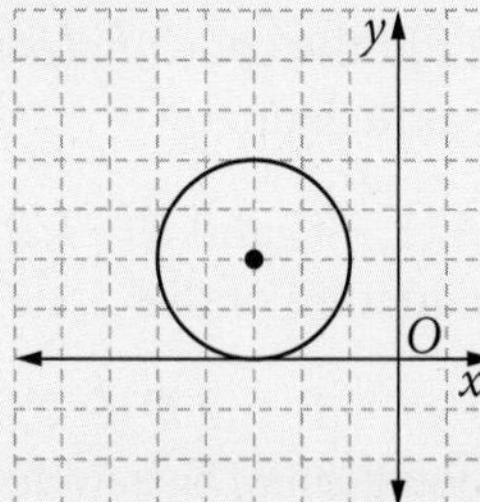

(ii)

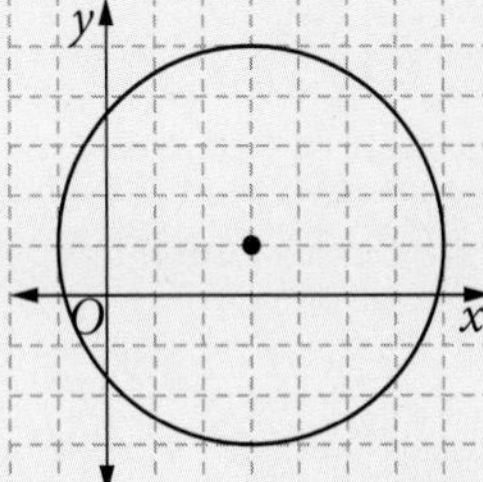

(v)

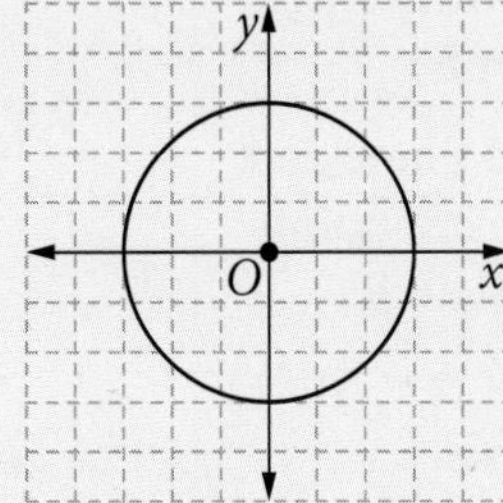

(viii)

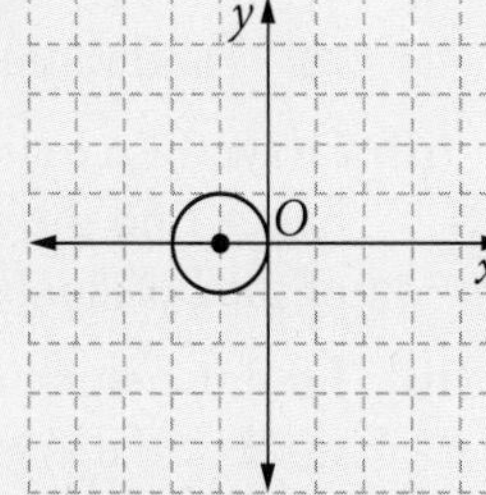

(iii)

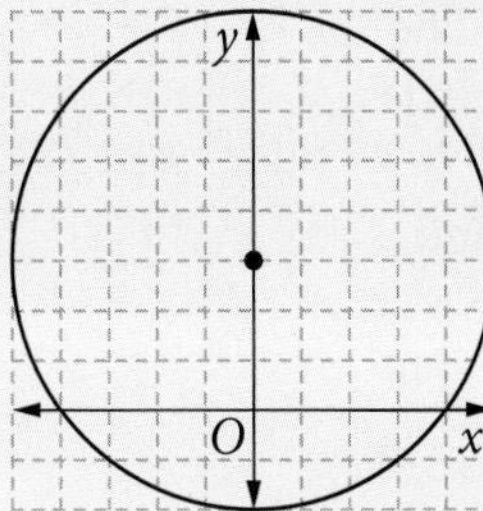

(vi)

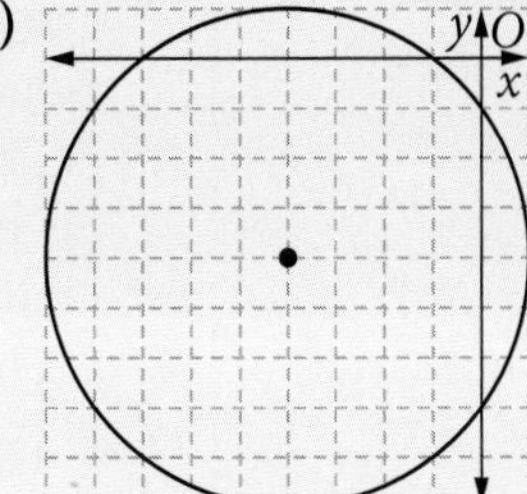

(ix)

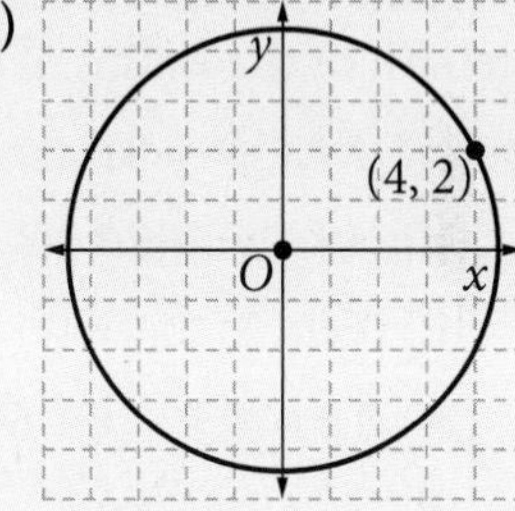

5. Find the equation of the circle with:
   - (i) centre $(0, 0)$, containing the point $(0, -7)$
   - (ii) centre $(-2, 4)$, containing the point $(1, 1)$
   - (iii) centre $(3, 1)$, containing the point $(-1, 4)$
   - (iv) centre $(0, 0)$, containing the point $(-3, 5)$
   - (v) centre $(5, -1)$, containing the point $(1, 3)$
   - (vi) centre $(0, 0)$, containing the point $(2, 1)$
   - (vii) centre $(0, 0)$, containing the point $(-6, -4)$
   - (viii) centre $(-2, -1)$, containing the point $(2, -2)$.

6. $P(5, 7)$ and $Q(-5, -7)$ are two points on the coordinated plane. A circle has $[PQ]$ as its diameter.

Plot the given points and draw a sketch of the circle.

   - (i) Find the centre of the circle.
   - (ii) Find the length of the radius of the circle.
   - (iii) Hence, write down the equation of the circle.

7. The diagram shows four circles of equal radius. The circles are touching as shown.

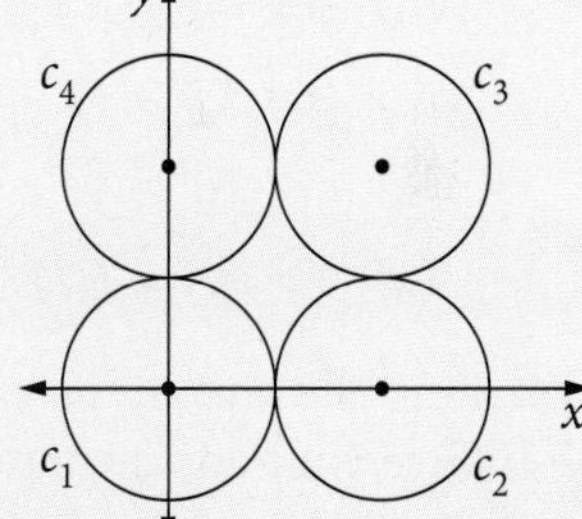

   - (i) The equation of c_1 is $x^2 + y^2 = 49$. Write down the radius of c_1.
   - (ii) Write down the coordinates of the centre of c_2.
   - (iii) Write down the coordinates of the centre of c_3.
   - (iv) Hence, find the equation of the circle c_3.
   - (v) The equation $x^2 + (y - 14)^2 = 49$ represents which circle?

8. The diagram shows two circles, k and s, which are touching internally.

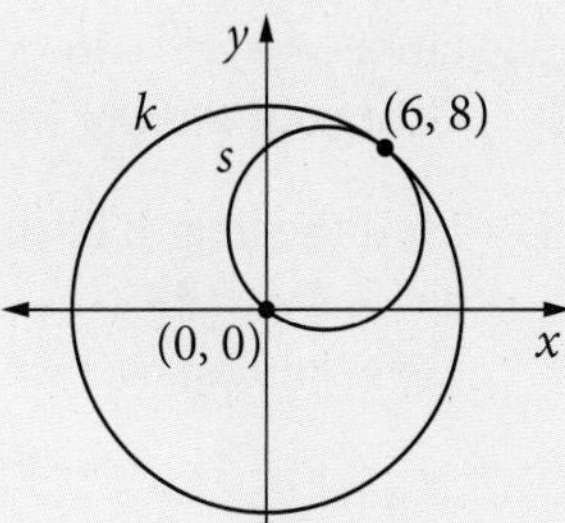

   - (i) Find the centre and radius of each of the circles.
   - (ii) Hence, find the equation of k and the equation of s.

9. $(-6, 2)$ is an extremity (a point at one end) of a diameter of the circle $x^2 + y^2 = 40$.
Find the coordinates of the other extremity of the same diameter.

10. $A(3, -1)$ and $B(-3, 3)$ are two points. Find the equation of the circle with $[AB]$ as diameter.

11. $P(-2, 4)$ and $Q(6, 2)$ are two points. Find the equation of the circle with $[PQ]$ as diameter.

12. (i) Write the equation of the circle with centre $(2, 3)$ and radius of length five units.
(ii) Draw this circle on a coordinated plane and hence find the coordinates of the endpoints of the horizontal diameter of this circle.
(iii) Find the equation of the image of this circle, under axial symmetry in the x-axis.

13. Write down the coordinates of the centre and the length of the radius of each of the following circles.
(i) $x^2 + y^2 = 81$
(ii) $x^2 + y^2 = 20$
(iii) $(x - 5)^2 + (y - 1)^2 = 16$
(iv) $(x + 4)^2 + (y + 6)^2 = 10$
(v) $x^2 + y^2 = 80$
(vi) $(x - 3)^2 + (y + 2)^2 = 49$
(vii) $16x^2 + 16y^2 = 121$
(viii) $(x + 1)^2 + (y - 4)^2 = 12$
(ix) $(x - 6)^2 + y^2 = 18$
(x) $4x^2 + 4(y + 7)^2 = 25$

14. Find the area of the circle $x^2 + y^2 = 24$.
Give your answer in terms of π.

Area of a circle = πr^2

15. Find the area of the circle $2x^2 + 2y^2 = 11$.
Give your answer in terms of π.

16. Find the length of the circumference of the circle $x^2 + y^2 = 36$.
Give your answer in terms of π.

Circumference of a circle = $2\pi r$

17. Find the length of the circumference of the circle $4x^2 + 4y^2 = 49$.
Give your answer in terms of π.

18. The diagram shows two concentric circles, s and t. The centre of each circle is $(0, 0)$ and the distance between the circles is four units.

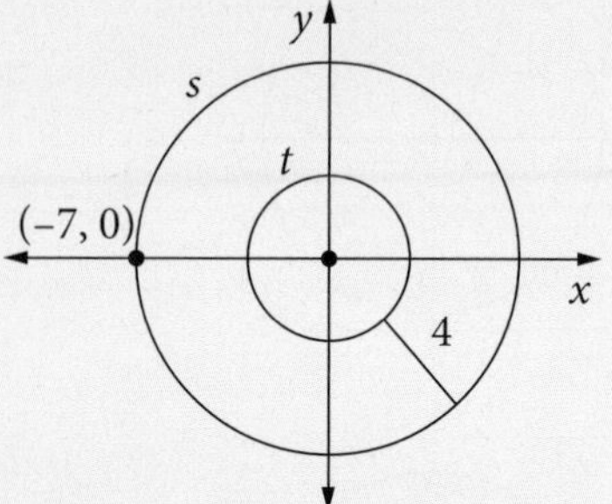

Find the equation of each of the circles.

Concentric circles are circles which have the same point as their centre.

19. The point P has coordinates $(-10, 8)$ and O is the origin. The diagram shows two circles, c_1 and c_2.
c_1 has centre $(0, 0)$ and radius $|OP|$.
c_2 has a diameter of $[OP]$.

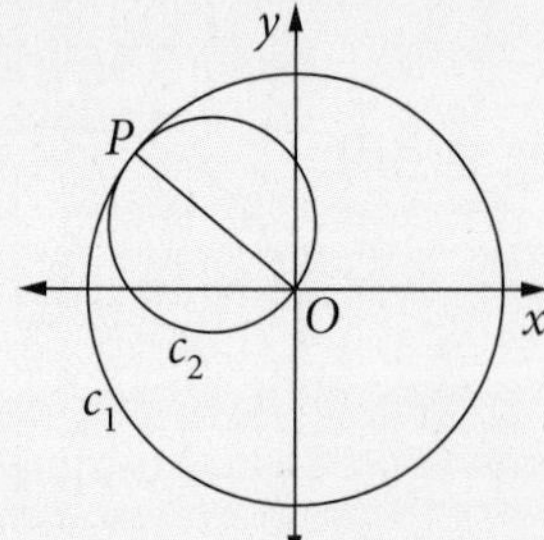

(i) Find the equation of c_1.
(ii) Find the equation of c_2.
(iii) Find the equation of a third circle, c_3, the image of c_2 under central symmetry in the origin.

20. $(-2, 2)$ is an extremity of a diameter of the circle $(x - 2)^2 + (y - 3)^2 = 17$.
Find the coordinates of the other extremity of the same diameter.

21. (i) A circle c_1 has centre $(2, 1)$ and diameter 12. Show c_1 on a coordinated plane.
(ii) Find the equation of c_1.
(iii) Another circle c_2 has centre $(-7, 1)$ and just touches c_1.
Show c_2 on your diagram drawn in part **(i)** and find the equation of c_2.

22. $P(-5, 1)$, $Q(3, 7)$ and $R(9, -1)$ are three points.
(i) Show that the triangle PQR is right-angled.
(ii) Hence, find the centre of the circle that passes through P, Q and R and write down the equation of the circle.

 **Links across the syllabus**

The theorem stating that a triangle in a semi-circle is right-angled is covered in Chapter 11: Geometry II.

23. The point $C(2, -5)$ is the centre of the circle k, as shown.

The point $S(8, 0)$ is on the circle.

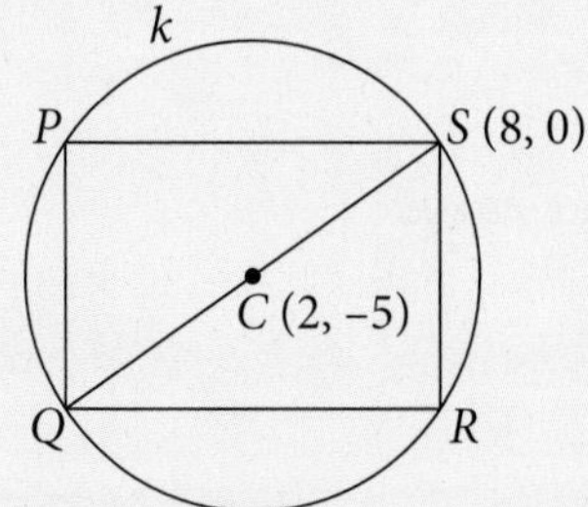

(i) Find the radius of k.

(ii) Write down the equation of k.

The vertices of the rectangle $PQRS$ are on the circle and PS is horizontal.

(iii) Find the coordinates of the points P, Q and R.

24. (i) The point A has coordinates $(0, 2)$.

The line l passes through A and has slope $\frac{1}{3}$.

Find the equation of l.

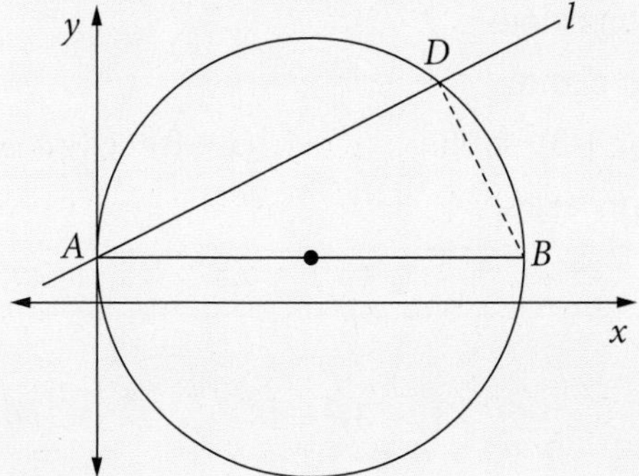

(ii) $[AB]$ is a diameter of a circle, where B is the point $(10, 2)$.

Find the centre and radius of the circle and hence write down its equation.

(iii) The line l crosses the circle at the points A and D.

Write down the slope of DB and explain how you know that this is the slope.

25. A graphic designer is tasked with creating a logo for a renewable energy company. She creates the image shown, using concentric circles, evenly spaced apart.

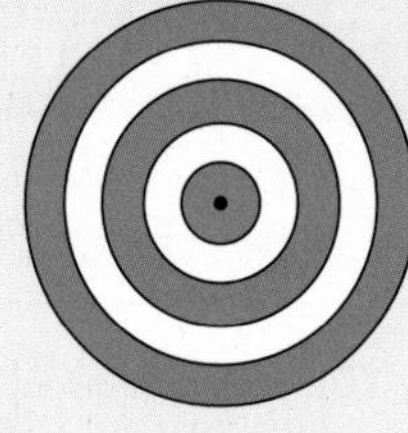

The entire logo is 20 mm in width.

(i) How many circular lines will need to be drawn to create this logo?

(ii) Taking the centre of each of the circles to be $(0, 0)$, find the equation of each of the circles drawn.

26. The circle s, with equation $x^2 + y^2 = 144$, has four smaller circles, of equal radius, inside it, as shown in the diagram.

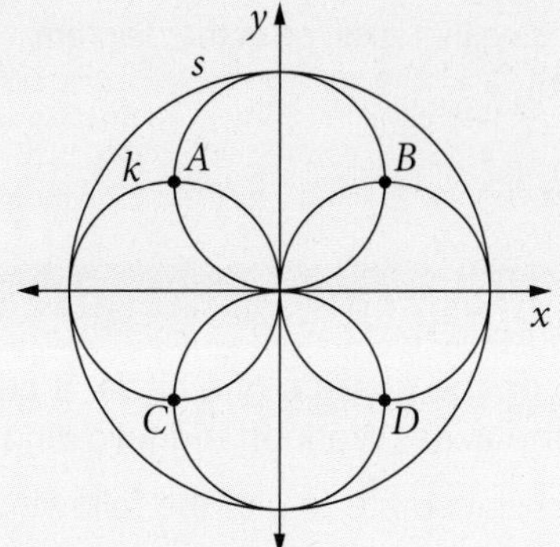

(i) Find the radius of the circle s.

(ii) Find the centre and radius of the circle k and hence find the equation of k.

(iii) The four circles intersect at the points A, B, C and D, as shown in the diagram. Write down the coordinates of the points A, B, C and D.

(iv) Find the area of the square $ABDC$.

(v) A circle c can be drawn, such that $[CB]$ is its diameter. Find the equation of the circle c.

The points A, B, C and D are in line with the centres of the circles.

Section 15.2: A Circle Intersecting the Axes

Learning Outcome:

You should be able to:

- find the coordinates of the points where a circle intersects the x and y axes

To find the points where a circle intersects the axes, we use the same method for finding the x and y-intercepts, as covered in the chapter on Coordinate Geometry of the Line.

From the diagram we can see: At the x-axis, $y = 0$

At the y-axis, $x = 0$

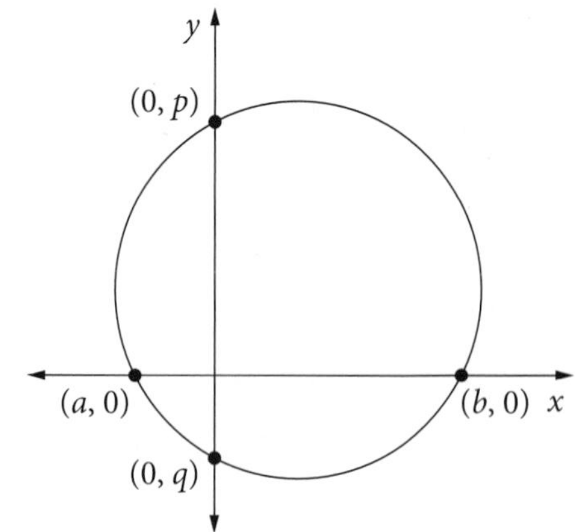

Depending on its position, it may be the case that a circle only crosses one of the axes, or doesn't cross either axis, as in the diagram shown here.

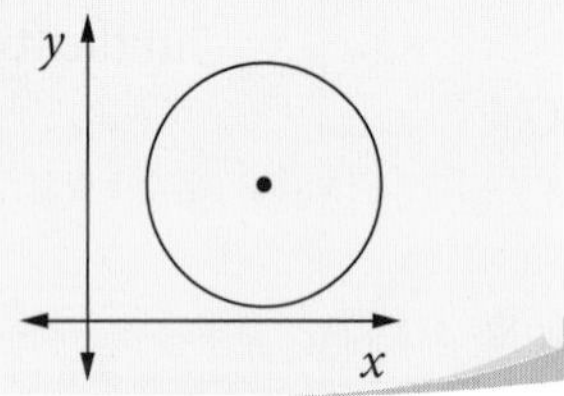

Discussion Time 

Depending on the position of a circle, it can sometimes be quite straightforward to find the points where a circle intersects the axes. Work on the following tasks to further explore this idea.

Work with a classmate to plot the following circles on a coordinated plane.

1. $(x - 4)^2 + y^2 = 25$
2. $x^2 + y^2 = 49$
3. $x^2 + (y + 3)^2 = 36$
4. $(x - 8)^2 + (y + 5)^2 = 9$

Hence find the points where each of the circles intersects the x and y axes.

EXAMPLE 1

Find the length of the chord which the x-axis makes through the circle $(x - 5)^2 + (y - 3)^2 = 18$.

Solution

At the x-axis, $y = 0$:

$$(x - 5)^2 + (y - 3)^2 = 18$$
$$(x - 5)^2 + (0 - 3)^2 = 18$$
$$(x - 5)(x - 5) + (-3)^2 = 18$$
$$x^2 - 10x + 25 + 9 - 18 = 0$$
$$x^2 - 10x + 16 = 0$$
$$(x - 2)(x - 8) = 0$$
$$x - 2 = 0 \quad \text{and} \quad x - 8 = 0$$
$$x = 2 \quad \text{and} \quad x = 8$$

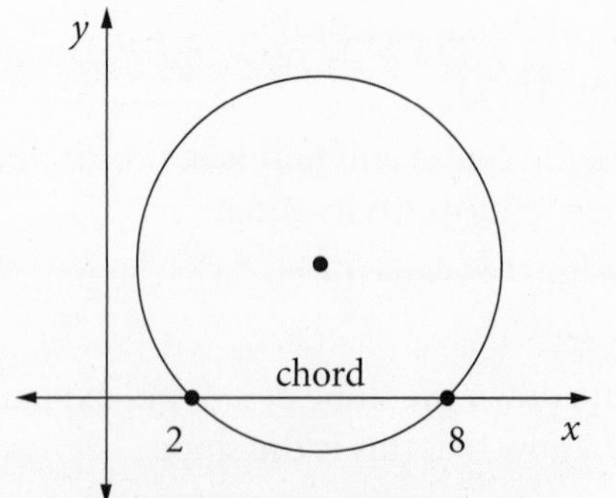

Therefore, the chord goes from 2 to 8 and so it is six units in length.

Links across the syllabus

Solving a quadratic equation is a basic skill and is covered in Chapter 4: Algebra III.

Practice Questions 15.2

1. Sketch the following circles. Hence, or otherwise, find the coordinates of the points where each of the circles intersect the x-axis.
   (i) $x^2 + y^2 = 25$
   (ii) $(x - 3)^2 + (y - 4)^2 = 41$
   (iii) $(x + 5)^2 + (y - 3)^2 = 45$

2. Sketch the following circles. Hence, or otherwise, find the coordinates of the points where each of the circles intersect the y-axis.
   (i) $x^2 + y^2 = 49$
   (ii) $(x + 2)^2 + (y + 4)^2 = 13$
   (iii) $(x - 2)^2 + (y + 2)^2 = 53$

3. Find the length of the chord which the y-axis makes through the circle $(x - 1)^2 + (y - 1)^2 = 26$.

4. Find the length of the chord which the x-axis makes through the circle $(x + 3)^2 + (y - 2)^2 = 40$.

5. The diagram shows the circle c, drawn on a coordinated plane.
   Both the x-axis and the y-axis are tangents to c.

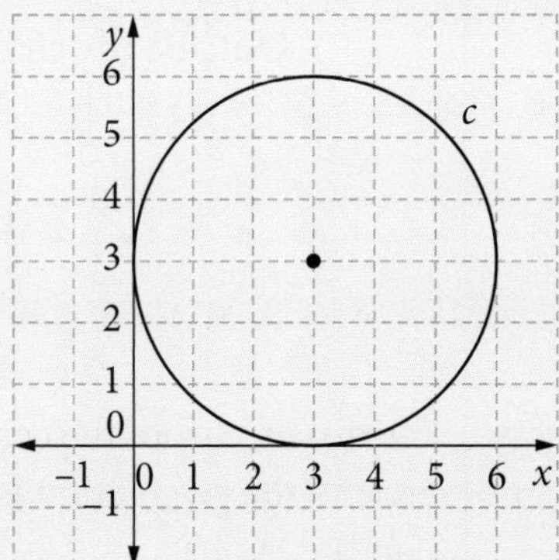

   Using the diagram, write down:
   (i) the centre of the circle c
   (ii) the length of the radius of the circle c.
   (iii) Hence, the equation of the circle c.
   (iv) Find the equation of the image of circle c, under axial symmetry in the y-axis.

6. The point $(-5, 3)$ is the centre of a circle s. The y-axis is a tangent to s.
   (i) Sketch the circle on a coordinated plane.
   (ii) Find the length of the radius of s.
   (iii) Find the equation of s.

7. The diagram shows a circle, drawn on a coordinated plane.

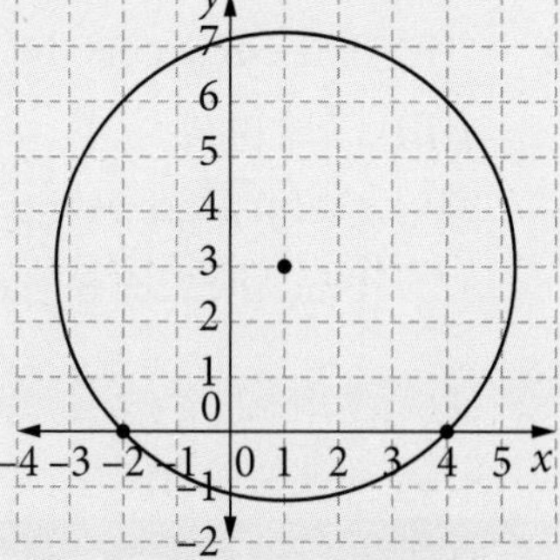

   (i) Use the diagram to write down the centre of the circle.

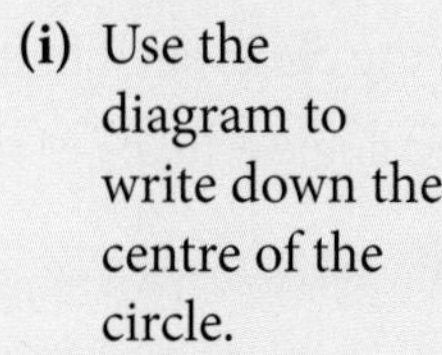

   (ii) Use the diagram to write down the points where the circle intersects the x-axis.
   (iii) Write down the length of the chord which the x-axis makes through the circle.
   (iv) Calculate the length of the radius of the circle. Give your answer in surd form.
   (v) Hence, find the equation of the circle.

8. s is the circle of centre $(3, 3)$. The circle s intercepts the y-axis at the points $(0, -1)$ and $(0, 7)$.
   (i) Using a compass, draw the circle s on a coordinated plane.
   (ii) Find the length of the radius of s.
   (iii) Hence, write down the equation of the circle s.

9. The diagram shows a circle of centre $(4, 3)$ and radius 5.
   Using the diagram, or otherwise, find the coordinates of the points A and B.

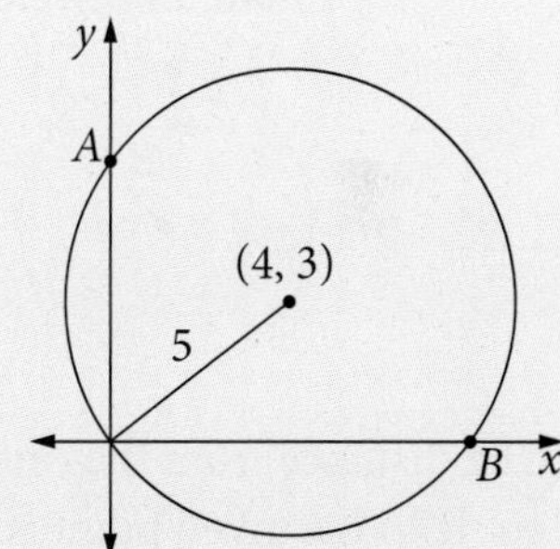

10. k is a circle such that its centre is on the x-axis.
   The circle k intercepts the x-axis at the points $(-11, 0)$ and $(3, 0)$.
   (i) Draw a sketch of the circle k.
   (ii) Find the centre of k.
   (iii) Find the length of the radius of k.
   (iv) Hence write down the equation of the circle k.
   (v) Find the equation of the image of circle k, under central symmetry in the origin.

11. The end points of a diameter of a circle are (2, −3) and (−8, 3).
   (i) Find the equation of the circle.
   (ii) The circle cuts the y-axis at the points A and B. Find the coordinates of A and B.
   (iii) Find $|AB|$.
   (iv) C and D are points on the circle such that $ABCD$ is a rectangle.
   Find the area of the rectangle $ABCD$.

Draw a sketch of the circle to better understand the problem.

Section 15.3: Position of Points in Relation to a Circle

Learning Outcome:

You should be able to:
- determine the position of a point relative to a circle

In relation to a circle, a point can either be inside the circle, on the circle or outside the circle.

Method 1:

To determine position of a point, we calculate the distance between the centre of the circle and the given point. Then compare this distance to the radius of the circle.

Inside the circle

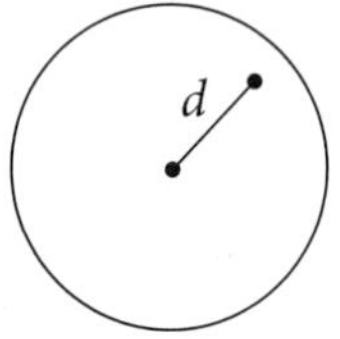

The distance from the centre of the circle to the given point is **less** than the radius.

$d <$ **radius**

On the circle

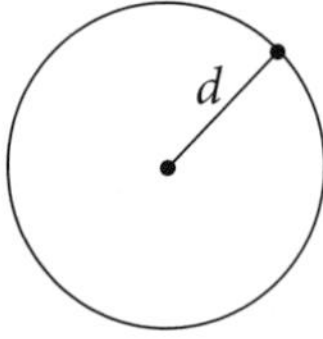

The distance from the centre of the circle to the given point is **equal** to the radius.

$d =$ **radius**

Outside the circle

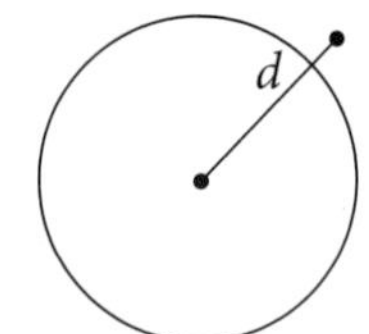

The distance from the centre of the circle to the given point is **greater** than the radius.

$d >$ **radius**

Method 2:

In coordinate geometry of the line, to determine if a point is on a line, you substitute the coordinates of the point into the equation of the line. The same method is used here. We substitute the coordinates of the given point in for x and y into the equation of the circle. If:

LHS < RHS then the point is **inside** the circle

LHS = RHS then the point is **on** the circle

LHS > RHS then the point is **outside** the circle

LHS means 'left hand side', RHS means 'right hand side'.

EXAMPLE 1

Determine whether the following points are inside, on or outside of the circle $(x-4)^2+(y+3)^2=25$.

(i) $(4, 2)$ **(ii)** $(-3, 2)$ **(iii)** $(1, -5)$

Solution

(i) Using method 1: $(x-4)^2+(y+3)^2=25$ has centre $(4, -3)$ and radius $= \sqrt{25} = 5$

Find the distance between the centre $(4, -3)$ (x_1, y_1) and the point $(4, 2)$ (x_2, y_2)

$$\text{Distance} = \sqrt{(x_2-x_1)^2+(y_2-y_1)^2}$$
$$= \sqrt{(4-4)^2+(2-(-3))^2}$$
$$= \sqrt{(0)^2+(5)^2}$$
$$= \sqrt{0+25}$$
$$\text{Distance} = \sqrt{25} = 5 = \text{Radius}$$

Therefore, the point $(4, 2)$ is on the circle $(x-4)^2+(y+3)^2=25$

(ii) Using method 2: Substitute $(-3, 2)$ into the circle $(x-4)^2+(y+3)^2=25$

LHS: $(x-4)^2+(y+3)^2$

$(-3-4)^2+(2+3)^2$

$(-7)^2+(5)^2$

$49+25$

74

Since $74 > 25$, the point $(-3, 2)$ is outside of the circle $(x-4)^2+(y+3)^2=25$

(iii) Using method 2: Substitute $(1, -5)$ into the circle $(x-4)^2+(y+3)^2=25$

LHS: $(x-4)^2+(y+3)^2$

$(1-4)^2+(-5+3)^2$

$(-3)^2+(-2)^2$

$9+4$

13

Since $13 < 25$, the point $(1, -5)$ is inside the circle $(x-4)^2+(y+3)^2=25$

Practice Questions 15.3

1. **(i)** Sketch the circle $x^2+y^2=13$, on a coordinated plane.
   (ii) Investigate whether the point $(2, 4)$ is inside, on or outside of the circle $x^2+y^2=13$.
2. **(i)** Verify that the point $(1, -3)$ is on the circle $x^2+y^2=10$.
   (ii) Write down the coordinates of two other points on this circle.
3. Determine whether each of the following points are inside, on or outside of the circle $x^2+y^2=29$.
   (i) $(5, 2)$ **(ii)** $(2, 6)$ **(iii)** $(-2, -5)$ **(iv)** $(4, -3)$ **(v)** $(-3, 2)$ **(vi)** $(4, -4)$
4. Verify that the point $(-1, 3)$ is on the circle $(x+3)^2+y^2=13$.
5. Determine whether each of the following points are inside, on or outside of the circle $(x+2)^2+(y-1)^2=32$.
   (i) $(2, 3)$ **(ii)** $(-6, 5)$ **(iii)** $(4, -2)$ **(iv)** $(2, -4)$ **(v)** $(2, 5)$ **(vi)** $(-4, 5)$

6. Which of the following points are outside of the circle $(x - 2)^2 + (y + 2)^2 = 68$?
   (i) $(-6, 0)$ **(ii)** $(7, 5)$ **(iii)** $(6, -5)$

7. s is the circle $x^2 + y^2 = 16$.
   (i) Write down the centre and radius of the circle s.
   (ii) Use a compass to draw the circle s on a coordinated plane.
   (iii) Write down the coordinates of two points on the circle s.
   (iv) Using your diagram, or otherwise, determine whether the point $(2, -2)$ is inside, on or outside of the circle s.

8. k is the circle $(x - 2)^2 + (y - 1)^2 = 36$.
   (i) Write down the centre and radius of the circle k.
   (ii) Use a compass to draw the circle k on a coordinated plane.
   (iii) Write down the coordinates of two points on the circle k.
   (iv) Using your diagram, or otherwise, determine whether the point $(-3, 6)$ is inside, on or outside of the circle k.

9. The point $(6, k)$ is a point on the circle $x^2 + y^2 = 40$. Find two possible values for k.

10. The point $(p, -1)$ is a point on the circle $(x + 3)^2 + (y - 2)^2 = 25$. Find two possible values for p.

11. The point $(2, b)$ is a point inside the circle $(x - 1)^2 + (y - 3)^2 = 20$.
    Find the largest possible value for b, given $b \in \mathbb{N}$.

Section 15.4: Intersection of a Line and a Circle

Learning Outcome:

You should be able to:
- find the points of intersection between a line and a circle, of centre (0, 0)

When a line and a circle are graphed on the same coordinated plane, one of three situations will occur:

The line passes through the circle, in which case there are two points of intersection.

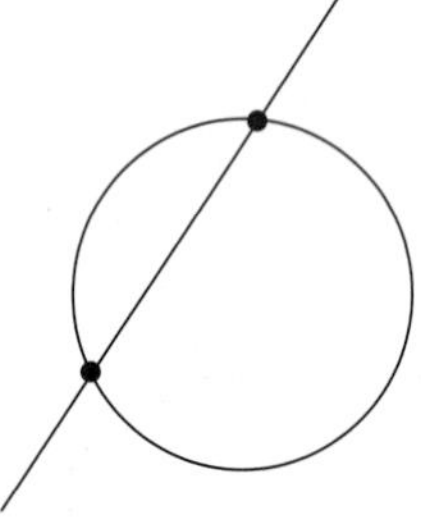

The line touches the edge of the circle, in which case there is one point of intersection.

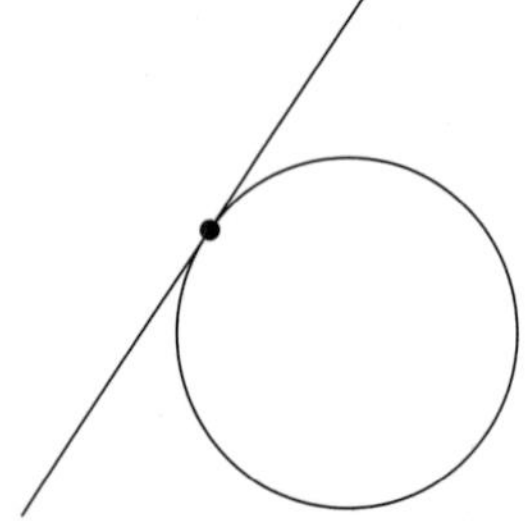

The line does not intersect the circle at all, in which case there are no points of intersection.

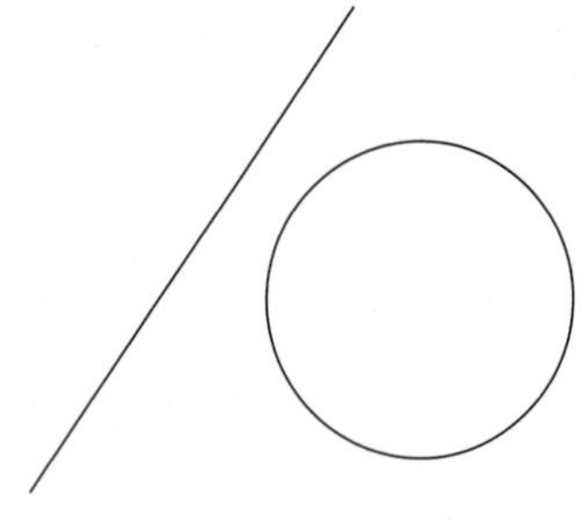

To find the points where a line and a circle intersect (meet each other), we must solve the equations simultaneously. To solve a linear and a quadratic equation, we use the method of substitution.

Follow these steps to solve the equations:

Step 1: Rearrange the equation of the line to get the x or the y on its own. Take care to select the variable which will make the work easier and avoid fractions, if possible.

Step 2: Substitute for this variable into the equation of the circle and solve the resulting quadratic equation.

Step 3: Substitute separately the value or values obtained in Step 2 into the linear equation in Step 1 to find the corresponding value(s) of the other variable.

Links across the syllabus

Solving simultaneous equations involving a linear and a quadratic equation is covered in Chapter 4: Algebra III.

If there is only one point of intersection between a line and a circle, then the line is a **tangent** to the circle.

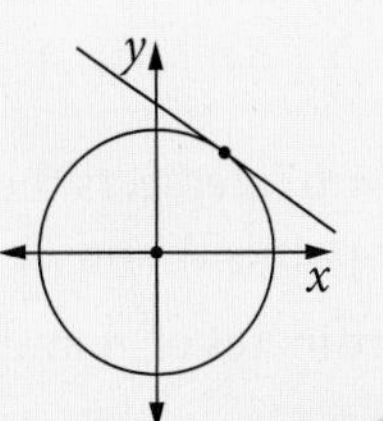

EXAMPLE 1

The diagram shows the circle $x^2 + y^2 = 40$ and the line $x + y - 4 = 0$.
Find the coordinates of the two points where the line and the circle intersect.

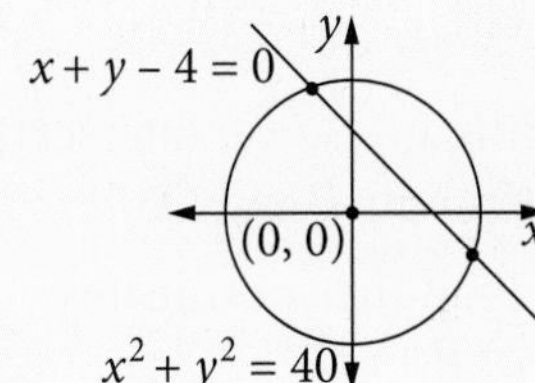

Solution

Step 1:

Equation for the line: $x + y - 4 = 0$

Rearrange to get x on its own: $x = -y + 4$

Step 2:

Substitute $x = -y + 4$ into the equation of the circle:

$$x^2 + y^2 = 40$$
$$(-y + 4)^2 + y^2 = 40$$
$$y^2 - 8y + 16 + y^2 = 40$$
$$2y^2 - 8y + 16 - 40 = 0$$
$$2y^2 - 8y - 24 = 0 \quad \text{(divide both sides by 2)}$$
$$y^2 - 4y - 12 = 0$$
$$(y - 6)(y + 2) = 0$$
$$y - 6 = 0 \quad \text{and} \quad y + 2 = 0$$
$$y = 6 \quad \text{and} \quad y = -2$$

Step 3:

Find corresponding x-coordinates:

$y = 6$	$y = -2$
$x = -y + 4$	$x = -y + 4$
$x = -6 + 4$	$x = -(-2) + 4$
$x = -2$	$x = 2 + 4$
$(-2, 6)$	$x = 6$
	$(6, -2)$

Therefore, the points of intersection are $(-2, 6)$ and $(6, -2)$.

Practice Questions 15.4

1. The diagram shows the line $x + y + 1 = 0$ and the circle $x^2 + y^2 = 13$.
   (i) Use the diagram to determine the coordinates of the points of intersection between the line and the circle.
   (ii) Using algebra, confirm your answer for part **(i)**.

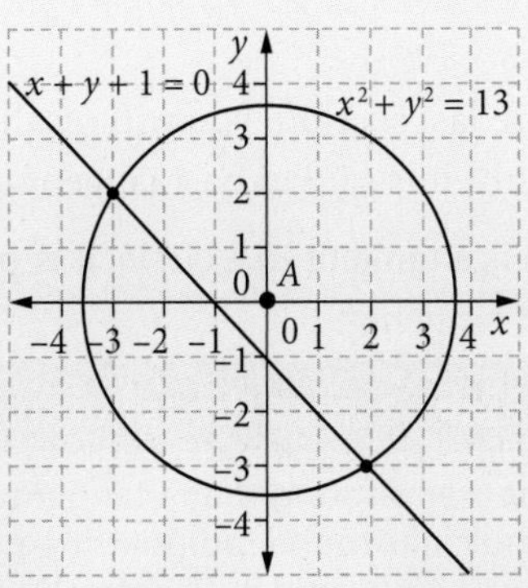

2. Find the coordinates of the point, or points, of intersection of the given line and circle. State, in each case, whether or not the line is a tangent to the circle.
   (i) Line: $x - y = 0$ Circle: $x^2 + y^2 = 18$
   (ii) Line: $x + y - 2 = 0$ Circle: $x^2 + y^2 = 20$
   (iii) Line: $x - y + 2 = 0$ Circle: $x^2 + y^2 = 10$
   (iv) Line: $2x + y + 5 = 0$ Circle: $x^2 + y^2 = 5$
   (v) Line: $x - 5y + 13 = 0$ Circle: $x^2 + y^2 = 13$

3. The line $x - y + 1 = 0$ intersects the circle $x^2 + y^2 = 13$ at the points A and B.
   (i) Find the coordinates of A and B.
   (ii) Find $|AB|$, giving your answer in surd form.
   (iii) Investigate whether $[AB]$ is a diameter of the circle.

4. The line $x - 3y = 0$ intersects the circle $x^2 + y^2 = 10$ at the points P and Q.
   (i) Find the coordinates of P and Q.
   (ii) Find the midpoint of $[PQ]$.
   (iii) Find $|PQ|$, giving your answer in surd form.
   (iv) Investigate whether $[PQ]$ is a diameter of the circle.

Diameter = 2(radius)
Midpoint of diameter = centre of the circle

5. The line $x - y - 1 = 0$ intersects the circle $x^2 + y^2 = 5$ at the points A and B.
   (i) Find the coordinates of A and B.
   (ii) Find the midpoint of $[AB]$.
   (iii) Find $|AB|$, giving your answer in surd form.
   (iv) Investigate whether $[AB]$ is a diameter of the circle.

6. Find the coordinates of the points at which the line $x - y - 2 = 0$ intersects a circle with centre $(0, 0)$ and radius of length $\sqrt{20}$.

7. Investigate whether the line $x + y - 4 = 0$ is a tangent to a circle with centre $(0, 0)$ and radius of length 4.

8. A graphic designer is designing a logo. He wants to construct a square inside of a circle, as shown in the diagram. He graphs the circle $x^2 + y^2 = 10$. The lines $2x - y + 5 = 0$ and $2x - y - 5 = 0$ form two sides of the square.

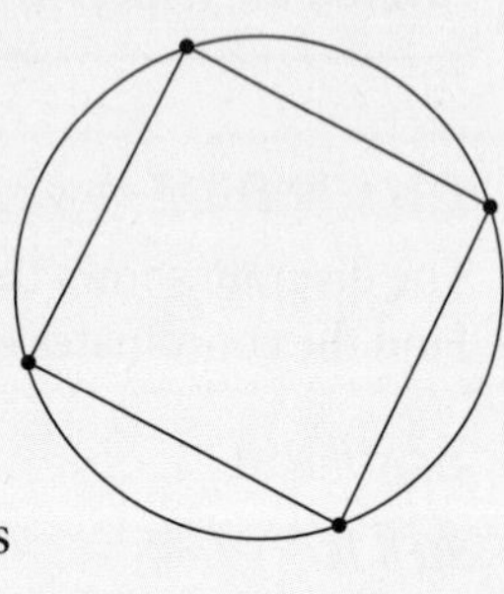

   (i) Find the points where the two lines intersect the circle.
   (ii) Draw a sketch of the circle on a coordinated plane, plot the points of intersection and hence construct the square.
   (iii) Find the area of the square.

Section 15.5: Equation of a Tangent to a Circle

Learning Outcome:

You should be able to:
- find the equation of a tangent to a circle at a given point

From the last section, you will recall that when a line touches a circle at one point only, it is said to be a tangent to the circle.

If a line is a tangent to a circle, it is perpendicular to the radius drawn to the point of tangency.

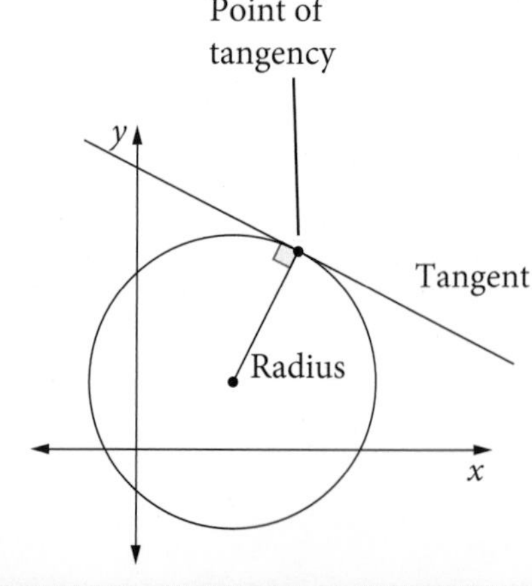

Links across the syllabus

The theorem stating that a tangent is perpendicular to the radius at the point of tangency, is covered in Chapter 11: Geometry II.

EXAMPLE 1

The circle $(x - 3)^2 + (y - 4)^2 = 34$ has a tangent at the point $(-2, 7)$. Find the equation of this tangent.

Solution

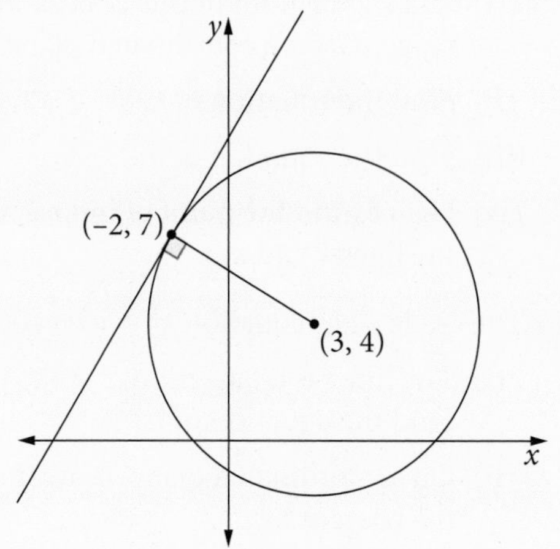

Circle $(x - 3)^2 + (y - 4)^2 = 34$ has centre $(3, 4)$

Find the slope of the radius from the centre to the point of tangency:

$(3, 4)$ to $(-2, 7)$

(x_1, y_1) (x_2, y_2)

Slope of radius $= \dfrac{y_2 - y_1}{x_2 - x_1}$

Slope of radius $= \dfrac{7 - 4}{-2 - 3} = \dfrac{3}{-5} = -\dfrac{3}{5}$

Since radius $\perp$ tangent

$\therefore$ Slope of tangent $= \dfrac{5}{3}$

Find equation of the tangent: Point $(-2, 7) = (x_1, y_1)$ and slope $= \dfrac{5}{3}$

$$y - y_1 = m(x - x_1)$$
$$y - 7 = \frac{5}{3}(x - (-2))$$
$$3(y - 7) = 5(x + 2)$$
$$3y - 21 = 5x + 10$$
$$0 = 5x - 3y + 10 + 21$$

Therefore, the equation of the tangent is $5x - 3y + 31 = 0$

Practice Questions 15.5

1. The circle $x^2 + y^2 = 8$ has a tangent at the point $(-2, 2)$, as shown in the diagram. Find the equation of this tangent.

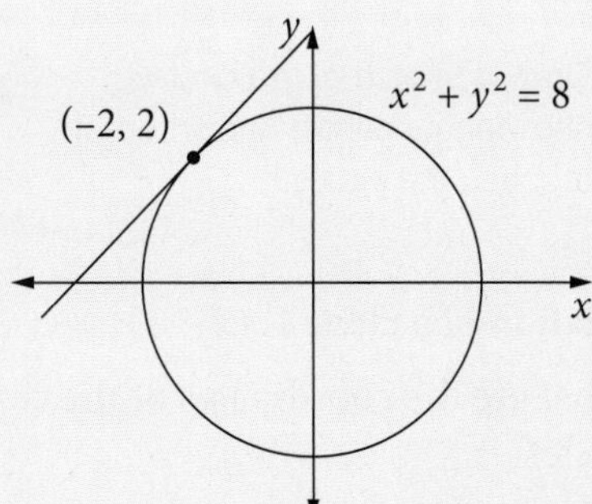

2. The circle $x^2 + y^2 = 20$ has a tangent at the point $(2, -4)$.
   (i) Draw a sketch of the circle and tangent.
   (ii) Find the equation of this tangent.
   (iii) Find the coordinates of the points where this tangent intersects the x and y axes.

3. The circle $x^2 + y^2 = 13$ has a tangent at the point $(2, 3)$. Find the equation of this tangent.

4. The circle $(x - 5)^2 + (y - 2)^2 = 45$ has a tangent at the point $(-1, -1)$. Find the equation of this tangent.

5. The circle $(x + 1)^2 + (y - 2)^2 = 50$ has a tangent at the point $(4, -3)$. Find the equation of this tangent.

6. The circle $x^2 + y^2 = 25$ has a tangent s, at the point $(-4, -3)$ and another tangent n, at the point $(-3, 4)$, as shown in the diagram.

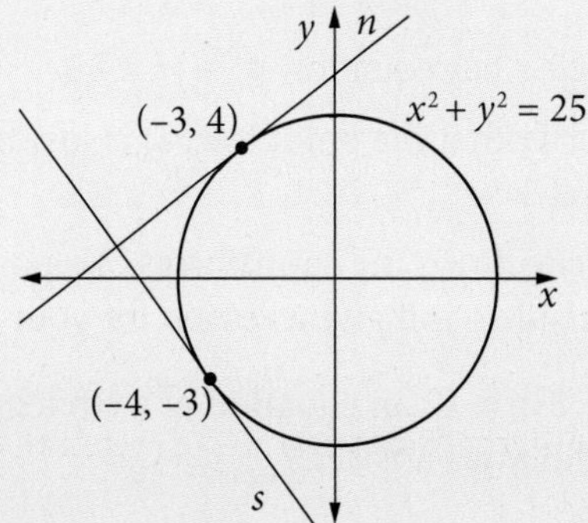

   (i) Find the equation of s.
   (ii) Find the equation of n.
   (iii) Hence, find the point of intersection between the lines s and n.

7. The circle $(x - 2)^2 + (y - 4)^2 = 52$ has a tangent k, at the point $(-2, -2)$ and another tangent m, at the point $(-2, 10)$.
   (i) Draw a diagram of this circle and the two tangents, on a coordinated plane.
   (ii) Find the equation of k.
   (iii) Find the equation of m.
   (iv) Hence, find the point of intersection between the lines k and m.

8. The circle c has equation $x^2 + y^2 = 100$.
   (i) The line t is a tangent to c at the point $(-6, 8)$. Find the equation of t.
   (ii) On a coordinated plane, draw the circle c and the tangent t.
   (iii) The line k is a tangent to c and k is parallel to the x-axis. Find the two possible equations of k.

9. The circle c has equation $(x + 4)^2 + (y - 3)^2 = 29$.
   (i) Show that the point $A(-6, 8)$ lies on the circle c.
   (ii) Find the equation of k, the tangent to c at the point A.
   (iii) A second line, t, is a tangent to c at the point B such that $k \parallel t$. Find the coordinates of the point B.
   (iv) Hence, or otherwise, find the equation of the line t.

Draw a sketch of the circle c, the point A and the tangent k.

10. The line $2x + 3y - 13 = 0$ is a tangent to a circle, with centre $(-2, k)$ at the point $(2, 3)$.
   (i) Find the slope of the tangent.
   (ii) Find the slope of the radius from the centre of the circle to the point of tangency.
   (iii) Hence, find the value of k.
   (iv) Hence, find the equation of the circle.

Revision and Exam Style Questions – Section A

1. (i) Find the equation of the circle which has centre $(0, 0)$ and passes through the point $(2, 6)$.
   (ii) Verify that the point $(4, 3)$ lies inside of the circle.

2. (i) Find the centre of the circle $(x + 4)^2 + (y - 4)^2 = 41$.
   (ii) Find the coordinates of the points where the circle crosses the y-axis.
   (iii) Hence, draw the circle on a coordinated plane. Show your scale on both axes.

3. The circle s has equation $x^2 + y^2 = 36$.
   (i) Verify that the point $(-2, 4)$ is inside the circle.
   (ii) Write down the coordinates of a point that lies outside s and give a reason for your answer.

4. Is $3x^2 + 3y^2 = 12$ an equation of a circle? Give a reason for your answer.

5. (i) Find the centre and radius of the circle c $x^2 + y^2 = 100$.
   (ii) Hence, draw the circle c on a coordinated plane. Show your scale on both axes.
   (iii) Verify, using algebra, that $(-8, 6)$ is on c.

6. A circle has centre $(4, 7)$ and it touches the y-axis.
   (i) Find the length of the radius of the circle.
   (ii) Hence, find the equation of the circle.
   (iii) Find the equation of the image of this circle under axial symmetry in the x-axis.

Draw a sketch of the circle, showing its centre and where it touches the y-axis.

7. The equation of a circle is $(x - 1)^2 + (y - 5)^2 = 36$.
   (i) What are the coordinates of the centre of the circle?
   (ii) What is the length of the radius of the circle?
   (iii) Write down the coordinates of any two points on the circle.

8. Is $x^2 + 2y^2 = 8$ an equation of a circle? Give a reason for your answer.

9. (i) The circle k has equation $(x + 4)^2 + (y + 3)^2 = 49$. Write down the centre and radius of k.
   (ii) James claims that the point $(1, 1)$ is inside k. Is he correct? Verify your answer.
   (iii) Write down the equation of the circle c, the image of k under axial symmetry in the y-axis.

10. Write down the coordinates of any three points that lie on the circle with equation $x^2 + y^2 = 64$.

11. **(i)** Plot the points $A(-3, 2)$, $B(-1, 6)$ and $C(7, 2)$ on a coordinated plane and hence construct the triangle ABC.

(ii) Find D, the midpoint of $[AC]$, and label this point on the diagram.

(iii) Hence, construct on the diagram the circle with diameter $[AC]$.

(iv) Show that angle $\angle ABC$ is a right-angle.

12. **(i)** Write the equation of the circle with centre $(-4, 2)$ and radius of length 7 units.

(ii) What are the coordinates of the endpoints of the vertical diameter of this circle?

(iii) Find the image of this circle under central symmetry in the origin.

Revision and Exam Style Questions – Section B

More challenging problems

1. Prove that the line $x - 3y + 10 = 0$ is a tangent to the circle with equation $x^2 + y^2 = 10$ and find the coordinates of the point of contact.

2. **(i)** Show that the points $A(-1, 7)$ and $B(5, 7)$ lie on a circle whose radius is 5 and centre is $(2, 3)$.

(ii) What is the distance from the centre of the circle to the chord $[AB]$?

3. s is the circle $(x - 5)^2 + (y + 4)^2 = 32$. s intersects the x-axis at the points A and B.

(i) Find the coordinates of the points A and B.

(ii) Show that $|AB|$ is less than the diameter of s.

(iii) Find the equation of the circle with $[AB]$ as diameter.

4. **(i)** The circle, c, has centre $(-1, 2)$ and radius 5. Write down the equation of c.

(ii) The circle k has equation $(x - 11)^2 + (y - 11)^2 = 100$. Prove that the point $A(3, 5)$ is on c and k.

(iii) Show that A lies on the line which joins the centres of the two circles.

(iv) Hence, or otherwise, draw circles c and k on a coordinated plane.

5. c is the circle with centre $(0, 0)$. It passes through the point $(-1, 5)$, as shown in the diagram.

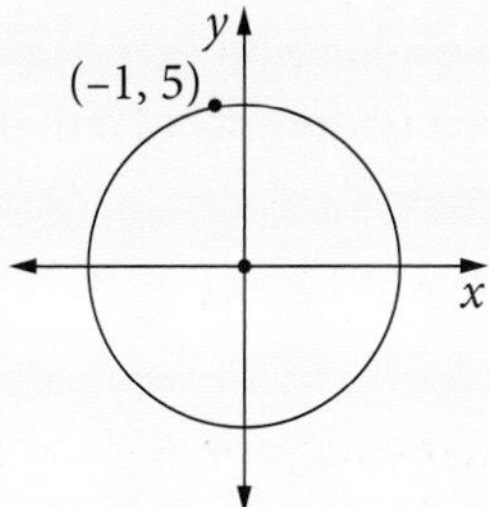

(i) Find the equation of c.

(ii) The point (k, k) lies inside c, where $k \in \mathbb{Z}$. Find all possible values of k.

6. The line $x - 4y = 0$ intersects the circle $x^2 + y^2 = 17$ at the points P and Q.

(i) Find the coordinates of P and Q.

(ii) Show that $[PQ]$ is a diameter of the circle.

7. Joshua claims that if the x-coordinate of the centre of a circle is equal to the length of the radius of the circle, then the y-axis is a tangent to the circle.

(i) Investigate Joshua's claim by sketching the circle with centre $(3, 2)$ and radius of length 3.

(ii) Is Joshua's claim correct? Justify your answer.

8. The diagram shows two circles c and s, of equal radius.

The circles touch at the point $P(5, 2)$.
The circle c has centre $(0, 0)$.

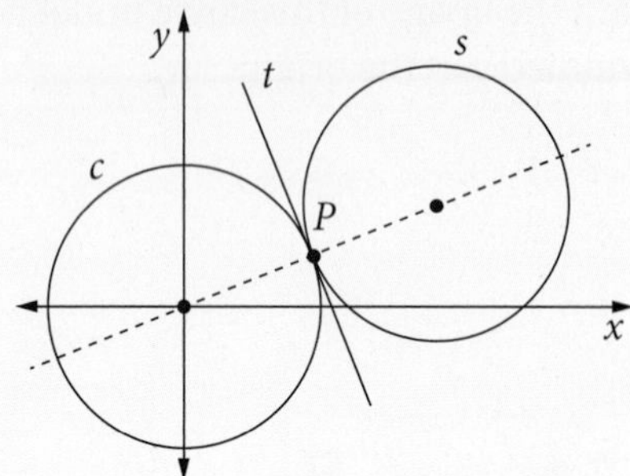

(i) Find the equation of c.

(ii) Find the equation of s.

(iii) The line t is a tangent to the circles at the point P. Find the equation of t.

9. The circle k has equation $(x - 2)^2 + (y - 4)^2 = 36$. P and Q are the endpoints of a diameter of k and PQ is horizontal.

(i) Find the coordinates of P and Q.

(ii) Hence, or otherwise, write down the equations of the two vertical tangents to k.

(iii) Another circle also has these two vertical lines as tangents.
The centre of this circle is on the x-axis.
Find the equation of this circle.

Drawing a sketch of the situation will help when solving these types of questions.

10. The circle k has equation $(x - 5)^2 + (y + 1)^2 = 34$.

(i) Verify that the point $A(8, 4)$ lies on the circle k.

(ii) Find the equation of t, the tangent to k at the point A.

(iii) A second line, s, is a tangent to k at the point B such that $t \parallel s$.
Find the coordinates of the point B.

(iv) Hence, or otherwise, find the equation of the line s.

(v) Find the coordinates of the points where the line s crosses the x and y axes.

11. A circle k has equation $x^2 + y^2 = 20$. The points $P(2, -4)$, $Q(-2, 4)$ and $R(4, -2)$ are on the circle.

(i) Verify that $[PQ]$ is a diameter of the circle.

(ii) Draw the circle, showing the points P, Q and R on a coordinated plane.

(iii) Verify that $|\angle PRQ|$ is a right-angle.

(iv) Find the equation of the image of the circle k under the translation $(1, 3) \rightarrow (4, 7)$.

12. A stationary submarine is positioned at the point $(0, 0)$ on a coordinated plane. Using its radar, the submarine can detect an approaching ship. At noon, the ship is at the position $(12, 5)$ on the coordinated plane. Two hours later, the ship has moved closer to the submarine and is now found to be on the circle $x^2 + y^2 = 64$.

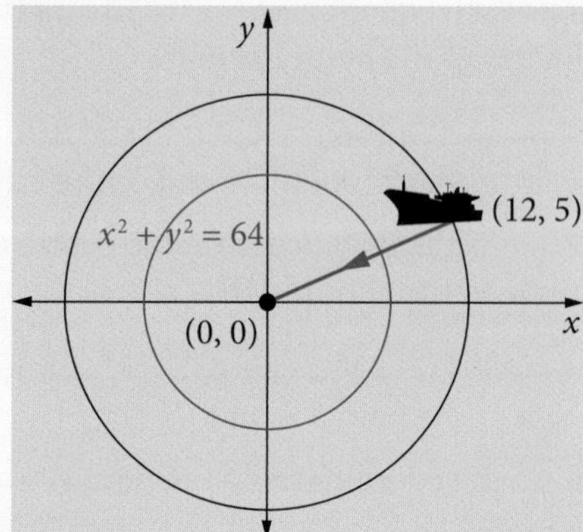

(i) Find the speed of the ship, in kilometres per hour.

(ii) Find the equation of the circle, which the ship will be on, at 3 pm, if the speed of the ship remains constant.

(iii) If the ship continues to move in a straight line at this speed, at what time, to the nearest minute, will the ship pass over the submarine?

(iv) If the ship doubled its speed from 2 pm onwards, at what time, to the nearest minute, will the ship pass over the submarine?

Now that you have completed the chapter, revisit the 'Something to think about…' question.

Area and Perimeter

CHAPTER 16

Sections covered within this chapter:

KEY WORDS

- Area
- Sector
- Perimeter
- Arc
- Quadrilateral
- Scaled diagram
- Trapezium

SOMETHING TO THINK ABOUT... 

A square tile of length 1 m has a pattern as shown in the diagram.

The arc of the sector ABC and the arc of the sector ADC intersect to form the pink section in the middle of the tile, as shown.

Find the area of the pink section, correct to the nearest square centimetre.

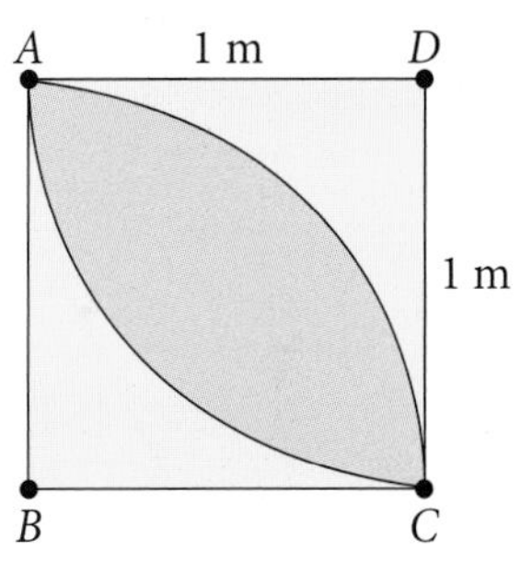

Introduction

This chapter will deal with finding the area and perimeter of a variety of shapes.

The **area** of a shape is the amount of space enclosed within its boundary.

The **perimeter** of a shape is the length of its boundary line.

It is very important that you know your units and always put them as part of your answer.

Length: mm, cm, m, km

Area: mm^2, cm^2, m^2, km^2

Throughout this chapter, taking the following steps will help when solving problems:

Step 1: Identify the shape and draw a sketch, if not given.

Step 2: Identify what values are given and what values are required.

Step 3: Select the relevant formula.

Step 4: Put the values into the formula.

Step 5: Solve the resulting equation.

Section 16.1: Quadrilaterals and Triangles

Learning Outcomes:

You should be able to:

- find the area and perimeter of quadrilateral shapes
- find the area and perimeter of triangles
- find the area and perimeter of compound shapes
- solve problems involving a variety of shapes

A **quadrilateral** is a four-sided shape.

Quadrilaterals and their properties were covered in Chapter 11: Geometry II.

Rectangle

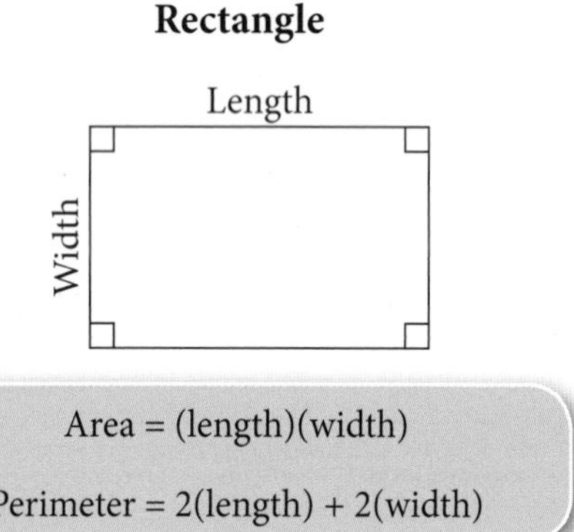

Area = (length)(width)

Perimeter = 2(length) + 2(width)

Square

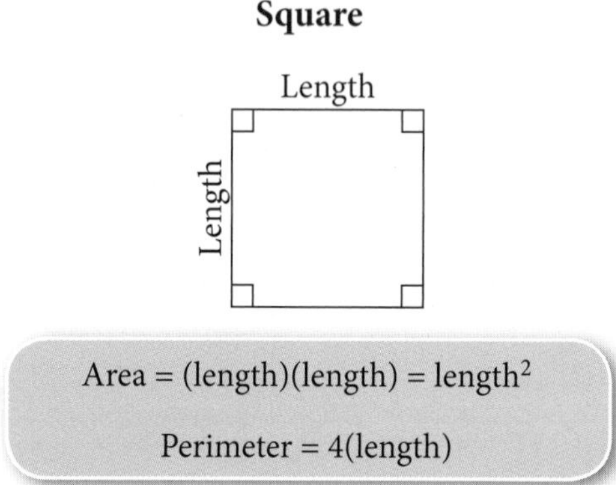

Area = (length)(length) = length^2

Perimeter = 4(length)

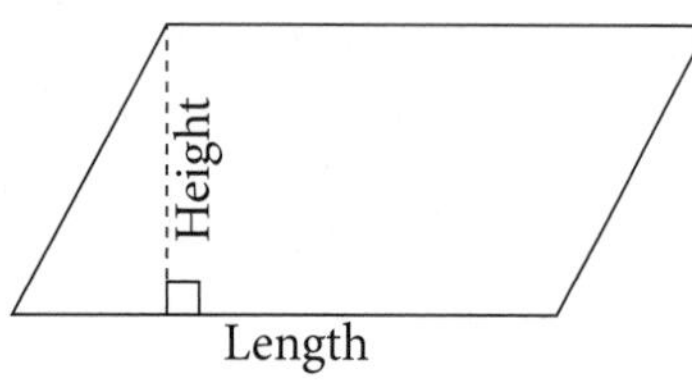

Area = (length)($\perp$height)

Perimeter = Sum of all the side lengths

The formula for the **area of a parallelogram** appears on page 8 of the booklet of *formulae and tables*, as shown:

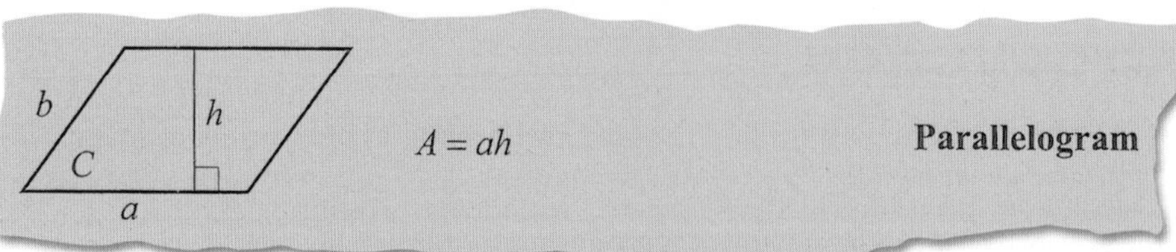

Trapezium

A **trapezium** is a shape in which only two sides are parallel.

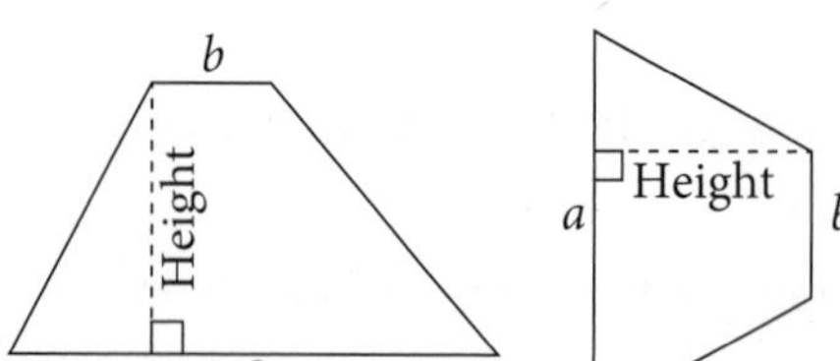

a Height b

Area = $\left(\frac{a+b}{2}\right)$($\perp$ height)

Perimeter = Sum of all the sides

It is worth noting that the formula for the area of a trapezium is found by averaging the lengths of the two parallel sides and multiplying this average by the perpendicular height.

The formula for the **area of a trapezium** appears on page 8 of the booklet of *formulae and tables*, as shown:

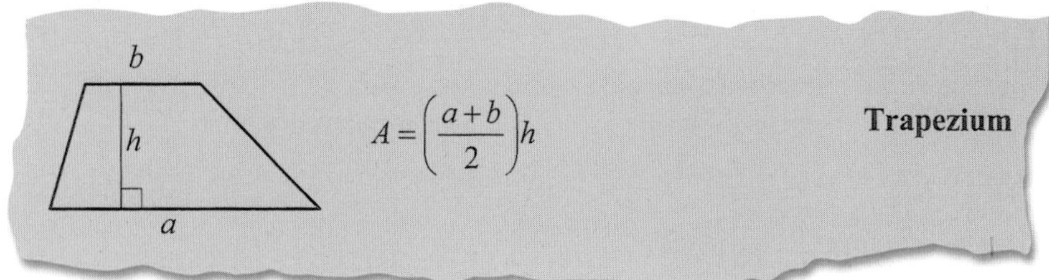

Triangle

Acute **Right-angled** **Obtuse**

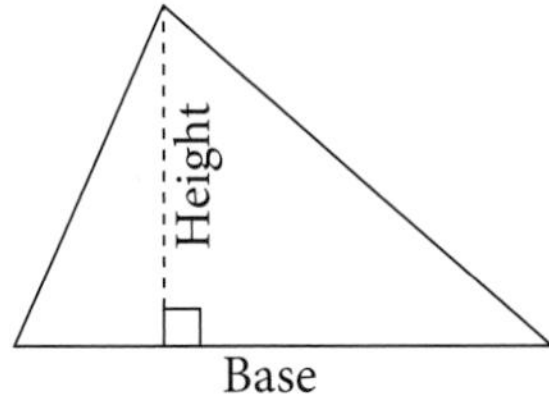

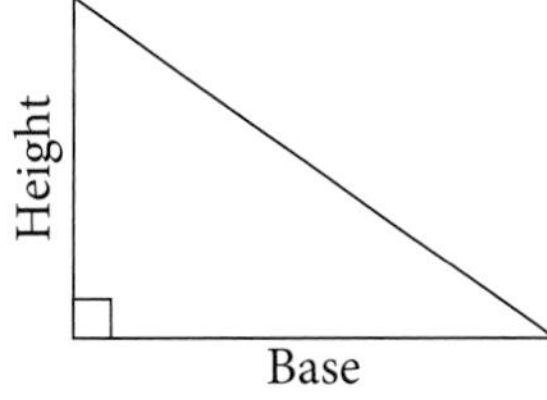

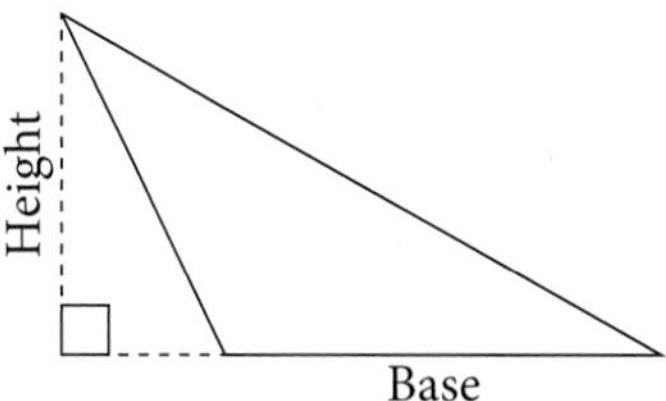

Area $= \frac{1}{2}$(base)($\perp$ height)

Perimeter = Sum of all the sides

A triangle is half of a rectangle or a parallelogram. Therefore, its area is half of the area of a rectangle or parallelogram.

Formula for the **area of a triangle** appears on page 9 of the booklet of *formulae and tables*, as shown:

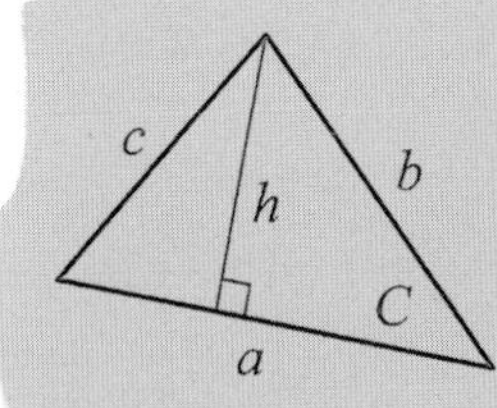

$$A=\frac{1}{2}ah$$

$$=\frac{1}{2}ab\sin C$$

$$=\sqrt{s(s-a)(s-b)(s-c)}$$

Triangle

taking $s=\dfrac{a+b+c}{2}$

The last formula shown is not mentioned in the syllabus, but you can use it to find the area of a triangle, when given three sides, if you wish.

Links across the syllabus

The formula Area $= \frac{1}{2}ab \sin C$ is covered in Chapter 21: Trigonometry II.

Discussion Time 

Working with a classmate, find the area of the triangle shown, using 15 as the base.

Then find the area of the triangle, using 10 as the base.

Discuss your findings and how they relate to Theorem 16: For a triangle, base times height does not depend on the choice of base, as covered in Chapter 11: Geometry II.

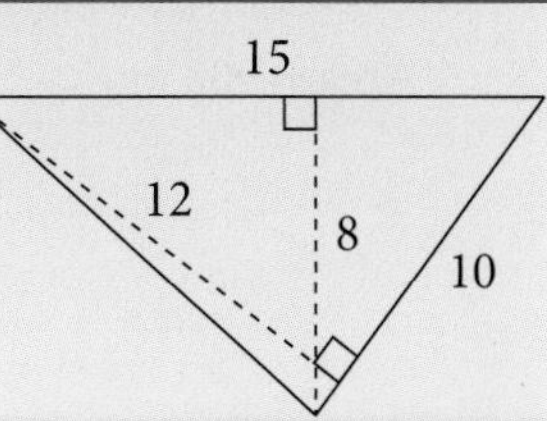

Area and Perimeter

EXAMPLE 1

A rectangle has a length of 8 cm and a width of 6 cm. Find:

(i) its area **(ii)** its perimeter **(iii)** the length of its diagonal.

Solution

Draw a diagram of the rectangle:

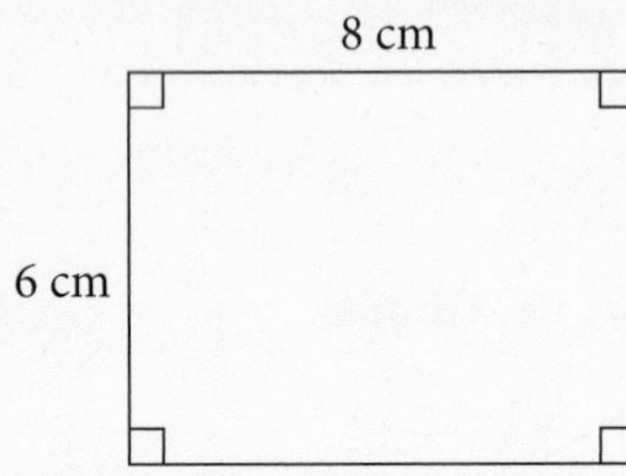

It is good practice to draw a sketch and write out the formula at the start of a question.

(i) Length = 8, width = 6, area = ?:

Area = (length)(width)

Area = (8)(6)

Area = 48 cm^2

(ii) Length = 8, width = 6, perimeter = ?

Perimeter = 2(length) + 2(width)

Perimeter = 2(8) + 2(6)

Perimeter = 16 + 12

Perimeter = 28 cm

(iii) The diagonal of the rectangle is the hypotenuse of a right-angled triangle. Use Pythagoras' Theorem to find the length of the hypotenuse:

$a = 8$, $b = 6$, $c = ?$

$c^2 = a^2 + b^2$

$x^2 = (8)^2 + (6)^2$

$x^2 = 64 + 36$

$x^2 = 100$

$x = \sqrt{100} = 10$ cm

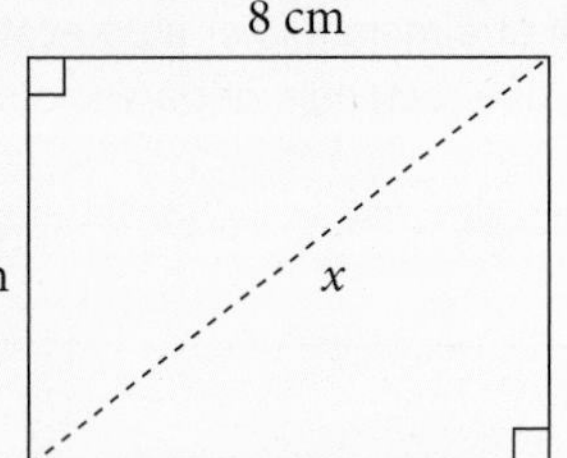

Pythagoras' Theorem is covered in Chapter 11: Geometry II and Chapter 20: Trigonometry I.

EXAMPLE 2

Find the area of the following shapes:

(i)

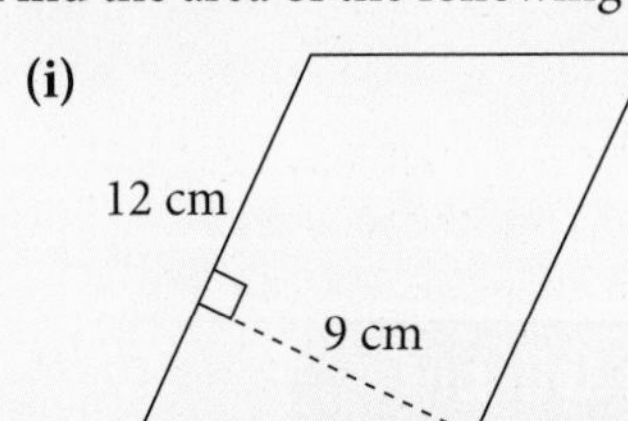

(ii)

10 cm

8 cm

5 cm

Solution

(i) Parallelogram where length = 12, ⊥ height = 9

Area = (length)(⊥ height)

Area = (12)(9)

Area = 108 cm^2

(ii) Trapezium where $a = 10$, $b = 5$, ⊥ height = 8

Area = $\left(\frac{a+b}{2}\right)$(⊥ height)

Area = $\left(\frac{10+5}{2}\right)(8)$

Area = $\left(\frac{15}{2}\right)(8)$

Area = (7·5)(8)

Area = 60 cm^2

EXAMPLE 3

An architect has drawn up the plans of the ground floor of an office block. As can be seen from the diagram, the ground floor is rectangular in shape, with a square entrance way and a triangular courtyard.

Find the area of the floor space available on the ground floor of this building (i.e. the shaded area).

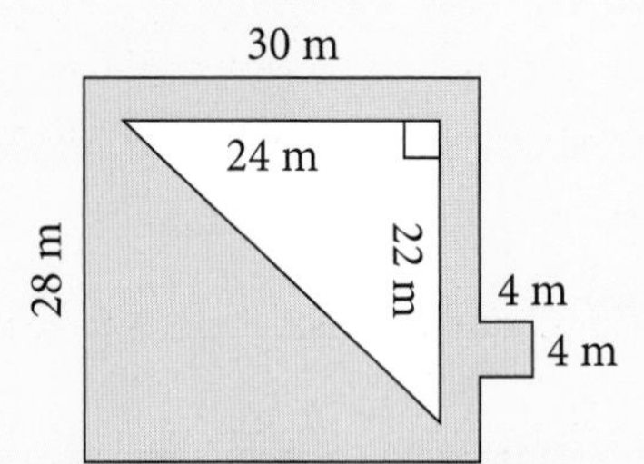

Solution

Break up the composite shape to identify all shapes involved:

Shaded area = rectangle + square − triangle

Rectangle:
Length = 30, width = 28
Area = (length)(width)
Area = (30)(28)
Area = 840 m^2

Square:
Length = 4
Area = (length)(length)
Area = (4)(4)
Area = 16 m^2

Triangle:
Base = 24, $\perp$ height = 22
Area = $\frac{1}{2}$(base)($\perp$ height)
Area = $\frac{1}{2}$(24)(22)
Area = 264 m^2

Shaded area = rectangle + square − triangle
Shaded area = 840 + 16 − 264
Shaded area = 592 m^2

EXAMPLE 4

Find the height of the following triangle, given that its area is 44 cm^2.

Solution

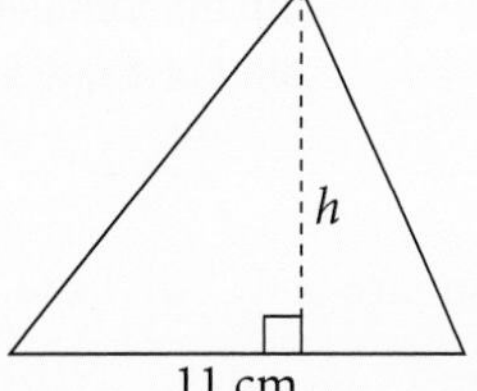

Base = 11, $\perp$ height = h, area = 44

Area = $\frac{1}{2}$(base)($\perp$ height)

$44 = \frac{1}{2}(11)(h)$

$44 = (5{\cdot}5)(h)$

$\frac{44}{5{\cdot}5} = h$

8 cm = h

We are sometimes given the area or the perimeter of a shape and need to work backwards to find one of the dimensions of the shape. In this case, we must use our algebra skills to establish and solve an equation.

Practice Questions 16.1

1. Find the area of each of the following quadrilaterals:

(i)

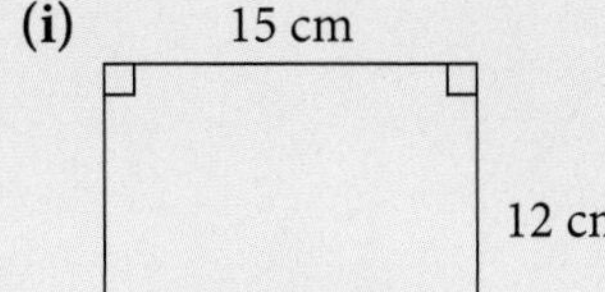

(ii)

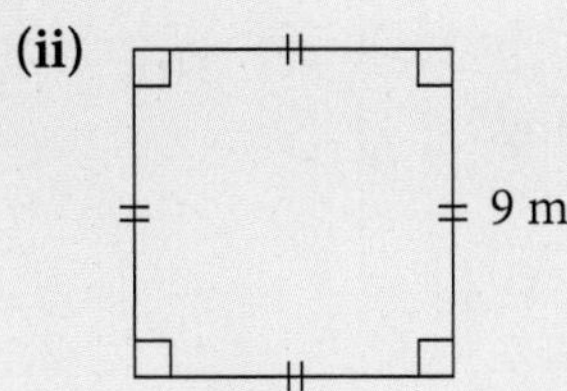

(iii)

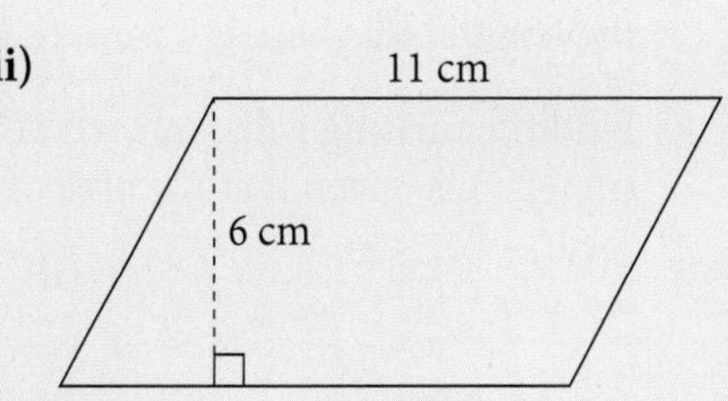

(iv)

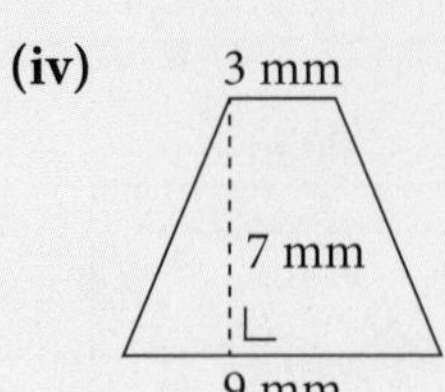

(v)

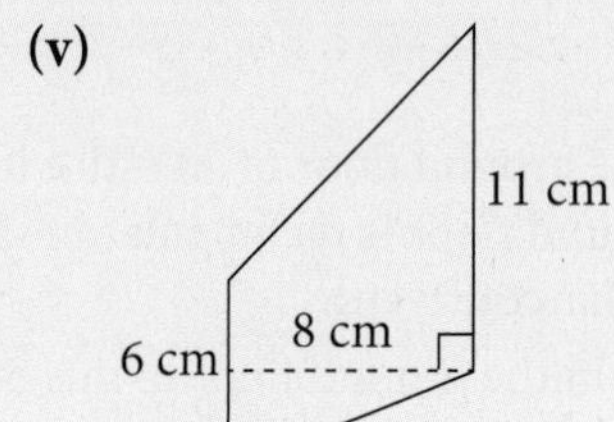

(vi)

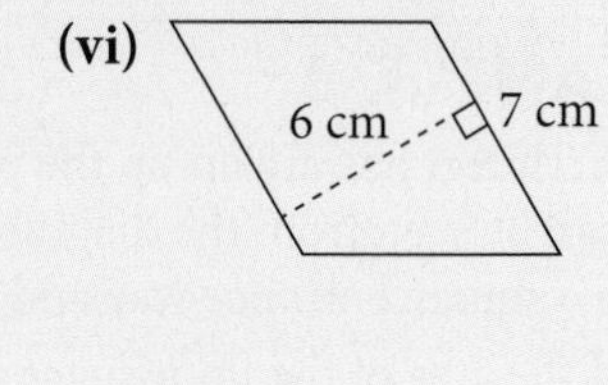

(vii)

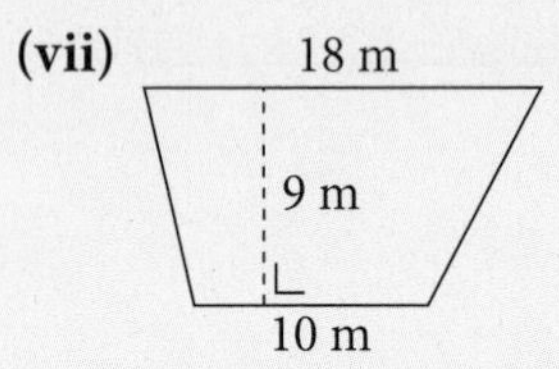

(viii)

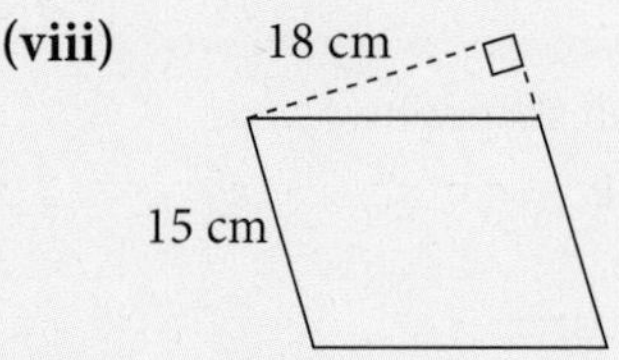

2. Find the area of each of the following triangles:

(i)

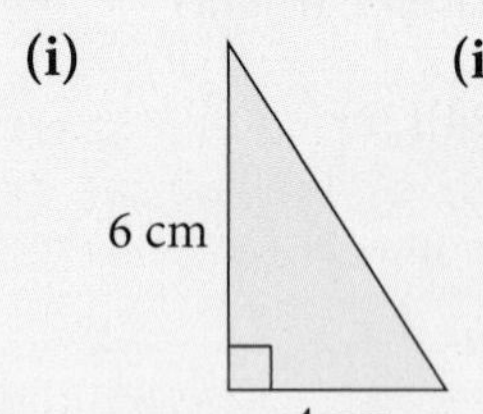

(ii)

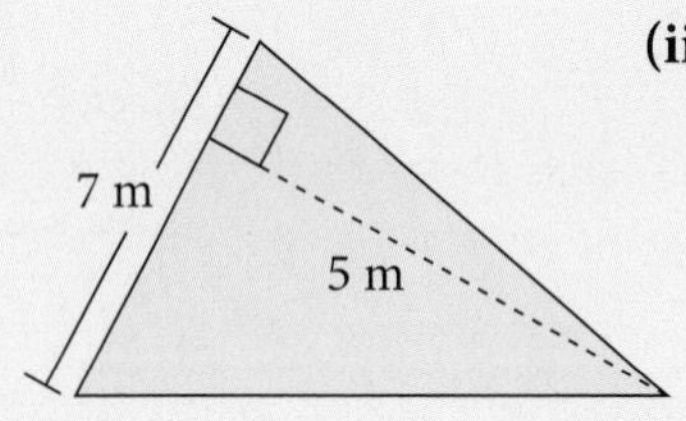

(iii) (iv)

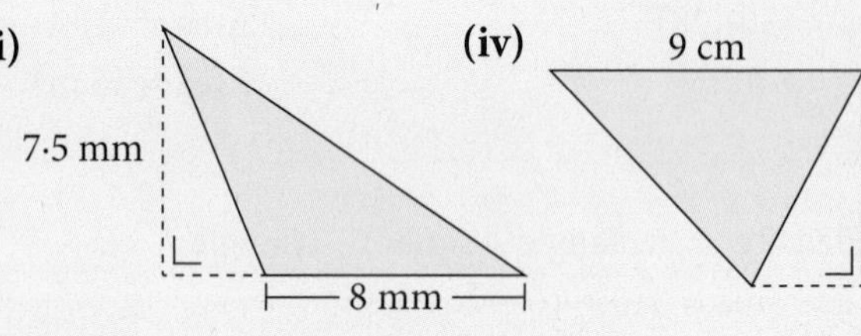

3. The area of a rectangle is 108 cm^2. Given that its width is 9 cm, find its:
   (i) length
   (ii) perimeter.

It is good practice to draw a sketch and write out the formula at the start of a question.

4. The perimeter of a square is 64 cm. Find:
   (i) the length of one of its sides (ii) its area.

5. The perimeter of a rectangle is 36 cm. Given that its length is 10 cm, find its:
   (i) width (ii) area.

6. The area of a rectangle is 12 cm^2. Given that its length is 4 cm, find:
   (i) its width (ii) the length of its diagonal.

7. The area of a parallelogram is 90 cm^2. Given that its height is 6 cm, find the length of its base.

8. The area of a parallelogram is 72 mm^2. Given that the length of its base is 6 mm, find its height.

9. Find the missing value in each of the following trapeziums, given that the area of each is 85 cm^2.

(i)

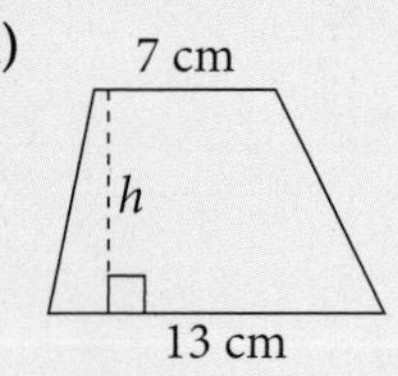

(ii)

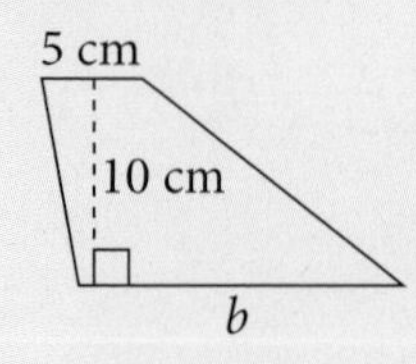

(iii)

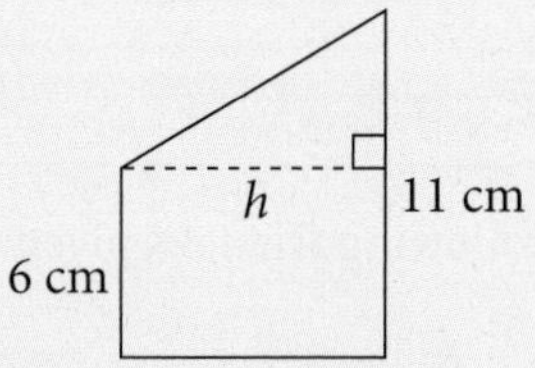

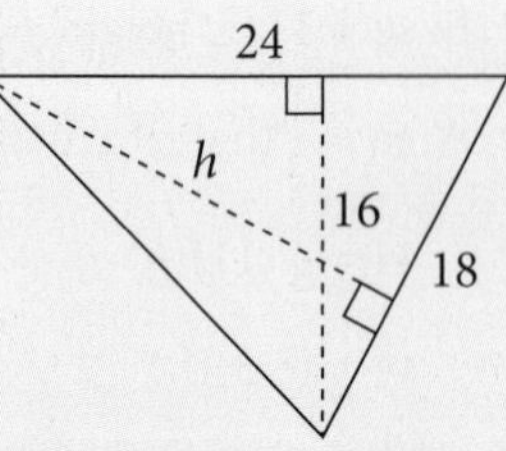

10. (i) Taking 24 as the base and 16 as the height, find the area of the triangle shown. All units shown are in centimetres.
    (ii) Hence, using 18 as the base, find the value of the height, h.

11. Find the value of h in each of the following triangles.

(i)

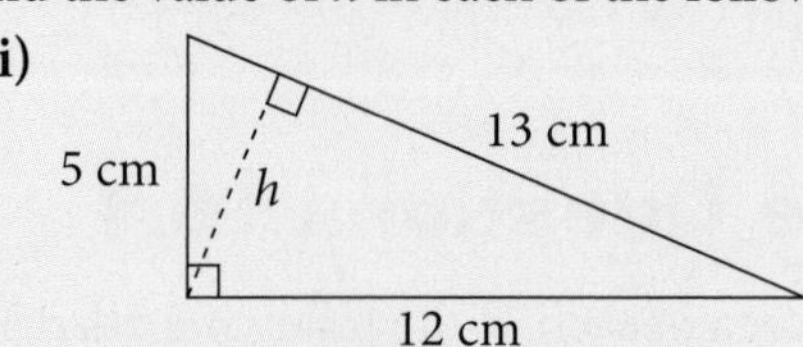

(ii)

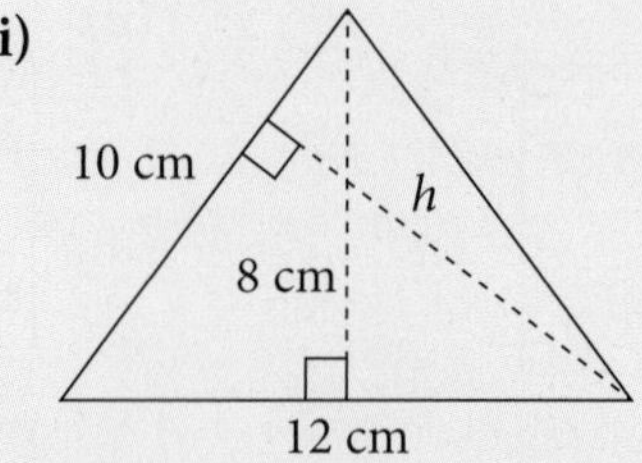

12. The diagram shows three quadrilaterals plotted on a coordinated plane. Each box is one unit in length and one unit in width.

Use Pythagoras' Theorem to find the lengths of the slanted lines.

Find **(i)** the area and **(ii)** the perimeter of each of the shapes *A*, *B* and *C*. Give your answers to two decimal places, where appropriate.

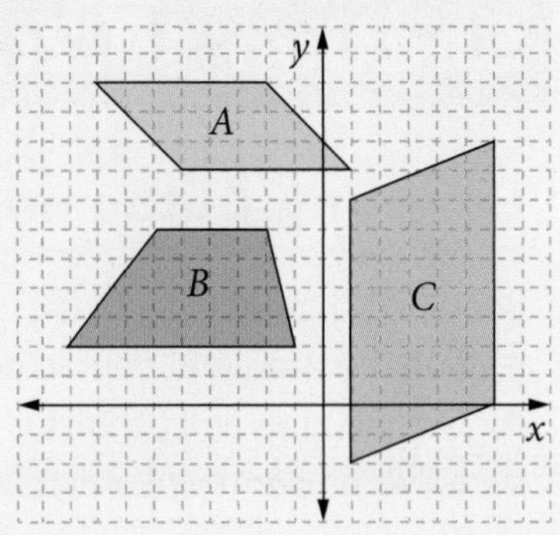

13. Find the area of the shaded portion of each of the following shapes:

(i)

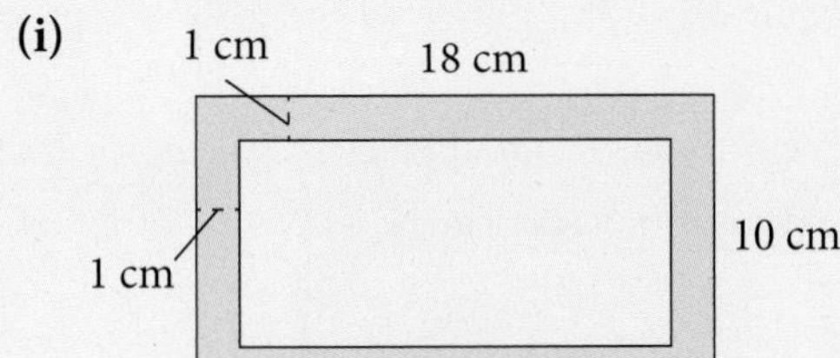

(ii)

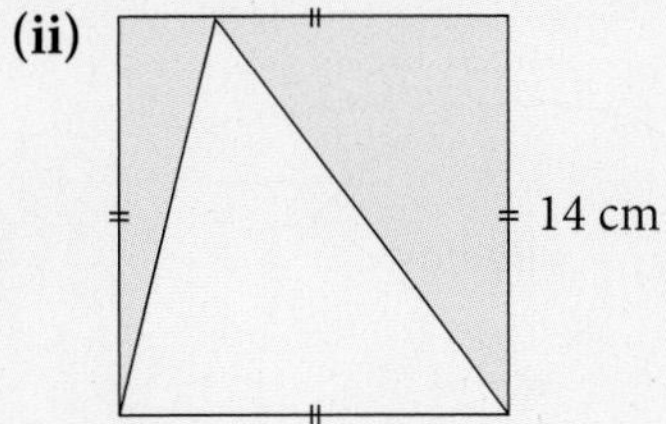

(iii)

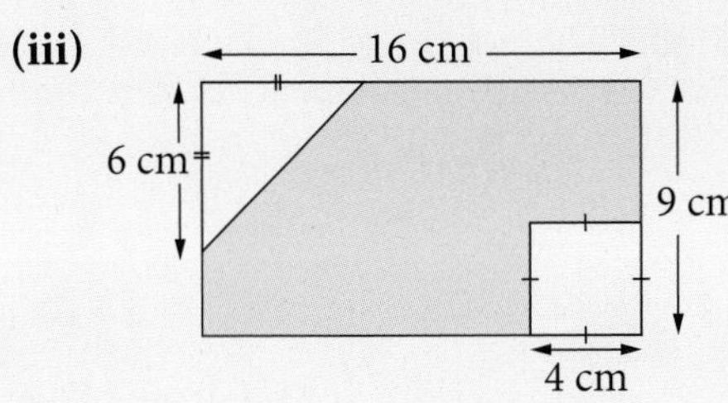

(iv)

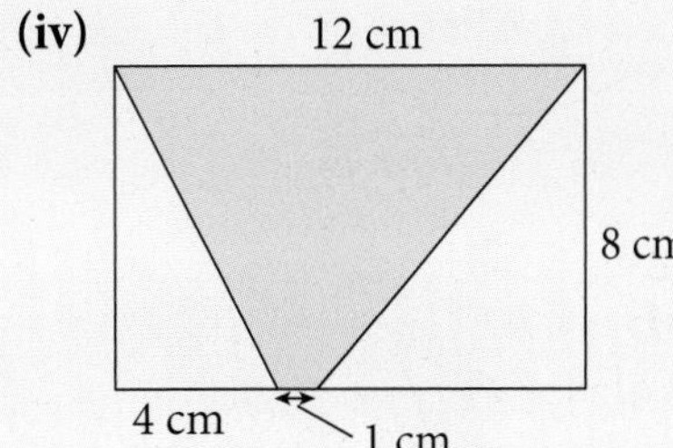

14. Find the area of each of the following shapes:

(i)

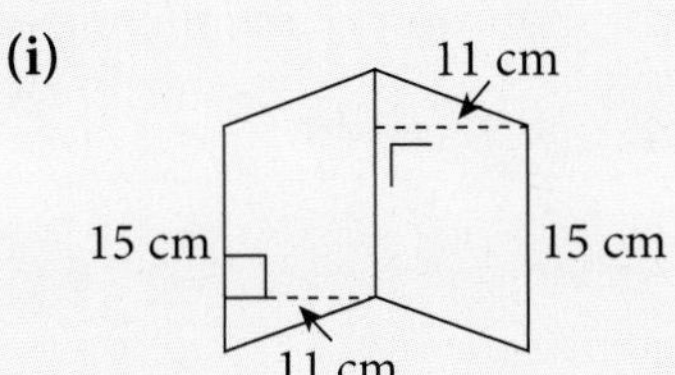

(ii)

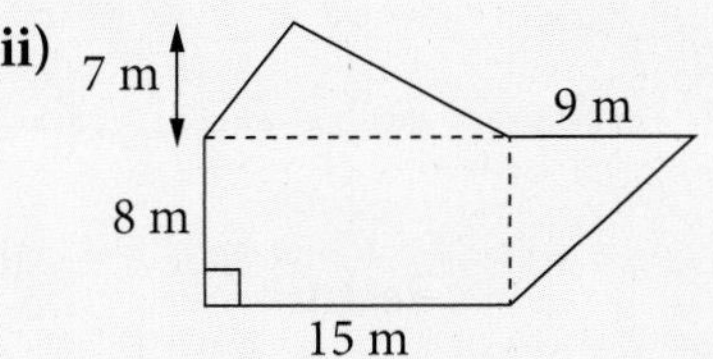

(iii)

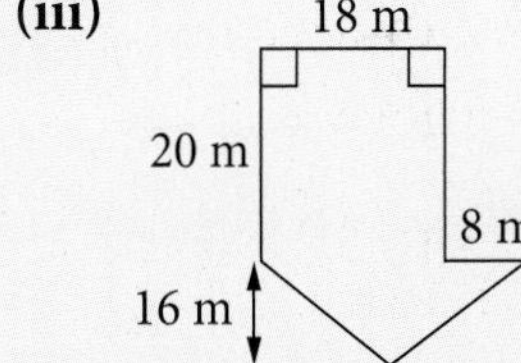

(iv)

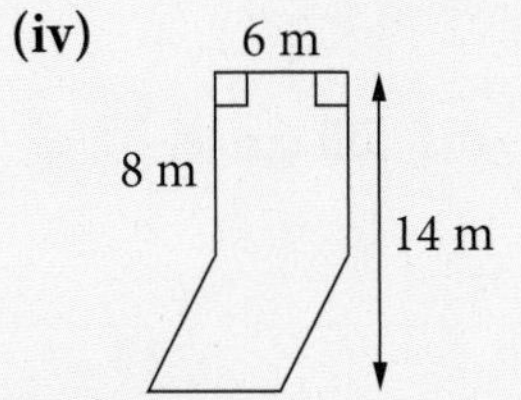

(v)

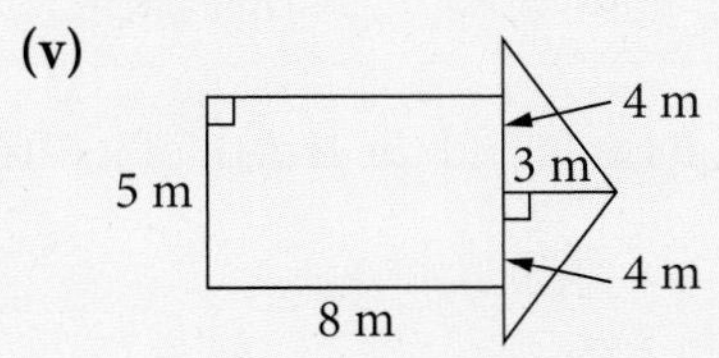

(vi)

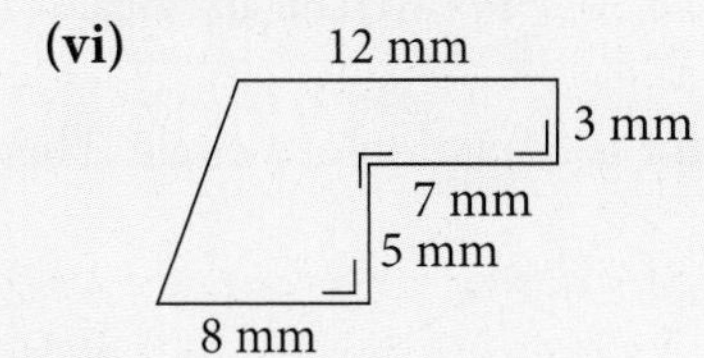

15. Find the area and perimeter of each of the following shapes:

(i)

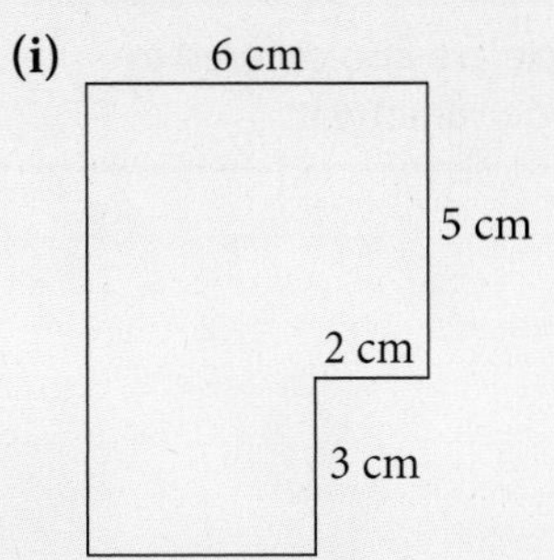

(ii)

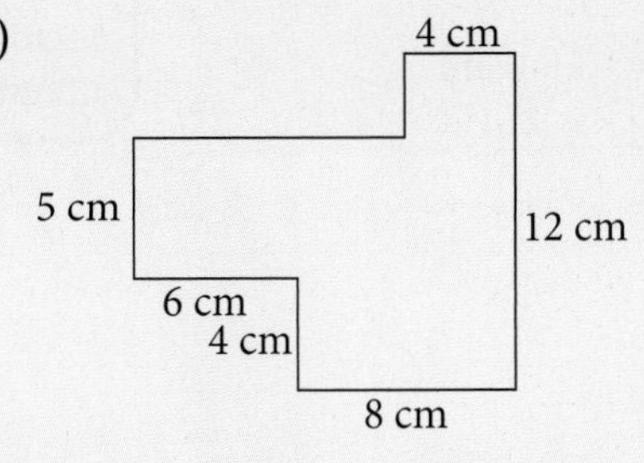

(iii)

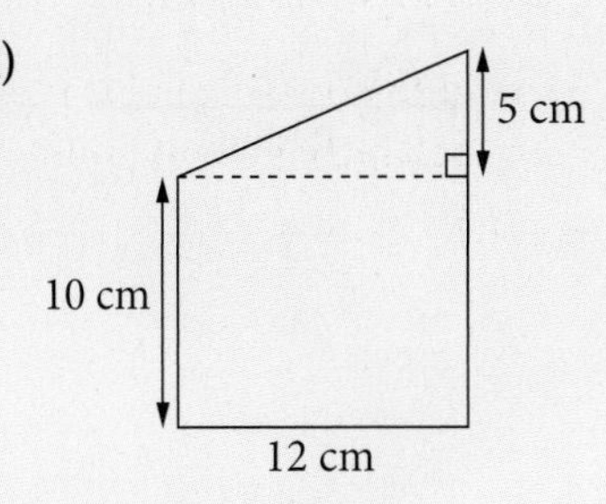

Section 16.2: Circles and Sectors

Learning Outcomes:

You should be able to:

- find the area and perimeter of circles and sectors
- find the area and perimeter of compound shapes
- solve problems involving a variety of shapes

Circle

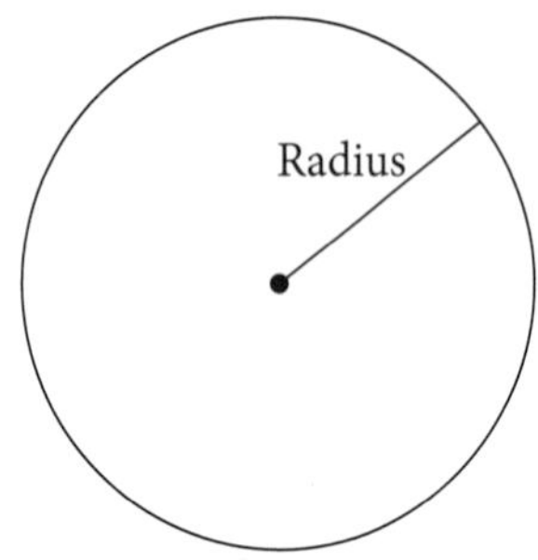

Circumference (length) = π (diameter)

= π (2(radius))

= 2π (radius)

Area = π (radius)^2

The formulae for the **length of a circle** and the **area of a circle** appear on page 8 of the booklet of *formulae and tables*, as shown:

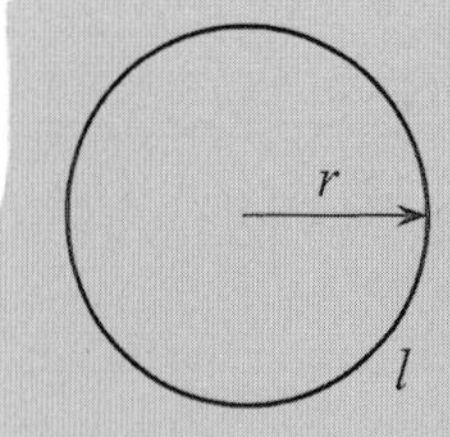

$l = 2\pi r$

$A = \pi r^2$

Circle / Disc

length l
(circumference l)

Sector

A **sector** is a portion of a circle enclosed by two radii and an arc.

An **arc** is a portion of the circumference of a circle.

A sector is a fraction of a circle. Therefore, its area and the length of its arc are fractions of a full circle.

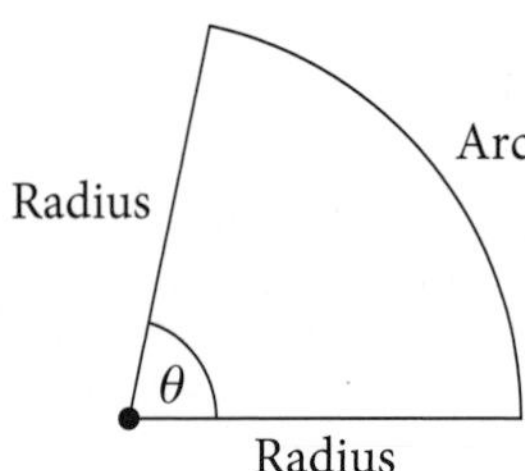

$$\text{Arc} = \frac{\theta}{360^\circ}(2\pi r)$$

$$\text{Perimeter} = \text{Arc} + 2(\text{radius})$$

$$\text{Area} = \frac{\theta}{360^\circ}(\pi r^2)$$

Links across the syllabus

Sectors of a circle are also covered in Chapter 21: Trigonometry II.

The formulae for the **length of the arc** and the area of the **sector of a circle** appear on page 9 of the booklet of *formulae and tables*, as shown:

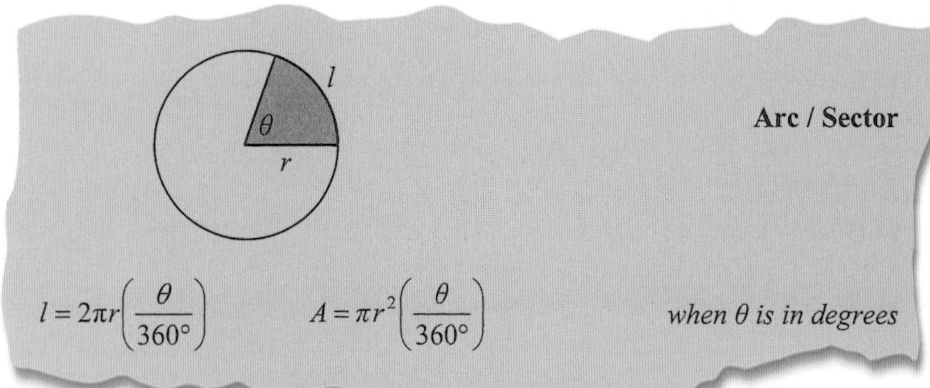

EXAMPLE 1

Find the area and perimeter of the following sector. Give your answers in terms of π.

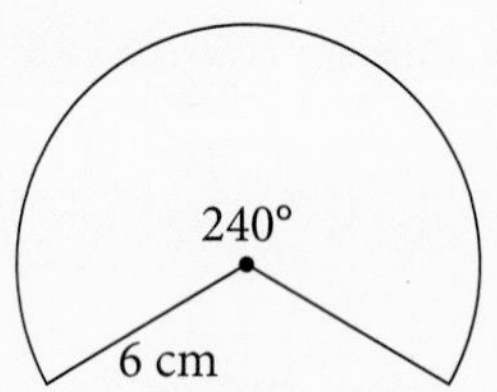

Solution

Area of the sector:

$\theta = 240°$, radius = 6

$$\text{Area} = \frac{\theta}{360°}\pi r^2$$
$$= \frac{240°}{360°}(\pi(6)^2)$$
$$= \frac{2}{3}(36\pi)$$
$$= 24\pi \text{ cm}^2$$

Arc of the sector:

$\theta = 240°$, radius = 6

$$\text{Arc} = \frac{\theta}{360°}(2\pi r)$$
$$= \frac{240°}{360°}(2\pi(6))$$
$$= \frac{2}{3}(12\pi)$$
$$= 8\pi \text{ cm}$$

Perimeter = Arc + 2(radius)

Arc = 8π, radius = 6

$= 8\pi + 2(6)$

$= (8\pi + 12)$ cm

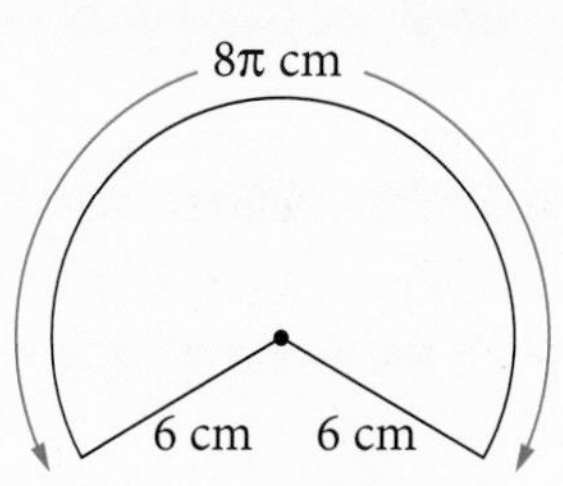

EXAMPLE 2

The diagram shows a circle inside of a trapezium.

Using the π button on your calculator, find the area of the shaded region.

Give your answer to one decimal place.

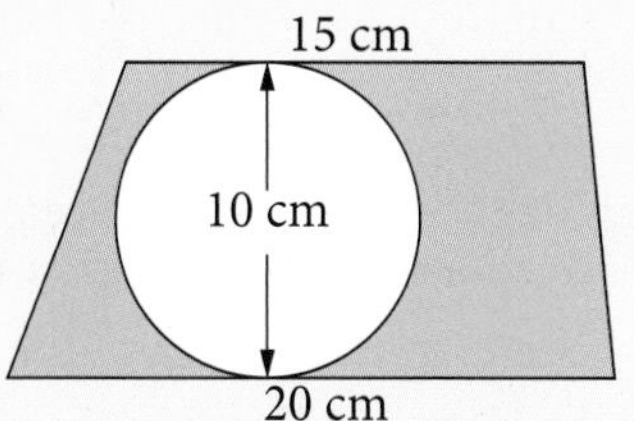

Solution

Trapezium where $a = 15$, $b = 20$, $\perp$ height = 10

$$\text{Area} = \left(\frac{a+b}{2}\right)(\perp \text{ height})$$
$$= \left(\frac{15+20}{2}\right)(10)$$
$$= \left(\frac{35}{2}\right)(10)$$
$$= (17{\cdot}5)(10)$$
$$= 175 \text{ cm}^2$$

Circle where radius = 5

$$\text{Area} = \pi r^2$$
$$= \pi(5)^2$$
$$= 25\pi$$
$$= 78{\cdot}539 \text{ cm}^2$$

Unless otherwise stated, use the π button on your calculator. This will give the most accurate solution.

Area of shaded region = Trapezium − Circle

Area of shaded region = 175 − 78·539

Area of shaded region = 96·461 = 96·5 cm^2 (to one decimal place)

Practice Questions 16.2

1. Find the area and circumference of each of the following circles.
Use the π button on the calculator and give your answer correct to one decimal place.

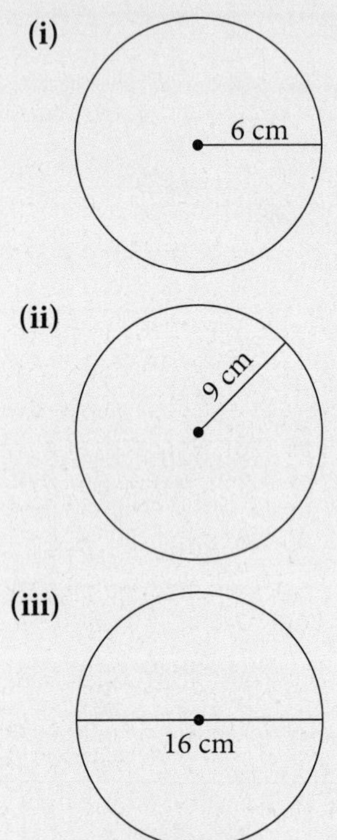

2. Given the area of a circle is $6{\cdot}25\pi$ m^2, find the length of its radius and hence the circumference of the circle, in terms of π.

3. Given the area of a circle is 154 cm^2, find the length of its radius and hence the circumference of the circle. Take π as $\frac{22}{7}$.

4. Given the circumference of a circle is 30π m, find the length of its radius and hence the area of the circle, in terms of π.

5. Given the circumference of a circle is 157 cm, find the length of its radius and hence the area of the circle. Take π as $3{\cdot}14$.

6. A sector of angle 30° is removed from a circle of radius 5 cm, as shown.
   (i) What fraction of the circle has been removed?
   (ii) Find the area of the circle remaining.
   Give your answer to one decimal place.

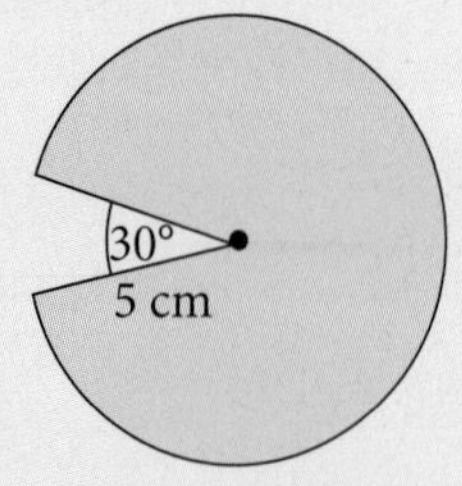

7. For each of the following sectors, find the **(a)** area and **(b)** length of the arc.
Give your answers in terms of π.

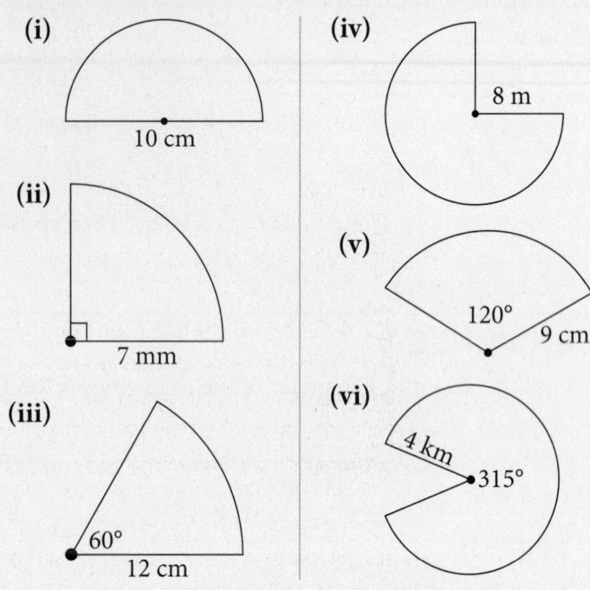

8. Find the perimeter of each of the following sectors.
Use the π button on the calculator and give your answer correct to one decimal place.

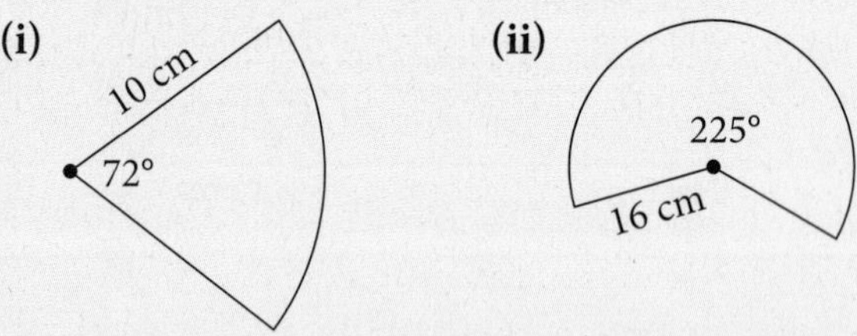

9. Find the area of the shaded region for each of the following.
Give your answer correct to one decimal place.

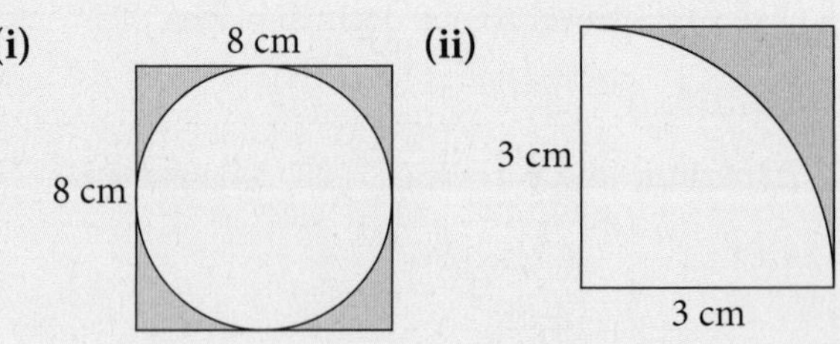

10. A game at a fun fair consists of spinning a spinner, which has five equal sectors.
If the radius of the spinner is 35 cm, find the area of one of the sectors of the spinner. Give your answer correct to one decimal place.

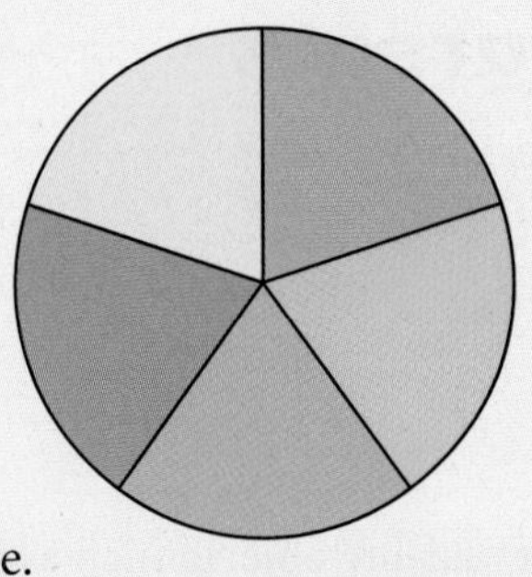

11. A sports club is having a target painted on a wall so that its members can practise taking shots.
If the target is to be painted as shown, what area of the wall will be painted with pink paint? Give your answer correct to one decimal place.

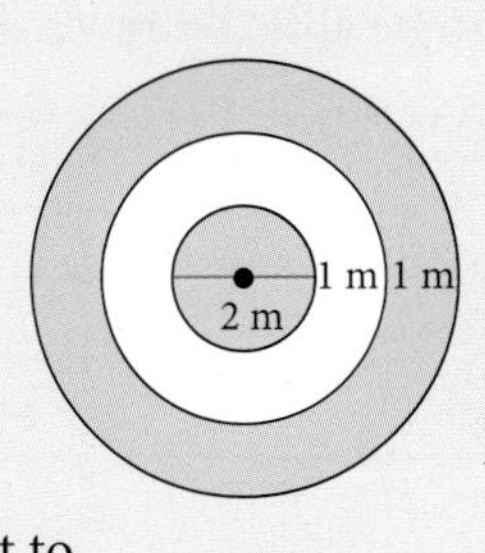

12. Find the area of the following compound shapes. Give your answer correct to two decimal places.

(i)

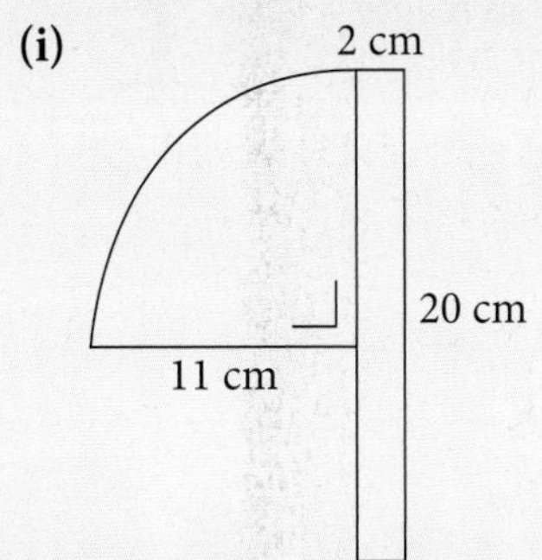

(ii)

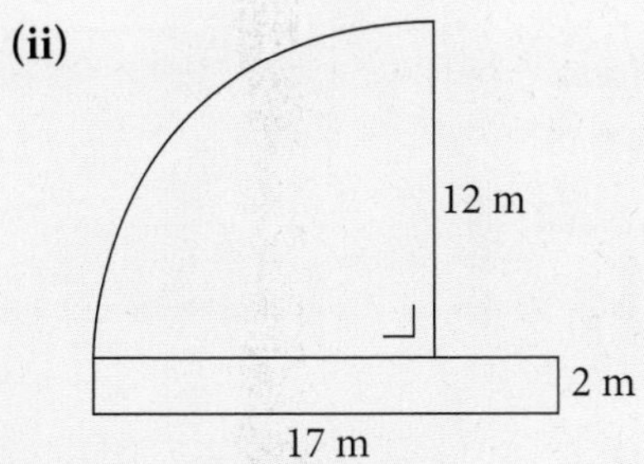

(iii)

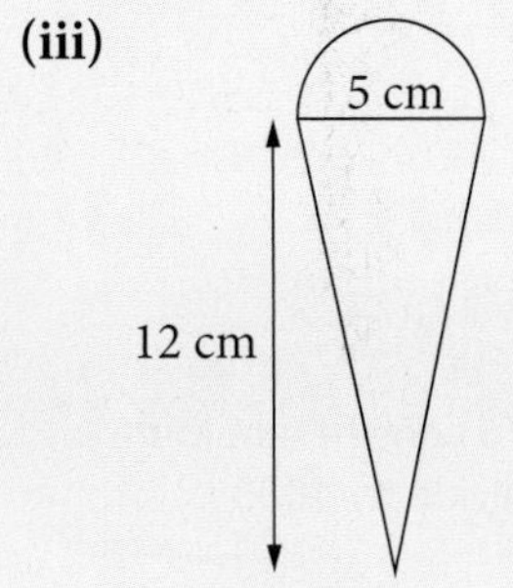

13. A garden has a shape as shown.

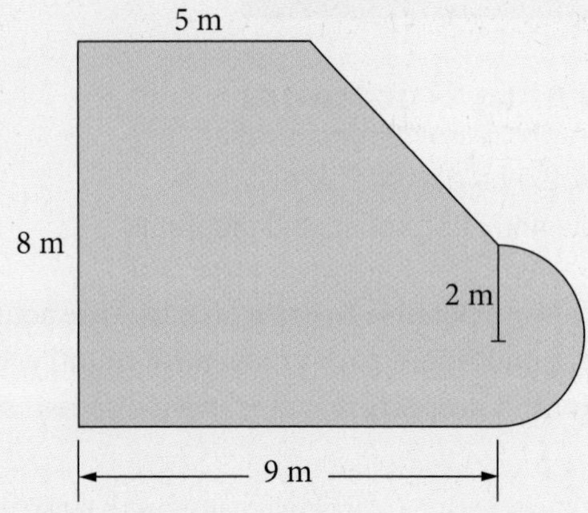

(i) Find the area of the garden, giving your answer correct to two decimal places.

(ii) The garden is to be covered with artificial grass. The cost of the grass is €35 per square metre, plus €7·50 per square metre for fitting. VAT of 18% is then applied. Find the total cost of buying and fitting the grass. Give your answer to the nearest euro.

14. Circular lids are cut out of a rectangular sheet of tin. The factory wants to waste as little tin as possible, so the three identical circles fit perfectly inside the rectangle, as shown.
Given the width of the rectangle is 22 cm, find the area of the tin remaining, after the lids have been cut out. Take $\pi = 3{\cdot}14$ and give your answer correct to one decimal place.

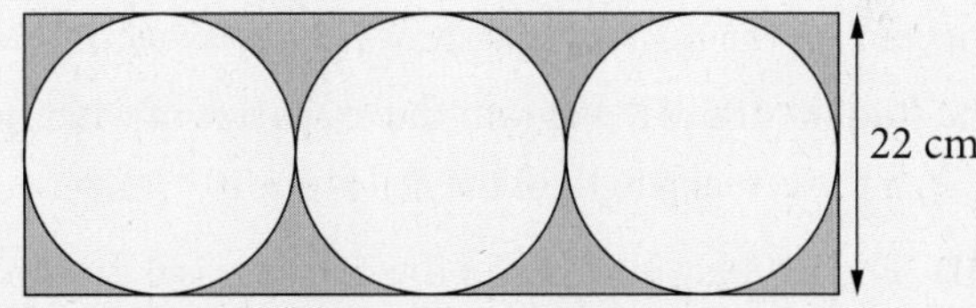

15. A sector of a circle, centre P and radius $|PQ| = 8$ cm is drawn inside a square $PQRS$.

(i) Find the area of the triangle PQS.

(ii) Find the area of the sector, correct to one decimal place.

(iii) Hence find the area of the segment from Q to S (shaded area).

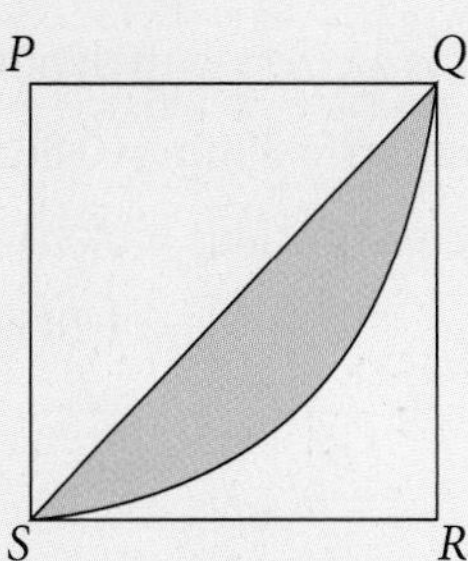

Area and Perimeter

Section 16.3: Scaled Diagrams

Learning Outcome:

You should be able to:

- draw and interpret scaled diagrams

It is not always possible to draw on paper the actual size of real-life objects such as a blood cell, a bacterium, an airplane, a building, a park or an entire country. We need to be able to draw a diagram of the object, keeping all dimensions in proportion, but just at a different size.

A **scaled diagram** is a drawing that shows a real object with accurate sizes reduced or enlarged by a certain amount, called the scale.

EXAMPLE 1

The scale on a drawing of a tree is 1 : 40.
If the height of the tree on paper is 12 cm, what is the height of the tree in reality?

Solution

A scale of 1 : 40 means that every 1 unit on the scale drawing is representing 40 units in reality.

For this tree: 1 cm = 40 cm

12 cm = (40)(12) (multiply both sides by 12)

12 cm = 480 cm

Therefore, the tree is 480 cm = 4·8 m tall.

EXAMPLE 2

A student uses a microscope to look at some plant cells.
The lens on the microscope shows $a \times 700$ magnification.

The student draws a diagram the exact size of what he views through the eyepiece.

(i) If the actual length of the cell is 6×10^{-5} m, what length is the student's diagram?

(ii) The circular nucleus on the diagram is 6 mm in diameter. Find the true radius of the nucleus and hence find the area of the nucleus.
Give your answer in square metres and in the form $a \times 10^n$, where $1 \leq a < 10$.

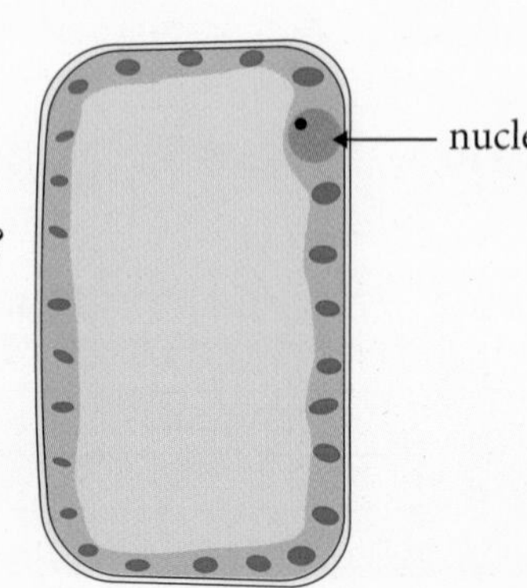

Solution

(i) The length of the diagram is 700 times the actual length of the cell

Length of the diagram: $(6 \times 10^{-5})(700)$

0·042 m

4·2 cm

(ii) The nucleus is a circle with diameter = 6 mm = 0·006 m

Therefore, radius = 3 mm = 0·003 m

Radius of actual nucleus = 0·003 ÷ 700 (divide by the scale factor)

$= 4{\cdot}2857 \times 10^{-6}$ m

Area of a circle $= \pi r^2$

$= \pi(4{\cdot}2857 \times 10^{-6})^2$

$= 5{\cdot}77027 \times 10^{-11}$ m^2

To convert mm to m, divide by 1000

Practice Questions 16.3

1. A scaled drawing of a boat is made to a scale of 1 : 20.
   - (i) If the scaled diagram of the boat is 25 cm in length, what is the length of the actual boat?
   - (ii) If the boat has a mast of height 4 m, how high is the mast on the scaled diagram?

2. The area of a rectangular sports pitch is 7875 m^2. The width of the pitch is 75 m.

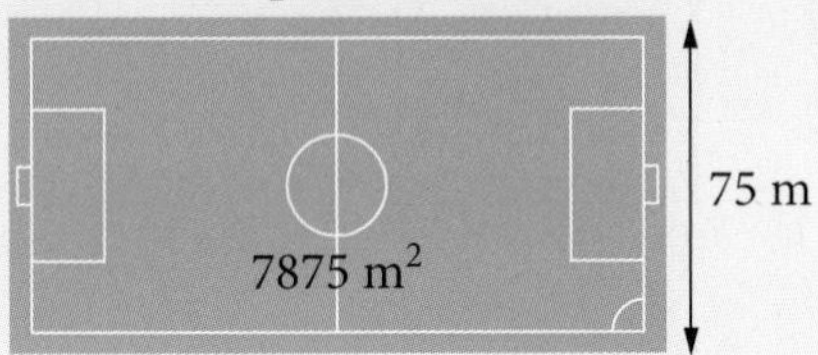

   - (i) Find the length of the playing pitch.
   - (ii) Find the perimeter of the playing pitch.
   - (iii) In your copybook, draw a scaled diagram of the sports pitch, using the scale 1 : 1500.

3. The diagram shows a square patio. Paving slabs are laid such that there is a smaller square inside of the bigger square, as shown. The lengths 6 m and 10 m are shown.

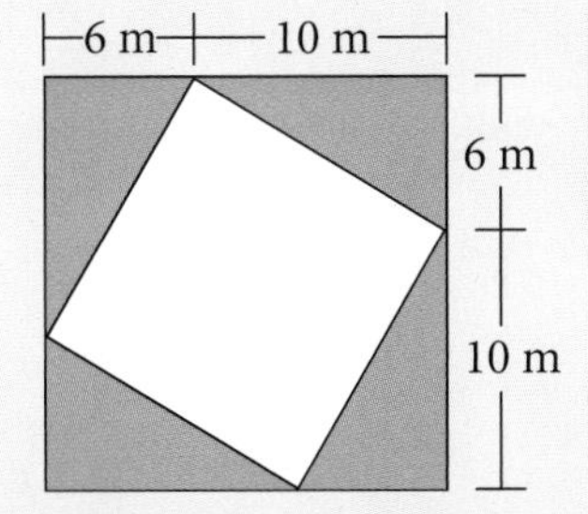

   - (i) Find the length of one side of the smaller square. Give your answer in surd form.
   - (ii) Find the exact area of the smaller square.
   - (iii) Using the scale 1 : 200, draw a scaled diagram of the patio into your copybook.
   - (iv) Taking measurements from your scaled diagram, verify your answer to part **(ii)**.

4. A Geography class is using a scaled map of Ireland.
   - (i) The direct distance between Dublin and Letterkenny is 220 km. The distance shown on a map is 50 cm. Find the scale which was used to draw the map.
   - (ii) On the same map, Cork is 22 cm from Limerick. How far apart are these two cities in reality? Give your answer correct to the nearest kilometre.

5. A tourist is on a driving holiday in France. They are using a scaled map of France.
   - (i) The direct distance between Bordeaux and Lyon is 500 km. The distance shown on a map is 20 cm. Find the scale which was used to draw the map.
   - (ii) On the same map, Montpellier is 28 cm from Paris. How far apart are these two cities in reality?

6. A shop has a large cut-out sign of an ice cream cone attached to its outside wall. The dimensions of the sign are as shown in the diagram. The shop owner wants to make smaller versions of the sign, for hanging inside the shop. He decides to redraw the ice cream cone, using a scale of 1 : 20.

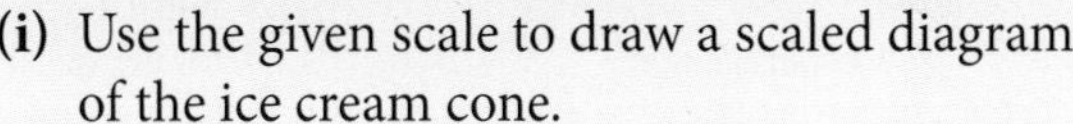

   - (i) Use the given scale to draw a scaled diagram of the ice cream cone.
   - (ii) Write down the height of both the large sign and the scaled diagram.
   - (iii) Find the area of both the large sign and the scaled diagram. Give your answers correct to two decimal places.
   - (iv) Find the ratio of the height of the scaled diagram to the height of the sign.
   - (v) Find the ratio of the area of the scaled diagram to the area of the sign.
   - (vi) Comment on the relationship between the answers to part **(iv)** and **(v)**. Explain why this is the case.

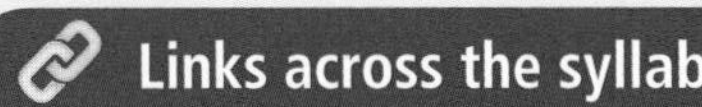

Links across the syllabus

Enlargements are covered in Chapter 13: Geometry IV.

Section 16.4: The Trapezoidal Rule

Learning Outcome:

You should be able to:

- use the trapezoidal rule to approximate area

The trapezoidal rule is a method that can be used for finding the approximate area of a shape.

The shape is divided into strips of equal width along the horizontal line. Each strip approximates a trapezium, as shown. As you can see, some of the trapeziums come above the boundary of the shape and some are below it.

The trapezoidal rule adds up the area of each of these trapeziums and hence, gives an approximation for the total area of the shape.

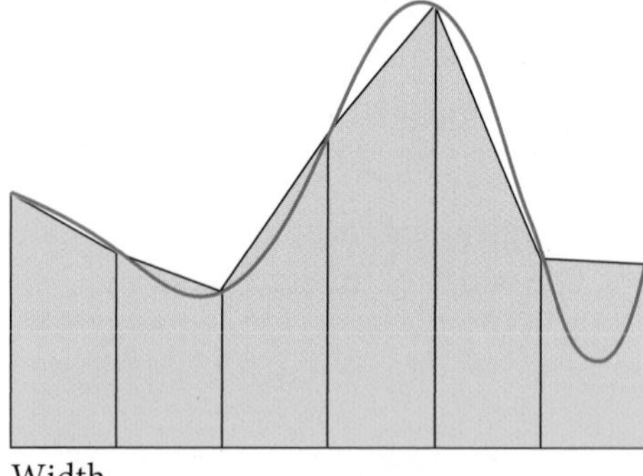

The more strips the shape is divided into, the closer the approximation is to the true area of the shape. That is, more strips give a more accurate estimate for the area.

$$\text{Trapezoidal rule: Area} = \frac{\text{width}}{2}[\text{First height} + \text{Last height} + 2(\text{sum of all other heights})]$$

The formula for the **trapezoidal rule** appears on page 12 of the booklet of *formulae and tables*, as shown:

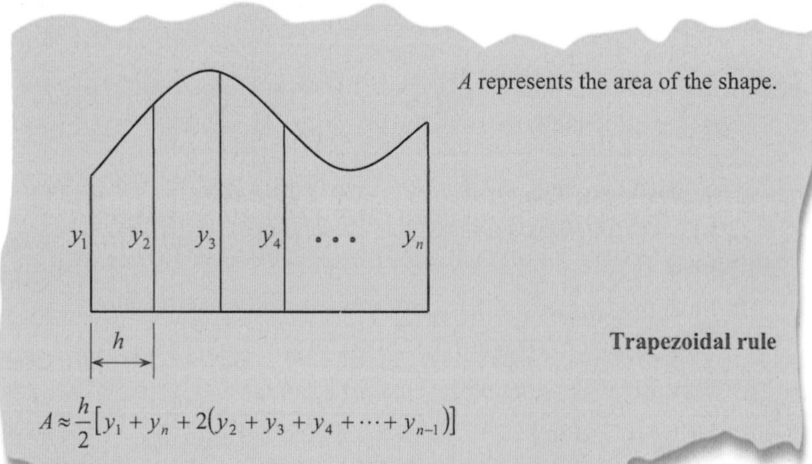

h is the width of each strip, not the height.

EXAMPLE 1

Use the trapezoidal rule to estimate the area of the shape, given the width of each strip is 5 cm and all heights are in centimetres.

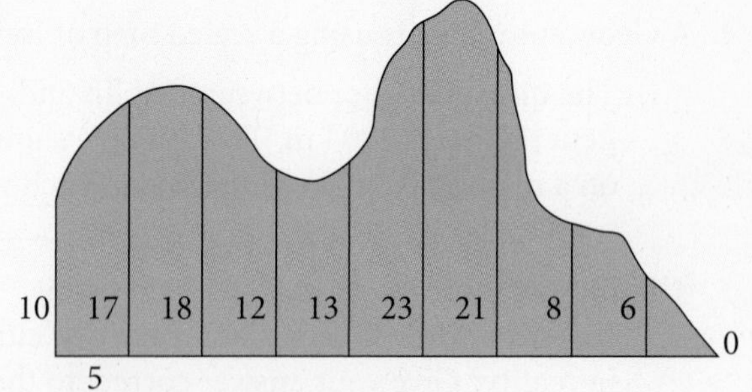

Area and Perimeter

Solution

$$\text{Area} = \frac{h}{2}[y_1 + y_{10} + 2(y_2 + y_3 + y_4 + \ldots + y_9)]$$

$$= \frac{5}{2}[10 + 0 + 2(17 + 18 + 12 + 13 + 23 + 21 + 8 + 6)]$$

$$= \frac{5}{2}[10 + 0 + 2(118)]$$

$$= \frac{5}{2}[10 + 236]$$

$$= \frac{5}{2}[246] = 615 \text{ cm}^2$$

Note that the last height is zero.

EXAMPLE 2

Use the trapezoidal rule to estimate the area of the shape below, given the width of each strip is 4 m and all dimensions are in metres.

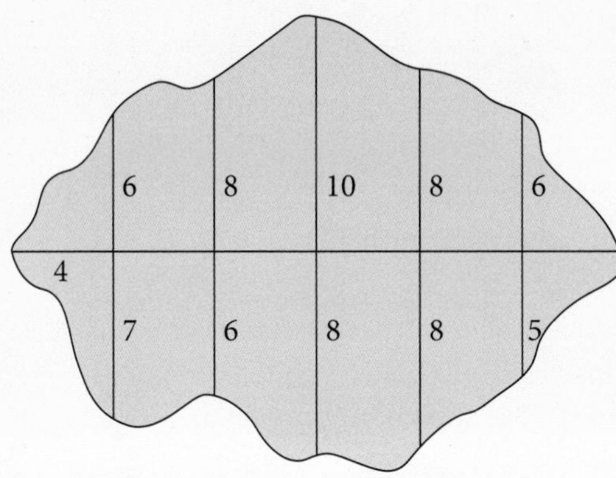

When the horizontal axis is passing through the shape you can:

1. Use the trapezoidal rule to find the area of the top and bottom parts of the shape separately, and then add them up.
2. Add the vertical heights to get the total height of each strip and then use these heights in the trapezoidal rule.

Solution

$$\text{Area} = \frac{h}{2}[y_1 + y_n + 2(y_2 + y_3 + y_3 + \ldots + y_{n-1})]$$

$$= \frac{4}{2}[0 + 0 + 2((6 + 7) + (8 + 6) + (10 + 8) + (8 + 8) + (6 + 5))]$$

$$= \frac{4}{2}[0 + 0 + 2(13 + 14 + 18 + 16 + 11)]$$

$$= 2[0 + 2(72)]$$

$$= 2[144]$$

$$= 288 \text{ m}^2$$

Note that the first and last heights are zero.

EXAMPLE 3

Using the trapezoidal rule, the area of the following shape was estimated to be 732 cm^2. Find the value of x. (All units are in centimetres.)

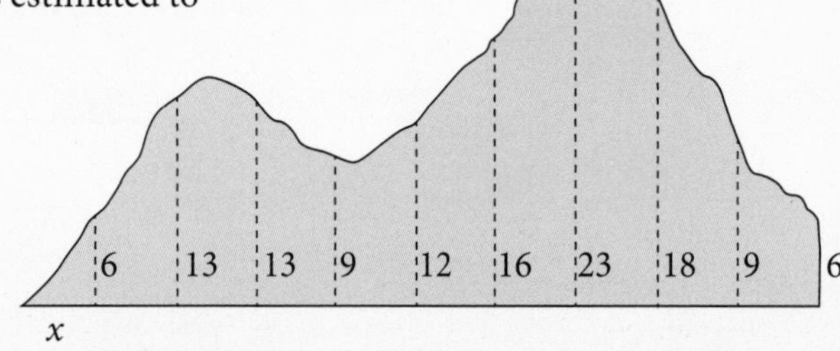

Solution

$$\text{Area} = \frac{h}{2}[y_1 + y_n + 2(y_2 + y_3 + y_3 + \ldots + y_{n-1})]$$

$$732 = \frac{x}{2}[0 + 6 + 2(6 + 13 + 13 + 9 + 12 + 16 + 23 + 18 + 9)]$$

$$732 = \frac{x}{2}[6 + 2(119)]$$

$$732 = \frac{x}{2}[6 + 238]$$

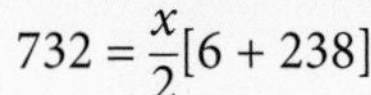

$$732 = \frac{x}{2}[244]$$

$$732 = x[122]$$

$$\frac{732}{122} = x \quad \Rightarrow \quad x = 6 \text{ cm}$$

Area and Perimeter

Practice Questions 16.4

1. Use the trapezoidal rule to estimate the area of the following shapes:

(i)

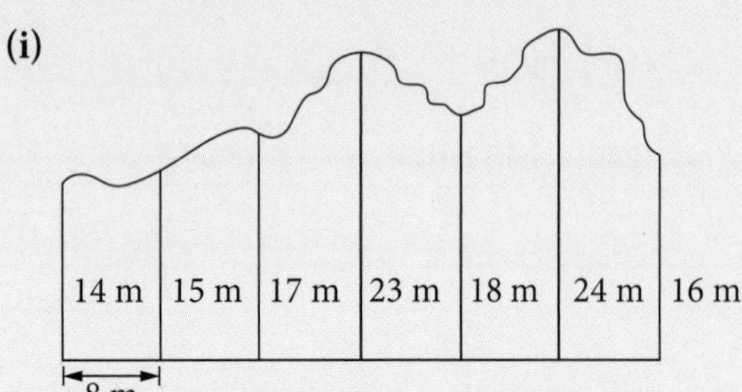

(ii)

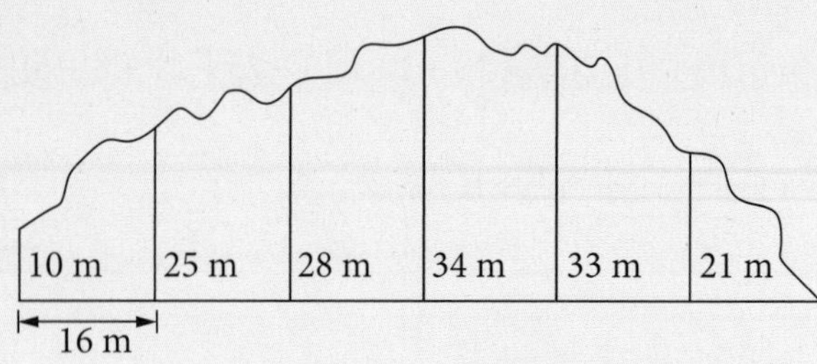

2. A sketch of a piece of land is shown.
At equal intervals of 16 m, perpendicular measurements are made to the top boundary.
   (i) Use the trapezoidal rule to estimate the area of the piece of land.
   (ii) Give the area as a percentage of a hectare.
   [1 hectare = 10,000 m^2]

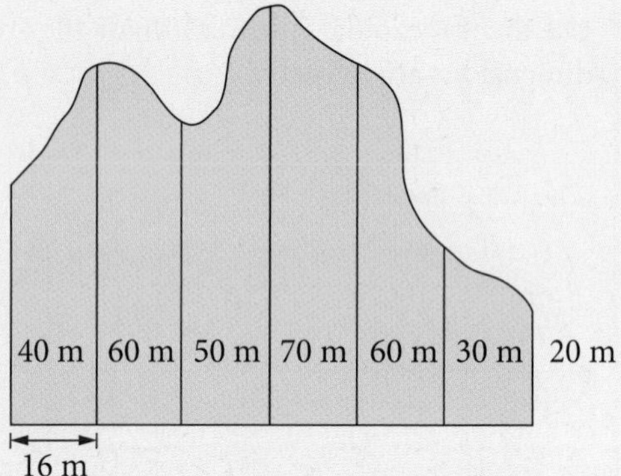

3. The sketch shows the garden of a house. At equal intervals of 3·6 m along one side, perpendicular measurements are made to the boundary, as shown on the sketch.

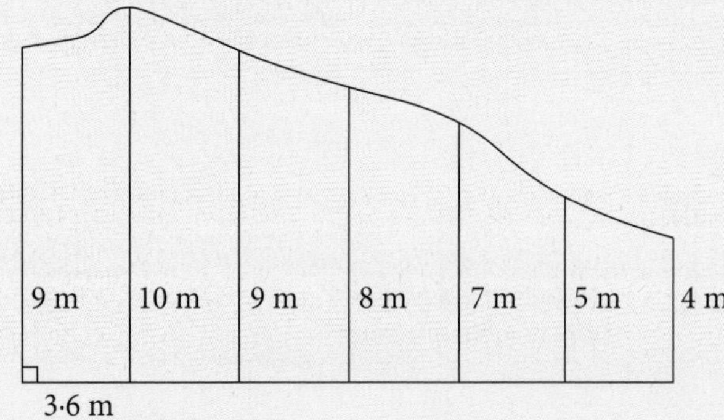

   (i) Use the trapezoidal rule to estimate the area of the garden.
   (ii) The owner of the house digs an ornamental pond in the garden.
   The surface area of the pond is 11 m^2. What percentage of the area of the garden is taken up by the pond?
   Give your answer correct to the nearest percent.

4. The sketch shows a piece of land covered by forest, which lies on one side of a straight road.
Measurements were taken, as shown, at equal intervals of 50 m along the road.
Use the trapezoidal rule to estimate the area of land covered by the forest.
Give your answer in hectares. [1 hectare = 10,000 m^2]

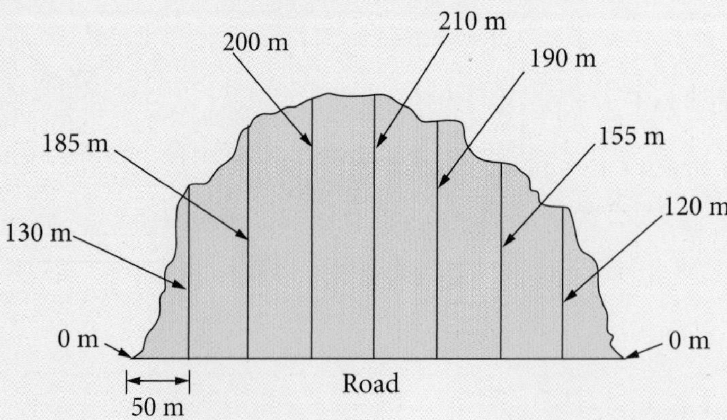

5. Use the trapezoidal rule to estimate the area of the following shape:

(i)

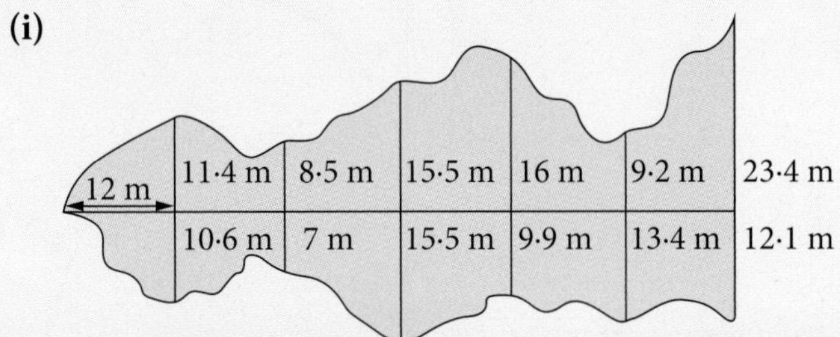

(ii)

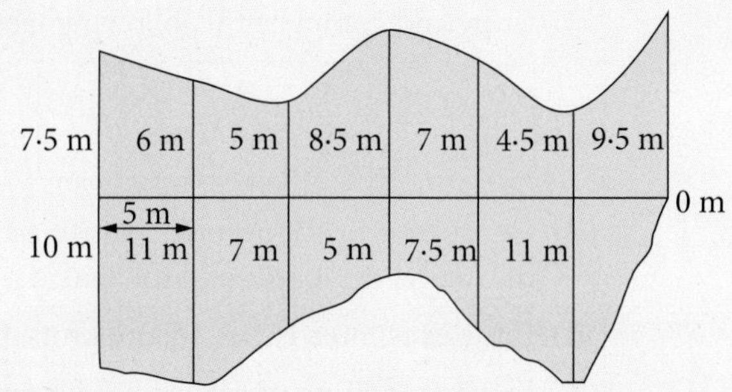

6. Use the grid to estimate the vertical height of each strip and hence use the trapezoidal rule to estimate the area under the curve (shaded area) for the following four graphs:

(i)

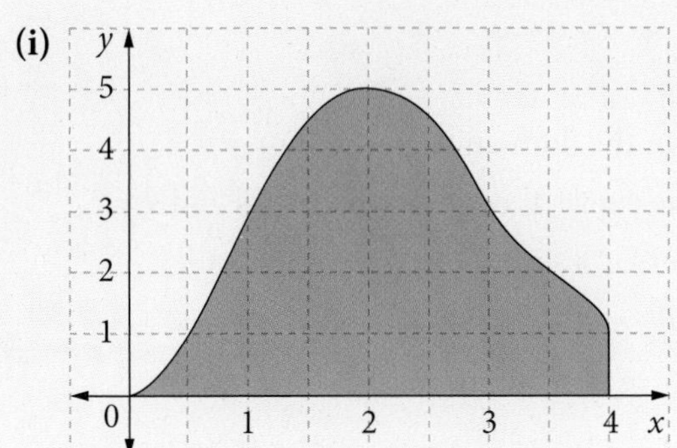

(ii)

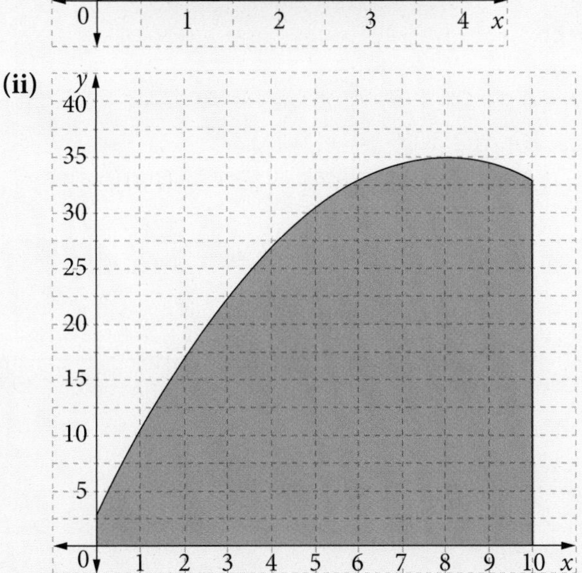

(iii)

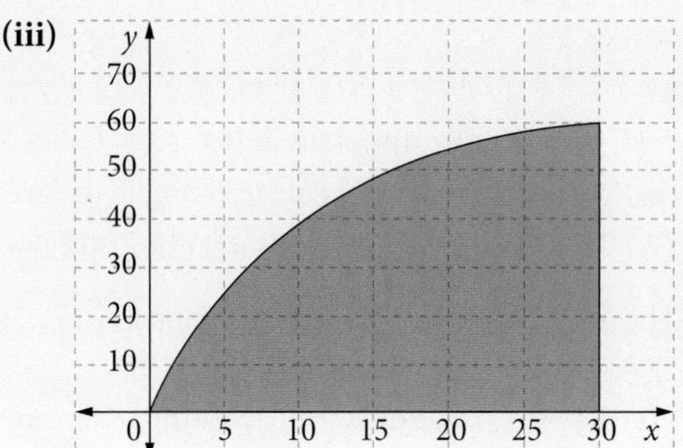

(iv)

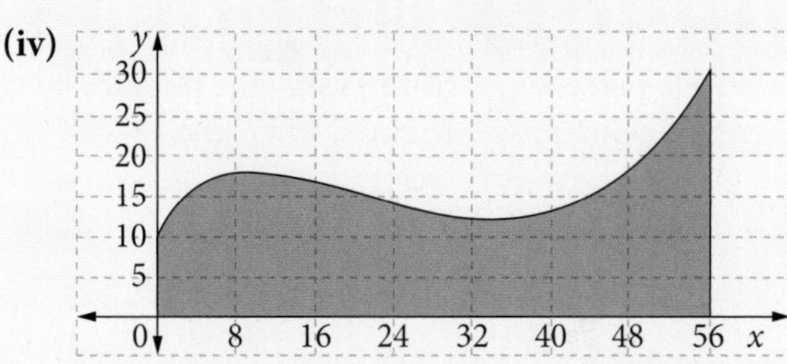

7. Archaeologists excavating a rectangular plot *ABCD* measuring 120 m by 60 m divided the plot into eight square sections as shown on the diagram. At the end of the first phase of the work the shaded area had been excavated. To estimate the area excavated, perpendicular measurements were made to the edge of the excavated area, as shown.

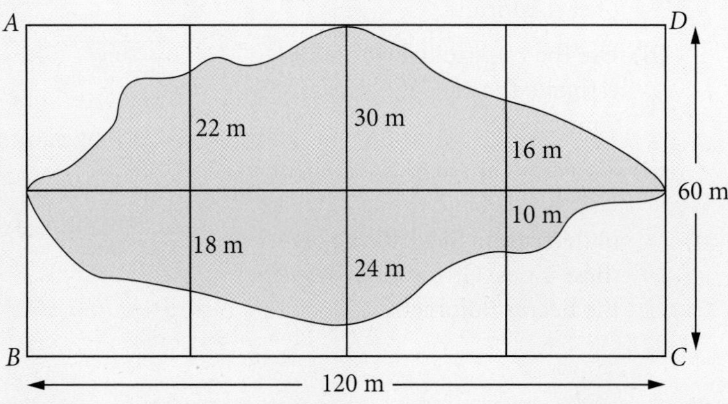

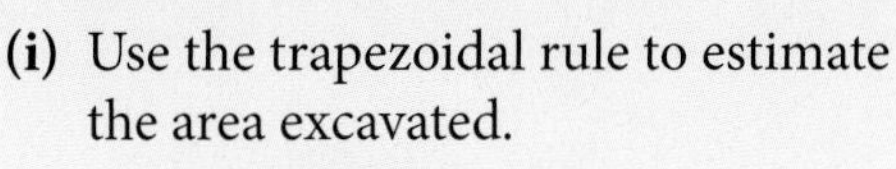

(i) Use the trapezoidal rule to estimate the area excavated.

(ii) If it has taken the team 12 days to excavate the area shown, how long will it take for them to excavate the entire plot, assuming they continue to work at the same rate?

8. The diagram shows the curve $y = -x^2 + 3x + 4$ in the domain $0 \le x \le 4$.

(i) Copy and complete the following table.

x	0	1	2	3	4
y					

(ii) Hence, use the trapezoidal rule to estimate the area between the curve, the x-axis and the y-axis.

(iii) If the exact area is $18\frac{2}{3}$ square units, find the percentage error in using the trapezoidal rule. Give your answer to two decimal places.

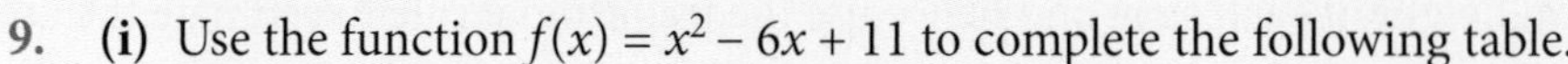

9. (i) Use the function $f(x) = x^2 - 6x + 11$ to complete the following table.

x	0	1	2	3	4	5	6
y							

(ii) Hence, draw the graph of the curve $f(x) = x^2 - 6x + 11$ in the domain $0 \le x \le 6$.

(iii) Use the trapezoidal rule to estimate the area between the curve, the x-axis, the y-axis and $x = 6$.

(iv) If the exact area is 30 square units, find the percentage error in using the trapezoidal rule.

10. The diagram shows a curve in the domain $-1 \le x \le 4$. The coordinates of the points are shown.

(i) Use the trapezoidal rule to estimate the area between the curve, the x-axis, $x = -1$ and $x = 4$ the shaded area.

(ii) If the exact area is 34·6 square units, find the percentage error in using the trapezoidal rule. Give your answer to two decimal places.

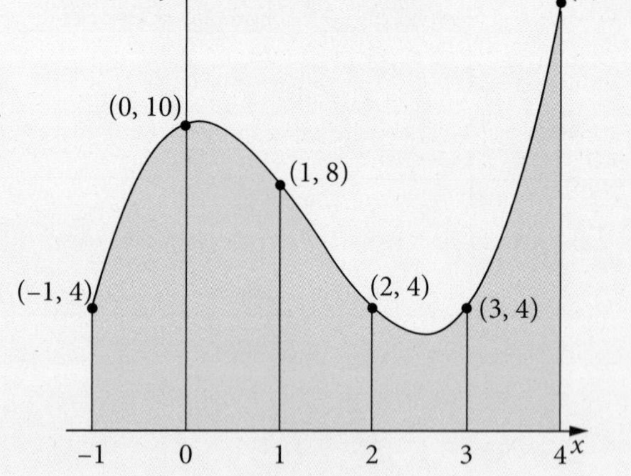

11. The diagram shows a scaled drawing of a section of Slovakia. The scale is 1 unit = 22 km.

(i) Construct vertical altitudes and use the grid to estimate the heights of each altitude.

(ii) Use the trapezoidal rule to estimate the area of Slovakia. Give your answer to two decimal places.

(iii) Two cities are marked on the map. Use the grid and the scale factor to determine the distance between these cities. Give your answer to the nearest kilometre.

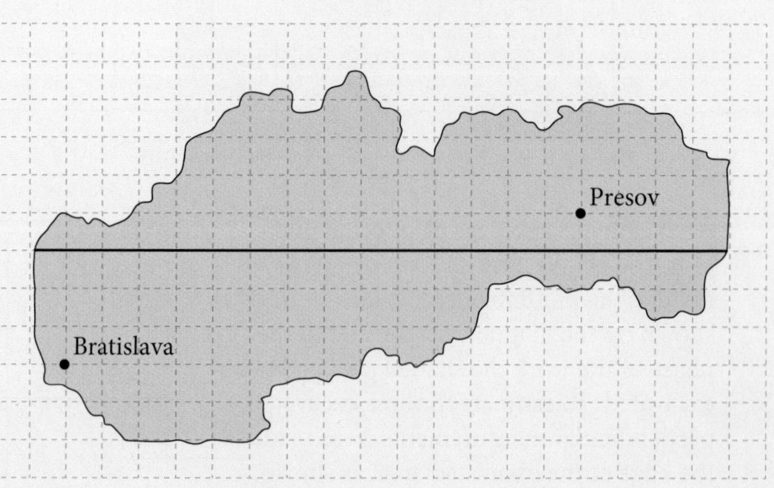

12. Using the trapezoidal rule, the area of the following shape was found to be 618 m^2. Find the value of x.

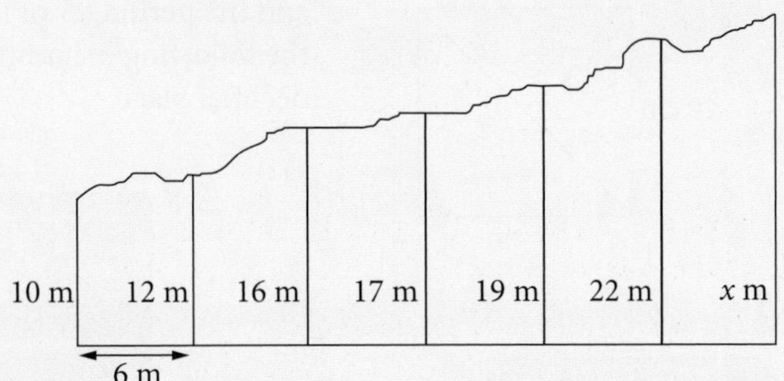

13. The sketch shows a flood caused by a leaking underground pipe that runs from A to B.

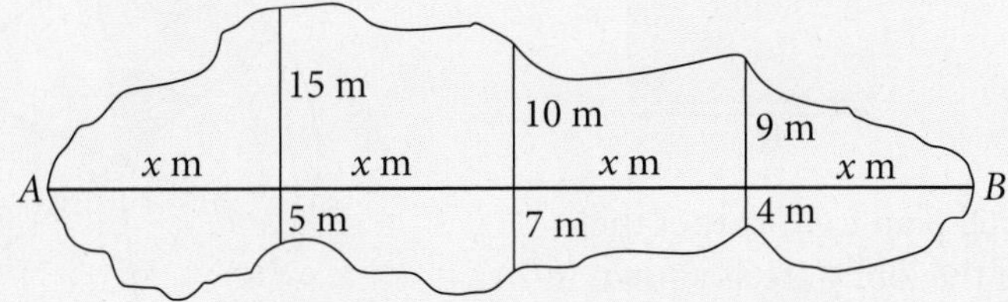

Using the trapezoidal rule, the area of the flood is estimated to be 1,100 m^2.
Find x and hence, write down the length of the pipe.

14. A curve is graphed as shown.
The height of each altitude is shown.
If the area under the curve (shaded area) is 8200 square units, find the value of k, the height of the fifth altitude.

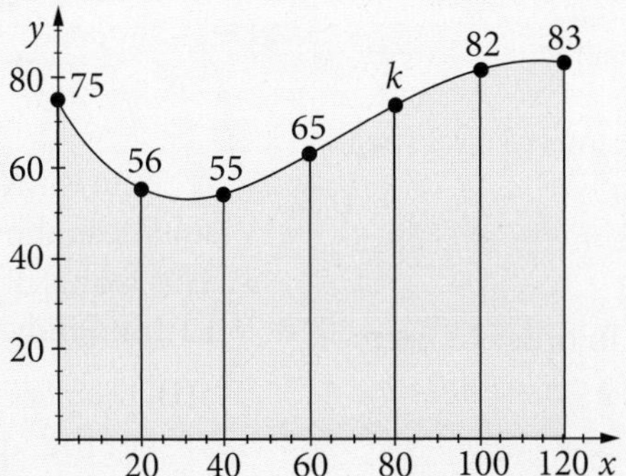

Revision and Exam Style Questions – Section A

1. The right-angled triangle shown in the diagram has sides of length 10 cm and 24 cm.

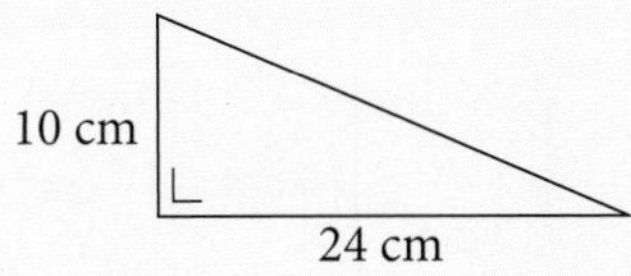

Find:

(i) the length of the third side

(ii) the length of the perimeter of the triangle.

2. The area of a square is 64 cm^2.
Find the length of a side of the square and hence, find the perimeter of the square.

3. Find the area of the figure in the diagram:

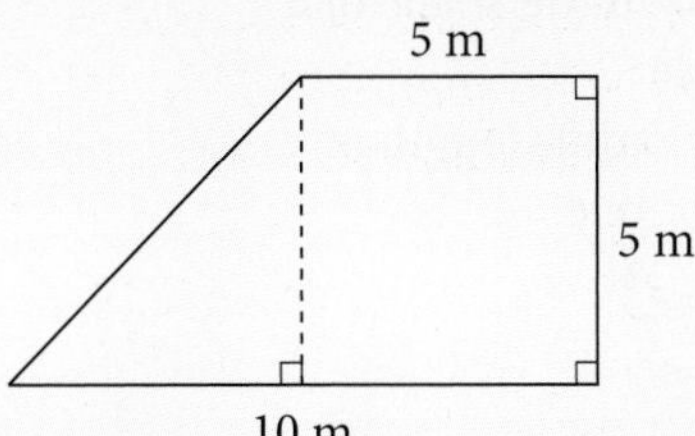

4. A rectangle has length 21 cm and width 20 cm. Find:
   - **(i)** the perimeter of the rectangle
   - **(ii)** the area of the rectangle
   - **(iii)** the length of the diagonal.

20 cm

21 cm

5. Calculate the area of the shaded region in the diagram.

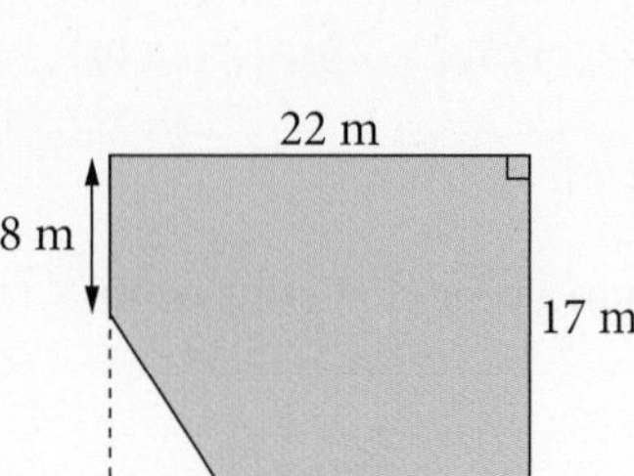

6. The management of a hotel plan to re-carpet their lobby. The dimensions of the lobby are as shown in the diagram.

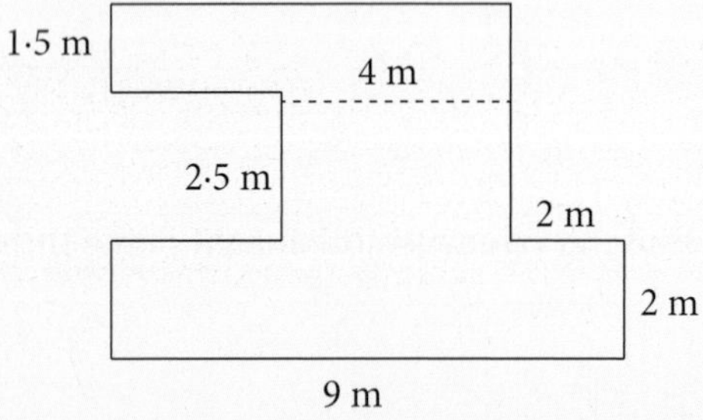

Company A charge €25 per square metre of carpet and €8 per square metre for fitting.
Company B charge €32 per square metre of carpet and a flat charge of €50 for fitting.
Which company should they use, in order to keep the cost of the re-carpeting as low as possible?

7. A sector of a circle has radius 18 cm and forms the angle 120°. Give the following answers in terms of π.
   - **(i)** The area of the sector.
   - **(ii)** The length of the arc of the sector.
   - **(iii)** The perimeter of the sector.

120°

18 cm

8. A piece of wire of length 154 cm is in the shape of a semicircle.
   Find the radius length of the semicircle.
   Take $\pi = \frac{22}{7}$

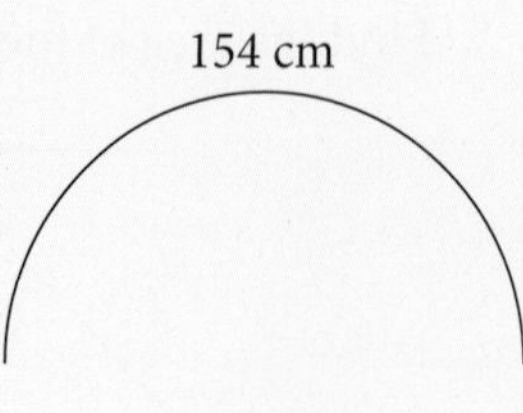

9. Using the π button on your calculator, find the area and the perimeter of the shaded region in each of the following diagrams. Give your answer to one decimal place.

(i)

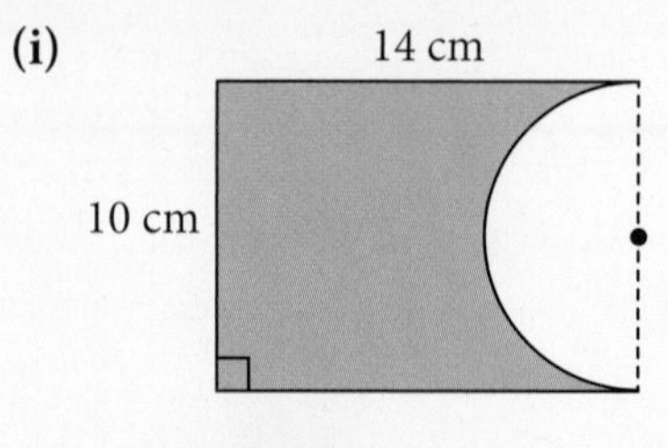

(ii)

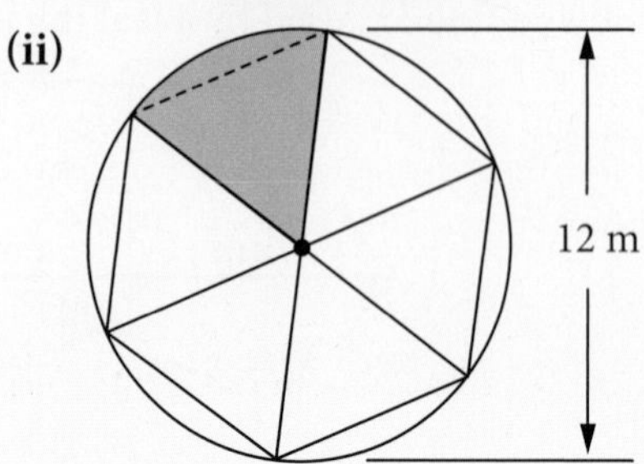

10. Find the area of the following compound shape. Give your answer correct to two decimal places.

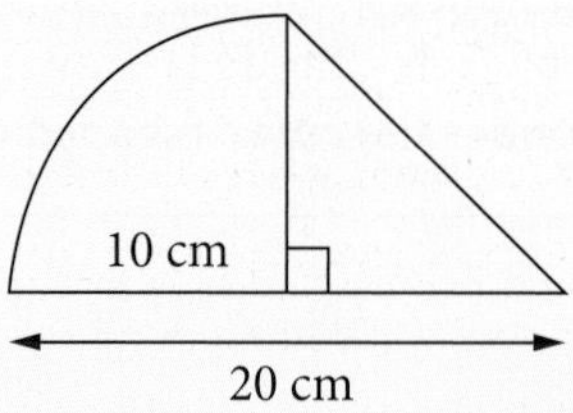

11. A circle is inscribed in a square as shown. The radius of the circle is 12 cm. Find:
   - **(i)** the perimeter of the square
   - **(ii)** the area of the square
   - **(iii)** the area of the shaded region.

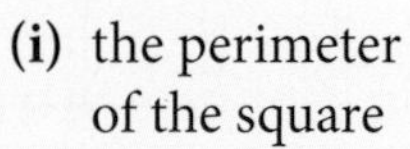

12 cm

12. Use the trapezoidal rule to find the area of the following shape:

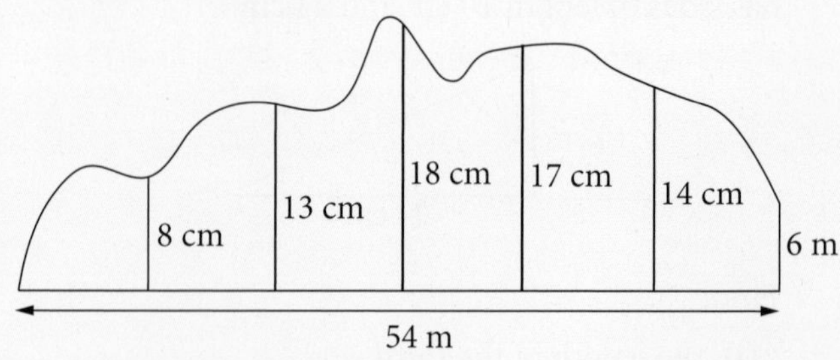

Area and Perimeter

13. Use the grid to estimate the vertical height of each strip and hence use the trapezoidal rule to estimate the area under the curve (shaded area) for the following graph:

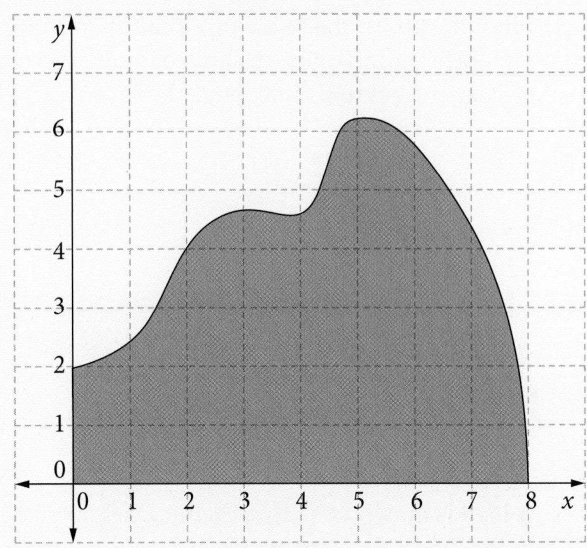

Revision and Exam Style Questions – Section B

More challenging problems

1. The diagram shows a rectangle of length 32 cm. The area of the rectangle is 576 cm^2.

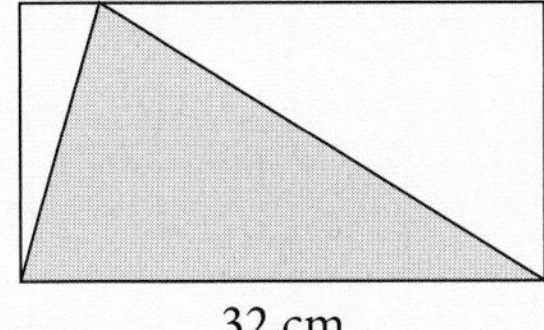

Find:

(i) the height of the rectangle

(ii) the area of the shaded triangle.

2. Find the area of the shaded region in the following shape. Let $\pi = 3{\cdot}14$ and give your answer to two decimal places.

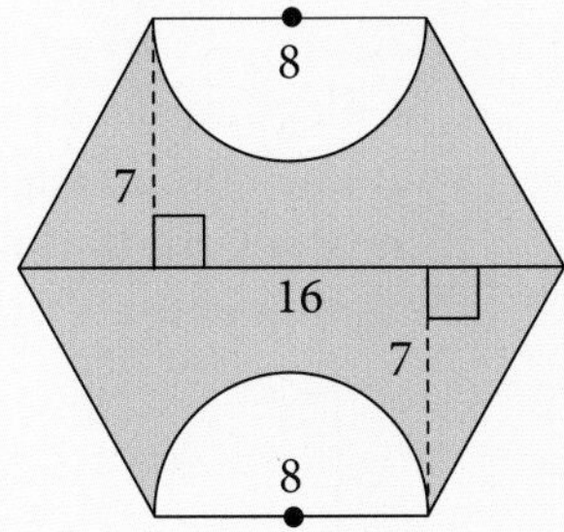

3. The sector shown in the diagram has radius of length 8 cm. Find:

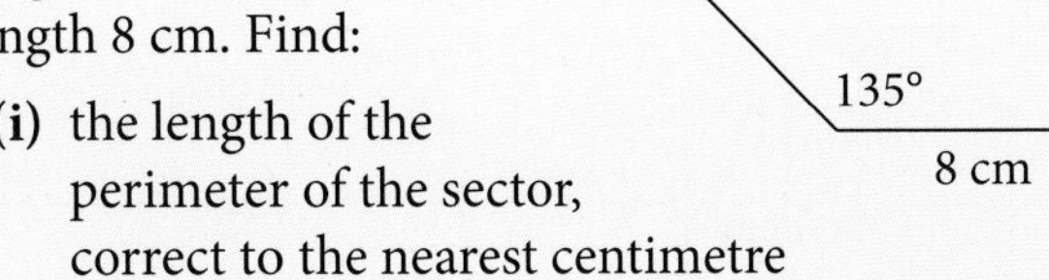

(i) the length of the perimeter of the sector, correct to the nearest centimetre

(ii) the area of the sector, correct to the nearest square centimetre.

4. A running track is made up of two straight parts and two semicircular parts, as shown in the diagram.

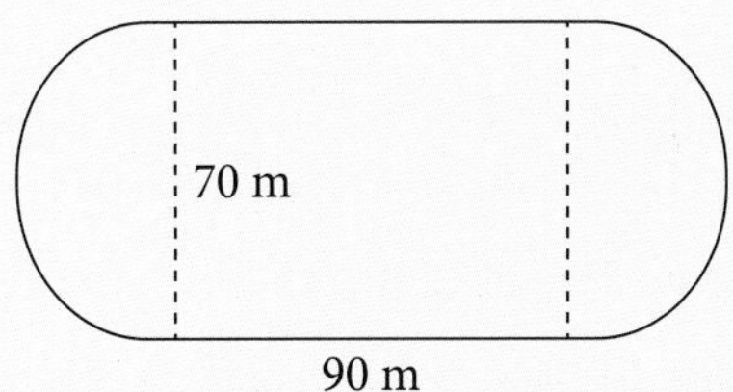

The length of each of the straight parts is 90 m
The diameter of each of the semicircular parts is 70 m.

(i) Calculate the area enclosed by the running track, correct to two decimal places.

(ii) Calculate the length of the running track, correct to the nearest metre.

(iii) How many laps of the track will the athletes need to complete in order to finish a 2000 m race?

(iv) An athlete completes 12 laps of this track in 15 minutes. Find the speed of the athlete in kilometres per hour.

5. Find the area of the following compound shape. Use the π button on the calculator and give your answer correct to two decimal places.

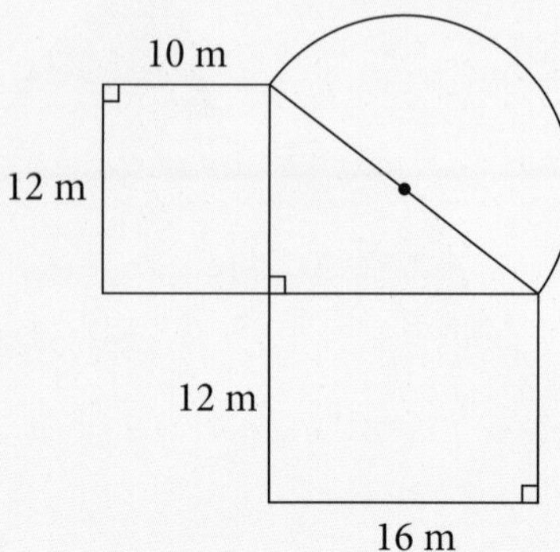

6. A logo is drawn from three semicircles, as shown in the diagram.

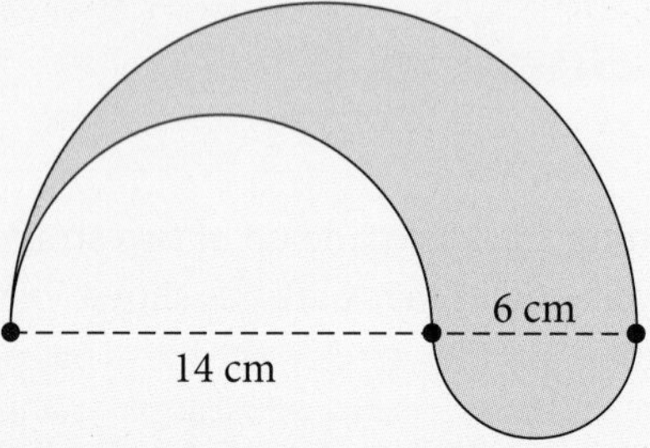

Find, in terms of π:

(i) the area of the logo (shaded area)

(ii) the perimeter of the logo.

7. The diagram shows the curve $y = x^2 - 2x + 4$ in the domain $-1 \leq x \leq 5$

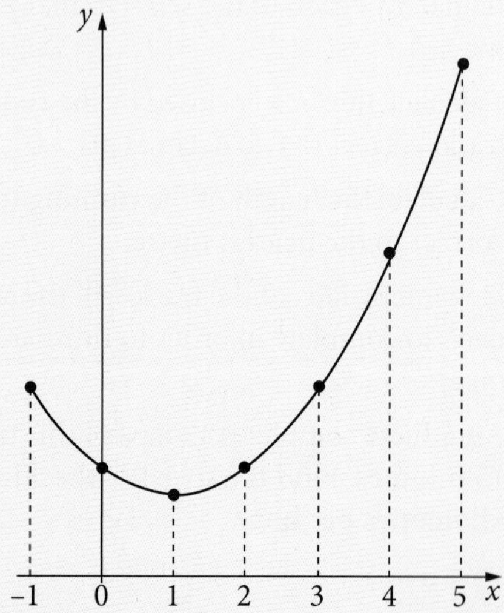

(i) Copy and complete the following table.

x	-1	0	1	2	3	4	5
y							

(ii) Hence, use the trapezoidal rule to estimate the area between the curve, the x-axis and the lines $x = -1$ and $x = 5$.

(iii) Given that the true area of this region is 42 square units, find the percentage error in the estimated area given by the trapezoidal rule. Give your answer to two decimal places.

8. The diagram below shows the outline of a park, drawn onto a grid.
The scale of the grid is 1 unit = 30 m.
Use the grid to estimate the vertical height of each strip and hence use the trapezoidal rule to estimate the area within the boundary of the park.

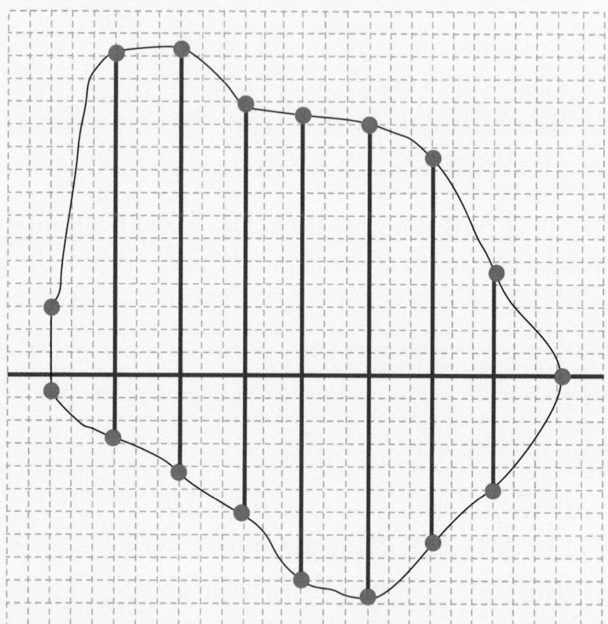

9. The diagram shows a sketch of a piece of paper with one uneven edge. At equal intervals of h cm along the bottom edge, perpendicular measurements are made to the top edge.

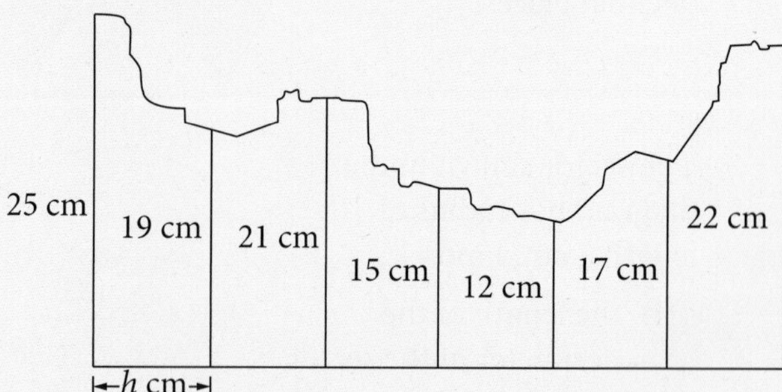

Using the trapezoidal rule, the area of the piece of paper is estimated to be 1075 cm^2.
Find h.

Now that you have completed the chapter, revisit the 'Something to think about…' question.

Volume and Surface Area

CHAPTER 17

Sections covered within this chapter:

KEY WORDS

- Volume
- Prism
- Frustum
- Capacity
- Cross-section
- Recast
- Surface area
- Hemisphere
- Displacement
- Net
- Cone

SOMETHING TO THINK ABOUT... 

A rectangular block of wax of length 40 cm, width 33 cm and height 7 cm is melted down and recast into 16 cylindrical candles, each of height 15 cm.

These candles are packaged into a box, with a square base.

Find the volume of the smallest box into which the 16 candles can fit.

Take $\pi = \frac{22}{7}$.

Introduction

This chapter will deal with finding the volume and surface area of a variety of objects.

The **volume** of an object is the amount of space the object takes up.

Capacity is a measure of the amount of space inside an object. It can also be called the internal volume.

The **surface area** of an object is the area of the outside of the shape.

Throughout this chapter, taking the following steps will help when solving problems:

Step 1: Identify the shape and draw a sketch, if not given.

Step 2: Identify what values are given and what values are required.

Step 3: Select the relevant formula.

Step 4: Put the values into the formula.

Step 5: Solve the resulting equation.

It is very important that you know your units and always put them as part of your answer.

Length: mm, cm, m, km

Area: mm^2, cm^2, m^2, km^2

Volume: mm^3, cm^3, m^3, km^3

Section 17.1: Regular Solids – Cuboids, Cubes and Prisms

Learning Outcomes:

You should be able to:

- find the volume and surface area of regular solids – cuboids, cubes and prisms
- use the nets of prisms
- solve problems in real-world contexts

Rectangular solid (cuboid)

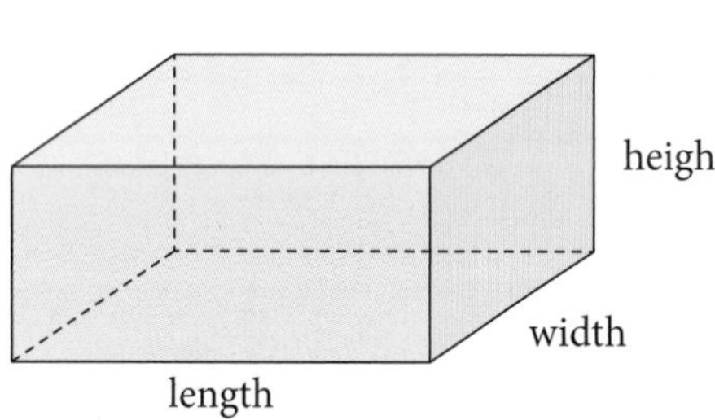

Net of a cuboid

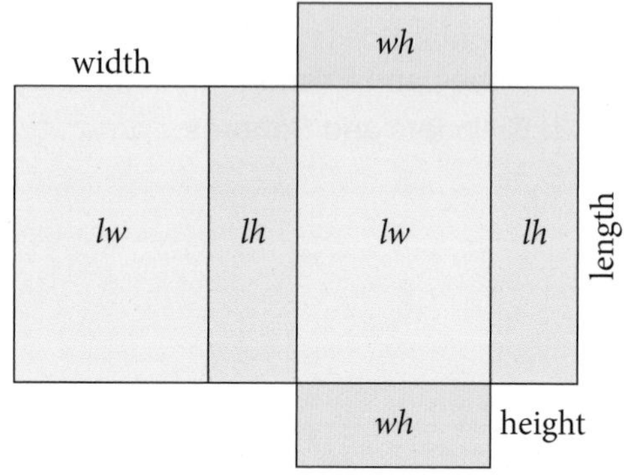

Volume = (length)(width)(height)

Surface area = $2lw + 2lh + 2wh$

A **net** is what a 3D shape would look like if it were opened out flat.

Cube

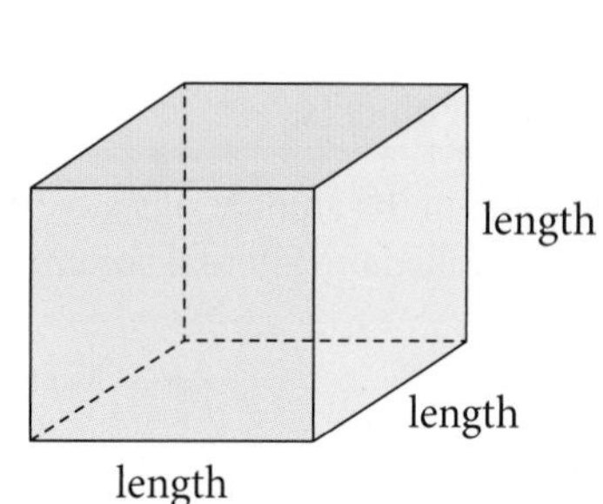

Net of cube

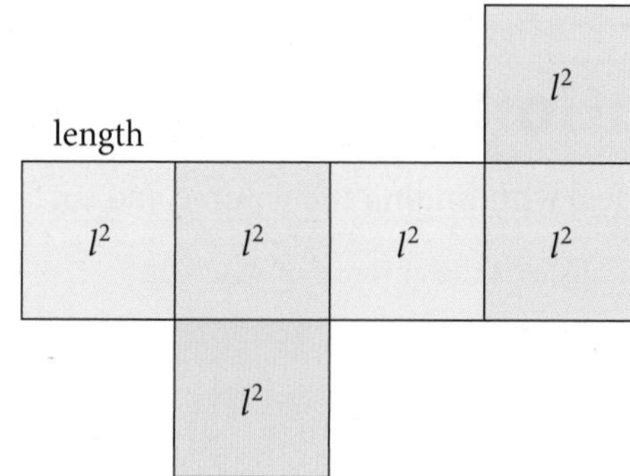

Volume = length^3

Surface area = $6l^2$

Prisms

A **prism** is a solid object which has the same cross-section throughout its length and its sides are parallel.

The **cross-section** is the shape we get when cutting straight through an object

For prisms, the cross-section is the same throughout the object. Therefore, the cross-section is the shape shown at the end of the object (marked as A in the following diagrams).

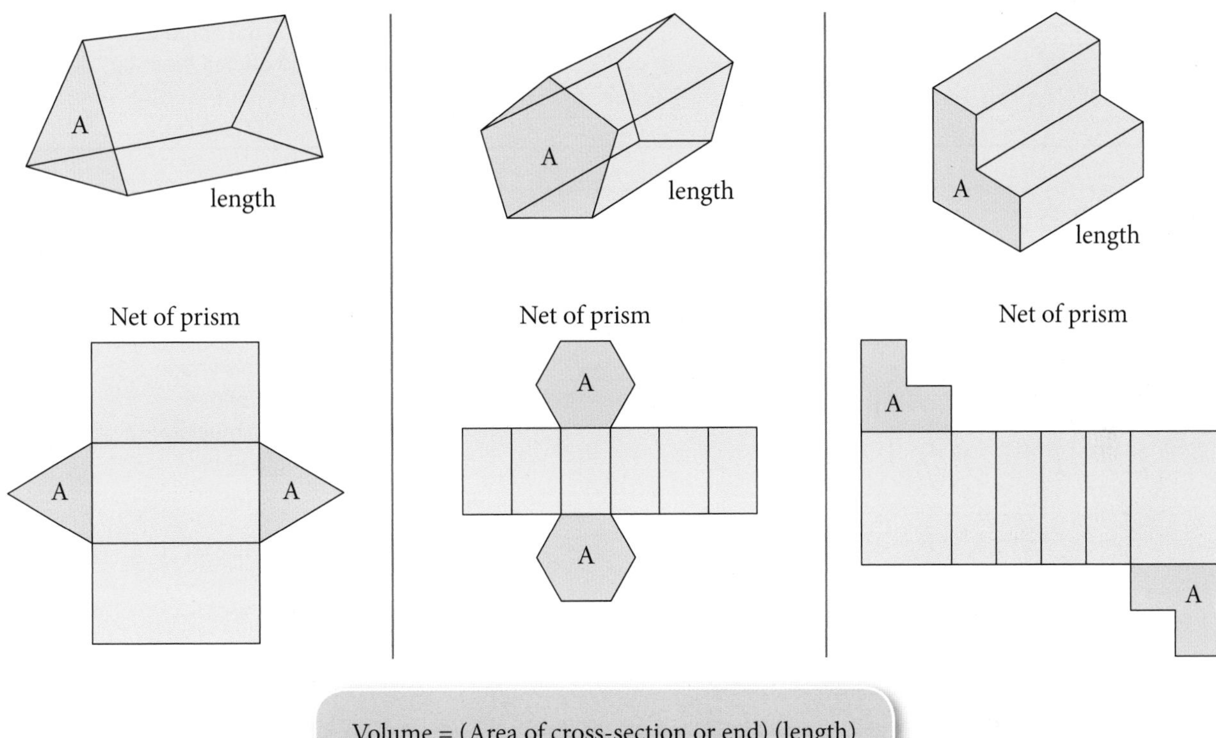

Volume = (Area of cross-section or end) (length)

The formula for the **volume** of a prism appears on page 11 of the booklet of *formulae and tables,* as shown:

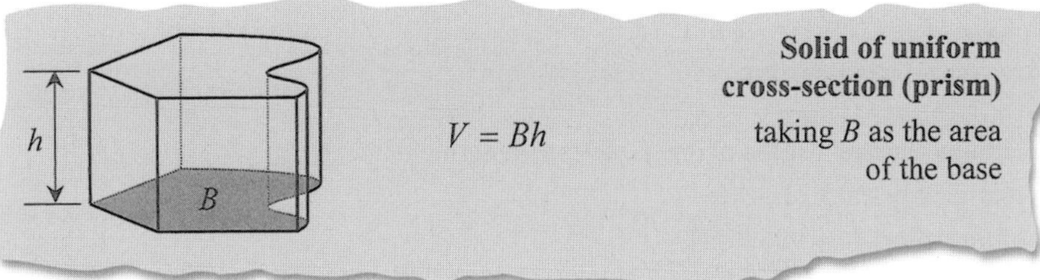

EXAMPLE 1

Given the volume of the box shown is 480 cm^3, find:

(i) the width of the box

(ii) the surface area of the box.

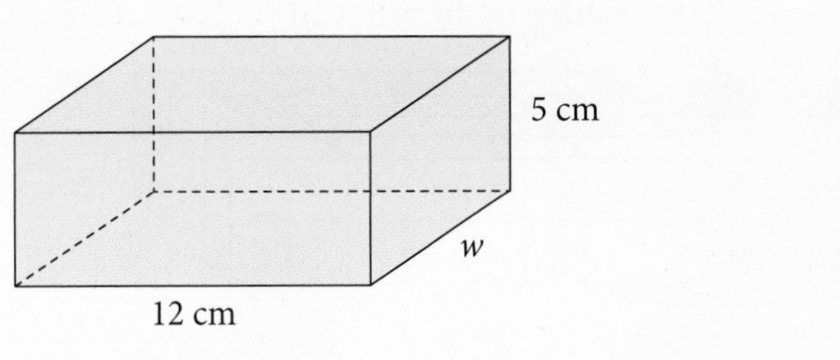

Solution

(i) Volume = 480, length = 12, height = 5

width = ?

Volume = (length)(width)(height)

$480 = (12)(w)(5)$

$480 = (60)(w)$

$\frac{480}{60} = w$

$8 \text{ cm} = w$

(ii) Length = 12, width = 8, height = 5

Surface area = ?

Surface area $= 2lw + 2lh + 2wh$

$= 2(12)(8) + 2(12)(5) + 2(8)(5)$

$= 192 + 120 + 80$

$= 392 \text{ cm}^2$

Finding the surface area is the same as finding the area of each face and adding them up.

EXAMPLE 2

The diagram shows a prism with dimensions as shown.
Find the volume of the prism.

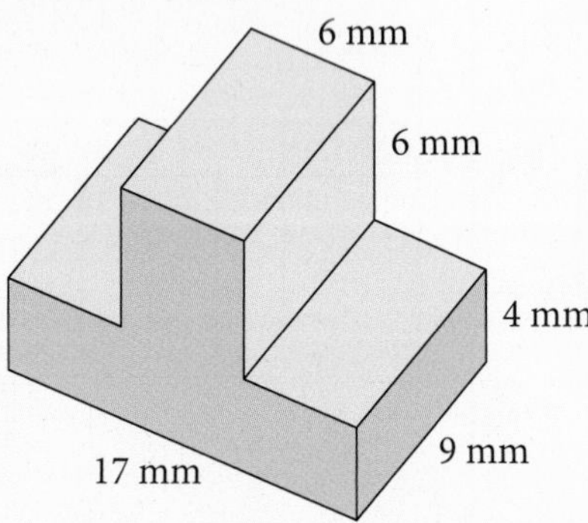

To find the volume of this shape, we firstly find the area of the cross-section and then multiply this area by the length of the shape.

Solution

Find the area of the cross-section.

Divide the shape up into a square ① and a rectangle ②.

Area of ① = (6)(6) = 36 mm^2

Area of ② = (17)(4) = 68 mm^2

Area of the cross-section = 36 + 68 = 104 mm^2

Volume of prism = (area of cross-section)(length)

Volume of prism = (104)(9)

Volume of prism = 936 mm^3

cross-section:

6 mm
1
6 mm
2
4 mm
17 mm

Practice Questions 17.1

1. Find the volume of the following cuboids, given [cube] = 1 cm^3

(i)

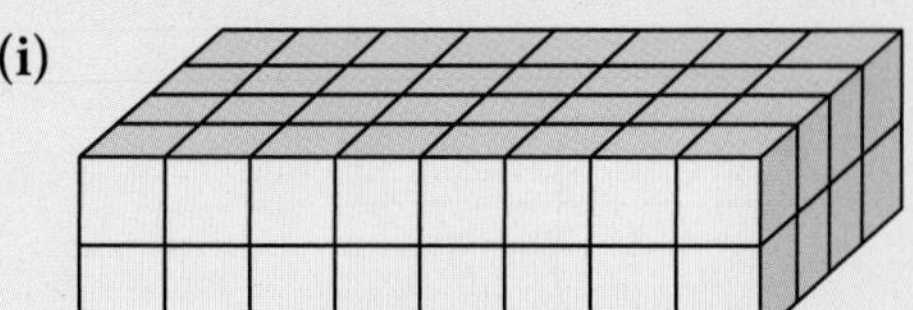

(ii)

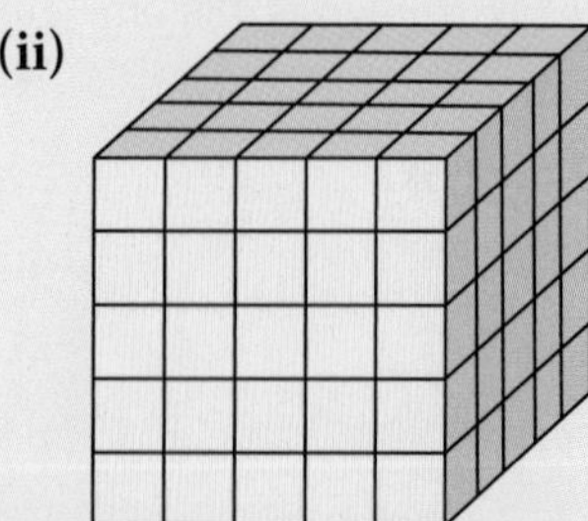

(iii)

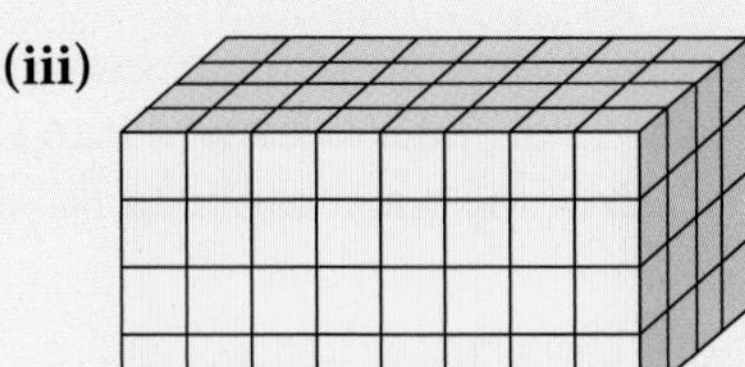

(iv)

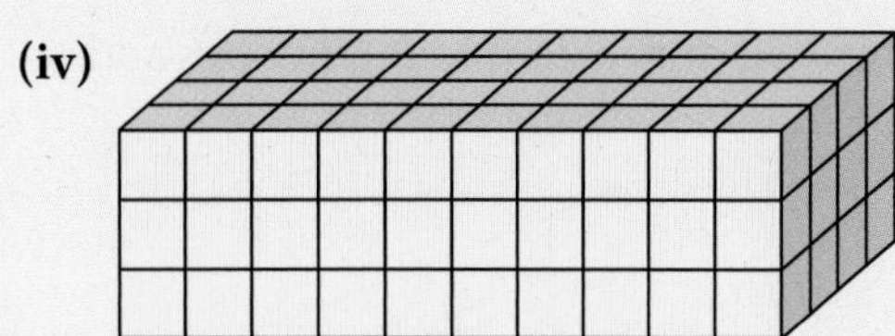

2. Which of the nets below could have been folded to make the rectangular solid shown?

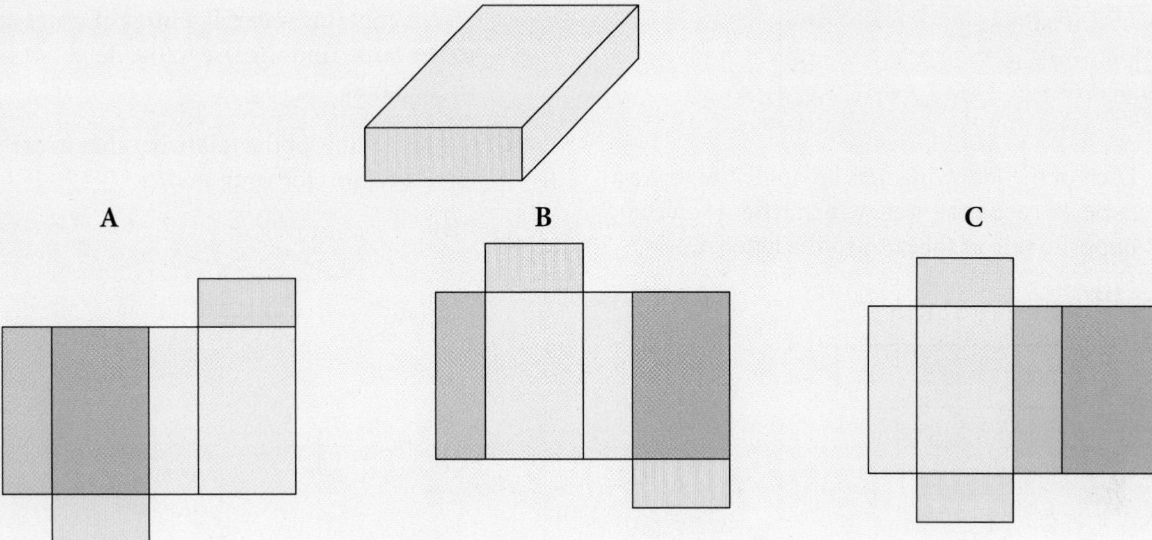

3. Find the volume and surface area of the following rectangular solids:

(i)

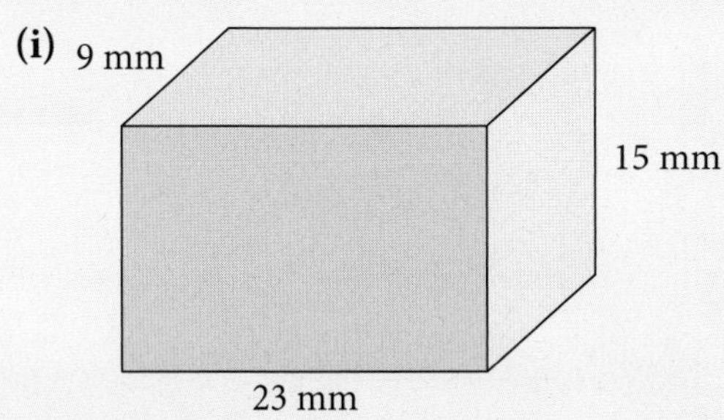

(ii)

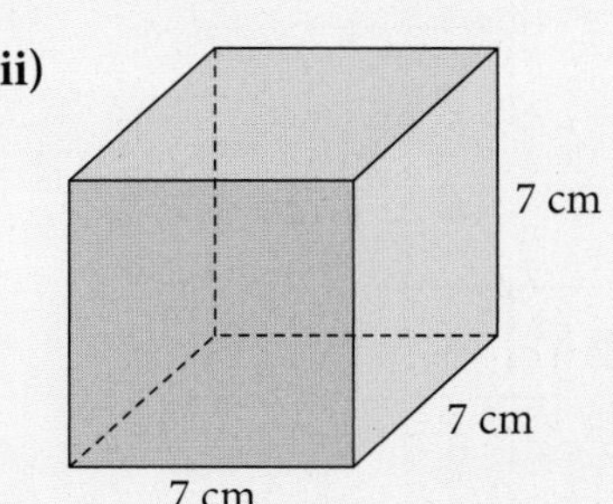

4. A rectangular block has length 30 cm, width 10 cm and height 14 cm.
   (i) Draw a diagram of the block, clearly showing all dimensions.
   (ii) Find its volume.
   (iii) Find its surface area.

5. A cube has a length of 12 cm. Find:
   (i) its volume
   (ii) its surface area.

6. Convert all dimensions to centimetres and hence find the capacity of the cuboid.

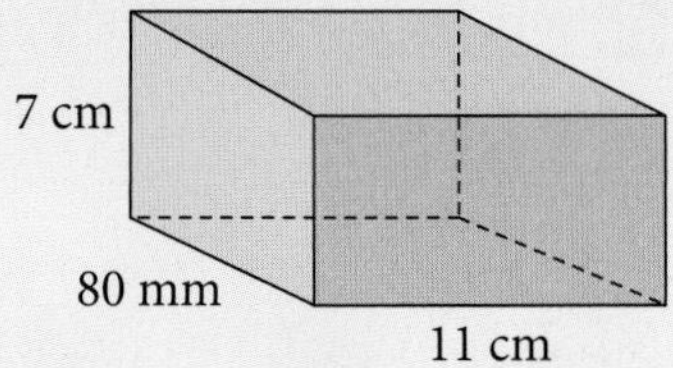

It is vital to convert all dimensions into the same units of measurement before starting a question.

7. Convert all dimensions to millimetres and hence find the volume of the cuboid.

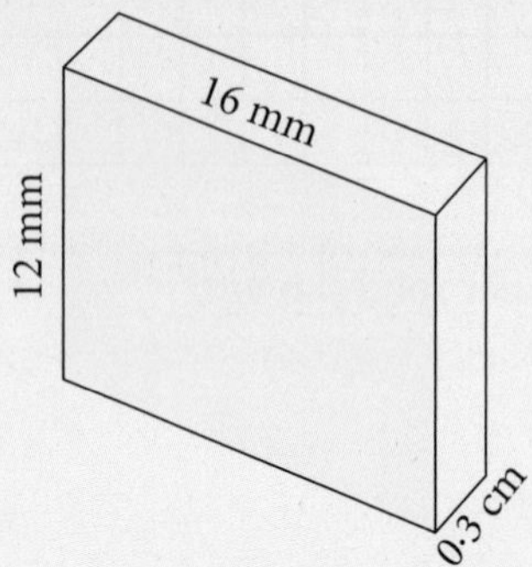

8. Each of the following nets are folded to make a cube. In each case, state which letter is on the opposite side of the cube to the letter A.

(i)

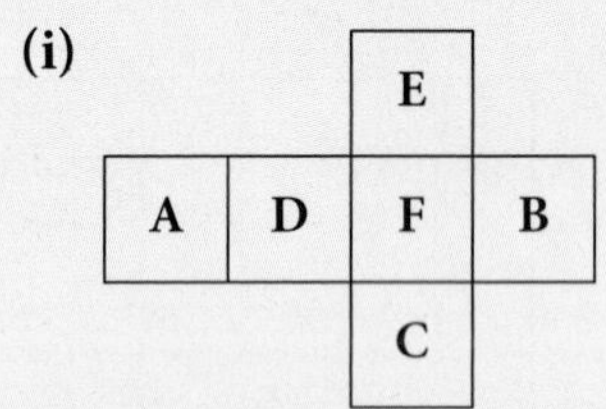

(ii)

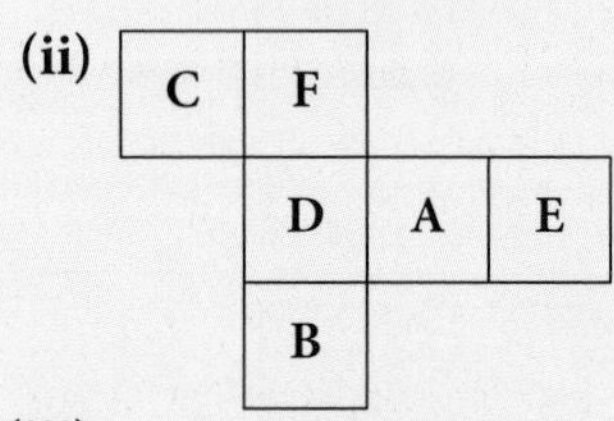

(iii)

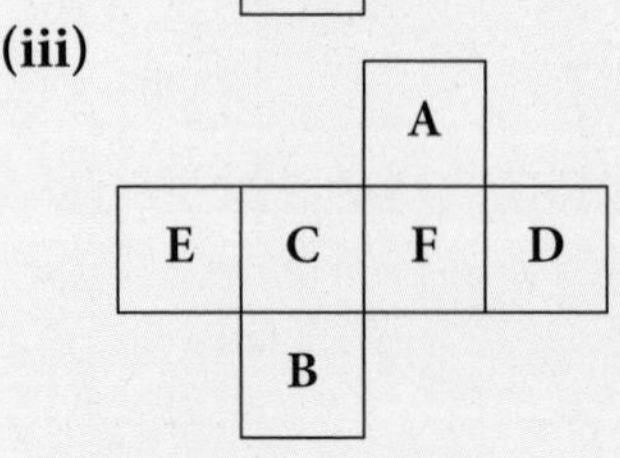

9. A cuboid has a volume of 378 cm^3. Given that its length is 9 cm and its height is 6 cm, find:

(i) its width

(ii) its surface area.

It is good practice to draw a sketch of each shape.

10. A cuboid has a volume of 440 m^3. Given that its length is 11 m and its width is 800 cm, find:

(i) its height (ii) its surface area.

11. A cube has a volume of 729 cm^3. Find:

(i) its length (ii) its surface area.

12. A cube has a volume of 1,331 m^3. Find:

(i) its length (ii) its surface area.

13. How many rectangular biscuit packets measuring 12 cm by 4 cm by 6 cm can be packed into a cardboard box measuring 84 cm by 32 cm by 54 cm?

14. An empty rectangular tank has a square base of length 80 cm. 96 litres of water is poured into the tank. Find the depth of the water in the tank.

1,000 cm^3 = 1 litre

15. A rectangular tank of length 40 cm and width 25 cm contains water. If 4 litres of water are added to the tank, find the rise in the height of the water in the tank.

16. Which, if any, of the following shapes are prisms? Give a reason for your answer.

(i)

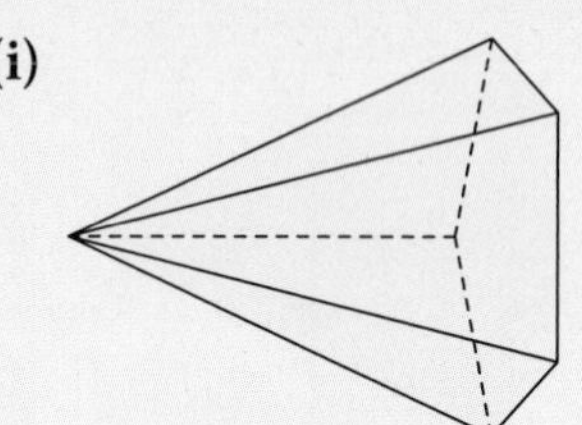

(ii)

(iii)

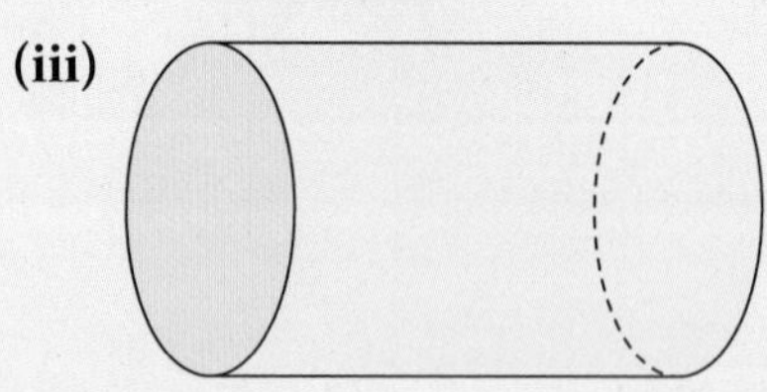

17. Given the area of the cross-section in each case, find the volume of these prisms.

(i)

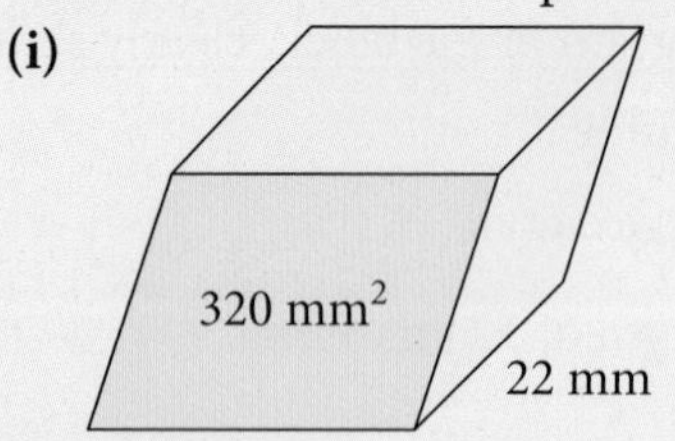

(ii)

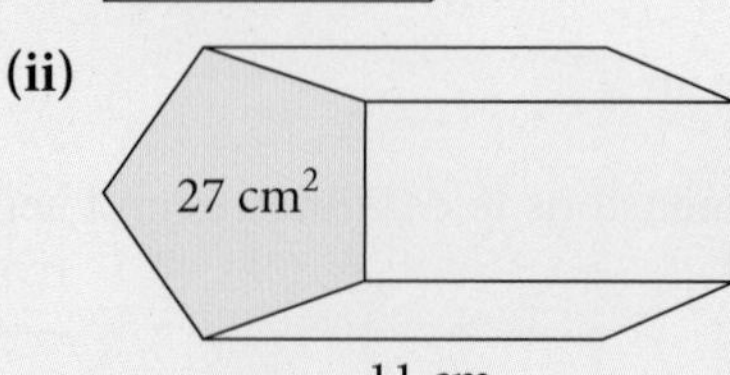

(iii)

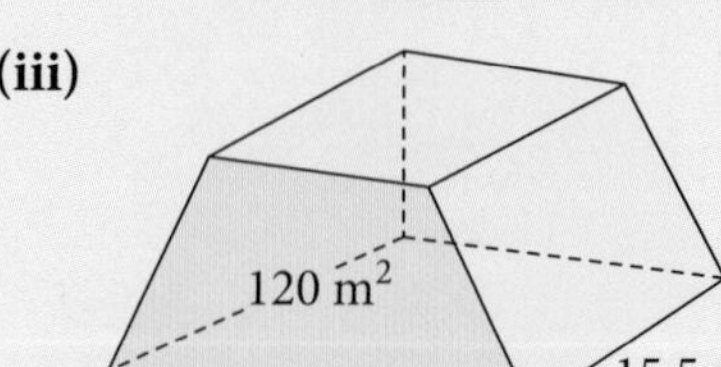

18. The diagram shows a wooden wedge. Find:
   (i) the area of the cross-section
   (ii) the volume of the wedge
   (iii) the surface area of the wedge, correct to two decimal places.

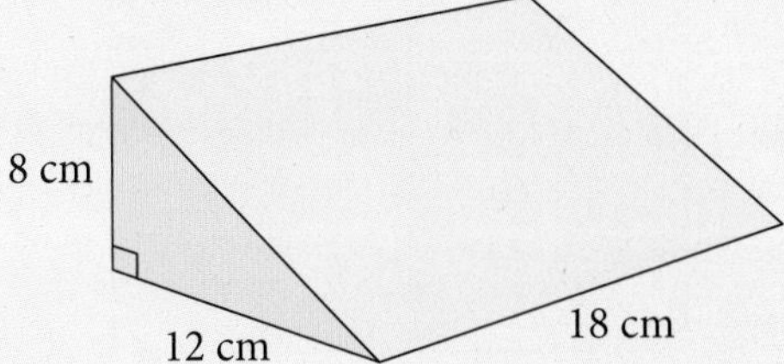

19. Find the volume of the following prisms:

(i)

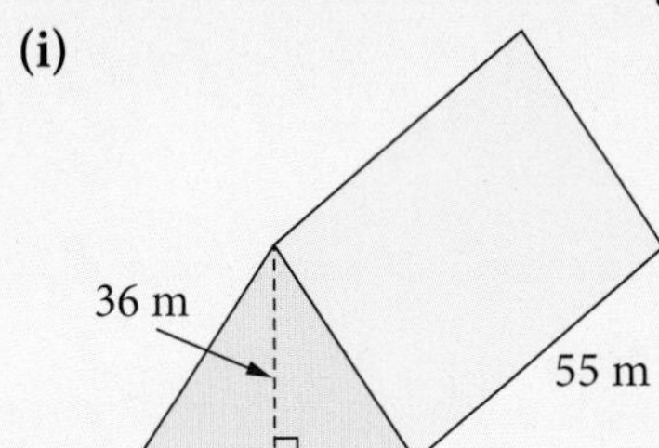

(ii)

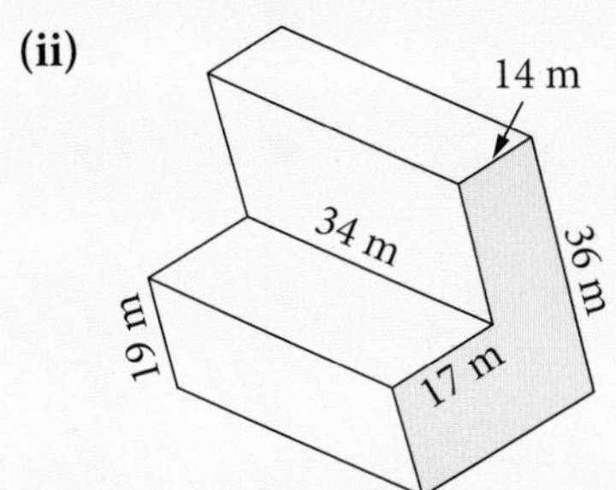

(iii)

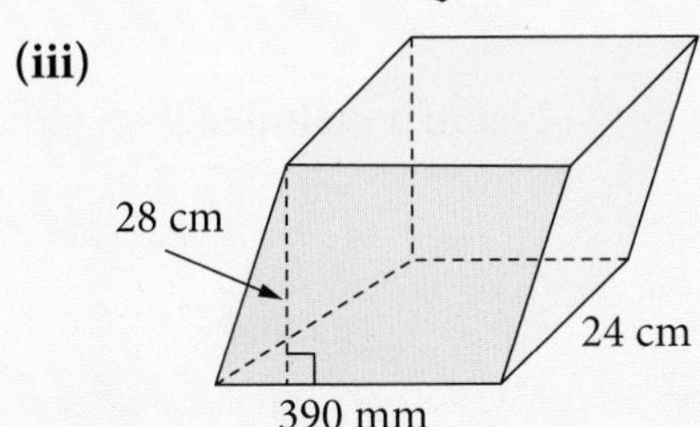

(iv)

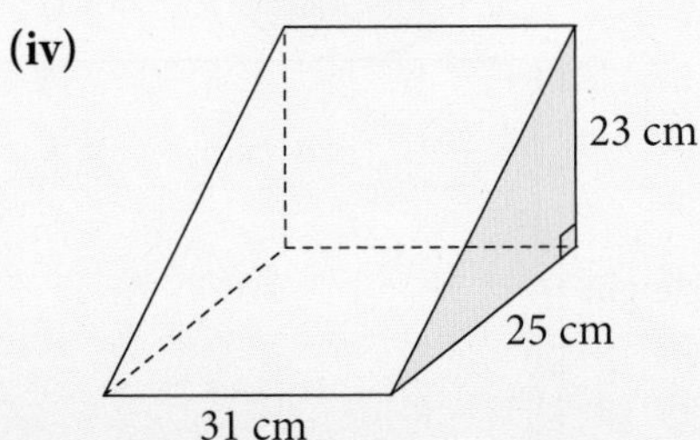

(v)

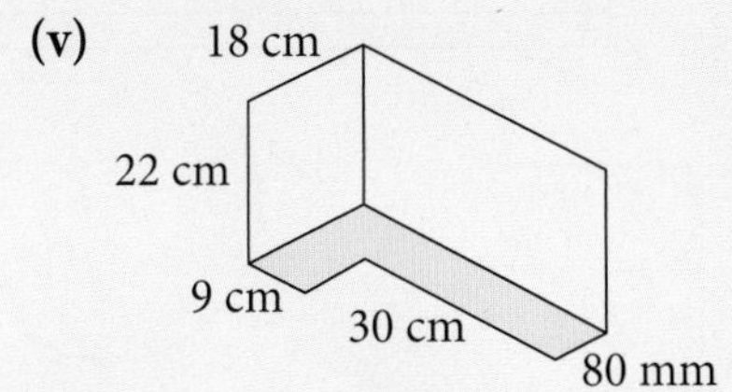

(vi)

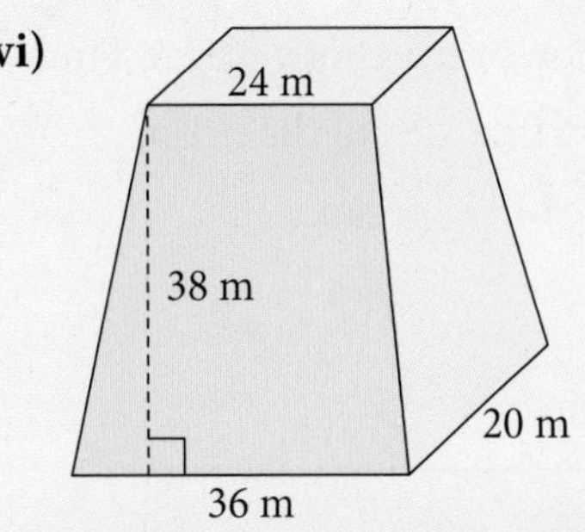

20. The diagram shows a swimming pool. Find the capacity of the pool. Give your answer in litres, given $1\ m^3 = 1{,}000$ litres

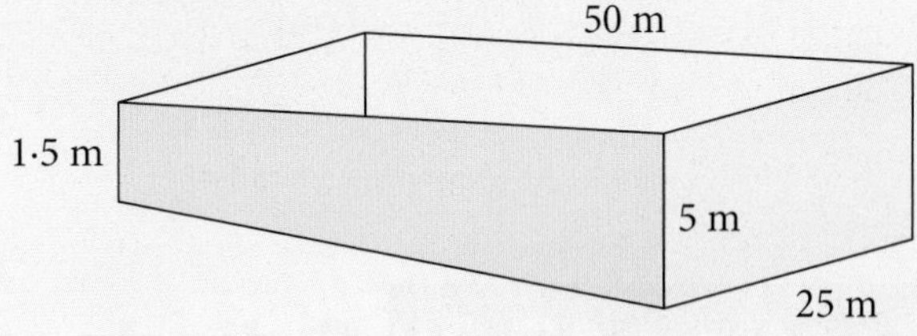

21. Which of the cubes could have been formed by folding the net shown below?

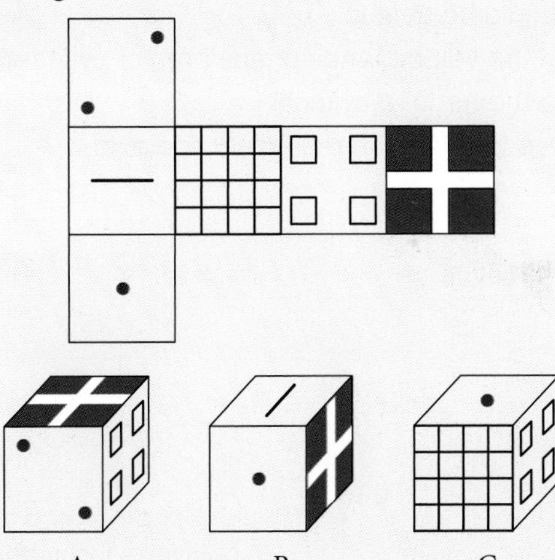

22. The diagram shows the net of a prism.
   (i) Find the total surface area of the prism.
   (ii) Find the volume of the prism.

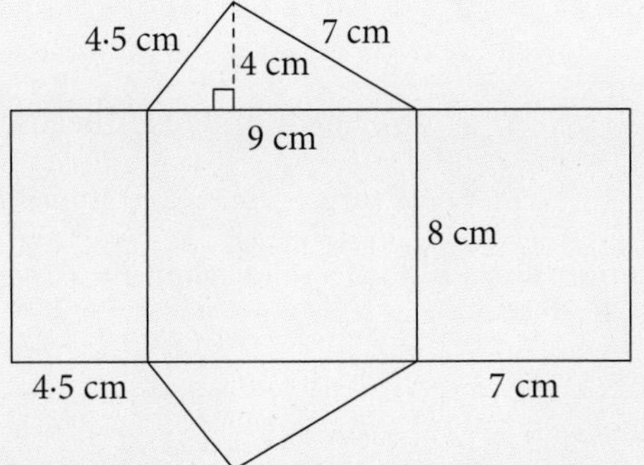

Volume and Surface Area

23. The diagram shows the net of a prism. Find:
   (i) the total surface area of the prism
   (ii) the volume of the prism.

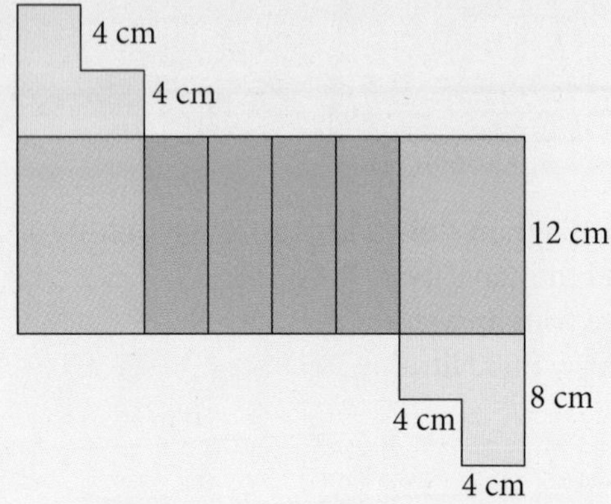

24. The diagram shows the net of a prism. Find:
   (i) the total surface area of the prism
   (ii) the volume of the prism.

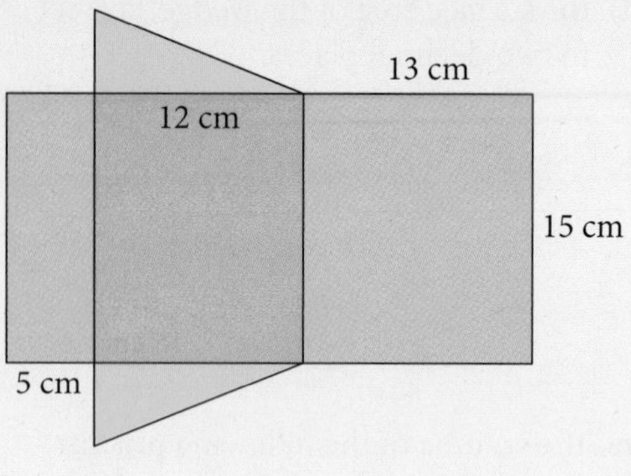

Section 17.2: Cylinders and Spheres

Learning Outcomes:

You should be able to:

- find the volume and surface area of cylinders and spheres
- use the net of a cylinder
- solve problems in real-world contexts

Cylinder

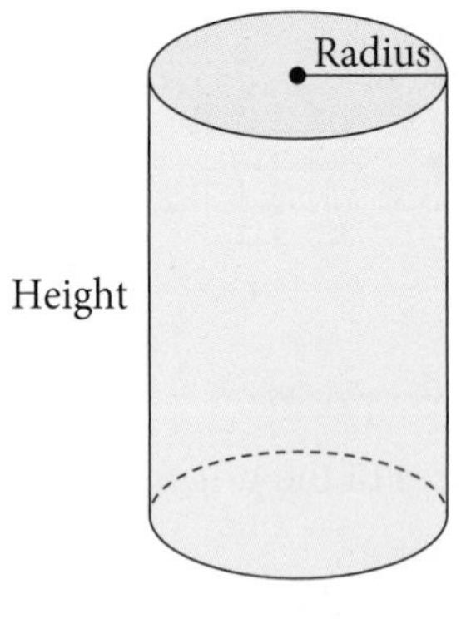

A cylinder is technically a prism, since it has a uniform cross-sectional area.

Net of a cylinder

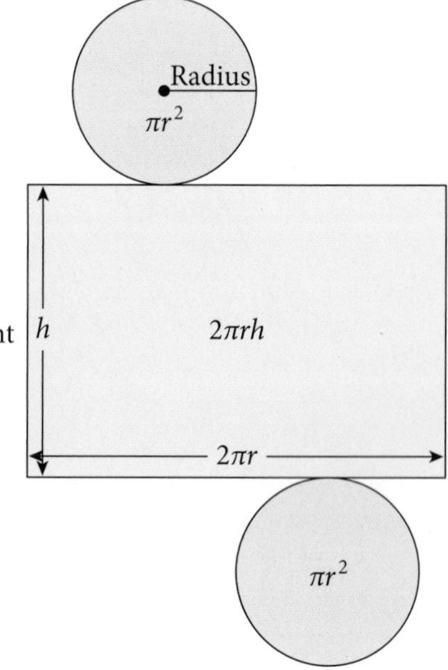

Volume = π(radius)^2(height) = $\pi r^2 h$

Curved surface area = 2π(radius)(height) = $2\pi rh$

Total surface area (TSA) of a solid cylinder = curved surface area + top + bottom

$= 2\pi rh + \pi r^2 + \pi r^2$

$= 2\pi rh + 2\pi r^2$

The formulae for the **volume** and the **curved surface area** of a cylinder appear on page 10 of the booklet of *formulae and tables,* as shown:

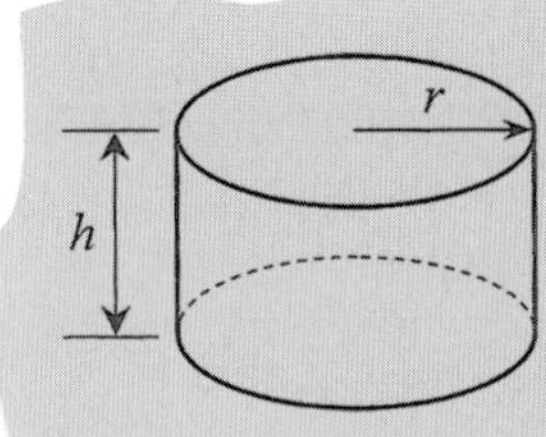

$A = 2\pi rh$

$V = \pi r^2 h$

Cylinder

Sphere

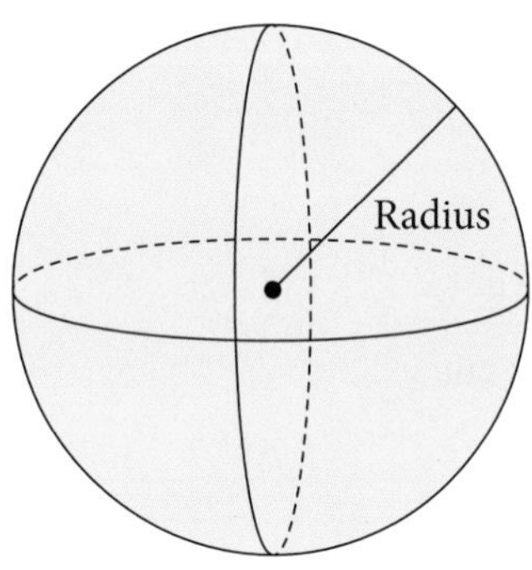

Volume $= \frac{4}{3}\pi(\text{radius})^3 = \frac{4}{3}\pi r^3$

Surface Area $= 4\pi(\text{radius})^2 = 4\pi r^2$

The formulae for the **volume** and the **curved surface area** of a sphere appear on page 10 of the booklet of *formulae and tables,* as shown:

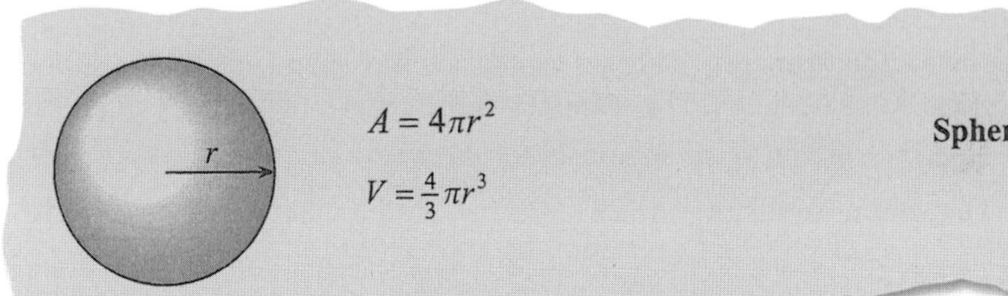

Hemisphere

A **hemisphere** is half of a sphere.

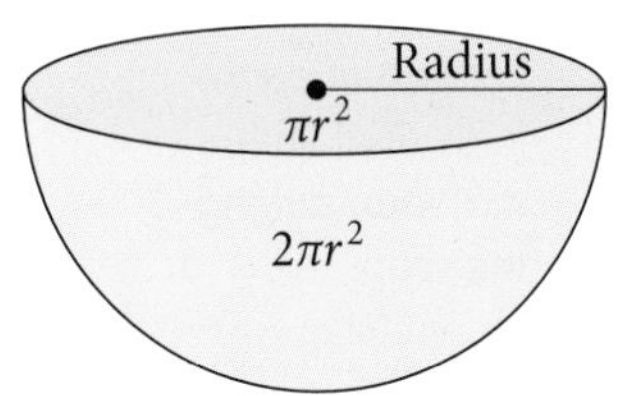

Volume $= \frac{1}{2}(\text{sphere}) = \frac{1}{2}\left(\frac{4}{3}\pi(\text{radius})^3\right)$

$= \frac{2}{3}\pi(\text{Radius})^3 = \frac{2}{3}\pi r^3$

Curved Surface Area $= \frac{1}{2}(\text{sphere}) = 2\pi r^2$

Total Surface Area of solid hemisphere = curved surface area + top

$= 2\pi r^2 + \pi r^2$

$= 3\pi r^2$

EXAMPLE 1

Find the volume and surface area of the following solid objects. Give your answers to one decimal place.

(i)

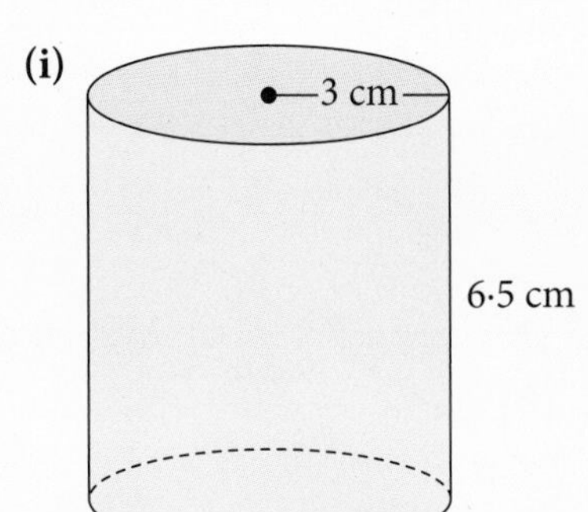

(ii)

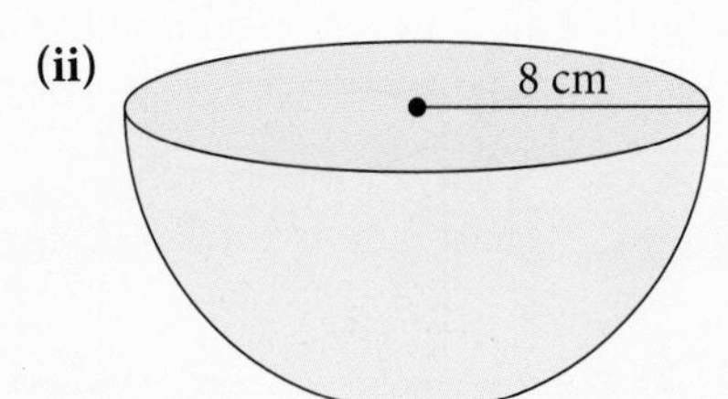

For the most accurate solution, use the π button on the calculator. Only use $\pi = 3{\cdot}14$ or $\frac{22}{7}$ if asked to do so.

Solution

(i) Cylinder with $r = 3$ cm and $h = 6\cdot5$ cm

Volume $= \pi r^2 h$

$= \pi(3)^2(6\cdot5)$

$= 58\cdot5\pi$

$= 183\cdot783$

$= 183\cdot8 \text{ cm}^3$

Total surface area $= 2\pi rh + 2\pi r^2$

$= 2\pi(3)(6\cdot5) + 2\pi(3)^2$

$= 39\pi + 18\pi$

$= 57\pi$

$= 179\cdot070$

$= 179\cdot1 \text{ cm}^2$

(ii) Hemisphere with $r = 8$ cm

Volume $= \frac{2}{3}\pi r^3$ $\left[\frac{1}{2}\text{ (volume of a sphere)}\right]$

$= \frac{2}{3}\pi(8)^3$

$= 341\cdot\dot{3}\pi$

$= 1072\cdot33029$

$= 1072\cdot3 \text{ cm}^3$

Total surface area $= 3\pi r^2$

$= 3\pi(8)^2$

$= 192\pi$

$= 603\cdot1857$

$= 603\cdot2 \text{ cm}^2$

EXAMPLE 2

A trophy for the winners of a soccer league is in the shape of a sphere supported on a cylindrical base, as shown. The diameter of the sphere and of the cylinder is 21 cm.

(i) Find the volume of the sphere, in terms of π.

(ii) The volume of the trophy is 6174π cm^3. Find the height of the cylinder.

Solution

(i) Sphere with diameter = 21 cm

radius $= \frac{1}{2}(21) = 10\cdot5$ cm

Volume $= \frac{4}{3}\pi r^3$

Volume $= \frac{4}{3}\pi(10\cdot5)^3$

Volume $= \frac{4}{3}\pi(1157\cdot625)$

Volume $= 1543\cdot5\pi \text{ cm}^3$

(ii) Total volume = sphere + cylinder

$6174\pi = 1543\cdot5\pi + \text{cylinder}$

$4630\cdot5\pi = \text{cylinder}$

$4630\cdot5\pi = \pi r^2 h$

$4630\cdot5\pi = \pi(10\cdot5)^2 h$

$4630\cdot5\pi = 110\cdot25\pi h$

$\frac{4630\cdot5\pi}{110\cdot25\pi} = h$

$42 \text{ cm} = h$

The volume of compound shapes is found by finding the volume of each individual shape and then adding them up.

Practice Questions 17.2

1. Find the volume and total surface area, in terms of π, of the following solid cylinders.

(i)

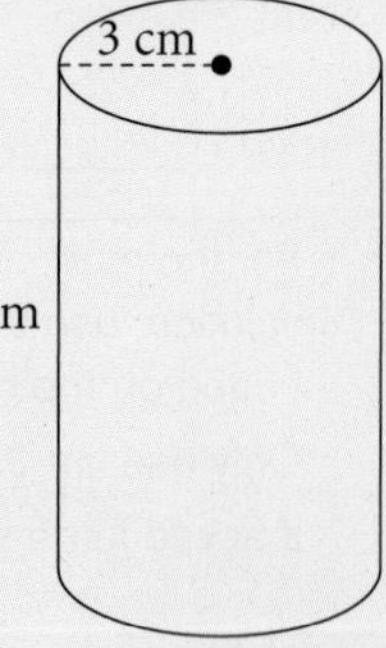

(ii)

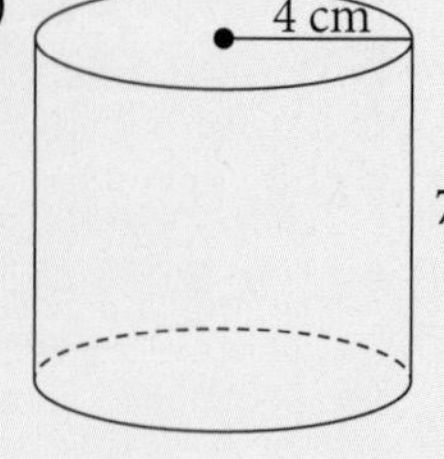

(iii)

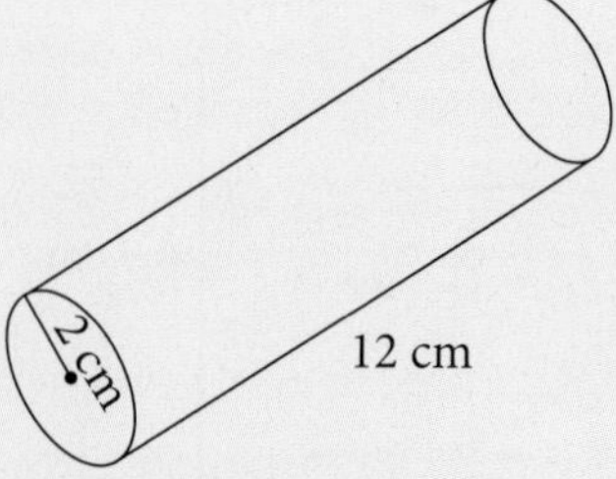

2. Find the volume and total surface area of the following spheres.
Give your answers to one decimal place.

(i)
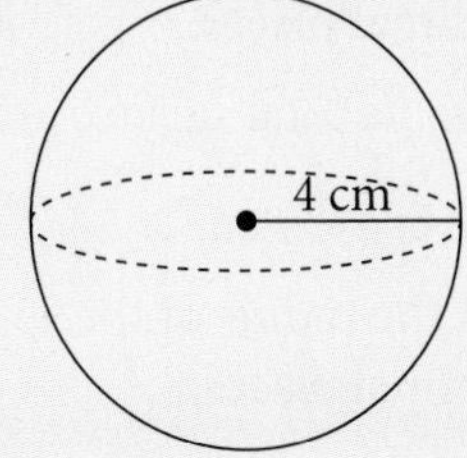

(ii)
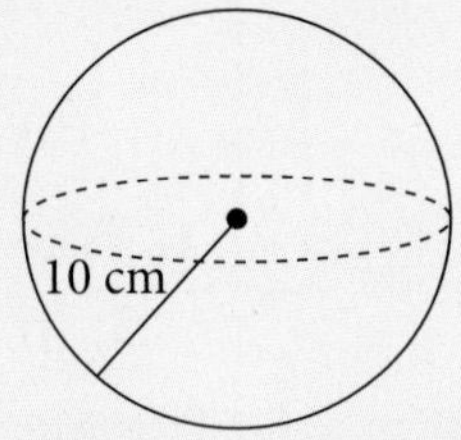

(iii)
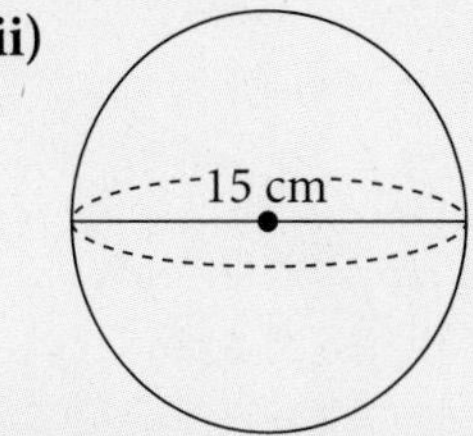

3. Find the volume and total surface area of the following solid hemispheres.
Give your answers to two significant figures.

(i)
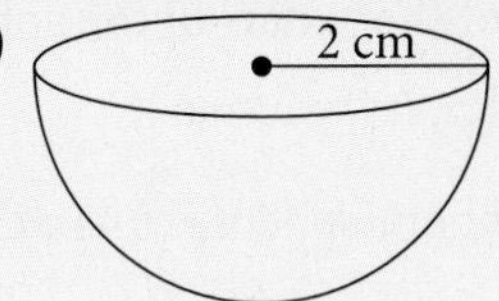

(ii)
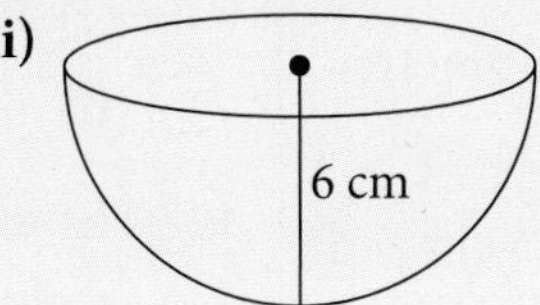

(iii)
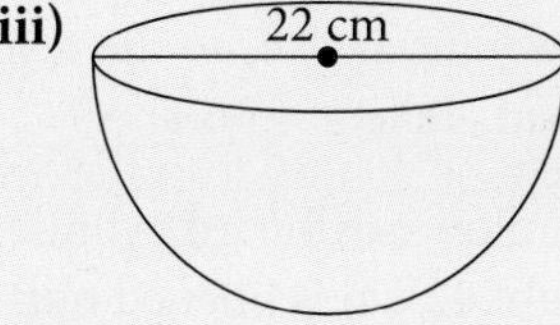

4. Find the volume and surface area of the following compound shapes. Take $\pi = \frac{22}{7}$.

(i)
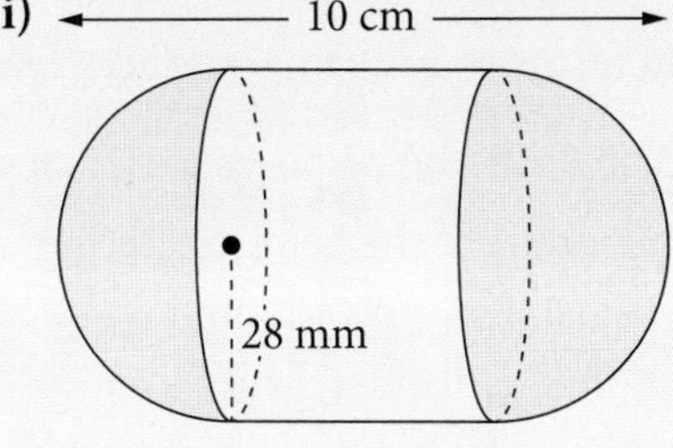

(ii)
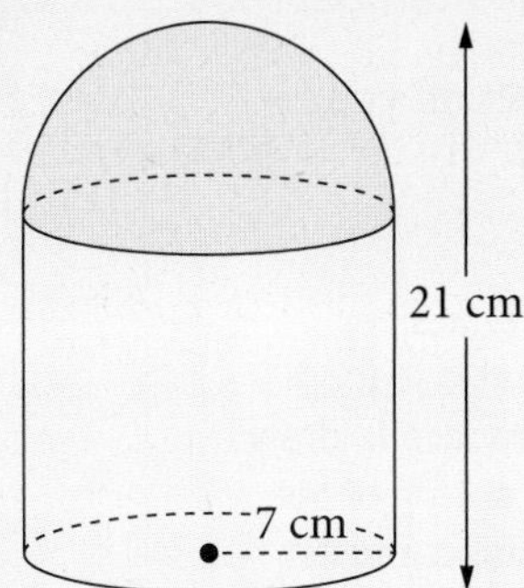

(iii)
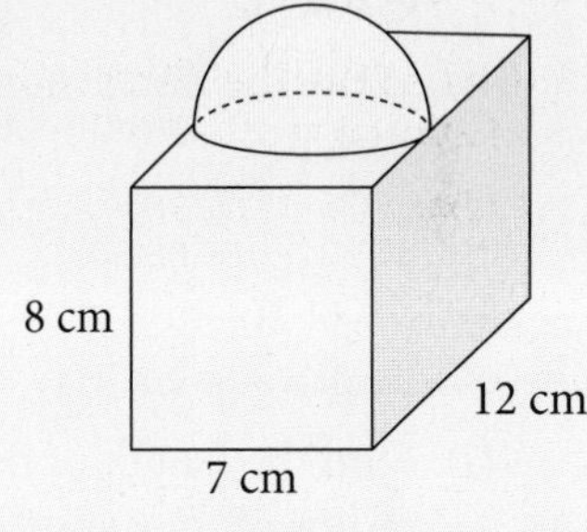

5. The diagram shows a curtain pole, which is made-up of a wooden cylinder of diameter 5 cm and two wooden spheres of diameter 7 cm. The total length of the pole is 1·8 m.

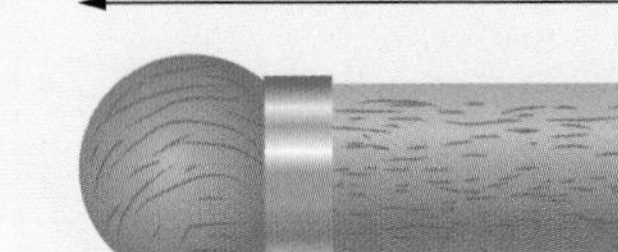
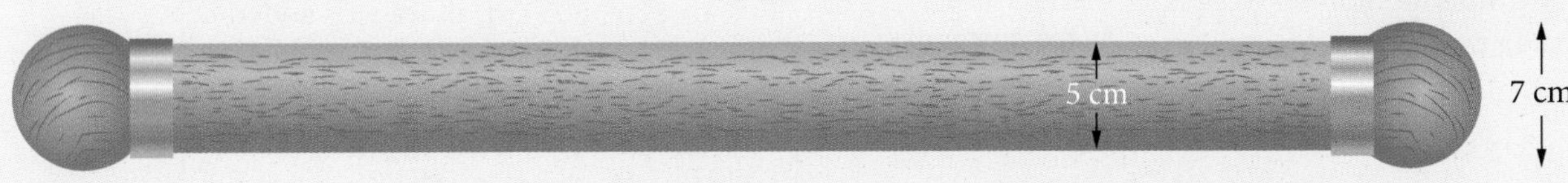

Find:

(i) the volume of wood in the curtain pole, correct to two decimal places

(ii) the surface area of wood in the curtain pole, correct to two decimal places.

6. The diagram shows a plastic cylindrical tube containing four tennis balls. The tennis balls fit exactly inside of the tube.

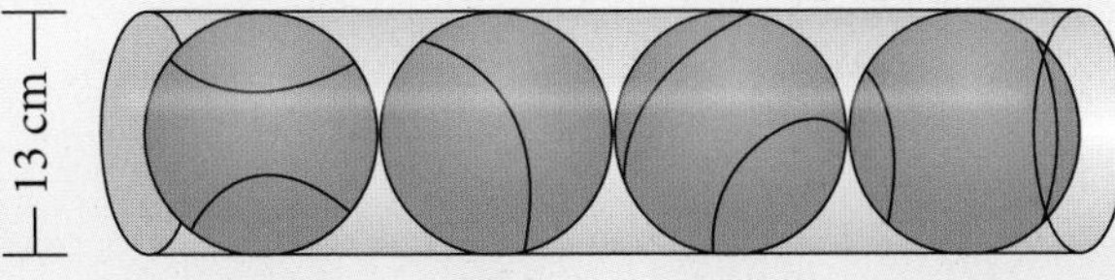

Given the diameter of the tube is 13 cm, find, correct to two decimal places:

(i) the volume of one tennis ball

(ii) the height of the cylindrical tube

(iii) the capacity of the cylindrical tube

(iv) the percentage of the space inside the tube, which is occupied by the tennis balls.

7. A plastic pipe, of outer diameter 8 cm, has a thickness of 1 cm.

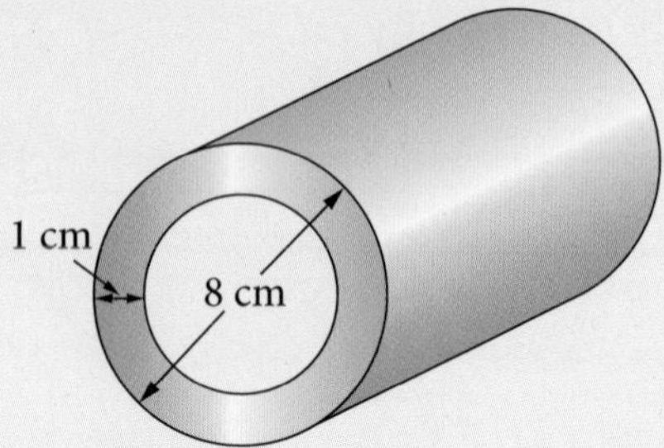

Find the volume of plastic required to produce 10 metres of this pipe.
Give your answer to the nearest whole centimetre cubed. Take $\pi = 3{\cdot}14$.

8. A hollow cardboard cylinder of diameter 5 cm and height 13 cm is opened out.
   (i) Draw a sketch of the net of the opened-out cylinder.
   (ii) Write the dimensions of the net on your sketch.

9. A hollow cylinder has a height of 16 cm and a volume of 100π cm^3.
   (i) Find the length of the radius of the cylinder.
   (ii) Find, in terms of π, its curved surface area.

10. The curved surface area of a cylinder of radius $3{\cdot}5$ cm is 84π cm^2.
    (i) Find the height of the cylinder.
    (ii) Find, in terms of π, its volume.

Remember that is it good practice to draw a sketch of the shape and list out what values you know and what you are looking for. Then select the appropriate formula.

11. The volume of a sphere is 64π cm^3.
    (i) Find the length of the radius of the sphere, correct to two decimal places.
    (ii) Find, in terms of π, its total surface area.

12. The volume of a sphere is 343π cm^3.
    (i) Find the length of the radius of the sphere, correct to two decimal places.
    (ii) Find, in terms of π, its total surface area.

13. The surface area of a sphere is 484π cm^2.
    (i) Find the length of the radius of the sphere.
    (ii) Find, in terms of π, its volume.

14. The volume of a solid hemisphere is 144π cm^3.
    (i) Find the length of the radius of the hemisphere.
    (ii) Find, in terms of π, its curved surface area.
    (iii) Find, in terms of π, its total surface area.

15. The volume of a solid hemisphere is $1{,}152\pi$ cm^3.
    (i) Find the radius of the hemisphere.
    (ii) Find the volume of the smallest rectangular box that the hemisphere will fit into.
    (iii) If the hemisphere is placed into the box, find the volume of space inside the box, which is not occupied by the hemisphere, correct to two decimal places.

16. A cylindrical glass has a radius of 4 cm. 603 cm^3 of water is added to the glass.
    Using the π button on your calculator, find the depth of the water in the glass. Give your answer to the nearest whole number.

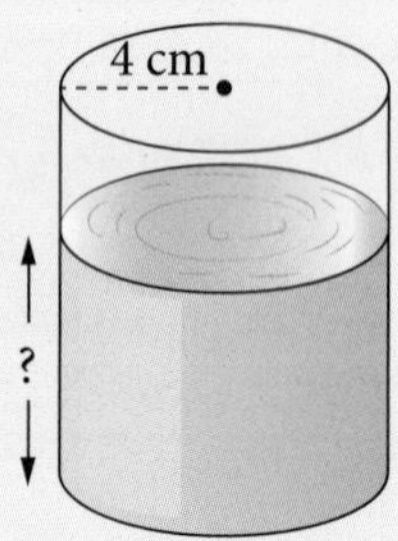

Section 17.3: Cones

Learning Outcomes:

You should be able to:
- find the volume and surface area of a cone
- use the net of a cone
- solve problems in real-world contexts

Cone

A **cone** is a solid or hollow object, which tapers from a circular base to a point.

A cone can sometimes be referred to as a **right circular cone**.

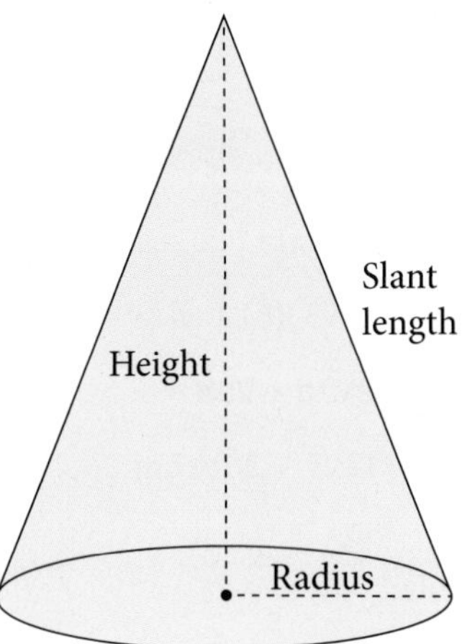

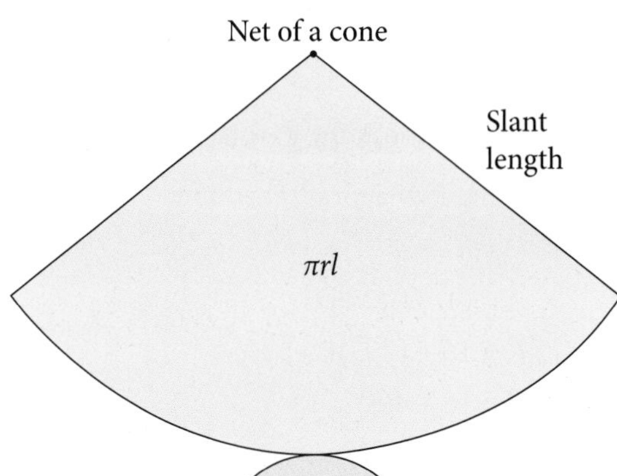

Volume $= \frac{1}{3}\pi(\text{radius})^2(\text{height}) = \frac{1}{3}\pi r^2 h$

Curved surface area $= \pi(\text{radius})(\text{slant length})$
$= \pi rl$

Total surface area = curved surface area + base
$= \pi rl + \pi r^2$

Pythagoras' Theorem:

$$(\text{slant length})^2 = (\text{radius})^2 + (\text{height})^2$$

$$l^2 = r^2 + h^2$$

Links across the syllabus

Pythagoras' Theorem is covered in Chapter 11: Geometry II and Chapter 20: Trigonometry I.

The formula for the **volume** (V) and the **curved surface area** (A) of a cone appear on page 10 of the booklet of *formulae and tables*, as shown:

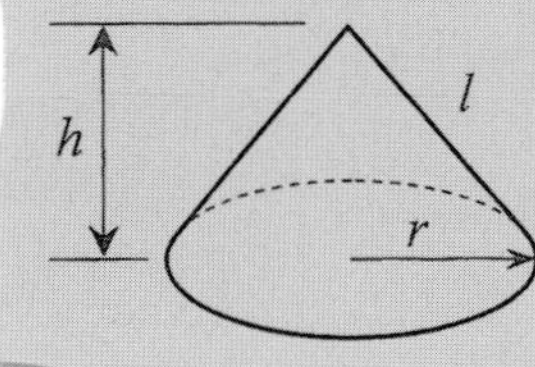

$A = \pi rl$

$V = \frac{1}{3}\pi r^2 h$

Cone

Frustum

A **frustum** is the portion of a solid (normally a cone or pyramid) which remains after the pointed top has been removed.

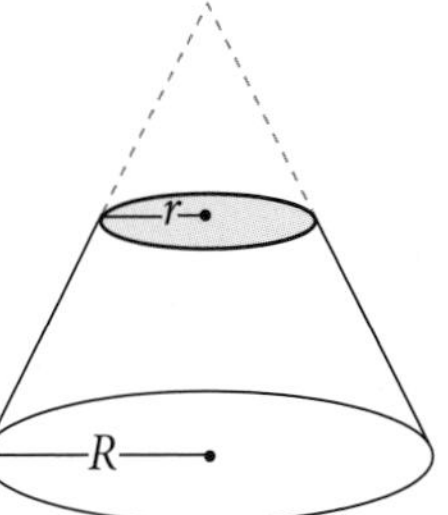

EXAMPLE 1

The diagram shows a solid cone of vertical height 4 cm and radius $2\sqrt{5}$ cm.

(i) Find the slant length, l, of the cone.

(ii) Find the volume of the cone, in terms of π.

(iii) Find the total surface area (TSA) of the cone, in terms of π.

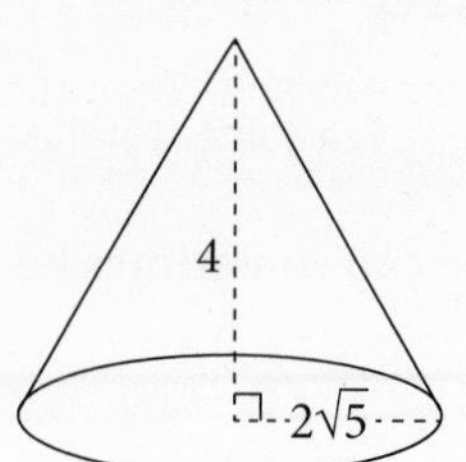

Solution

(i) $h = 4, r = 2\sqrt{5}, l = ?$

Using Pythagoras' Theorem:

$l^2 = h^2 + r^2$

$l^2 = (4)^2 + (2\sqrt{5})^2$

$l^2 = 16 + (2\sqrt{5})(2\sqrt{5})$

$l^2 = 16 + 4(5)$

$l^2 = 16 + 20$

$l^2 = 36$

$l = \sqrt{36}$

$l = 6$ cm

(ii) $h = 4, r = 2\sqrt{5}, V = ?$

$\text{Volume} = \frac{1}{3}\pi r^2 h$

$= \frac{1}{3}\pi(2\sqrt{5})^2(4)$

$= \frac{1}{3}\pi(20)(4)$

$= \frac{80}{3}\pi$

$= 26\frac{2}{3}\pi \text{ cm}^3$

(iii) $r = 2\sqrt{5}, l = 6$

$\text{TSA} = \pi r l + \pi r^2$

$= \pi(2\sqrt{5})(6) + \pi(2\sqrt{5})^2$

$= 12\sqrt{5}\pi + 20\pi$

$= (12\sqrt{5} + 20)\pi \text{ cm}^2$

EXAMPLE 2

The diagram shows a cone of height 18 cm and radius 9 cm. A portion of height 6 cm and base radius r cm is removed from the top of the cone.

(i) Find the value of r.

(ii) Find the volume of the portion removed, in terms of π.

(iii) Find the volume of the portion of the cone remaining (the frustum), in terms of π.

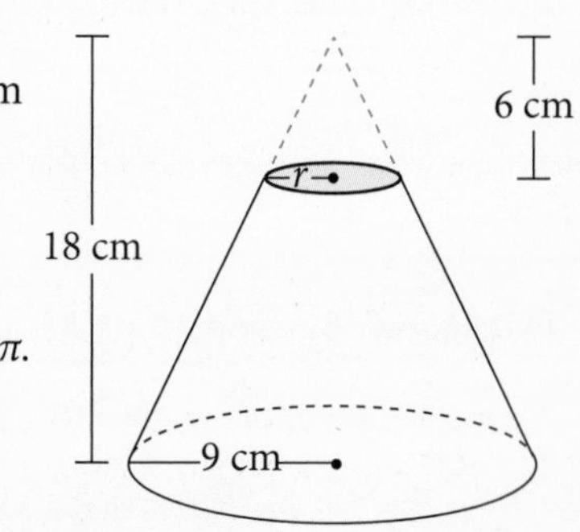

Solution

(i)

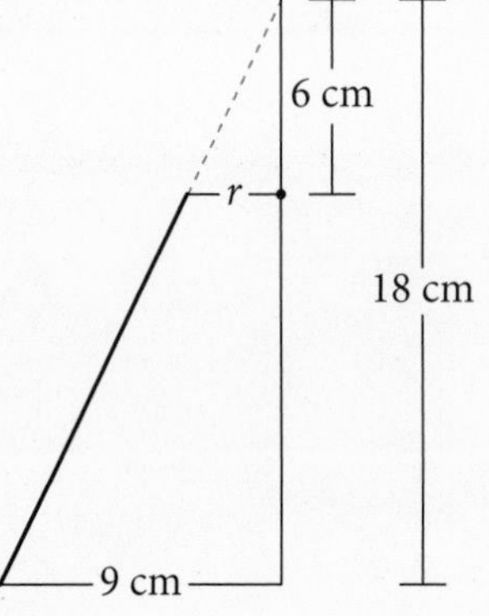

We can see two similar triangles.
The sides are in proportion, therefore:

$\frac{r}{6} = \frac{9}{18}$

$r = \frac{(6)(9)}{18}$

$r = \frac{54}{18}$

$r = 3$ cm

Links across the syllabus

Similar triangles are covered in Chapter 11: Geometry II.

(ii) Find the volume of a cone of height 6 cm and radius 3 cm: $\text{Volume} = \frac{1}{3}\pi r^2 h$

$= \frac{1}{3}\pi(3)^2(6)$

$= 18\pi \text{ cm}^3$

(iii) Volume of portion remaining = Volume of total cone – Volume of cone removed

$= \frac{1}{3}\pi(9)^2(18) - 18\pi$

$= 486\pi - 18\pi$

$= 468\pi \text{ cm}^3$

Practice Questions 17.3

1. Find the volume and total surface area, in terms of π, of the following solid cones.

(i)

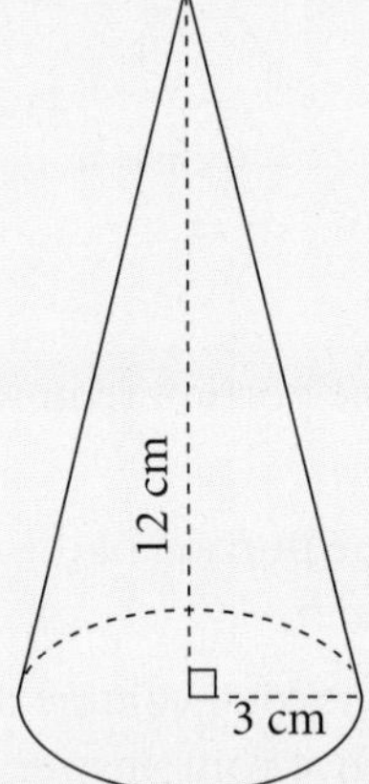

(ii)

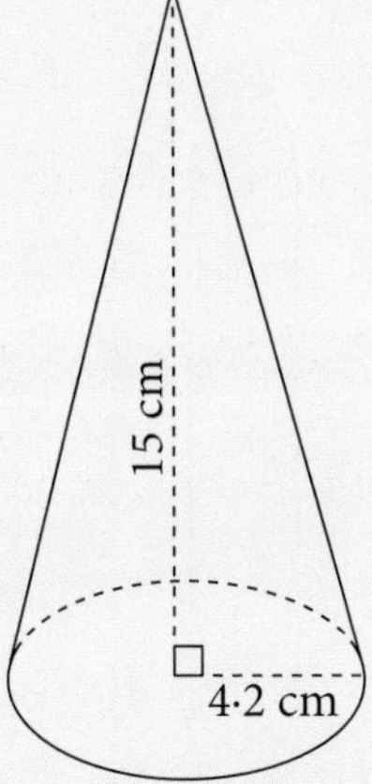

(iii)

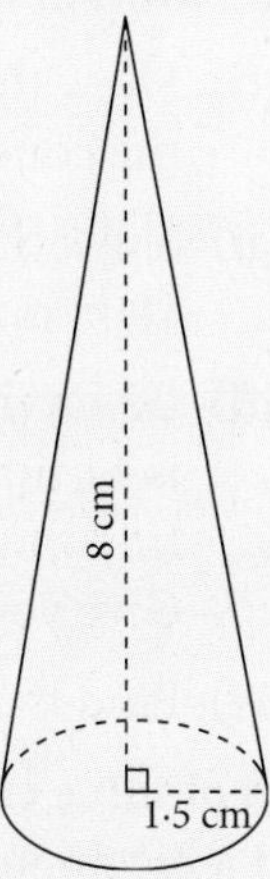

2. The diagram shows the net of a cone.
   (i) Draw a diagram of the completed cone, showing dimensions where appropriate.
   (ii) Find the volume of the cone.
   (iii) Find the surface area of the cone.

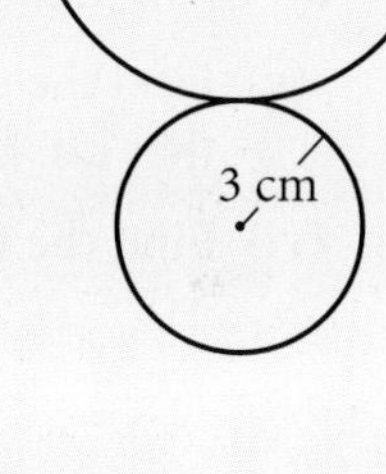

3. Find the volume of the compound shape shown in the diagram.
   Give your answer to the nearest whole number.

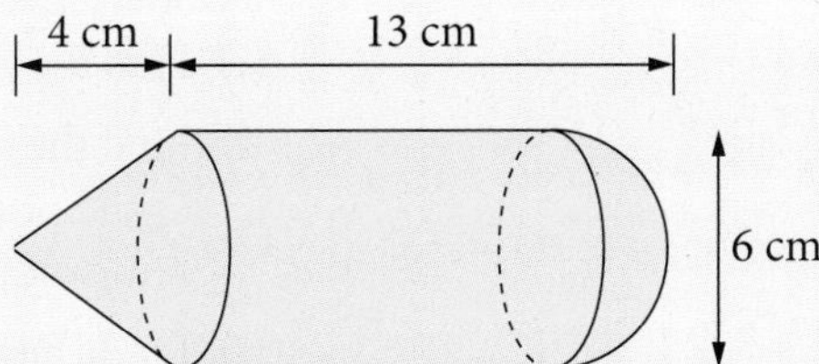

4. A right circular cone has radius 6 cm and height 8 cm.
   (i) Find the slant length of the cone.
   (ii) Draw a net of the cone, showing all dimensions of the net.
5. A buoy at sea is in the shape of a hemisphere with a cone on top, as in the diagram. The radius of the base of the cone is 0·9 m and its vertical height is 1·2 m.

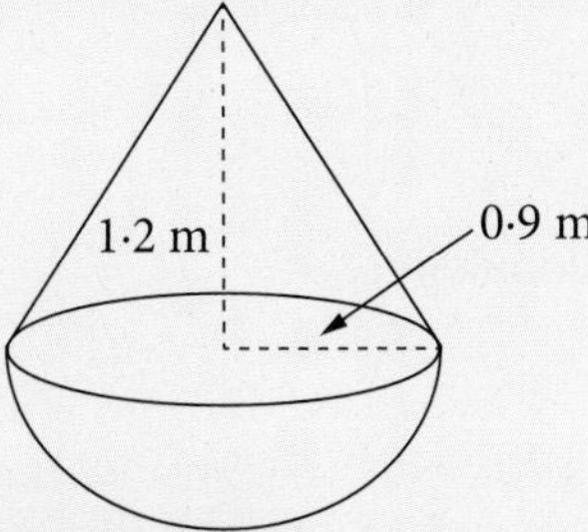

   (i) Find the slant height of the cone part of the buoy.
   (ii) Find the total vertical height of the buoy.
   (iii) Find the volume of the buoy, in terms of π.
   (iv) Find the total surface area of the buoy, in terms of π.
6. A right circular cone with a radius 5 cm has a volume of 100π cm^3. Find the height of the cone.
7. A right circular cone with a height 4·5 cm has a volume of $13{\cdot}5\pi$ cm^3. Find the radius of the cone.

8. A wax crayon is in the shape of a cylinder of diameter 10 mm, and a cone of slant length 13 mm, as shown in the diagram.
   - **(i)** Show that the vertical height of the cone is 12 mm.
   - **(ii)** Show that the volume of the cone is 100π mm^3.
   - **(iii)** Given that the volume of the cylinder is 11 times the volume of the cone, find the total volume of the crayon. Give your answer in terms of π.
   - **(iv)** Find the total height of the crayon.

   16 of these crayons are packaged in a rectangular box. The crayons are arranged in two rows of eight, and there is no space for them to move around inside the box.
   - **(v)** Find the dimensions of the smallest box that can be used to package the crayons.
   - **(vi)** Find the volume of this box.

9. The diagram shows a cone of height 8 cm and radius 6 cm. A portion of height 2 cm and base radius r cm is removed from the top of the cone.

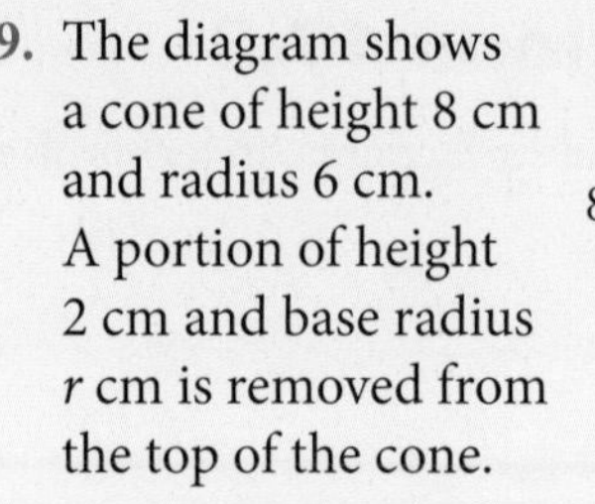

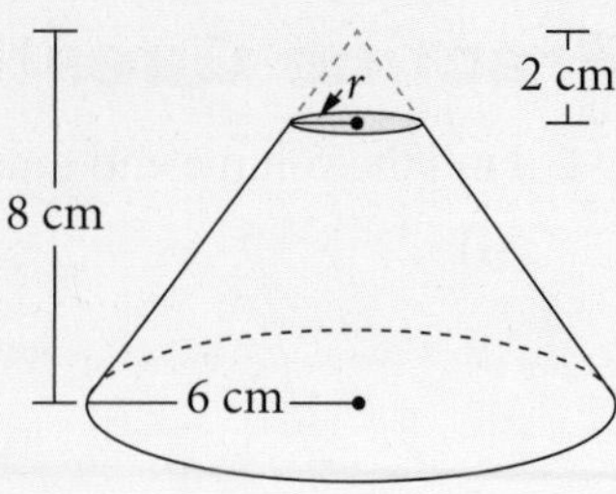

   - **(i)** Find the value of r.
   - **(ii)** Find the volume of the portion removed, in terms of π.
   - **(iii)** Find the volume of the portion of the cone remaining, in terms of π.
   - **(iv)** What percentage of the total volume of the cone was removed? Give your answer correct to two decimal places.

10. The diagram shows a cone of height 24 cm and radius 10·5 cm. A portion of height h cm and base radius 7 cm is removed from the top of the cone.

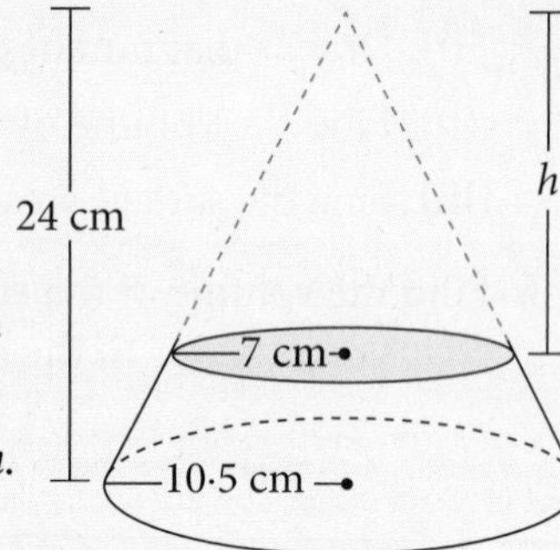

   - **(i)** Find the value of h.
   - **(ii)** Find the volume of the portion removed, in terms of π.
   - **(iii)** Find the volume of the portion of the cone remaining, in terms of π.

Section 17.4: Problems Involving Equating of Volumes

Learning Outcomes:

You should be able to:
- solve problems involving recasting or remoulding
- solve problems involving flowing liquids
- solve problems in real-world contexts

Recasting

To **recast** means to give a quantity of a substance a different form, by melting it down and reshaping it.

Volume of the original shape = volume of the new shape.

In the world around us, for various reasons, some solids are melted and recast into another solid. For example, a block of wax can be melted and recast to produce candles; a quantity of metal can be melted and recast to make metal components for cars or machinery; a block of plastic can be melted and recast to produce drinking bottles.

Any time one solid is melted and recast as a new solid, assuming that none of the substance is lost in the process, the volume of the substance stays the same.

EXAMPLE 1

A spherical ball, of radius length 24 cm, is made of a pure metal.

This ball is melted down and recast into 64 smaller balls, of equal size.

(i) Find the volume of each of the smaller balls.

(ii) Find the radius of each of the smaller balls.

(iii) Find the ratio of the surface area of the original ball to the total surface area of the 64 smaller balls.

Solution

(i) Volume of original ball, of radius 24 cm:

$$\text{Volume} = \frac{4}{3}\pi r^3$$
$$= \frac{4}{3}\pi(24)^3$$
$$= \frac{4}{3}\pi(13824)$$
$$= \frac{55296}{3}\pi$$

Volume = 18432π cm^3

This $18{,}432\pi$ cm^3 of metal is divided by 64 to make each of the smaller balls.

Therefore,

$$\text{Volume of a smaller ball} = \frac{\text{Volume of original ball}}{64}$$
$$\text{Volume of a smaller ball} = \frac{18432\pi}{64}$$

Volume of a smaller ball = 288π cm^3

(ii) Volume of a smaller ball = 288π cm^3:

$$\text{Volume} = \frac{4}{3}\pi r^3$$
$$288\pi = \frac{4}{3}\pi r^3$$
$$864\pi = 4\pi r^3 \quad (\times 3)$$
$$216 = r^3 \quad (\div 4\pi)$$
$$\sqrt[3]{216} = r$$
$$6 = r$$

Therefore, the radius of each of the small ball bearings is 6 cm.

(iii) Surface area of original ball, of radius 24 cm:

Surface area = $4\pi r^2$

Surface area = $4\pi(24)^2$

Surface area = $4\pi(576)$

Surface area = 2304π cm^2

Surface area of smaller ball, of radius 6 cm:

Surface area = $4\pi r^2$

Surface area = $4\pi(6)^2$

Surface area = $4\pi(36)$

Surface area = 144π cm^2

Surface area of the original ball : total surface area of the 64 smaller balls

$2304\pi : 64(144\pi)$

$2304\pi : 9216\pi$ (divide both ratios by $2{,}304\pi$)

$1 : 4$

Displacement

Discussion Time 

On a given day, a miner extracts a variety of raw diamond particles from a diamond mine. These diamond particles are all of different shapes and sizes.

The miner is paid a fixed rate per cubic centimetre of diamond particles extracted.

Work with a partner to come up with a suitable method for finding the ***exact*** volume of diamond particles extracted by the miner.

From the discussion time above, hopefully you came to the conclusion that when an object is submerged in a liquid, it pushes the liquid out of its way. The object takes up space in the liquid and hence the liquid rises up in the container.

The **displacement** of a fluid occurs when a fluid is pushed away by an object being placed in it. The volume of the object immersed in the fluid is equal to the volume of the displaced fluid.

volume of the immersed object = volume of the displaced fluid

EXAMPLE 2

A rectangular tank has a base of length 2 m and width 1·5 m. The tank contains some water.

A solid cylinder of radius 45 cm and height 120 cm is dropped into the tank.

Given that the cylinder is totally submerged in the water, find the increase in height of the water in the tank. Give your answer in centimetres, correct to one decimal place.

Solution

Draw a diagram of the situation.

When the cylinder goes into the tank, the water level in the tank rises.

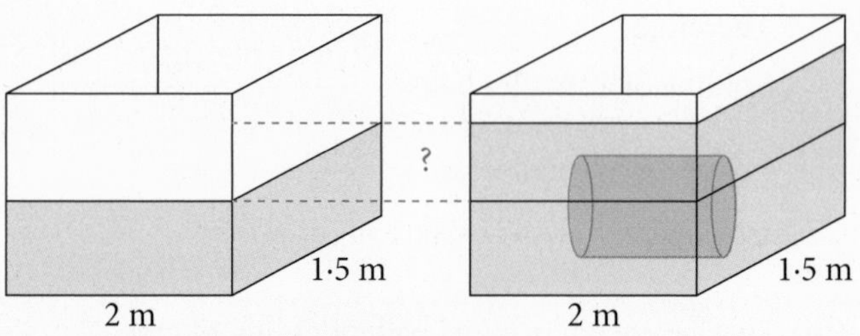

Volume of risen water (in rectangular shape) = Volume of the cylinder

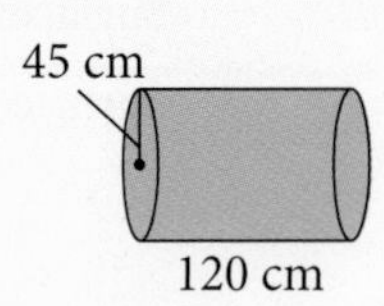

=

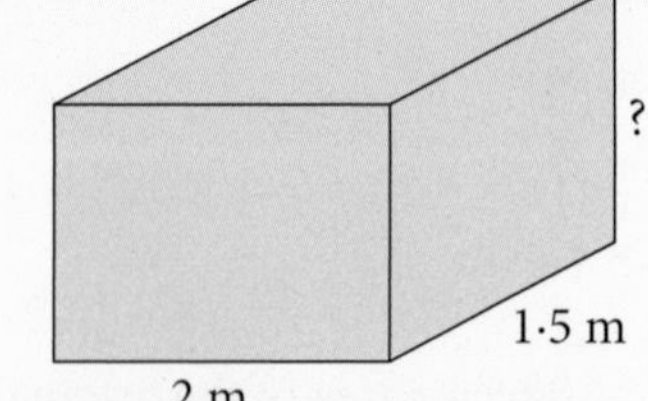

Find the volume of a cylinder of radius 45 cm and height 120 cm:

Volume of cylinder = $\pi r^2 h$

Volume of cylinder = $\pi(45)^2(120)$

Volume of cylinder = $243{,}000\pi$ cm^3

Volume of risen water = $243{,}000\pi$ cm^3

(length)(width)(height) = $243{,}000\pi$

(200)(150)(height) = $243{,}000\pi$

(30,000)(height) = $243{,}000\pi$

$$\text{height} = \frac{243{,}000\pi}{30{,}000}$$

height = 25·4469 cm

Therefore, the water rises by 25·4 cm in the tank.

Ratios

Some questions will ask us to compare the dimensions, volumes or surface areas of different shapes, given certain information. Always read these questions carefully and take time to ensure that you have set up the ratio correctly.

EXAMPLE 3

Cone A is a solid cone of height h and radius r. Cone B is a solid cone of height $\frac{1}{2}h$ and radius of $2r$.
Find volume of cone A : volume of cone B

Solution

$$\text{Volume of a cone} = \frac{1}{3}\pi r^2 h$$

Cone A: height = h, radius = r

Volume of cone A = $\frac{1}{3}\pi(r)^2(h)$

Volume of cone A = $\frac{1}{3}\pi r^2 h$

Cone B: height = $\frac{1}{2}h$, radius = $2r$

Volume of cone B = $\frac{1}{3}\pi(2r)^2\left(\frac{1}{2}h\right)$

Volume of cone B = $\frac{1}{3}\pi(4r^2)\left(\frac{1}{2}h\right)$

Volume of cone B = $\frac{4}{6}\pi r^2 h$

Volume of cone B = $\frac{2}{3}\pi r^2 h$

Volume of cone A : Volume of cone B

$\frac{1}{3}\pi r^2 h : \frac{2}{3}\pi r^2 h$ (divide both sides by $\frac{1}{3}\pi r^2 h$)

1 : 2

Flowing liquids

When a liquid is flowing at a constant rate, a fixed volume of liquid is passing through the end of the pipe, per second.

In general, we will be dealing mainly with cylindrical pipes.

You should visualise a filled section of the pipe with a length equal to the rate. The volume of this section is the volume of fluid flowing, per second.

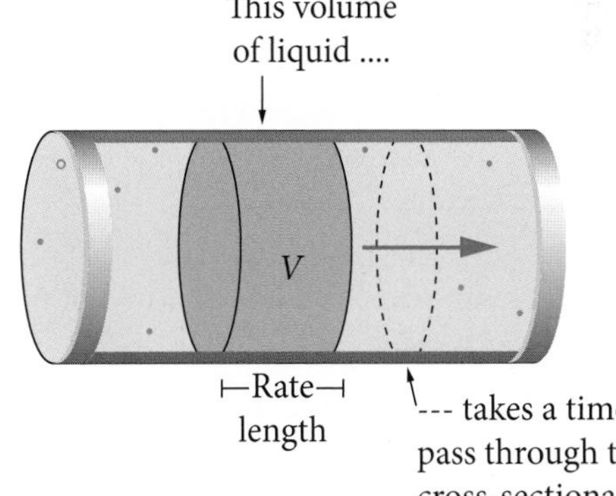

EXAMPLE 4

Water flows through a cylindrical pipe, of diameter 10 cm, at a rate of 14 cm per second.

(i) How much water flows out of the pipe in one second? Take $\pi = \frac{22}{7}$

(ii) How long would it take to pour out 33 litres of water?

Solution

A length of 14 cm of water pours out of the pipe, every second.
Draw a diagram to represent the situation:

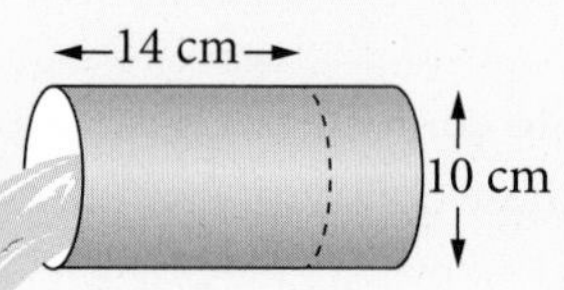

(i) Volume of water pouring per second = volume of cylinder of radius 5 cm and length 14 cm

Volume $= \left(\frac{22}{7}\right)(5)^2(14)$

Volume $= 1{,}100 \text{ cm}^3$

Therefore, $1{,}100 \text{ cm}^3$ of water pours through the pipe in one second.

For questions involving liquid flowing, find the volume flowing per second.

(ii) 33 litres $= 33 \times 1000 = 33{,}000 \text{ cm}^3$.

Time $= \frac{\text{Total volume}}{\text{Volume per second}} = \frac{33{,}000}{1{,}100} = 30$ seconds

Practice Questions 17.4

1. The volume of the metal prism shown is $1{,}144 \text{ cm}^3$.
   (i) Find the value of x.
   (ii) This prism is melted down and recast as 143 identical cubes.
   Find the side length of each of these cubes.

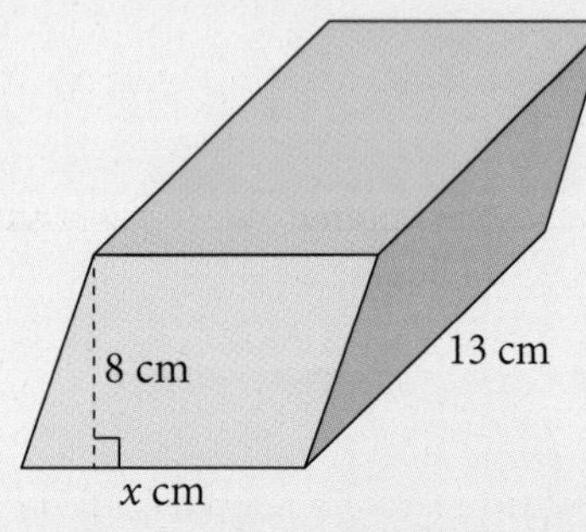

2. A solid metal cylindrical rod has a radius of 6 mm and a height of 216 mm.
   (i) Find the volume of the cylindrical rod, in terms of π.
   (ii) Find the surface area of the rod, in terms of π.
   This metal rod is melted down and recast as a metallic sphere, with no metal wasted.
   (iii) Find the radius length of this sphere.
   (iv) Find the surface area of the sphere, in terms of π.
   (v) Find surface area of rod : surface area of the sphere.

For the questions in this section, we can assume there is no wastage unless told otherwise.

3. A solid wax candle, in the shape of a cylinder, has a radius of 8 cm and a height of 15 cm.
   (i) Find the volume of the candle, in terms of π.
   This candle is melted down and remoulded into four identical conical candles, each of height 12 cm.
   (ii) Find the radius of these candles, correct to two decimal places.

4. A wax candle is in the shape of a right circular cone. The height of the candle is 7 cm and the diameter of the base is 9 cm.
   (i) Find the volume of the wax candle, correct to two decimal places.
   A rectangular block of wax measuring 30 cm by 15 cm by 12 cm is melted down and used to make a number of these candles.

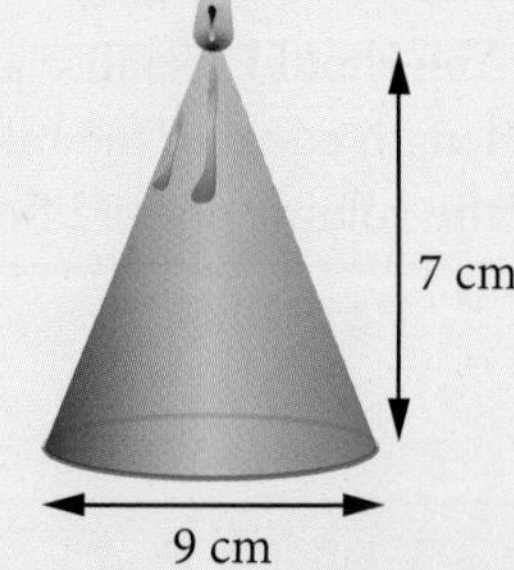

   (ii) Find the maximum number of candles that can be made from the block of wax, if 6% of the wax is lost in the process.

5. **(i)** A spherical golf ball has a diameter of 4 cm. Find the volume of the golf ball, in terms of π.

 (ii) A cylindrical hole on a golf course is 10 cm in diameter and 12 cm deep. The hole is half full of water. Calculate the volume of water in the hole, in terms of π.

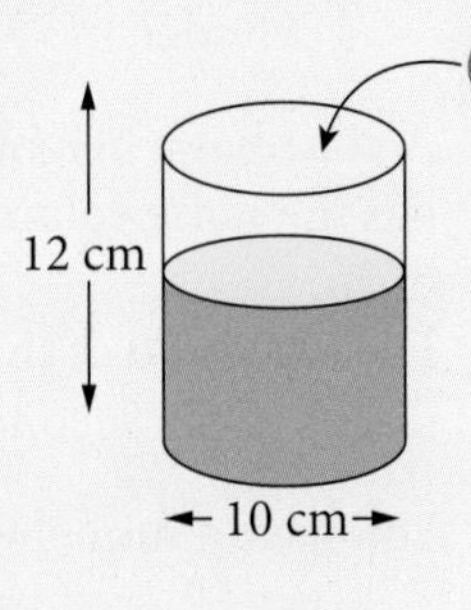

 (iii) The golf ball is dropped into the hole. Find the rise in the level of the water, correct to two decimal places.

Volume of rise = Volume of ball

6. **(i)** Find the volume of a solid sphere which has radius of length 2·1 cm. Give your answer correct to the nearest cm^3. Take $\pi = \frac{22}{7}$.

 (ii) A cylindrical container contains water. When this sphere and a solid cube of side length 3 cm are completely submerged in the water in the cylindrical container, the water level rises by 4 cm. Find the radius of the cylinder, correct to one decimal place. Take $\pi = \frac{22}{7}$.

7. Liquid is poured into a closed bottom cylinder, of radius 6 cm, at a volume of 18π cm^3 per second. Find the depth of the water after 33 seconds.

8. A cylindrical container has a radius of 6 cm and contains a volume of water. Water is poured into the container at a rate of 21 cm^3 per second. Using the π button on your calculator, find the rise in the level of the water in the container after 14 seconds. Give your answer to one decimal place.

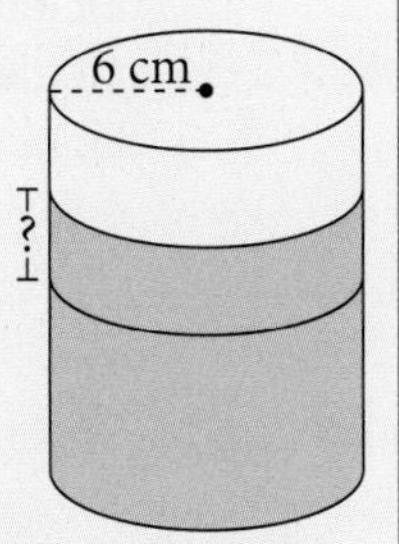

9. Water flows through a cylindrical pipe, of internal diameter 4 cm, at a rate of 12·5 cm per second.

 (i) Find, in terms of π, how much water flows out of the pipe in one second.

 (ii) Find how long it takes to fill a hemispherical bowl, of radius 15 cm, using this pipe.

10. Water flows through a cylindrical pipe, of radius 2 cm, at a rate of 5 cm/sec.

 (i) Find, in terms of π, the volume of water flowing out of the pipe per second.

 (ii) Water flows through this pipe into a conical-shaped cup, of base diameter 10 cm. If it takes 15 seconds for the cup to fill, find the depth of the cup.

11. Water flows through a cylindrical garden hose, of internal diameter 8 cm, at a rate of 52 cm per second.

 (i) Find, in terms of π, how much water flows out of the hose in one second.

 (ii) The pipe is used to fill a cylindrical paddling pool of internal diameter 1·2 m. Find the depth of the water in the pool after 4·5 minutes.

12. A sphere has a radius of 6 cm. A larger sphere has a radius of 18 cm.

 (i) Find surface area of smaller sphere : surface area of larger sphere.

 (ii) Find volume of smaller sphere : volume of larger sphere.

13. A hollow cylinder has a height, h, and radius r. A second hollow cylinder has dimensions which are double those of the first cylinder.

 (i) Find the ratio of the volume of the first cylinder to the volume of the second cylinder.

 (ii) Find the ratio of the curved surface area of the first cylinder to the curved surface area of the second cylinder.

14. A fuel storage tank is in the shape of a cylinder with a hemisphere at each end, as shown.
The capacity (volume) of the tank is 81π m^3.
The ratio of the capacity of the cylindrical section to the sum of the capacities of the hemispherical ends is 5 : 4.

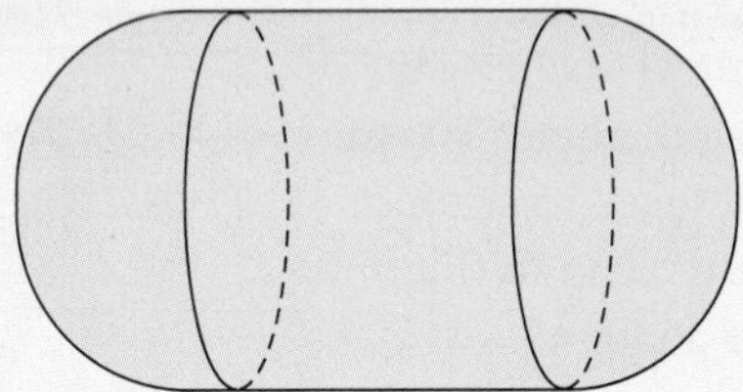

(i) Calculate the internal radius length of the tank.

(ii) Find the height of the cylindrical part of the tank.

(iii) The storage tank is to be painted. Find the curved surface area of the tank, correct to one decimal place.

(iv) The paint used is a special paint. One litre of the paint covers 2·5 m^2.
Find how many litres of paint are used, correct to the nearest litre.

(v) The paint is sold in five tins. Each tin costs €75. Find the total cost of the paint.

15. A sphere, of radius r, fits exactly inside an open-ended cylinder, as shown.

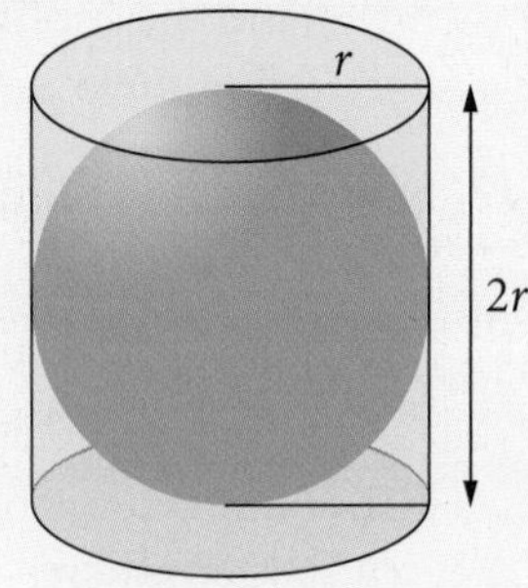

(i) Find the volume of the cylinder, in terms of r.

(ii) Find the ratio of the volume of the sphere to the volume of the cylinder.

(iii) Find the ratio of the curved surface area of the sphere to the curved surface area of the cylinder.

16. A cone has a height, h, and radius r. A second cone has the same volume as the first, but with a height of $2h$.
Find the ratio of the radius of the first cone to the radius of the second cone.

17. You have a funnel with the dimensions shown.

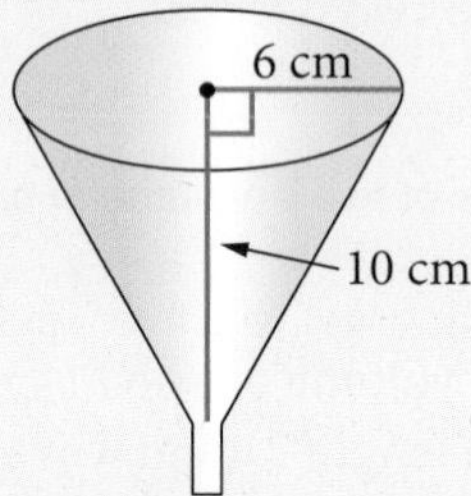

(i) Find the approximate volume of the funnel.

(ii) You use the funnel to put oil in a car. Oil flows out of the funnel at a rate of 45 millilitres per second. How long will it take to empty the funnel, when it is full of oil? (1 ml = 1 cm^3)

(iii) How long would it take to empty a funnel with a radius of 10 cm and a height of 6 cm, if oil flows out of the funnel at the same rate as in part **(ii)**?

(iv) Explain why you can claim that the time calculated in part **(iii)** is greater than the time calculated in part **(ii)**, without doing any calculations.

Revision and Exam Style Questions – Section A

1. Which of the cubes below could have been formed by folding the net on the right?

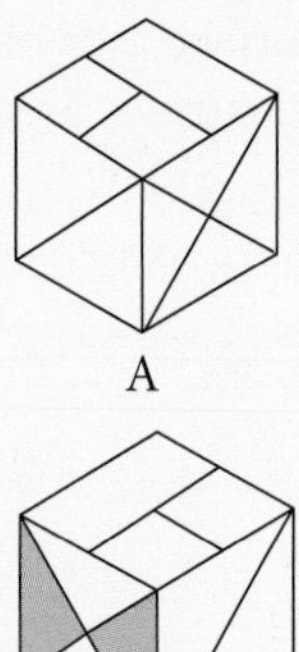
A

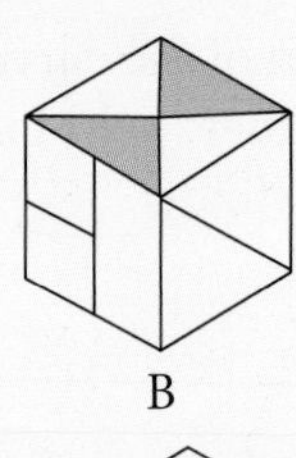
B

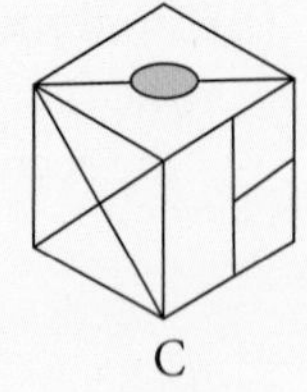
C

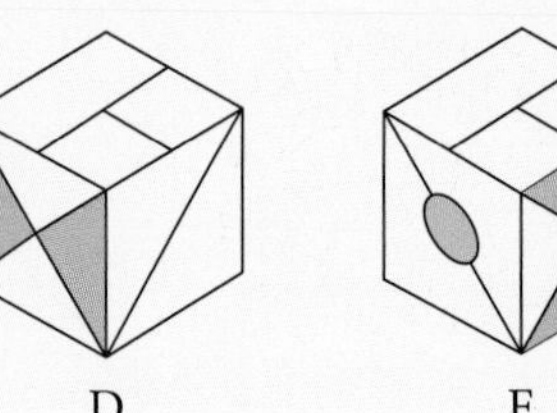
D E

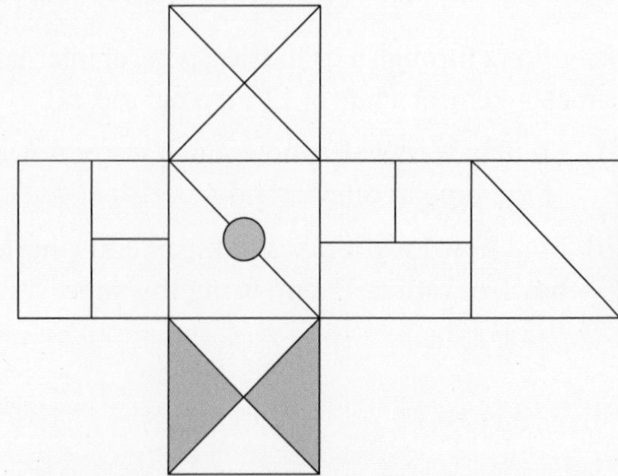

2. The diagram shows the net of a solid figure.

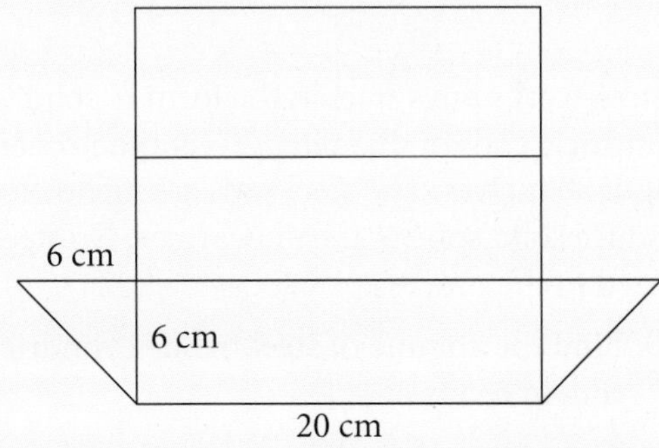

(i) Draw a sketch of the made-up solid.
(ii) How many edges does this solid have?
(iii) Find the volume of the solid.
(iv) Find the surface area of the solid. Give your answer to one decimal place.

3. The diagram shows a component used in a car motor. Find the volume of the metal needed to make 12 of these components.

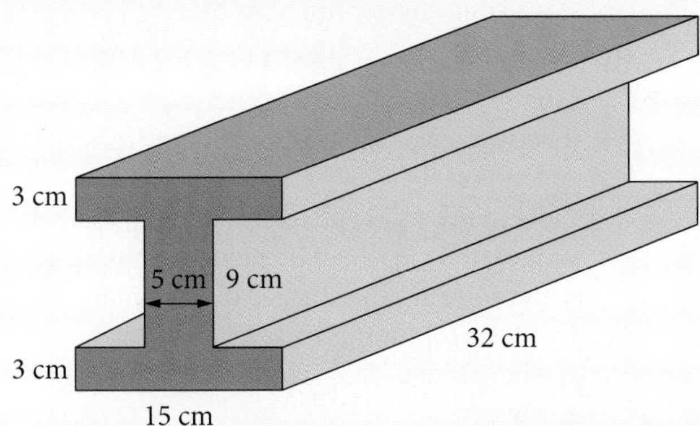

4. The diagram shows the net of a cylinder. Using the information in the diagram, calculate the radius of the cylinder.
Hence find the volume of the cylinder.
Take $\pi = \frac{22}{7}$.

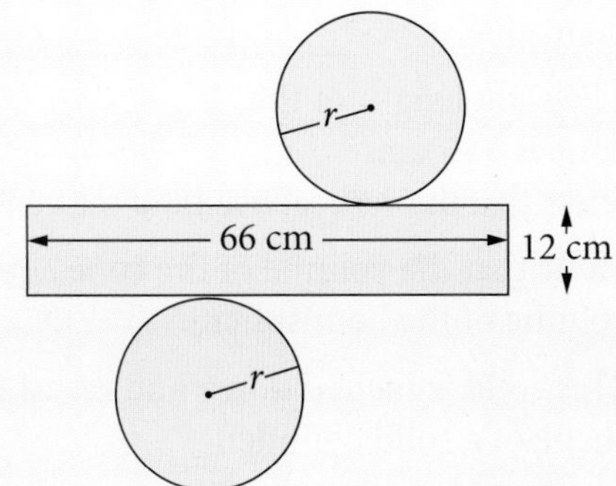

5. A hot water container is in the shape of a hemisphere on top of a cylinder as shown. The hemisphere has a radius of 25 cm and the container has a height of 90 cm. Find the capacity of the container in litres, giving your answer correct to the nearest litre.
[1 litre = 1,000 cm^3]

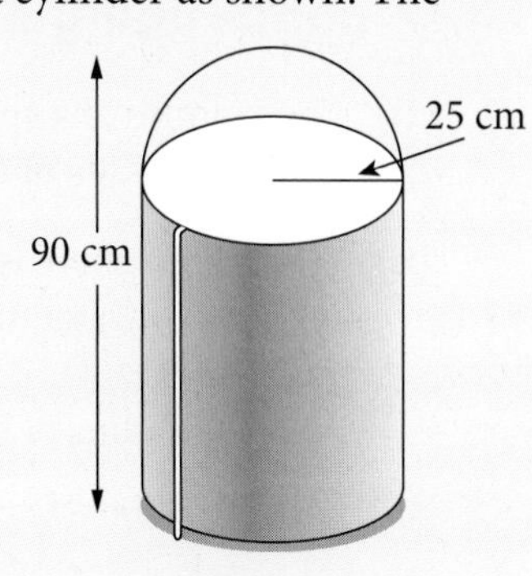

6. 49 ping pong balls, each of diameter 3 cm, fit exactly in a rectangular box which has internal height 3 cm.
(i) The base of the box is a square. How many balls are there in each row?
(ii) What is the internal volume of the box?

7. The diagram shows a cone with a perpendicular height of 4 cm and base with radius of length 3 cm.

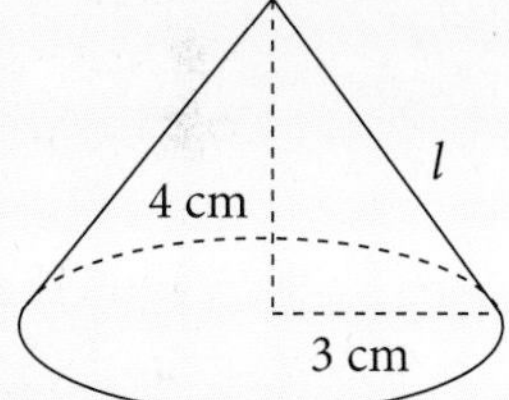

(i) Find the slant length of the cone.
(ii) Find the volume of the cone, correct to one decimal place.
(iii) Find the curved surface area of the cone, correct to one decimal place.

8. The diagram shows a canvas camping tent of volume 1·2 m^3.
(i) Find the height of the tent.
(ii) How much canvas is required to make this tent? Give your answer correct to one decimal place.

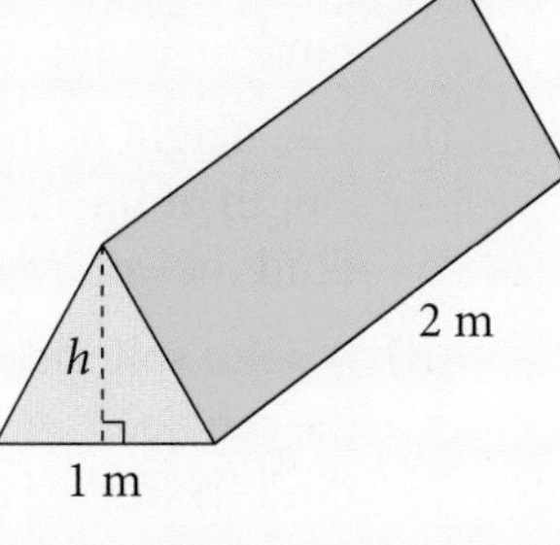

9. Find the volume of the concrete used to make the hollow block shown:

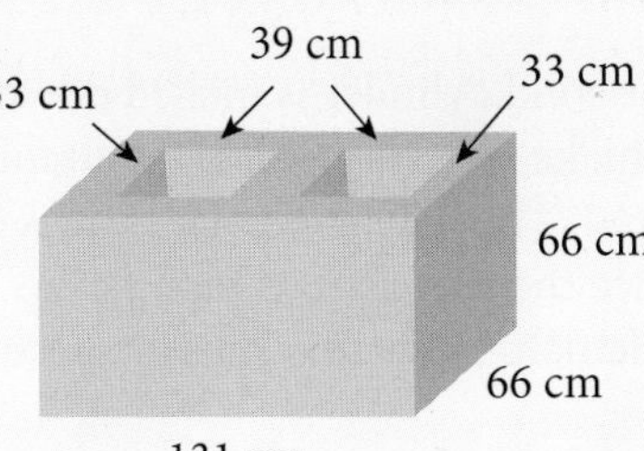

Volume and Surface Area

Revision Questions – Section B

More challenging problems

1. **(i)** The volume of a sphere is 288π cm^3.
Find the radius of the sphere.

   (ii) When the sphere is fully immersed in a cylinder of water, the level of the water rises by 2 cm.
Find the radius of the cylinder.

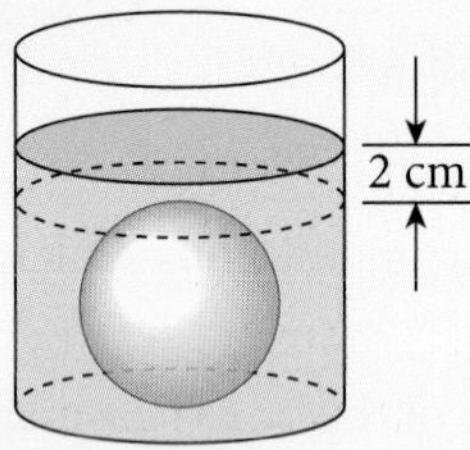

2. A candle is in the shape of a cylinder with a conical top, as shown in the diagram.

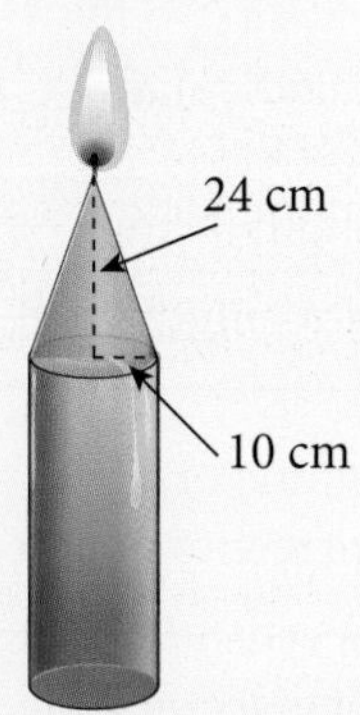

   (i) The cone has height 24 cm and the length of the radius of its base is 10 cm.
Find the volume of the cone in terms of π.

   (ii) The height of the cylinder is equal to the slant length of the cone.
Find the volume of the cylinder in terms of π.

   (iii) A solid spherical ball of wax was used to make the candle.
Find the radius of this spherical ball, correct to one decimal place.

3. **(i)** A solid cylinder, made of wax, has a radius of length 15 cm and height of 135 cm.
Find its volume in terms of π.

   (ii) The solid cylinder is melted down and recast to make four identical right circular solid cones. The height of each cone is equal to twice the length of its base radius.
Calculate the base radius length of the cones.

4. A steel-works buys steel in the form of solid cylindrical rods of diameter 20 centimetres and length 30 metres. The steel rods are melted to produce solid spherical ball bearings. No steel is wasted in the process.

   (i) Find the volume of steel in one cylindrical rod, in terms of π.

   (ii) The radius of a ball bearing is 2 cm.
How many such ball bearings are made from one steel rod?

   (iii) Ball bearings of a different size are also produced.
One steel rod makes 225,000 of these new ball bearings. Find the radius of the new ball bearings.

5. **(i)** Find the volume of a solid sphere with a diameter of length 3 cm.
Give your answer in terms of π.

   (ii) A cylindrical vessel with internal diameter of length 15 cm contains water.
The surface of the water is 11 cm from the top of the vessel.
How many solid spheres, each with diameter of length 3 cm, must be placed in the vessel in order to bring the surface of the water to 1 cm from the top of the vessel?
Assume that all the spheres are submerged in the water.

6. A solid is in the shape of a hemisphere with a cone on top, as in the diagram.

   (i) The volume of the hemisphere is 18π cm^3.
Find the radius of the hemisphere.

   (ii) The slant length of the cone is $3\sqrt{5}$ cm.
Show that the vertical height of the cone is 6 cm.

   (iii) Show that the volume of the cone equals the volume of the hemisphere.

   (iv) This solid is melted down and recast in the shape of a solid cylinder.
The height of the cylinder is 9 cm. Calculate its radius.

7. A solid wax candle is in the shape of a cylinder with a cone on top, as shown in the diagram. The diameter of the base of the cylinder is 6 cm and the height of the cylinder is 12 cm. The volume of the wax in the candle is 123π cm^3.

12 cm

6 cm

   (i) Find the total height of the candle.

   (ii) 20 of these candles fit into a rectangular box. The candles are arranged in five rows of four. Find the dimensions of the smallest rectangular box that the candles will fit into.

   (iii) When the 20 candles are packed into the box, what percentage of the box is air?

8. A test tube consists of a cylinder on top of a hemisphere, as shown in the diagram.

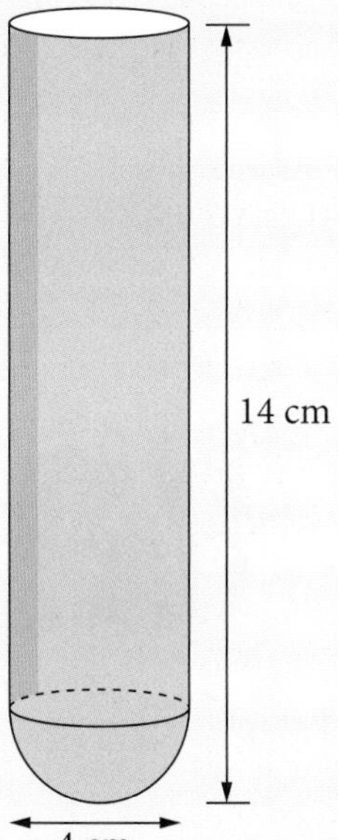

   (i) Find the capacity (internal volume) of the test tube, in terms of π.

   (ii) Water is added to the test tube, until it is three-quarters full. How far is the surface of the water from the top of the test tube?

9. **(i)** A solid metal sphere has a diameter of 9 cm. Find the volume of the sphere in terms of π.

   (ii) This sphere is melted down and all the metal is used to make a solid shape which consists of a cone on top of a cylinder, as shown in the diagram. The cone and the cylinder both have height 8 cm. The cylinder and the base of the cone both have radius r cm. Calculate r, correct to one decimal place.

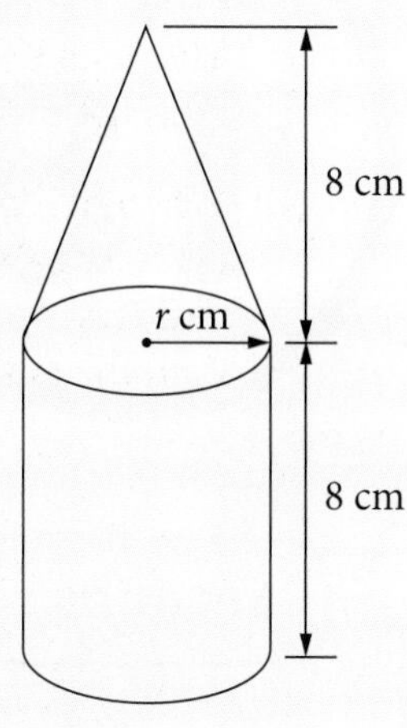

10. A cylindrical tank, of base diameter 40 cm, contains a quantity of water. A solid cone, of height 25 cm and base radius 15 cm is dropped into the cylinder, such that it is upright and some of the cone is above the water (as shown in the diagram). If the depth of the water in the tank is now 20 cm, find the original depth of the water before the cone was dropped into the tank.

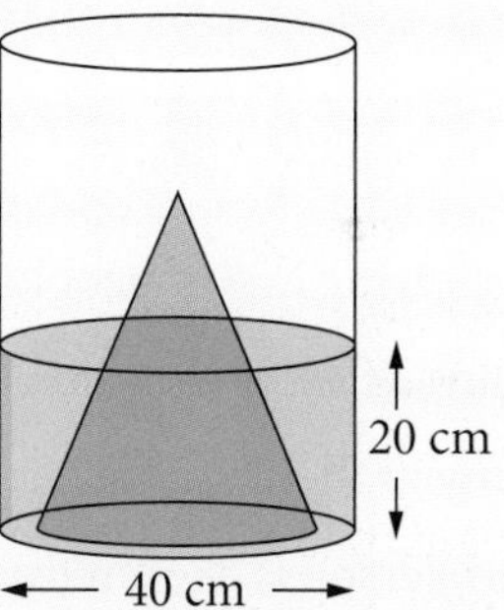

Now that you have completed the chapter, revisit the 'Something to think about…' question.

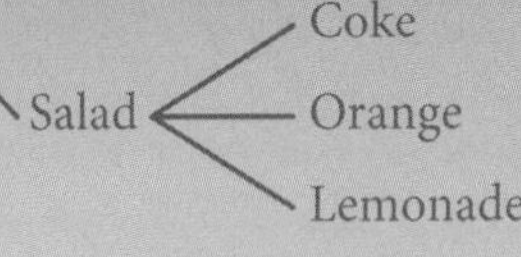

CHAPTER 18 Probability I

Sections covered within this chapter:

KEY WORDS

- Fundamental Principle of Counting
- Two-way table
- Probability
- Equally likely
- Outcome
- Tree diagram
- Experiment
- Sample space
- Permutation
- Event

SOMETHING TO THINK ABOUT...

Consider the following line of people.

(i) In how many different ways can this group of people line up?

(ii) In how many of these arrangements is the first and last person male?

(iii) If a random person is chosen from the line, what is the chance that the person:

(a) is male? **(c)** has long hair?

(b) is bald? **(d)** is using a phone?

Section 18.1: The Fundamental Principle of Counting

Learning Outcome:

You should be able to:

- understand and use the Fundamental Principle of Counting

Consider a situation where an ice cream van sells three different flavours of ice cream: vanilla, strawberry or chocolate. You can choose a regular cone or a waffle cone.

In how many different ways can you buy an ice cream from this van?

Some of you will have listed all the combinations as follows:

Vanilla waffle	Strawberry waffle	Chocolate waffle
Vanilla regular	Strawberry regular	Chocolate regular

This gives us six options. This method is called **systematic listing**.

Others will have noticed that there are two cone options and three ice cream options, so that gives a total of six combinations.

If you worked this out by multiplying the number of options, you used the Fundamental Principle of Counting (FPoC).

The Fundamental Principle of Counting can be used to work out the total number of possible ways two or more options can be combined.

The **Fundamental Principle of Counting** (FPoC) is a mathematical rule that allows you to find the number of ways that a combination of events can occur.

When there are m ways to do one thing, and n ways to do another, then there are $m \times n$ ways of doing both.

Sometimes we are not only asked the number of possible combinations but also to list all the possible combinations (outcomes).

An **outcome** is any possible result in a given situation.

When the number of choices increases, it can become difficult to list all combinations. To assist with this, we can use a sample space diagram. A sample space diagram makes sure we don't forget any outcomes.

There are two main types of sample space diagrams:

1. Two-way tables
2. Tree diagrams

A list of all possible outcomes is called a **sample space**.

Two-way table

A **two-way table** is a way of listing all possible outcomes when combining a number of choices within two categories.

All of the choices for one of the categories are listed in a vertical column. The choices for the other category are listed along a horizontal row.

EXAMPLE 1

If Jackie has a red t-shirt, a green t-shirt, a white t-shirt, a pair of blue jeans and a pair of black jeans.

(i) How many different outfits can she make?

(ii) List all the outfits possible.

Solution

(i) Using the Fundamental Principle of Counting:

Number of choices of t-shirt = 3

Number of choices of jeans = 2

Total number of outfits possible = $3 \times 2 = 6$ (FPoC)

(ii) It is possible to simply list all the outcomes systematically, since there are only six outfits. However, you can also use a two-way table.

The two categories in this case are colour of jeans and colour of t-shirt, so we can set up the table as shown.

The list of all the outfits possible is now contained in the table.

	Red t-shirt	**Green t-shirt**	**White t-shirt**
Blue jeans	Red t-shirt and blue jeans	Green t-shirt and blue jeans	White t-shirt and blue jeans
Black jeans	Red t-shirt and black jeans	Green t-shirt and black jeans	White t-shirt and black jeans

Tree diagram

A **tree diagram** is a way of listing all possible outcomes when combining a number of choices within two or more categories.

When there are more than two different categories, it is best to use a tree diagram to list the outcomes. Each branch of the tree represents a different outcome.

When the tree is complete, we follow the branches to see all of the possible outcomes.

EXAMPLE 2

Simon's local restaurant has a lunch special that includes a burger, one side and a drink for €5. He can choose a hamburger or a cheeseburger; salad or fries and coke; and orange or lemonade.

(i) How many different meals can Simon order?

(ii) List all the meals possible.

Solution

(i) Number of burger choices = 2

Number of side choices = 2

Number of drink choices = 3

Total number of choices = $2 \times 2 \times 3 = 12$ (FPoC)

(ii) Set up the tree diagram as shown. Follow each branch to list the different meals possible. We know from (i) we should have 12 meals.

When using tree diagrams, we could use shorthand instead of the full words; e.g. H = hamburger, etc.

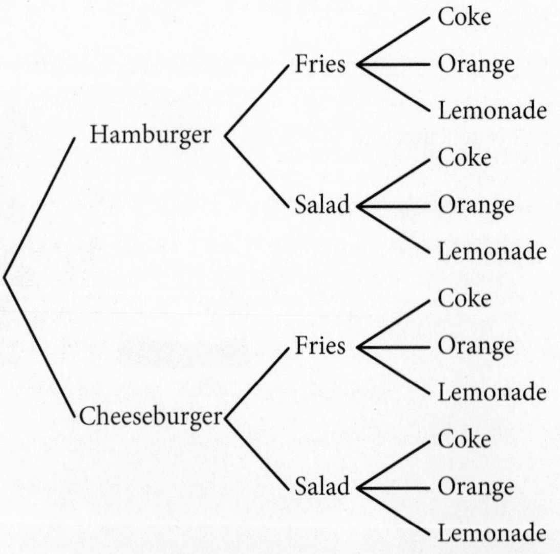

Hamburger, fries, coke
Hamburger, fries, orange
Hamburger, fries, lemonade
Hamburger, salad, coke
Hamburger, salad, orange
Hamburger, salad, lemonade
Cheeseburger, fries, coke
Cheeseburger, fries, orange
Cheeseburger, fries, lemonade
Cheesburger, salad, coke
Cheesburger, salad, orange
Cheesburger, salad, lemonade

Practice Questions 18.1

1. A university English course allows students to choose to study one novel from four, one poem from six and one short story from five.
   How many choices do students have?
2. Adam has four shirts, three pairs of trousers and two pairs of shoes.
   How many outfits can he put together?
3. How many different results are possible when two people play rock paper scissors?
   List all the possible outcomes.
4. A travel agent has nine holiday destinations available in three price ranges, with either full board or self-catering options.
   How many holiday combinations are there to choose from?
5. A pizza restaurant offers three sizes of pizza, two types of base, two types of crust and six toppings.
   How many different types of pizza with one topping is it possible to order?
6. A café has an offer that includes a hot drink and a snack. The choices of hot drinks are tea or coffee and the snack choices are a chocolate bar, a muffin or a scone.
   Use a two-way table to list all possible drink and snack combinations.
7. Grace loves to eat salad. How many salads can she put together if she can select one type of lettuce from two choices, one vegetable from four choices and one dressing from seven choices?
8. A website allows members to design an avatar (personal picture). Each picture is designed by choosing from male or female, eight face types, 48 eye types, 12 noses, 24 mouths and 82 hair styles.
   How many different pictures are possible?
9. Steph and Dan go for a meal to celebrate Steph's birthday.
   (i) How many different three-course meals can they order from the menu shown?
   (ii) Steph decides not to have a starter. How many meal options does she have now?
   (iii) Dan is allergic to fish. How many meal options does he have?
   (iv) Use a tree diagram to list all of Dan's meal options.

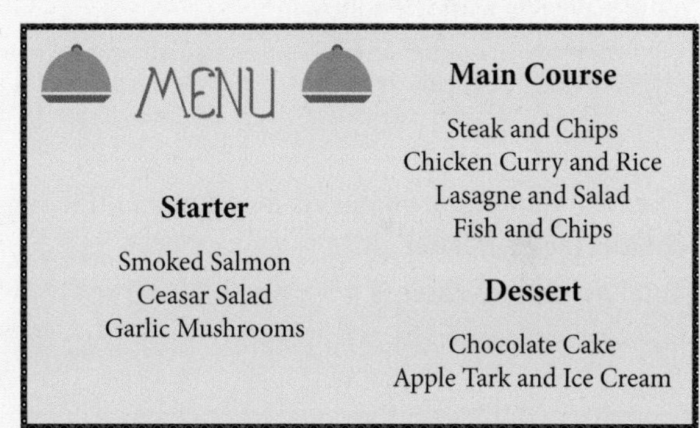

10. Lucy is planning a day out for herself and three friends to a nearby town.
    She must choose how they get there, what they will do when they are there, and what kind of food they will eat. To get there, she can choose to get a bus or a train. The activities available are mini golf, bowling or the cinema. The food options are Chinese, Italian or Mexican.
    (i) Use a tree diagram to list all the possible options available.

    The cost per person for each option is listed in the table:

Transport	Activity	Food
Bus €3	Mini golf €8	Chinese €12
Train €6	Bowling €6	Italian €13
	Cinema €7	Mexican €11

(ii) Find the difference between the maximum and minimum costs of the day out.

Lucy discovers that on the day she is planning to go, the bowling alley is closed.

(iii) How does this fact affect the number of choices available to the group?

Section 18.2: Permutations (Arrangements)

Learning Outcomes:

You should be able to:
- count the number of ways of arranging n objects
- count the number of ways of arranging r objects from n different objects

A **permutation** is an arrangement (or order) of a set of objects.

EXAMPLE 1

How many different ways can the letters of the word MATHS be arranged if no letter can be repeated?

Solution

The first letter can be M, A, T, H, or S, i.e. there are five choices of letter.

1st letter	2nd letter	3rd letter	4th letter	5th letter
5				

One letter has now been used up so there are only four left to choose from. Then two are used, leaving three to choose from. Next, three have been used leaving two choices and, finally, four have been used leaving only one choice for the final letter.

This leaves us with the following:

1st letter	2nd letter	3rd letter	4th letter	5th letter
5	4	3	2	1

The total number of choices is found by multiplying the number of choices for each letter.

Total number of choices = $5 \times 4 \times 3 \times 2 \times 1 = 120$ (FPoC)

$5 \times 4 \times 3 \times 2 \times 1 = 5!$ (5 factorial)
This can be done by using the factorial button ($x!$) on the calculator.

Restrictions

Restrictions are often put in place in permutations questions. When dealing with questions that contain restrictions, it is important that we deal with the restrictions first. Look at the next example to see how we do this.

EXAMPLE 2

How many of the arrangements of the letters of the word MATHS start with a consonant and end with T?

A, E, I, O and U are vowels.
All other letters are consonants.

Solution

Fill in the restricted options first. This time there is a restriction on the 1st letter.

It must be a consonant, so there are four choices of consonants: M, T, H and S.

T must be the final letter so that leaves three choices for the 1st letter and one choice for the final letter.

The situation can be represented as follows:

1st letter	2nd letter	3rd letter	4th letter	5th letter
M/H/S				T

Two letters are now used up so there are three choices for the 2nd letter, two choices for the 3rd letter and only one choice for the 4th letter, leaving us with the following:

1st letter	2nd letter	3rd letter	4th letter	5th letter
3	3	2	1	1
M/H/S				T

Total number of choices = $3 \times 3 \times 2 \times 1 \times 1 = 18$ (FPoC)

Another type of restriction would be where certain objects must come together. This situation is examined in the next example.

EXAMPLE 3

In how many of the arrangements of the letters M, A, T, H and S are the H and the S together?

Solution

If the two letters must always be together, they are taken as **one object**.

MAT[HS]

We now have four objects to rearrange, which can be done in four factorial (4!) ways.

However, H and S can come together in two different ways: HS or SH.

So the total numbers of choices is $2 \times 4! = 48$ (FPoC)

The number of arrangements possible is reduced by putting in restrictions.

Arranging r objects from n distinct objects ($^n\mathrm{P}_r$)

In general, arranging r objects from n distinct objects is called $^n\mathbf{P}_r$.

This means the number of permutations of n objects taking r at a time.

We can do this on our calculator using the $^n\mathbf{P}_r$ button.

EXAMPLE 4

How many four-letter arrangements can be made from the letters of the word LEAVING?

Solution

In this example we have 7 objects to permute in 4 ways.

This leads to the following:

1st letter	2nd letter	3rd letter	4th letter
7	6	5	4

Total number of choices = $7 \times 6 \times 5 \times 4 = 840$ (FPoC)

Alternatively, you could use $^7\mathrm{P}_4 = 840$

EXAMPLE 5

Eight horses run a race. How many ways can 1st, 2nd and 3rd place be awarded, assuming there are no dead heats?

Solution

There are eight horses possible for 1st place

There are seven horses possible for 2nd place (since one has already passed the line)

There are six horses possible for 3rd place (since two have already passed the line)

Using the FPoC:

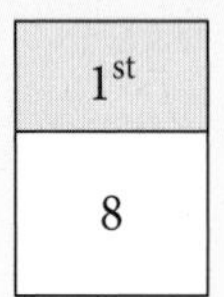
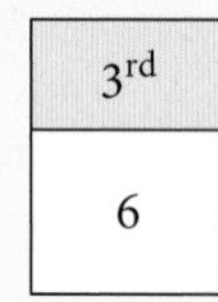

1st		2nd		3rd
8	$\times$	7	$\times$	6

There are $8 \times 7 \times 6 = 336$ different possible outcomes for the race winners.

Alternatively, you could use ${}^{8}P_{3} = 336$

Practice Questions 18.2

1. Evaluate each of the following
   - **(i)** $10!$
   - **(ii)** $7!$
   - **(iii)** $2 \times 4!$
   - **(iv)** $3! \times 4!$
   - **(v)** $9! \div 3!$
   - **(vi)** ${}^{6}P_{2}$
   - **(vii)** ${}^{10}P_{3}$
   - **(viii)** ${}^{16}P_{9}$
   - **(ix)** $\dfrac{3! \times 5!}{2!}$
   - **(x)** $\dfrac{7! \times 4!}{3! \times 2!}$
   - **(xi)** $\dfrac{7!}{2! \times 5!} + \dfrac{7!}{4! \times 3!}$
   - **(xii)** $3 \times \dfrac{11!}{5! \times 4!}$

2. How many ways can five pictures be hung in a line on a wall?

3. How many five-digit numbers can be formed using 1–9, without repetition of any digits?

4. The letters A, B and C are used to make a three-letter company name. Each letter is used only once. How many different company names can be made?

5. On sports day 18 students enter a race. In how many ways can 1st, 2nd and 3rd place be awarded assuming there were no dead heats?

6. A test consists of 15 questions, but you only have to answer 10. In how many different ways can these 10 questions be completed?

7. A book shop must display 31 books in its window. In how many ways can the books be arranged on the top shelf if this shelf holds 15 books?

8. From a group of 8 men and 10 women, in how many ways can three men and four women be arranged in a row if the men must be first?

9. How many five-number licence plates can be made using the digits 4, 5, 6, 7, 8 and 9 if:
   - **(i)** repetitions are **not** allowed?
   - **(ii)** repetitions are **not** allowed and the plate number is even?
   - **(iii)** repetitions **are** allowed?

10. Ahmed's playlist consists of 50 different songs that can be arranged in any order.
    - **(i)** How many arrangements are there for the 50 songs?
    - **(ii)** Ahmed decides that he wants to play his three favourite songs first, in any order. How many arrangements of the 50 songs are now possible?

11. How many four-digit ATM codes can be made if:
    - **(i)** each digit can only be used once (no repetition)?
    - **(ii)** all digits can be repeated?

    Assuming repetition is not allowed, how many arrangements are possible if:
    - **(iii)** the code can't start with 0?
    - **(iv)** the code must be an even number?
    - **(v)** the code must start with 2 and be an odd number?

12. If all letters must be used, how many different ways can the letters of the word COUNTS be arranged if:

    (i) none of the letters can be repeated?

    Assuming repetition is not allowed, how many arrangements are possible if:

    (ii) the first letter must be a vowel?

    (iii) the first letter is S, and the last letter is a vowel?

    (iv) the vowels must always come together?

13. How many of each of the following types of arrangements can be made from the letters of the word MATHEMATICS?

    (i) 2 letters (iii) 7 letters

    (ii) 4 letters (iv) 10 letters

14. A family is being arranged in a line for a photograph. The family consists of a mother, father, three children and a grandmother.
    How many different arrangements are possible if:

    (i) all family members can stand anywhere in the line?

    (ii) the parents must be on the outside?

    (iii) the grandmother is on the outside left and the father is on the outside right?

    (iv) the parents are beside each other?

    (v) the grandmother is not in the photograph, the parents are on the outside and the children line up according to age from oldest to youngest assuming there are no twins or triplets in the family?

15. A website requires a password consisting of two letters, followed by four numbers. Assume no letters or numbers can be repeated in the password.

    How many different passwords can be generated if:

    (i) no further restrictions apply?

    (ii) the first letter must be a vowel?

    (iii) the last number cannot be zero?

    (iv) the first letter must be a vowel and the first number must be odd?

    (v) the password starts with a consonant and the numerical part is even?

16. A security code used to consist of two odd digits followed by four even digits. To allow more codes to be generated, a new system uses two even digits, followed by any three digits. If repetition of digits is not allowed, what is the increase in the number of codes possible?

17. Assuming repetition is not allowed, how many four-letter word arrangements can be made from the word COMPUTER?
    Assuming repetition is not allowed, how many of these arrangements:

    (i) start with a vowel?

    (ii) start with a vowel and end with R?

    (iii) contain only the letters COMP?

18. A bank issues a unique six-digit password to each of its online customers. The password may contain any of the numbers 0 to 9 in any position and numbers may be repeated.

    (i) How many different passwords are possible?

    (ii) How many different passwords do not contain any zeros?

19. A type of padlock uses letters instead of numbers. There are two types of this lock available.

    (a) The first type of lock consists of a dial containing all the letters of the alphabet, as shown.
    This type of lock requires six letters to open it. How many arrangements are possible if:

    (i) all letters can be repeated?

    (ii) no letter can be repeated?

    (iii) the first letter must be a vowel (no repetition)?

    (iv) the first, third and last letter must be consonants (no repetition)?

    (v) the first three letters must be A, B and C, in any order (no repetition)?

    (b) The second type of lock is a barrel lock, as shown.
    This lock comes in four-letter and five-letter (shown) versions, which use four or five dials respectively, with 26 letters on each dial.

    The manufacturer claims the four-letter version provides 10,000 different letter

Probability I

arrangements and the five-letter version provides 100,000 different letter arrangements.

Are the manufacturers claims correct? Justify your answer.

20. The new Eircode postcode was introduced in 2015. An Eircode is a unique seven-character code consisting of letters and numbers.

- Each Eircode consists of a three-character routing key to identify the area and a four-character unique identifier.
- The routing key is the first three characters of an Eircode. The first character is always a letter, followed by two numbers.
- The unique identifier is made-up of a mixture of letters and numbers.
- The letter 'O' is not used to avoid confusion with the number zero.

For example, the Eircode for the 3 Arena is D01 EW90

(i) How many routing keys can be generated if:

(a) no repetition is allowed?

(b) repetition is allowed?

Assume no repetition is allowed. How many different arrangements of routing keys:

(c) start with a vowel?

(d) start with a vowel and end with zero?

(ii) How many unique identifiers can be generated if:

(a) no repetition is allowed?

(b) repetition is allowed?

(iii) How many Eircodes can be generated if

(a) no repetition is allowed?

(b) repetition is allowed?

(iv) If the population increased dramatically and new Eircodes were needed, suggest one simple change that would allow more codes to be generated?

Section 18.3: Basic Probability

Learning Outcomes:

You should be able to:

- understand that probability is a measure on a scale of 0–1 of how likely an event is to occur
- use the language of probability to discuss events

Probability is the branch of maths that allows us to calculate how likely something is to happen.

Probability is the maths of chance.

Probability has many everyday applications such as gambling, sports, medical decisions, insurance quotes and life expectancy, even down to deciding whether or not to bring a coat when leaving the house.

Discussion Time 

Work with a classmate to determine which statements are true and which are false. One third of the statements are true.

1. Six is the hardest number to throw on a die.
2. In a true/false test of 20 questions you will get 10 correct by just guessing.
3. If a family already has two boys, the next baby is more likely to be a girl.
4. If you buy a lot of raffle tickets, you are more likely to win a prize.
5. In the national lottery, you shouldn't pick a set of consecutive numbers because it's almost impossible for them to come up.
6. When picking a card at random from a standard deck of 52, you have a 25% chance of picking a club.

Probability questions often use situations involving playing cards and dice. It is very important that you know the basic facts about these situations.

Know your dice!

A die is a cube consisting of six faces.

Each face has a number of dots from one to six.

Opposite faces of a die add up to seven.

Know your cards!

There are a total of 52 cards in a deck, excluding the two joker cards.

There are four suits: hearts, diamonds, spades and clubs.

There are 13 cards in each suit.

There are 26 red cards and 26 black cards.

There are four cards of each value.

The jacks, queens and kings are picture cards. Thus there are a total of 12 picture cards in the deck.

	A	2	3	4	5	6	7	8	9	10	J	Q	K
Hearts	Ace ♥	2 ♥	3 ♥	4 ♥	5 ♥	6 ♥	7 ♥	8 ♥	9 ♥	10 ♥	Jack ♥	Queen ♥	King ♥
Diamonds	Ace ♦	2 ♦	3 ♦	4 ♦	5 ♦	6 ♦	7 ♦	8 ♦	9 ♦	10 ♦	Jack ♦	Queen ♦	King ♦
Spades	Ace ♠	2 ♠	3 ♠	4 ♠	5 ♠	6 ♠	7 ♠	8 ♠	9 ♠	10 ♠	Jack ♠	Queen ♠	King ♠
Clubs	Ace ♣	2 ♣	3 ♣	4 ♣	5 ♣	6 ♣	7 ♣	8 ♣	9 ♣	10 ♣	Jack ♣	Queen ♣	King ♣

Probability scale

The probability of something happening lies somewhere between impossible and certain.

Things that are certain to happen are given a probability of 1.

Things that will never happen are given a probability of 0.

Events that could happen are rated between 0 and 1 on what is known as the probability scale.

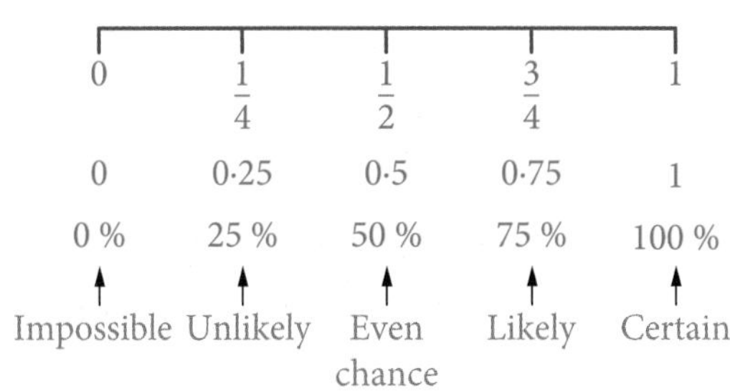

There are no negative probabilities and no probabilities greater than 1 or 100%.

Probabilities can be represented as fractions, decimals or percentages. For example, if something has an even chance of occurring we can say it has a probability of 50%, 0·5 or $\frac{1}{2}$.

The closer the probability is to 0, the less likely it is to happen.

The closer the probability is to 1, the more likely it is to happen.

Practice Questions 18.3

1. Which of the following could be the probability of an event occurring?

   (i) 1 **(ii)** $\frac{6}{5}$ **(iii)** 1·27 **(iv)** 145% **(v)** −0·75

2. Which letter represents each of the following:
   - **(i)** An event that is certain to happen?
   - **(ii)** An event that is impossible?
   - **(iii)** An event that has an even chance of happening?
   - **(iv)** An event that is very likely to happen?
   - **(v)** An event that is unlikely to happen?
   - **(vi)** An event that is likely to happen?

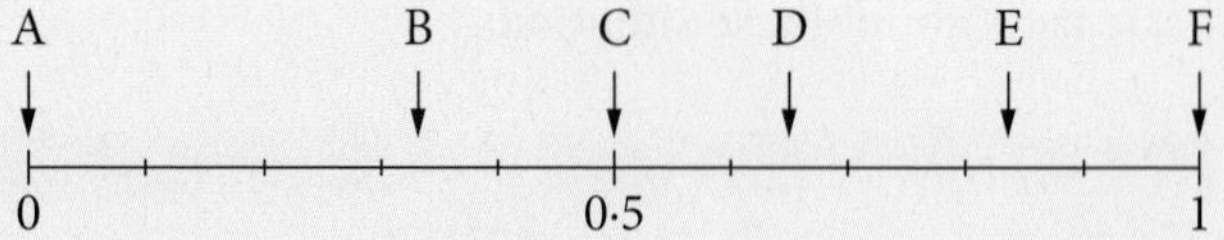

   A B C D E F

   0 0·5 1

3. Which of the arrows A, B, C or D shows the best position on the probability scale for each of the following events:
   - **(i)** A head is obtained when a coin is flipped?
   - **(ii)** You will visit Mars in your lifetime?
   - **(iii)** A number chosen at random from 0–9 will be prime?
   - **(iv)** It will snow in Florida tomorrow?

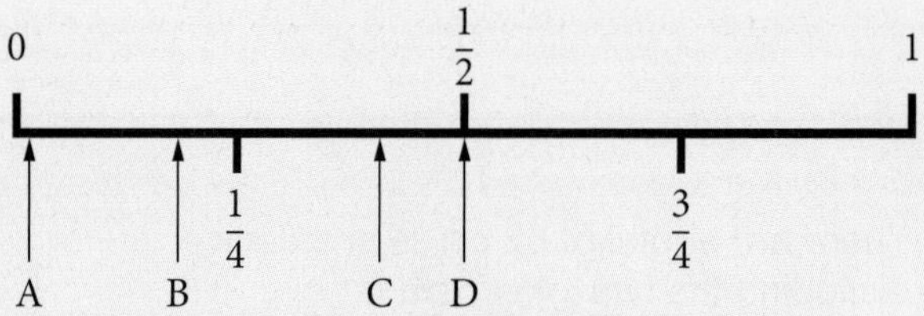

   0 $\frac{1}{2}$ 1

   $\frac{1}{4}$ $\frac{3}{4}$

   A B C D

4. Draw a probability scale and mark the following probabilities on it:

   A: You will get heads when you flip a coin.

   B: The day after Sunday will be Monday.

   C: Christmas day will fall on June 25th next year.

   D: You will choose a picture card from a standard deck.

   E: A month chosen at random will have more than 30 days.

5. Think of an example of a situation that could result in the following probabilities:

   (i) 0 **(ii)** 1 **(iii)** 0·5 **(iv)** 0·2 **(v)** 0·75

Section 18.4: Single Event Probabilities

Learning Outcomes:

You should be able to:

- list all possible outcomes of an experiment and estimate probabilities from experimental data
- understand that increasing the number of times an experiment is repeated generally leads to better estimates of probability
- understand how to calculate probabilities

An **experiment** or **trial** is the event or action of doing something and recording results. For example, flipping a coin, picking a card from a deck or throwing a die.

An **event** is a single result of an experiment.

If a fair die is thrown you have an equal chance of getting each of the numbers 1, 2, 3, 4, 5 and 6.

As previously mentioned, the sample space is a listing of all the possible outcomes that could arise from an experiment.

The words **fair**, **unbiased** and **random** are commonly used in probability questions. These are ways of saying that all outcomes are **equally likely**.

Calculating probability

To calculate the probability of an event (E) happening we use the following formula:

$$P(E) = \frac{\text{The number of outcomes of interest}}{\text{The total number of possible outcomes}}$$

When calculating probabilities, we can have different types of situations:

Theoretical situations

In theoretical situations we calculate probabilities based on what should happen in theory.

For example, the probability of getting an even number when a fair die is thrown is $\frac{3}{6} = \frac{1}{2}$, since there are three even numbers possible out of six numbers. This is known as the theoretical probability.

Experimental situations

In real life if we were to throw a fair die six times, we would be very unlikely to get one of each of the six numbers, as would be expected in theory. (Try it yourself!)

The experimental probability that something will happen is based on how often the event occurs after collecting data or running an experiment (or trial). It is based specifically on direct observations.

The number of times an event occurs is called the **frequency**.

The number of times an event occurs out of the total number of trials is called the **relative frequency**. Relative frequency can be referred to as **experimental probability**.

For example, Roisín throws a fair die 60 times and gets the following results:

Results	Number of times it happens (Frequency)	Number of times out of the total (Relative frequency)
1	6	$\frac{6}{60}$
2	12	$\frac{12}{60}$
3	9	$\frac{9}{60}$
4	16	$\frac{16}{60}$
5	4	$\frac{4}{60}$
6	13	$\frac{13}{60}$

So, the probability of getting a 5 in Roisín's experiment is $\frac{4}{60} = \frac{1}{15}$, not $\frac{1}{6}$ as we would expect.

This may be just a fluke in this case or it may indicate the die is unfair.

The larger the number of trials carried out the closer the experimental probability comes to theoretical probability.

Probability I

Probability of an event not occurring

If E is an event this means that it will either happen or not happen.

We use the notation P(event) to describe the probability of particular events.

For example,

P(6) means the probability of getting a 6 when a fair die is thrown.

You will either get a 6 or you will get a number other than 6.

Since there is only one 6 on a fair die, then: $P(6) = \frac{1}{6}$

When a fair die is thrown, it is certain that you will get a number between 1 and 6.

This means, the probability of getting a number between 1 and 6 is 1.

All probabilities in a given situation must add up to 1.

Therefore, we can work out the probability of not getting a 6 as follows:

$$P(\text{not a } 6) = 1 - P(6)$$
$$= 1 - \frac{1}{6}$$
$$= \frac{5}{6}$$

If E is an event, then:

P(E happening) + P(E not happening) = 1

P(E happening) = 1 − P(E not happening)

P(E not happening) = 1 − P(E happening)

EXAMPLE 1

A spinner with six equal segments numbered 1 to 6 was spun 50 times and the numbers of times it landed on each number was recorded in the table of results below.

Use the table to work out the answers to the following questions:

Outcome	Number of times recorded
1	5
2	10
3	14
4	8
5	9
6	4

(i) What is the theoretical probability of each outcome? Explain your answer.

(ii) What is the relative frequency/experimental probability of each outcome?

(iii) Find the sum of relative frequencies. Is this as expected? Justify your answer.

(iv) How could you ensure the experimental probability will be closer to the theoretical probability?

Solution

(i) The theoretical probability of each outcome is $\frac{1}{6}$.

There is one segment for each number, the total number of segments is six and each segment is of equal size, so:

$P(1) = \frac{1}{6}$ $P(2) = \frac{1}{6}$ $P(3) = \frac{1}{6}$ $P(4) = \frac{1}{6}$ $P(5) = \frac{1}{6}$ $P(6) = \frac{1}{6}$

(ii) Using the figures from the table, relative frequency/experimental probability can be calculated by:

$$P(E) = \frac{\text{The number of outcomes of interest}}{\text{The total number of possible outcomes}}$$

$P(1) = \frac{5}{50} = \frac{1}{10}$ $P(2) = \frac{10}{50} = \frac{1}{5}$ $P(3) = \frac{14}{50} = \frac{7}{25}$ $P(4) = \frac{8}{50} = \frac{4}{25}$ $P(5) = \frac{9}{50}$ $P(6) = \frac{4}{50} = \frac{2}{25}$

(iii) The sum of the relative frequencies = $\frac{1}{10} + \frac{1}{5} + \frac{7}{25} + \frac{4}{25} + \frac{9}{50} + \frac{2}{25} = 1$

This is as expected because the sum of all the probabilities in a given situation must be 1.

(iv) You could spin the spinner more times. The more times you do a trial/experiment, the closer your result will get to the theoretical probability.

Discussion Time 

Work with a classmate to carry out the following investigation:

1. Get a coin.
2. Flip it 50 times and record your results in a table.
3. What is your sample space?
4. Work out P(head) and P(tail).
5. Take results from five other pairs and work out P(head) and P(tail) for 300 flips. (Make sure that the coins used by the other pairs are the same shape and size.)

Now discuss the following:

When we do an experiment, are the results always the same?

Which probabilities are more reliable, your results from 50 flips or the group's results as a whole? Why?

Why does the number of times we do the experiment affect the accuracy of the experimental probabilities we get?

EXAMPLE 2

A marble is randomly selected from a bag containing three green, five red, and seven blue marbles. Calculate the probability that the marble is:

(i) red
(ii) green
(iii) blue
(iv) not red
(v) not green or blue
(vi) green or red
(vii) yellow.

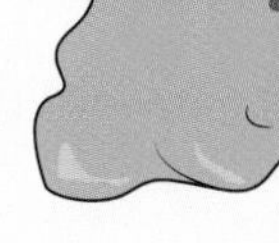

Solution

Calculate the total number of possible outcomes

$$3 + 5 + 7 = 15$$

(i) P(red) = $\frac{\text{number of red marbles}}{\text{total number of marbles}} = \frac{5}{15} = \frac{1}{3}$

(ii) P(green) = $\frac{3}{15} = \frac{1}{5}$

(iii) P(blue) = $\frac{7}{15}$

(iv) P(not red) = 1 − P(red)

$= 1 - \frac{1}{3}$

$= \frac{2}{3}$

(v) P(not green or blue) = $\frac{5}{15} = \frac{1}{3}$

(vi) P(green or red) = $\frac{3+5}{15} = \frac{8}{15}$

(vii) There are no yellow marbles in the bag, so P(yellow) = 0.

Fractions should always be expressed in their simplest form.

Probability I

Practice Questions 18.4

1. Identify the correct sample space in each case:
   - **(i)** Choosing one jelly bean at random from a jar containing 4 red, 6 blue and 5 green jelly beans.

     {4 red, 6 blue, 5 green} {4, 6, 5} {red, blue, green}
   - **(ii)** Choosing one letter from five vowels.

     {a, e, i, o, u} {1, 2, 3, 4, 5} {v, o, w, e, l}
   - **(iii)** Choosing one letter at random from the word PROBABILITY.

     {p, r, o, b, a, b, i, l, i, t, y} {p, r, o, b, a, i, l, t, y} {1, 2, 3, 4, 5, 6, 7, 8, 9, 10, 11}
   - **(iv)** Choosing an odd number at random between 1 and 10.

     {1, 2, 3, 4, 5, 6, 7, 8, 9, 10} {1, 3, 5, 7, 9} {2, 3, 5, 7}

2. Work out the probability of each of the following events and hence, determine which one is least likely.

   - **(i)** Flipping a fair coin and getting a head.
   - **(ii)** Rolling a standard six-sided die and getting a 3.
   - **(iii)** Randomly selecting the letter 'G' from the 26 letters of the alphabet.
   - **(iv)** Winning first prize in a raffle of 100 tickets, in which you have four tickets.

3. A basket of fruit contains four apples, six bananas and three oranges. What is the probability that a randomly selected piece of fruit is:
   (i) an apple? **(ii)** a banana? **(iii)** an orange? **(iv)** not an orange?

4. One letter is chosen at random from the word PROBABILITY. What is the probability that the letter is:
   - **(i)** a P?
   - **(ii)** a B?
   - **(iii)** a vowel?
   - **(iv)** a consonant?
   - **(v)** not an I?

5. A card is selected at random from a standard pack of cards. Find the probability that the chosen card will be:
   - **(i)** a black card
   - **(ii)** a spade
   - **(iii)** a 5
   - **(iv)** a red king
   - **(v)** a red picture card

6. A fair die is rolled. Calculate the probability the number rolled is:
   - **(i)** 4
   - **(ii)** 7
   - **(iii)** 3
   - **(iv)** a prime number
   - **(v)** an even number
   - **(vi)** an odd number
   - **(vii)** a 1 or a 6

7. A garage has eight red cars, six blue cars, 12 black cars and 10 silver cars for sale. What is the probability that a car chosen at random will be:
   - **(i)** red
   - **(ii)** blue
   - **(iii)** black or sliver
   - **(iv)** green
   - **(v)** not blue
   - **(vi)** not red or silver

Probability I

8. Below are some events that might happen when a fair die is thrown.
Decide where you would place them on the probability scale and explain your reasoning.

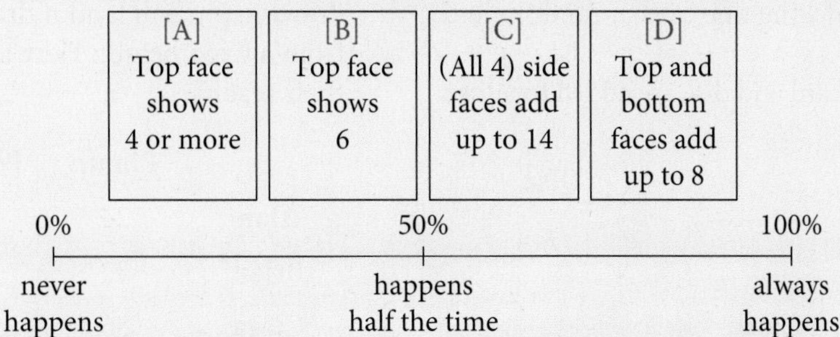

9. There are a number of different coloured marbles in a bag. The probability of picking a certain coloured marble is given in the table on the right.

Marble colour	Red	Blue	Green	Yellow
Probability	0·2	$\frac{1}{4}$	x	0·35

   (i) Find the value of x.

   (ii) The bag contains the same number of two of the marble colours. Based on your answer to part **(i)**, identify which two colours have the same number of marbles. Justify your answer.

Revision and Exam Style Questions – Section A

1. A student council committee consists of five members. The committee is going to have a photo taken.
   (i) In how many ways can the committee line up for the photo?
   (ii) The chairperson and the secretary like to stand together. How many arrangements allow this to happen?

2. Four cards, labelled 1, 3, 6 and 8, are placed on a table to form a four-digit number.
   (i) How many four-digit numbers can be formed?
   (ii) How many different numbers greater than 3,000 can be formed?
   (iii) How many different numbers less than 6,000 can be formed?

3. Read each of the statements below and decide whether you agree or disagree with the statement. Justify your answer.
   (i) The probability that it will rain tomorrow is $\frac{6}{5}$.
   (ii) In a box of chocolates there are 13 soft centres and 15 hard centres, so the probability of choosing a soft centre is $\frac{13}{28}$.
   (iii) Tom tosses a fair coin twice. He gets a head both times. He says, 'The probability that I will get a head the next time I throw the coin is $\frac{1}{8}$.'

4. You randomly choose a letter from a hat that contains the letters A to P.
   (i) What is the sample space for the experiment?
   (ii) What is the probability of choosing a vowel?

5. Julie does a statistical experiment. She throws a die 600 times. She scores six 200 times.
Is the die fair, in your opinion? Explain your answer.

6. A game uses a spinner to decide what move a player makes next. The player spins one of the spinners shown and the outcome is the move they make.

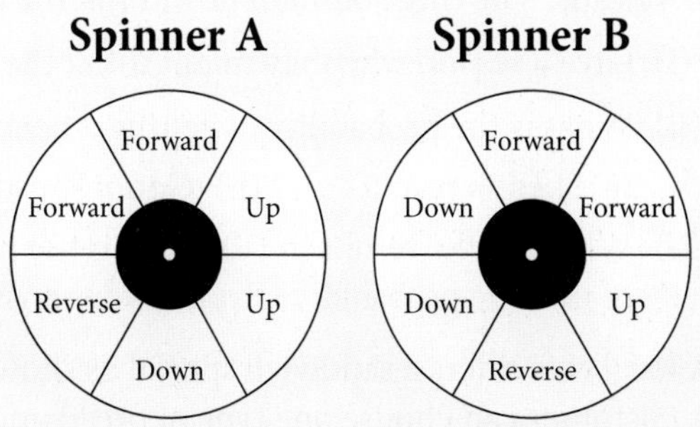

   (i) You want to move down. Which spinner should you spin? Explain.
   (ii) You want to move forward. Does it matter which spinner you spin? Explain.

7. Three cards are numbered 1, 3 and 4.
Three discs are numbered 2, 4 and 5.
A game consists of picking one card at random and one disc at random.
The numbers on the card and disc are added together.

   (i) Complete the two-way table to show all the possible totals.

		Disc		
		2	4	5
Card	1	3		
	3			
	4			

   (ii) What is the probability of getting a total that is an even number?

In a **different** game, the probability of getting a total that is an even number is $\frac{3}{5}$.

   (iii) What is the probability of getting a total that is an odd number?

8. Alan, Brian and Ciara collect data about which way up a drawing pin will land if dropped from a fixed height. Here are their results.

	Pin up	Pin down	Total
Alan	24	33	57
Brian	22	33	55
Ciara	86	102	188

Alan thinks 'a drawing pin can only land with its pin up or with its pin down so the probability of a drawing pin landing pin up is 0·5.'

   (i) Explain whether you agree or disagree with his statement and give a reason.

   (ii) Ciara's results give the best estimate of the probability of a pin landing pin up. Explain why.

Revision and Exam Style Questions – Section B

More Challenging Problems

Probability I

1. Using lettered tiles, Ann makes the word winter.

w i n t e r

   (i) How many different arrangements can be made of the six tiles?
   (ii) In how many of these arrangements is the first letter a vowel?
   (iii) In how many of these arrangements are the first and last letters vowels?
   (iv) In how many of these arrangements are the two vowels together?
   (v) A tile is chosen at random. Write down the probability that it has the letter R printed on it.
   (vi) Find the probability that the tile chosen at random does not have the letter W printed on it.
   (vii) Find the probability that the letter printed on the tile chosen at random has no lines of symmetry.

A line of symmetry is a line drawn through a shape such that each side is a mirror image.

2. Leon flipped a coin 300 times and got 156 heads. Conor flipped the same coin 400 times and got 212 heads and Georgia flipped the coin 600 times and got 324 heads. The three of them now think the coin is biased (unfair).

   (i) Give a reason why they might think the coin is biased.
   (ii) What is the probability of getting a head from:
      (a) Leon's results? **(b)** Conor's results? **(c)** Georgia's results? **(d)** Their combined results?
   (iii) Which of the results in **(ii)** above is the most accurate estimate of the true probability? Explain your answer.

3. A local café offers a sandwich special as shown in the picture.
A customer can choose one type of bread and one from each of fillings 1 and 2.

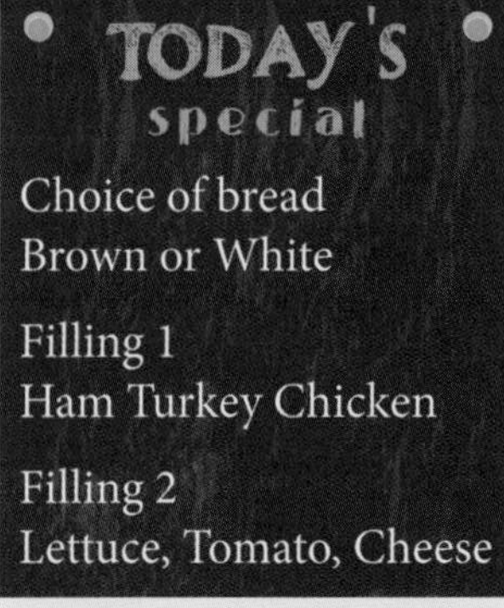

   (i) How many different sandwiches can be made?
   (ii) Draw a tree diagram to represent all the sandwich options available.

Use your tree diagram to answer the following.

(iii) What is the probability a customer chosen at random bought:

(a) a brown-bread sandwich?

(b) a sandwich with chicken and tomato?

(c) a white-bread sandwich with cheese?

The café decides to increase the cost of the special and add a choice of drink and crisps. The drink choices are soft drink, tea or coffee and the crisp choices are salt and vinegar or cheese and onion.

(iv) What is the increase in the number of choices after the new special is implemented?

4. There are a number of coloured counters in a bag. The probability of picking a certain coloured counter from the bag at random is given in the table below.

Colour	Red	Green	Yellow	White	Black
Probability	$\frac{1}{5}$	$\frac{1}{10}$	0·15	x	$\frac{1}{4}$

(i) What is the probability of picking a white counter?

(ii) Which colour are most of the counters in the bag? Explain.

(iii) The least number of counters in the bag are of which colour? Give a reason for your answer.

(iv) Is there an equal number of counters in any of the colours? Justify your answer.

5. Fifty people take a driving test at a test centre on one day.
The table shows the results.
A person is chosen at random from the group.

	Pass	Fail
Male	14	15
Female	8	13

(i) What is the probability that the person is male?

(ii) What is the probability that the person passed the test?

(iii) It is known that throughout Ireland the probability of a person passing their test is 0·6.
John says it is easier to pass the test at this test centre. Do you agree with John? Justify your answer.

6. The following items are on sale at a concert.

T-shirt	Signed Photograph	Baseball Cap	Poster	Key ring
€12	€8	€6	€5	€2

Sophie wants to buy three different items. She wants to spend a maximum of €20. One combination of three different items that Sophie can buy is shown in the table.

T-shirt €12	Signed Photograph €8	Baseball Cap €6	Poster €5	Key ring €2	Total Cost €
	✓	✓		✓	€16

(i) Draw a table to show all the possible combinations of three different items that Sophie can buy.

(ii) What is the probability that her three chosen items will include a key ring?

(iii) What is the probability that she will choose a poster and a baseball cap in her three items?

(iv) What is the probability that she will choose a baseball cap or a key ring in her three items?

(v) What is the probability that her chosen items will not include a baseball cap?

Now that you have completed the chapter, revisit the 'Something to think about…' questions.

CHAPTER 19 Probability II

Sections covered within this chapter:

KEY WORDS

- Independent
- Bernoulli trial
- Dependent
- Expected value
- Mutually exclusive

SOMETHING TO THINK ABOUT... 

You are the financial advisor to a large company. Your company plans to invest in a particular project.

There is a 35% chance that you will lose €40,000, a 40% chance that you will break even, and a 25% chance that you will make €65,000.

Based solely on this information, what would you advise the company directors to do?

Section 19.1: Representing Sample Space

Learning Outcome:

You should be able to:

- construct sample spaces for two independent events

In Chapter 18: Probability I we learned how to calculate the probability that a single event would take place. We will now learn how to calculate the probability of more than one event occurring.

If a fair die and a fair coin are thrown at the same time, the list of all possible outcomes, i.e. the sample space, is as follows:

1H, 2H, 3H, 4H, 5H, 6H, 1T, 2T, 3T, 4T, 5T and 6T. [H = head, T = tail]

When listing larger sample spaces like this it is easy to accidentally miss a possible outcome. To help us organise our sample spaces we can use the methods we met in Chapter 18: Probability I.

Two-way tables

A two-way table is used to list all the possible outcomes when two events occur.

A fair coin is flipped and a fair die is thrown.

Below is a two-way table to represent this sample space.

		Coin	
		Head	Tail
Die	1	1 Head	1 Tail
	2	2 Head	2 Tail
	3	3 Head	3 Tail
	4	4 Head	4 Tail
	5	5 Head	5 Tail
	6	6 Head	6 Tail

Tree diagrams

A tree diagram is used to list all possible outcomes when two or more events occur.

Following each branch from the start to the end allows us to list all possible outcomes.

Die	Coin	Outcome
1	H	1 Head
	T	1 Tail
2	H	2 Head
	T	2 Tail
3	H	3 Head
	T	3 Tail
4	H	4 Head
	T	4 Tail
5	H	5 Head
	T	5 Tail
6	H	6 Head
	T	6 Tail

Recall:
The expected number of outcomes can be calculated using the Fundamental Principle of Counting (Chapter 18: Probability I).
The number of outcomes for the die × number of outcomes for the coin = 6 × 2 = 12

In this section we will only look at events which are equally likely to occur.

EXAMPLE 1

A fair die is thrown twice. Use a two-way table to represent the sample space for this experiment.
Calculate the probability of getting:

(i) the same number on the die each time

(ii) two odd numbers

(iii) a total of 6.

Solution

(i) P(same number on the die each time)

The outcomes where we get the same number on the die each time are:
(1,1), (2,2), (3,3), (4,4), (5,5) and (6,6)

		Second throw					
		1	2	3	4	5	6
First throw	1	(1,1)	(1,2)	(1,3)	(1,4)	(1,5)	(1,6)
	2	(2,1)	(2,2)	(2,3)	(2,4)	(2,5)	(2,6)
	3	(3,1)	(3,2)	(3,3)	(3,4)	(3,5)	(3,6)
	4	(4,1)	(4,2)	(4,3)	(4,4)	(4,5)	(4,6)
	5	(5,1)	(5,2)	(5,3)	(5,4)	(5,5)	(5,6)
	6	(6,1)	(6,2)	(6,3)	(6,4)	(6,5)	(6,6)

The outcomes with the same number on the die each time are highlighted in orange.

P(same number on the die each time)

$= \frac{\text{number of outcomes of interest}}{\text{total number of outcomes}}$

$= \frac{6}{36}$

$= \frac{1}{6}$

(ii) P(two odd numbers)

		Second throw					
		1	2	3	4	5	6
First throw	1	(1,1)	(1,2)	(1,3)	(1,4)	(1,5)	(1,6)
	2	(2,1)	(2,2)	(2,3)	(2,4)	(2,5)	(2,6)
	3	(3,1)	(3,2)	(3,3)	(3,4)	(3,5)	(3,6)
	4	(4,1)	(4,2)	(4,3)	(4,4)	(4,5)	(4,6)
	5	(5,1)	(5,2)	(5,3)	(5,4)	(5,5)	(5,6)
	6	(6,1)	(6,2)	(6,3)	(6,4)	(6,5)	(6,6)

The outcomes where we get two odd numbers are highlighted in green.

P(two odd numbers)

$= \frac{\text{number of outcomes of interest}}{\text{total number of outcomes}}$

$= \frac{9}{36}$

$= \frac{1}{4}$

(iii) P(total of 6)

		Second throw					
		1	2	3	4	5	6
First throw	1	(1,1)	(1,2)	(1,3)	(1,4)	(1,5)	(1,6)
	2	(2,1)	(2,2)	(2,3)	(2,4)	(2,5)	(2,6)
	3	(3,1)	(3,2)	(3,3)	(3,4)	(3,5)	(3,6)
	4	(4,1)	(4,2)	(4,3)	(4,4)	(4,5)	(4,6)
	5	(5,1)	(5,2)	(5,3)	(5,4)	(5,5)	(5,6)
	6	(6,1)	(6,2)	(6,3)	(6,4)	(6,5)	(6,6)

The outcomes where we get a total of 6 are highlighted in red.

P(total of 6)

$= \frac{\text{number of outcomes of interest}}{\text{total number of outcomes}}$

$= \frac{5}{36}$

EXAMPLE 2

A fair coin is flipped three times. Draw a tree diagram to represent the sample space for this experiment. Calculate the probability of:

(i) three tails

(ii) exactly two tails

(iii) at least two heads.

Solution

The tree diagram is constructed as shown on the right.

(i) P(three tails) highlighted in yellow

$= \frac{1}{8}$

Since the probability of each branch is $\frac{1}{2}$, we can also find this result by multiplying along the branches: $\frac{1}{2} \times \frac{1}{2} \times \frac{1}{2} = \frac{1}{8}$

See 'AND' rule later.

(ii) P(exactly two tails) highlighted in pink

$= \frac{3}{8}$

(iii) P(at least two tails) highlighted in green

$= \frac{4}{8} = \frac{1}{2}$

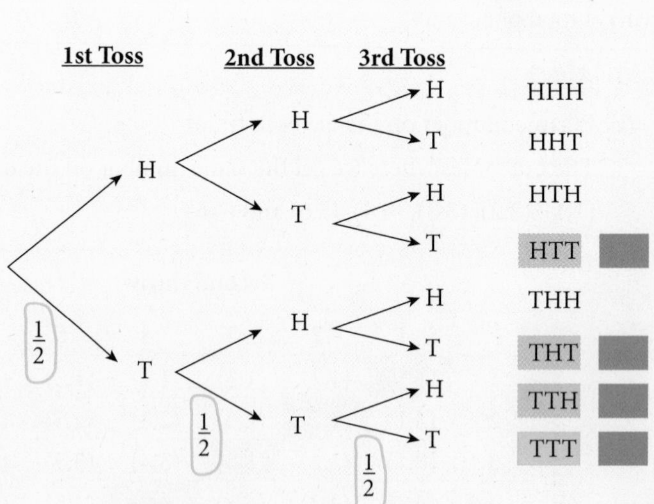

Practice Questions 19.1

1. An ice cream shop has vanilla, chocolate or strawberry ice cream and you can have either chocolate or caramel sauce on top.
   (i) Represent this information on a tree diagram.
   (ii) Use the tree diagram to answer the following questions:
   What is the probability that a customer chosen at random will order
   (a) a chocolate ice cream?
   (b) an ice cream with caramel sauce?
   (c) a strawberry ice cream with caramel sauce?

2. You are buying a jumper from a shop. You have to choose a size, colour and style. You can choose between small, medium or large for size; blue, pink, red or brown for colour; and round-neck or V-neck for style.
   (i) Draw a tree diagram to represent the sample space.
   (ii) Use the tree diagram to answer the following questions:
   (a) How many different options do you have?
   (b) What is the probability that you pick a brown jumper?
   (c) What is the probability that you pick a jumper that has a V-neck?
   (d) What is the probability that you pick a large, red, round-neck jumper?
   (e) What is the probability that the jumper you pick doesn't have a round neck?

---

3. A fair die is thrown and a fair coin is flipped at the same time.
   (i) Draw a two-way table to represent this sample space.
   (ii) Use the two-way table to calculate the probability of getting:
   (a) a head
   (b) a 3
   (c) a head and a 3
   (d) a tail and an even number
   (e) a tail or a prime number.

4. Suppose we flip a coin and spin a spinner with four coloured sections of equal size at the same time.

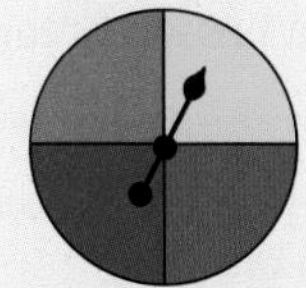

   (i) What is the sample space for the coin?
   (ii) What is the sample space for the spinner?
   (iii) Draw a sample space diagram and use it to write out the sample space for when we throw both the coin and spin the spinner.
   (iv) Using your sample space diagram, calculate the probability of getting:
   (a) a tail on the coin
   (b) red on the spinner
   (c) a tail on the coin and red on the spinner
   (d) a tail on the coin or red on the spinner
   (e) the colour on the spinner is not red
   (f) green on the spinner
   (g) a head on the coin and either blue or yellow on the spinner.

AND means both events happen
OR means either (or both) events happen.

5. A spinner with four equal segments, numbered 1 to 4, is spun twice.

   (i) Represent the sample space for this experiment using a two-way table.
   (ii) Use your two-way table to calculate the probability that:
   (a) the same number comes up on both spins
   (b) both numbers are odd
   (c) the number on both the first and second spinner is even
   (d) the sum of the two numbers is 6
   (e) 1 doesn't come up on either spin.

6. Sean and Colin are playing a game involving throwing two fair dice one after the other. Sean wins if both dice are odd and Colin wins if either die is a five.

   (i) Draw a sample space diagram to represent this information.
   (ii) How many different outcomes are there?

   Use your sample space diagram to answer the following questions:

   (iii) What is the probability that Sean wins?
   (iv) What is the probability that Colin wins?
   (v) Is the game fair? Explain your answer.
   (vi) Will any of the outcomes result in a tie?

7. A fair, six-sided die and four-sided die are thrown.
   (i) Represent this information on a sample space diagram.
   (ii) Use your sample space diagram to work out the probability that:
      (a) the numbers on both dice are the same
      (b) the numbers on both dice are even
      (c) the sum of the numbers on both dice is greater than six
      (d) a four appears on at least one die
      (e) the sum of the two numbers is a multiple of 3.

8. A spinner with three equal sectors coloured red, green and blue is spun three times.

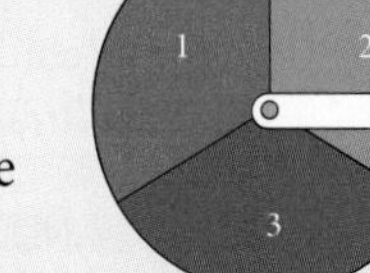

   (i) Represent the sample space on a tree diagram.
   (ii) Use the tree diagram to work out the probability of getting:
      (a) the same colour on all three spins
      (b) the same colour on two of the three spins
      (c) a green and two reds in any order
      (d) a different colour on all three spins
      (e) not blue on any of the spins.

9. When Joselyn comes home from school she has a snack, which is either a ham sandwich or a chicken wrap. After that she either does her homework or studies. Then she has her dinner. After dinner she either watches TV, plays on her Xbox or reads a book.
   (i) To list all of Joselyn's options, is it better to use a two-way table or a tree diagram? Justify your answer.
   (ii) Use either of the methods above to list all the possible ways Joselyn could spend her evening.
   (iii) With the help of your sample space diagram, determine the probability that Joselyn:
      (a) has a ham sandwich, does her homework and then reads a book
      (b) watches TV
      (c) eats a chicken wrap and plays on her Xbox
      (d) doesn't study.

10. Anita and Rebecca both think of a number between 1 and 10 inclusive.
    Draw a two-way table to list all the possible outcomes and use it to determine the probability that:
    (i) they both chose the same number
    (ii) Anita chooses an even number and Rebecca chooses an odd number
    (iii) at least one of them chooses a prime number
    (iv) Anita chooses a multiple of two and Rebecca chooses a multiple of three
    (v) neither of them choose 5.

11. A lunch menu has 'made to order' sandwiches. You can pick one type of bread, one meat and one other item.

    There are two choices of bread: brown or white; three choices of meat: ham, chicken or turkey; and four other items: coleslaw, cheese, tomato or lettuce.
    Draw a sample space diagram and use it to work out the probability that a customer chosen at random purchased:
    (i) a brown bread sandwich
    (ii) a sandwich with chicken or coleslaw
    (iii) a sandwich with cheese on it
    (iv) a sandwich with turkey and lettuce
    (v) a white bread sandwich with ham and tomato.

Probability II

Section 19.2: The 'AND' Rule

Learning Outcomes:

You should be able to:
- understand the basic rules of probability, particularly the 'AND' rule
- find the probability that two events both occur

Consider the following situation:

Bag A contains 2 blue and 2 green marbles. Bag B contains 3 red and 1 white marble. A marble is randomly selected from each bag.

Calculate the probability of getting a blue marble from bag A and a red marble from bag B.

Using a two-way table to illustrate the sample space, we get:

		Bag A			
		Blue	Blue	Green	Green
Bag B	Red	(B,R)	(B,R)	(G,R)	(G,R)
	Red	(B,R)	(B,R)	(G,R)	(G,R)
	Red	(B,R)	(B,R)	(G,R)	(G,R)
	White	(B,W)	(B,W)	(G,W)	(G,W)

Total number of outcomes possible = 16

Number of outcomes of interest = 6

P(blue from A and red from B) = $\frac{6}{16} = \frac{3}{8}$

Is there a quicker way to do this? Could we do this without drawing a two-way table? Can we make a rule to work out this probability?

Let's take a look at each probability separately.

What is the probability that a blue marble will be picked from bag A?

P(blue) = $\frac{\text{number of outcomes of interest}}{\text{total number of outcomes}} = \frac{2}{4} = \frac{1}{2}$

What is the probability that a red marble will be picked from bag B? P(red) = $\frac{3}{4}$

So, P(blue) = $\frac{1}{2}$ P(red) = $\frac{3}{4}$ And P(blue and red) = $\frac{3}{8}$

Do you see a link?

Let's look at the other probabilities:

P(green) = $\frac{2}{4} = \frac{1}{2}$ P(red) = $\frac{3}{4}$ P(green and red) = $\frac{6}{16} = \frac{3}{8}$

P(blue) = $\frac{2}{4} = \frac{1}{2}$ P(white) = $\frac{1}{4}$ P(blue and white) = $\frac{2}{16} = \frac{1}{8}$

P(green) = $\frac{2}{4} = \frac{1}{2}$ P(white) = $\frac{1}{4}$ P(green and white) = $\frac{2}{16} = \frac{1}{8}$

Hopefully you can now see that if we multiply the individual probabilities in each case, we get the probability of one event and another event occurring at the same time.

This is sometimes known as the 'AND' rule.

If a question asks for the probability of A and B, we simply find the probability of each event and multiply them together.

> Probability of A and B equals the probability of A multiplied by the probability of B.
>
> P(A and B) = P(A) × P(B)

EXAMPLE 1

The probability that Toby is late for school on any given day is 0·14.

What is the probability that:

(i) Toby is not late for school on a randomly chosen day?

(ii) Toby is late on three consecutive days?

(iii) Toby is late on Wednesday and Thursday but not late on Friday?

(iv) Toby is not late for a whole week?

Solution

(i) P(not late) = 1 – P(late)

1 – 0·14 = 0·86

> The sum of all the probabilities in a given situation is 1.

(ii) Late on three consecutive days = P(late **and** late **and** late)

0·14 × 0·14 × 0·14 = 0·002744

(iii) P(late **and** late **and** not late)

0·14 × 0·14 × 0·86 = 0·016856

(iv) P(not late **and** not late **and** not late **and** not late **and** not late)

0·86 × 0·86 × 0·86 × 0·86 × 0·86 = $(0·86)^5$ = 0·4704270176

Independent events

All of the events we have been looking at up to now are independent events.

> Events are **independent** if the outcome of the first event *does not affect* the outcome of the second event.

For example: you throw a coin three times and it comes up 'heads' each time. What is the chance that the next throw will also be a 'head'?

The chance is simply $\frac{1}{2}$, just like any other throw of the coin. The outcome in the past will not affect the current throw, as the coin does not know it came up heads before. Each throw is an independent event.

We can calculate the probability of two or more independent events by multiplying the probabilities of each single event.

Did you know?

There is a commonly held misconception that after a 'run' of one outcome, the other outcome is 'due'. This is known as the 'gambler's fallacy'. One example of the gambler's fallacy in action took place at the Monte Carlo Casino on August 18, 1913. In a game of roulette, the ball landed on black 26 times in a row. As a result, many punters began betting heavily on red as they believed that the roulette wheel was now due a red. However, since each roulette spin is independent of the previous spins, this was not the case. The casino made millions of francs as a consequence of this misconception.

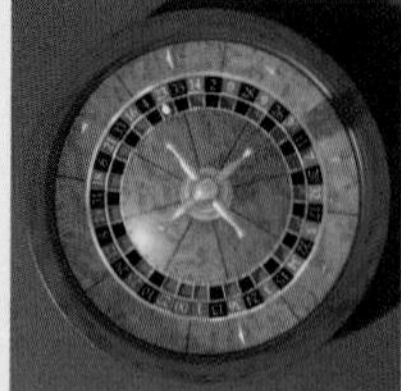

EXAMPLE 2

A fair coin and a fair die are thrown at the same time. Calculate the probability that you get:

(i) a head **and** a 6

(ii) a tail **and** an even number.

Solution

(i) $P(\text{head}) = \frac{1}{2}$ $\quad P(6) = \frac{1}{6}$

$P(\text{head } \textbf{and } 6) = \frac{1}{2} \times \frac{1}{6} = \frac{1}{12}$

(ii) $P(\text{tail}) = \frac{1}{2}$ $\quad P(\text{even number}) = \frac{3}{6} = \frac{1}{2}$

$P(\text{tail } \textbf{and } \text{even number}) = \frac{1}{2} \times \frac{1}{2} = \frac{1}{4}$

Dependent events

Consider this situation:

There are 2 green and 3 yellow marbles in a bag.

What is the probability of getting a green marble?

$P(\text{green}) = \frac{2}{5}$

But after taking one marble out the chances change, as there are now only 4 marbles in the bag.

So the next time:

If we got a green marble before, then the probability of a green marble next is $\frac{1}{4}$.

If we got a yellow marble before, then the probability of a green marble next is $\frac{2}{4} = \frac{1}{2}$.

Events are **dependent** when what happens in the first event *does affect* the outcome of the second event.

Each event depends on what happened in the previous event.

When reading questions that ask us to pick multiple objects, we must consider what happens after each pick. Questions may refer to replacement so take note that:

With replacement: the events are independent (the probabilities don't change).

Without replacement: the events are dependent (the probabilities change).

EXAMPLE 3

A bag contains 4 yellow, 5 green and 6 orange sweets. If we pick out two sweets without replacement, find the probability that both sweets are green.

Solution

$P(1^{st} \text{ sweet green}) = \frac{5}{15} = \frac{1}{3}$

Now, since we are not replacing the sweet, there are only 4 green sweets left and a total of 14 sweets. So,

$P(2^{nd} \text{ sweet green}) = \frac{4}{14} = \frac{2}{7}$

Therefore,

$P(1^{st} \text{ and } 2^{nd} \text{ sweet green}) = \frac{1}{3} \times \frac{2}{7} = \frac{2}{21}$

Before attempting to calculate the probabilities in a question you must firstly decide whether the events are dependent or independent.

EXAMPLE 4

Jake has a deck of regular playing cards and a bag of 6 marbles. In the bag, there are 2 blue marbles, 3 green marbles and 1 white marble.

He has to pick 1 card and 1 marble.

(i) Are these events dependent or independent? Explain.

What is the probability of Jake picking:

(ii) an ace from the deck of cards and a blue marble from the bag?

(iii) a black card from the deck and a green marble from the bag?

Solution

(i) These events are independent because the card he picks has no effect on his choice of marble.

(ii) $P(\text{ace}) = \frac{4}{52} = \frac{1}{13}$; $\quad P(\text{blue}) = \frac{2}{6} = \frac{1}{3}$

$P(\text{ace } \textbf{and} \text{ blue}) = \frac{1}{13} \times \frac{1}{3} = \frac{1}{39}$

(iii) $P(\text{black card}) = \frac{26}{52} = \frac{1}{2}$; $\quad P(\text{green}) = \frac{3}{6} = \frac{1}{2}$

$P(\text{black } \textbf{and} \text{ green}) = \frac{1}{2} \times \frac{1}{2} = \frac{1}{4}$

EXAMPLE 5

Dave has a deck of regular playing cards.

He picks three cards from the deck without replacement.

(i) Are these events dependent or independent? Explain.

What is the probability of Jake picking:

(ii) a three, a seven and a picture card in that order?

(iii) three aces?

Solution

(i) These events are dependent because if he doesn't replace the card each time, each event will affect the following events.

(ii) $P(\text{three}) = \frac{4}{52}$

$P(\text{seven}) = \frac{4}{51}$, since there are 4 sevens but one less card in total

$P(\text{picture card}) = \frac{12}{50}$, since there are 3 in each suit and 2 less cards in total

$P(\text{three } \textbf{and} \text{ seven } \textbf{and} \text{ picture})$

$= \frac{4}{52} \times \frac{4}{51} \times \frac{12}{50} = \frac{8}{5525}$

(iii) $P(1^{st} \text{ ace}) = \frac{4}{52}$

3 of the remaining 51 cards are aces

$P(2^{nd} \text{ ace}) = \frac{3}{51}$

2 of the remaining 50 cards are aces

$P(3^{rd} \text{ ace}) = \frac{2}{50}$,

$P(3 \text{ aces}) = \frac{4}{52} \times \frac{3}{51} \times \frac{2}{50} = \frac{3}{16250}$

EXAMPLE 6

A fruit bowl contains 10 apples and 6 bananas. Sophie picks 2 pieces of fruit without replacement.

(i) Are these events dependent or independent?

(ii) Draw a tree diagram to represent this information. Write the probability of each event on each branch.

Use your tree diagram to work out the probabilities that:

(iii) Sophie picks an apple and a banana in that order

(iv) Sophie picks two bananas.

Solution

(i) Since the fruit is not replaced after the first pick, these events are dependent.

(ii) Working out the probabilities for each branch gives the following:

1st pick

$$P(\text{apple}) = \frac{10}{16} = \frac{5}{8}$$

$$P(\text{banana}) = \frac{6}{16} = \frac{3}{8}$$

2nd pick

$$P(\text{apple if apple } 1^{st}) = \frac{9}{15} = \frac{3}{5}$$

$$P(\text{apple if banana } 1^{st}) = \frac{10}{15} = \frac{2}{3}$$

$$P(\text{banana if apple } 1^{st}) = \frac{6}{15} = \frac{2}{5}$$

$$P(\text{banana if banana } 1^{st}) = \frac{5}{15} = \frac{1}{3}$$

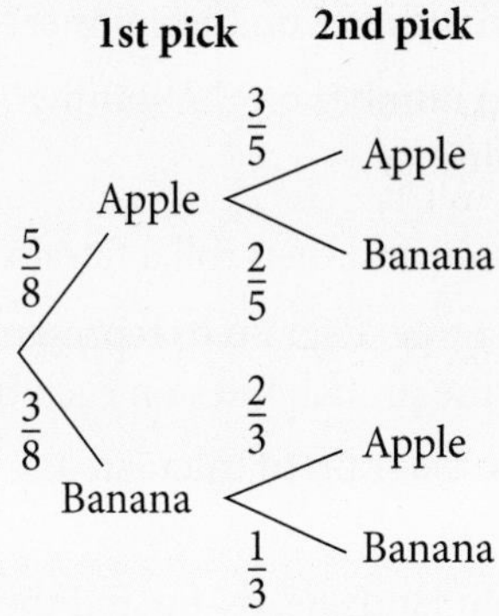

To answer these questions we simply multiply along the relevant branch.

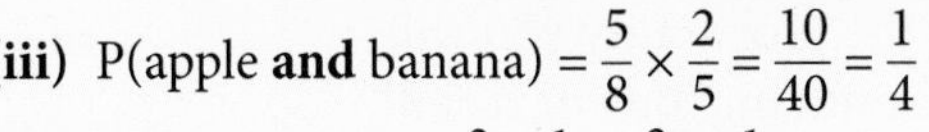

(iii) $P(\text{apple } \textbf{and} \text{ banana}) = \frac{5}{8} \times \frac{2}{5} = \frac{10}{40} = \frac{1}{4}$

(iv) $P(\text{two bananas}) = \frac{3}{8} \times \frac{1}{3} = \frac{3}{24} = \frac{1}{8}$

Practice Questions 19.2

1. Decide whether these events are independent or dependent.
   (i) You have a jar with 24 chocolates and 14 jellies. You take one sweet at random from the jar, eat it, and then take a second sweet at random from the jar.
   (ii) Derek has a blue, a red, and a green tie. He also has a blue and a green shirt. He chooses a random tie and shirt for work today.
   (iii) Amy plays card games. She picks a card at random. Then without putting the first card back, she picks a second card at random.
   (iv) Ian has 14 coins. He takes three of them at random, then he puts these back, and then picks two more coins at random.
   (v) Jeff has three children. His first two children are boys. His last child is a girl.
   (vi) A plant has four red flowers and two blue flowers. Brenda picks one flower from the plant. After some time, her sister picks a flower from the same plant.

Questions 2 to 5 are based on independent events

2. You roll a fair six-sided die twice. What is the probability the first roll shows a five and the second roll shows a six?

Probability II

3. There are nine mugs in Tom's cupboard, four blue and five green.
He randomly selects one to use on Monday, washes it and replaces it.
He randomly selects another on Tuesday.
What is the probability that:
   (i) he uses a blue mug both days?
   (ii) he uses a blue mug on Monday and a green mug on Tuesday?

4. Shannon spins a spinner numbered 1 to 7, and tosses a coin.
What is the probability she gets:
   (i) an odd number on the spinner?
   (ii) an odd number on the spinner and a tail on the coin?

5. You flip a coin and then roll a fair six-sided die.
   (i) Draw a tree diagram to represent this situation. Write the probabilities on each branch.

   Use the tree diagram to calculate the probability that:
   (ii) the coin lands heads-up and the die shows a three?
   (iii) the coin lands tails-up and the die shows a number greater than four?
   (iv) the coin lands heads-up and the die shows an even number?
   (v) the coin lands heads-up and the die shows a prime number?

Questions 6 to 9 are based on dependent events

6. The names of 9 boys and 11 girls from your class are put into a hat. Two names are selected without replacement.
   (i) Draw a tree diagram to represent this situation. Write the probabilities on each branch.

   What is the probability that:
   (ii) the two names chosen will both be girls?
   (iii) the first name will be a boy and the second will be a girl?
   (iv) both names will be boys?

7. A card is chosen at random from a standard deck of 52 playing cards. Without replacing it, a second card is chosen.
What is the probability that the first card chosen is a queen and the second card chosen is a jack?

8. A bowl of fruit is on the table. It contains four apples, six oranges and three bananas. Alan and Kenneth come home from school and randomly grab one fruit each. What is the probability that both grab apples?

When two items are chosen together, we consider it as choosing one immediately after the other with no replacement.

9. Your drawer contains 11 red socks and six blue socks. It's too dark to see which are which, but you grab two anyway.
   (i) Draw a tree diagram to represent this information. Write the probabilities on each branch.

   What is the probability that:
   (ii) the first sock is red and the second is blue?
   (iii) the first sock is blue and the second is red?
   (iv) both socks are blue?
   (v) both sock are red?

10. The game of backgammon uses two standard dice, each with the numbers one through six. You need to roll double twos to win the game.
What is the probability you will get that result on your next roll?

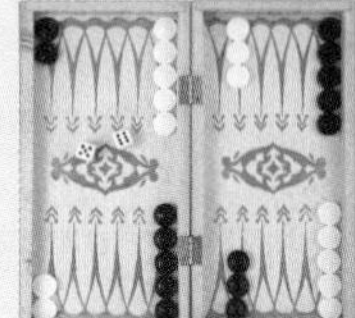

11. I roll three dice.
   (i) Are these events dependent or independent?
   (ii) What is the probability that I get three ones?

12. I draw a card from a standard deck, replace it, and draw another.
   (i) Are these events dependent or independent?
   (ii) What is the probability I get two aces?

13. Four cards are chosen at random from a deck of 52 cards, one after the other, without replacement.
   (i) Are these events dependent or independent?
   (ii) What is the probability of choosing a ten, a nine, an eight and a seven in that order?

14. Henry has three black shirts and seven blue shirts in his wardrobe. Two shirts are drawn without replacement from the wardrobe. What is the probability that both of the shirts are black?

15. An archer always hits a circular target with each arrow shot. He hits the bullseye two out of every five shots on average. If he takes three shots at the target, calculate the probability that he hits the bullseye:

  (i) every time

  (ii) the first two times but not the third

  (iii) on no occasion.

16. A class has 14 boys and 16 girls. Three students are chosen at random to represent the class at a school event. What is the probability that:

  (i) they are all girls?

  (ii) they are all boys?

17. Emma says that it is very difficult to get five heads in a row when you flip a coin. Brian disagrees and says he has done it loads of times.

  (i) Which person do you agree with?

  Neither of them have a coin to try it so they decide to work the chances out mathematically.

  (ii) Show the calculations they would use to do this.

  (iii) Do you want to change your answer to (i) above? Justify your answer using the calculations in (ii) above.

Section 19.3: The 'OR' Rule

Learning Outcomes:

You should be able to:

- understand the basic rules of probability, particularly the 'OR' rule
- understand mutually and non-mutually exclusive events

Consider the following situation:

A fair die is thrown. What is the probability of rolling a 2 or a 5?

$$P(2 \text{ or } 5) = \frac{\text{number of outcomes of interest}}{\text{total number of outcomes}}$$

$= \frac{2}{6} = \frac{1}{3}$, since there are two possible outcomes, a 2 or a 5, out of 6 total outcomes

If we look at each of the probabilities individually we see

$P(2) = \frac{1}{6}$ and $P(5) = \frac{1}{6}$

$P(2 \text{ or } 5) = \frac{1}{6} + \frac{1}{6} = \frac{2}{6} = \frac{1}{3}$

The probability of getting a 2 or a 5 when a fair die is thrown are said to be mutually exclusive events because they cannot happen at the same time. We cannot get both a 2 and a 5 in a single throw of a die.

Mutually exclusive

Mutually exclusive means we can't get both events at the same time.

It is either **one or the other, but not both.**

Examples of mutually exclusive events:

- Turning left or right (you can't do both at the same time)
- Tossing a coin and getting a head and a tail
- Picking a card and getting a king and an ace

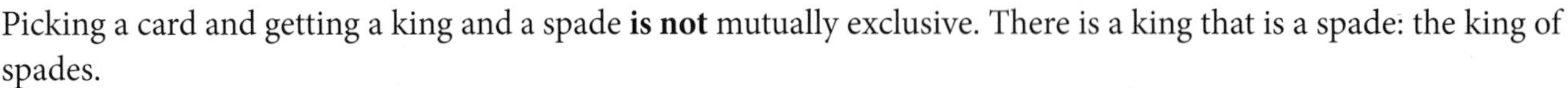

Picking a card and getting a king and a spade **is not** mutually exclusive. There is a king that is a spade: the king of spades.

When two events are **mutually exclusive**, it is **impossible** for them to happen together.

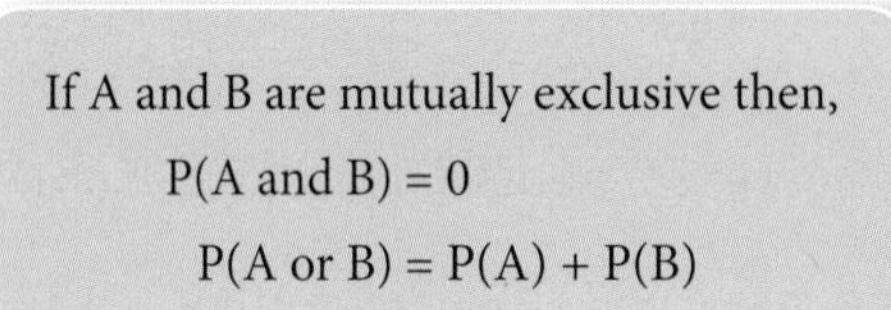

If A and B are mutually exclusive then,

P(A and B) = 0

P(A or B) = P(A) + P(B)

But what happens if we have **non-mutually exclusive events?**

Consider a pack of 52 playing cards. A card is selected at random. What is the probability that the card is either a diamond or a ten?

The card selected can be a diamond; a ten; or a diamond and a ten.

It is very important in this case to avoid **double counting**, i.e. counting the ten of diamonds twice, once as a diamond and once as a ten. It is only one card.

These events are **not mutually exclusive,** since they can occur at the same time. It is possible to select a card that is both a diamond and a ten: the ten of diamonds.

How do we find the probabilities of these events that are **not mutually exclusive** events?

Looking at the image on the right, we can see:

The probability that a diamond is picked is $\frac{13}{52}$.

The probability that the card is a ten is $\frac{4}{52}$.

Ace	2	3	4	5	6	7	8	9	10	Jack	Queen	King
♥	♥	♥	♥	♥	♥	♥	♥	♥	♥	♥	♥	♥
♦	♦	♦	♦	♦	♦	♦	♦	♦	♦	♦	♦	♦
♠	♠	♠	♠	♠	♠	♠	♠	♠	♠	♠	♠	♠
♣	♣	♣	♣	♣	♣	♣	♣	♣	♣	♣	♣	♣

The probability that the card is a diamond and a ten (the ten of diamonds) is $\frac{1}{52}$, highlighted in yellow.

P(ten **or** diamond) = P(ten) + P(diamond) – **P(ten and diamond)** avoiding **double counting**

$$\text{P(ten or diamond)} = \left(\frac{4}{52} + \frac{13}{52}\right) - \frac{1}{52}$$

$$= \frac{17}{52} - \frac{1}{52}$$

$$= \frac{16}{52}$$

$$= \frac{4}{13}$$

In general, P(A or B) means the probability that A occurs, B occurs or both occur. The general formula is

P(A or B) = P(A) + P(B) – P(A and B)

Note: If A and B are mutually exclusive events, then **P (A and B) = 0**, which leads to the simplified formula:

P (A or B) = P (A) + P(B)

EXAMPLE 1

A bag contains 20 balls. 10 are red with an even number from 1 to 20 on them and the other 10 are blue with an odd number from 1 to 20 on them. One ball is selected at random.

Find the probabilities of the following events:

(i) the ball is red and a multiple of 3

(ii) the ball is blue or a prime number

(iii) the number is not a square number.

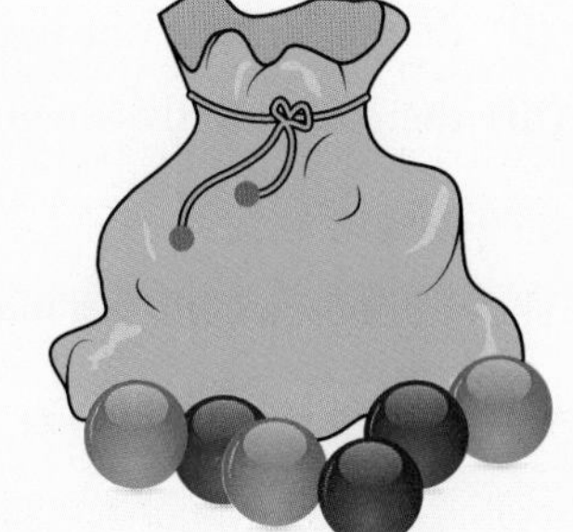

Solution

(i) P(red and multiple of 3)

There are 10 red balls having the numbers: 2 4 6 8 10 12 14 16 18 and 20

The multiples of three are highlighted in red: 6 12 18

P(red and multiple of 3) $= \frac{3}{20}$

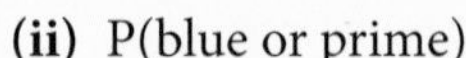

(ii) P(blue or prime)

These events are **not mutually exclusive** as they can happen at the same time, e.g. 3 is prime and blue. We must be careful to avoid double counting.

P(blue or prime) = P(blue) + P(prime) − P(blue and prime)

P(blue) $= \frac{10}{20}$

The prime numbers between 1 and 20 are 2, 3, 5, 7, 11, 13, 17 and 19. The prime numbers are all odd and therefore blue except 2. There are 7 prime numbers that are blue.

P(prime) $= \frac{8}{20}$

P(prime and blue) $= \frac{7}{20}$

P(blue or prime) = P(blue) + P(prime) − P(blue and prime)

$= \frac{10}{20} + \frac{8}{20} - \frac{7}{20} = \frac{11}{20}$

(iii) P(not a square number)

$1^2 = 1, 2^2 = 4, 3^2 = 9, 4^2 = 16$

There are four square numbers between 1 and 20. So P(square number) $= \frac{4}{20}$

P(not a square number) = 1 − P(square number) $= 1 - \frac{4}{20} = \frac{16}{20} = \frac{4}{5}$

P(square number) + P(not a square number) = 1
(It is certain that the number is either a square number or not)

Summary: To find the probability of event A or B, we must first determine whether the events are mutually exclusive or non-mutually exclusive. Then we can apply the appropriate **addition** 'OR' **rule**:

Mutually exclusive: P(A or B) = P(A) + P(B)

Non-mutually exclusive: P(A or B) = P(A) + P(B) − P(A and B)

EXAMPLE 2

A family has three children. Calculate the probability that:

(i) all children are the same sex

(ii) there is **at least** one boy

(iii) there are exactly two girls.

Solution

The sex of each child is a mutually exclusive event.

$P(\text{girl}) = \frac{1}{2}$ $\quad P(\text{boy}) = \frac{1}{2}$

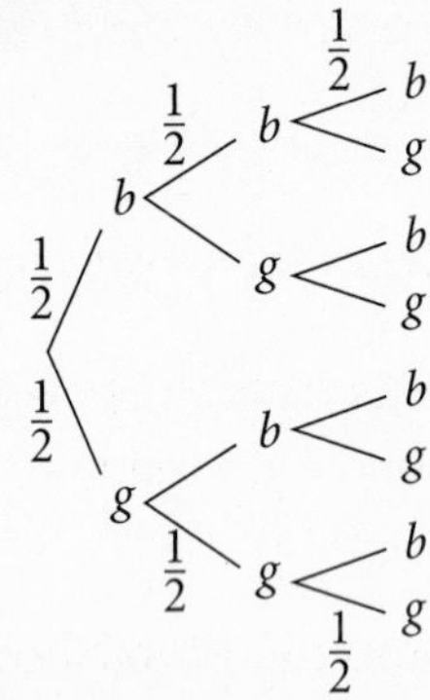

(i) P(all children same sex)

= P(girl **and** girl **and** girl) **or** P(boy **and** boy **and** boy)

$= \left(\frac{1}{2} \times \frac{1}{2} \times \frac{1}{2}\right) + \left(\frac{1}{2} \times \frac{1}{2} \times \frac{1}{2}\right)$

$= \frac{1}{8} + \frac{1}{8} = \frac{2}{8} = \frac{1}{4}$

(ii) P(at least one boy)

= 1 – P(all girls)

$= 1 - \left(\frac{1}{2} \times \frac{1}{2} \times \frac{1}{2}\right)$

$= 1 - \frac{1}{8} = \frac{7}{8}$

(iii) P(two girls)

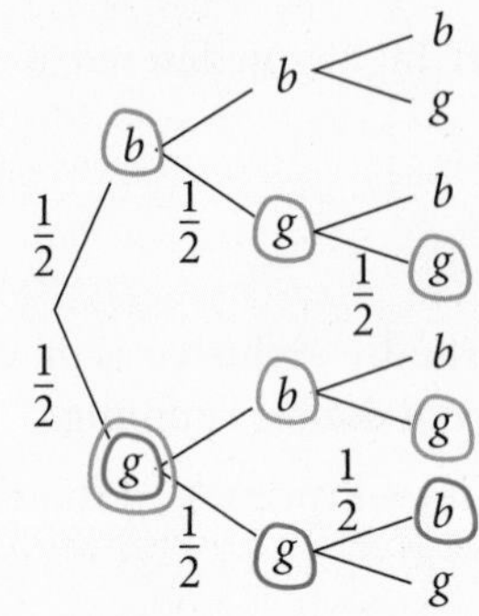

= P(girl **and** girl **and** boy) **or** (boy **and** girl **and** girl) or (girl **and** boy **and** girl)

$= \left(\frac{1}{2} \times \frac{1}{2} \times \frac{1}{2}\right) + \left(\frac{1}{2} \times \frac{1}{2} \times \frac{1}{2}\right) + \left(\frac{1}{2} \times \frac{1}{2} \times \frac{1}{2}\right)$

$= \frac{1}{8} + \frac{1}{8} + \frac{1}{8}$

$= \frac{3}{8}$

Practice Questions 19.3

1. Decide whether these events are mutually exclusive or not. Explain.
   - **(i)** Roll a die; get an even number and a number less than 3.
   - **(ii)** Roll a die; get a prime number and an odd number.
   - **(iii)** Roll a die; get a number greater than 3 and a number less than 3.
   - **(iv)** Select a student in the classroom; student has blond hair and blue eyes.
   - **(v)** Select a student in your school; the student is a second year and does business.
   - **(vi)** Select a card from a standard deck; the card is red and a king.

Before attempting each question, decide if the events are mutually exclusive or not.

2. A shop decides to pick a month for its annual sale. Calculate the probability that:
   - **(i)** it is a month beginning with J
   - **(ii)** it is a month with 30 days
   - **(iii)** it is either September or March
   - **(iv)** it has less than five letters or has an 'A' in it.

3. A card is picked at random from a standard deck. What is the probability that it is:
   (i) a red card?
   (ii) a picture card?
   (iii) a red card or a picture card?
   (iv) a king or a black card?
   (v) a red queen or a black king?

4. A bag contains 20 chocolates; 5 are milk chocolate, 6 are dark chocolate, and 9 are white chocolate. If a chocolate is selected at random, what is the probability that the chocolate chosen is:
   (i) milk chocolate?
   (ii) dark chocolate?
   (iii) either milk chocolate or white chocolate?

5. The probability of a student owning a mobile phone is 0·83. The probability of a student owning an iPad is 0·58. The probability of a student owning both devices is 0·46. What is the probability that a student chosen at random will own either a phone or an iPad?

6. A number between 1 and 10 is chosen at random. What is the probability that it is:
   (i) an even number?
   (ii) a number greater than 3?
   (iii) an even number or a number greater than 3?
   (iv) a prime number or an odd number?

7. At a particular school with 400 students, 116 play football, 80 play basketball and 16 play both. What is the probability that a randomly selected student:
   (i) plays football?
   (ii) plays basketball?
   (iii) plays basketball or football?

8. The probability that a man will be alive in 15 years is $\frac{4}{5}$ and the probability that his wife will also be alive is $\frac{3}{4}$.
   What is the probability that in 15 years:
   (i) they will both be alive?
   (ii) at least one of them will be alive?
   (iii) neither of them will be alive?
   (iv) only the wife will be alive?

9. A shop carried out a survey and found that 40% of the customers were male. They also found that 75% of the males spent over €100 on an average visit to the shop and 55% of the females spent over €100. What is the probability that a customer chosen at random is:
   (i) a female or a customer who spends less than €100 on average?
   (ii) a customer that spends more than €100?

10. A box contains nine green marbles, eight blue marbles and eleven yellow marbles. Dave picks two marbles without looking.
   (i) Draw a tree diagram to represent this information. Write the probabilities on each branch.
   Use your tree diagram to work out the probability that:
   (ii) the 1st will be blue and the 2nd will be yellow?
   (iii) both will be green?
   (iv) the first will be green and the second will be blue?
   (v) both will be yellow?
   (vi) one will be green and the other will be yellow?
   (vii) at least one will be yellow?

11. Fourteen coloured discs are placed in a bag. Six are red, five are blue and three are yellow. Two discs are picked from the bag without replacement.
   What is the probability that:
   (i) both discs are red?
   (ii) one disc is blue and the other is yellow?
   (iii) both discs are blue?
   (iv) the first is blue and the second is not blue?
   (v) one is red and the other is blue?
   (vi) at least one is yellow?

12. A jar contains coloured stones consisting of four pink stones, nine orange stones and five green stones. Ryan picks one stone, records its colour and puts it back in the jar. Then he draws another stone.
   (i) Are these events dependent or independent?
   What is the probability of taking out:
   (ii) an orange stone followed by the green stone?
   (iii) two pink stones?
   (iv) at least one green stone?

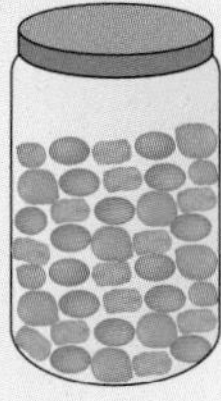

Section 19.4: Using Venn Diagrams

Learning Outcome:

You should be able to:

- use set theory and Venn diagrams to discuss experiments, outcomes and sample spaces

It is often useful to use a Venn diagram to visualise the probabilities of multiple events. Let's recap on some set notation.

P(A)

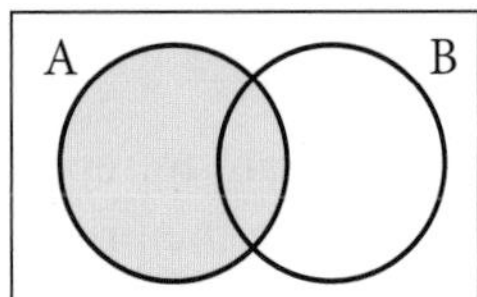

P(A) represents the probability that event A takes place.

Everything inside circle A is included.

P(A∪B)

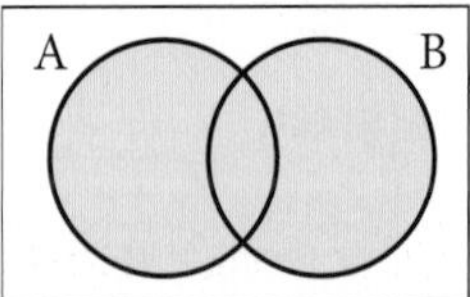

P(A **OR** B) means the probability that either A **OR** B (**OR** both) occurs, that is everything inside circles A and B is included.

In set notation this is written **A∪B** and read 'A union B'.

P(A′)

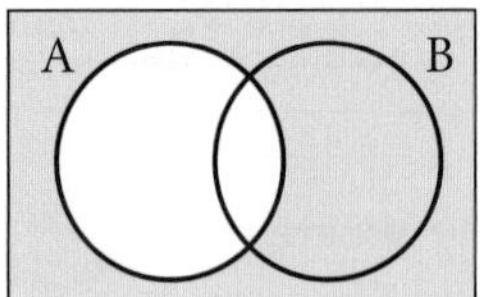

P(not A) means the probability that event A does not occur. Everything outside A is included.

In set notation it is written **A′** and read 'A complement'.

P(B\A)

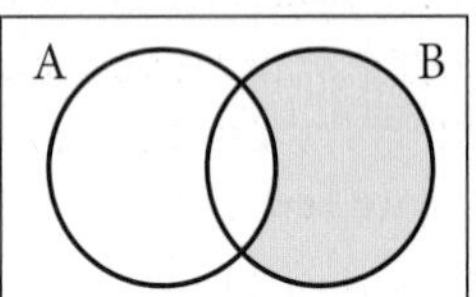

P(B only) represents the probability that **only** event B takes place. Everything in circle B that doesn't overlap with circle A is included.

In set notation it is written B\A and read 'B less A'.

P(A∩B)

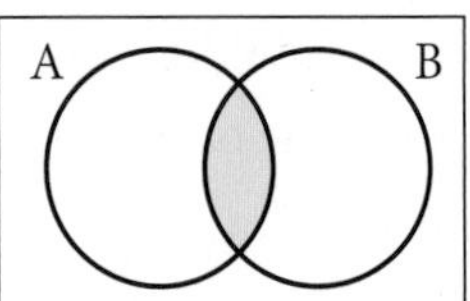

P(A **AND** B) means the probability that A **AND** B occur.

Everything in the overlapping section of circles A and B is included.

In set notation it is written **A∩B** and is read 'A intersection B'.

P(A∩B) = 0

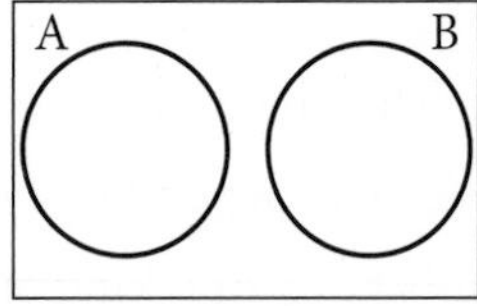

If A∩B is empty (null intersection) it means that these events can't occur at the same time, i.e. they are mutually exclusive.

EXAMPLE

The Venn diagram shown represents the favourite sports of a group of students.

Use the Venn diagram to calculate the probability that a student chosen at random:

(i) likes tennis
(ii) likes tennis **or** soccer
(iii) likes tennis **and** soccer
(iv) doesn't like either sport
(v) likes soccer only
(vi) doesn't like soccer.

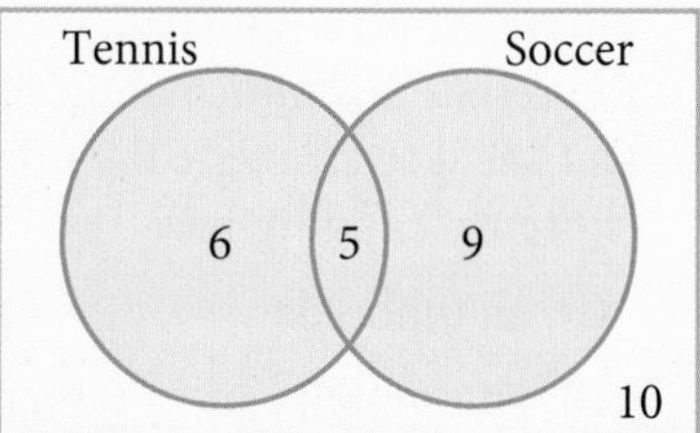

Solution

Since each probability will be expressed as a fraction of the total number of students, we must first work this out.

Total number of students = 6 + 5 + 9 + 10 = 30 students.

(i) P(like tennis) $= \frac{6+5}{30} = \frac{11}{30}$ — everything inside tennis circle

(ii) P(like tennis or soccer) = P(tennis or soccer or both)

$= \frac{6+5+9}{30} = \frac{20}{30} = \frac{2}{3}$ — everything inside both circles ($T \cup S$)

(iii) P(like tennis and soccer) $= \frac{5}{30} = \frac{1}{6}$ — everything in the overlapping section ($T \cap S$)

(iv) P(doesn't like either sport) $= \frac{10}{30} = \frac{1}{3}$ — everything outside both circles $(T \cup S)'$

(v) P(like soccer only) $= \frac{9}{30} = \frac{3}{10}$ — everything in the part of the soccer circle that doesn't overlap with the tennis circle ($S \setminus T$)

(vi) P(doesn't like soccer) $= \frac{6+10}{30} = \frac{16}{30} = \frac{8}{15}$ — everything outside the soccer circle (S')

Practice Questions 19.4

1. On separate Venn diagrams of events A and B, shade the regions that represent the following:
   (i) P(A)
   (ii) P(B)
   (iii) P(A or B)
   (iv) P(A and B)
   (v) P(not A)
   (vi) P(B only).

2. In a class of 30 students, 25 passed their Christmas Maths exam, 24 passed their Irish exam and 23 passed both exams.
   Draw a Venn diagram to represent this information and use it to calculate the probability that a student chosen at random:
   (i) didn't pass maths
   (ii) passed maths or Irish but not both
   (iii) passed both exams
   (iv) passed maths only
   (v) didn't pass either exam.

3. Twenty-six people were surveyed about their choice of mobile phones. The survey finds that 14 people have Apple iPhones, 10 have Samsungs and five have Nokias. Four have Apple iPhones and Samsungs, three have Apple iPhones and Nokias and one has a Samsung and a Nokia. No one has all three types of phone.
   Represent this information on a Venn diagram and use it to calculate the probability that a person chosen at random has:
   (i) an iPhone
   (ii) a Samsung or a Nokia
   (iii) two phones
   (iv) no phone
   (v) no iPhone.

4. A group of 20 people are waiting at a bus stop one morning. Nine of them have an umbrella, six have a raincoat and three have both an umbrella and a raincoat.

Represent this information on a Venn diagram and use it to calculate the probability that a person chosen at random has:

(i) an umbrella
(ii) an umbrella and a raincoat
(iii) an umbrella or a raincoat
(iv) neither.

5. A group of students were asked if they preferred soccer, rugby or Gaelic football. The results are shown on the Venn diagram.

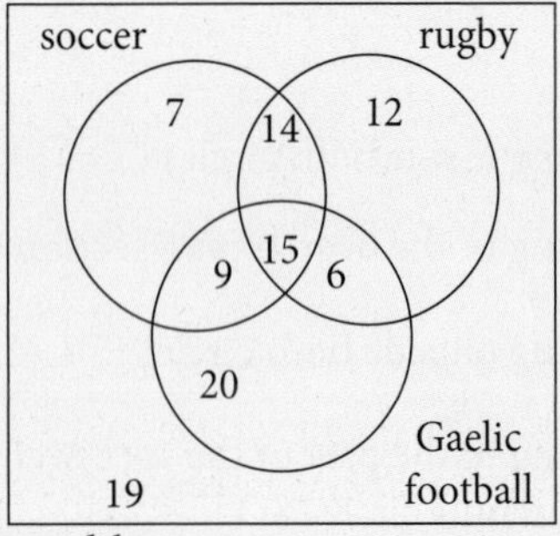

Calculate the probability that a randomly chosen students likes:

(i) soccer or rugby
(ii) rugby or Gaelic football
(iii) soccer and Gaelic football but not rugby
(iv) only Gaelic football
(v) none of these sports.

6. Two events A and B have the following probabilities:
$P(A) = 0{\cdot}4$ $P(B) = 0{\cdot}6$ $P(A \cap B) = 0{\cdot}2$
Draw a Venn diagram to represent these probabilities and use it to calculate:

(i) $P(A \cup B)$
(ii) $P(A \cup B)'$

7. Let A and B be independent events, where $P(A) = 0{\cdot}4$ and $P(B) = 0{\cdot}7$.

(i) Find $P(A \cap B)$
(ii) Find $P(A \cup B)$
(iii) Draw a Venn diagram and shade the region that represents $A \cap B'$
(iv) Find $P(A \cap B')$.

8. A driving test consists of a practical test and theory test. One day everyone who took the test passed at least one section. 64% passed the practical section and 78% passed the theory section.

(i) Represent this information on a Venn diagram showing the probabilities of candidates in each section of the diagram.

One person is chosen at random from all the people who took the test that day. What is the probability that this person:

(ii) passed the practical section and the theory section?
(iii) passed the theory section only?

Section 19.5: Bernoulli Trials

Learning Outcomes:

You should be able to:

- understand Bernoulli trials and solve problems involving up to three Bernoulli trials
- calculate the probability that the first success occurs on the nth Bernoulli trial where n is given

Very often in real life an event may have only two outcomes of interest. For example, either you pass an exam or you don't pass an exam, either you get the job you applied for or you don't get the job, etc. In probability terms such situations are called Bernoulli trials.

Bernoulli trial is an experiment with only two possible outcomes.

The outcomes are said to be 'success' and 'failure'.

The probability of success plus the probability of failure is equal to 1.

$$P(\text{success}) + P(\text{failure}) = 1$$
$$P(\text{success}) = 1 - P(\text{failure})$$
$$P(\text{failure}) = 1 - P(\text{success})$$

For example, if a fair die is thrown and you are only interested in whether you get a 6, getting a 6 is a success and not getting a 6 is a failure.

Therefore, P(success) $= \frac{1}{6}$ P(failure) $= 1 - \frac{1}{6} = \frac{5}{6}$

Imagine you throw the die six times and you want to work out the probability that you throw the first six on the fourth throw.

This would be P (F and F and F and S) = P(F) × P(F) × P(F) × P(S)

$$= P(F)^3 \times P(S)$$
$$= \left(\frac{5}{6}\right)^3 \times \frac{1}{6}$$
$$= \frac{125}{1296}$$

To calculate the probability that the first successful outcome occurs after n trials when n is given means that you will fail $n - 1$ times and be successful on the nth trial. To do this we use the following formula:

$$P(\text{failure})^{n-1} \times P(\text{success})$$

EXAMPLE

A soccer player has scored 75% of his goal opportunities during the season. In his next game, what is the probability that:

(i) he scores for the first time on his first goal opportunity?

(ii) he scores any two of the first three shots?

(iii) he scores for the first time on his eight goal opportunity?

(iv) he misses for the first time on his fourth goal opportunity?

Success = score P(S) = **0·75**

Failure = miss P(F) = **0·25**

(i) P(score on 1st shot) = 0·75

(ii) Any two of 1st three shot
= P(SSF) or P(SFS) or P(FSS)
= (0·75 × 0·75 × 0·25) + (0·75 × 0·25 × 0·75) + (0·25 × 0·75 × 0·75)
= 0·140625 + 0·140625 + 0·140625
= 0·421875

(iii) P(1st score on 8th shot)
P(FFFFFFFS)
$n = 8$
P(failure)^7 × P(success)
= $(0\cdot25)^7 \times 0\cdot75$
= 0·00045776

(iv) P(1st miss on 4th shot)
= P(SSSF)
= 0·75 × 0·75 × 0·75 × 0·25 = 0·10546875

Practice Questions 19.5

1. Jamie is playing a game where he must toss a coin until he gets a head. What is the probability that he gets a head for the first time on:

   (i) the first throw?

   (ii) the second throw?

   (iii) the third throw?

   (iv) his fifth throw?

2. Ciaran is playing a game using a fair die. He must throw the die until he gets a 6.
What is the probability that he throws a 6 in:
   (i) one throw?
   (ii) two throws?
   (iii) three throws?
   (iv) his tenth throw?

3. A fair die is thrown three times.
What is the probability that a 2 or a 3 is thrown:
   (i) for the first time on the third throw?
   (ii) once in three throws?

4. A spinner has five equal sections. Three of them are green and two of them are yellow. Chloe is playing a game where she has to spin the spinner until it lands on yellow.

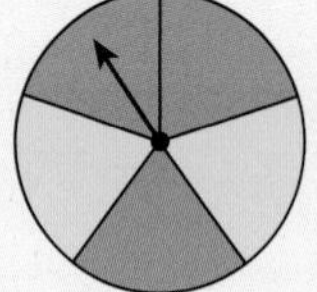

What is the probability that she lands on yellow for the first time on:
   (i) the first spin?
   (ii) the third spin?
   (iii) the sixth spin?
   (iv) the ninth spin? Give your answer in scientific notation.

5. Zoe is the best free-throw taker on her basketball team. Her average probability of scoring from a free shot is 0·78.
If she takes three free throws in a game, what is the probability that she will:
   (i) score all three?
   (ii) score two out of three?
   (iii) score only on the final throw?
   (iv) not score at all?
   (v) score at least once?

6. At the end of Maths class, a teacher gives her students a three-question multiple-choice test to check if they have understood the lesson. Each question has three options. A student guesses on all questions.
What is the probability that he gets:
   (i) all questions correct?
   (ii) two questions correct?
   (iii) no questions correct?
   (iv) the first two correct and the final question incorrect?

7. In a survey of her class, Olivia found that 35% of the students walk to school. Three students are selected at random from the class. Giving your answers as a decimal, what is the probability that:
   (i) all three students walk to school?
   (ii) none of the three students walk to school?
   (iii) two out of the three students walk to school?

8. Charlie is the goalkeeper on the school soccer team. His average success rate for saving goals is $\frac{5}{8}$. If there are three scoring opportunities in a match, what is the probability that:

   (i) he saves all three?
   (ii) he doesn't save any of them?
   (iii) he saves the first two but not the third?
   (iv) he saves one?

9. Stephen comes to school by car. On his way to school he passes three sets of traffic lights. The probability that the lights will be red is $\frac{4}{7}$. What is the probability that:

   (i) the first set of lights will be green?
   (ii) the first time the lights are red is at the last set of lights?
   (iii) all three sets of lights are red?
   (iv) at least one set of lights are red?

10. Suppose a student takes a multiple choice test. The test has 10 questions, each of which has four possible answers (only one correct).
   (i) If the student guesses the answer to each question, do the questions form a sequence of Bernoulli trials? Explain your answer.
   (ii) List the possible outcomes.
   (iii) Write the probability associated with each outcome.

Section 19.6: Expectation

Learning Outcome:

You should be able to:

- calculate expected value, use its value in decision making and explore the issue of fair games

Consider the following situation:

A fair die is thrown 300 times. How many times would you expect to get a six?

In one thrown, $P(6) = \frac{1}{6}$. Therefore, in 300 throws we would expect to get a six in $\frac{1}{6}$ of the throws.

We would expect to get a six $\frac{1}{6} \times 300 = 50$ times.

This does not mean we will always get fifty 6's in 300 throws, it is just our expectation. Remember the Gambler's Fallacy.

If there are n trials of an experiment and the probability of an event occurring in each trial is p, then the number of times we expect the event to occur is given as $n \times p$

EXAMPLE 1

Each time a footballer takes a kick at goal he has a $\frac{3}{4}$ chance of scoring. How many goals would you expect him to score out of 36 kicks at goal?

Solution

$P(\text{goal}) = \frac{3}{4}$

$n = 36$

Therefore, the expected number of goals is $n \times p = 36 \times \frac{3}{4} = 27$ goals.

Expected value

The **expected value**, **E(*x*)** of an experiment is described as the average outcome if the experiment is run many times.

When calculating the expected value for all possible outcomes in a situation, we multiply each outcome by the probability of that outcome and add these values together.

E(*x*) = the sum of all outcomes times their respective probabilities. Mathematically,

$$E(x) = \Sigma x.p(x)$$

where **Σ** = the sum of

x = the outcome

. = multiply

***p*(*x*)** = the probability of the outcome

EXAMPLE 2

What is the expected value of throwing a fair die?

Solution

Outcome (x)	Probability of outcome $p(x)$	$x.p(x)$
1	$\frac{1}{6}$	$1 \times \frac{1}{6} = \frac{1}{6}$
2	$\frac{1}{6}$	$2 \times \frac{1}{6} = \frac{2}{6}$
3	$\frac{1}{6}$	$3 \times \frac{1}{6} = \frac{3}{6}$
4	$\frac{1}{6}$	$4 \times \frac{1}{6} = \frac{4}{6}$
5	$\frac{1}{6}$	$5 \times \frac{1}{6} = \frac{5}{6}$
6	$\frac{1}{6}$	$6 \times \frac{1}{6} = \frac{6}{6}$

$$\text{E}(x) = \Sigma x.p(x) = \frac{1}{6} + \frac{2}{6} + \frac{3}{6} + \frac{4}{6} + \frac{5}{6} + \frac{6}{6} = \frac{21}{6} = 3{\cdot}5$$

So the expected value of throwing a fair die is 3·5.

This means that if we were to roll a die a large number of times and average the values we would get 3·5.

An outcome of 3·5 is not actually possible when throwing a die.

E(x) does not have to be an actual outcome.

Applications of expected value

Expected value can be used in decision making and risk management; for example, taking calculated risks. This forms the basis of many personal and business decisions. It is also the basis for calculating insurance premiums.

Expected value can also be used in gambling to see if a game is fair. A game is said to be fair if the amount bet is equal to the expected value. To calculate the expected value in this case, we multiply each pay out by its associated probability and add these results.

$$\text{E}(x) = \Sigma(\text{payout})(\text{probability})$$

Did you know?

You may have heard the phrase 'the house always wins' in relation to gambling in casinos. This is because the games are arranged so that the expected value for the customer is always negative. It is possible for a person to win but over the long term the casino will always win, thereby ensuring it is a profitable business.

EXAMPLE 3

A stall owner charges €2 to play a certain game by throwing a fair die once.

If a 1 or a 2 comes up, the player wins nothing. If a 3, 4, 5, or 6 comes up they win the difference between the number rolled and the €2 to play the game.

(i) Find the expected value for this game.

(ii) Is this game fair?

Solution

(i)

Outcome	Payout (€)	Probability of outcome P(x)	Payout × probability
1	0	$\frac{1}{6}$	$\frac{1}{6} \times 0 = 0$
2	0	$\frac{1}{6}$	$\frac{1}{6} \times 0 = 0$
3	1	$\frac{1}{6}$	$\frac{1}{6} \times 1 = 0{\cdot}17$
4	2	$\frac{1}{6}$	$\frac{1}{6} \times 2 = 0{\cdot}33$
5	3	$\frac{1}{6}$	$\frac{1}{6} \times 3 = 0{\cdot}5$
6	4	$\frac{1}{6}$	$\frac{1}{6} \times 4 = 0{\cdot}67$

$E(x) = 0 + 0 + 0{\cdot}17 + 0{\cdot}33 + 0{\cdot}5 + 0{\cdot}67 = 1{\cdot}67$

(ii) You pay €2 to play with an expectation of 'winning' €1·67 so your net 'winnings' are

$$1{\cdot}67 - 2 = -0{\cdot}33$$

That means you are down €0·33. This is not a fair game. It is unfair against the player.

The expected value is the same for both the stall owner and the player, however the player's loss will be the stall owners gain and vice versa. It's all about perspective!

Practice Questions 19.6

1. A goalkeeper has a probability of $\frac{3}{5}$ of saving a penalty. How many penalties would you expect him to save out of 50 penalties taken?

2. A batch of 1,600 items is examined. The probability that an item from this batch is defective is 0·04. How many items from this batch are defective?

3. In an experiment, a standard six-sided die was rolled 72 times. The results are shown in the table. Which number on the die was obtained the expected number of times?

Number on the die	1	2	3	4	5	6
Frequency	11	8	12	15	16	10

4. In a random survey of the voting intentions of a local electorate, the following results were obtained:

Politician A	Politician B	Politician C
165	87	48

   (i) Calculate the probability that a randomly selected voter will vote for:
      (a) Politician A
      (b) Politician B
      (c) Politician C.
   (ii) If there are 7,500 people in the electorate, how many votes would you expect to be for:
      (a) Politician A?
      (b) Politician B?
      (c) Politician C?

5. In a raffle, 250 tickets are sold at €1 each for three prizes of €100, €50 and €10. You buy one ticket.
   (i) What is the expected value of this raffle.
   (ii) Does it represent a good investment of €1? Explain your answer.

6. Jennifer is playing a game at an amusement park. There is a 0·1 probability that she will score 10 points, a 0·2 probability that she will score 20 points, and a 0·7 probability that she will score 30 points. How many points can Jennifer expect to receive by playing the game?

7. You take out a fire insurance policy on your home. The annual premium is €300. In case of fire, the insurance company will pay you €200,000. The probability of a house fire in your area is 0·0002.
   (i) What is the expected value?
   (ii) What is the insurance company's expected value?
   (iii) Suppose the insurance company sells 100,000 of these policies. What can the company expect to earn?

8. A hundred tickets are sold for a movie at the cost of €10 each. Some tickets have cash prizes as a part of a promotional campaign: one prize of €50, three prizes of €25 and five prizes of €20. What is the expected value if you buy one ticket?

9. You pay €10 to play the following game of chance. There is a bag containing 12 balls, five are red, three are green and the rest are yellow. You are to draw one ball from the bag. You will win €14 if you draw a red ball and you will win €12 if you draw a green ball. How much do you expect to win or lose if you play this game 100 times?

10. A sports club decides to hold a field day to raise money for local charities. One of the games involves spinning the wheel shown on the right. You win the amount the pointer lands on. It costs €5 to play the game.
   (i) What is the expected value of the game?
   (ii) How could they adjust the wheel to ensure they make more money for the charities?

11. A child asks his parents for some money. The parents make the following offers.
Father's offer: The child flips a coin. If the coin lands heads-up, the father will give the child €20. If the coin lands tails-up, the father will give the child nothing.
Mother's offer: The child rolls a 6-sided die. The mother will give the child €3 for each dot on the up side of the die.
   (i) Which offer has the greater expected value?
   (ii) Which offer would you choose if you were the child? Justify your answer.

12. (i) What is the expected value for each of the following investment packages for a €1,000 investment?

Speculative investment
- Complete loss: 40% chance
- No gain or loss: 15% chance
- 100% gain: 15% chance
- 400% gain: 15% chance
- 900% gain: 15% chance

Conservative investment
- Complete loss: 1% chance
- No gain or loss: 35% chance
- 10% gain: 59% chance
- 20% gain: 5% chance

A speculative investment is one in which there is a high risk of loss.

A conservative investment is one in which there is a low risk of loss.

   (ii) Which would you choose? Why?

13. A biased die is used in a fairground game. The probabilities of getting the six different numbers on the die are shown in the table below.

Number	1	2	3	4	5	6
Probability	0·12	0·26	0·1	0·23	0·18	0·11

(i) Find the expected value of the random variable x, where x is the number thrown.

(ii) It costs €3·50 to play the game. The player rolls a die once and wins the number of euro shown on the die. By doing the calculations required, complete the following sentence:

'If you play the game many times with a fair die, you will win an average of ______ per game, but if you play with the biased die you will lose an average of ______ per game.'

Revision and Exam Style Questions – Section A

1. The probability that Ben's soccer team wins this weekend is $\frac{3}{5}$. The probability that his rugby league team wins this weekend is $\frac{2}{3}$.
   (i) What is the probability that neither team wins this weekend?
   (ii) What is the probability that only one of the teams wins?

2. A packet of lollipops contains eight red lollipops and 14 blue lollipops. Two lollipops are selected at random without replacement.
   (i) Draw a tree diagram to show the possible outcomes. Write the probabilities on each branch.
   (ii) What is the probability that the two lollipops are of different colours?
   (iii) What is the probability that the two lollipops are the same colour?

3. The probability of winning a game is $\frac{5}{8}$. If the game is played three times, what is the probability of winning:
   (i) three consecutive games?
   (ii) at least two games?

4. A bag contains five yellow marbles and seven green marbles. Two marbles are selected at random without replacement.
   (i) What is the probability that at least one of the marbles selected is yellow?
   (ii) If a marble is selected at random and replaced 72 times, how many times would you expect to get a yellow marble?

5. Two boxes each contain green balls and yellow balls. Box A contains four green and three yellow balls. Box B contains four green and five yellow balls. Chris randomly chooses one ball from each box.
   (i) What is the probability that both balls are green?
   (ii) What is the probability that at least one of the balls is yellow?
   (iii) What is the probability that both balls are the same colour?

6. Jake has four blue t-shirts and three white t-shirts. On each of the three days, Friday, Saturday and Sunday, he selects one t-shirt at random to wear. Jake wears each t-shirt that he selects only once.
   (i) What is the probability that Jake wears a blue t-shirt on Friday?
   (ii) What is the probability that Jake wears a t-shirt of the same colour on all three days?
   (iii) What is the probability that Jake does not wear a t-shirt of the same colour on consecutive days?

7. There are 12 chocolates in a box. Four of the chocolates have caramel centres, four have orange centres and four have strawberry centres. Abdul randomly selects two chocolates and eats them.
   (i) What is the probability that the two chocolates have orange centres?
   (ii) What is the probability that the two chocolates have the same centre?
   (iii) What is the probability that the two chocolates have different centres?

8. Sarah often oversleeps and arrives late for school. She has estimated the probability that she will oversleep on Monday as 25% and on Tuesday as 35%. The tree diagram shows these probabilities.

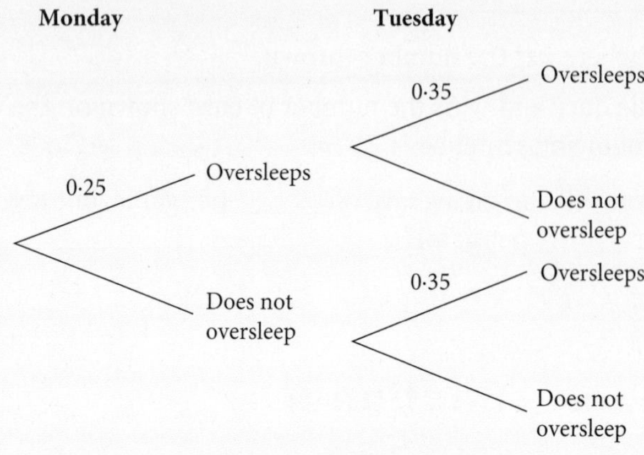

(i) Copy the tree diagram and fill in the probabilities that Sarah does not oversleep.
(ii) Calculate the probability that Sarah oversleeps on both Mondays and Tuesdays.
(iii) Calculate the probability that Sarah oversleeps on exactly one of the two days.

9. A card is taken from a standard deck. This card is replaced and a second card is drawn. What is the probability that the cards drawn are:
(i) a seven and a queen?
(ii) two red tens?
(iii) a spade or an ace?
(iv) not picture cards?

10. If you draw three cards from a deck without replacement, what is the probability that:
(i) all three cards are red?
(ii) you don't draw any spades?
(iii) you draw a club, a heart and a diamond (in that order)?
(iv) you draw a club, a heart and a diamond in any order?

11. A survey of 154 people was carried out. Participants were asked whether they liked tea or coffee. Some of the results are recorded in the Venn diagram below.

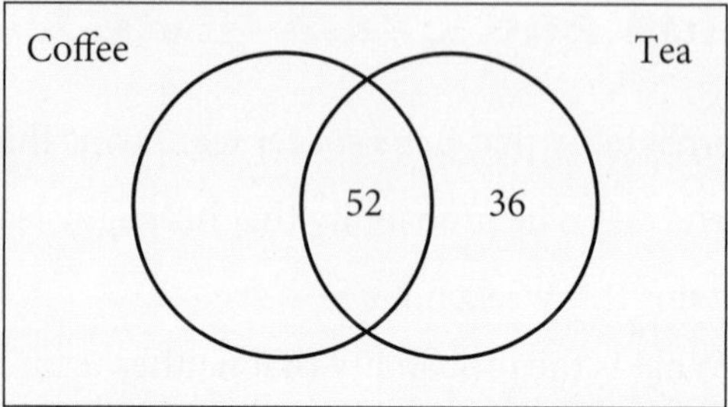

(i) Of those surveyed, 21 people did not like either tea or coffee. Complete the diagram.
(ii) A person is chosen at random from those surveyed. What is the probability that the person liked both coffee and tea?
(iii) What percentage of the people surveyed liked one beverage only? Give your answer correct to one decimal place.

Revision and Exam Style Questions – Section B

More challenging problems

1. Jane plays a game which involves two coins being tossed. The amounts to be won for the different possible outcomes are shown below:
Win €6 for two heads
Win €1 for one head and one tail
Win €2 for two tails
It costs €4 to play one game.
(i) Will Jane expect a gain or a loss, and how much will it be? Justify your answer with suitable calculations.
(ii) Is this a fair game? Justify your answer.

2. Conor says that the probability of getting two tails in three throws is higher than the probability of getting three heads in a row.
(i) Do you agree with Conor? Justify your answer by showing the calculations for each situation.

Georgia says that if you get three heads in a row you are more likely to get a tail on the next throw because a tail is due.
(ii) Do you agree with Georgia? Explain your answer.

3. The table shows the probability of choosing each of the different coloured sweets from packets containing red, green, yellow, brown and blue sweets.

Colour of sweet	Red	Green	Yellow	Brown	Blue
Probability	0·3	0·15		0·26	0·18

(i) What is the probability of choosing a yellow sweet?

(ii) What is the probability of not choosing a red sweet?

(iii) If three sweets are chosen at the same time, what is the probability of choosing a green, a blue and a brown sweet?

4. Weather records for a town suggest the following:

If it rains (R) on a given day, the probability it will rain the next day is $\frac{1}{6}$.

If it is sunny (S) on a given day, the probability of the next day being sunny is $\frac{1}{2}$.

In a particular week Tuesday is sunny. The tree diagram shows the possible outcomes for the next three days.

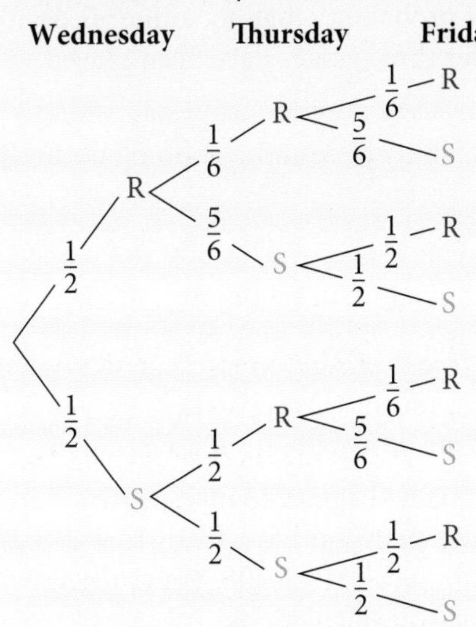

(i) Show that the probability of Thursday being sunny is $\frac{2}{3}$.

(ii) What is the probability of rain on both Thursday and Friday?

(iii) What is the probability of at least one of Thursday and Friday being sunny?

5. Judy is playing a game in which she rolls a fair dice three times and tries to get '6' as many times as she can.

(i) Using the options '6' and 'not a 6', draw a tree diagram to represent this game. Fill in the probabilities on the branches of the tree diagram.

(ii) Calculate the probability that Judy gets a '6' on all three tries.

(iii) Calculate the probability that Judy gets a '6' on at least two of her three tries.

6. A bag contains 10 counters with the letters of the word STATISTICS written on them. A counter is chosen at random and not replaced before choosing another one.

(i) Draw a tree diagram to represent this situation.

(ii) What is the probability of getting two consonants?

(iii) What is the probability of getting a vowel at least once?

(iv) What is the probability of getting exactly one vowel?

(v) What is the probability of not getting exactly one vowel?

7. In a certain game, you pick a card from a standard deck of 52 cards. If the card is a heart, you win. If the card is not a heart, you replace the card to the deck, reshuffle, and draw again. What is the probability that you will pick the first heart on the third draw?

8. A biased die is used in a game. The probabilities for each outcome are given below.

Outcome	1	2	3	4	5	6
Probability	0·22	0·12	0·25	0·14	0·18	0·09

(i) The die is thrown once. What is the probability of getting:

(a) an even number?

(b) a prime number or an odd number?

(c) a 4 or less?

(d) a multiple of 3?

(ii) Calculate the expected value of the biased die above.

This die was used in a game where the player rolls the die once and wins back the number of euro shown on the die. The game costs €3 to play.

(iii) By doing the necessary calculations, show the difference between using the biased die and a fair die to play the game.

9. While shuffling a deck of cards, two cards are accidently dropped. What is the probability that the cards are:

(i) a king and a queen?

(ii) both red fours?

(iii) both of the same suit?

(iv) both black picture cards?

(v) one is a spade and the other is not a spade?

(vi) at least one is a diamond?

10. A team from school A and a team from school B are in the finals of a Gaelic football competition. In this competition the final round consists of a best-of-three game series. Each game continues until one team has a winning score. The team that wins two games wins the competition. Both teams are equally likely to win a game.

(i) Find the probability that team A will win the competition at the end of the first two games.

(ii) Find the probability that no winner is decided until after three games have been played.

From an analysis of previous games, it is found that the probability of winning at home for both teams is $\frac{5}{8}$.

The first game is played at school A, the second at school B and the third at school A.

(iii) Draw a tree diagram to represent all possible outcomes for the three matches. Include the probabilities on each branch.

(iv) Use your tree diagram to investigate a claim that team A is more likely to win the competition. Clearly justify your answer with mathematical calculations.

Now that you have completed the chapter, revisit the 'Something to think about...' question.

Trigonometry I

CHAPTER 20

Sections covered within this chapter:

KEY WORDS

- Hypotenuse
- Angle of depression
- Trigonometric ratios
- Clinometer
- Angle of elevation
- Reference angle

SOMETHING TO THINK ABOUT... 

Colin stands in front of an 8 m tall vertical pole, at a point R, and measures the angle of elevation from the ground to the top of the pole to be 48·8°.

Colin then moves along the same line to the point S and measures the angle of elevation from the ground to the top of the pole to be 36°.

Find the distance Colin walked from R to S, correct to the nearest centimetre.

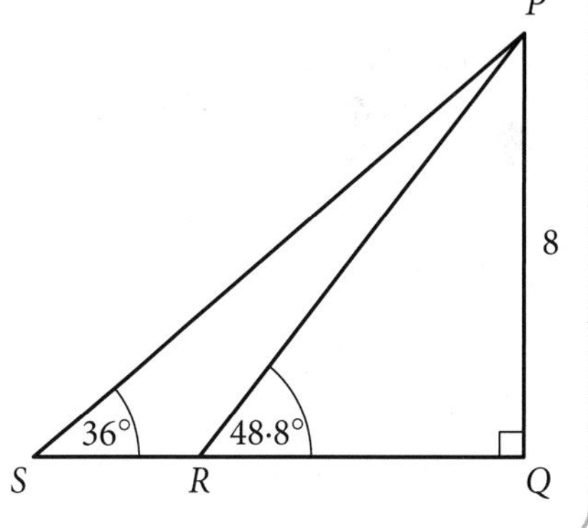

Introduction

Trigonometry is the area of mathematics that studies relationships between the sides and angles of triangles. Trigonometry is heavily linked with geometry. It is important that you are familiar with the geometry theorems before studying trigonometry, as you will need to use some of the theorems when solving trigonometric problems.

This chapter will look at how to solve for missing sides and missing angles in right-angled triangles.

A right-angle can be denoted in two ways, as shown.
An L-shape or a box indicates the 90° angle.

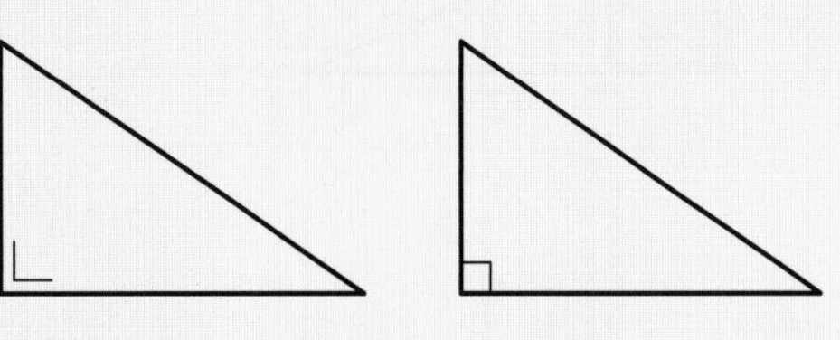

Section 20.1: Pythagoras' Theorem

Learning Outcome:

You should be able to:

- apply Pythagoras' Theorem when solving for a missing side in a triangle

The **hypotenuse** is the longest side in a right-angled triangle. It is always the side directly facing the right-angle.

In any right-angled triangle, the hypotenuse squared equals the sum of the squares of the other two sides.

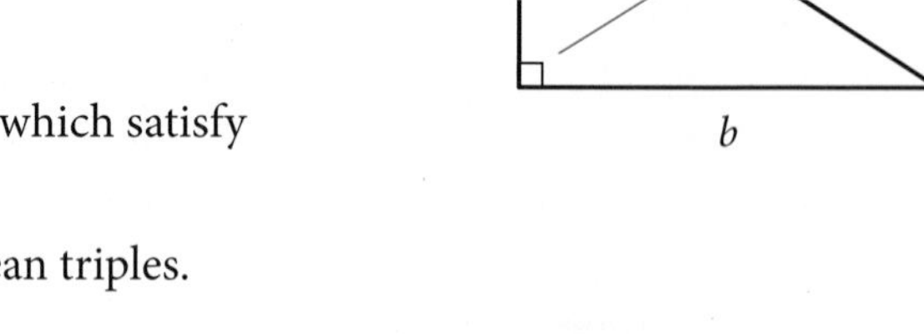

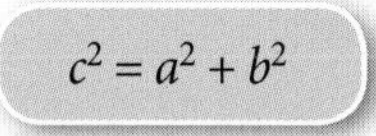

Pythagroean triples are a set of three integers (whole numbers) which satisfy Pythagoras' Theorem.

You should be familiar with the more commonly used Pythagorean triples. These would be:

- 3, 4, 5 (shown in the diagram)
- 6, 8, 10
- 5, 12, 13
- 8, 15, 17

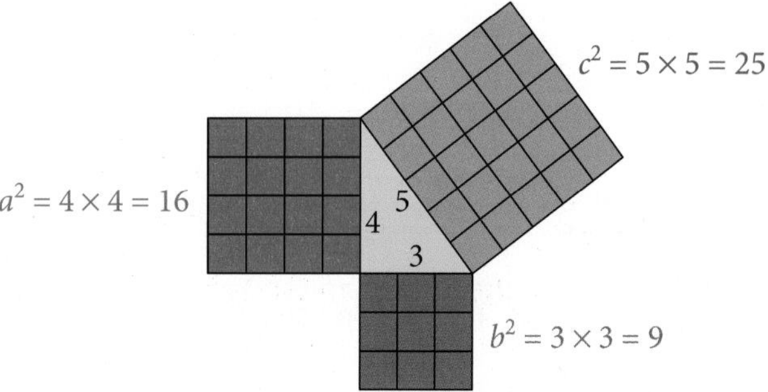

Links across the syllabus

Pythagoras' Theorem is also covered in Chapter 11: Geometry II.

EXAMPLE

The diagram shows two right-angled triangles.
Find:

(i) the value of p

(ii) the value of q. Leave your answer in surd form.

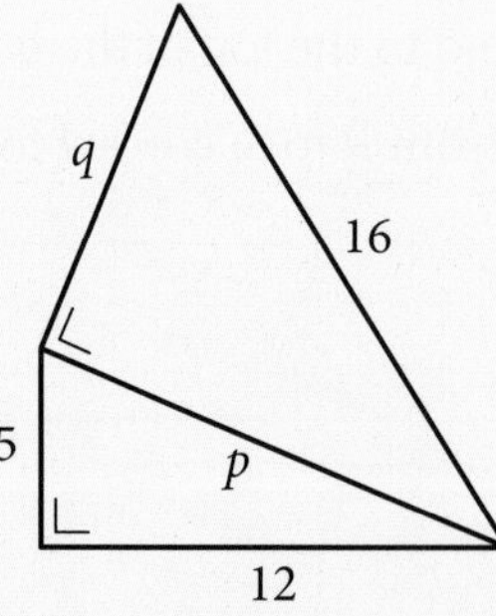

Solution

(i) Identify the hypotenuse as p:

$c^2 = a^2 + b^2$

Let: $a = 5$, $b = 12$ and $c = p$

$p^2 = 5^2 + 12^2$

$p^2 = 25 + 144$

$p^2 = 169$

$p = \sqrt{169}$

$p = 13$

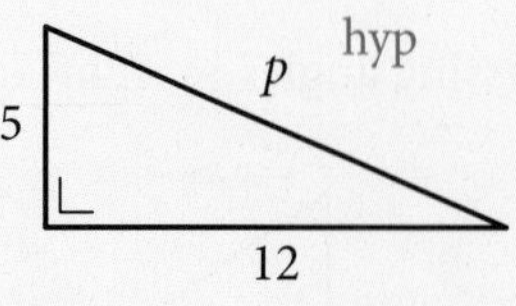

(ii) Identify the hypotenuse as 16:

$c^2 = a^2 + b^2$

Let: $a = 13$, $b = q$ and $c = 16$

$16^2 = 13^2 + q^2$

$256 = 169 + q^2$

$256 - 169 = q^2$

$87 = q^2$

$\sqrt{87} = q$

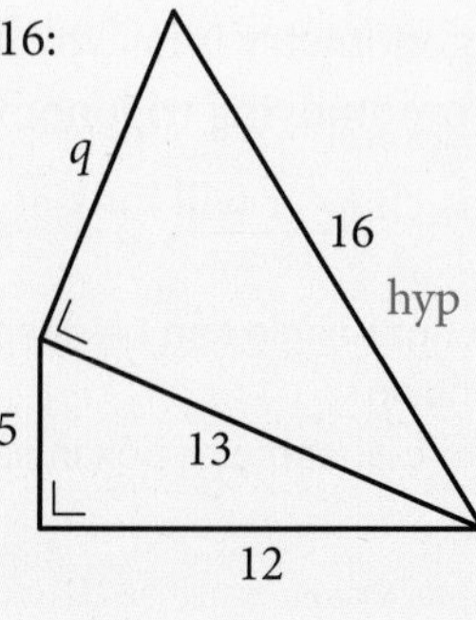

Practice Questions 20.1

1. In each of the following, find the length of the missing side.
   Give your answer in simplest surd form, where appropriate.

   (i)

   5 cm
   12 cm

   (iv)

   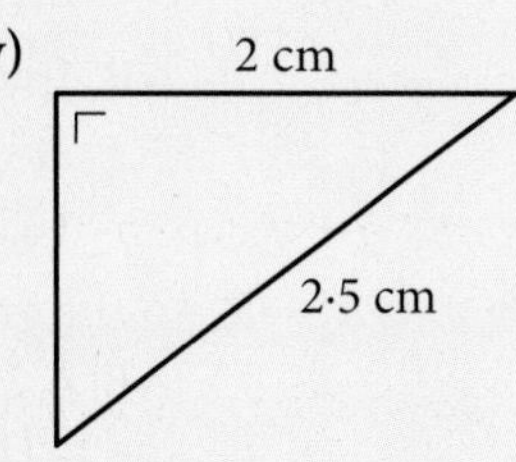

   (vii)

   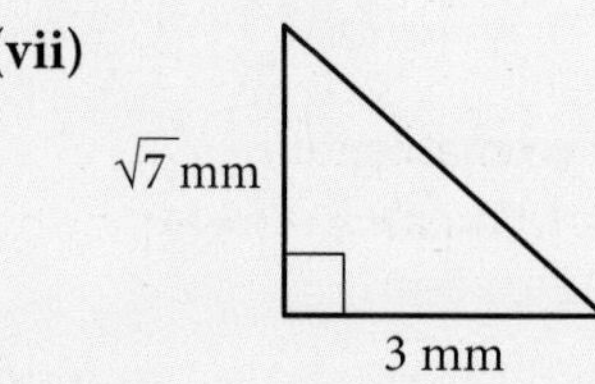

   (ii)

   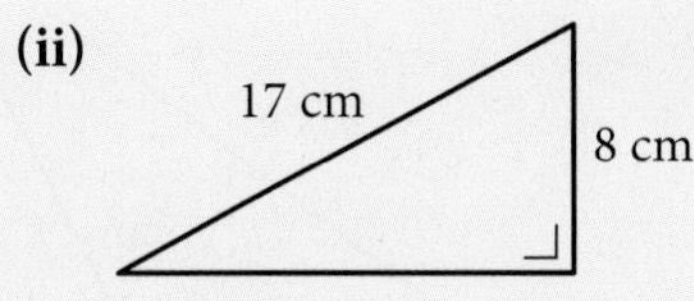

   (v)

   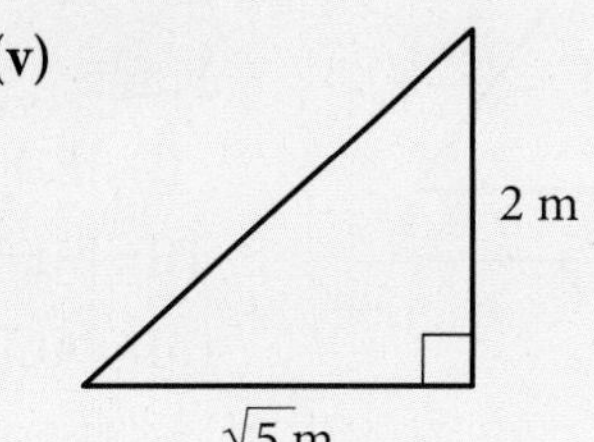

   (viii)

   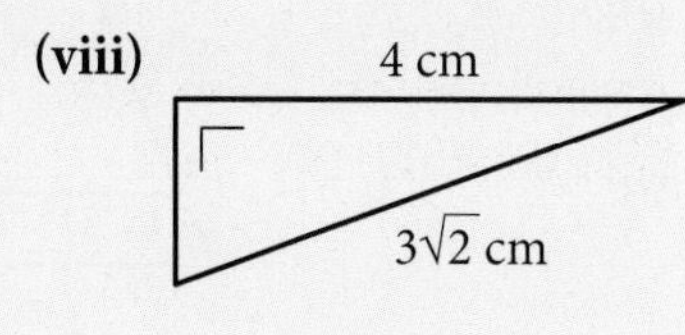

   (iii)

   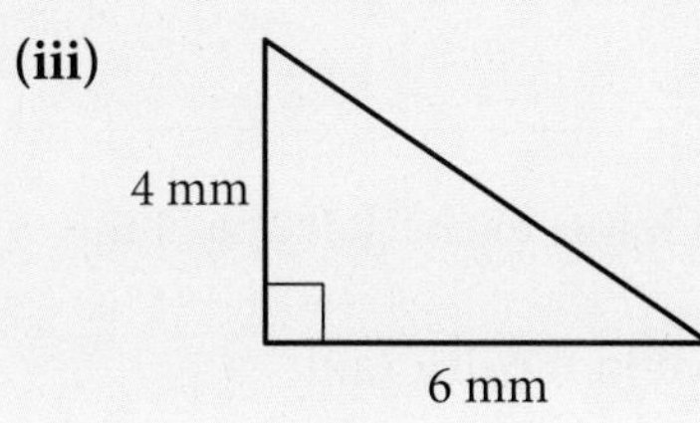

   (vi)

   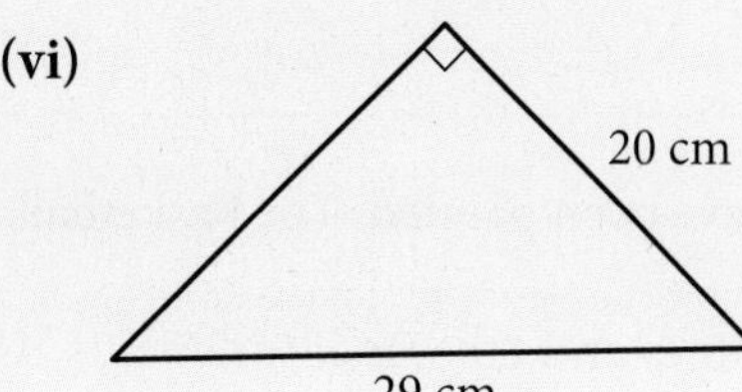

   (ix)

   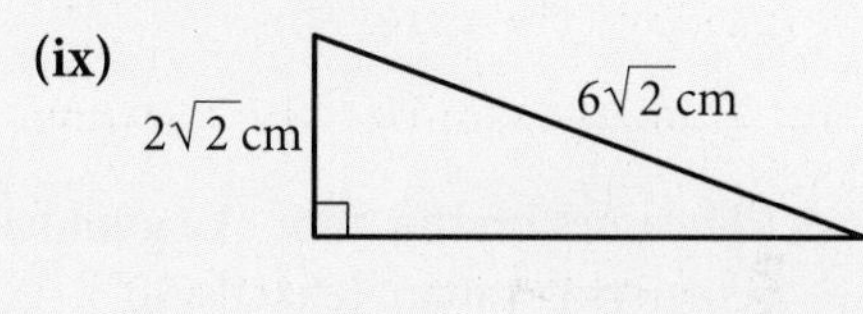

2. Use Pythagoras' Theorem to determine whether the following triangles are right-angled.

   (i)

   15 cm
   25 cm
   20 cm

   (ii)

   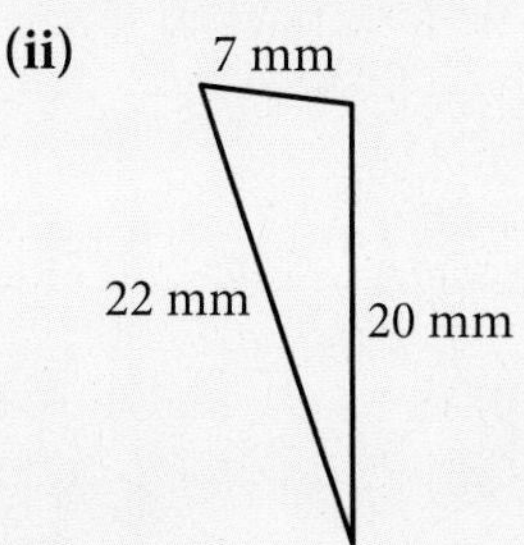

   (iii)

   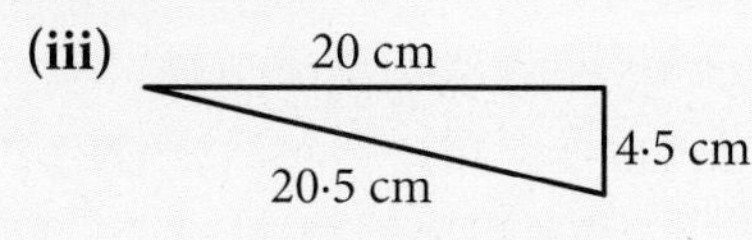

3. Find the vertical height of the following triangles.
   Give your answer in simplest surd form, where appropriate.

   (i)

   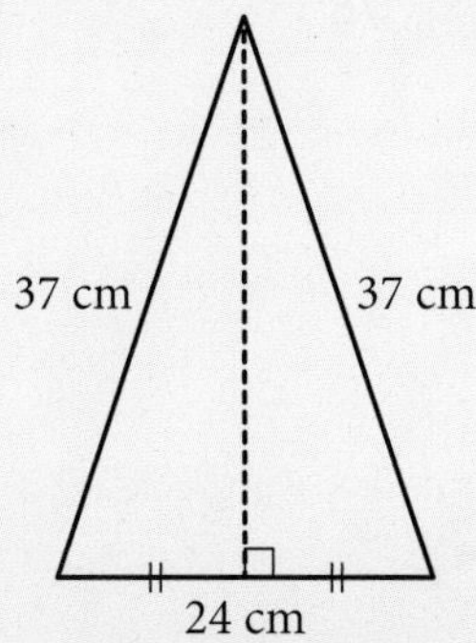

   (ii)

   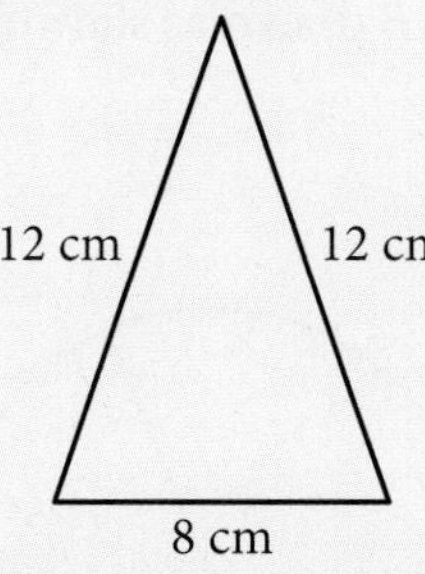

   The vertical height of an isosceles triangle bisects the base.

4. A wire is tied from the horizontal ground to the top of a vertical flag pole to secure it.
   The flag pole is 9 m tall and it is to be anchored 5·5 m away from its base.
   How long must the wire be to do this?
   Give your answer to the nearest centimetre.

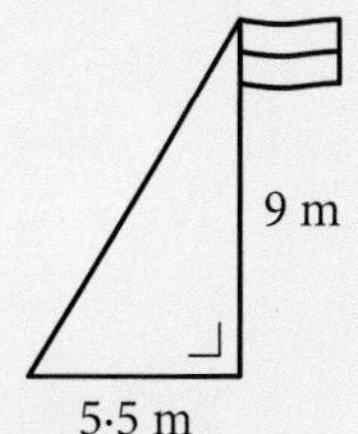

When solving problems, you can never assume that a triangle is right-angled. You must be told or be able to prove it.

5. A rectangular door measures 2·5 m by 1 m. How long is the diagonal of the door? Give your answer to two decimal places.

   Draw a diagram.

6. In the given diagram $|AB| = 13$ m, $|AC| = 14$ m and $|AD| = 5$ m.

   Find:

   (i) $|BD|$

   (ii) $|CD|$

   (iii) $|BC|$

   and

   (iv) investigate if ΔABC is right-angled.

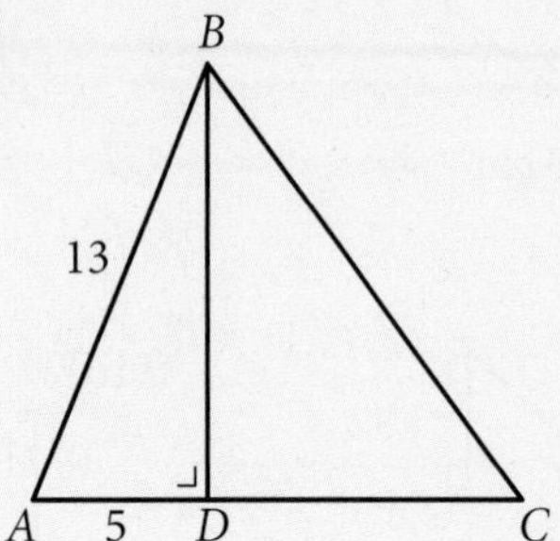

7. In the given diagram $|AD| = 7$ mm, $|DC| = 3$ mm and $|BC| = 5$ mm.

   (i) Find $|AB|$. Give your answer in surd form.

   (ii) Investigate if ΔABC is right-angled.

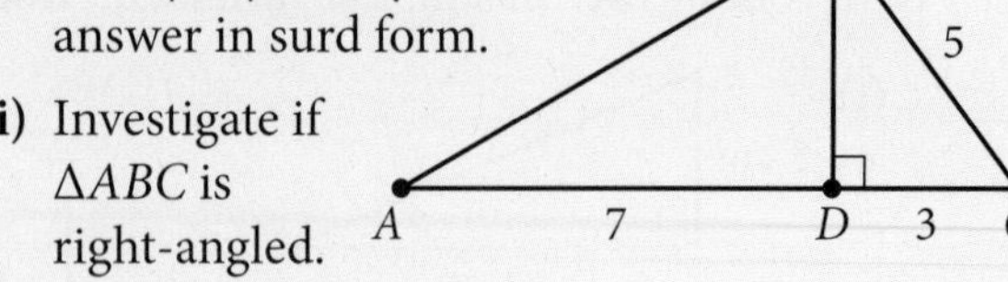

8. In the given diagram, $|AB| = 25$ cm, $|BC| = 17$ cm and $|CD| = 8$ cm.

   Find:

   (i) $|BD|$

   (ii) $|AD|$

   (iii) $|AC|$

9. The lines on the floor of a gym hall have been painted. The basketball coach wants to check if one of the corners is square (exactly 90°).
   He marks out three points along the lines and takes measurements, as shown in the diagram.
   Using his measurements, determine if the corner of the hall is in fact square. Justify your answer.

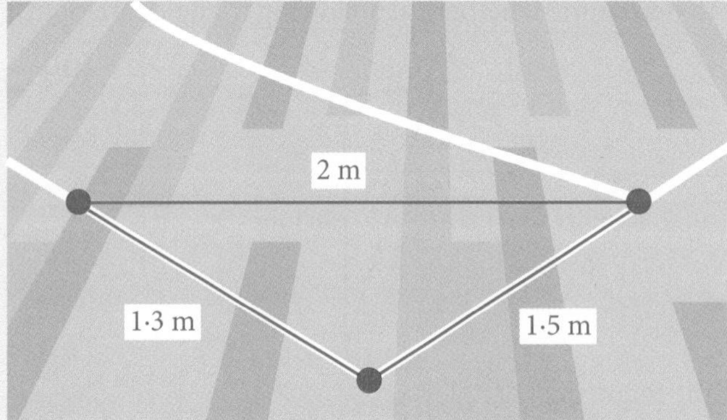

10. The diagram shows a circle with a tangent AB drawn as shown. $|AB| = 15$ and $|CB| = 9$

    (i) Explain why $|\angle OAB| = 90°$

    (ii) Find the radius of the circle.

    Let the radius of the circle be r.

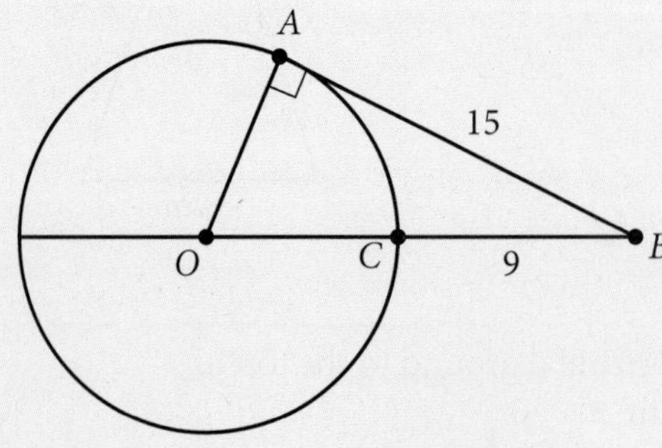

Trigonometry I

Section 20.2: Trigonometric Ratios

Learning Outcome:

You should be able to:

- understand the trigonometric ratios and know how to apply them to a right-angled triangle

In some situations, we may need to find a missing angle, when given two sides of the triangle. Or a missing side, when given an angle and another side. When this is the case, Pythagoras' Theorem will not work. Therefore, we need to use the trigonometric ratios to solve these triangles.

The **trigonometric ratios** connect the angles and sides in a right-angled triangle. Each ratio is related to two sides of the triangle.

We label the sides of the triangle as:

Hypotenuse – the side facing the right-angle

Opposite – the side facing the angle in question

Adjacent – the side beside the angle in question.

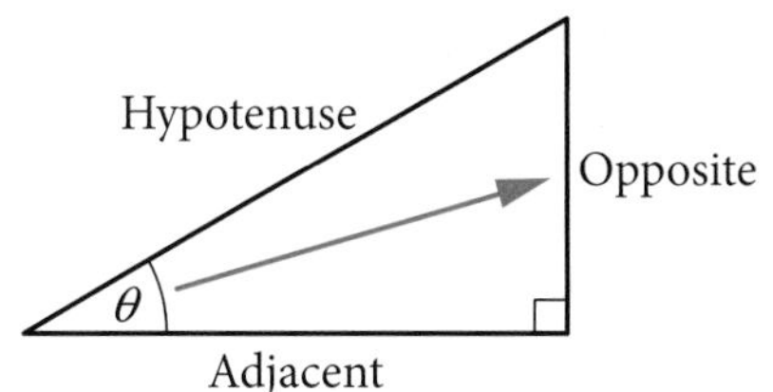

Label the sides in relation to the marked angle.

$$\sin \theta = \frac{\text{opposite}}{\text{hypotenuse}}$$

$$\cos \theta = \frac{\text{adjacent}}{\text{hypotenuse}}$$

$$\tan \theta = \frac{\text{opposite}}{\text{adjacent}}$$

The formulae for the **trigonometric ratios** appears on page 16 in the booklet of *formulae and tables* as shown:

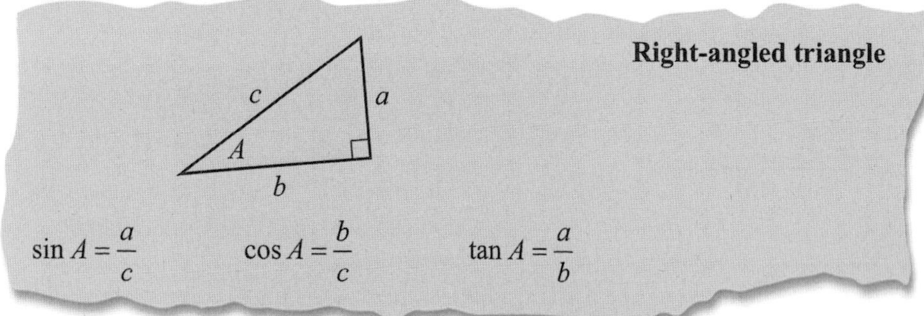

It is important to realise that the formulae in the booklet do not use the words 'opposite', 'adjacent' and 'hypotenuse'.

Discussion Time

The diagram shows a right-angled triangle with three sides, p, q and r, and two angles, P and Q.

Work with a classmate to perform the following tasks:

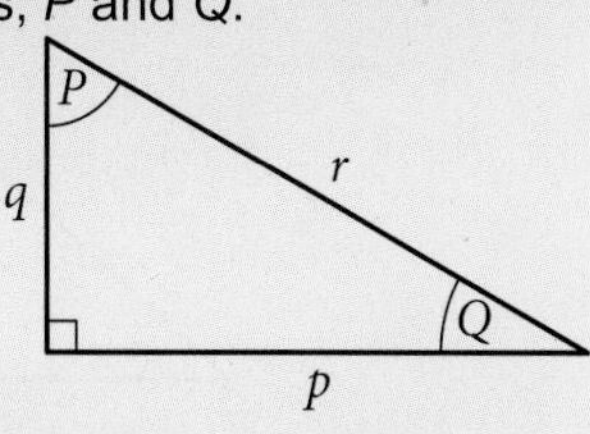

1. In relation to angle P, label the sides of the triangle and hence find the trigonometric ratios sin P, cos P and tan P.
2. In relation to angle Q, label the sides of the triangle and hence find the trigonometric ratios sin Q, cos Q and tan Q.
3. Compare your answers to parts **1** and **2** and comment on any findings you may have.

EXAMPLE

A is an angle, such that $\cos A = \frac{\sqrt{11}}{6}$. Without finding the angle A, find $\sin A$ and $\tan A$.

Solution

$\cos A = \frac{\sqrt{11}}{6} = \frac{\text{adjacent}}{\text{hypotenuse}}$

Draw a triangle with the angle A,
adjacent = $\sqrt{11}$
hypotenuse = 6

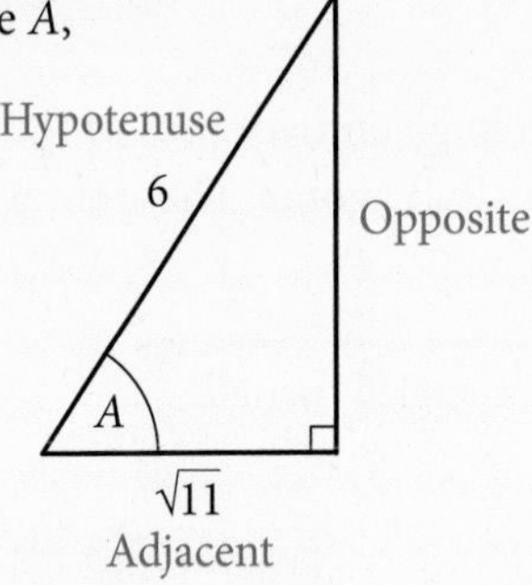

It is always good practice to draw a sketch of the situation, if no diagram is given.

Use Pythagoras' Theorem to find the opposite side:

$$c^2 = a^2 + b^2$$
$$6^2 = \sqrt{11}^2 + (\text{opposite})^2$$
$$36 = 11 + (\text{opposite})^2$$
$$25 = (\text{opposite})^2$$
$$\sqrt{25} = \text{opposite}$$
$$5 = \text{opposite}$$

$$\sin A = \frac{\text{opposite}}{\text{hypotenuse}} = \frac{5}{6}$$

$$\tan A = \frac{\text{opposite}}{\text{adjacent}} = \frac{5}{\sqrt{11}}$$

Practice Questions 20.2

1. For each of the following triangles, write down $\sin A$, $\cos A$ and $\tan A$. Give your answers in simplest form.

(i)

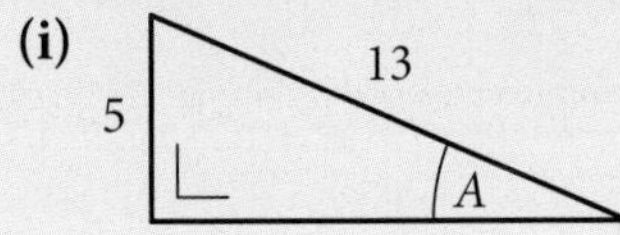

(iii)

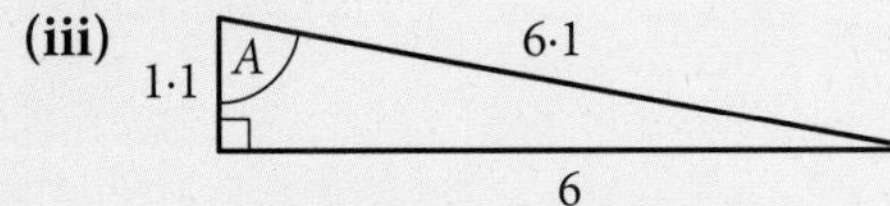

(v)

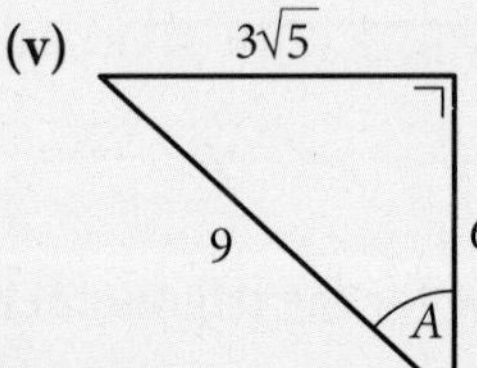

(ii)

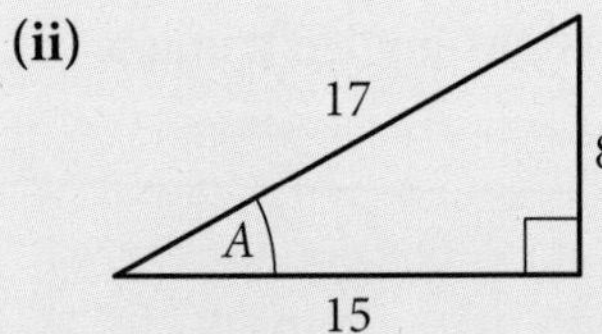

(iv)

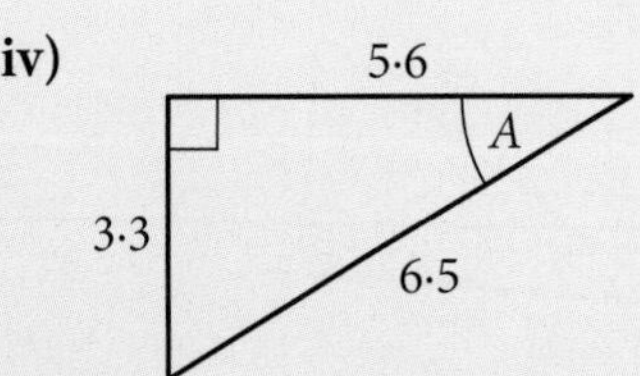

(vi)

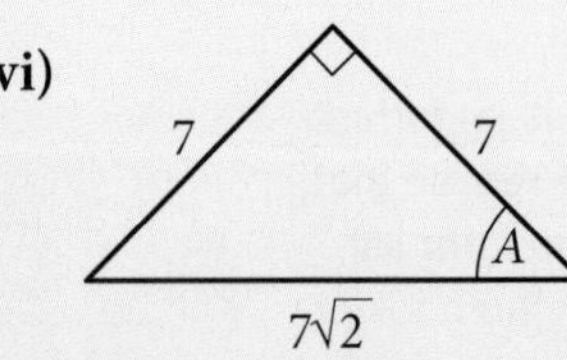

2. (i) Find the measure of the missing side, in the triangle shown.
   (ii) Hence write down $\sin A$, $\cos A$ and $\tan A$. Give your answers in simplest form.

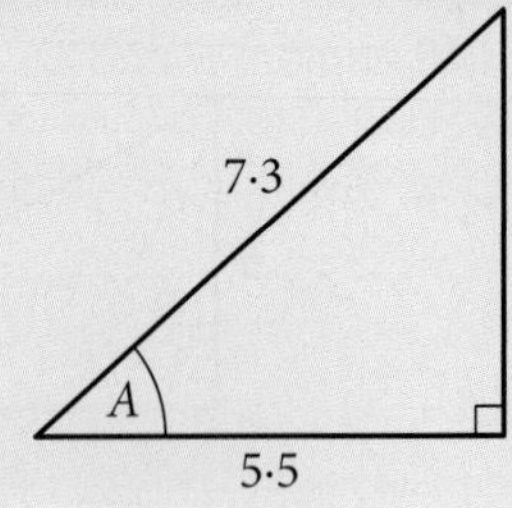

3. (i) Use your calculator to find the value of tan 45°.
   (ii) Hence, find $|PQ|$, in the triangle shown.
   (iii) Find $|PR|$. Give your answer in surd form.

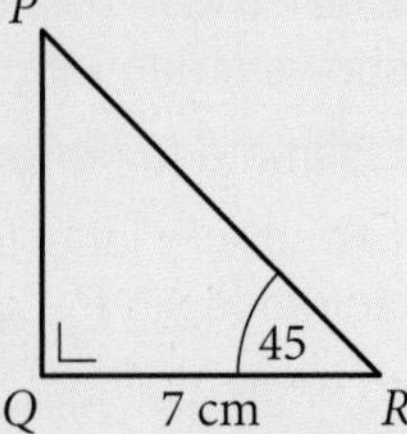

4. The diagram shows a right-angled triangle, ABC.

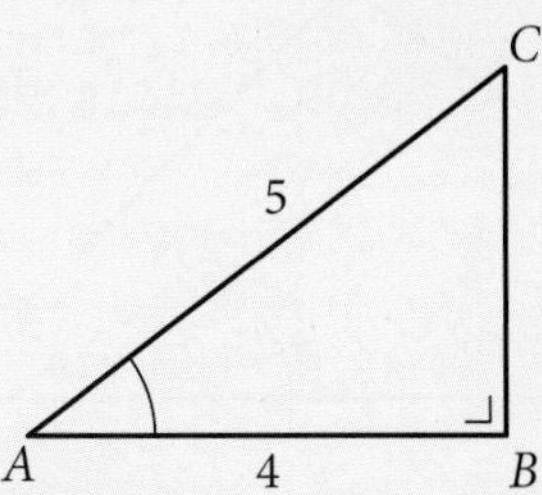

(i) Find $|BC|$.

(ii) Write down $\sin\angle BAC$, $\cos\angle BAC$ and $\tan\angle BAC$

(iii) Show that $\tan\angle BAC = \dfrac{\sin\angle BAC}{\cos\angle BAC}$

5. A is an angle, such that $\cos A = \dfrac{3}{5}$
Without finding the angle A, find $\sin A$ and $\tan A$.

6. B is an angle, such that $\sin B = \dfrac{12}{37}$
Without finding the angle B, find $\cos B$ and $\tan B$.

7. θ is an angle, such that $\tan\theta = \dfrac{1}{\sqrt{3}}$

(i) Without finding the angle θ, find $\sin\theta$ and $\cos\theta$.

(ii) Show that $\sin^2\theta + \cos^2\theta = 1$

$\sin^2\theta = (\sin\theta)^2$

8. Use the information given in the diagram to show that $\sin\theta + \cos\theta > \tan\theta$

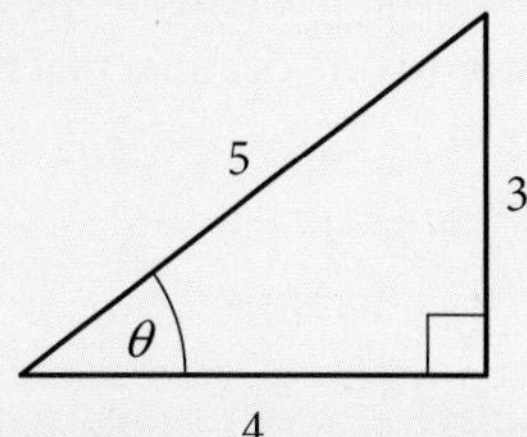

9. The diagram shows two right-angled triangles.

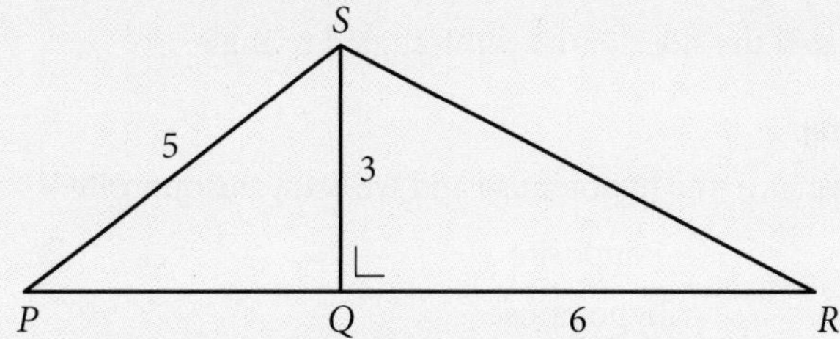

Find each of the following. Where appropriate, give your answer in surd form.

(i) $|SR|$

(ii) $|PQ|$

(iii) $\sin\angle SRQ$

(iv) $\tan\angle SPQ$

(v) $\cos\angle RSQ$

and

(vi) investigate whether ΔSPR is right-angled.

Section 20.3: Solving Right-Angled Triangles

Learning Outcome:

You should be able to:

- use the trigonometric ratios to solve for missing sides or missing angles in a right-angled triangle

To solve for a missing side or angle, in a right-angled triangle, follow these steps:

Step 1: Label the sides of the triangle, in relation to the marked angle.

Step 2: By identifying the two sides involved in the given question, select which of the formulae to use.

Step 3: Substitute the known values into the relevant formula and solve for the missing variable.

EXAMPLE 1

Find the vertical height of the triangle shown.
Give your answer to one decimal place.

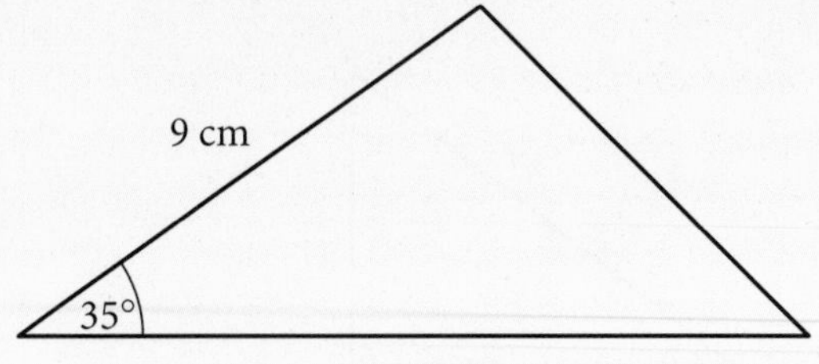

Solution

Draw in the vertical height and the right-angle.

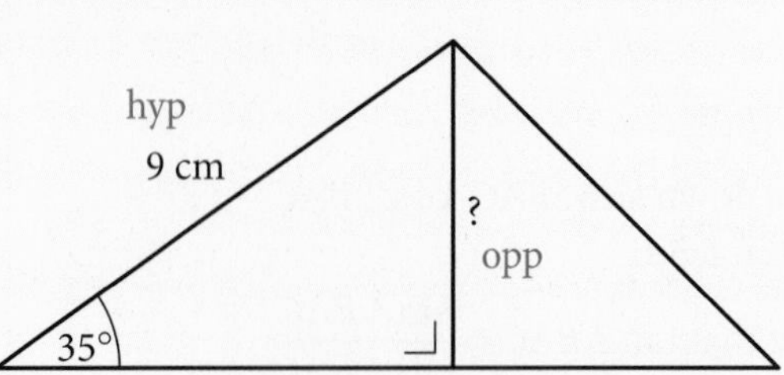

Step 1:
Label the sides of the right-angled triangle.

Step 2:
We have the hypotenuse and we want the opposite.

Use $\sin A = \dfrac{\text{opposite}}{\text{hypotenuse}}$

Step 3:

$$\sin 35° = \frac{\text{opposite}}{9}$$
$$9(\sin 35°) = \text{opposite}$$
$$5{\cdot}1621879 = \text{opposite}$$
$$5{\cdot}2 = \text{opposite}$$

Enter 9(sin 35°) into the calculator all together.

Therefore, height of the triangle = 5·2 cm.

EXAMPLE 2

Find the value of x.
Give your answer to one decimal place.

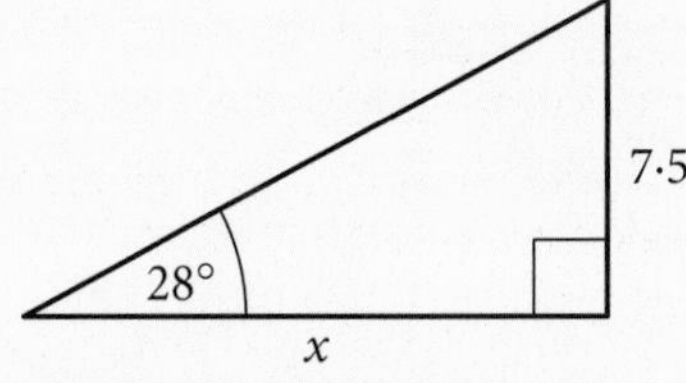

Solution

Step 1:
Label the sides of the triangle:

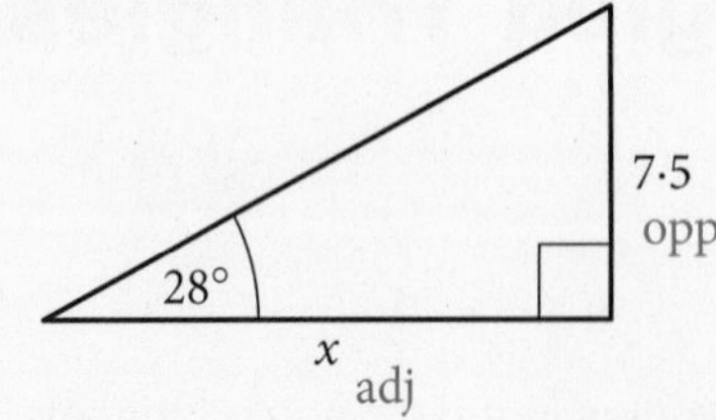

Step 2:
We have the opposite and we want the adjacent.

Use $\tan A = \dfrac{\text{opposite}}{\text{adjacent}}$

Step 3:

$$\tan 28° = \frac{7{\cdot}5}{x}$$
$$x(\tan 28°) = 7{\cdot}5$$
$$x = \frac{7{\cdot}5}{\tan 28°}$$
$$x = 14{\cdot}1$$

For the most accurate answer, enter $\dfrac{7{\cdot}5}{\tan 28°}$ into the calculator all together.

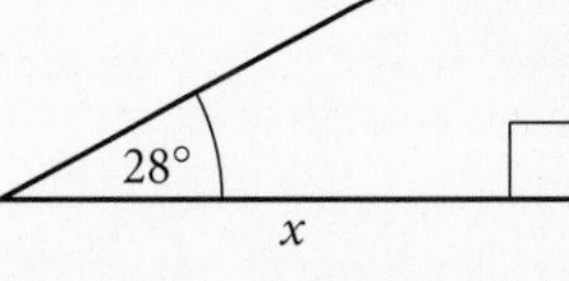

EXAMPLE 3

Find the measure of the angle A, in the given triangle.
Give your answer to the nearest minute.

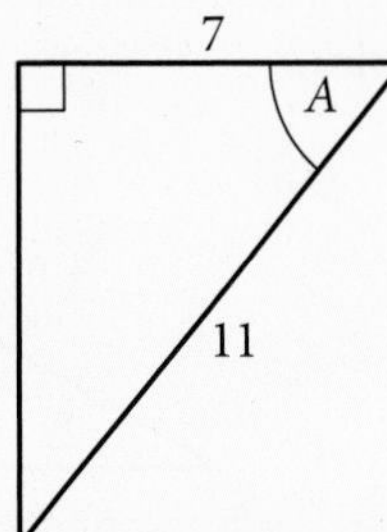

Solution

Step 1:
Label the sides of the triangle:

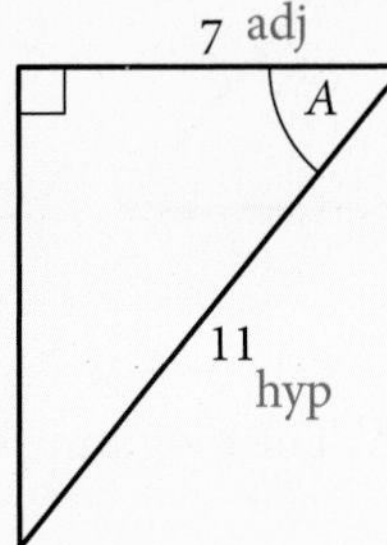

Step 2:
We have the hypotenuse and the adjacent.

Use $\cos A = \dfrac{\text{adjacent}}{\text{hypotenuse}}$

Step 3:

$$\cos A = \frac{7}{11}$$

$$A = \cos^{-1}\left(\frac{7}{11}\right) \quad \text{(apply inverse cos)}$$

$$A = 50° \, 28' \, 44''$$

$A = 50° \, 29'$ to the nearest minute.

Use the degrees button on your calculator to convert angles from degrees in decimal form, to degrees, minutes and seconds. For rounding purposes, recall that there are 60 seconds in a minute and 60 minutes in a degree.

Practice Questions 20.3

1. Given all dimensions are in centimetres, find the measure of the or angle side x, in each of the following triangles. Give your answers to one decimal place.

(i)

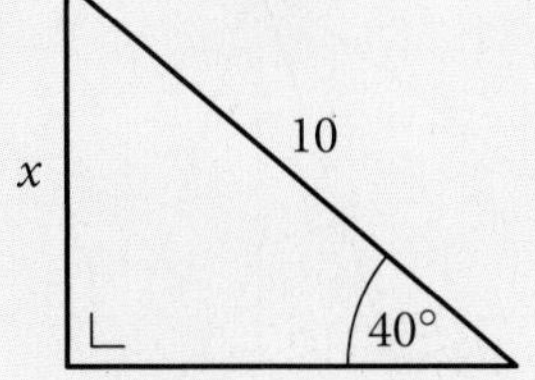

(ii)

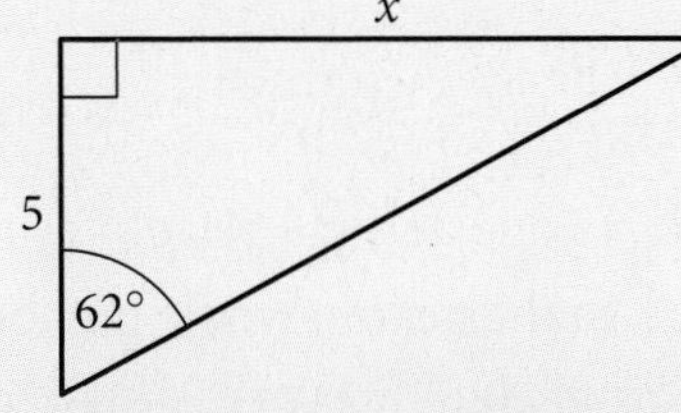

(iii)

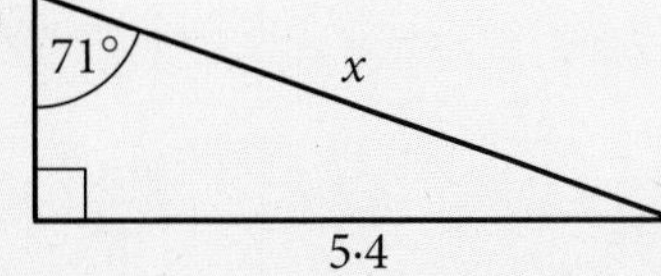

(iv)

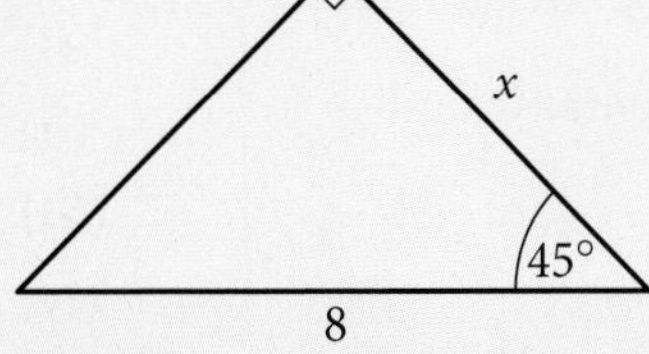

(v)

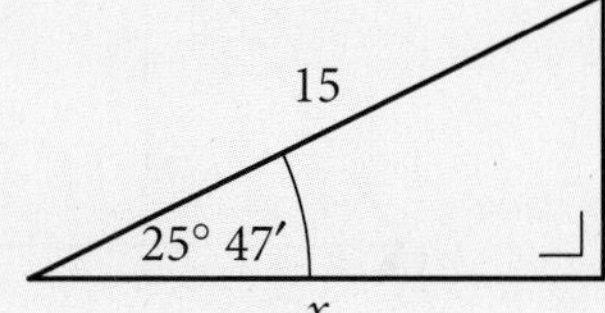

(vi)

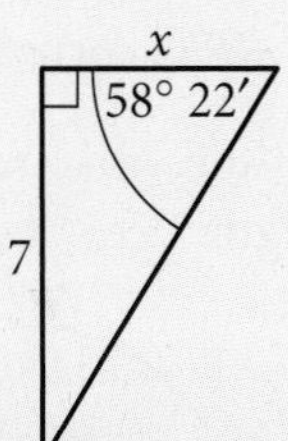

2. Find the measure of the angle A, in each of the following triangles. Give your answers to the nearest minute.

(i)

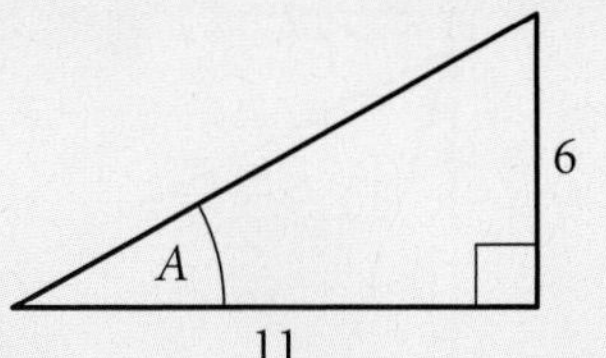

(ii)

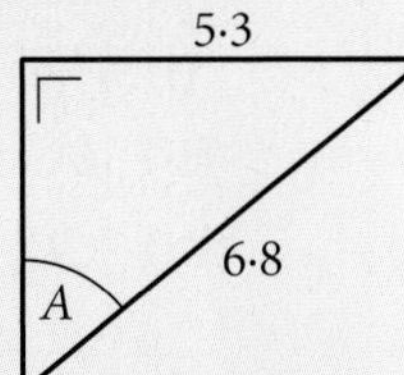

(iii)

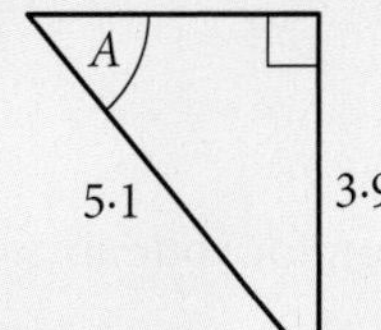

(iv)

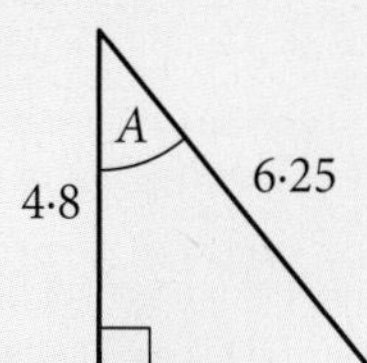

3. Given all dimensions are in centimetres, find the measure of the side or angle x, in each of the following triangles. Give your answers to one decimal place.

(i) x, 38°, 9·5

(iii) 3·4, x, 29°

(v)

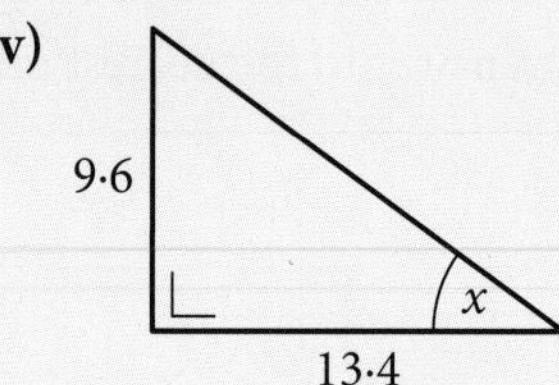

(ii) 7·2, x, 10

(iv)

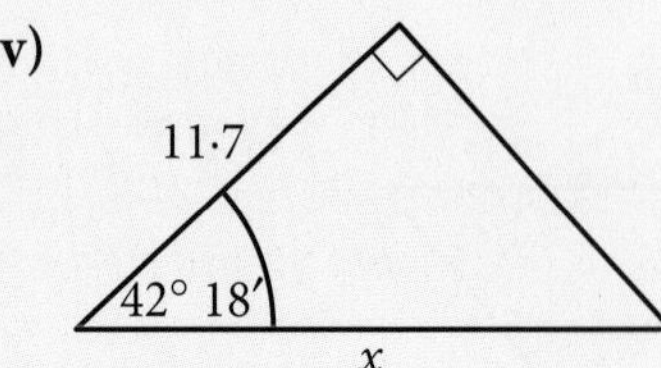

4. The diagram shows two right-angled triangles.

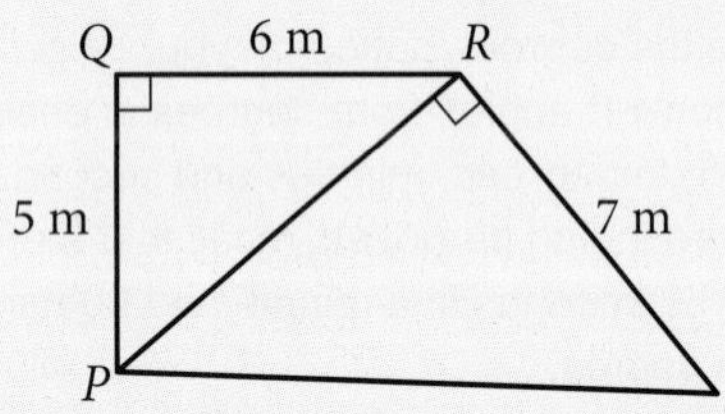

(i) Find $|PR|$, in surd form.

(ii) Find $|\angle RSP|$, correct to one decimal place.

5. The diagram shows two right-angled triangles.

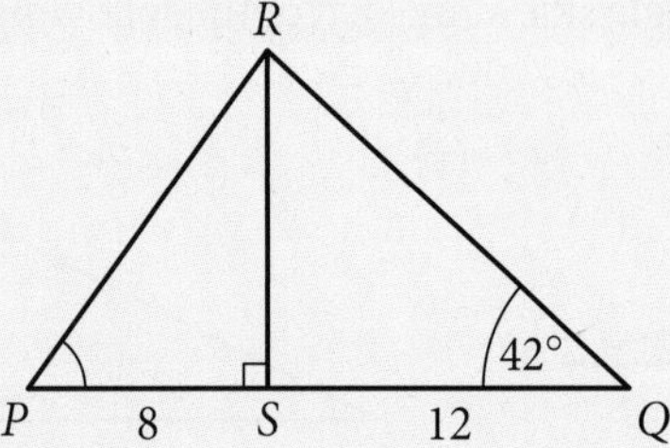

(i) Find $|RS|$.

(ii) Find $|\angle RPS|$, correct to two significant figures.

6. The diagram shows a circle, with centre O and radius of length 5 cm.

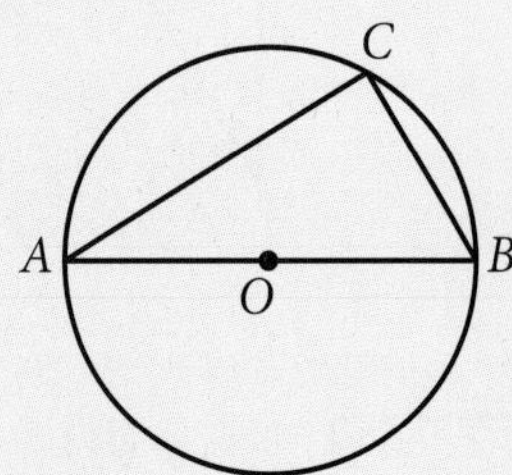

Given $|BC| = 6$ cm, find:

(i) $|\angle ACB|$. Give reason for your answer.

(ii) $|AC|$

(iii) $|\angle CAB|$, correct to the nearest minute.

7. The diagram shows an isosceles triangle.

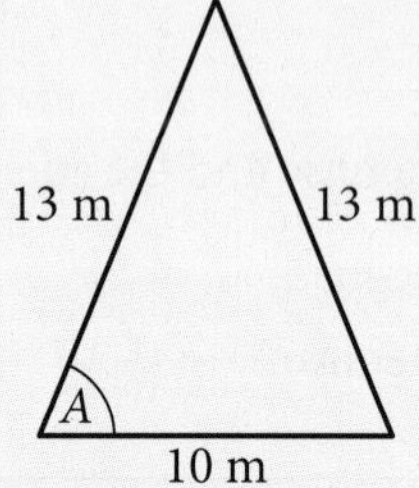

(i) Find the vertical height of the triangle.

(ii) Hence, find the measure of the angle A. Give your answer to the nearest degree.

8. For the given diagram $|AB| = |BD| = |CD| = 6$.

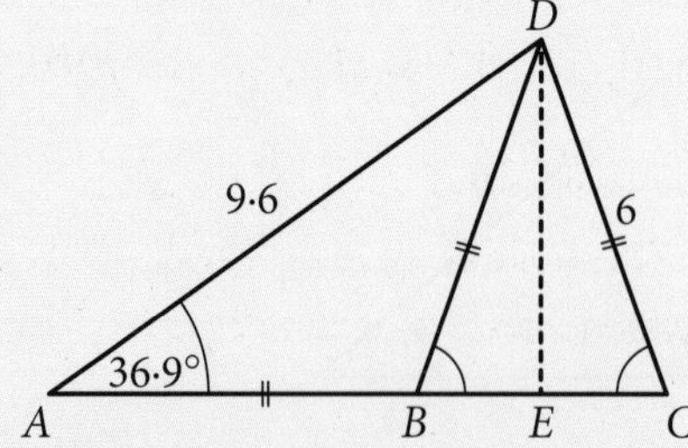

(i) Find $|\angle ADB|$

(ii) Find $|\angle DBE|$

(iii) Find $|DE|$, to one decimal place.

(iv) Find $|AC|$, to the nearest whole number.

(v) Investigate whether ΔACD is a right-angled triangle.

9. For the diagram shown find the following, correct to two decimal places.

(i) $|AB|$

(ii) $|BC|$

(iii) $|CD|$

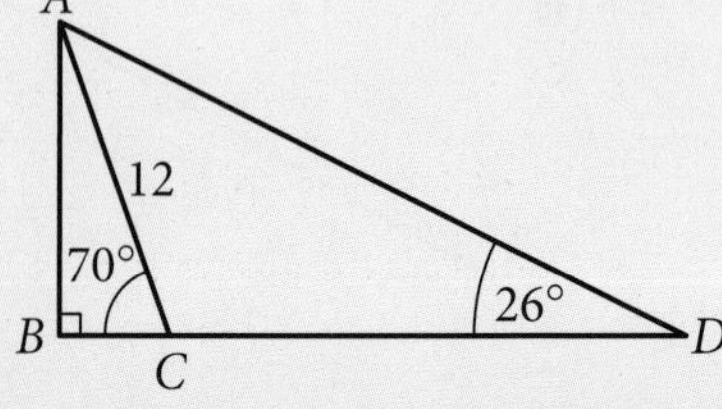

ing Triangles in Real-World
exts

ısing trigonometry

eying, engineering and geography involve solving a triangle. When
y, represent each situation with a right-angled triangle. Mark on
d label what you need to find. Then solve the triangle using the skills

Vhen a question involves a tree, building, wall, etc., we can assume that a
ght-angle is formed between the vertical object and the horizontal ground.

ver:

ne observer, is the angle between
erver's eye to the object.

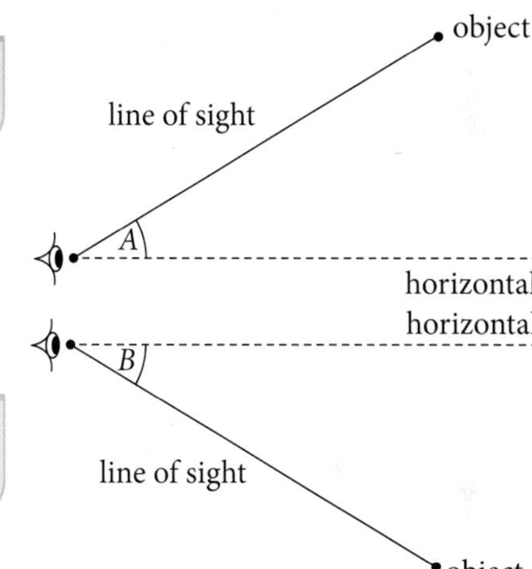

ne an ect be tl ev of a obs er:

The **angle of depression** of the object, as seen by the observer, is the angle between the horizontal and the line of sight, from the observer's eye to the object.

In the given diagram, **B = angle of depression**

An angle of elevation has an equal angle of depression. The angle of elevation from P to Q is equal to the angle of depression from Q to P.
The angles are alternate angles, as the horizontal lines are parallel.

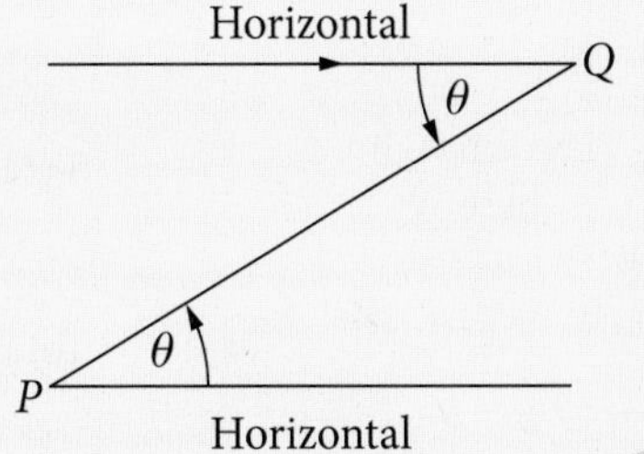

Compass directions

The directions north, south, east and west are at right-angles to each other.

- North-east is exactly halfway between north and east.
  It can be written as N 45° E.

Likewise:

- North-west is written as N 45° W.
- South-east is written as S 45° E.
- South-west is written as S 45° W.

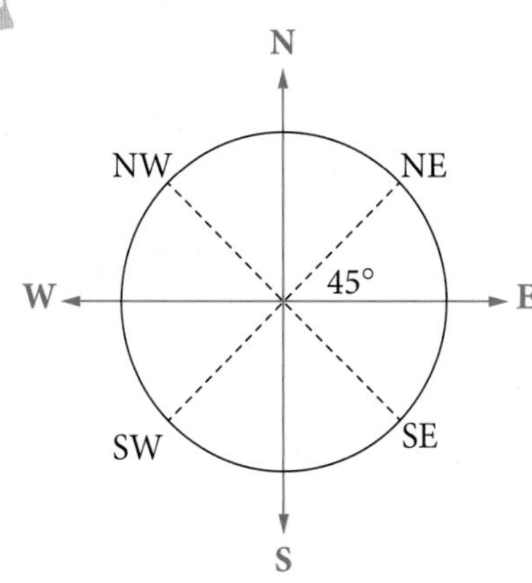

A bearing is used to represent the direction of one point relative to another point.

The direction of a point is stated as the number of degrees east or west of north or south. Some points and their directions are shown in the diagram given.

For example, for N 70° E, start by heading towards the north and then turn by 70° towards the east.

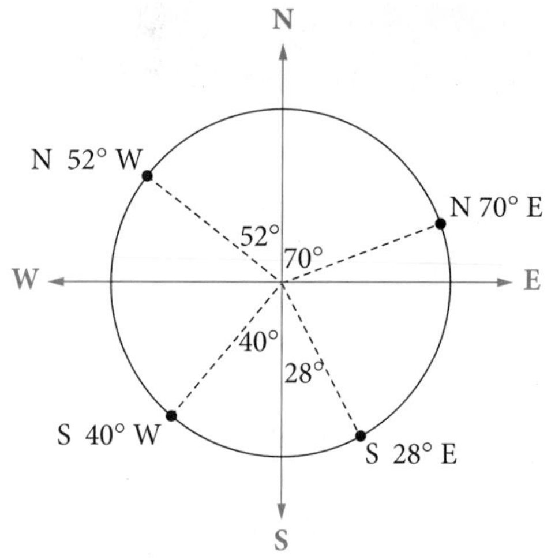

EXAMPLE 1

Deirdre wants to measure the height of a vertical tower. When she stands a distance of 5 m away from the base of the tower, she measures the angle of elevation to the top of the tower to be 32°. Deirdre is 1·7 m tall.

(i) What did Deirdre use to measure the angle of elevation of the tower?

(ii) Find the vertical height of the tower. Give your answer to the nearest centimetre.

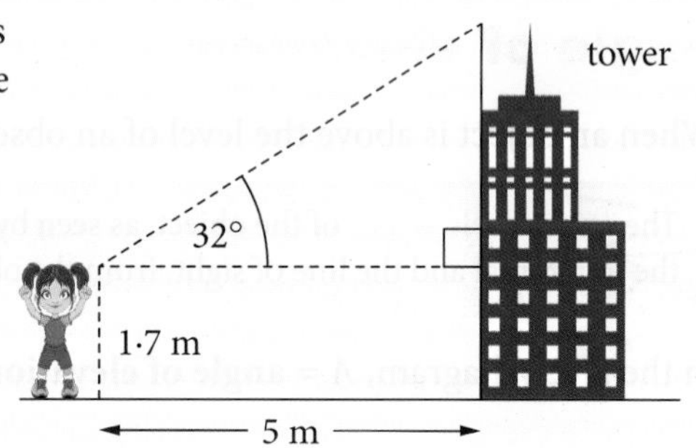

Solution

(i) Deirdre would have used a clinometer to measure the angle of elevation.

A **clinometer** is a device used to measure angles of elevation and/or angles of depression.

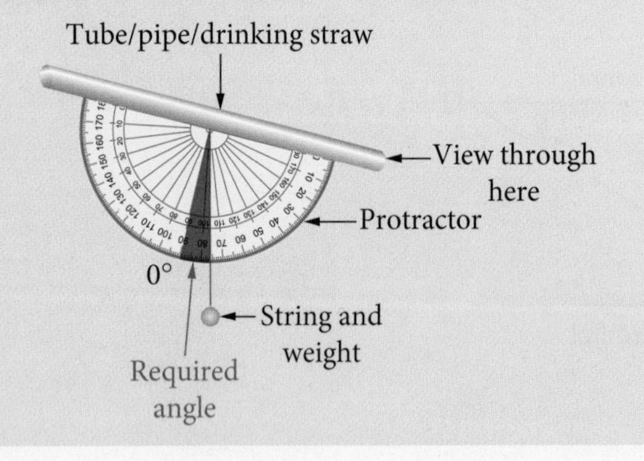

(ii) Draw the right-angled triangle and label the side we have and the side we want:

opp ?
32°
5 m
adj

$$\tan\theta = \frac{\text{opposite}}{\text{adjacent}}$$

$$\tan 32° = \frac{\text{opposite}}{5}$$

$$5(\tan 32°) = \text{opposite}$$

$$3{\cdot}1243 = \text{opposite}$$

Total height of the tower = 1·7 + 3·1243
= 4·8243 m

Therefore, to the nearest centimetre, height of the tower = 482 cm.

EXAMPLE 2

Two ships, A and B, leave the port P at noon. A travels due east at a speed of 30 km/hr and B travels in the direction S 20° E. At 2 pm B is due south of A.

(i) Draw a mathematical model of the situation.

(ii) Find the distance between ships A and B at 2 pm. Give your answer to two decimal places.

(iii) Find the speed of ship B. Give your answer to one decimal place.

Solution

(i) Ship A is travelling at 30 km/hr for two hours.

Distance = speed × time

Distance travelled by $A = 30 \times 2 = 60$ km.

Direction S 20° E means a 70° angle inside the triangle.

The information is presented in a diagram, as shown.

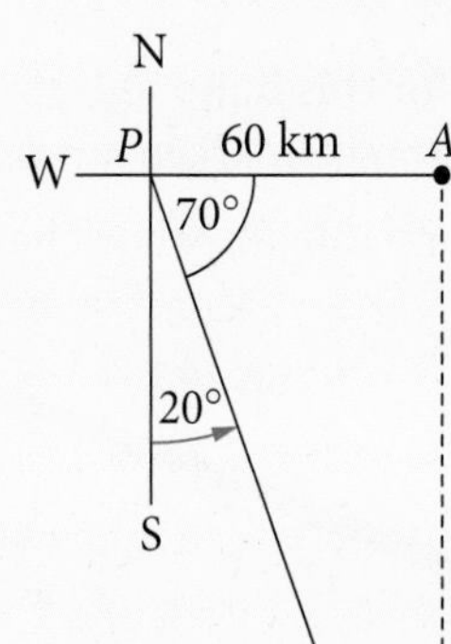

(ii) Find $|AB|$:

Label the sides

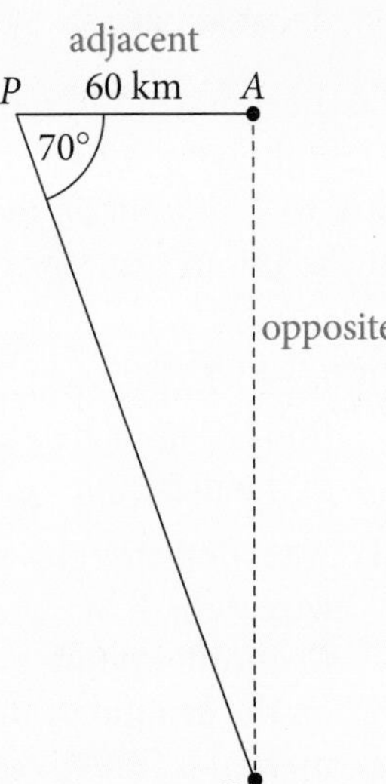

$$\tan A = \frac{\text{opposite}}{\text{adjacent}}$$

$$\tan 70° = \frac{|AB|}{60}$$

$$60\,(\tan 70°) = |AB|$$

$$164{\cdot}848 = |AB|$$

$$164{\cdot}85 \text{ km} = |AB|$$

(iii) Find $|PB|$:

Label the sides

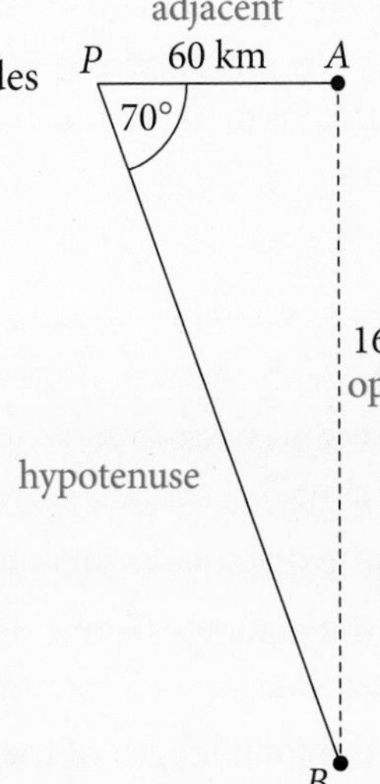

$$\cos A = \frac{\text{adjacent}}{\text{hypotenuse}}$$

$$\cos 70° = \frac{60}{|PB|}$$

$$|PB| \cos 70° = 60$$

$$|PB| = \frac{60}{\cos 70°}$$

$$|PB| = 175{\cdot}428 \text{ km}$$

Since we already know two of the sides, we could also have used Pythagoras' Theorem to solve for $|PB|$.

Time = 2 hours

Distance = 175·428 km

$$\text{Speed} = \frac{\text{Distance}}{\text{Time}}$$

$$= \frac{175{\cdot}428}{2} = 87{\cdot}714$$

Therefore, the speed of ship B is 87·7 km/hr.

Practice Questions 20.4

1. A boat leaves a port and sails 10 km north. It then turns and sails 24 km west.
   - **(i)** Draw a diagram to represent this information.
   - **(ii)** At this point, what is the shortest distance between the boat and the port?

2. A ramp is four metres long and 304 millimetres high.

   In order for this ramp to be safe for wheelchair users, the angle marked x must be 4° or less.

   Is this ramp safe for wheelchair users?

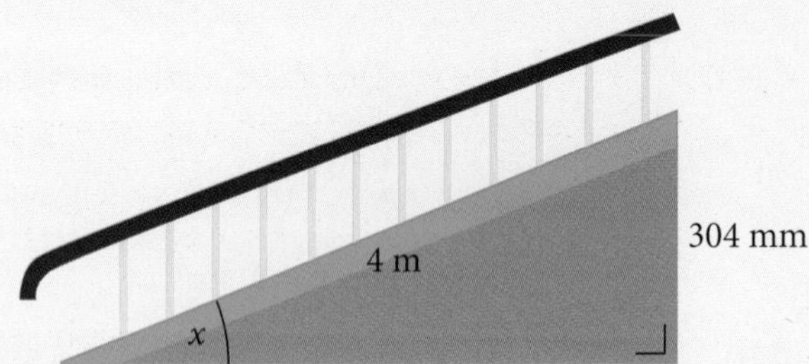

3. For a ladder to be safe, it must be inclined at between 70° and 80° to the ground. The diagram shows a ladder resting against a wall.
   - **(i)** Is this ladder safe?
   - **(ii)** Find the length of the ladder, correct to the nearest centimetre.

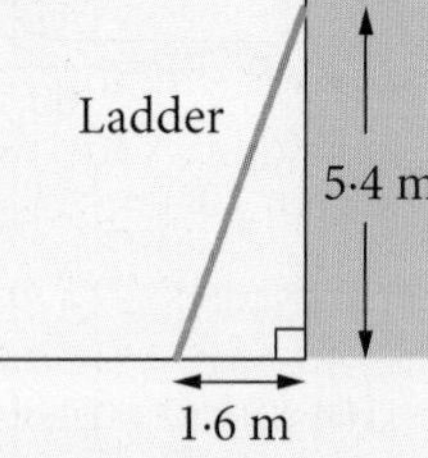

4. Freya stands at a point P, 7 m from the base of a 9 m tall vertical pole, and measures the angle of elevation, A, from the ground to the top of the pole.
   - **(i)** Find the angle of elevation, A, correct to the nearest minute.

   Freya then moves a further distance from the pole, to a point Q, and measures the angle of elevation from the ground to the top of the pole to be 31°.
   - **(ii)** Find the distance Freya moved from P to Q. Give your answer to one decimal place.

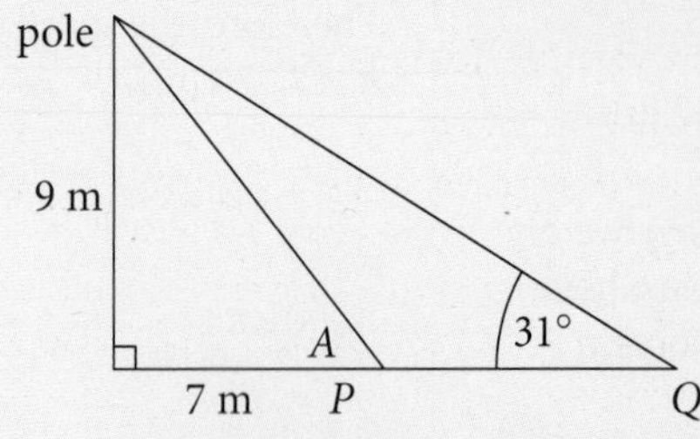

5. A vertical pole stands on level ground. A cable joins the top of the pole to a point on the ground, which is 50 m from the base of the pole. The angle of depression from the top of the pole to the cable is 66° 25′.
   - **(i)** Find the height of the pole, correct to the nearest metre.
   - **(ii)** Find the length of the cable, to three significant figures.

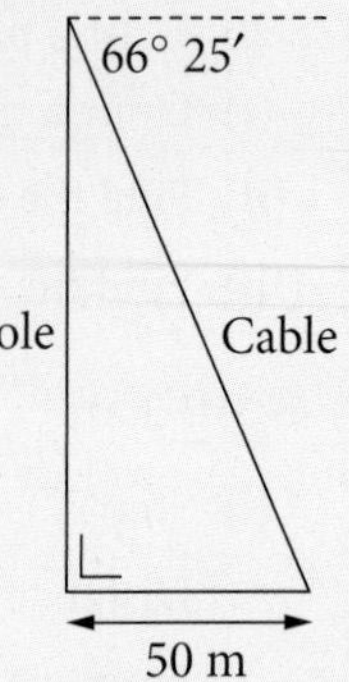

6. From a point on the horizontal ground 12 m from the base of a building, the angle of elevation to the top of the building is 72° 24′.
   - **(i)** Draw a mathematical model to represent this information.
   - **(ii)** Find the height of the building, correct to two decimal places.

7. A vertical mast $[XY]$ stands on level ground. A straight wire joins Y, the top of the mast, to T, a point on the ground, which is 50 m from the bottom of the mast.
   - **(i)** If $|\angle YTX| = 56{\cdot}31°$, find $|XY|$, the height of the mast.
   - **(ii)** A second straight wire joins Y to K, another point on the ground. If the length of this wire is 100 m, find $|\angle YKX|$, correct to the nearest degree.

8. In the diagram opposite, $ABCD$ represents the course in an adventure race. Competitors must row the 9 km from A to B, then run the 12 km from B to C and cycle from C to D and back to A.
   $|\angle ADC| = 36{\cdot}87°$
   - **(i)** Find the distance from A to C.
   - **(ii)** Find the distance from C to D, correct to the nearest km.
   - **(iii)** Find the total length of the course.

9. The angle of elevation of the top of a building, as viewed from a point A, 94 m from the base of the building, is 27°.
 (i) Find the height of the building, correct to the nearest metre.

 The bottom of a balloon is 72 m above the top of the building, as shown.
 (ii) Find the angle of elevation of the bottom of the balloon, as viewed from the point A. Give your answer correct to the nearest degree.

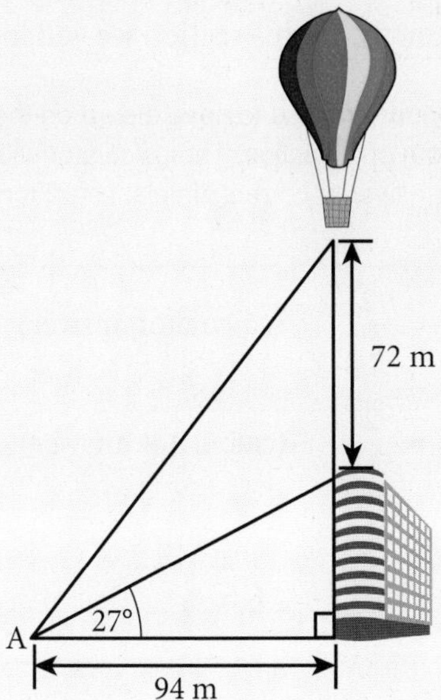

10. Two airplanes leave an airport, at noon. Plane S travels in the direction N 37° W at a speed of 410 km/hr. Plane T travels in the direction N 53° E at a speed of 280 km/hr.
 (i) Find the distance each plane has travelled by 2:30 pm.
 (ii) Find the distance between the planes at this time. Give your answer to the nearest kilometre.

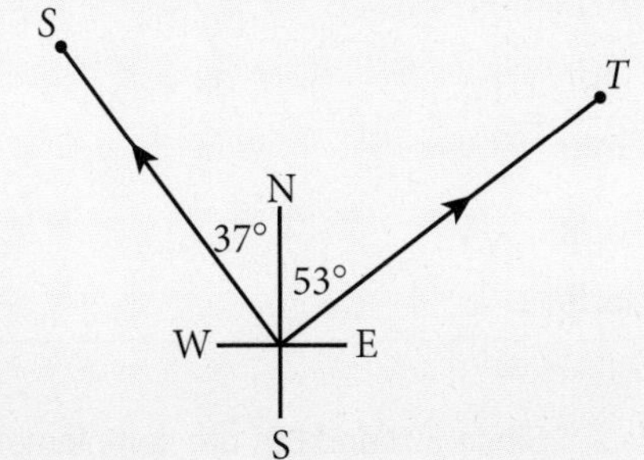

11. A boat sails due east from the base A of a 30 metre-high lighthouse, $[AD]$. At the point B, the angle of depression of the boat from the top of the lighthouse is 68°. Ten seconds later the boat is at the point C and the angle of depression is now 33°.

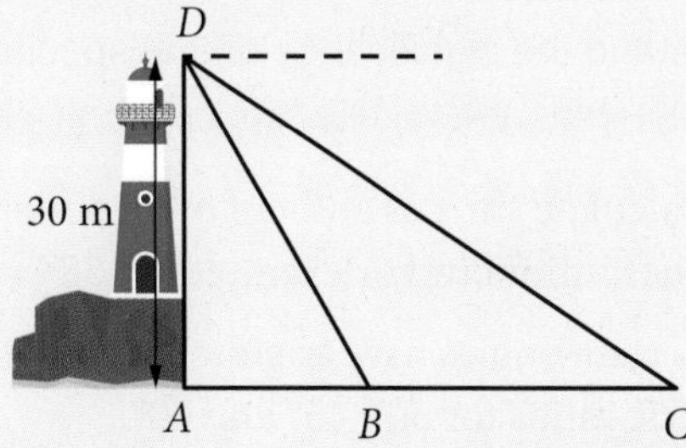

 (i) Find $|BC|$, the distance the boat has travelled in this time. Give your answer to the nearest whole number.
 (ii) Calculate the average speed at which the boat is sailing between B and C. Give your answer in metres per second, correct to one decimal place.

12. A cyclist is on a straight road heading directly north. At 10:30 am he passes point A and observes a mobile phone mast on a bearing of N 40° E. At 11:20 am, he passes point B and observes the same mobile phone mast on a bearing of S 70° E. The shortest distance between the road and the mobile phone mast is 4·7 km.
 (i) Draw a mathematical model to illustrate this information.
 (ii) Find the distance between the points A and B.
 (iii) Hence, find the average speed of the cyclist, in km/hr, correct to one decimal place.

13. Two swimmers leave the same point, P, on the edge of a lake. Abby swims at a speed of 24 m/s in the direction N 20·32° W from P. Jed swims at a speed of 15·5 m/s in the direction S 32·52° W from P. After six minutes Jed is due south of Abby.

 (i) Draw a mathematical model to illustrate this information.
 (ii) Find the distance between Abby and Jed after six minutes.

Section 20.5: Special Angles

Learning Outcome:

You should be able to:

- understand the significance of the 'special angles', 30°, 45° and 60°

When we calculate sin, cos and tan of angles on our calculator, we often get an irrational number, i.e. a decimal that continues infinitely. For example sin 58° = 0·848048096…

However, certain angles have trigonometric ratios that may be computed exactly. In this section we will look at the trigonometric ratios for 30°, 45° and 60°.

It is poor practice to have a surd on the bottom of a fraction. The calculator will give the answer in correct simplest surd form.

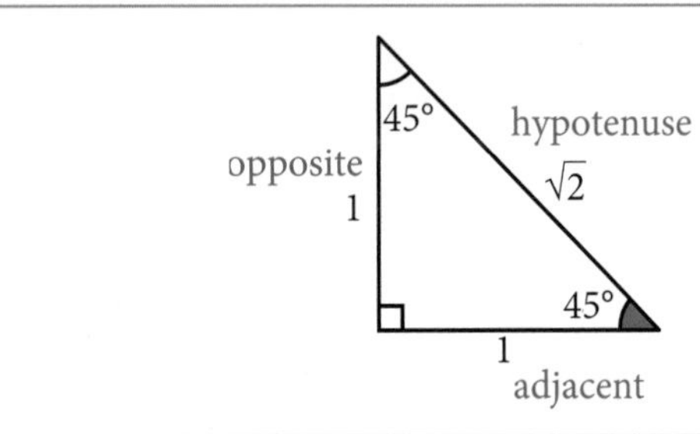

$\sin 45° = \frac{\text{opp}}{\text{hyp}} = \frac{1}{\sqrt{2}} = \frac{\sqrt{2}}{2}$ (calculator answer)

$\cos 45° = \frac{\text{adj}}{\text{hyp}} = \frac{1}{\sqrt{2}} = \frac{\sqrt{2}}{2}$ (calculator answer)

$\tan 45° = \frac{\text{opp}}{\text{adj}} = \frac{1}{1} = 1$

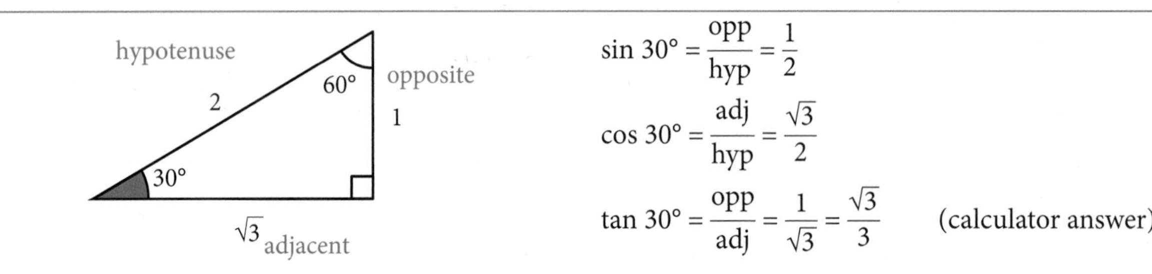

$\sin 30° = \frac{\text{opp}}{\text{hyp}} = \frac{1}{2}$

$\cos 30° = \frac{\text{adj}}{\text{hyp}} = \frac{\sqrt{3}}{2}$

$\tan 30° = \frac{\text{opp}}{\text{adj}} = \frac{1}{\sqrt{3}} = \frac{\sqrt{3}}{3}$ (calculator answer)

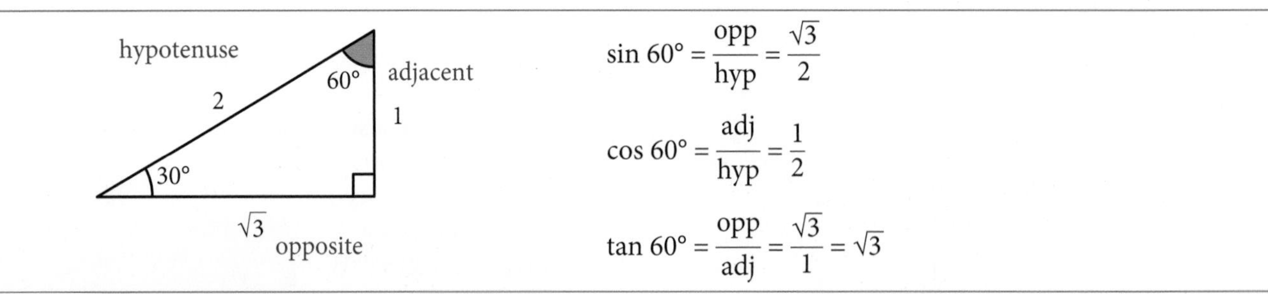

$\sin 60° = \frac{\text{opp}}{\text{hyp}} = \frac{\sqrt{3}}{2}$

$\cos 60° = \frac{\text{adj}}{\text{hyp}} = \frac{1}{2}$

$\tan 60° = \frac{\text{opp}}{\text{adj}} = \frac{\sqrt{3}}{1} = \sqrt{3}$

Links across the syllabus

Surds are covered in Chapter 1: Number Systems.

Since 30° and 60° are complementary angles in the same triangle, sin 30° = cos 60° and sin 60° = cos 30°.

These **special angles and their trigonometric ratios** appear on page 13 of the booklet of *formulae and tables* as shown:

The format of the ratios presented in the booklet of *formulae and tables* does not follow best practice, regarding not having surds as a denominator.

30°	45°	60°	A (degrees)
$\frac{\pi}{6}$	$\frac{\pi}{4}$	$\frac{\pi}{3}$	A (radians)
$\frac{\sqrt{3}}{2}$	$\frac{1}{\sqrt{2}}$	$\frac{1}{2}$	$\cos A$
$\frac{1}{2}$	$\frac{1}{\sqrt{2}}$	$\frac{\sqrt{3}}{2}$	$\sin A$
$\frac{1}{\sqrt{3}}$	1	$\sqrt{3}$	$\tan A$

$1° \approx 0.01745$ rad.

EXAMPLE

Without using a calculator, find the value of x in the given right-angled triangle.

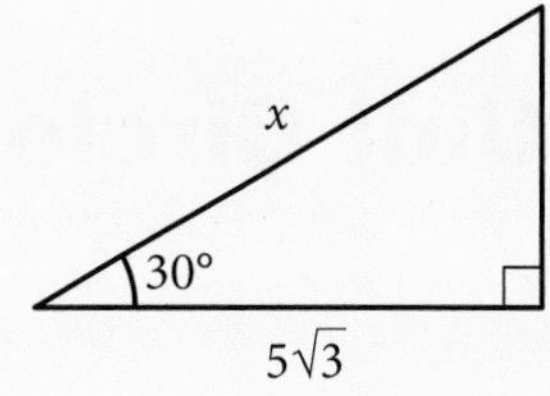

Solution

Label the sides:

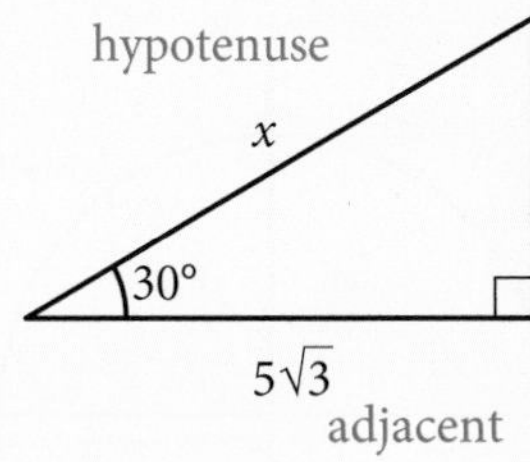

$$\cos A = \frac{\text{adj}}{\text{hyp}}$$

$$\cos 30° = \frac{5\sqrt{3}}{x}$$

$$\frac{\sqrt{3}}{2} = \frac{5\sqrt{3}}{x} \qquad \left(\cos 30° = \frac{\sqrt{3}}{2} \text{ from tables}\right)$$

$$2x\left(\frac{\sqrt{3}}{2}\right) = 2x\left(\frac{5\sqrt{3}}{x}\right) \qquad \text{(multiply both sides by } 2x)$$

$$x\sqrt{3} = 10\sqrt{3}$$

$$x = 10$$

Practice Questions 20.5

1. Using the table from the booklet of *formulae and tables*, find the exact value of each of the following. Leave your answer in surd form, where appropriate.
   - **(i)** $\sin 60°$
   - **(ii)** $\tan 30°$
   - **(iii)** $\cos 45°$
   - **(iv)** $\sin 30° + \cos 60°$
   - **(v)** $\tan 60° - \sin 60°$
   - **(vi)** $\cos^2 30°$
   - **(vii)** $\sin^3 30°$
   - **(viii)** $\sqrt{\tan 45°}$
   - **(ix)** $6 \tan^2 30°$

   $\cos^2 \theta = (\cos \theta)^2$

2. Without using a calculator, prove that:
   - **(i)** $\sin 60° = 2 \sin 30° \cos 30°$
   - **(ii)** $\cos 60° = \cos^2 30° - \sin^2 30°$
   - **(iii)** $\cos^2 45° + \sin^2 45° = 1$
   - **(iv)** $\cos^2 60° = 1 - \sin^2 60°$

3. In the given triangle, without using a calculator, find the values of x and y. Give your answer in simplest surd form, where appropriate.

4. Without using a calculator, find the vertical height of the given parallelogram. Give your answer in simplest surd form.

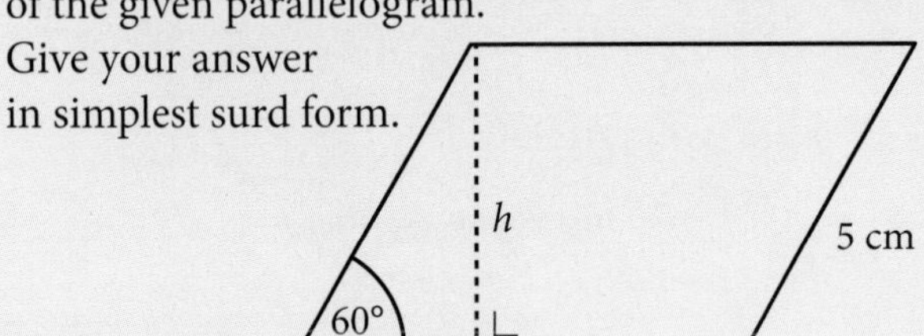

5. In the given triangle, without using a calculator, find the values of x, y and z. Give your answer in simplest surd form, where appropriate.

6. Given $\sin(A + B) = \sin A \cos B + \cos A \sin B$, by letting $A = 30°$ and $B = 60°$, without using a calculator, show that $\sin 90° = 1$.

7. Given $\cos(A + B) = \cos A \cos B - \sin A \sin B$, without using a calculator, find the value of $\cos 75°$ in simplest surd form.

Section 20.6: Unit Circle

Learning Outcome:

You should be able to:

- understand the unit circle and how to use it

The unit circle is a circle of radius length 1, centred at the origin. When using the unit circle:

The x-axis is referred to as the $\cos A$ axis

The y-axis is referred to as the $\sin A$ axis.

The coordinates of any point on the circle, making an angle θ with the positive $\cos A$ axis is $(\cos \theta, \sin \theta)$.

For 0°, 90°, 180°, 270°, 360° the point is on one of the axes, which means that the sine and cosine of these angles will be 0, 1 or −1.

From the diagram, and knowing that $\tan A = \dfrac{\sin A}{\cos A}$, we can complete the following table:

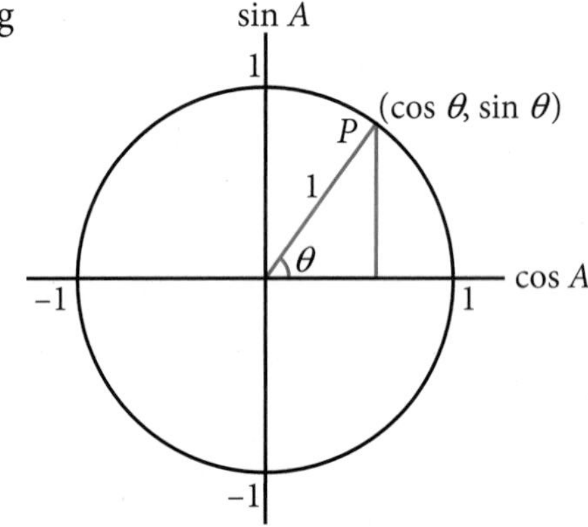

	0°	90°	180°	270°	360°
sin A	0	1	0	−1	0
cos A	1	0	−1	0	1
tan A	0	Undefined	0	Undefined	0

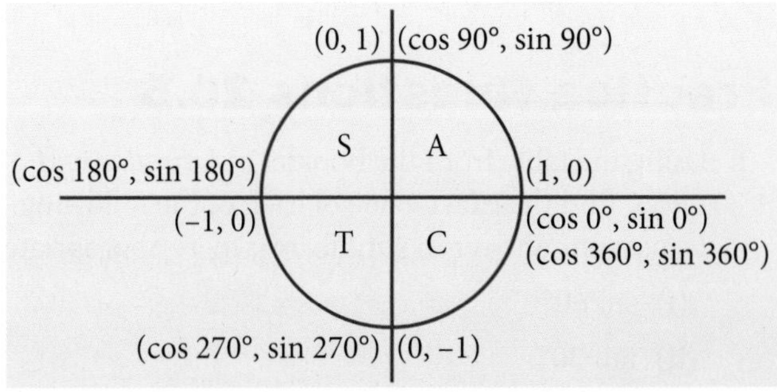

Since $\tan A = \dfrac{\sin A}{\cos A}$ when $\cos A = 0$, $\tan A$ is undefined.

The four quadrants

The circle is divided into four quadrants, as shown in the diagram. The sign of each ratio will vary in each quadrant, as also shown.

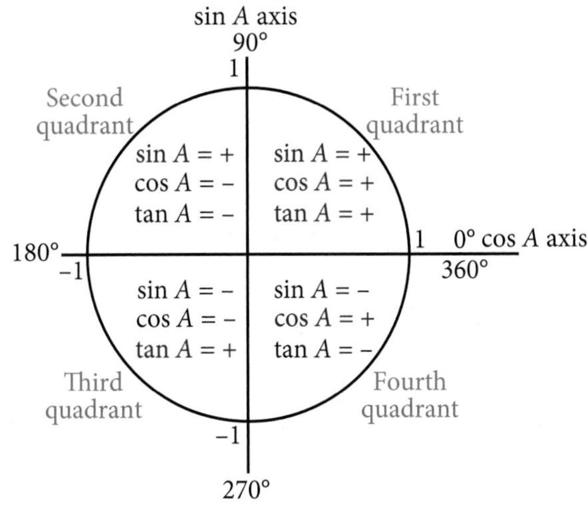

When answering questions on the unit circle, it is vital that you know the sign of each ratio in each quadrant. The following diagram will help you remember the positive ratios in the four quadrants.

In the first quadrant all (**A**) ratios are positive

In the second quadrant sin A (**S**) is positive

In the third quadrant tan A (**T**) is positive

In the fourth quadrant cos A (**C**) is positive

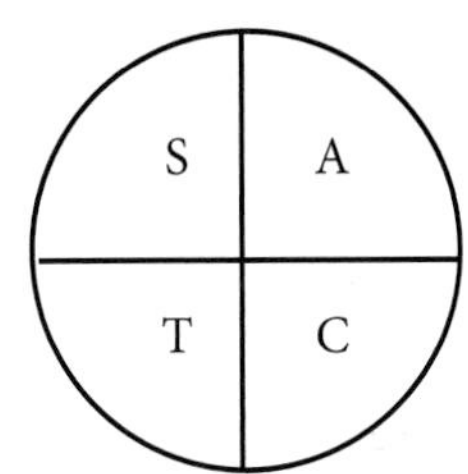

Memory aid:

ASTC – starting in the first quadrant and moving anti-clockwise.

All **S**tudents **T**rust **C**alculators.

Finding a ratio when given the angle

When given an angle between 0° and 360° and asked to find a trigonometric ratio, we do the following:

Step 1: Draw a sketch of the unit circle and mark in the given angle.

Step 2: From the marked quadrant, determine whether the ratio will be positive or negative.

Step 3: Find the reference angle, which is the acute angle between the marked position and the horizontal axis.

Step 4: Use your tables or calculator to find the ratio of the reference angle and then apply the sign determined in step 2.

The **reference angle** is the acute angle between any marked position between 0° and 360° and the horizontal axis.

EXAMPLE 1

Find the value of tan 285°. Give your answer correct to three decimal places.

Solution

Step 1: Starting from 0° and moving anti-clockwise, 285° is in the fourth quadrant.

Step 2: tan is **negative** in the fourth quadrant.

Step 3: The reference angle = 360° – 285° = 75°

Step 4: tan 285° = –(tan 75°) = –3·732

It is important to show your steps when solving these problems. You can, however, use your calculator to verify your answers.

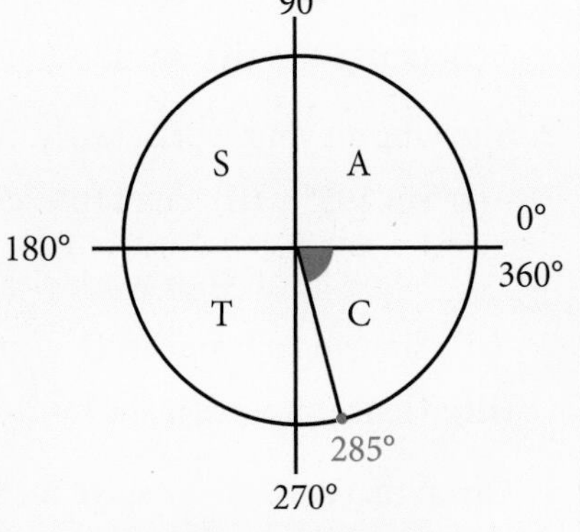

Finding the angle when given the ratio

Between 0° and 360° there may be two angles with the same trigonometric ratio.

For example, you can use your calculator to verify that $\tan 150° = -\frac{1}{\sqrt{3}}$ and $\tan 330° = -\frac{1}{\sqrt{3}}$.

When given the value of the ratio and asked to find the two values, we do the following:

Step 1: Ignore the sign and evaluate the reference angle using your tables or calculator.

Step 2: From the sign of the given ratio, decide in which quadrants the angles lie.

Step 3: Draw a sketch of the unit circle and mark the reference angle from the horizontal line into each of the relevant quadrants.

Step 4: Starting from the 0° mark and moving anti-clockwise, find the measure of the two angles.

EXAMPLE 2

Given that $\tan\theta = \sqrt{3}$, solve for all possible values of θ for $0 \leq \theta \leq 360°$.

Solution

Step 1: Find the reference angle:
Reference angle = $\tan^{-1}(\sqrt{3}) = 60°$

Step 2: tan is **positive** in the first and third quadrants.

Step 3: Mark 60° from the horizontal axis into each of these quadrants.

Step 4: Read the angle from the 0° around anti-clockwise to these two marked positions.
This gives: $\theta = 60°, 240°$

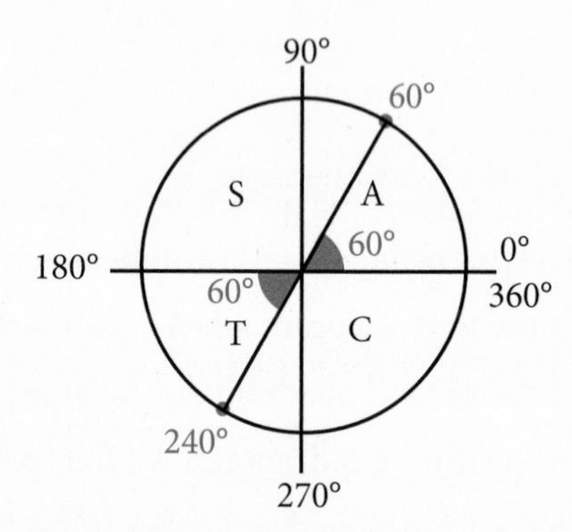

EXAMPLE 3

Given that $\sin\theta = -0{\cdot}629$, solve for all possible values of θ for $0 \leq \theta \leq 360°$. Give your answers to the nearest degree.

Solution

Step 1: Ignore the negative sign and find the reference angle:
Reference angle = $\sin^{-1}(0{\cdot}629) = 38{\cdot}98° = 39°$

Step 2: sin is **negative** in the third and fourth quadrants.

Step 3: Mark 39° from the horizontal axis into each of these quadrants.

Step 4: Read the angle from the 0° around anti-clockwise to these two marked positions.
This gives: $\theta = 219°, 321°$

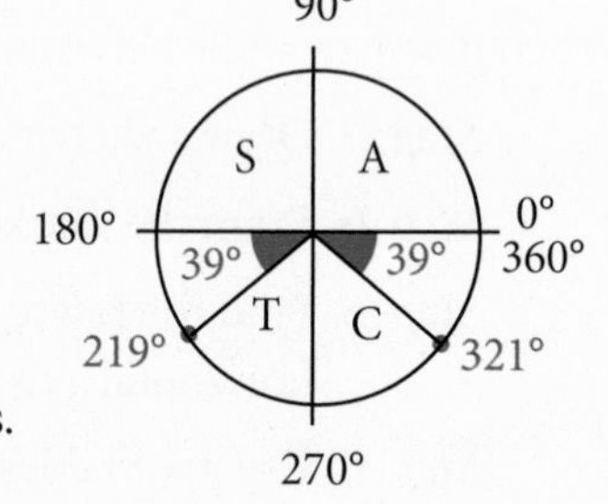

Practice Questions 20.6

1. Without using your calculator, find the exact value of each of the following:
   (i) tan 180° **(ii)** sin 135° **(iii)** cos 210° (iv) cos 315° **(v)** sin 240° **(vi)** tan 300°

2. Showing all your work clearly, find the value of the following, correct to four decimal places.
   (i) sin 295° **(ii)** cos 110° **(iii)** tan 230°

3. **(i)** Showing all your work clearly, find sin 160°, correct to four decimal places.
   (ii) Showing all your work clearly, find cos 250°, correct to four decimal places.
   (iii) Hence show that $\sin 160° - \cos 250° > 0$.

4. Given that $\sin\theta = \frac{1}{\sqrt{2}}$, solve for all possible values of θ for $0° \leq \theta \leq 360°$.

5. Given that $\cos\theta = -\frac{1}{2}$, solve for all possible values of θ for $0° \leq \theta \leq 360°$.

6. Given that $\tan\theta = -1$, solve for all possible values of θ for $0° \leq \theta \leq 360°$.

7. Find, correct to the nearest degree, the two values of θ for $0° \leq \theta \leq 360°$, given that:
   (i) $\sin\theta = -0{\cdot}9744$
   (ii) $\tan\theta = 1{\cdot}28$
   (iii) $\cos\theta = -0{\cdot}3748$.

8. Given that $\sin A = -\frac{\sqrt{3}}{2}$ and $\cos A$ is positive, find the value of A in the range $0° \leq A \leq 360°$.

9. Given that $\tan B = \frac{1}{\sqrt{3}}$ and $\sin B$ is negative, find the value of B in the range $0° \leq B \leq 360°$.

10. If $\sin A = \frac{5}{13}$ and $90° \leq A \leq 180°$, without finding A, find the values of $\tan A$ and $\cos A$.

Revision and Exam Style Questions – Section A

1. A ladder, 7·2 m long, leans against the vertical wall of a house. The foot of the ladder is 275 cm from the base of the wall on horizontal ground. Calculate the height of the top of the ladder above the ground to the nearest centimetre.

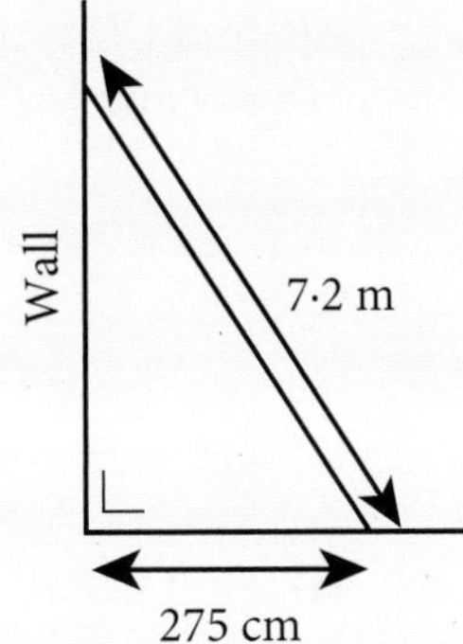

2. (i) Write 225° as the sum of two of the 'special angles'.
   (ii) Hence, without using your calculator, find the exact value of tan 225°.

3. In the diagram ABC is a right-angled triangle, with AC perpendicular to BC. $|AC| = 2\sqrt{2}$ and $|BC| = 3\sqrt{3}$

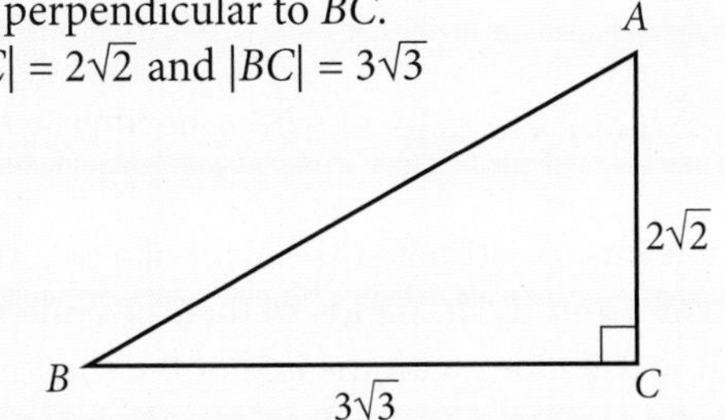

   (i) Find $|AB|$, leaving your answer in surd form.
   (ii) Find $|\angle ABC|$, correct to the nearest degree.

4. In the given triangle, $\tan A = \frac{7}{5}$
   (i) Copy the triangle into your copybook and mark in the angle A.
   (ii) Find, in surd form, the length of the third side of the triangle.

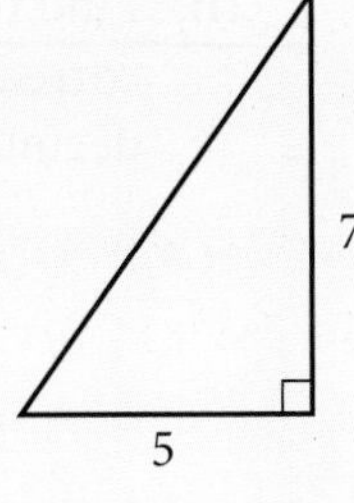

5. In the diagram MNO is a triangle with $[OP]$ perpendicular to $[MN]$. $|MP| = 10$ cm, $|ON| = 30$ cm and $|\angle PMO| = 65°$.

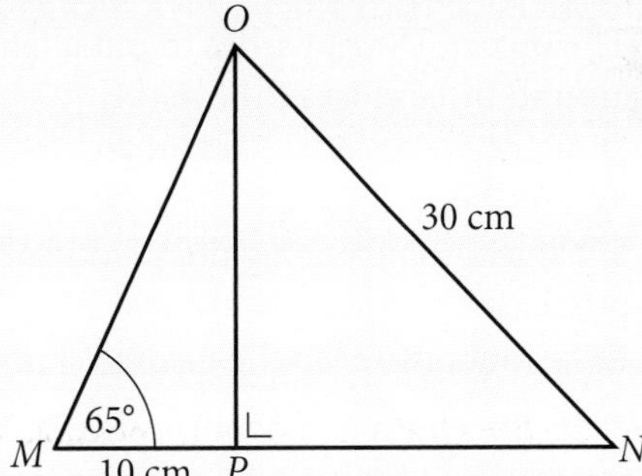

Calculate:
   (i) $|OP|$, correct to one decimal place
   (ii) $|\angle MON|$, correct to one decimal place.

6. From a point on the horizontal ground 25 m from the base of a tree, the angle of elevation to the top of the tree is 42° 15'.
   (i) Draw a mathematical model to represent this information.
   (ii) Find the height of the tree.

7. The path of a running track is in the shape of a triangle. A runner must start by going 6 km due south, then 4·5 km due west and then return directly to the starting position.
   (i) Draw a mathematical model to represent the running track.
   (ii) Find the length of the last leg of the track.
   (iii) Find the total length of one lap of the track.

8. The isosceles triangle shown in the diagram has a base of length 12 cm and the other two sides are each 10 cm in length.
Find h, the perpendicular height of the triangle.

10 cm
h
12 cm

9. A is an acute angle such that $\tan A = \frac{21}{20}$
   (i) Find, as fractions, the value of $\cos A$ and the value of $\sin A$.
   (ii) Find the measurement of angle A, correct to the nearest degree.

10. Showing all your work clearly, find the exact value of sin 305°. Give your answer correct to four decimal places.

Revision and Exam Style Questions – Section B

More challenging problems

1. The distance diagonally across a square patio is 11 metres long.
   (i) Find, to the nearest centimetre, the length of the sides of the patio.
   (ii) The owner, Doug, wishes to put a fence around three sides of the patio.
   Doug needs to get 15% extra fencing, to allow for cutting.
   What length of fencing does Doug need to purchase?
   Give your answer to the nearest centimetre.
   (iii) A 90 cm length of fencing costs €19·50. How much will Doug spend on the fencing, if he must buy it in 90 cm lengths?

2. θ is an angle, such that $\tan \theta = \frac{5}{12}$
   (i) Without finding the angle θ, find $\sin \theta$ and $\cos \theta$.
   (ii) Show that $\sin^2 \theta + \cos^2 \theta = 1$.

3. For a ladder to be safe, it must be inclined at between 70° and 80° to the ground. The diagram shows an 8 m ladder resting against a wall. If the ladder is to be inclined safely,
   (i) what is the shortest, distance to the nearest centimetre, that the base of the ladder can be from the wall?
   (ii) what is the furthest distance, to the nearest centimetre, that the base of the ladder can be from the wall?

Ladder
8 m
A

4. ABC is a triangle where $|BC| = 6$. D is a point on $[AB]$ and CD is perpendicular to AB, where $|CD| = 4$ and $|AD| = 9$.

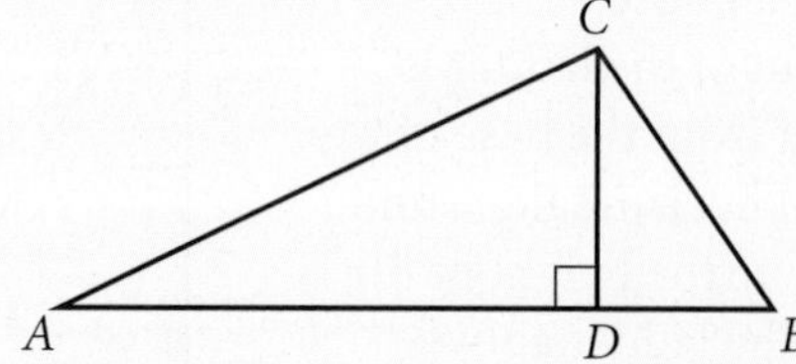

   (i) Find $|\angle CBD|$, correct to the nearest minute.
   (ii) Find $|\angle CAD|$, correct to the nearest minute.

5. Find the perimeter of the isosceles triangle shown. Give your answer to the nearest centimetre.

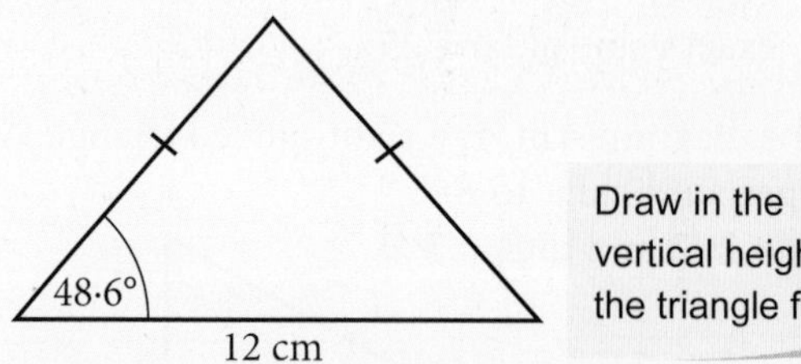

Draw in the vertical height of the triangle first.

6. Steve wants to estimate the height of a tree standing on level ground. He stands so that the end of his shadow coincides with the end of the shadow of the tree, as shown in the diagram. He measures the distances shown in the diagram. Steve is 1·6 m tall.
   (i) Find angle A, correct to the nearest minute.
   (ii) Find the height of the tree correct to one decimal place.

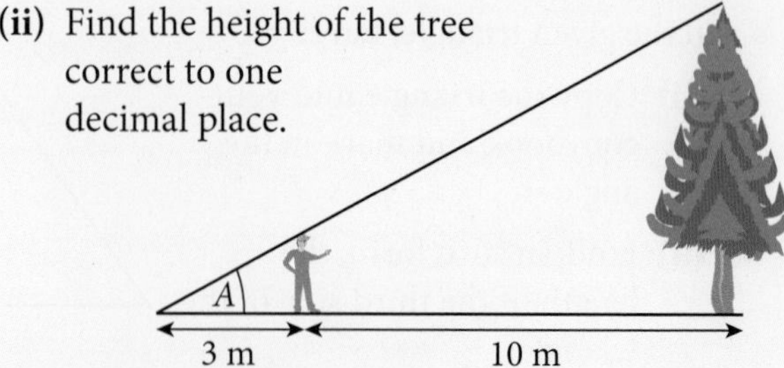

Trigonometry I

7. If $\tan A = -\frac{\sqrt{5}}{2}$ and $270° \leq A \leq 360°$, without finding A, find the values of $\sin A$ and $\cos A$, in surd form.

8. In the right-angled triangle ABC, $|AB| = 5$ cm. The area of the triangle is 15 cm^2. Find:

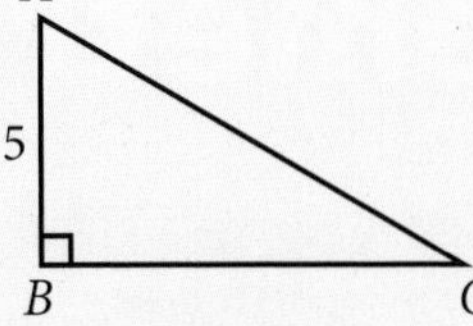

(i) $|BC|$
(ii) $|AC|$, in surd form
(iii) $|\angle CAB|$, correct to the nearest degree
(iv) $|\angle BCA|$, correct to the nearest minute.

9. Two vertical poles A and B, each of height h, are along a straight level road. They are 24 m apart. The point P, on the road directly between the two poles, is a distance x from pole A. The angle of elevation from P to the top of pole A is 60°.

(i) Write h in terms of x.
(ii) From P, the angle of elevation to the top of pole B is 30°. Find h, the height of the two poles.

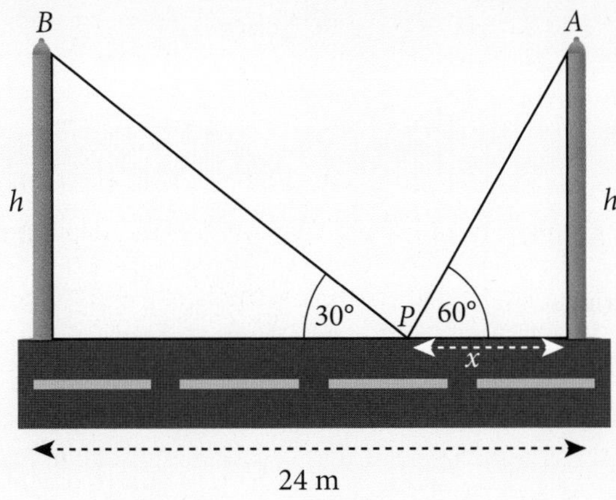

10. A and B are acute angles, where $\sin A = \frac{3}{5}$ and $\cos B = \frac{5}{13}$

(i) Find, as fractions, the value of $\cos A$ and the value of $\sin B$.
(ii) Given $\sin(A + B) = \sin A \cos B + \cos A \sin B$, find the value of $\sin(A + B)$, giving your answer as a single fraction.

11. Given that $\sin \theta = -\frac{1}{2}$, solve for all possible values of θ for $0 \leq \theta \leq 360°$.

12. A square, of side length 20 cm, has a circle inscribed inside it. The circle then has a smaller square (shaded in blue) inscribed inside it, as shown.
Find the length of a side of the smaller square. Give your answer in simplest surd form.

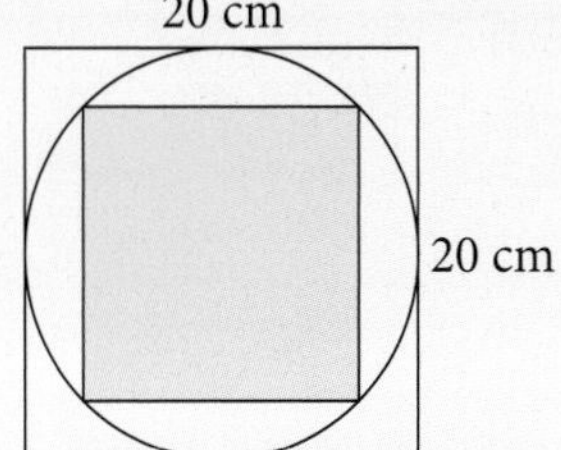

Find the diagonal length of the blue square.

Now that you have completed the chapter revisit the 'Something to think about…' question.

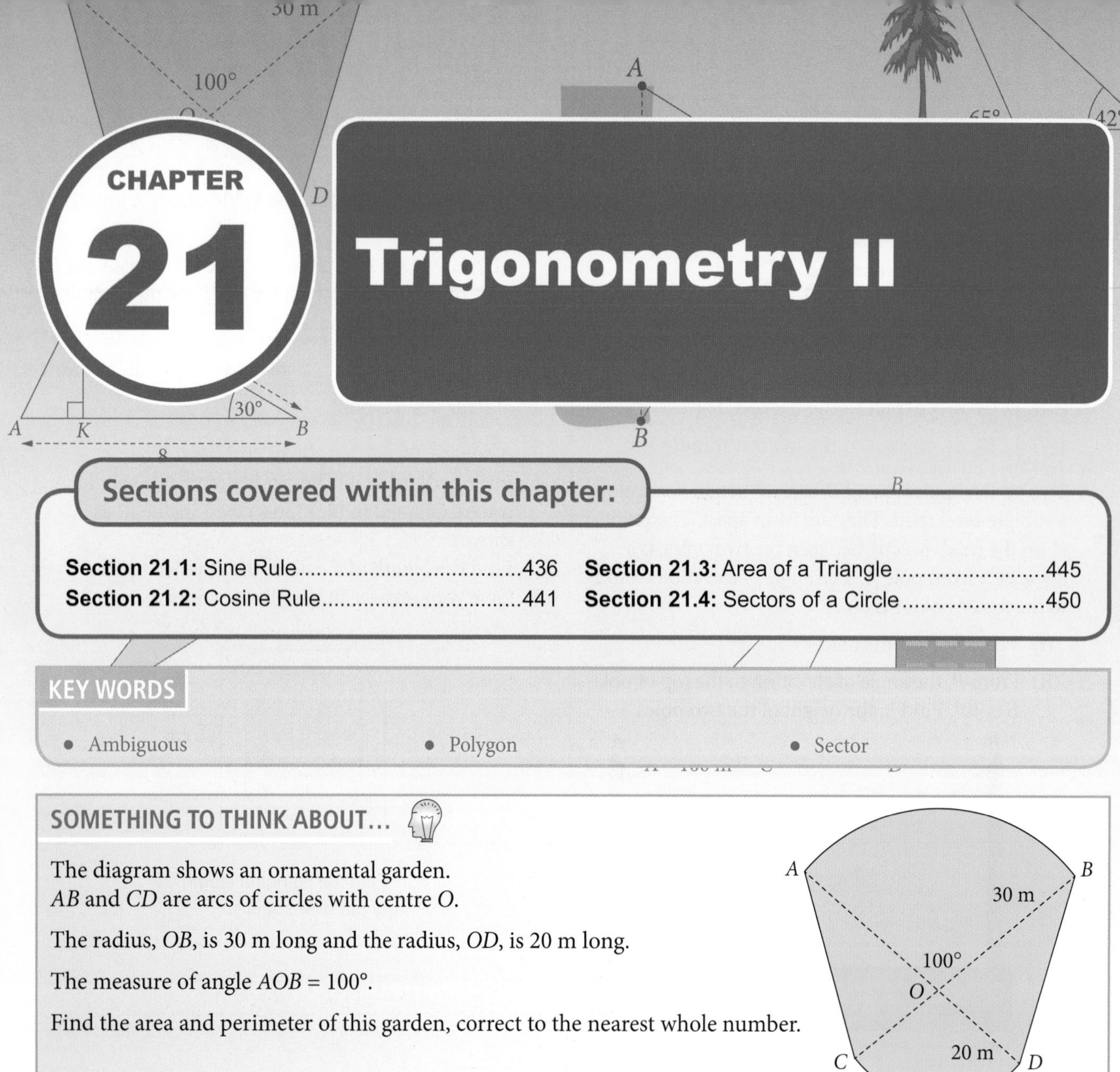

CHAPTER 21 Trigonometry II

Sections covered within this chapter:

KEY WORDS

- Ambiguous
- Polygon
- Sector

SOMETHING TO THINK ABOUT…

The diagram shows an ornamental garden.
AB and *CD* are arcs of circles with centre *O*.

The radius, *OB*, is 30 m long and the radius, *OD*, is 20 m long.

The measure of angle *AOB* = 100°.

Find the area and perimeter of this garden, correct to the nearest whole number.

Introduction

In Chapter 20: Trigonometry I we covered how to solve for missing sides or angles in right-angled triangles. However, if the triangle is not right-angled, then we need a new set of rules. These rules are covered in this chapter.

Section 21.1: Sine Rule

Learning Outcomes:

You should be able to:

- use the sine rule to solve for missing sides and angles in a triangle
- solve problems in real-life contexts

There are many relationships that exist between the sides and angles in a triangle. The sine rule uses the fact that the ratio of the sine of an angle to the side opposite that angle is a constant in any triangle.

The sine rule is used when working with two angle/side pairs. An angle/side pair occurs when a side is paired with the angle directly facing it.

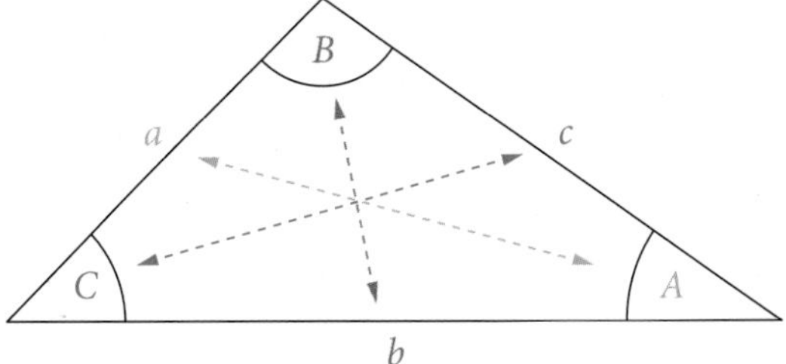

$$\frac{a}{\sin A} = \frac{b}{\sin B} = \frac{c}{\sin C} \quad \text{or} \quad \frac{\sin A}{a} = \frac{\sin B}{b} = \frac{\sin C}{c}$$

The sine rule can also be used on right-angled triangles.

The formula for the **sine rule** appears on page 16 of the booklet of *formulae and tables*, as shown:

The version of the sine rule with the angles on top is not given in the booklet of *formulae and tables*.

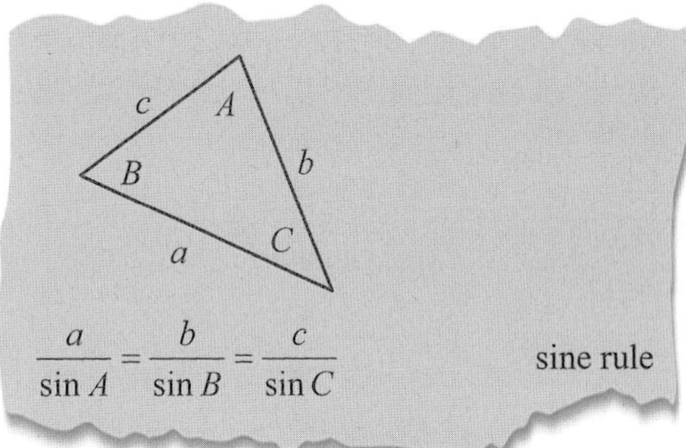

$$\frac{a}{\sin A} = \frac{b}{\sin B} = \frac{c}{\sin C}$$ sine rule

To solve a problem using the sine rule

Step 1: Identify the unknown quantity (side or angle).

Step 2: Identify two angle/side pairs.

Step 3: Label one pair as a and the other pair as b.

Step 4: If the unknown quantity is a side, use : $\frac{a}{\sin A} = \frac{b}{\sin B}$.

Step 5: If the unknown quantity is an angle, use : $\frac{\sin A}{a} = \frac{\sin B}{b}$.

In practice you will only use two of the three parts of the formula.

EXAMPLE 1

Find the value of x. Give your answer to one decimal place.

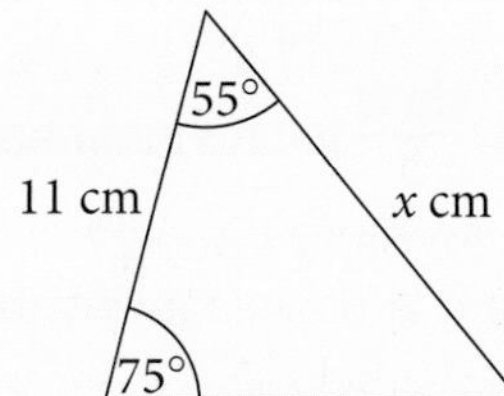

Solution

We do not have two angle/side pairs, therefore we need to find the third angle within the triangle:

Third angle = 180° − 55° − 75°

Third angle = 50°

Label one pair as a and one pair as b

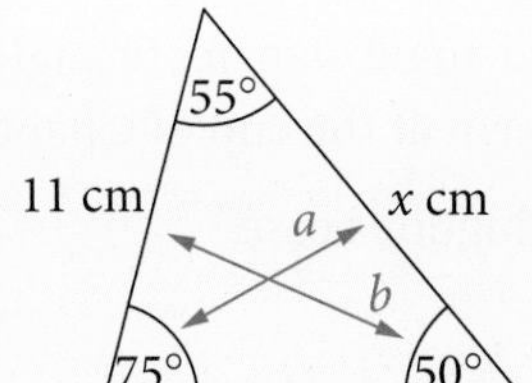

$a = x$, $A = 75°$, $b = 11$, $B = 50°$

We are looking for a side, so we put the sides on top:

$$\frac{a}{\sin A} = \frac{b}{\sin B}$$

$$\frac{x}{\sin 75°} = \frac{11}{\sin 50°} \quad \text{(multiply both sides by sin 75°)}$$

$$x = \frac{11(\sin 75°)}{\sin 50°}$$

$x = 13{\cdot}87019276$

$x = 13{\cdot}9$ cm

EXAMPLE 2

Find the value of the acute angle, θ. Give your answer in degrees and minutes, correct to the nearest minute.

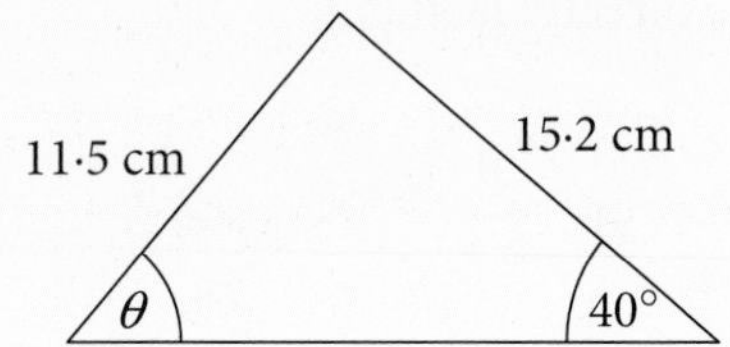

Solution

Pick out the two angle/side pairs.

Label one pair as a and the other pair as b.

We are looking for an angle, so we put the angles on top:

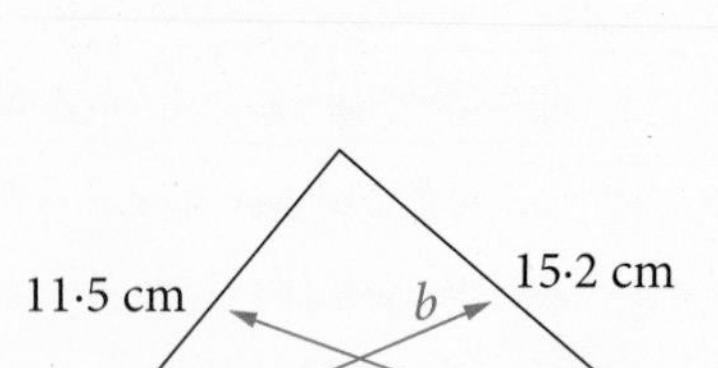

$$\frac{\sin A}{a} = \frac{\sin B}{b}$$

$$\frac{\sin 40°}{11{\cdot}5} = \frac{\sin \theta}{15{\cdot}2}$$

$$\frac{15{\cdot}2(\sin 40°)}{11{\cdot}5} = \sin \theta$$

$$0{\cdot}8495975363 = \sin \theta$$

$$\sin^{-1}(0{\cdot}8495975363) = \theta$$

$$58{\cdot}16792216 = \theta$$

$$58°\ 10'\ 4{\cdot}52'' = \theta$$

$$58°\ 10' = \theta$$

Use the degrees button on your calculator to convert angles from degrees in decimal form, to degrees, minutes and seconds.

Discussion Time

The diagram shows a right-angled triangle with dimensions as shown.

Work with a classmate to perform the following tasks:

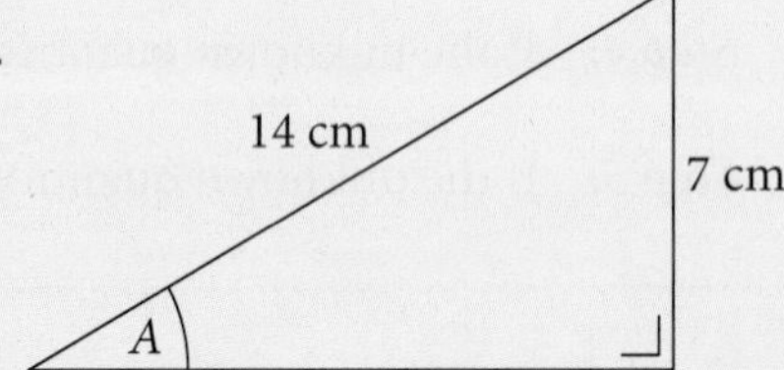

1. Label the sides of the triangle as hypotenuse, opposite and adjacent.
   Hence, use the formula $\sin A = \frac{\text{Opposite}}{\text{Hypotenuse}}$ to find the measure of the angle A.
2. Label the two angle/side pairs in the triangle.
   Hence, use the formula $\frac{\sin A}{a} = \frac{\sin B}{b}$ to find the measure of the angle A.
3. Did you get the same answers for parts **1** and **2**?
   Use your solutions to parts **1** and **2** to explain why this is the case.

The ambiguous case

In some cases it is possible to find two values for the required angle – an acute angle and an obtuse angle. To find these two angles we must use the unit circle and the skills learnt at the end of Chapter 20: Trigonometry I.

Look at the following example to further understand the ambiguous case.

Ambiguous means that something is unclear or undecided.

EXAMPLE 3

The triangle PQR has dimensions $|PQ| = 41$ cm, $|PR| = 54$ cm, $|\angle PRQ| = 38°$.

(i) Find two possible values for $|\angle PQR|$, correct to the nearest degree.

(ii) Draw a sketch of the two possible triangles PQR.

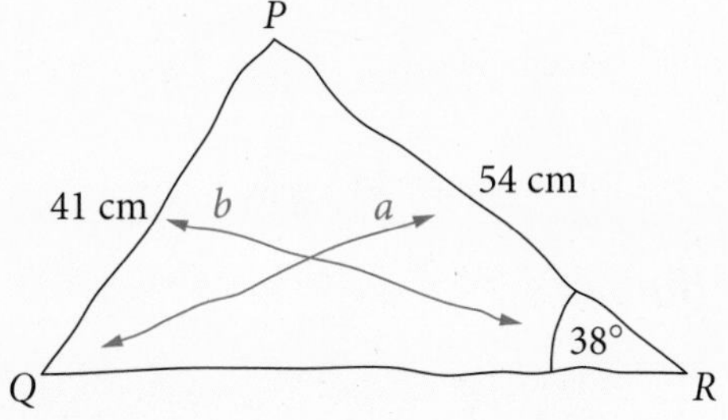

Solution

(i) Draw a sketch of the triangle PQR and label the two angle/side pairs:

$a = 54$, $A = |\angle PQR|$, $b = 41$, $B = 38°$

$$\frac{\sin A}{a} = \frac{\sin B}{b}$$

$$\frac{\sin |\angle PQR|}{54} = \frac{\sin 38°}{41}$$

$$\sin |\angle PQR| = \frac{54\ (\sin 38°)}{41}$$

$$\sin |\angle PQR| = 0{\cdot}8108712114$$

Reference angle = 54·18°

The two quadrants where sine is positive are the first and the second quadrants.

Therefore,

$|\angle PQR| = 54{\cdot}18° = 54°$

$|\angle PQR| = 180° - 54{\cdot}18° = 125{\cdot}82° = 126°$

Recall how to use the unit circle to find the two possible values for the angle.
This was covered in Chapter 20: Trigonometry I.

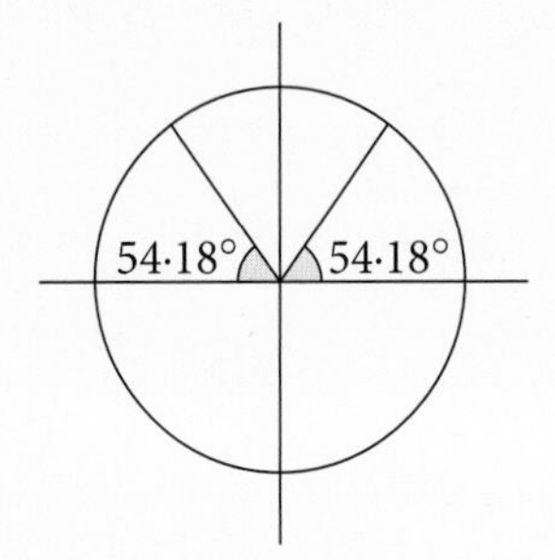

(ii) $|\angle PQR| = 54°$

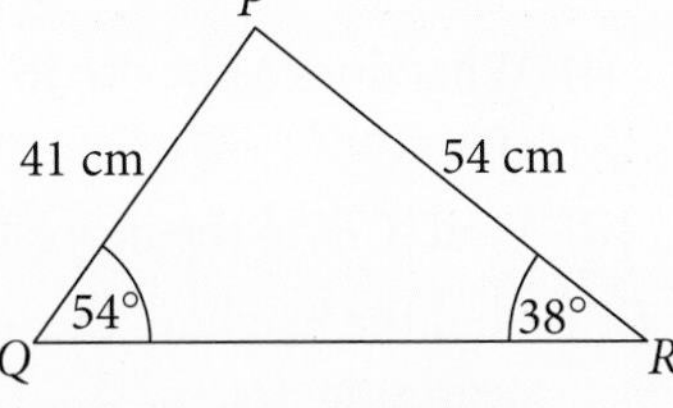

$|\angle PQR| = 126°$

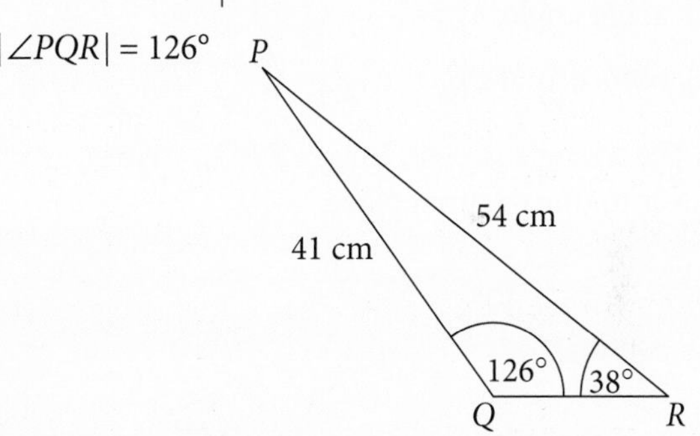

Practice Questions 21.1

1. Using the sine rule, find side x in each of the following triangles. Give your answers to one decimal place.

(i)

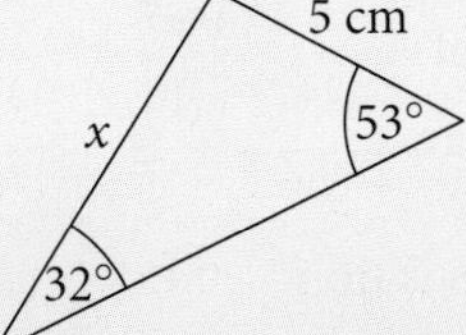

(ii)

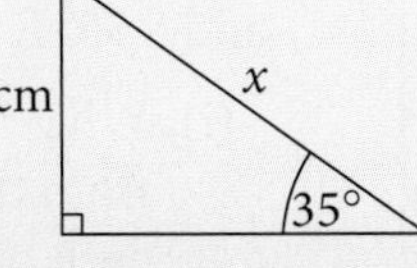

(iii)

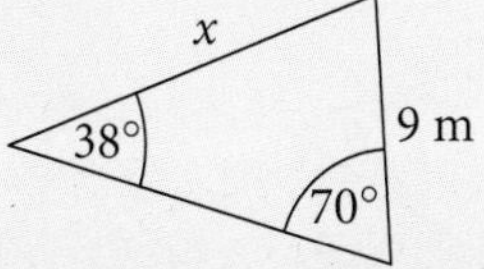

(iv)

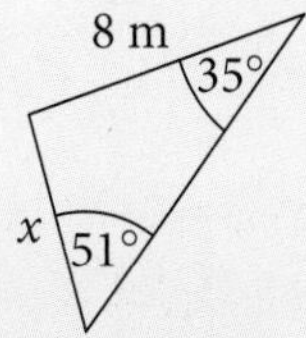

2. Using the sine rule, find the side x in each of the following triangles. Give your answers to one decimal place.

(i)

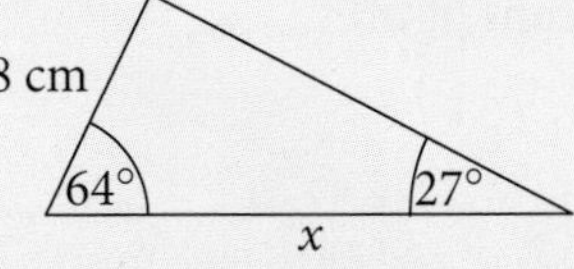

(ii)

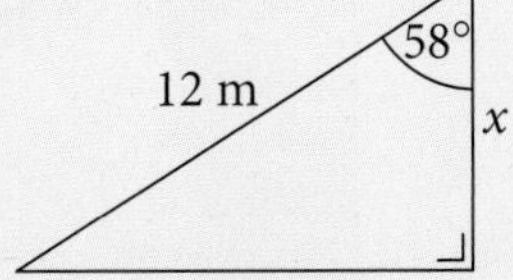

(iii)

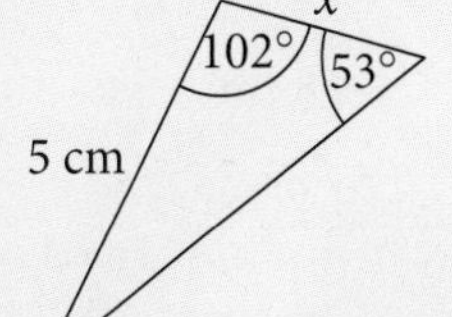

(iv)

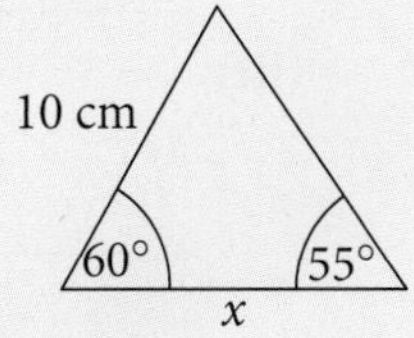

3. Use the sine rule to find the measure of the acute angle θ in each of the following triangles. Give your answers to one decimal place.

(i)

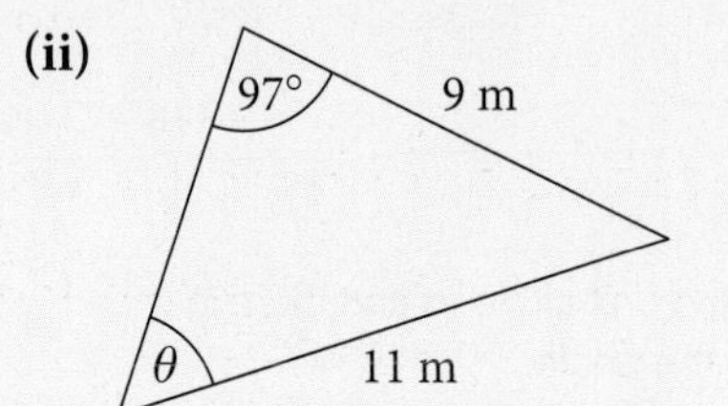

(ii)

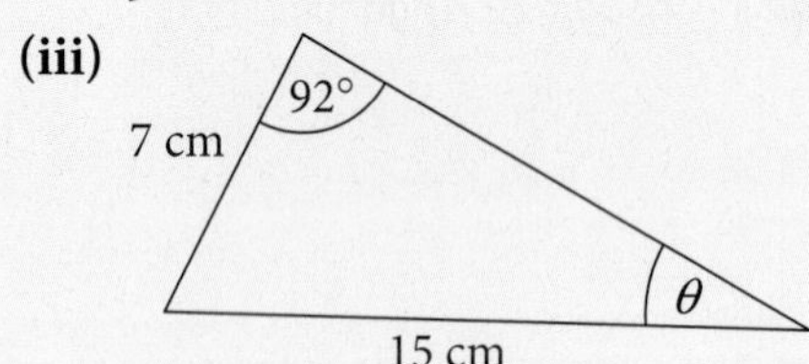

(iii)

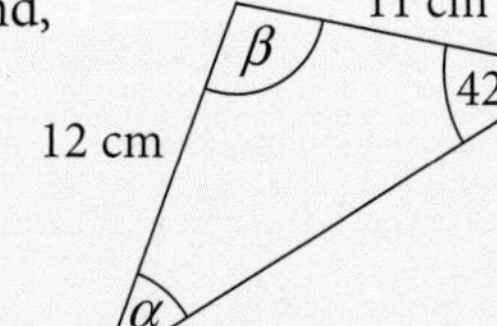

4. For the triangle shown, find, correct to one decimal place the measure of:

(i) acute angle, α

(ii) obtuse angle, β.

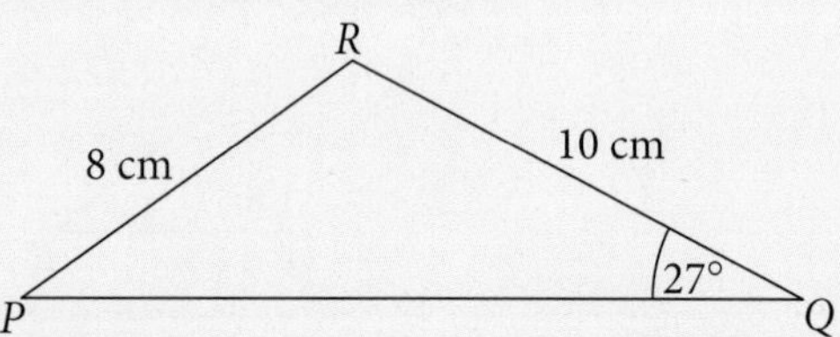

5. For the triangle shown, find $|\angle PRQ|$. Give your answer to one decimal place.

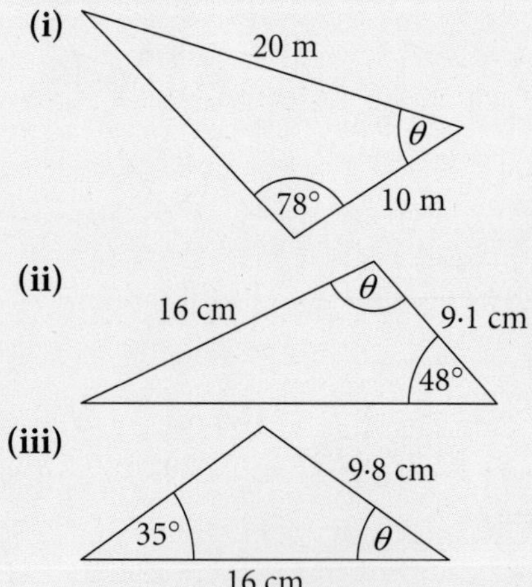

6. Find the measure of the acute angle θ in each of the following triangles. Give your answers in degrees and minutes, correct to the nearest minute.

(i)

20 m, 78°, 10 m, θ

(ii)

16 cm, θ, 9·1 cm, 48°

(iii)

9·8 cm, 35°, θ, 16 cm

7. The diagram shows two triangles PQS and QRS. Find, in surd form:

(i) $|SQ|$

(ii) $|SR|$

(iii) $|PS|$.

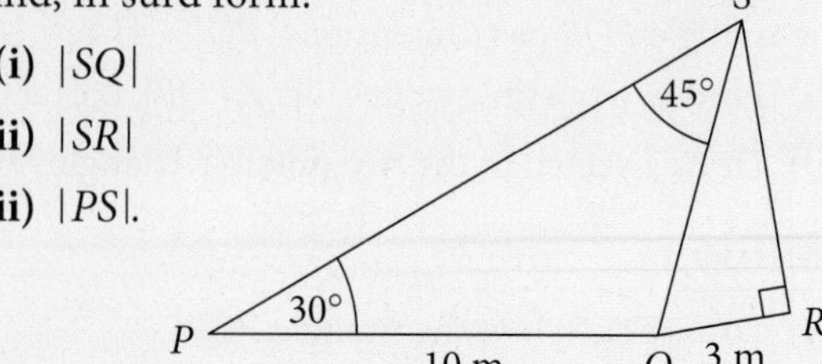

8. Mike wants to know the height of a vertical building. He stands at the point A and measures the angle of elevation to the point B, at the top of the building, to be 46°. He then walks 100 m towards the building until he gets to the point C. He measures the angle of elevation from C to B to be 63°.

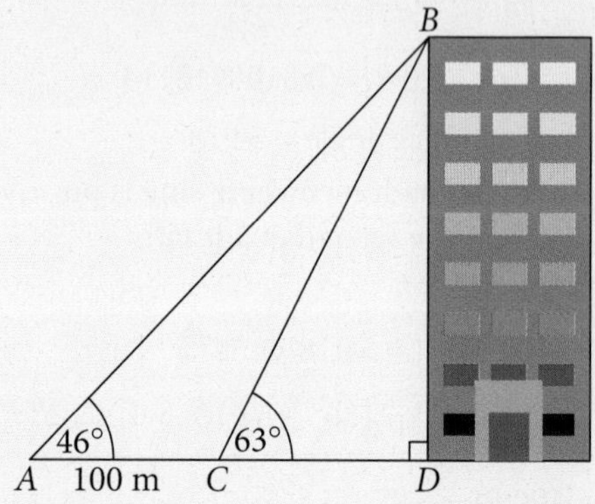

(i) What does Mike use to measure the angles of elevation?

(ii) Find $|CB|$ to the nearest metre.

(iii) Find the height of the building, $|DB|$ to the nearest metre.

9. A ship is anchored off a long straight shoreline that runs north to south. From two observation points, A and B, 18 km apart on the shore, the bearings of the ship are N 30° E from point B and S 55° E from point A.

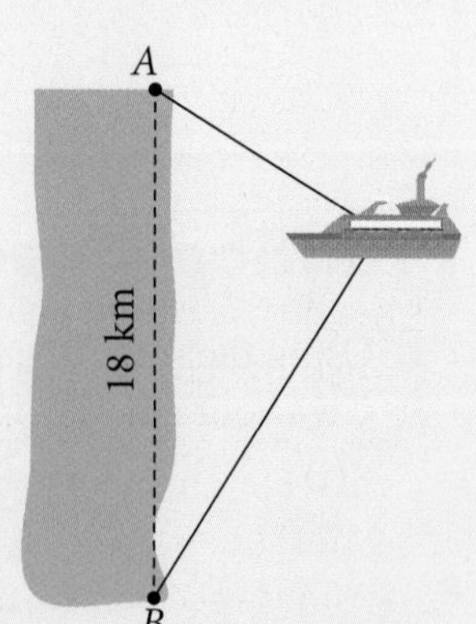

(i) What is the distance from the ship to each of the observation points? Give your answer to one decimal place.

(ii) Find the shortest distance from the ship to the shoreline. Give your answer to in metres, to two significant figures.

10. Suraj and Graham want to measure the height of a vertical telephone mast. They stand on opposite sides of the mast, a distance 80 m apart. Suraj measures the angle of elevation to the top of the mast to be 57°. Graham measures the angle of elevation to the top of the mast to be 48°.
    (i) Draw a mathematical model of the information given.
    (ii) Find the height of the mast. Give your answer to the nearest metre.

11. The diagram shows a vertical telephone pole, $[PQ]$, of height 8 m. Two wires $[PR]$ and $[PS]$ are connected from the top of the pole to the horizontal ground.

    $|PQ| = 8$ m, $|\angle PRQ| = 48{\cdot}8°$ and $|\angle PSQ| = 36°$.

    Find:
    (i) the length of the wire, $|PR|$, correct to one decimal place
    (ii) the distance between the two points S and R, where the wires are connected to the ground. Give your answer to the nearest metre.

12. The triangle PQR has dimensions $|PQ| = 34{\cdot}7$ cm, $|PR| = 42{\cdot}5$ cm, $|\angle PRQ| = 28°$.
    (i) Find **two** possible values for $|\angle PQR|$, correct to the nearest degree.
    (ii) Draw a sketch of the two possible triangles PQR.

13. The triangle XYZ has dimensions $|XY| = 6{\cdot}8$ cm, $|XZ| = 7{\cdot}5$ cm, $|\angle XZY| = 63°$.
    (i) Find **two** possible values for $|\angle XYZ|$, correct to the nearest degree.
    (ii) Draw a sketch of the two possible triangles XYZ.

14. The diagram shows two triangles ABD and BCD. Find, correct to one decimal place:
    (i) the **obtuse** angle, $|\angle ADB|$
    (ii) $|\angle CDB|$
    (iii) $|DC|$.

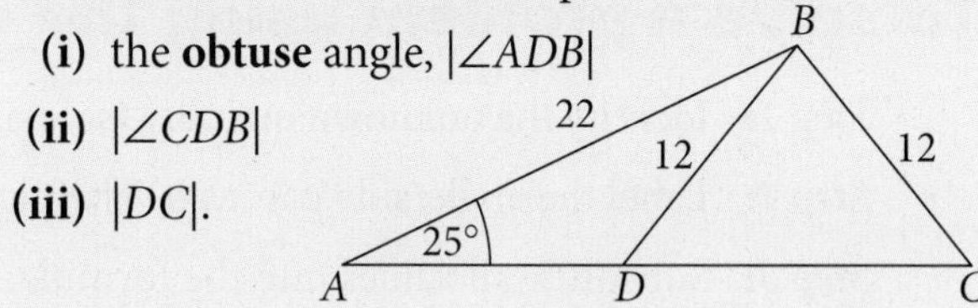

15. The diagram shows two triangles ABD and BCD. Find, correct to one decimal place:
    (i) the **obtuse** angle, $|\angle ADB|$
    (ii) $|\angle BDC|$
    (iii) $|DC|$.

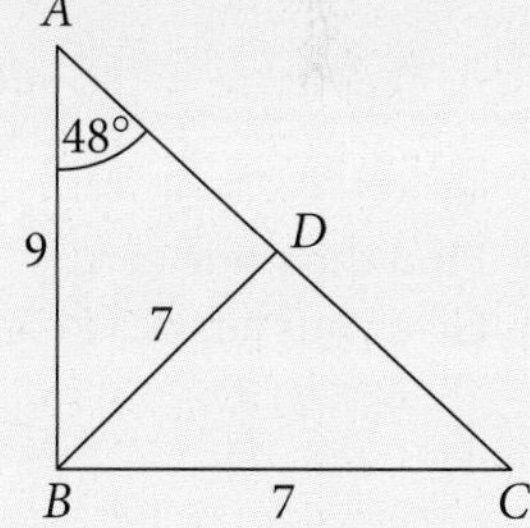

Section 21.2: Cosine Rule

Learning Outcomes:

You should be able to:
- use the cosine rule to solve for missing sides and angles in a triangle
- solve problems in real-life contexts

If it is not possible to find two angle/side pairs, then we must use the cosine rule. The cosine rule involves the three sides of a triangle and one of the angles.

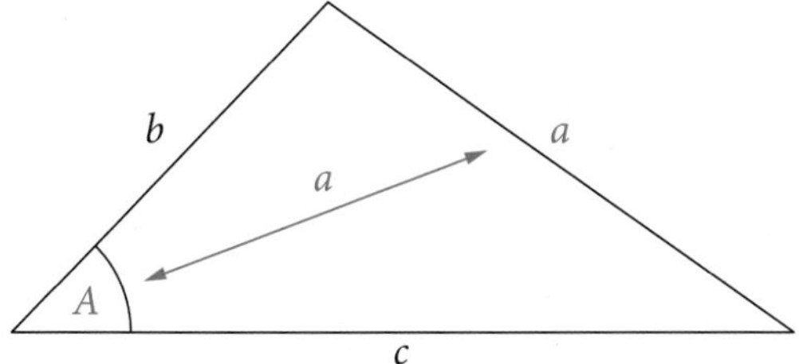

$$a^2 = b^2 + c^2 - 2bc\cos A$$

The angle-side pair must be labelled as the a's.

The formula for the **cosine rule** appears on page 16 of the booklet of *formulae and tables*, as shown:

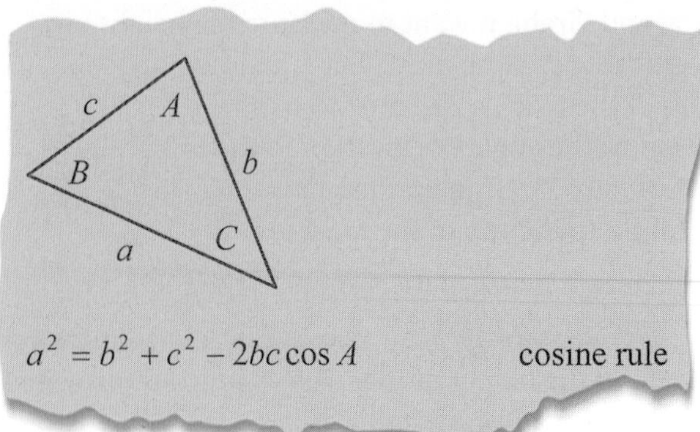

We use the cosine rule in the following two situations:

- We have all three sides of the triangle and we are looking for an angle.
- We have two sides of the triangle and the angle in between them, and we are looking for the third side.

The cosine rule can also be used on right-angled triangles.

To solve a problem using the cosine rule

Step 1: Identify the unknown quantity (side or angle).

Step 2: Label the angle/side pair as *a*. Then label the other two sides as *b* and *c*.

Step 3: Substitute all values into the formula: $a^2 = b^2 + c^2 - 2bc \cos A$.

Step 4: Solve the resulting equation to find the missing value.

EXAMPLE 1

Find the value of *x*.
Give your answer to one decimal place.

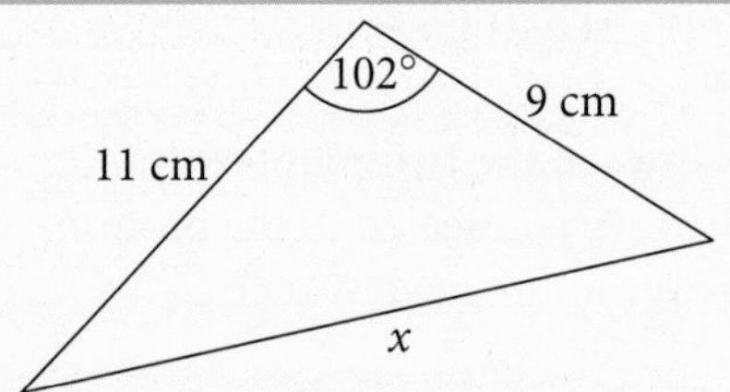

Solution

Label the angle/side pair as *a*.
Label one of the other sides *b* and the third side *c*.

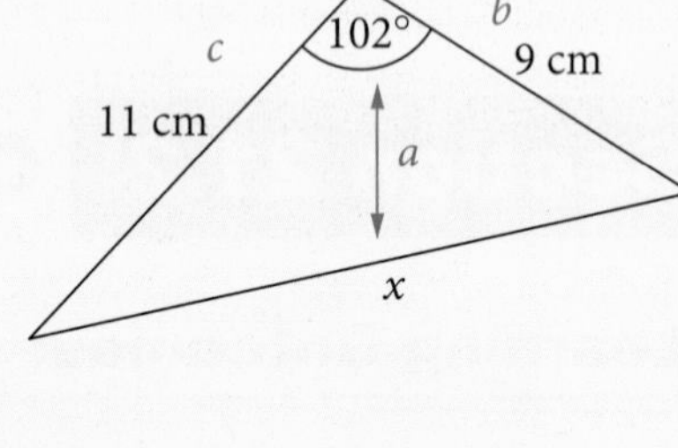

$a = x, \quad b = 9, \quad c = 11, \quad A = 102°$

$a^2 = b^2 + c^2 - 2bc \cos A$

$x^2 = (9)^2 + (11)^2 - [2(9)(11) \cos 102°]$

$x^2 = 81 + 121 - [198 \cos 102°]$

$x^2 = 202 - [-41{\cdot}16651478]$

$x^2 = 202 + 41{\cdot}16651478$

$x^2 = 243{\cdot}16651478$

$x = \sqrt{243{\cdot}16651478}$

$x = 15{\cdot}593797$

$x = 15{\cdot}6$ cm

It will help to put the $2bc \cos A$ part into a bracket, to get: $a^2 = b^2 + c^2 - [2bc \cos A]$

Note that the cosine of an obtuse angle is a negative value.

EXAMPLE 2

The diagram shows triangle PQR.

Find $|\angle PRQ|$.

Give your answer to two decimal places.

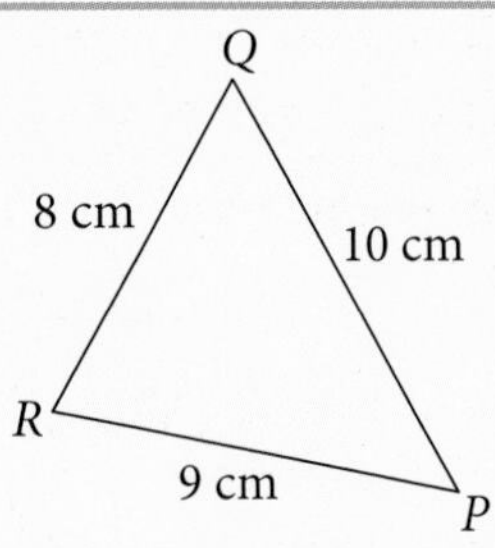

Solution

Label the angle/side pair as a.

Label one of the other sides b and the third side c.

$a = 10, \quad b = 8, \quad c = 9, \quad A = |\angle PRQ|$

$$a^2 = b^2 + c^2 - 2bc\cos A$$

$$(10)^2 = (8)^2 + (9)^2 - [2(8)(9)\cos A]$$

$$100 = 64 + 81 - [144\cos A]$$

$$100 = 145 - [144\cos A]$$

$$[144\cos A] = 145 - 100 \qquad \text{(rearrange)}$$

$$144\cos A = 45$$

$$\cos A = \frac{45}{144}$$

$$A = \cos^{-1}\left(\frac{45}{144}\right)$$

$$A = 71{\cdot}79^\circ$$

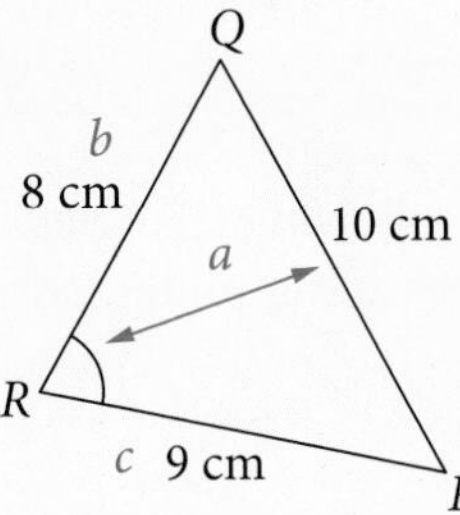

If you are given a triangle to solve, use the following flowchart to work out which formula to use:

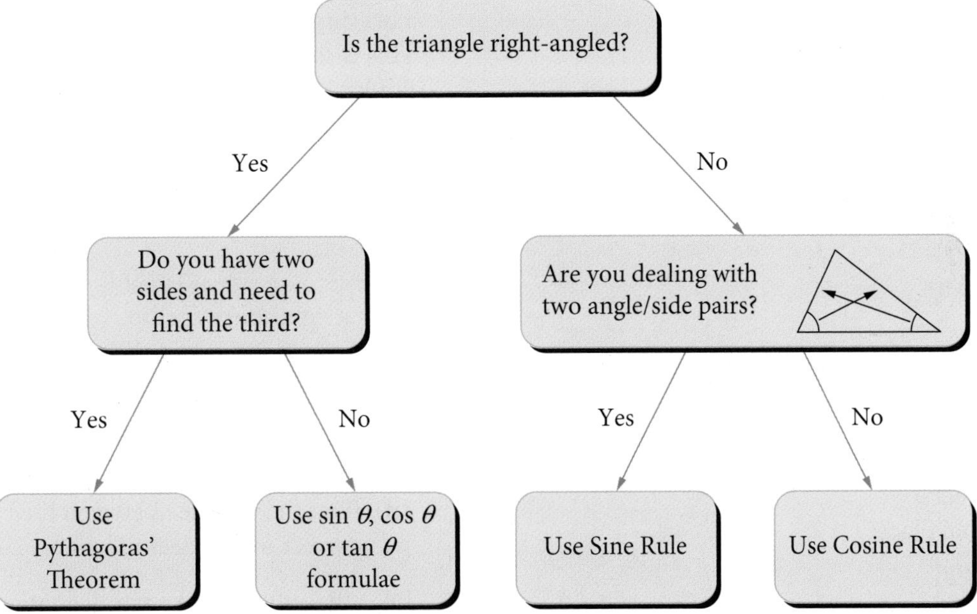

Practice Questions 21.2

1. Find side x in each of the following triangles. Give your answers to one decimal place.

(i)

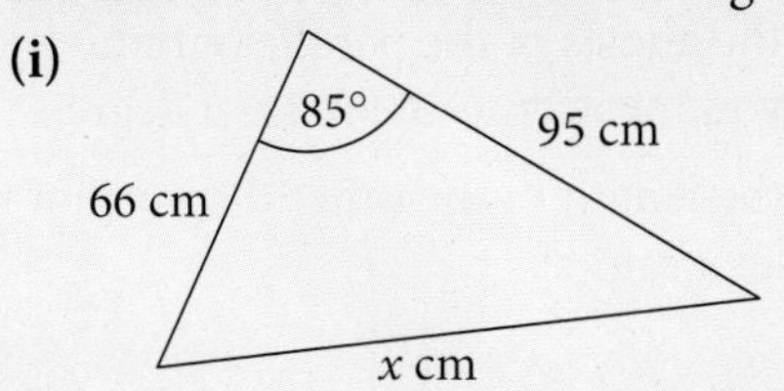

(ii)

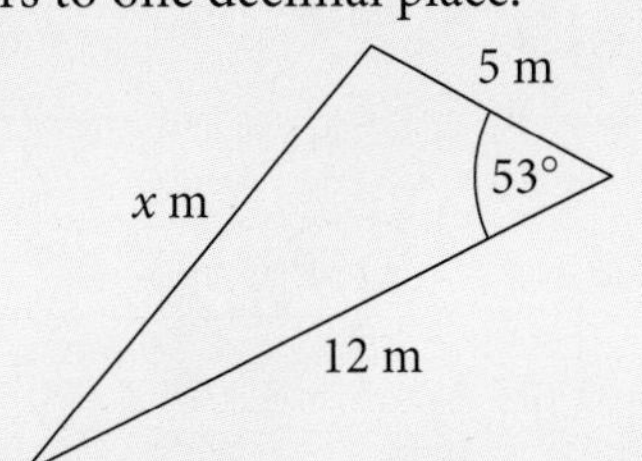

(iii)

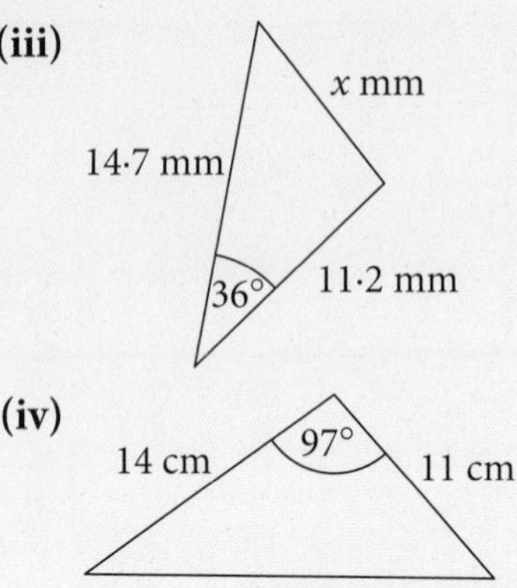

2. Find angle θ in each of the following triangles. Give your answers in degrees and minutes, correct to the nearest minute.

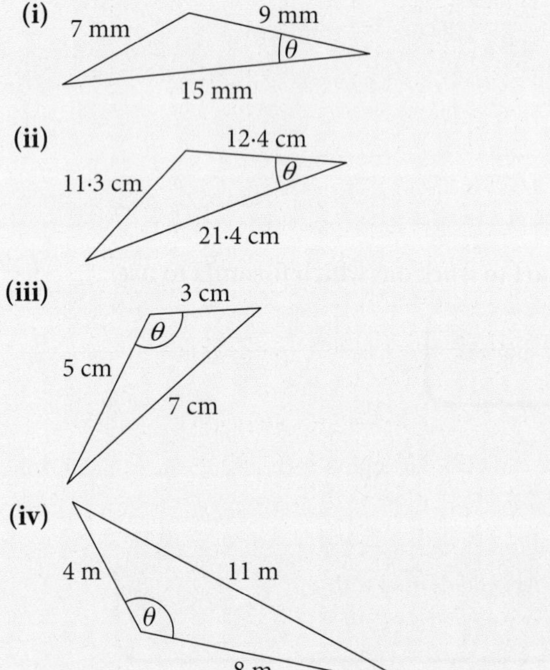

3. The diagram shows the triangle PQR. Find, correct to one decimal place:

(i) $|\angle QPR|$

(ii) $|\angle PQR|$

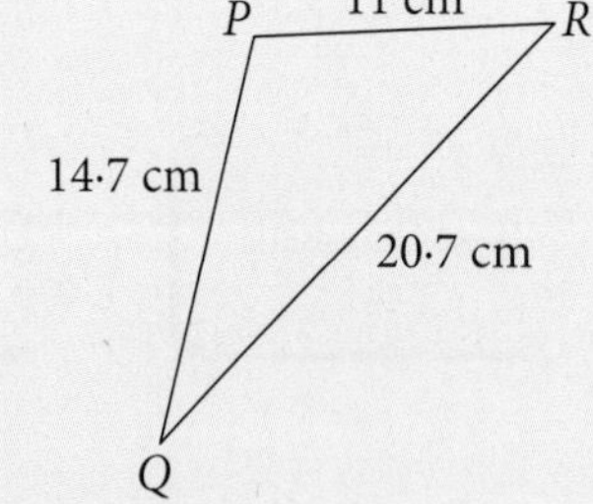

4. The diagram shows the triangle ABC. Find, correct to one decimal place:

(i) $|AC|$

(ii) $|\angle BAC|$

A
6·5 m
131°
B
9·3 m
C

5. (i) Use the cosine rule to find the length marked x in the given diagram.

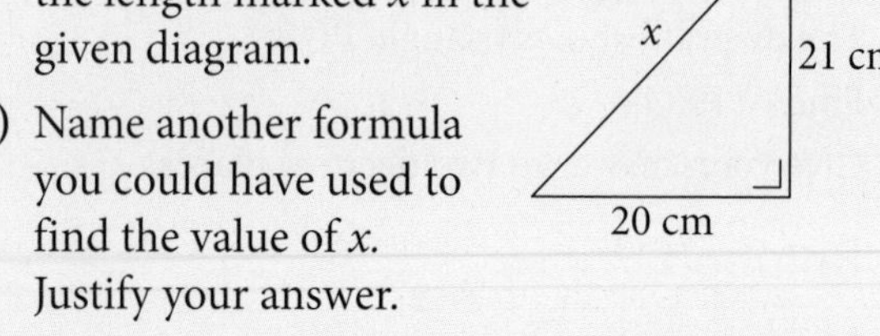

(ii) Name another formula you could have used to find the value of x. Justify your answer.

(iii) State a reason why both the formulae used in part (i) and (ii) are equal, for this triangle.

6. The hands of a clock have lengths 6·5 cm and 8 cm.

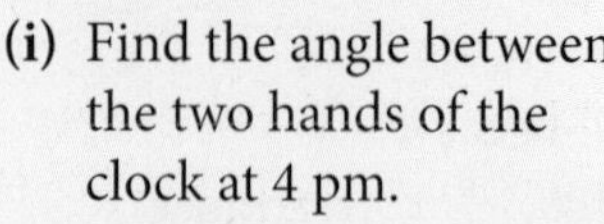

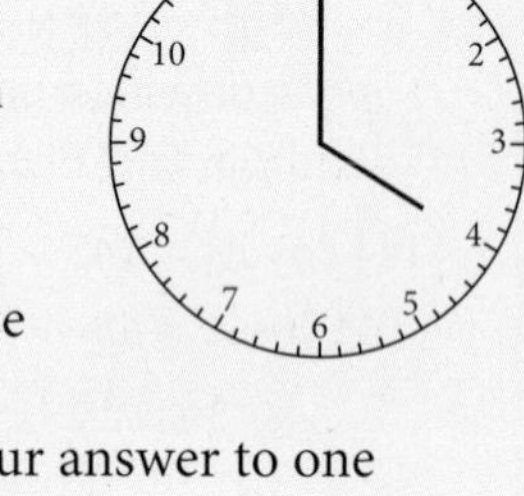

(i) Find the angle between the two hands of the clock at 4 pm.

(ii) Hence, find the distance between the tips of the hands at 4 pm. Give your answer to one decimal place.

7. From a lighthouse, L, a ship P is 8 km away on a bearing of N 52° W and ship Q is 10·2 km away on a bearing of S 49° W. This is shown in the diagram. Find:

(i) $|\angle PLQ|$

(ii) the distance between the two ships.

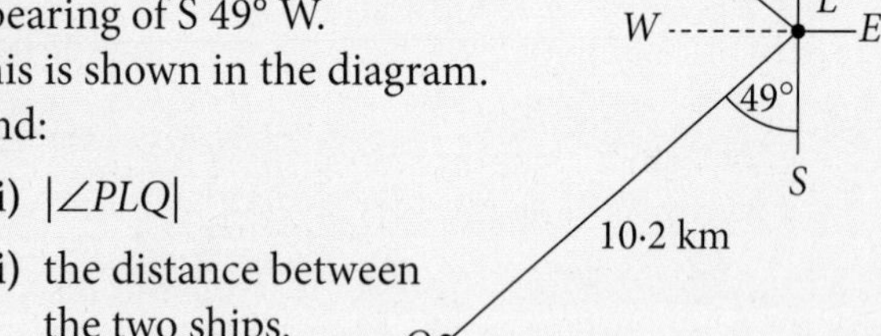

8. From a lighthouse L, ship A is 4 km away on a bearing of N 35° E and ship B is 6 km away on a bearing of S 48° E for the lighthouse.

(i) Draw a mathematical model of the information given.

(ii) Find the distance between the two ships, correct to one decimal place.

9. Two adjacent sides of a parallelogram are of length 9·5 cm and 7 cm, and the shorter diagonal is of length 8 cm.

(i) Draw a diagram of the parallelogram, showing all known dimensions.

(ii) Find the angles of the parallelogram. Give your answer to the nearest degree.

(iii) Find the length of the other diagonal of the parallelogram.

10. A boat sets off from a point A and sails for 5·6 km in the direction N 23° E to a point B. At point B it turns and begins to move in the direction N 48° W. It then stays on this course for 8·7 km until it reaches a point C.
    (i) Draw a mathematical model to represent the information given.
    (ii) Find the distance from A to C, correct to one decimal place.
    (iii) Find the bearing of C from A.

11. Two ships leave a port P, at the same time. *Princess Sophie, S*, sails on a bearing N 75° W at a speed of 16 km/hr, and *Princess Regina, R*, sails on a bearing of N 10° W. After three hours the angle PRS is 80°.
    (i) Draw a mathematical model to represent the information given.
    (ii) Find the distance between the ships at this time. Give your answer to two decimal places.
    (iii) Find the speed of the *Princess Regina*, to the nearest whole number.

12. In the diagram, the triangle XYZ is right-angled. XP is parallel to ZY and $|XP| = |XZ|$, as shown. $|XY| = 8$ m and $|ZY| = 15$ m. Find:
    (i) $|XZ|$
    (ii) $|PZ|$, correct to the nearest metre.

13. In the triangle PQR, $|PQ| = |PR|$, $|QR| = 15$ cm and $|\angle RPQ| = 40°$. S is a point on QR such that $|RS| = 10$ cm.

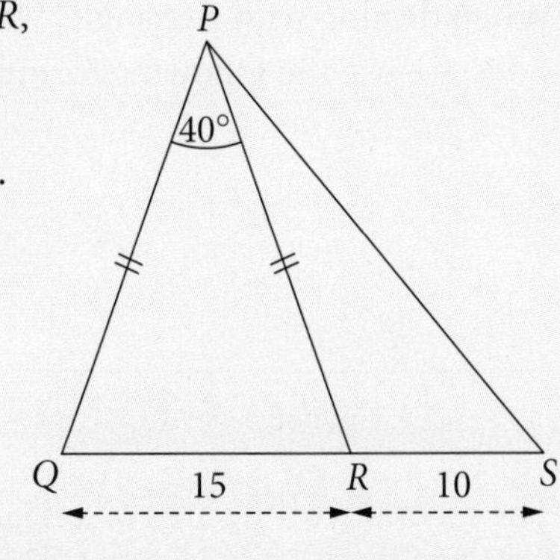

    (i) Find $|PR|$, correct to the nearest centimetre.
    (ii) Find $|PS|$, correct to the nearest centimetre.

14. A lighthouse, L, is observed from a ship sailing a straight course due north. The distance from P to L is 2·1 km and the bearing of the lighthouse from P is N 41·3° E. The distance from Q to L is 2·73 km.

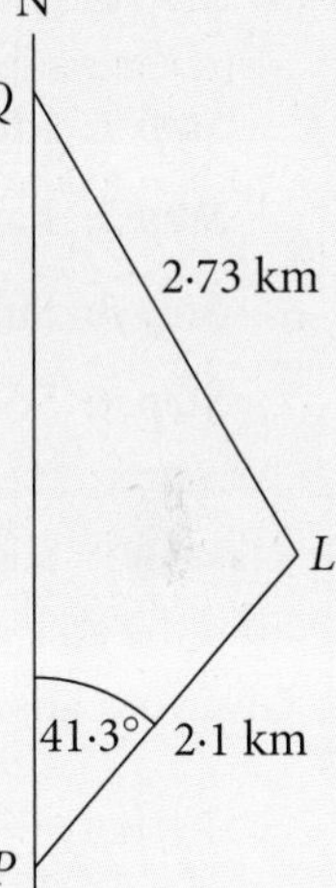

    (i) Find the bearing of the lighthouse from Q, to the nearest minute.
    (ii) The ship is sailing at a speed of 18 km/hr.
    Find, correct to the nearest minute, the time taken to sail from P to Q.

Section 21.3: Area of a Triangle

Learning Outcomes:

You should be able to:
- find the area of a triangle
- solve problems in real-life contexts

Links across the syllabus

Finding the area of a triangle is a procedure which arises in different topics of your maths course.

When dealing with a triangle where we have the base and the perpendicular height, we use the following formula:

$$\text{Area} = \frac{1}{2}(\text{base})(\perp \text{height})$$

(covered in Chapter 16: Area and Perimeter)

When dealing with a triangle, which is plotted on a coordinated plane, we use the following formula:

$$\text{Area} = \frac{1}{2}|x_1y_2 - x_2y_1|$$

(covered in Chapter 14: Coordinate Geometry I)

When dealing with a triangle, where we are given two sides, a and b, and measure of the angle in between these sides, we use the following formula:

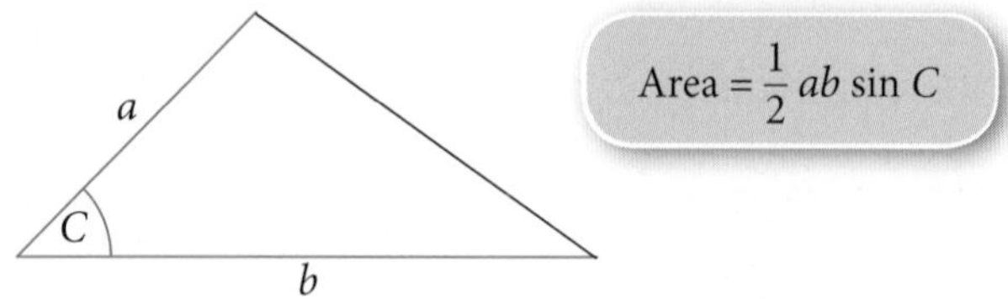

$$\text{Area} = \frac{1}{2}ab \sin C$$

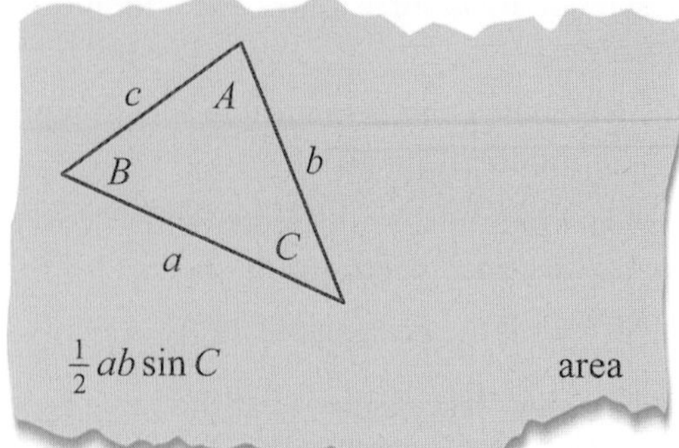

The formula for the area of a triangle appears on page 9 of the booklet of *formulae and tables*, as shown:

To find the area of a triangle

Step 1: Identify or calculate the angle between the two given sides.

Step 2: Label the sides as a and b and the angle as C.

Step 3: Substitute all values into the formula Area $= \frac{1}{2}ab \sin C$.

Step 4: Solve the resulting equation.

EXAMPLE 1

Find the area of the triangle shown.
Give your answer to the nearest whole number.

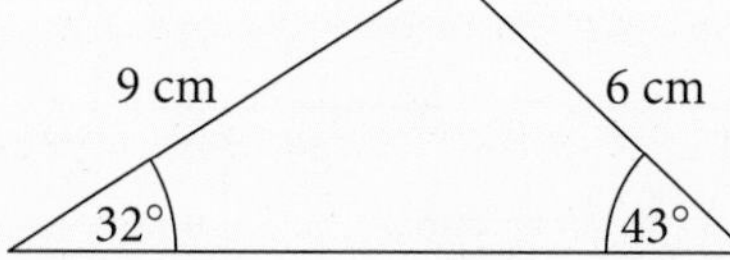

Solution

Find the missing angle:

$C = 180° - 32° - 43°$

$C = 105°$

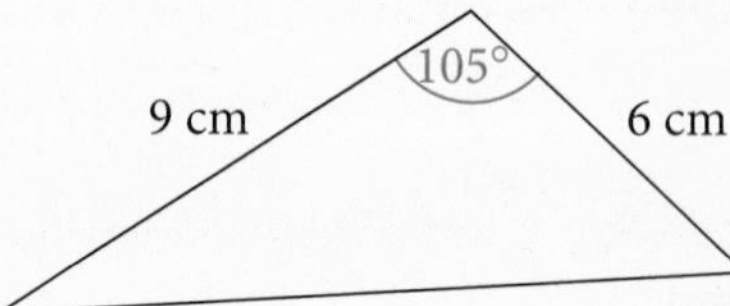

Area $= \frac{1}{2}ab \sin C$ $\quad a = 9$, $b = 6$ and $C = 105°$

Area $= \frac{1}{2}(9)(6) \sin 105°$

Area $= \frac{1}{2}(54) \sin 105°$

Area $= 27 \sin 105°$

Area $= 26{\cdot}08$

Area $= 26 \text{ cm}^2$

EXAMPLE 2

The area of the triangle shown is 36 cm^2. Find the value of x.

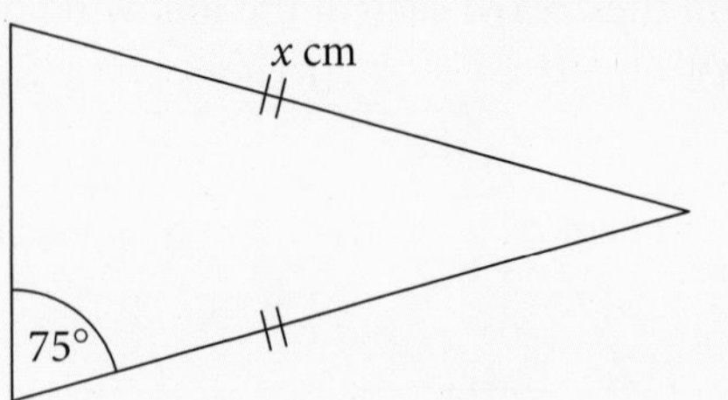

Solution

The triangle is isosceles, therefore the two marked sides are equal and the angles on the left are 75°.

Third angle = 180° − 75° − 75°

Third angle = 30°

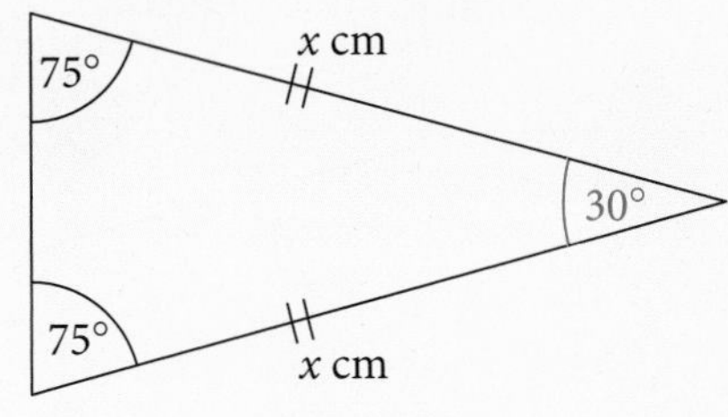

Area $= \frac{1}{2}ab \sin C$ $a = x$, $b = x$ and $C = 30°$

$$36 = \frac{1}{2}(x)(x)\sin 30°$$

$$36 = \frac{1}{2}(x^2)\left(\frac{1}{2}\right)$$

$$36 = \frac{1}{4}(x^2)$$

$$144 = x^2$$

$$\sqrt{144} = x$$

$$12 = x$$

Practice Questions 21.3

1. Find the area of each of the following triangles. Give your answer in surd fom.

(i)

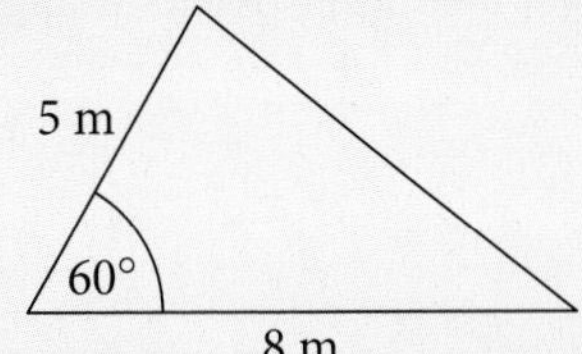

(ii)

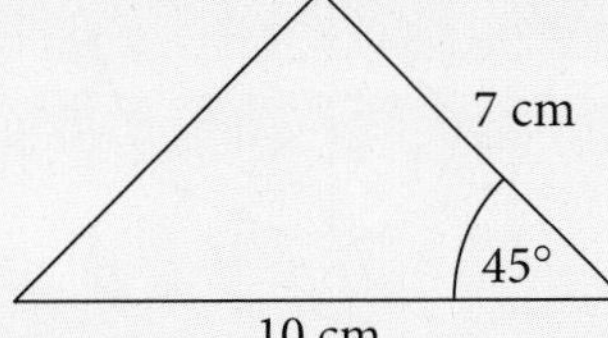

(iii)

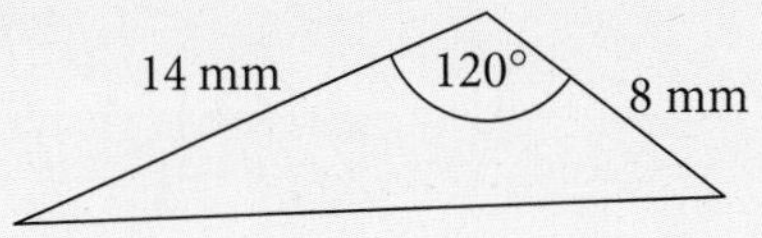

2. Find the area of each of the following triangles. Give your answer correct to one decimal place.

(i)

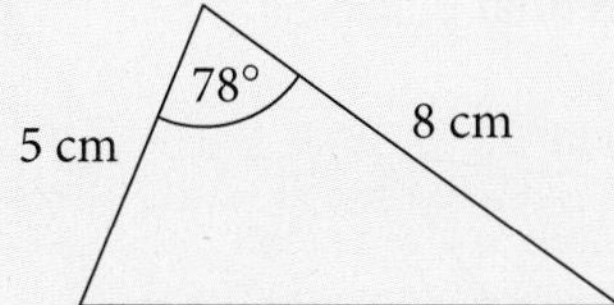

(ii)

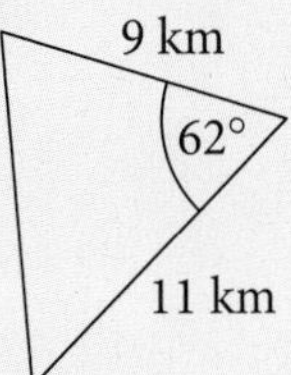

(iii)

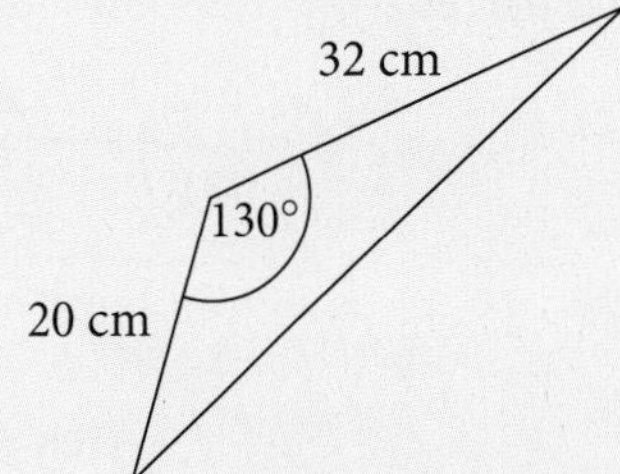

3. Find the missing angle in each of the following triangles and hence find the area of the triangle. Give your answer correct to one decimal place.

(i)

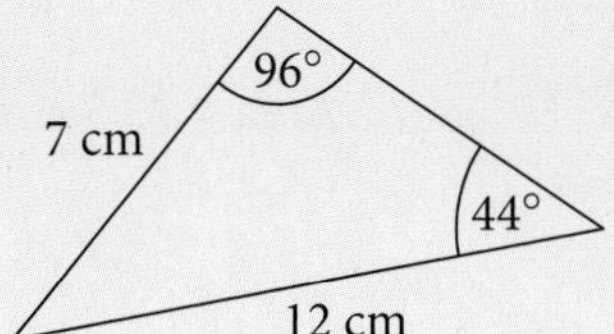

(ii)

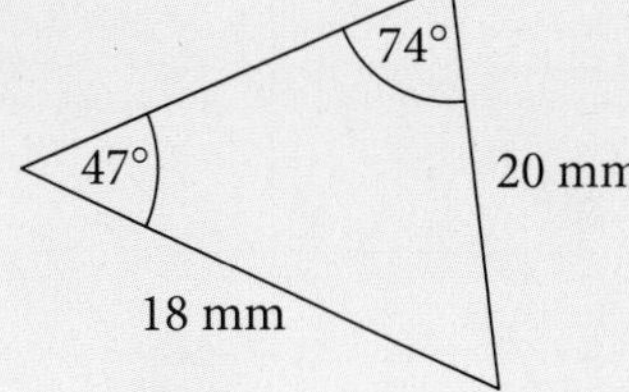

(iii)

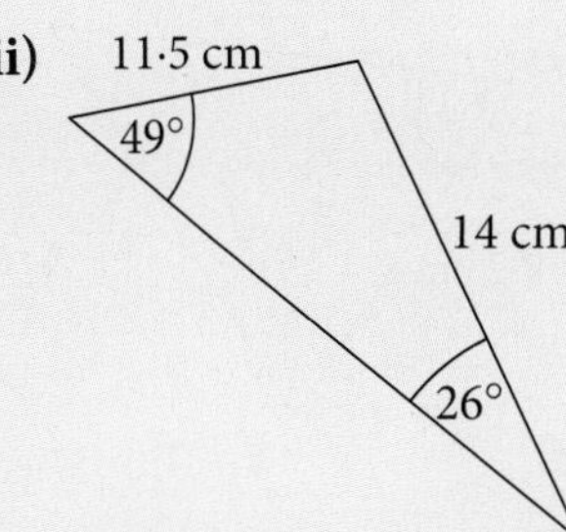

4. Find the area of each of the following quadrilaterals. Give your answer correct to one decimal place.

(i)

16 cm
122°
12 cm
9 cm
82°
28 cm

(iii)

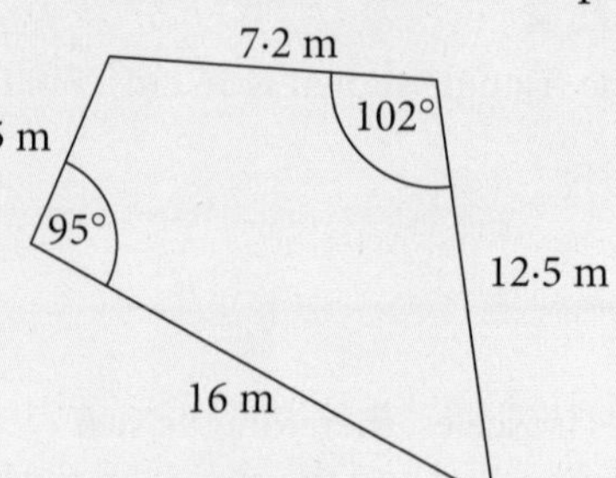

Hint: Divide the quadrilaterals into two triangles.

(ii)

56°
15 cm
11 cm
6 cm
110°
9 cm

(iv)

49°
7·5 cm
12·6 cm
9·5 cm
37°

5. Find the area of each of the following polygons. Give your answer to two decimal places.

(i)

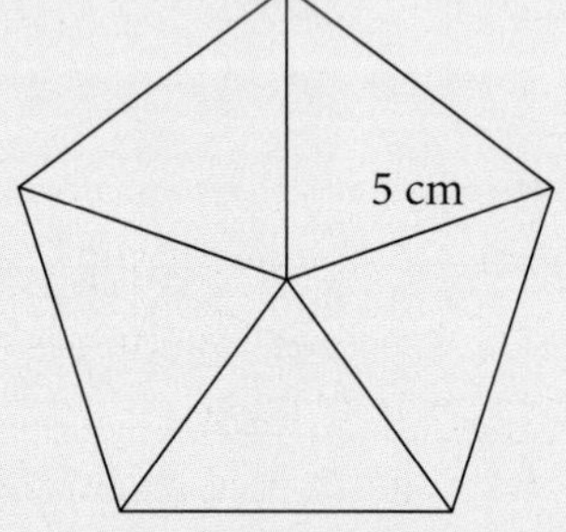

(ii)

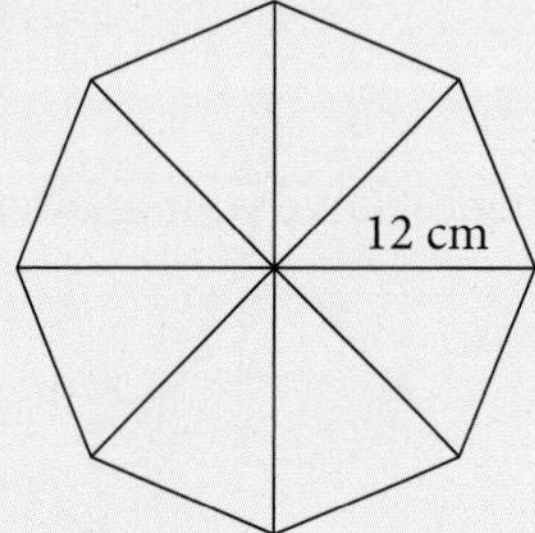

A **polygon** is a plane shape with three, or more, straight edges.
Regular polygons are symmetrical and made up of identical isosceles triangles.

6. Find the value of x, in each case, given the area of the triangle shown. Give your answer to two decimal places.

(i)

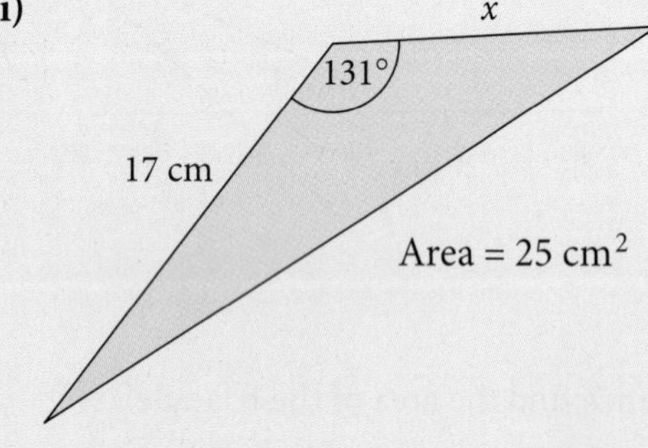

(ii)

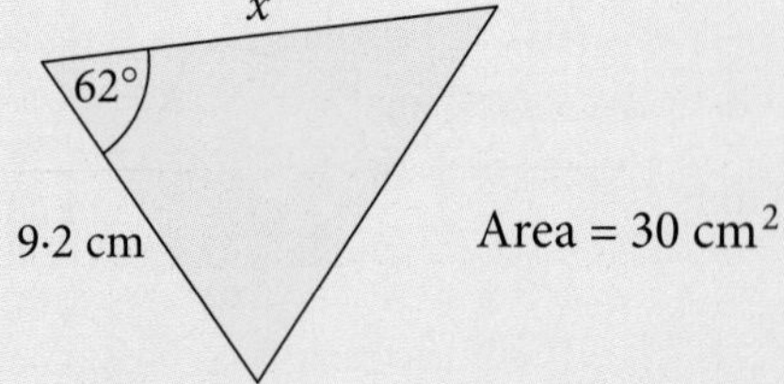

7. Find the measure of the acute angle X in each case, given the area of the triangle shown. Give your answer to two decimal places.

(i)

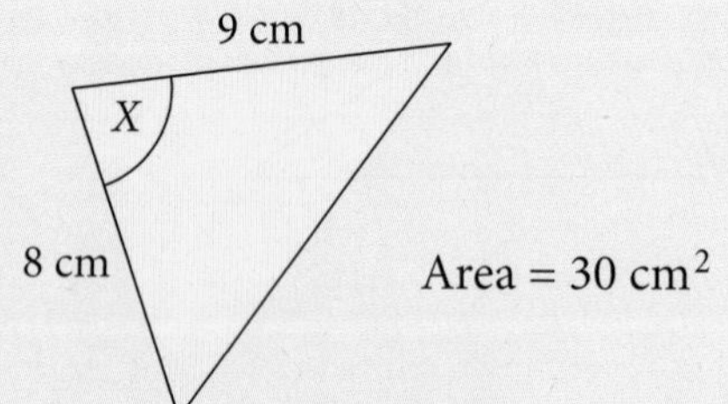

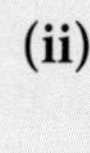

(ii)

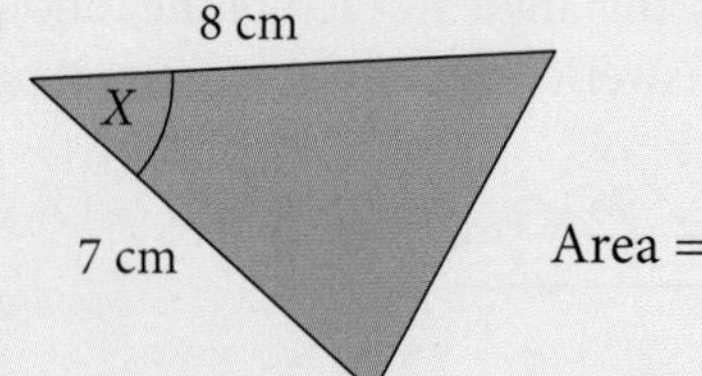

8. The diagram shows an equilateral triangle.

   The area of the triangle is $16\sqrt{3}$ cm^2.

   Find the measure of the sides of the triangle.

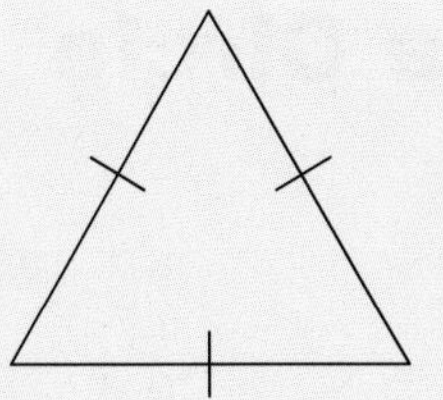

9. ABC is a triangle and D is a point on $[BC]$, as shown.
   $|BD| = 3$ cm, $|AC| = 6$ cm
   $|\angle ACD| = 65°$ and $|\angle DAC| = 70°$.

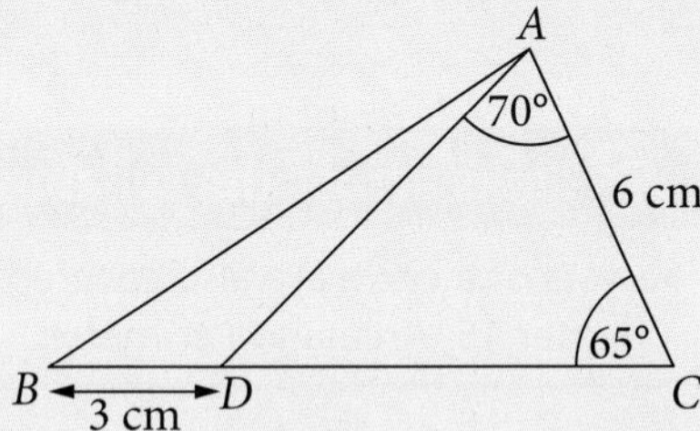

   Find:

   (i) $|DC|$, correct to the nearest whole number

   (ii) the area of the triangle ABC, correct to one decimal place.

10. In the triangle ABC, D is a point on $[BC]$, as shown.
    $|BD| = 5$ cm, $|AC| = 8$ cm, $|\angle DCA| = 82°$ and $|\angle CAD| = 50°$.

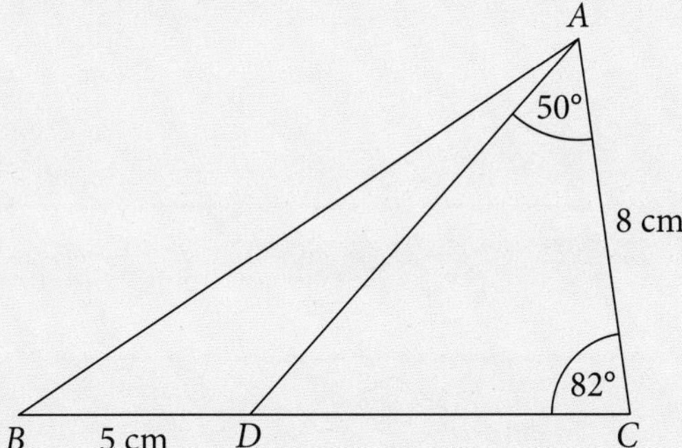

   Find:

   (i) $|DC|$, correct to the nearest centimetre

   (ii) $|AB|$, correct to the nearest centimetre

   (iii) the area of triangle ABC, to the nearest whole number.

11. The area of the triangle ABC is 33 cm^2.
    $|AB| = 8$ cm and $|\angle CAB| = 55°$.
    Find:

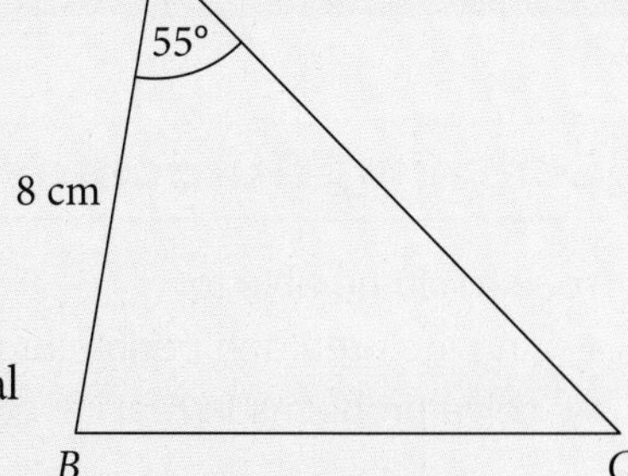

   (i) $|AC|$, correct to one decimal place

   (ii) $|BC|$, correct to one decimal place

   (iii) $|\angle ABC|$, correct to the nearest degree.

12. The lengths of the sides of the triangle PQR are $|PQ| = 20$, $|QR| = 14$ and $|PR| = 12$.

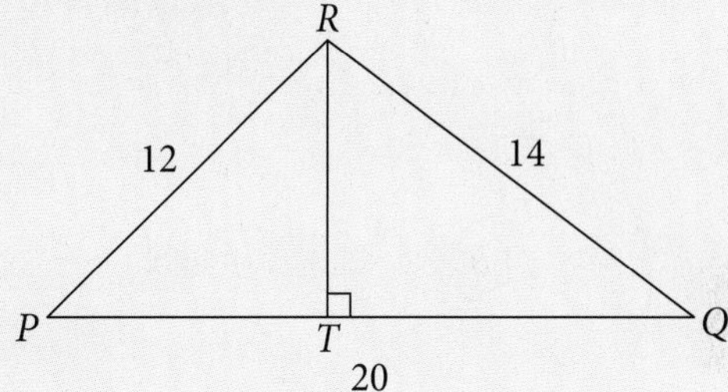

   Find:

   (i) $|\angle RPQ|$, correct to one decimal place

   (ii) $|RT|$, where $RT \perp PQ$. Give your answer correct to two decimal places.

   (iii) the area of the triangle PQR by two different methods.

13. The triangle ABC has an area of 20 cm^2.
    $|AB| = 8$ cm and $|AC| = 10$ cm.

   (i) Find **two** possible values for $|\angle BAC|$.

   (ii) Draw a sketch of the two possible triangles ABC.

   (iii) Find the two possible values for $|BC|$. Give your answer correct to one decimal place.

   Recall the ambiguous case which was covered in Section 21.1 of this chapter.

14. The triangle PQR has an area of 51 cm^2.
    $|PQ| = 6$ cm and $|PR| = 18$ cm.

   (i) Find **two** possible values for $|\angle QPR|$. Give your answer correct to two decimal places.

   (ii) Draw a sketch of the two possible triangles PQR.

   (iii) Find the two possible values for $|QR|$.

   Give your answer to one decimal place.

Section 21.4: Sectors of a Circle

Learning Outcomes:

You should be able to:
- find the area and perimeter of a sector of a circle
- solve problems in real life contexts

A **sector** is a portion of a circle enclosed by two radii and an arc.

$$\text{Area} = \pi r^2\left(\frac{\theta}{360°}\right)$$
$$\text{Arc} = 2\pi r\left(\frac{\theta}{360°}\right)$$
$$\text{Perimeter} = \text{Arc} + 2(\text{radius})$$

Links across the syllabus

Sectors of a circle are also covered in Chapter 16: Area and Perimeter.

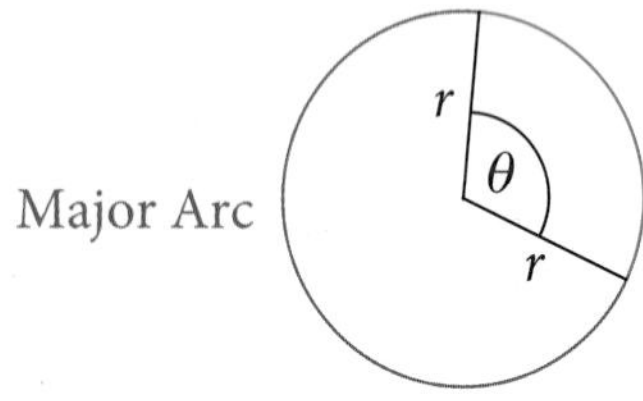

The formula for the **length of the arc** and the **area of the sector** of a circle appears on page 9 of the booklet of *formulae and tables*, as shown:

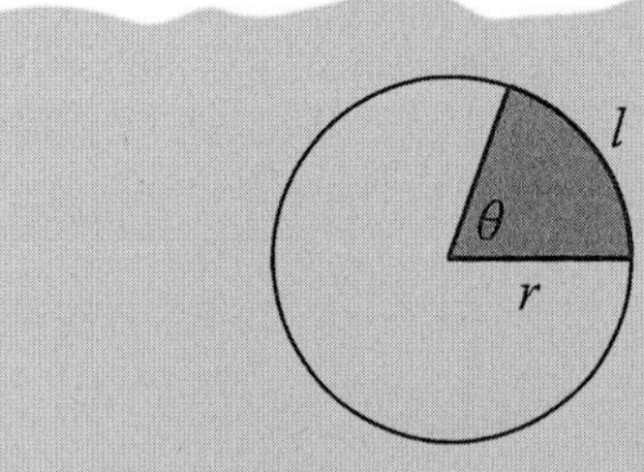

Arc / Sector

$$l = 2\pi r\left(\frac{\theta}{360°}\right) \qquad A = \pi r^2\left(\frac{\theta}{360°}\right)$$ *when θ is in degrees*

EXAMPLE 1

Find the **(i)** area and **(ii)** perimeter of the sector shown.
Give your answer to one decimal place.

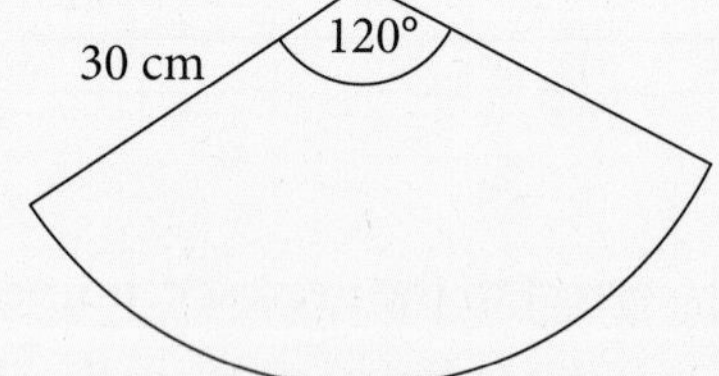

Solution

(i) $\text{Area} = \pi r^2\left(\frac{\theta}{360°}\right)$

$= (\pi(30)^2)\left(\frac{120°}{360°}\right)$

$= (900\pi)\left(\frac{1}{3}\right)$

$= 300\pi$

$= 942{\cdot}477$

$\text{Area} = 942{\cdot}5 \text{ cm}^2$

(ii) $\text{Arc} = 2\pi r\left(\frac{\theta}{360°}\right)$

$= (2\pi(30))\left(\frac{120°}{360°}\right)$

$= (60\pi)\left(\frac{1}{3}\right)$

$= 20\pi$

$= 62{\cdot}8318$

$\text{Arc} = 62{\cdot}8$

$\text{Perimeter} = \text{Arc} + 2(\text{radius})$

$= 62{\cdot}8 + 2(30)$

$= 62{\cdot}8 + 60$

$\text{Perimeter} = 122{\cdot}8 \text{ cm}$

Trigonometry II

EXAMPLE 2

A sector of a circle, of angle 225°, has an arc of length 7·5π cm.
Find the area of this sector, in terms of π.

Solution

We must first find the radius

$$\text{Arc} = 2\pi r\left(\frac{\theta}{360°}\right)$$

$$7·5\pi = 2\pi r\left(\frac{225°}{360°}\right)$$

$$7·5\pi = 2\pi r\left(\frac{5}{8}\right)$$

$$8(7·5\pi) = 5(2\pi r) \quad \text{(multiplied by 8)}$$

$$60\pi = 10\pi r$$

$$6 = r \quad \text{(divided by } 10\pi\text{)}$$

Now find the area of the sector with radius 6 cm and angle 225°:

$$\text{Area} = \pi r^2\left(\frac{\theta}{360°}\right)$$

$$= (\pi(6)^2)\left(\frac{225°}{360°}\right)$$

$$= 36\pi\left(\frac{5}{8}\right)$$

$$= \frac{180\pi}{8}$$

$$\text{Area} = 22·5\pi\,\text{cm}^2$$

EXAMPLE 3

Find the area of the shaded region (segment) in the given diagram.
Give your answer to the nearest whole number.

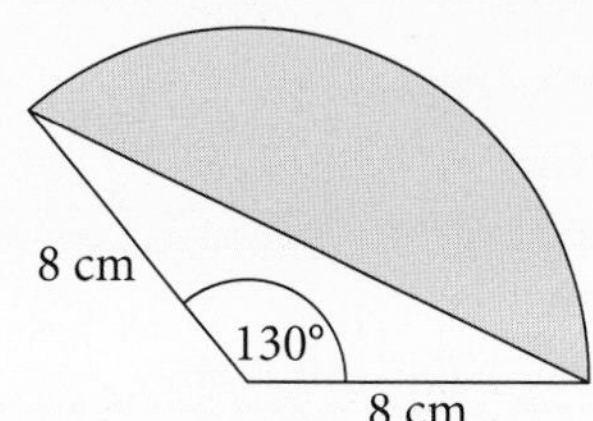

Solution

Area of the segment = Area of the sector − Area of the triangle

Area of the sector:

$$\text{Sector} = \pi r^2\left(\frac{\theta}{360°}\right)$$

$$= (\pi(8)^2)\left(\frac{130°}{360°}\right)$$

$$= (64\pi)\left(\frac{13}{36}\right)$$

$$\text{Sector} = 72·6\ \text{cm}^2$$

Area of the triangle:

$$\text{Triangle} = \frac{1}{2}ab\sin C$$

$$= \frac{1}{2}(8)(8)\sin 130°$$

$$= 32\sin 130°$$

$$\text{Triangle} = 24·51\ \text{cm}^2$$

Area of the segment:

$$\text{Segment} = \text{Sector} - \text{Triangle}$$

$$= 72·6 - 24·51$$

$$= 48·09$$

$$\text{Segment} = 48\ \text{cm}^2$$

Practice Questions 21.4

1. Find **(a)** the area, **(b)** the length of the arc and **(c)** the perimeter of the following sectors. Give your answer in terms of π.

(i)

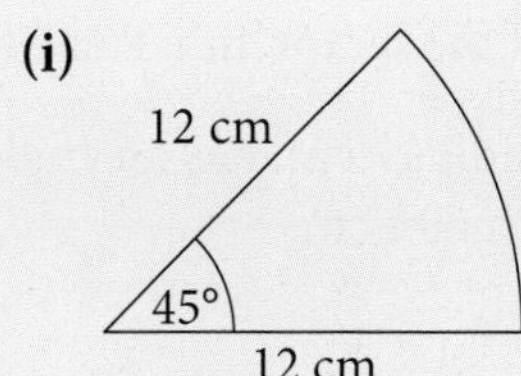

(ii)

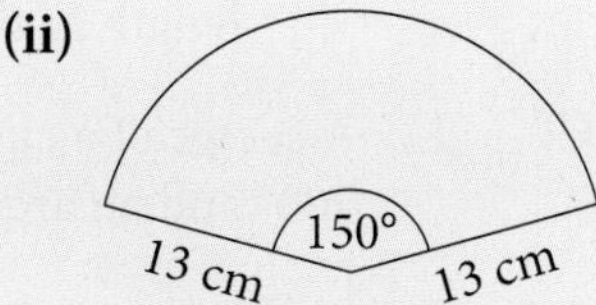

(iii)

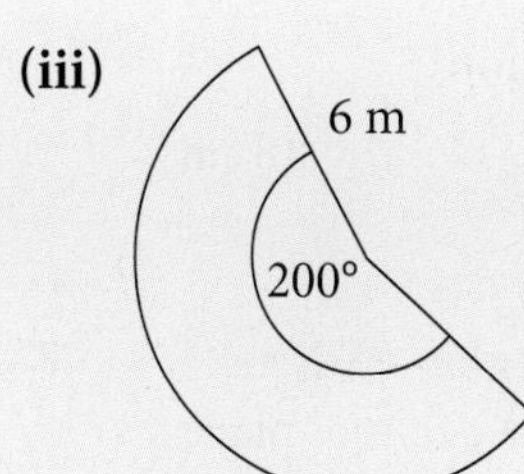

2. A circle, of radius 7·2 cm, contains a sector AOB, of angle 30°, as shown. Find, in terms of π, the length of the **major** arc AB.

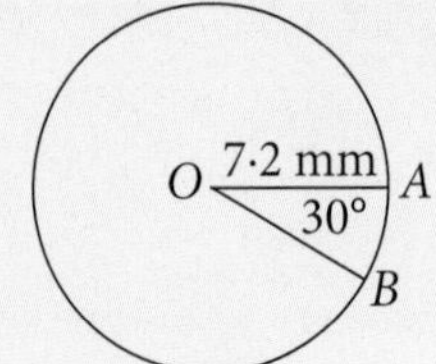

3. The diagram shows an equilateral triangle ABC with side length 8 cm. P is the midpoint of AC and Q is the midpoint of AB. APQ is a sector of a circle, centre A. Calculate the area of the shaded region. Give your answer correct to one decimal place.

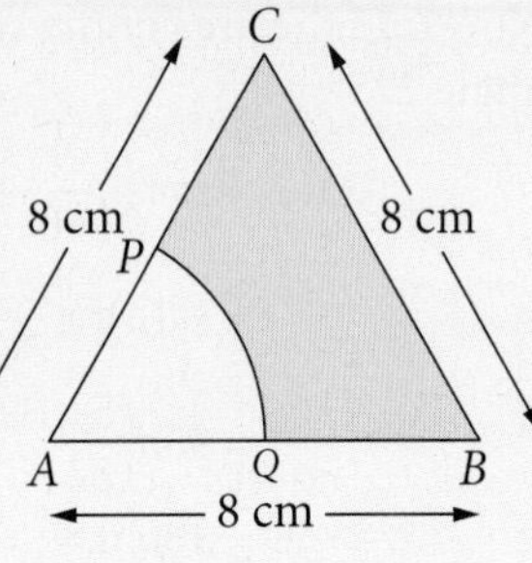

4. The diagram shows a sector of a circle inscribed inside a triangle. Find the area of the shaded region. Give your answer to the nearest whole number.

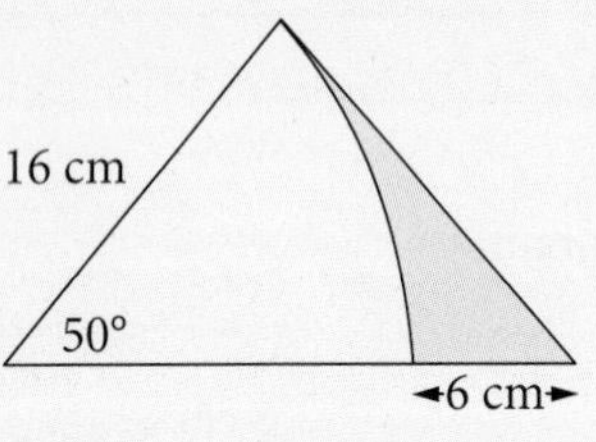

5. The diagram shows a pentagon inscribed inside a circle, of radius 8 cm. Find the area of the shaded region, correct to one decimal place.

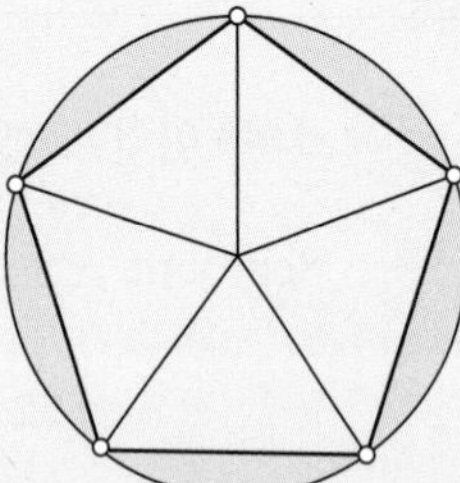

6. The diagram shows a circle, of radius 20 cm, with a segment removed, as shown. Find the perimeter of this shape, correct to one decimal place.

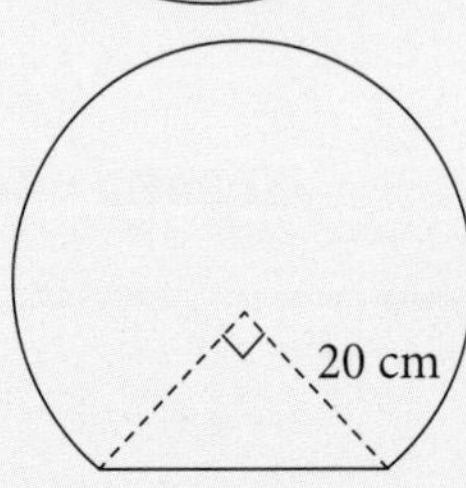

7. The diagram shows a sector of a circle with centre O. The radius of the circle is 18 cm. PS is a chord of the circle. Calculate:

   (i) the area of the shaded region PSR, correct to one decimal place

   (ii) the perimeter of the segment PSR, correct to one decimal place.

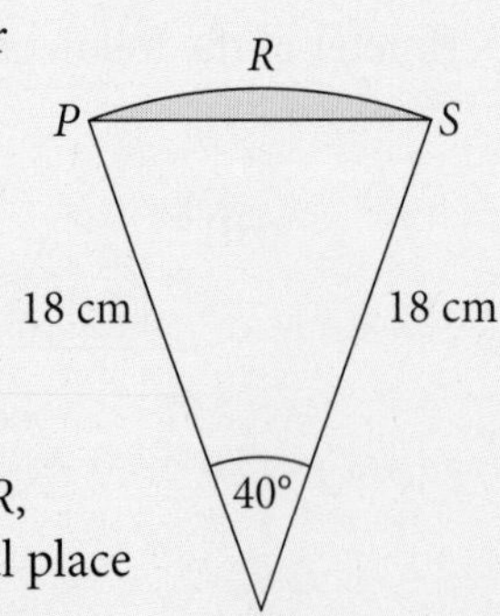

8. The diagram shows a sector of a circle with centre O. The radius of the circle is 75 m. AB is a chord of the circle.

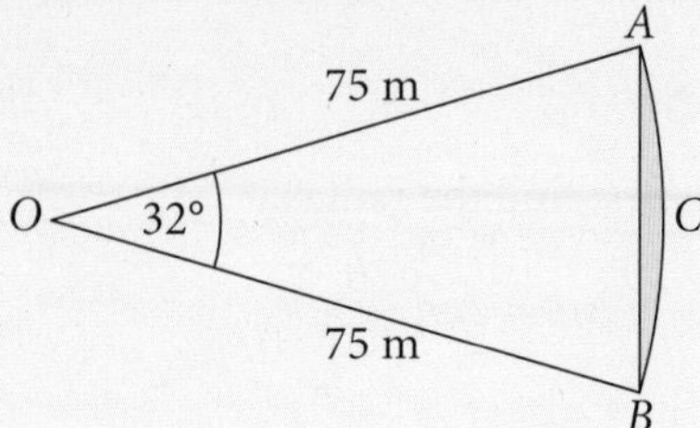

Calculate:

   (i) the area of the shaded region ABC, correct to one decimal place

   (ii) the perimeter of the segment ABC, correct to one decimal place.

9. The diagram shows a flowerbed (shaded in green), formed by two sectors.

   (i) Find the area of the flowerbed, to the nearest square metre.

   (ii) The gardener wants to surround the flowerbed with a fence. What length of fencing will the gardener need?

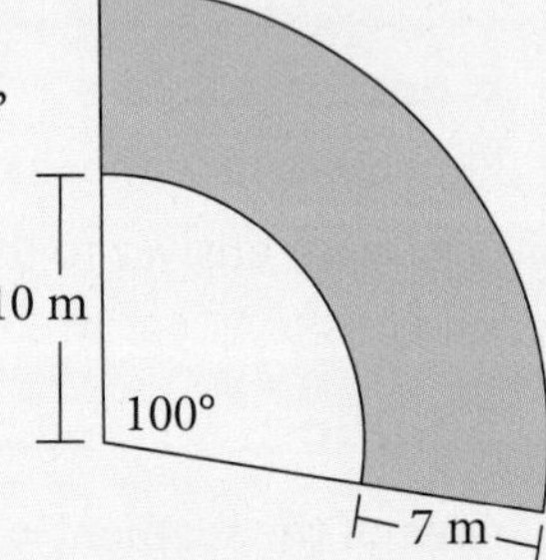

10. OAB is a sector of a circle, centre O. The length of the arc AB is 4π cm.

    (i) Find the measure of the angle θ.

    (ii) Hence, find the area of the sector AOB, in terms of π.

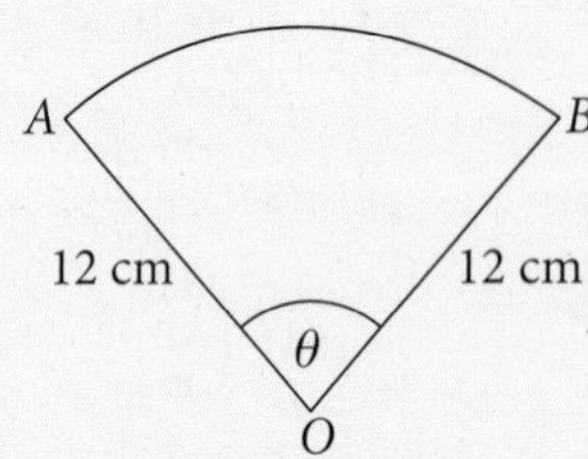

11. The sector shown has an area of 81π cm^2.

    (i) Find the measure of the angle θ.

    (ii) Hence, find the length of the arc of the sector, in terms of π.

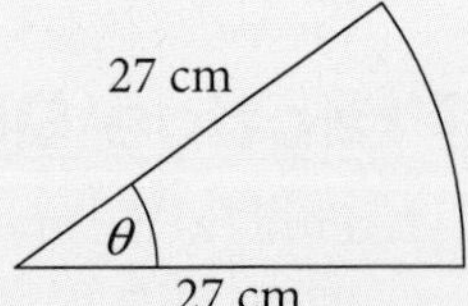

12. A sector of a circle, of radius r cm, has an angle of 200° and an arc of length 60π cm.

    Find:

    (i) the value of r, the radius of the sector

    (ii) the area of the sector, in terms of π.

13. A sector of a circle, of radius 16 cm, has an arc of length 12π cm.
Find the area of this sector, to the nearest whole number.

14. A sector of a circle, of radius 6 cm, has an area of 24π cm^2.
Find the length of the arc of this sector.

15. A sector of a circle, of angle 72°, has an arc of length 6π cm.
Find the area of this sector.

16. Two identical circles, of radius 9 mm, intersect as shown.
The centre of one circle is A and the centre of the other circle is B.

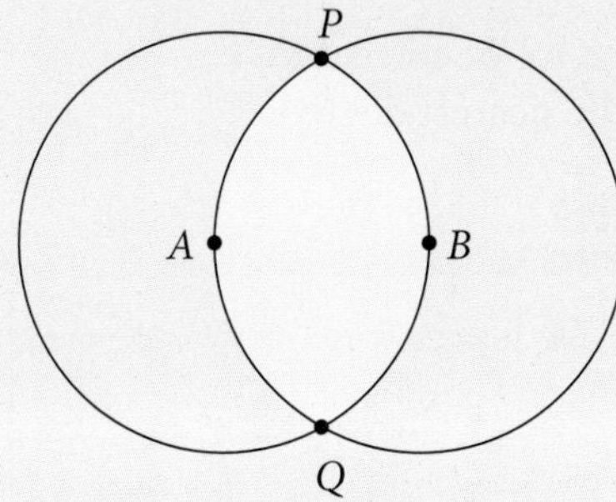

(i) Find the measure of the angle PAB.
(ii) Hence, find the measure of the angle PAQ.
(iii) Find the area of the sector PAQ, in terms of π.
(iv) Find the area of the shaded region.
Give your answer to one decimal place.

17. The diagram shows a church window.
The centre for the arc AB is C and the centre of the arc AC is B.
$|DE| = 120$ cm and $|CE| = 160$ cm.

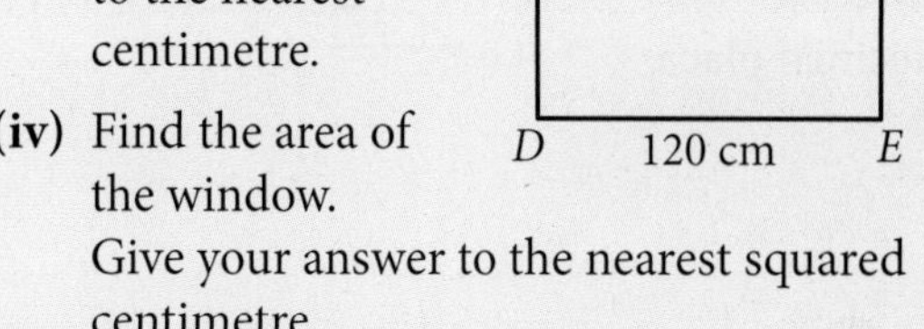

(i) Show that $|\angle ABC| = 60°$.
(ii) Find the length of the arc AB. Give your answer to the nearest centimetre.
(iii) Find the perimeter of the window. Give your answer to the nearest centimetre.
(iv) Find the area of the window. Give your answer to the nearest squared centimetre.
(v) Find the vertical height of the window. Give your answer to the nearest centimetre.

Revision and Exam Style Questions – Section A

1. Find the value for x, the length of the side shown in the triangle. Give your answer to one decimal place.

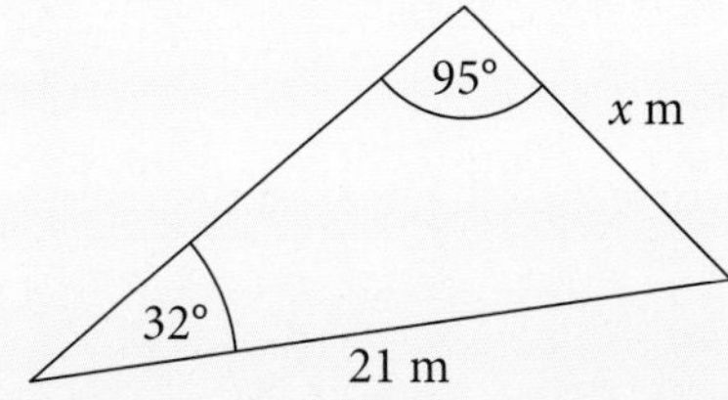

2. In the triangle ABC, $|AB| = 18{\cdot}4$, $|BC| = 14$ and $|\angle CAB| = 44°$.

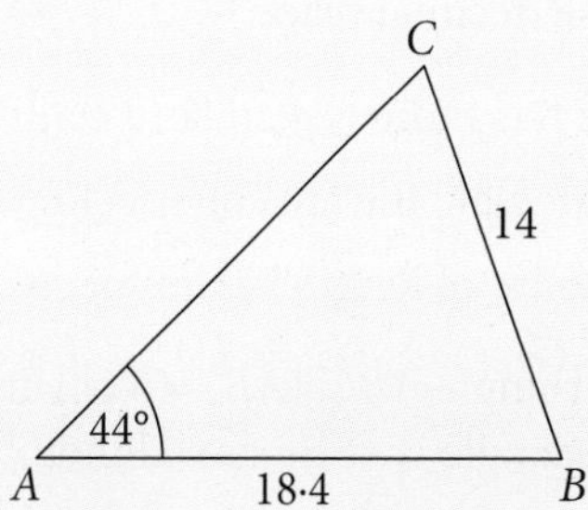

Find:
(i) $|\angle BCA|$, correct to the nearest degree
(ii) the area of the triangle ABC, correct to the nearest whole number.

3. For the triangle shown, find to the nearest whole number the measure of:

   (i) α (ii) β

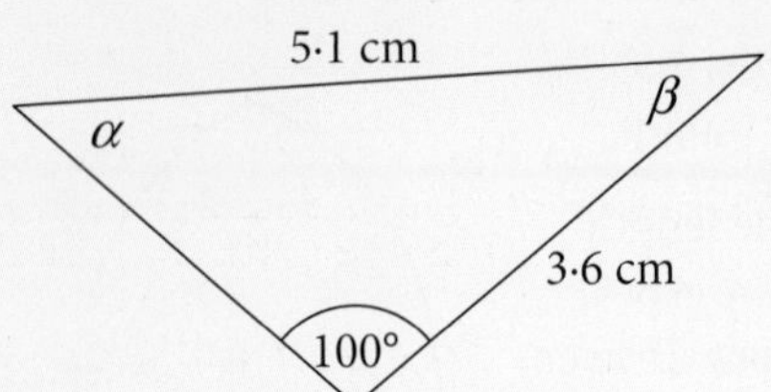

4. Find the value for x, the length of the side shown in the triangle. Give your answer correct to one decimal place.

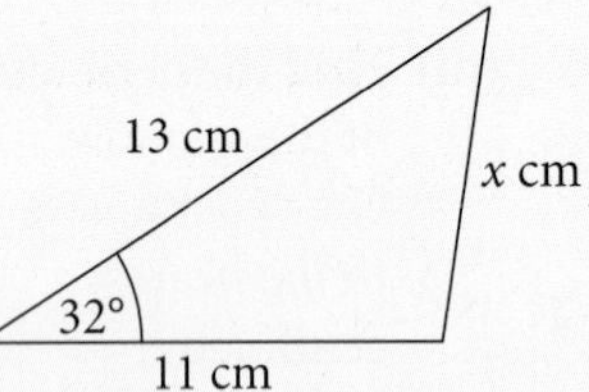

5. In the triangle ABC, $|AB| = 5$ cm, $|BC| = 9$ cm and $|\angle ABC| = 67°$.

   (i) Find the area of the triangle ABC, correct to one decimal place.

   (ii) Calculate $|AC|$, correct to the nearest whole number.

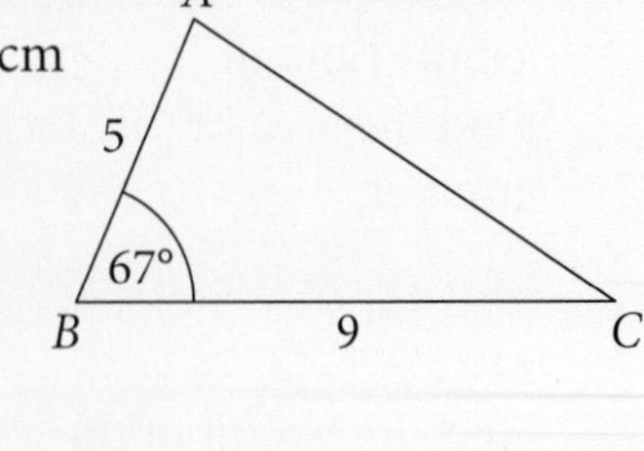

6. XYZ is a triangle where $|XY| = 15$ cm, $|YZ| = 22$ cm and $|\angle XYZ| = 74°$. Find:

   (i) $|XZ|$, correct to the nearest centimetre

   (ii) $|\angle YZX|$, correct to the nearest degree.

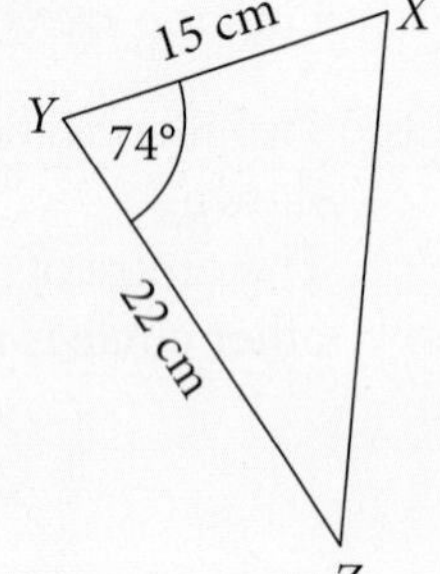

7. A circle has centre O and radius 8 cm. A and B are two points on the circle and $|\angle AOB| = 150°$. Find:

   (i) the area of the circle, correct to the nearest cm^2

   (ii) the area of the sector AOB, correct to the nearest cm^2

   (iii) the length of the minor arc AB, correct to the nearest cm.

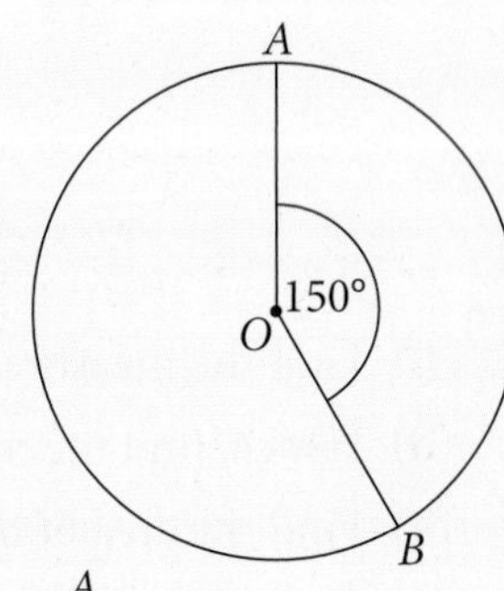

8. The diagram shows a wooden structure used for supporting a roof. Find:

   (i) $|BD|$ to the nearest metre

   (ii) $|EG|$ to two decimal places

   (iii) $|\angle CAF|$

   (iv) $|CF|$ to two decimal places

   (v) Hence, find the total length of wood needed to make this structure, correct to one decimal place.

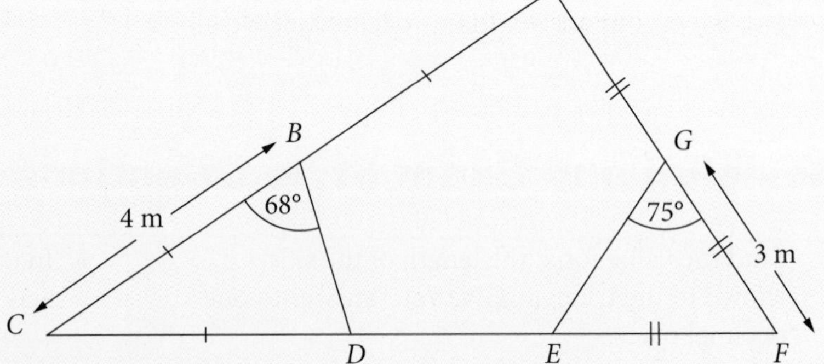

9. A circle has radius 24 cm and centre O.

   (i) Calculate the area of a sector which has 75° at its centre, in terms of π.

   (ii) An arc of length 52 cm forms an angle A at O. Calculate A, correct to the nearest degree.

10. In the triangle ABC, $|AB| = 5$ cm and $|BC| = 8$ cm. The area of the triangle is 16·58 cm^2. Find:

   (i) $|\angle ABC|$, correct to the nearest degree

   (ii) $|AC|$, correct to the nearest centimetre.

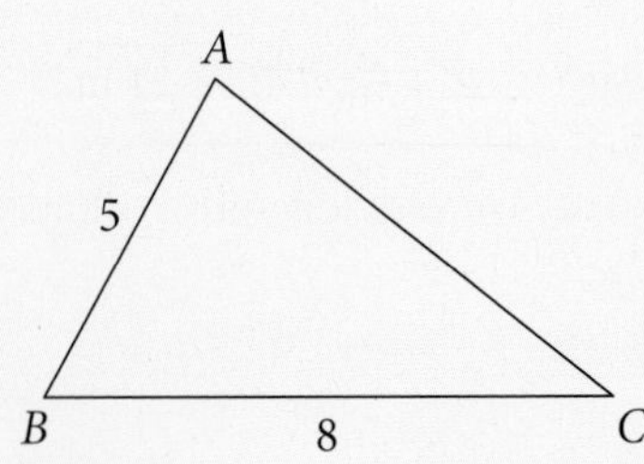

11. Two ships, A and B, leave port K at noon. A is travelling due East and B is travelling E 70° S, as shown.

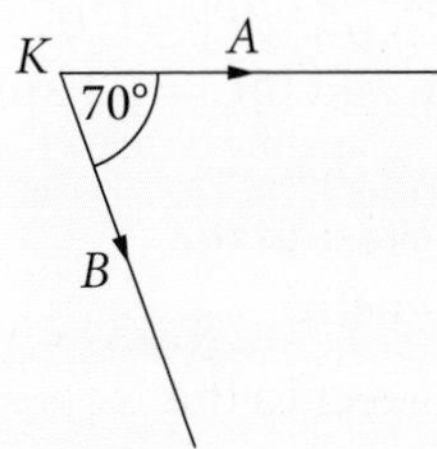

A is travelling at 3 km/hr and B is travelling at 4·5 km/hr. Find the distance between the ships at 4 pm. Give your answer to one decimal place.

12. In the triangle ABC, $|AB| = 8$ cm, $|BC| = 7$ cm and $|\angle ABC| = 30°$.

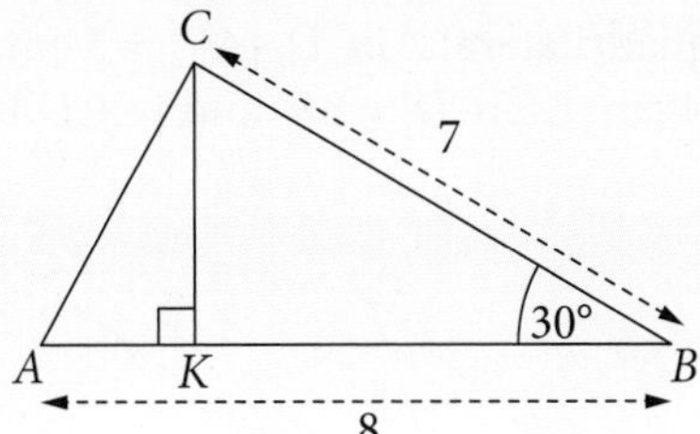

(i) Find the area of the triangle ABC.

(ii) Given that $CK \perp AB$, find $|CK|$.

(iii) Find $|AC|$.

(iv) Find $|\angle BAC|$, correct to the nearest degree.

(v) Hence, find $|\angle KCA|$.

13. A harbour is 8 km due east of a lighthouse. A boat is 6·5 km from the lighthouse. The bearing of the boat from the lighthouse is N 30° W.

Boat
6·5 km
30°
Lighthouse
8 km
Harbour

(i) How far is the boat from the harbour? Give your answer to the nearest metre.

(ii) Find the bearing of the boat from the harbour. Give your answer correct to the nearest degree.

14. A plane is flying due north. There is an air traffic control tower located as shown. Two points, A and B, are 12 km apart along the plane's path. From A the bearing of the tower is N 40° E.

North
Tower
70°
B
12 km
40°
A

From B the bearing of the tower is N 70° E. Find:

(i) the distance from B to the tower, correct to one decimal place

(ii) the shortest distance from the path of the plane to the tower, correct to the nearest metre.

Revision and Exam Style Questions – Section B

More challenging problems

1. Nia wants to measure the height of a tree. She stands at the point A and measures the angle of elevation to the point C, at the top of the tree, to be 65°. She then walks 3 m away from the tree until she gets to the point B. She measures the angle of elevation from B to C to be 42°. Find:

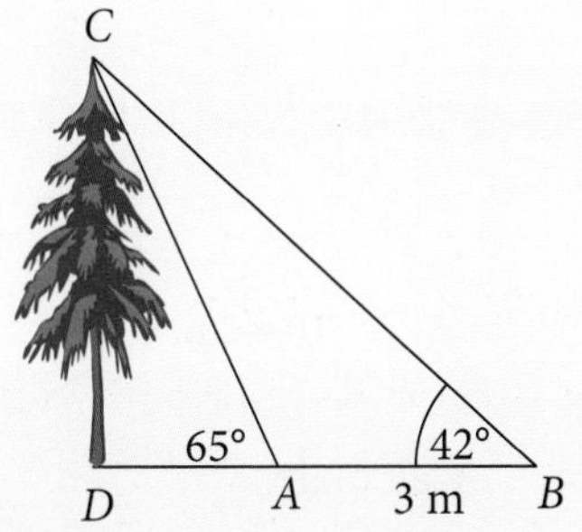

(i) $|AC|$. Give your answer to the nearest centimetre.

(ii) the height of the tree, $|CD|$. Give your answer to the nearest centimetre.

2. The triangle XYZ has dimensions $|XY| = 54$ cm, $|XZ| = 62$ cm, $|\angle XZY| = 40°$.

(i) Find two possible values for $|\angle XYZ|$, correct to the nearest degree.

(ii) Draw a sketch of the two possible triangles XYZ.

3. The diagram shows a circle, of radius 40 cm, with a segment removed.

40 cm
120°

Find:

(i) the area of this shape, correct to one decimal place

(ii) the perimeter of this shape, correct to one decimal place.

4. Two adjacent sides of a parallelogram are of length 7·5 cm and 9·3 cm, and the longer diagonal is of length 12 cm.
   (i) Draw a diagram of the parallelogram, showing all known dimensions.
   (ii) Find the angles of the parallelogram. Give your answer to the nearest degree.
   (iii) Find the length of the other diagonal of the parallelogram, correct to one decimal place.

5. The diagram shows a sketch of a field $ABCD$. A farmer needs to buy fertiliser for this field and to put a new fence around the perimeter of the field.

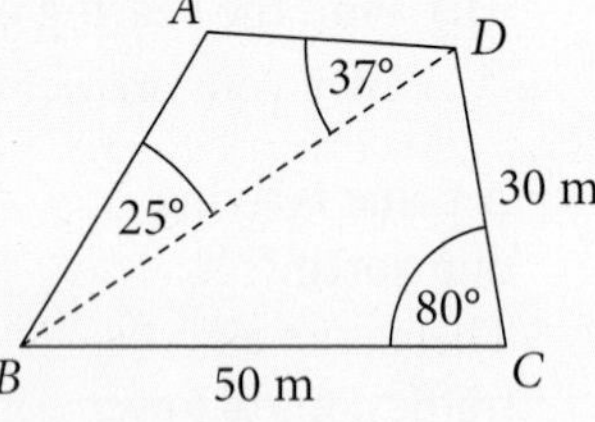

A bag of fertiliser costs €25 and can cover 18 m^2.

Fencing comes in 2 m lengths, each costing €45. Find:
   (i) $|BD|$, correct to one decimal place
   (ii) $|AD|$, correct to one decimal place
   (iii) the perimeter of the field, to the nearest whole number
   (iv) the area of the field, to the nearest whole number
   (v) the total amount the farmer will pay for the fertiliser and the fencing.

6. A circle, of radius 8 cm, is divided into six equal sectors, as shown.
   (i) Find $|\angle AOB|$.
   (ii) Find $|FD|$, correct to one decimal place.

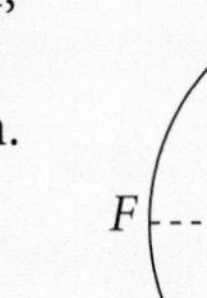

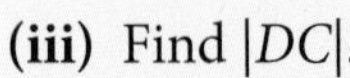

   (iii) Find $|DC|$.
   (iv) Given $|\angle FDC| = |\angle FAC| = 90°$, find the area of the rectangle $FDCA$.
   (v) What percentage of the circle is occupied by the rectangle $FDCA$? Give your answer to one decimal place.

7. Three ships are situated in a straight line at points A, B and C.
   P is a port such that:
   $|\angle BAP| = 55°$, $|\angle ABP| = 110°$
   $|AB| = 10$ km and $|BC| = 22$ km.
   Find:
   (i) $|BP|$, correct to the nearest metre
   (ii) $|CP|$, correct to the nearest metre
   (iii) the area of the triangle APC, correct to one decimal place.

P
55° 110°
A 10 km B 22 km C

8. In the quadrilateral $ABCD$, $|AC| = 5$ cm, $|BC| = 4$ cm, $|\angle ACD| = 35°$ and $|\angle CDA| = 22°$.

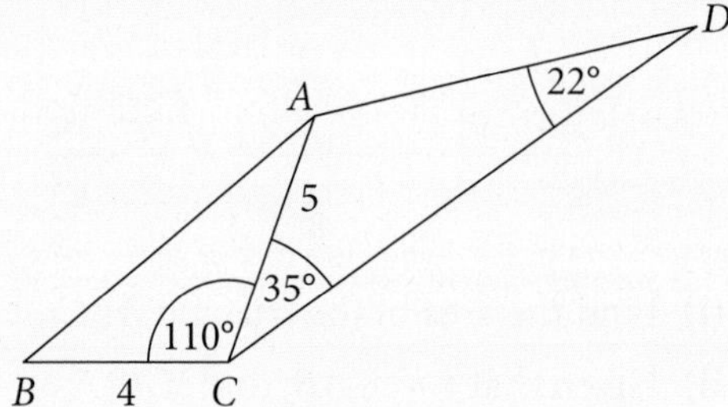

Find:
   (i) $|AB|$, correct to two decimal places
   (ii) $|CD|$, correct to one decimal place
   (iii) the area of the quadrilateral $ABCD$, correct to one decimal place.

9. The diagram shows a sector of a circle with centre O. The radius of the circle is 10·4 cm. AC is a chord of the circle.

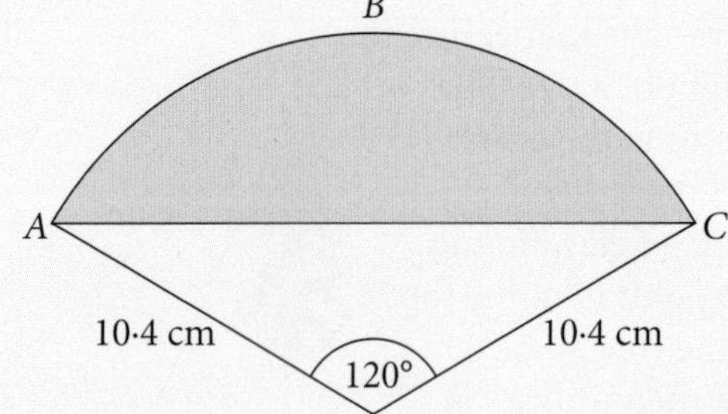

Calculate:
   (i) the area of the shaded region ABC, correct to one decimal place
   (ii) the perimeter of the segment ABC, correct to one decimal place.

Now that you have completed the chapter, revisit the 'Something to think about…' question.

Types of Data

Statistics I – Collecting Data

CHAPTER 22

DATA

Sections covered within this chapter:

KEY WORDS

- Data
- Numerical data
- Bivariate
- Primary data
- Categorical data
- Discrete
- Population
- Secondary data
- Nominal
- Continuous
- Census
- Bias
- Ordinal
- Univariate
- Sample

SOMETHING TO THINK ABOUT… 

Look at the questionnaire below. Do you think it is a well-designed questionnaire? Why or why not? What changes would you make and why?

Questionnaire to find out about eating habits of teenagers

Name: …………………………..

Age: 1st Year ☐ 2nd Year ☐ 3rd Year ☐ 4th Year ☐ 5th Year ☐ 6th Year ☐

Do you think junk food is bad for you? Yes ☐ No ☐
Why? ……………………………………………………………

Do you eat a lot of junk food? Yes ☐ No ☐

How often do you do your maths homework?
Always ☐ Sometimes ☐ Never ☐

Do you or do you not like eating at the following restaurants?
McDonalds ☐ Burger King ☐ KFC ☐ Subway ☐

Introduction

Statistics are used by governments, businesses, sports organisations and many others to make informed decisions when they are providing services, such as in health, transport and business, or developing new strategies or products. These organisations are also interested in using statistics as a means of analysing the effects of certain changes that may have been made, or in predicting and planning for what might happen in the future.

Statistics are collected by carrying out questionnaires and surveys, or by conducting experiments.

Section 22.1: Describing Data

Learning Outcome:

You should be able to:
- identify different types of data

Data is the actual information obtained from surveys, questionnaires or experiments. Data can be either words or numbers.

Discussion Time 

Work with a classmate to answer the following questions, which could appear on a survey.

1. What colour are your eyes?
2. What height are you?
3. How would you rate the last movie you saw, on a scale from excellent to poor?
4. How many siblings do you have?
5. Now work with a classmate and try to put your answers into two separate groups that have something in common.
   (i) Can you see anything in common between questions **1** and **3**?
   (ii) Can you see anything in common between questions **2** and **4**?
   (iii) Both questions **1** and **3** have word answers. Can you see any way that they are different?
   (iv) Both questions **2** and **4** have numerical answers. Can you see any way they are different?

Categorical data

Word answers are known as categorical data.

Categorical data can be either **nominal** or **ordinal**.

Nominal data is made-up of word responses that have **no particular rank**, e.g. eye colour, favourite sport etc.

Ordinal data is text data that can be categorised into groups in a **particular order/rank** e.g. shirt sizes (S, M, L), exam grades (O1, O2, O3 etc.)

Numerical data

Number answers are known as numerical data.

Numerical data can be either **discrete** or **continuous**.

In general, discrete data is made-up of number answers that can only take on **certain values**. It is data that can be counted, e.g. number of people (you can't have half a person!)

Continuous data is number answers that can take on **any value within a range**. It is data that can be measured, e.g. height, time, etc.

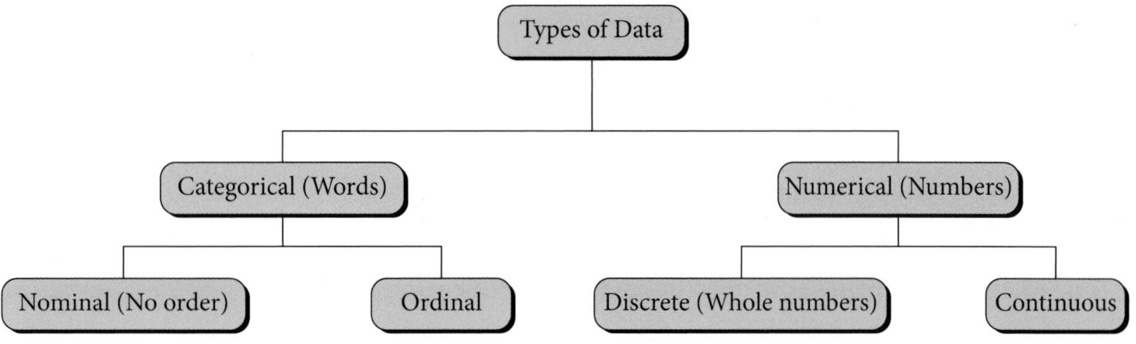

Data can also be **univariate** or **bivariate**.

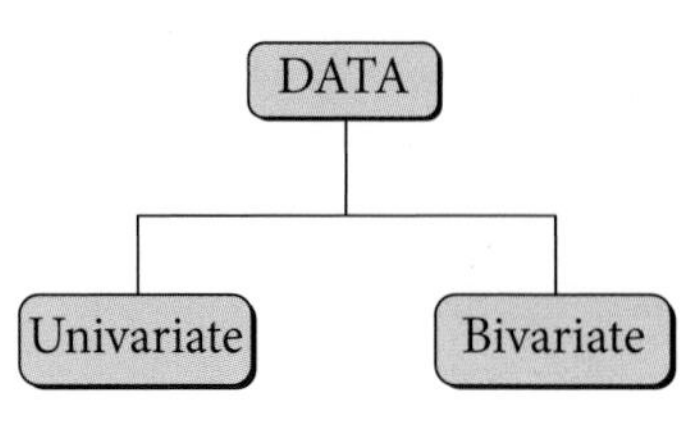

Univariate data looks at **one** variable at a time, e.g. number of siblings, time to get to school, etc. We can find averages, distributions and measures of spread for this type of data.

Bivariate data looks at **two** variables at a time, e.g. ice cream sales and temperature, weight and height. We can compare these two variables and look for relationships between the variables.

EXAMPLE

Explain why:

(i) the weight of a dog is continuous numerical data
(ii) the number of leaves on a tree is univariate discrete numerical data
(iii) people's names are categorical nominal data
(iv) how often you exercise per week is categorical ordinal data
(v) the weight of a vehicle and its fuel consumption is bivariate continuous data.

Solution

(i) The answer is a number and it has been measured, e.g. the average weight of a King Charles Spaniel is 5·4–8·1 kg.
(ii) The answer is a number and it has been counted.
(iii) The answer is in words and one name is not better or worse than another, i.e. there is no order.
(iv) The answer is in words and there is an order, e.g. twice is more often than never.
(v) Two variables are being examined and both are numbers that have been measured.

Practice Questions 22.1

1. Classify the following data as categorical or numerical.
   (i) Jumper size
   (ii) Flavour of crisps
   (iii) Waist measurement
   (iv) Musical genre
   (v) Age
   (vi) Hair colour
   (vii) Type of car
   (viii) Weekly wage
   (ix) Petrol price
   (x) Breed of dog
2. State whether each of these numerical variables is continuous or discrete.
   (i) Chocolates in a box
   (ii) Hand span
   (iii) Altitude of capital cities
   (iv) People in a cinema
   (v) Lifetime of a light bulb
   (vi) Length of a foot
   (vii) Students in a class
   (viii) Distance to school
   (ix) Children in family

3. Name the type of data described in each of the statements below:
   (i) Data that can take on any value.
   (ii) Not a number, often descriptive.
   (iii) Combination of two variables.
   (iv) Data where you can't have 'in-between' values.
4. Abraham bought a new school bag. He wrote down the colour of the bag and the number of pockets in the bag. State whether each of these data types is numerical or categorical.
5. There are three pieces of data relating to the car in this sentence: 'Niall bought a five-door car for €18,000 and drove home at a steady speed of 40 km/hr.'
   (i) What are the three pieces of data?
   (ii) Identify the type of data in each case.
6. Mr Jones starts to make a database for his first-year tutor group. Below is some of his data.

Name	Age	Transport to school	Height (cm)	Punctual	No. of siblings
Amy Andrews	12	Bus	151	Always	0
Barry Bacon	12	Car	145	Usually	1
Chloe Coleman	11	Walk	139	Never	3
Damien Doyle	13	Walk	146	Always	2
Elaine Edwards	12	Cycle	142	Always	3
Fred Flynn	11	Car	156	Usually	1
Grace Gorman	12	Walk	149	Never	2
Hugh Harmon	12	Car	150	Always	1

   (i) From the table above, give an example of:
      (a) categorical nominal data
      (b) numerical discrete data
      (c) numerical continuous data.
   (ii) What type of data is shown in the punctual column?

Discussion Time 

Work with a classmate to come up with a question that could be used to gather:

1. discrete data
2. categorical data
3. bivariate data
4. ordinal data
5. continuous data
6. nominal data

Section 22.2: Collecting Data

Learning Outcomes:

You should be able to:
- understand the difference between a population and a sample
- discuss different ways of collecting data
- understand bias and how it can affect interpretation of data
- select a simple random sample that is representative and without bias from a population

Populations and samples

A **population** is the entire group being studied.

Collection of data from a whole population is called a **census**.

Suppose you wanted to find out the favourite sport of students in your school. It would not be very practical to question every single student in the school, so you might decide to ask a group of students and use their results to predict the numbers for the entire school.

All the students in the school are known as the student population.

If you take a group of students from the population this group is known as a sample.

A **sample** is a group taken from within the population, it is a subset of the population.

Simple random sampling is the most widely used statistical sampling method, mainly because it is easy to implement and easy to analyse. In a simple random sample, each member of the population is equally likely to be chosen. For example, picking names out of a hat, as long as the names are returned to the hat each time.

It is very important that a sample is representative of the entire population.

When choosing a sample from a population, we must consider the following:

1. The sample must be large enough to ensure it is representative of the entire population. For populations of 1,000 or more, a sample size of 400 is typically used.
2. The sample must be random.
3. All members of the population must have an equal chance of being selected.
4. The likely response rate should be as high as possible.

If the sample is not selected correctly, the data gathered from it may be useless.

Generating a simple random sample

Step 1: Identify and list your entire population, e.g. all the students enrolled in the school.

Step 2: Assign each member of the population a number.

Step 3: Decide on your sample size.

Step 4: Use a random number generator to generate random numbers.

Step 5: Select the members of your population using the random numbers generated.

You can use your calculator to generate random numbers.

Methods of collecting data

There are many ways to collect data. Some of these ways include:

- **Direct observations** – e.g. standing at a set of traffic lights and counting the colours of the cars passing.
- **Surveys and questionnaires** – if these are completed by the entire population, this is called a census. More commonly, they are completed by a sample of the population.
- **Experiments** – often carried out to test a new drug or medical treatment.
- **Interviews** – can be face to face or over the phone.
- **Databases** – this involves looking up information that has been gathered by others, e.g electoral register, etc.

If the data is collected by the person carrying out the investigation, it is called **primary data.** Direct observations, interviews and experiments would produce primary data.

Primary data is data that is collected first-hand by the person carrying out the investigation.

If the data is taken from a source such as the internet, records or registers, it is called **secondary data**. Using databases would produce secondary data.

Secondary data is not collected by the person carrying out the investigation.

DATA

Primary | Secondary

Data collection methods have advantages and disadvantages, as shown below:

Method	Advantages	Disadvantages
Direct observations	Cheap Easy to do	May have observer bias Not suitable for all data collection
Surveys and questionnaires: **(a)** Phone	Easily carried out Questions can be explained	Response rate can be low Limited to phone owners
Surveys and questionnaires: **(b)** Internet	Many questions can be asked Cheap and easily carried out Anonymous	Limited to people with internet access
Experiments	Accurate data, as long as it is carried out properly	Expensive Time consuming Requires expertise Focused on one task
Interviews	Questions can be explained High response rate Many questions can be asked	Expensive Interviewers can influence answers Respondents may not be totally honest
Databases	Cheap Fast Easy to do	Limited to databases available May be out of date Collection method unknown

Bias and becoming statistically aware

Bias is an in-built error that causes data collected to be inaccurate. It can lead to misleading results.

Bias can occur in a number of ways, some of which are outlined below:

Choosing a sample that is not representative of the population

Example: If you are trying to find out if students want to get rid of the school uniform and you only ask one year group or all the boys, etc.

Choosing a sample size that is too small

Example: Asking only 10 students in the above example.

The way a question is phrased

Example: 'Don't you agree that we should get rid of the school uniform?'

Non-response to survey

The sample may be designed to be representative, but if a high proportion of people questioned don't respond this may affect the results.

Self-selecting responses

If people volunteer to answer a survey it may be because they have strong views on the issue and this may lead to bias.

As you can see, statistics are influenced by many different factors. It is even possible that statistics can be manipulated so that they tell the story that the person using them wants to tell.

Because of these influencing factors, it is important to understand how to evaluate statistical information.

In an attempt to prevent companies from misleading customers, there are laws and standards that companies have to adhere to when advertising their products. For example, you may have noticed in certain advertisements they will tell you how many people were surveyed.

The internet, however, is very difficult to regulate and so it is important not to believe everything you read online!

Discussion Time 

Work with a classmate to discuss the following questions:

1. Is it important to know who collected the data or paid for the study to be conducted?
2. Would you trust the results of a study on the effects of smoking if you knew it was carried out by a tobacco company? Can you think of other such conflicts of interest?
3. Do you think it is important to know how recent the study is? How could this affect the validity of the results?
4. How would knowing the sample size of the study affect your confidence in the results?
5. Which would you trust more: primary or secondary data?
6. What other things would you consider when evaluating the results of a study?
7. Can you think of other ways, not listed above, in which bias could occur?

Now design a short questionnaire to find out about teenagers' use of the internet.

EXAMPLE

Determine whether the conclusion is drawn from the population or a sample in each of the following:

(i) Four out of five doctors interviewed recommend aspirin.

(ii) Out of 2,000 women, 1,720 women were married.

(iii) All students in a class were asked how many pets they had and 36% of the students had no pet.

(iv) The average wages of a person in Dublin is €2,000 per month.

Solution

(i) Sample: only five doctors were interviewed not every doctor.

(ii) Sample: 2,000 women surveyed not every woman.

(iii) Population: all students in the class were asked.

(iv) Sample: it is unlikely that every person in Dublin was asked!

Note: If the results from **(iii)** about students in one class were used to generalise about a larger group of students, they would be classed as a sample.

Practice Questions 22.2

1. Something is wrong with each of the following questions.
Identify the problem and rewrite the question to improve it.
   (i) Don't you agree that Xbox is better than PS4?
   Yes______
   (ii) How much TV do you watch?
   None______ Up to an hour______
   1–2 hours______ More than 2 hours______
   (iii) How much pocket money do you get a week?
   None______ A lot______
   (iv) How many pets do you have?
   1____ 2______ 3______
   (v) Do you agree that maths is boring?
   (vi) The prices in the school canteen have not increased for two years. Do you think the prices are good value?

2. Identify the population and the sample in each of the following:
   (i) A survey of 1,353 Irish households found that 18% of the households own a computer.
   (ii) A recent survey of 2,625 primary school children found that 28% of the children could be classified as obese.
   (iii) The average weight of every sixth person entering a shopping centre within a three-hour period was 75 kg.
   (iv) In a 'Teens Today' Internet poll, readers responded voluntarily to the question 'Do you drink at least one caffeinated beverage every day?'

3. Explain the difference between primary and secondary data.

4. Decide which method of data collection you would use for each of the following studies: observational study, experiment, interview, database or survey. Give a reason for your choice in each case.
   (i) A study of the salaries of teachers in a particular country.
   (ii) A study where a political pollster wishes to determine if his candidate is leading in the polls.
   (iii) A study where you would like to determine the chance of getting three girls in a family of three children.
   (iv) A study of the effects of a fertiliser on a wheat crop.
   (v) A study of the effect of declining grey squirrel numbers on the red squirrel population.

5. Explain what bias there is in a study done entirely online.

6. A local newspaper ran a survey by asking 'Do you support the development of a weapon that could kill millions of innocent people?'
Do you think this question is biased? Justify your answer.

7. Describe how you could select a simple random sample from:

   (i) your class
   (ii) your school
   (iii) your town
   (iv) your county.

8. Which of the following questions are biased? Give a reason in each case.

   (i) Does the Principal have the right to enforce a dress code?
   (ii) Do you think the Taoiseach is doing a good job in spite of all the stories in the news?
   (iii) Do you prefer daytime or evening television?
   (iv) Do you think the government should be allowed to cut down trees willy-nilly to build a new motorway?
   (v) Should there be a school uniform?
   (vi) Do you prefer current affairs programmes or mindless sitcoms?
   (vii) Do you think a new motorway should be built?

9. Reword each of the following survey questions to eliminate bias.

   (i) A random sample of residents of a town with high traffic congestion is asked: 'Are you in favour of widening the main street to reduce congestion?'
   (ii) During an election campaign, voters are asked: 'Do you agree that, because they have reduced taxes to an all-time low, the current government should be re-elected to continue their great work?'
   (iii) A marketing firm hired by a movie company asks: 'Which of the following movies should be named Movie of the Year?'
   (iv) A government pollster asks: 'Unemployment is at an extremely high level. Are you in favour of government policies to spend money to create jobs in your community?'

10. You want to conduct a study to determine the average student height at your school. The following are possible samples. Decide whether the potential sample is unbiased or biased and explain your reasoning.

    (i) Every third student entering the school on Monday
    (ii) The basketball team
    (iii) All the third-years
    (iv) Every tenth person selected from an alphabetical list of all students
    (v) All the girls
    (vi) The first three students who report to the office on Monday

11. A telephone directory has 500 pages with 350 names on each page.

    (i) Describe how you could generate a simple random sample from the telephone book.
    (ii) Is this a random sample of the population of the area? Justify your answer.

12. Are these samples representative? Justify your answer.

    (i) To determine the percentage of teenage girls with long hair, a teen magazine published a mail-in questionnaire. Of the 500 respondents, 85% had shoulder-length or longer hair.
    (ii) A college psychology professor needs subjects for a research project to determine which colours average Irish adults find restful. From the list of all 743 students taking introductory psychology at her college, she selects 25 students using a random number table.
    (iii) To evaluate the reliability of cars owned by its subscribers, *Consumer Reports* magazine publishes a yearly list of cars and their frequency-of-repair records. The magazine collects the information by mailing a questionnaire to subscribers and tabulating the results from those who return it.
    (iv) Oranges from an orchard need to be sampled to see if they are sweet enough for juice. The orchard has 25,000 orange trees. Each tree has at least 500 oranges. Claire decides to randomly choose 800 trees and test one orange from each tree.
    (v) For a survey of student opinions about school extracurricular programmes, a member of the school board obtains a sample of students by listing all students in the school and using a random number table to select 30 of them. Six of the students say that they don't have time to participate, and they are eliminated from the sample.

13. Do the sampling methods below produce a simple random sample from a class of 30 students?
    (i) A teacher selects the first five students that enter the room.
    (ii) A teacher wants to select ten students from the class. She lists students in alphabetical order, then selects every third student.
    (iii) A teacher wants to select five students from the class. Suppose that the classroom has six rows of chairs with five chairs in each row. The teacher assigns the rows the digits 1 through 6. She throws a die and selects all the students in the row corresponding to the number on the die in the sample.
    (iv) Assign each student a number from 1 to 30. The girls get the numbers 1 to 15 and the boys the numbers from 16 to 30. Use a random number table to select six two-digit numbers from 1 to 30, and select the corresponding students in the sample.
    (v) There are fifteen boys and fifteen girls in a maths class. Each student's name is placed in a hat and the names are thoroughly mixed. Seven names are drawn and all names correspond to the boys in the class.

Revision and Exam Style Questions

1. On a school report, a student's record of completing homework is graded using the following codes:
   C = consistently
   U = usually
   S = sometimes
   R = rarely
   N = never
   What type of data is this?

2. When a new patient arrives at a doctor's surgery they must fill in a form containing the following headings:
   (i) Name
   (ii) Age
   (iii) Distance of home from surgery
   (iv) How often do you exercise?
   (v) Do you smoke?
   (vi) Number of siblings
   Name the type of data produced when each of the questions above are answered.

3. Faye read that reaction time varies depending on whether you are using your right or left hand. She decided to investigate this with the students in her school.
   (i) What is the population for her investigation?
   She selects a group of students from her class to use as a sample for her investigation.
   (ii) Is this a good way of taking a sample? Give a reason for your answer.
   (iii) Suggest a better way to take a sample.

4. A roadside garage is doing a survey on the colours of cars.
   An employee is going to count how many cars of each colour pass the garage.
   (i) What type of data is recorded when the colour of the car is recorded?
   (ii) What type of data is recorded when the number of cars is recorded?
   The manager has three suggestions for when the employee should do the survey:
   A: between 7.30 am and 9.30 am on a weekday
   B: between 1.00 pm and 3.00 pm on a Saturday
   C: at a randomly selected 1 hour period between 7.30 am and 5.30 pm every day for a week
   (iii) Which suggestion is best? Give a reason for your answer.

5. People regularly provide ratings for products, sellers and companies through websites.
   (i) Who are the sample providing these ratings?
   (ii) Do you think this sample is a representative sample?
   (iii) If 50% of online reviews for a product are negative, do you think this means that 50% of buyers are dissatisfied with the product? Justify your answer.

6. Some students wrote a questionnaire to find out if people liked a new app.

   (a) One question was:
   How old are you (in years)?

   ☐ 20 or younger ☐ 20 to 30 ☐ 30 to 40 ☐ 40 to 50 ☐ 50 or older

   Mary said, 'The labels for the middle three boxes need changing.'
   Explain why Mary was right.

   (b) A different question was:
   How much would you pay for an app?

   ☐ A lot ☐ A little ☐ Nothing ☐ Don't know

   Mary said: 'Some of these labels need changing too.'
   Write new labels for any boxes that need changing. You may change as many labels as you like.

7. State whether the data collected in each of the following is primary or secondary data:

   (i) Ann visits several websites to investigate the average time spent in school for 17-year-olds in Europe.

   (ii) Brian carries out a survey of the students in his year to determine the most popular genre of music of Irish teenagers.

   (iii) Colin conducts an experiment to compare the reaction times of boys versus girls.

   (iv) Denise uses census data to calculate the average number of children per family in Ireland.

   (v) Eamonn counts the number of each colour of car passing the school gates for half an hour to work out the most popular car colour.

   (vi) Fiona interviews a group of students in her school about getting rid of the school uniform.

8. A market research company is going to do a national opinion poll to find out what people think about getting rid of the Presidency.
   The company are going to do a telephone poll.
   First they will pick 10 towns at random.
   Then they will pick 10 telephone numbers from the telephone book for each town.
   They will ring these 100 telephone numbers.
   The people who answer will form the sample.

   (i) Discuss whether this will form a satisfactory sample for the poll.

   Two of the questions suggested for the telephone poll are:
   A: Do you think that the Presidency is working well? Yes or No?
   B: What do you think of the Presidency?

   (ii) Which question, in your opinion, is the most suitable? Discuss the reasons for your choice.

9. The local council is planning to build a new sports centre, and the councillors want to get the views of the local people.

   Councillor Adams suggests taking a census of the population of the town.

   (i) Give one advantage and one disadvantage of taking a census.

   Councillor Byrne suggests taking a sample from the people who attend the local swimming pool.

   (ii) Is this a representative sample? Justify your answer.

   Councillor Clarke suggests taking a simple random sample of 100 people.

   (iii) Describe, in detail, how the council could take a simple random sample.

   The council decides to use either face-to-face interviews or a questionnaire.

   (iv) What are the advantages and disadvantages of these two methods of data collection?

   (v) Outline the main features of a good question to use when collecting data.

Now that you have completed the chapter, revisit the 'Something to think about...' questions.

CHAPTER 23

Statistics II – Representing Data

Sections covered within this chapter:

KEY WORDS

- Distribution
- Positive skewed
- Uniform distribution
- Scatterplot
- Symmetric distribution
- Correlation
- Negative skewed
- Causality

SOMETHING TO THINK ABOUT...

As part of the Census at School 2014 students were asked if they were to become famous in the future, what area would they like to be famous in. The results are shown in the graph below.

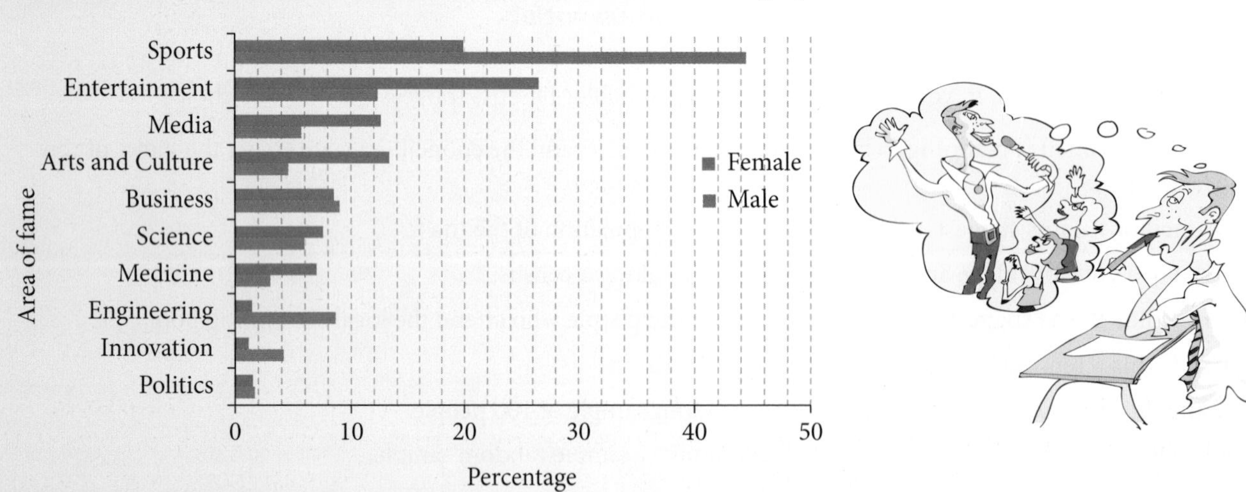

Study the graph above. Write as many different statements as you can about the information displayed.

Displaying data

Once data is collected one of the first things we usually do with it is represent it visually. This makes it easier to read and analyse. It allows us to highlight similarities, differences, trends and other relationships more easily.

Section 23.1: Line Plots, Bar Charts and Pie Charts

Learning Outcomes:

You should be able to:
- use line plots, bar charts and pie charts to display data
- use suitable graphs to compare data sets

Line plots

A line plot is a display of data along a number line with Xs or dots used to show the number of times a response appears in the data. A line plot consists of a horizontal line with equal intervals.

Line plots are best used for categorical data.

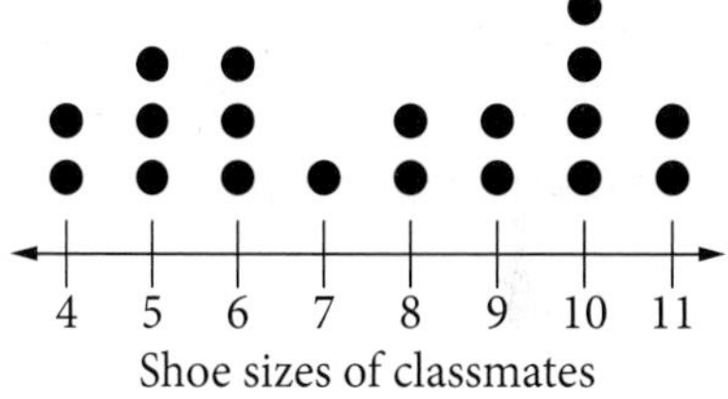

Bar charts

A bar chart uses bars to show comparisons between categories of data. These bars can be displayed horizontally or vertically. A bar graph has two axes. One axis will generally have numerical values, and the other will describe the types of categories being compared.

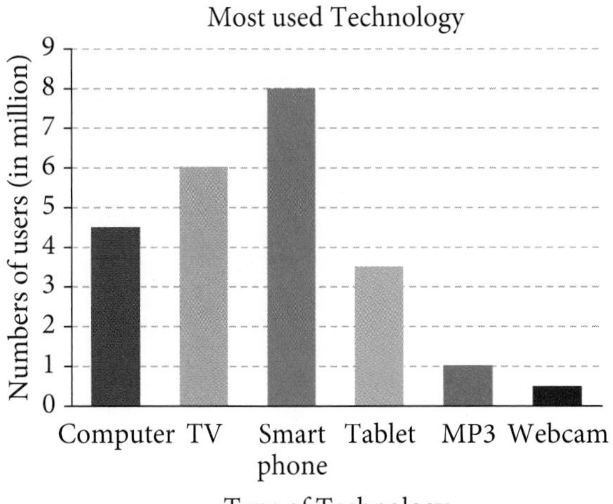

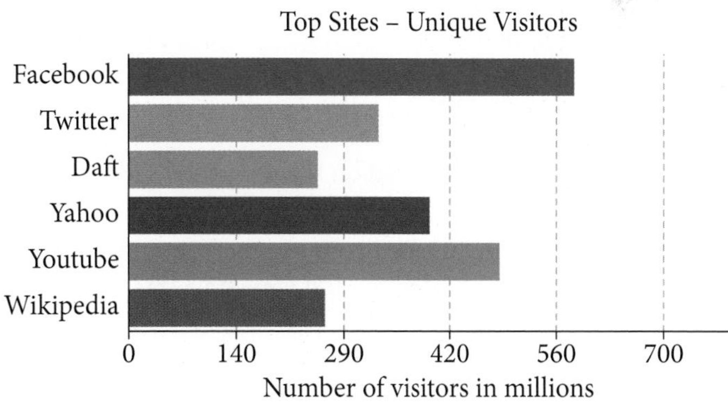

The most common way to draw a bar chart is vertically. The horizontal axis represents the different categories and so has no scale. In order to emphasise the fact that the categories are discrete, a gap is left between the bars on the horizontal axis. The width of the bars and the gap is the same for each bar. The vertical axis is a linear scale to measure the heights of the bars, which gives us the frequency.

Pie charts

A pie chart is a circular graph that shows the proportion that different categories contribute to an overall total.

Each 'slice' of the pie chart represents the contribution of a particular category to the total. Pie charts are particularly useful for representing categorical data.

In the pie chart shown here you can clearly see that yellow was the preferred colour of the people questioned and green was the least favourite colour.

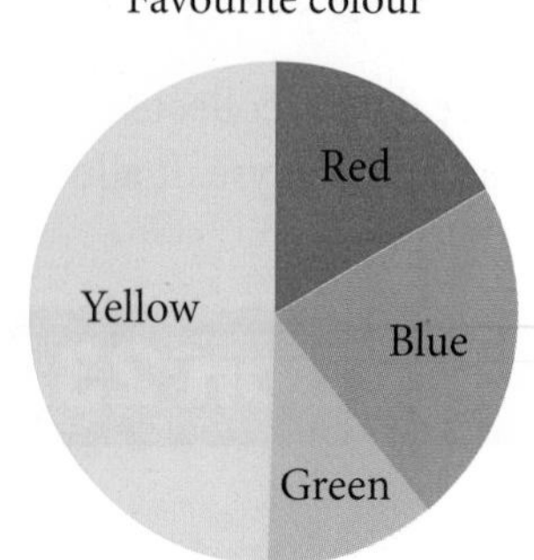

To draw a pie chart

Step 1: Find the total number surveyed.

Step 2: Represent each category as a fraction of the total.

Step 3: Work out the angle for each category by multiplying the fraction by 360°.

Step 4: Mark a centre, draw a circle and a start line from the centre to one side of the circle.

Step 5: Use a protractor placed on the start line to begin measuring each of the angles around the circle. Each line drawn becomes the start line for the next angle.

EXAMPLE

Represent the following data on a pie chart.

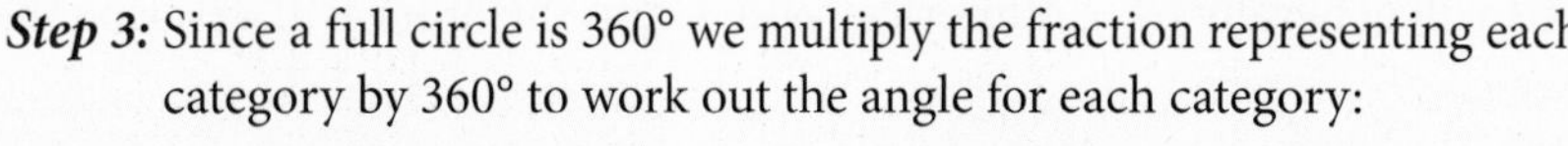

How you get to school	Bicycle	Bus	Car	Walk
Number of students	7	3	8	12

Solution

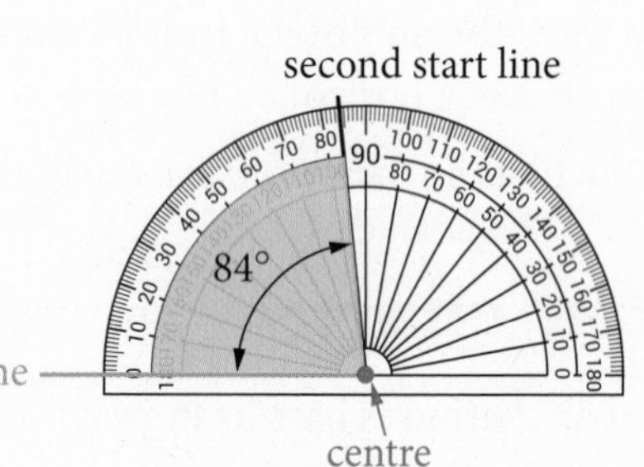

Step 1: Find the total number of people surveyed: $7 + 3 + 8 + 12 = 30$

Step 2: Represent each category as a fraction of the total:

Bicycle: $\frac{7}{30}$ Bus: $\frac{3}{30}$ Car: $\frac{8}{30}$ Walk: $\frac{12}{30}$

Step 3: Since a full circle is 360° we multiply the fraction representing each category by 360° to work out the angle for each category:

Bicycle: $\frac{7}{30} \times 360° = 84°$ Bus: $\frac{3}{30} \times 360° = 36°$

Car: $\frac{8}{30} \times 360° = 96°$ Walk: $\frac{12}{30} \times 360° = 144°$

Step 4: Mark a centre, draw a circle and a start line from the centre to one side of the circle.

Step 5: Use a protractor placed on the start line to measure each of the angles around the circle.

When you are finished your pie chart should look similar to the one shown, depending on where you put your start line.

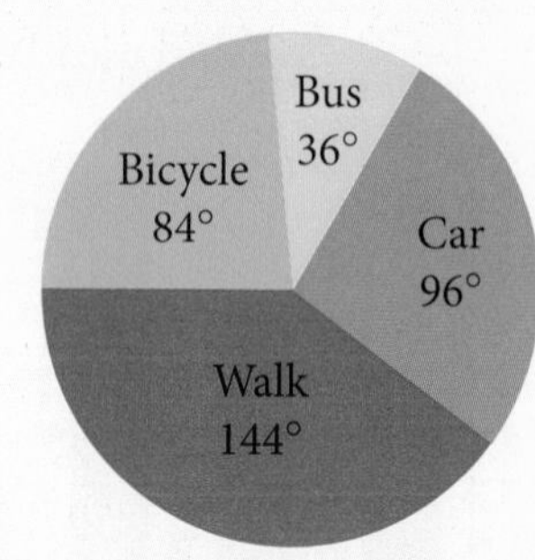

Practice Questions 23.1

1. The graph below shows the amount of money spent in a supermarket in three months.

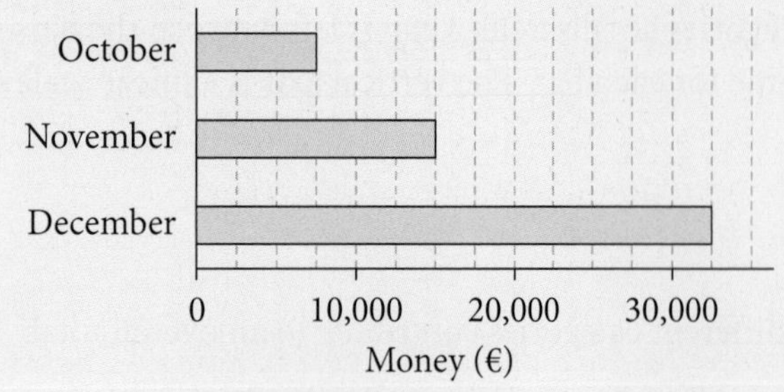

(i) Is this data discrete or continuous? Justify your answer.

(ii) In what month was the least money spent?

(iii) How much more money was spent in December than October?

(iv) Karla says, 'In November there was a 100% increase on the money spent in October'. Is she correct? Justify your answer with reference to the chart.

2. The following bar chart shows the favourite subjects of a group of students.

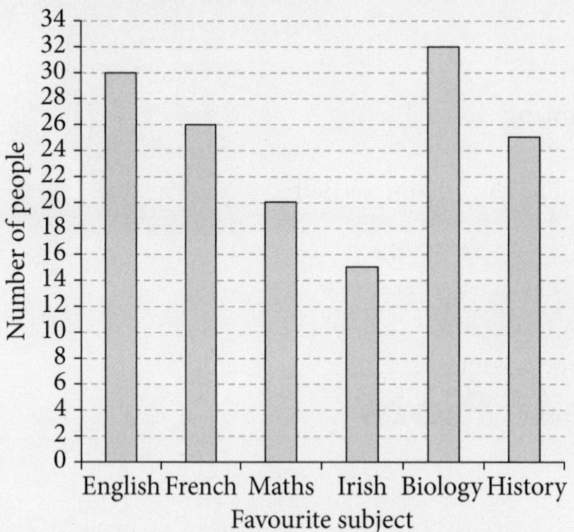

(i) How many students were questioned?

(ii) What was the difference in the number of people between the most popular and the least popular subject?

(iii) How many more students picked English as their favourite than picked Irish?

(iv) What two subjects combined were picked by three more students than the most popular subject?

3. The bar chart below shows the favourite social media sites of boys and girls.

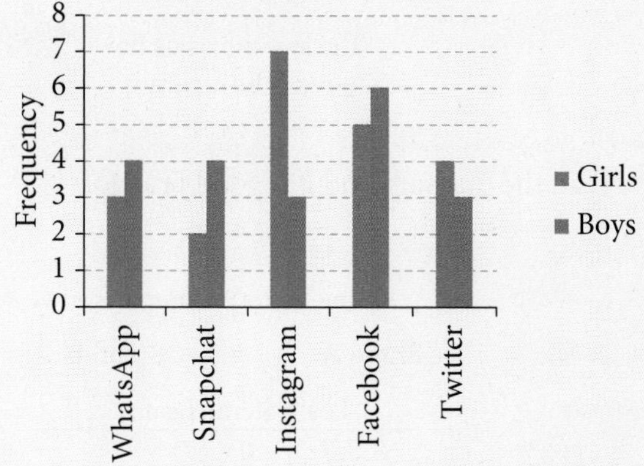

(i) True or false

(a) Girls' favourite site is Facebook.

(b) More boys than girls chose WhatsApp.

(c) Instagram is the most popular site in the class.

(ii) How many girls are in the class?

(iii) How many students are in the class?

4. The following line plot shows the number of students that were late over a two-week period (day 1 represents the Monday of the first week, day 6 the Monday of the second week).

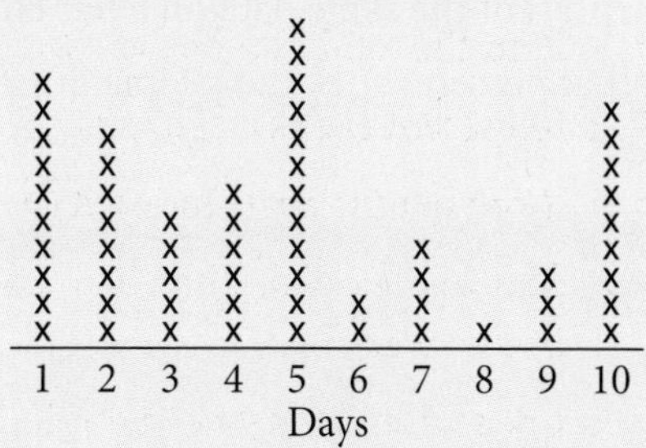

(i) On what day were the least students late?

(ii) On what day were the most students late?

(iii) What is the difference between the number of late students on the first and second Monday?

(iv) What similarities are there between the two weeks?

(v) In which week were there more late students?

5. Andrew recorded the number of hours' sleep received by his fellow classmates the previous night and found the results listed below:

6, 5, 7, 4, 6, 8, 9, 4, 6, 7, 8, 4, 7, 7, 6,
5, 4, 8, 7, 6, 8, 7, 8, 9, 5, 7, 8, 6, 5, 6.

(i) Is this data discrete or continuous? Explain your answer.

(ii) Draw a line plot to represent Andrew's results.

(iii) What is the least number of hours' sleep received?

(iv) What is the greatest number of hours' sleep received?

(v) What is the most common number of hours' sleep received?

6. A group of 120 children were asked to name their favourite flavour of ice cream. The results are shown in the table below.

Flavour	Number of Children
Chocolate	35
Vanilla	22
Strawberry	46
Chocolate chip	17

Show this information in a pie chart.

Statistics II

7. The following pie chart shows the instruments played by 30 students in a music class.
   (i) How many people play piano?
   (ii) Represent the same data on a bar chart.
   (iii) What percentage of the people don't play any instrument?

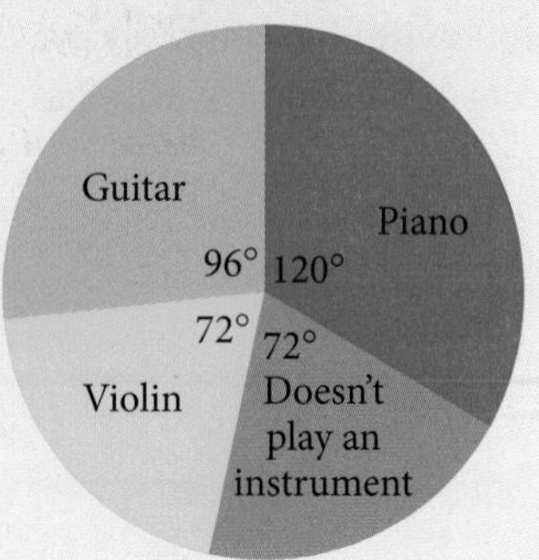

Section 23.2: Stem-and-Leaf Plots

Learning Outcomes:

You should be able to:
- use stem-and-leaf plots to display data
- use suitable graphs to compare data sets

Stem-and-leaf plots are used to represent both discrete and continuous data. In a stem-and-leaf plot the data is spread evenly along a branch in **numerical order**.

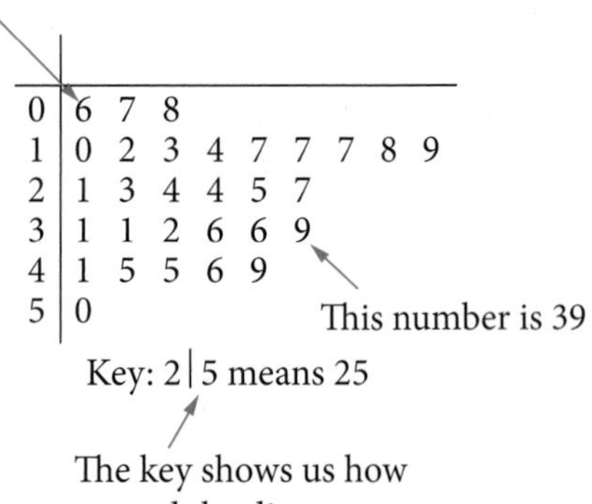

- Each data value is split into a stem and a leaf. The digits in the front are referred to as the stem and the last digit is referred to as the leaf.
- The stem is placed in a column and the leaves are placed in rows to the right (and/or left) of the column corresponding to their stems.
- Data is displayed similarly to a horizontal bar chart but each value is seen and data is sorted in numerical order.
- Each stem-and-leaf plot must include a key to explain how to read the diagram and it is good practice to include units on the key.

A stem-and-leaf plot is also useful for comparing two data sets. This can be done by using a back-to-back stem-and-leaf plot.

Phone Battery Comparison

'Brand A' 'Brand B'

Leaf	Stem	Leaf
8 8 7 5	0	7
9 7 4 1 0	1	0 5 5 5 7 9
2 2 2 1	2	0 2 2 6 7
8 6 4 2 0	3	0 2 4 6 8
	4	
	5	6
1	6	
	7	5

Key: 1|2 = 2·1 hours Key: 3|2 = 3·2 hours

Drawing a stem-and-leaf plot

The results (%) of a maths test were as follows:

63, 61, 45, 52, 63, 57, 38, 40, 64, 37, 53, 63, 54, 35, 43, 57, 62, 65, 69

Construct a stem-and-leaf plot to represent these results.

Step 1: Arrange the data in ascending numerical order.

35, 37, 38, 40, 43, 45, 52, 53, 54, 57,
57, 61, 62, 63, 63, 63, 64, 65, 69

Step 2: Split the data into a stem and leaf and place the stems in a column.

Stem
3
4
5
6

Step 3: Place the leaves in rows that correspond to their stem, in ascending order.

Stem	Leaf
3	5 7 8
4	0 3 5
5	2 3 4 7 7
6	1 2 3 3 3 4 5 6

It is important that the leaves are placed directly under each other to maintain the correct shape of the graph. Also if a number occurs more than once it is repeated in the diagram.

Step 4: A key must always be included. Key: 4|3 = 43%

EXAMPLE

The heights (in cm) of a group of first year and sixth year students were recorded as shown below.

First years: 144, 141, 145, 138, 150, 152, 146, 135, 129, 145, 151, 146, 147, 137, 136, 146, 148, 131, 139, 140

Sixth years: 163, 161, 158, 149, 157, 161, 170, 156, 164, 168, 147, 155, 162, 166, 156, 160, 155, 172, 139, 163

Draw a stem-and-leaf plot and compare the heights of the two groups of students.

Solution

Sixth years		First years
	12	9
9	13	1 5 6 7 8 9
9 7	14	0 1 4 5 5 6 6 6 7 8
8 7 6 6 5 5	15	0 1 2
8 6 4 3 3 2 1 1 0	16	
2 0	17	

Key: 9|13 = 139 cm Key: 15|0 = 150 cm

Comparing the two groups:

- The sixth years are taller than the first years. The smallest sixth year is 139 cm, and most of the sixth years are between 150 and 170 cm.
- Most of the first years are between 130 and 150 cm.
- The difference between the tallest and smallest first year is 152–129 = 23 cm
  The difference between the tallest and smallest sixth year is 172–139 = 33 cm
  This means the heights of the sixth years are more spread out.

Practice Questions 23.2

1. The first row of a stem-and-leaf plot showing the arm span of primary school students appears as follows:

   13 | 2 3 3 4 6 7

   (i) Assuming whole number values, write the key for this stem-and-leaf plot.
   (ii) How many data values are in this row?
   (iii) List the actual values in this row.

2. Write the stems that would be used to plot each set of data.
   (i) 23, 45, 56, 12, 27, 56, 37
   (ii) 8, 11, 23, 37, 31, 42, 59
   (iii) 230, 236, 234, 235, 233, 237
   (iv) 4·5, 6·1, 5·8, 9·8, 4·1, 3·2

3. The stem-and-leaf plot shows the results in a German test.

Stem	Leaf
6	1 1 4 6 7 8
7	2 3 5 7 9
8	1 3 5 6 6 7 7 8 9
9	0 0 3 4 6 8 9 9
10	0 0

   Key: 6 | 1 = 61%

   (i) What is the best test result?
   (ii) How many students took the test?
   (iii) How many students scored 90?
   (iv) What is the lowest result?
   (v) Find the difference between the highest and lowest results.

4. The following stem-and-leaf plot shows the number of objects produced per day in a factory.

Stem	Leaf
3	8
4	
5	6
6	0 1 3 3 5 5 9
7	0 2 3 6 7 7 8
8	5 9
9	0 0 1 5 6
10	3 6

   Key: 3|8 = 38 objects

   (i) How many days were studied?
   (ii) What are the largest and smallest values in the data?
   (iii) List the actual values in the fourth row.
   (iv) List the actual values in the second row.
   (v) How many values are less than 70?
   (vi) How many values are 80 or more?
   (vii) How many values are between 60 and 89?

5. Draw stem and leaf diagrams for each of the following sets of data:
   (i) 12, 8, 6, 15, 14, 11, 19, 21, 23, 7, 28, 16, 3, 31, 25, 18, 9, 11, 12, 15
   (ii) 101, 127, 134, 123, 107, 111, 118, 129, 148, 142, 115, 104, 123
   (iii) 8·3, 8·6, 9·2, 1·3, 2·8, 5·3, 4·9, 2·8, 4·9, 6·6, 5·0, 8·1, 1·8, 2·7, 6·8, 8·1, 4·5

6. A survey of the number of text messages sent by a sample of people last week revealed the following information:

   52, 43, 30, 38, 30, 42, 12, 46, 39, 37, 34, 46, 32, 18, 41, 5

   (i) Draw a stem-and-leaf plot to represent this data.
   (ii) What were the largest and the smallest number of texts sent?

7. The test scores (out of 100) for the students in a Geography class are listed below.

   92, 78, 73, 89, 98, 89, 83, 75, 83, 100, 69, 71, 96, 67, 81, 73, 88, 86, 82, 94

   (i) Draw a stem-and-leaf plot of the scores.
   (ii) Use the stem-and-leaf plot to determine the number of test scores greater than 84.
   (iii) Use the stem-and-leaf plot to make a statement about the test scores of the class.

8. The time taken (in mins) for a certain journey by bus and by car is shown:

   Bus: 24, 14, 25, 28, 47, 13, 9, 17, 30, 35, 16, 39

   Car: 17, 18, 12, 23, 32, 36, 20, 11, 41, 25, 26, 29

   Draw a back to back stem-and-leaf plot to represent this data and use it to compare the data.

9. The following are the ages of the people who took part in a soccer blitz.

19, 17, 13, 16, 15, 16, 17, 18, 24, 23, 28, 45, 48, 36, 12, 23, 15, 14, 13, 15, 17, 18, 19, 15, 15, 16, 16, 16, 16, 17

(i) Draw a stem-and-leaf plot of the data.

(ii) How many people attended the blitz?

(iii) What are the ages of the youngest and oldest persons attending?

(iv) Which age group was more widely represented?

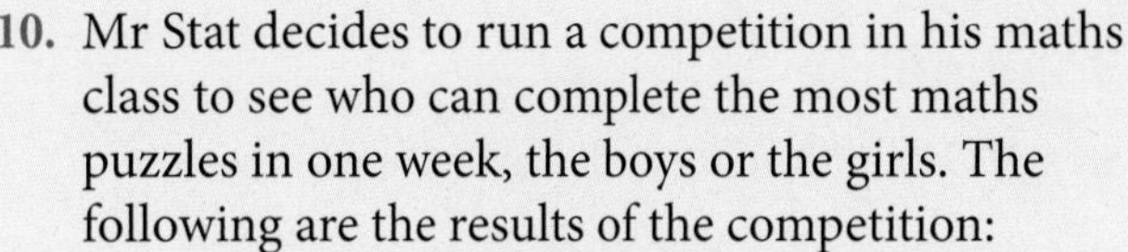

10. Mr Stat decides to run a competition in his maths class to see who can complete the most maths puzzles in one week, the boys or the girls. The following are the results of the competition:

Girls: 11, 12, 12, 17, 18, 23, 23, 23, 24, 33, 34, 35, 44, 45, 47, 50, 51, 51

Boys: 15, 18, 22, 22, 23, 26, 34, 35, 35, 35, 40, 40, 42, 47, 49, 50, 50, 51

(i) Draw a back-to-back stem-and-leaf plot to represent this data.

(ii) What was the most common number of puzzles completed by each group?

(iii) Mr Stat is having difficulty deciding who won the competition. Who do you think won? Justify your answer.

Section 23.3: Histograms

Learning Outcomes:

You should be able to:

- use histograms to display data
- use suitable graphs to compare data sets

Histograms are a special form of bar chart where the data represented is **continuous** rather than discrete. It is very similar to a bar chart except:

- There are no gaps between the bars (shows the data is continuous).
- The data in a histogram is often grouped to reduce the number of categories and these groups are called classes.

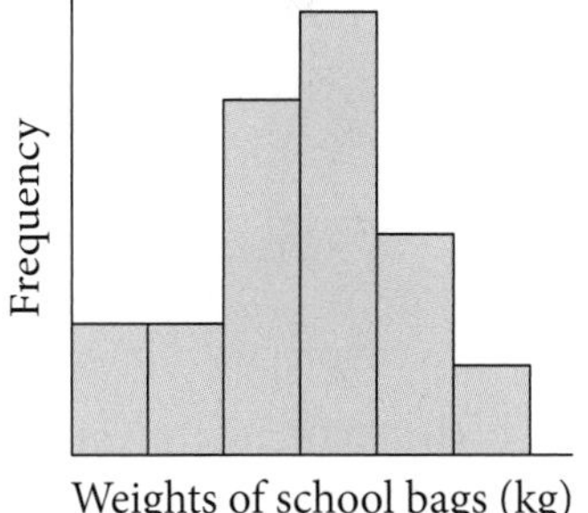

EXAMPLE

The following data represents the number of minutes spent on maths homework by a particular maths class on a given night:

15, 7, 22, 16, 24, 31, 8, 12, 23, 13, 27, 9, 11, 35, 26, 11, 17, 28, 34, 15, 5, 24, 19

Draw a histogram to represent this data.

(i) Use the histogram to determine the most frequent class.

(ii) What is the maximum number of students who could have spent more than 25 minutes on their maths homework?

Solution

Step 1: Group the data and draw a frequency table

Time (mins)	0–10	10–20	20–30	30–40
Tally	||||	~~||||~~ ||||	~~||||~~ ||	|||
Frequency	4	9	7	3

Note: 0–10 means 0 or more but less than 10.

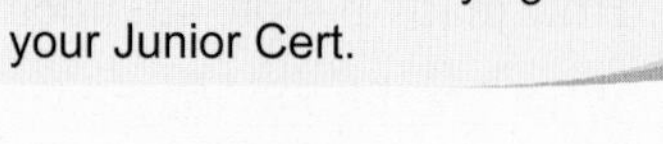
Recall the skills of tallying from your Junior Cert.

Step 2: Draw the histogram putting the variable (time in this case) on the horizontal axis and the frequency (number of students in this case) on the vertical axis. Make sure to label each axis and scale the axes correctly.

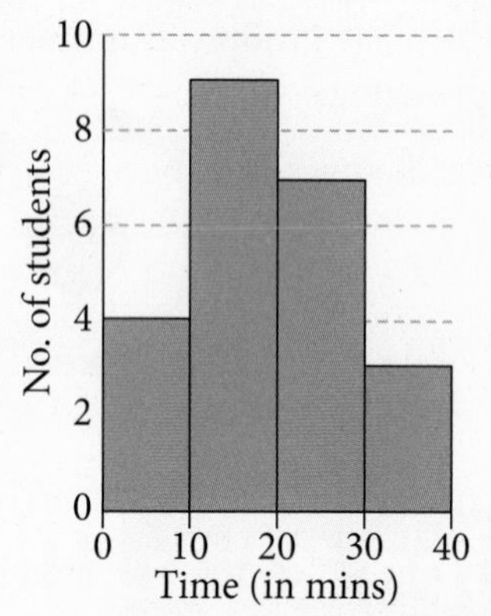

(i) The most frequent class is 10–20 mins.

(ii) The maximum number of students who could spend more than 25 minutes:

The students in the 30–40 mins class definitely spent > 25 mins = 3 students

If maximum, we assume all the students in the 20–30 mins class spent > 25 mins = 7 students

Maximum = 3 + 7 = 10 students

Practice Questions 23.3

1. Kamila is the top scorer on the school basketball team. The following are the number of points she scored in her last twenty games.

   35, 28, 25, 34, 41, 26, 19, 23, 32, 20, 11, 8, 38, 48, 22, 25, 16, 19, 22, 40

   (i) Copy and complete the following frequency table in your copybook.

Points scored	0–10	10–20	20–30	30–40	40–50
Frequency					

   Note: 0–10 means 0 or more but less than 10, etc.

   (ii) Which interval contains the greatest frequency?

   (iii) In what percent of these 20 games did Kamila score 30 or more points?

   (iv) Draw a histogram to represent this data.

2. The table show the speeds in km/hr of 100 cars that pass a speed camera on a certain day.

Speed (km/hr)	60–70	70–80	80–90	90–100	100–110
No. of cars	15	19	25	33	8

   Note: 60–70 means 60 or more but less than 70, etc.

   (i) Draw a histogram to represent this data.

   (ii) Is the speed discrete or continuous data? Explain.

   (iii) How many motorists travelled at a speed of 80 km/hr or more?

   (iv) If the camera is located in an 80 km/hr zone, what is the minimum number of motorists that could have exceeded the speed limit by at least 10%?

3. The table shows the weights in kg of parcels arriving at an office in a certain month.

Weight of parcel (kg)	10–15	15–20	20–25	25–30	30–35	35–40
Frequency (no. of parcels)	35	27	8	10	16	3

Note: 10–15 means 10 or more but less than 15, etc.

(i) Draw a histogram to represent this data.

(ii) What percentage of the parcels delivered that month are over 25 kg?

(iii) (a) Find the maximum possible number of parcels with a weight > 32 kg.

(b) Find the minimum possible number of parcels with a weight > 32 kg. Give reasons for these answers.

4. The tables below show the ages of two groups of 250 people.

Group A

Age	0–10	10–20	20–30	30–40	40–50	50–60	60–70	70–80
No. of people	15	25	55	40	50	50	10	5

Group B

Age	0–10	10–20	20–30	30–40	40–50	50–60	60–70	70–80
No. of people	35	55	65	30	20	20	10	15

Note: 0–10 means 10 or more but less than 10, etc.

(i) Draw a separate histogram to represent each of these data sets.

(ii) Use the histograms to compare the two sets of data.

5. The histogram below shows the results obtained by a group of students in a maths exam.

(i) How many students are represented in this histogram?

(ii) How many students got between 40% and 80%?

(iii) What percentage of students failed this exam? (given a pass is 40%)

(iv) What are the maximum and minimum number of students who could have gotten greater than or equal to 70%?

(v) Can you suggest a way in which this histogram could be changed to provide more information?

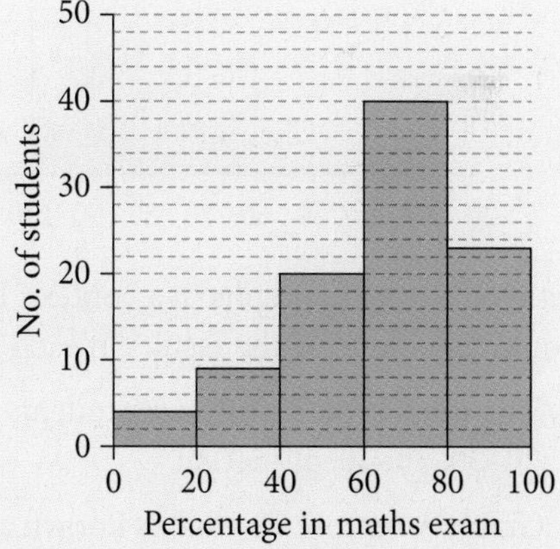

Hint: Think about the interval widths.

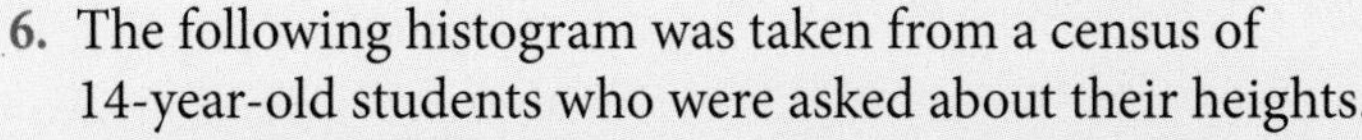

6. The following histogram was taken from a census of 14-year-old students who were asked about their heights.

(i) What was the smallest height interval recorded in this sample?

(ii) How many students were in the smallest interval?

(iii) Why are there gaps in the graph if it is a histogram?

(iv) If you were trying to work out the average height of a 14-year-old in Ireland, would this be a good sample to use? Justify your answer.

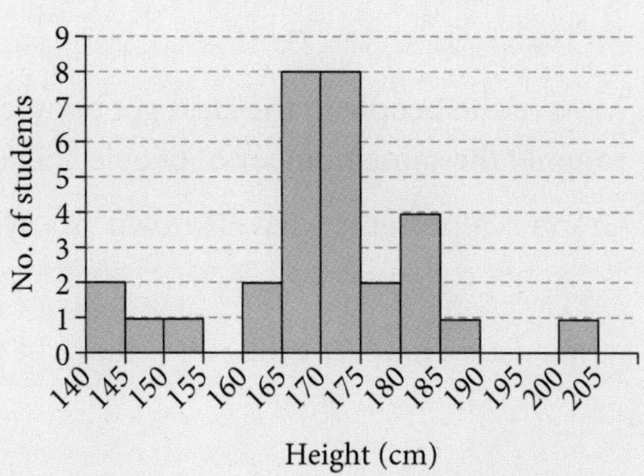

Source: censusatschool.ie

Statistics II

Section 23.4: Shape of a Distribution

Learning Outcome:

You should be able to:

- describe the distribution of data, including symmetry and skew

When data is presented on a graph, we can get a clearer picture of the distribution of this data

Distribution refers to how the data is spread.

Examine the graphs below and discuss the shape of them with the person beside you.

Think about the frequencies. Are they all the same, different, focused towards a central point or towards either end?

Write at least one sentence to describe each graph.

A.

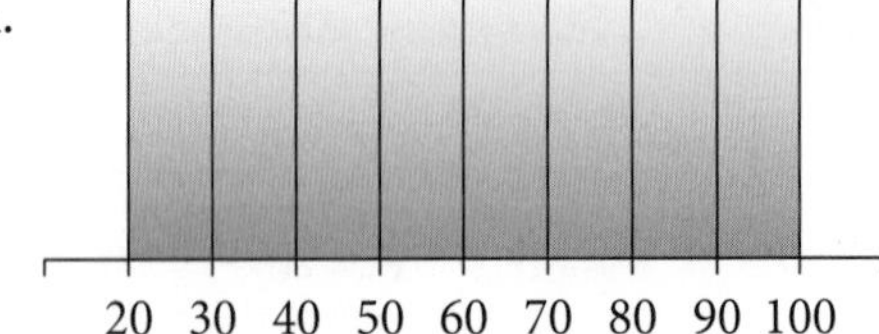

B.

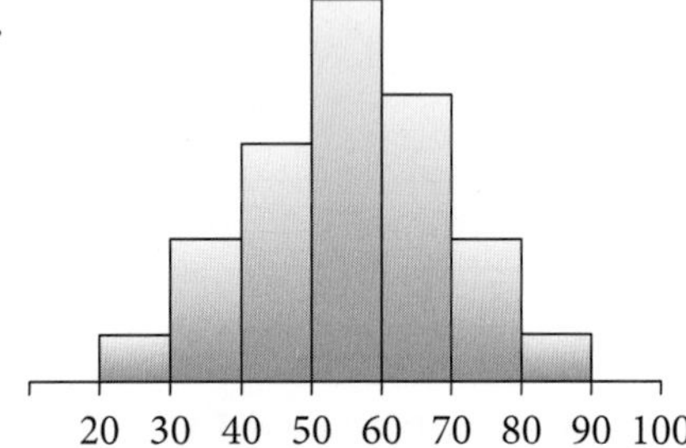

C.

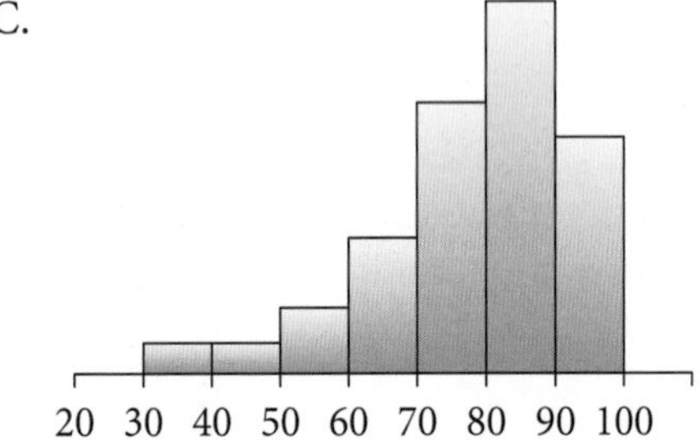

D.

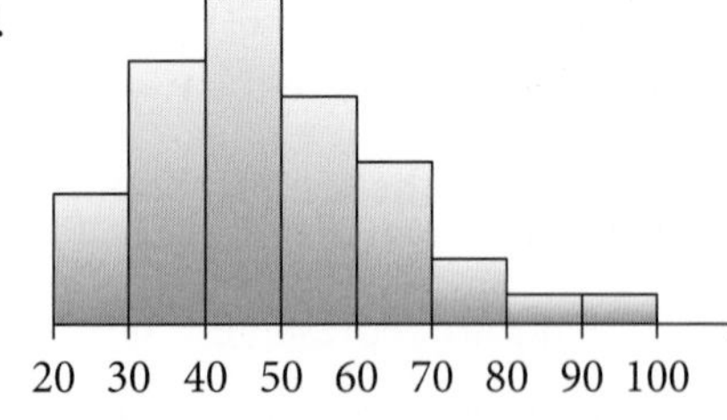

Let's look at these graphs in a context. Let's imagine they represent the results of a class in a maths exam. How would you describe the results in each case? Maybe something like this:

A. The exact same number of students are found in each interval 20–30, 30–40, 40–50 etc.

Graph A represents what is known as a **uniform distribution.**

In a **uniform distribution** the frequencies are evenly spread out among all values of the variable.

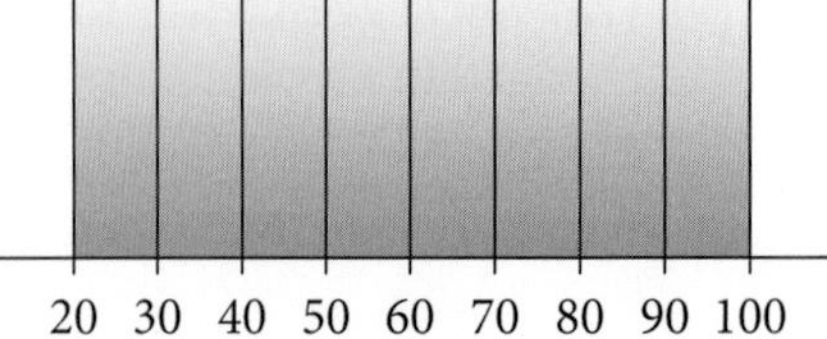

B. Most of the people in the class got between 50 and 60% and there are roughly the same number of people above and below this interval.

Graph B represents what is known as a **symmetric distribution.**

In a **symmetric distribution** the highest value is in the middle, with values tailing off to the right and left.

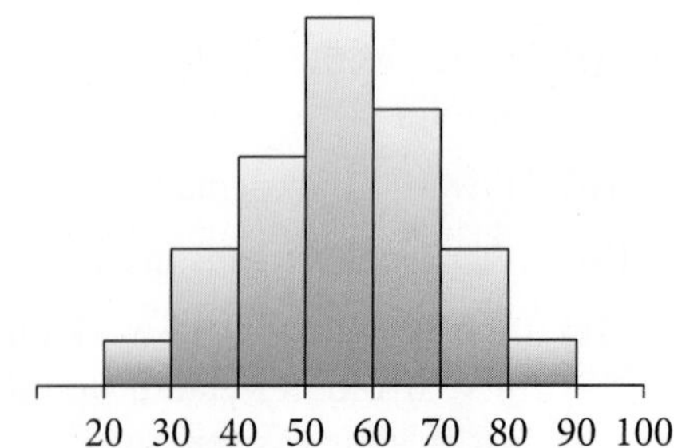

C. Most of the students got 60% or above with only a few getting lower than 60%.

Graph C represents a **negative (or left) skewed distribution.**

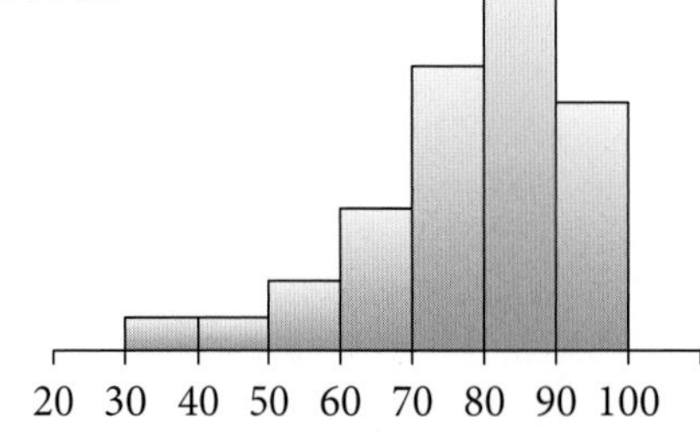

In a negative-skewed distribution, the highest value is on the right, with a longer left 'tail'.

It is referred to as negative skew because the tail heads towards the negative side of the number line.

D: Most of the students got below 70% with only a few getting above 70%.

Graph D represents **positive (or right) skewed distribution**.

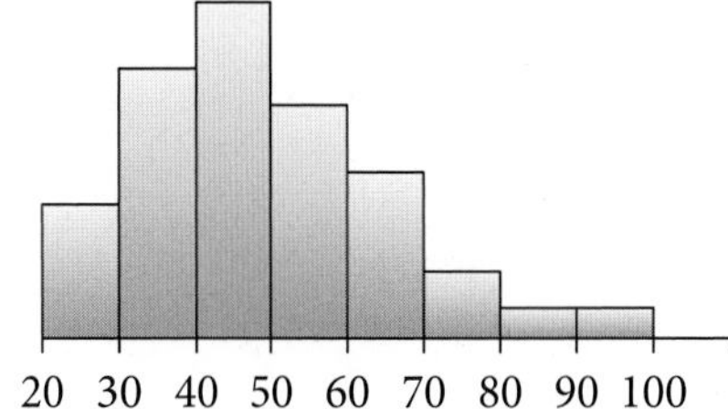

In a positive-skewed distribution, the highest value is on the left, with a longer right 'tail'.

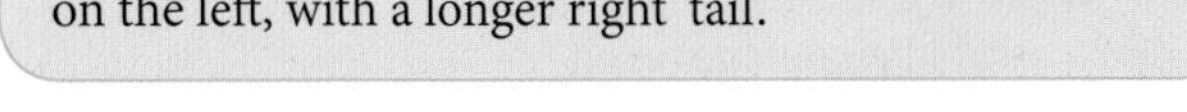

The tail heads towards the positive side of the number line.

Everyday examples of each type of distribution are shown in the table

Distribution	Examples
Uniform	theoretical probability of throwing a number on an unbiased die
Symmetric distribution (also known as normal distribution)	heights, IQs, blood pressure, Leaving Cert results
Negative-skewed distributions	retirement age, life expectancy, and hip replacement operations
Positive-skewed distributions	distribution of income, age of learning a new language and number of children in a family

Practice Questions 23.4

1. **(i)** Discuss the shape of each of the following distributions.

(a)
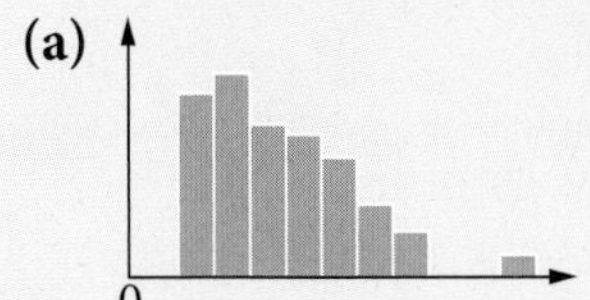

(b)
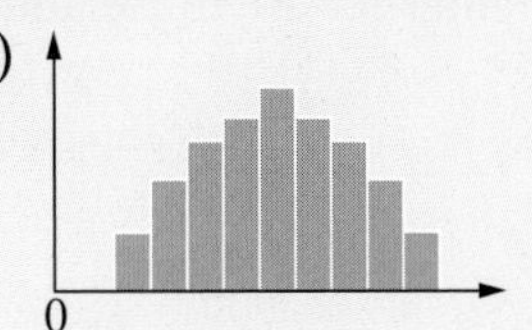

(c)
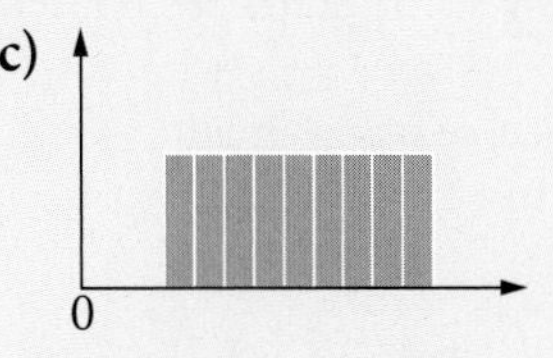

(d)
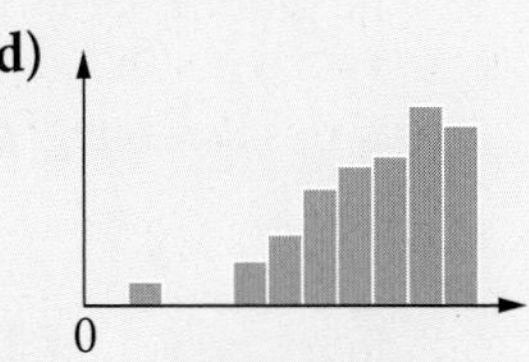

(ii) Give an example of data that could be represented by each graph.

2. Identify the type of data distribution most likely to be seen if the frequency of the following was graphed on a histogram:

(i) Marriage age

(ii) Number of children in a family

(iii) Annual income over a lifetime

(iv) Litres of blood in the body over an adult's lifetime

(v) Age of first-time parents

3. The following histograms show the results of a class in two tests on statistics.

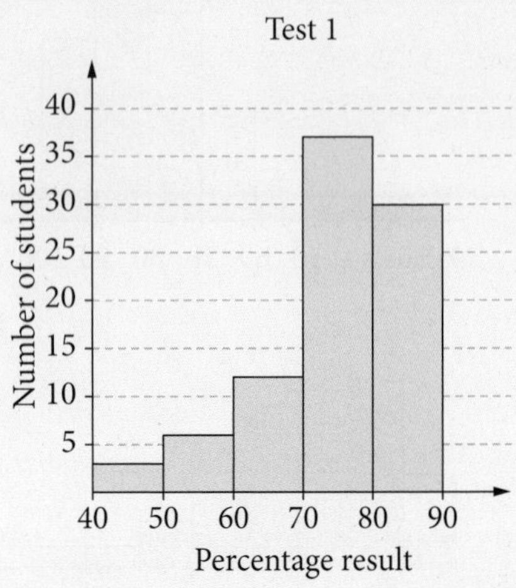

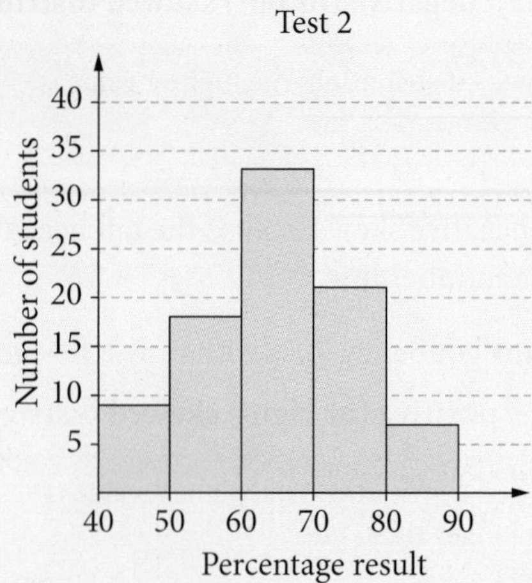

(i) Describe the shape of the distribution in each test.

(ii) Comment on the relative difficulty of each test using evidence from the histograms to back up your comments.

4. The graph below shows the population by county in the Republic of Ireland in 2011. (Source: CSO) Comment on the distribution of this data. Suggest a reason for this distribution.

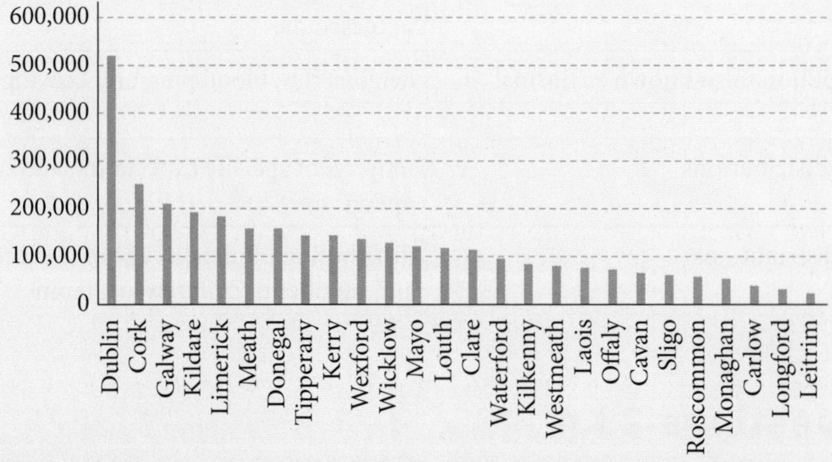

5. The graphs below show some statistics related to internet use in Ireland by age group. (Source: CSO)

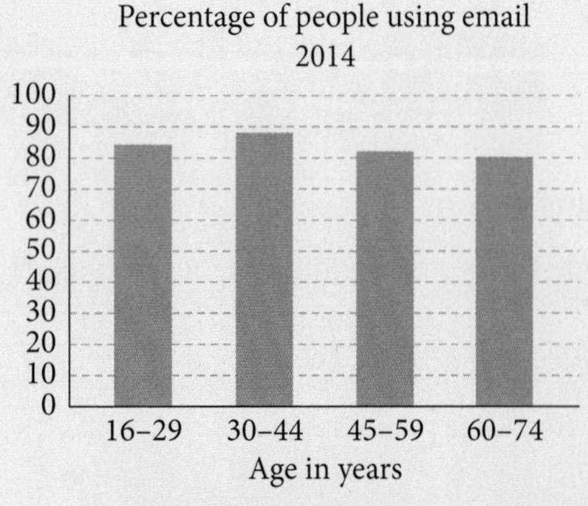

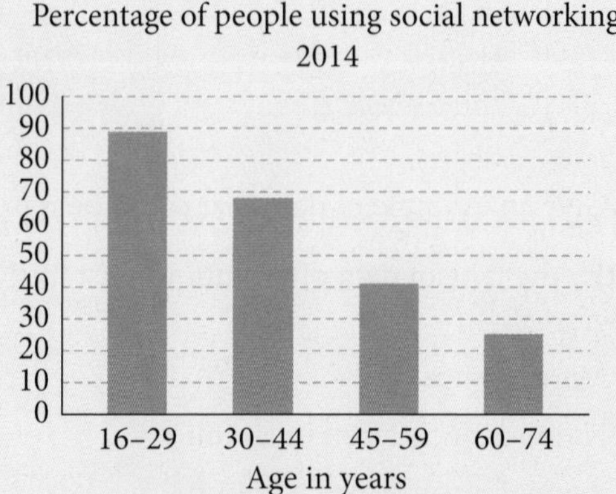

(i) Comment on the distribution of people using email.

(ii) Comment on the distribution of people using social media and suggest a possible reason for it.

Statistics II

6. The following stem-and-leaf diagram show the weights of the schoolbags belonging to students who walk to school. (Source: censusatschool.ie)

(i) How many students were surveyed?

(ii) How would you describe the shape of the distribution for females?

(iii) How would you describe the shape of the distribution for males?

(iv) Diana claims that 'girls' bags are heavier'. Do you agree with Diana? Justify your answer.

Stem-and-leaf plot of the bag weight of sixth-year students that walk to school classified by gender of student

Male		Female
200	1	024
	2	004
00000	3	00000000257
651	4	0
2000	5	0000459
000000	6	00023
	7	005
5	8	005
98500000000	9	056

Key: 0|1 = 1·0 kg Key: 2|4 = 2·4 kg

Section 23.5: Scatterplots

Learning Outcome:

You should be able to:

- draw a scatterplot to show relationships between two variables

Bivariate data means two variables are examined at the same time. The purpose of examining bivariate data is usually to show some sort of relationship between the two variables.

To examine the relationship between two variables we can draw a **scatterplot**.

A **scatterplot** is a graph of plotted points that shows the relationship between two sets of data.

EXAMPLE

Look at the table below that compares the number of ice creams sold to average daily temperature.

Temperature (°C)	22	25	14	26	16	28	21	29	20	15	31	18
Number of ice creams sold	73	83	48	84	52	95	69	96	77	44	105	59

Solution

It appears when you look at this table that more ice creams are sold when the temperature is higher (as you would probably expect). It is much easier to see this relationship by drawing a scatterplot.

To draw this graph we put temperature on the horizontal axis (top line of the table always goes on the horizontal axis) and number of ice creams sold on the vertical axis. We then plot the results in pairs just like on a coordinate graph.

(22, 73) (25, 83) (14, 48)...

 Links across the syllabus

Plotting points on a coordinated plane is covered in Chapter 14: Coordinate Geometry I.

We plot them as they appear on the table, without rearranging in ascending or descending order.

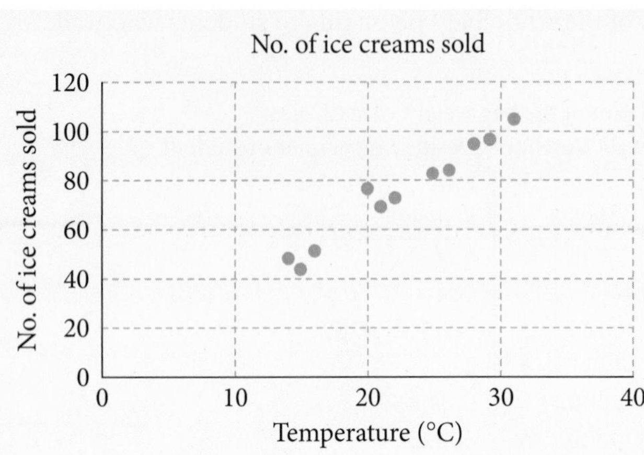

You can now clearly see that as the temperature rises the sales of ice creams also rise. Therefore we can say that there is a relationship between temperature and sales of ice cream.

A change in one of the variables causes a change in the other variable. In statistics we call this relationship a **correlation.**

The strength of the relationship between two sets of data is known as **correlation.**

Types of correlation

In the example above we saw that as temperature increased, ice cream sales increased. This is an example of a **positive correlation**.

A **positive correlation** exists when the **values increase together**.

Points form a band that increases from left to right.

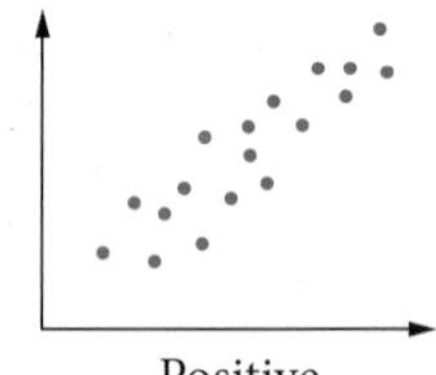

Positive

We can also have a **negative correlation.**
A **negative correlation** exists when as **one value increases the other decreases**.

Points form a band that decreases from left to right.

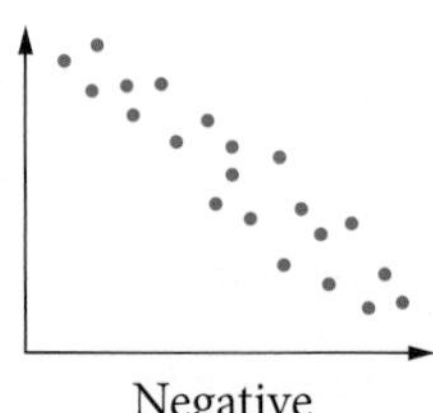

Negative

Sometimes we suspect a correlation but when the scatter graph is drawn the points are randomly scattered with no detectable relationship. The variables are said to have **no correlation**.

Points are randomly spread out.

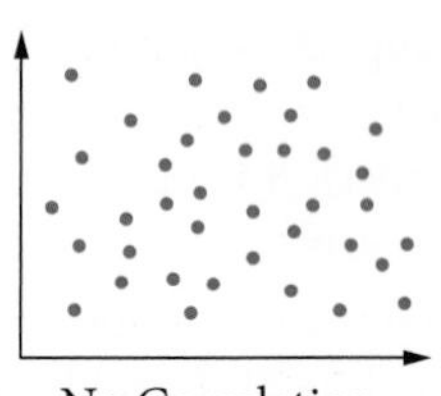

No Correlation

Practice Questions 23.5

1. Copy and complete the following:
   (i) If the variables x and y are positively correlated, then as x increases y ________?
   (ii) If there is negative correlation between the variables m and n then as m increases, n ________?
   (iii) If there is no correlation between two variables, then the points on the scatterplot appear to be ________?

2. Describe the correlation shown in each of the following graphs:

(i) 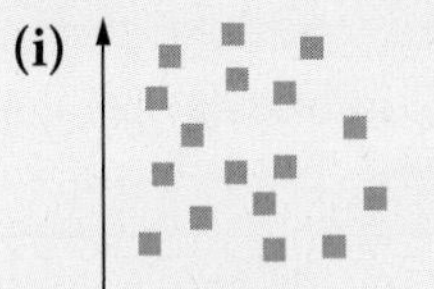

(ii) 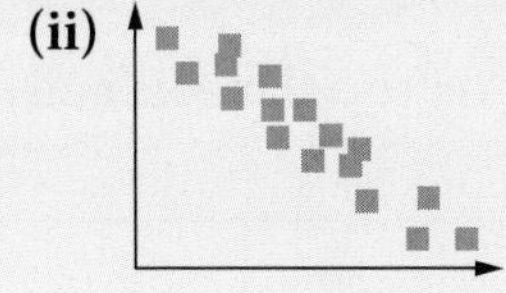

(iii) 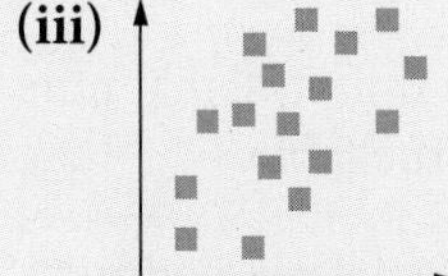

3. The scatterplot shows the relationship between weight and kilometres ran per week.
   (i) What was the heaviest weight recorded?
   (ii) What was the longest distance recorded?
   (iii) What weight corresponds to a distance of 6 km?
   (iv) What distance did the person weighing 84 kg run?
   (v) How would you describe the relationship between these two variables?

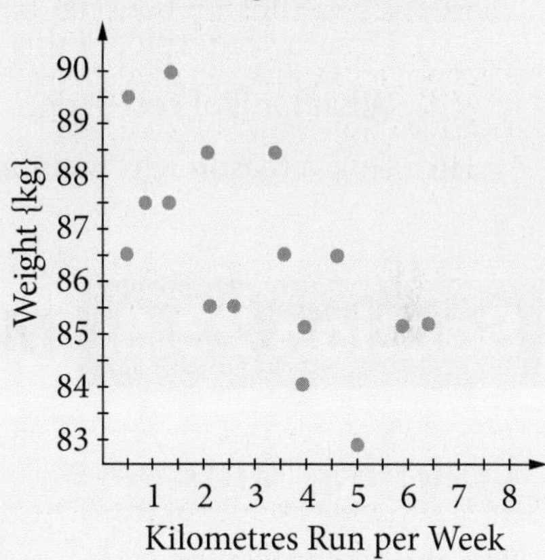

4. Decide whether each of the following examples shows a positive, negative or no correlation. Give a reason for your answer in each case.
   (i) Age and height.
   (ii) Size of vehicle and fuel consumption.
   (iii) Absence from class and test result.
   (iv) Calorie intake and weight.
   (v) The number of your house and your IQ.
   (vi) Temperature and sales of gloves.
   (vii) Hours spent studying and exam results.
   (viii) Speed of a cyclist and time to destination.
   (ix) Shoe size and wages.
   (x) The year of a car and its value.

5. Match the scatterplot to the variables being studied. Give a reason for your answer.

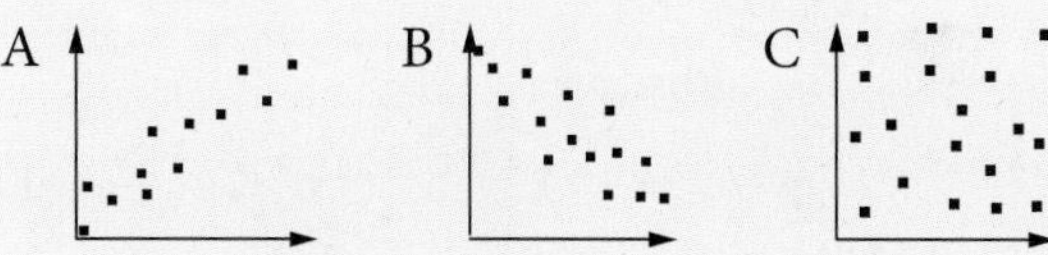

   (i) Time spent in the sun and degree of sunburn.
   (ii) Hair length and finger nail length.
   (iii) The number of students in a school and the number of teachers in the school.
   (iv) Distance run and speed of the runner.
   (v) Age of a child and size of clothing.
   (vi) Amount of exercise and weight.
   (vii) Time spent on social media and size of family.
   (viii) Temperature and layers of clothing.
   (ix) Distance from school and results in a maths test.

6. Ms Newton teaches maths and physics to the same class. She thinks that the students who do well in maths also do well in physics. She decides to compare the results of two tests to see if she is correct. When she arranges the students alphabetically, their results in each test are as follows:

   Maths test results: 54, 48, 83, 67, 41, 57, 74, 53, 87, 79, 25, 63, 64, 66, 78

   Physics test results: 62, 39, 92, 73, 45, 63, 76, 49, 93, 82, 30, 57, 55, 70, 79

   (i) Draw a scatterplot to represent this data.

   (ii) Do you agree with Ms Newton's claim? Justify your answer.

7. The time, in minutes, that nine teenagers spent on social media and spent watching TV on one day is recorded in the table.

Time on Social media (min)	10	5	30	35	45	55	60	20	40
Time watching TV (min)	50	25	45	40	30	30	20	40	40

   (i) Draw a scatterplot of this data.

   (ii) What kind of correlation, if any, exists between these two sets of data?

   (iii) Give a reason why you think this type of correlation might exist.

Section 23.6: Measuring the Strength of a Correlation

Learning Outcome:

You should be able to:

- understand the idea of correlation and decide the strength of a correlation

The closer the points plotted on a scatter graph are to a **straight line** the **stronger** the **correlation**.

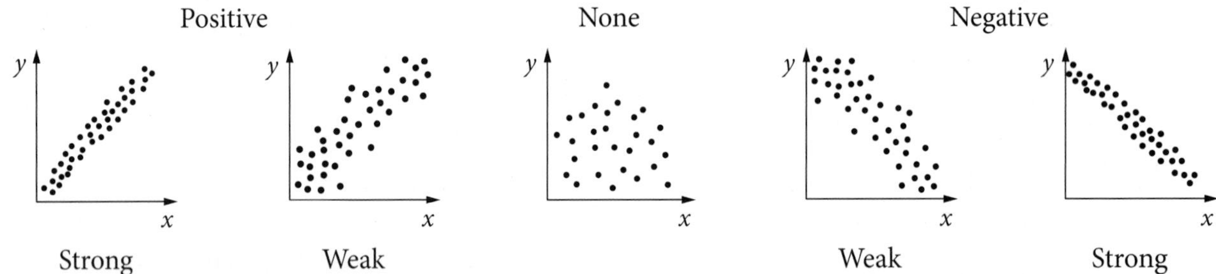

Sometimes it can be difficult to tell by eye how strong or weak a correlation is so it is necessary to calculate a **correlation coefficient** to determine the strength of the correlation. For this course, you are not required to calculate the correlation coefficient exactly, but you must be able to estimate it by eye.

The correlation coefficient is given the symbol r and has values ranging from -1 to $+1$.

$$-1 \le r \le +1$$

A **perfect positive correlation** means that the data points are in an exact straight line and have a correlation coefficient of $r = 1$.

The closer the r value is to 1, the stronger the positive correlation.

A **perfect negative correlation** means that the data points are in an exact straight line and have a correlation coefficient of $r = -1$.

The closer the r value is to -1, the stronger the negative correlation.

If there is **no correlation,** $r = 0$. The closer the r value is to 0 the weaker the correlation.

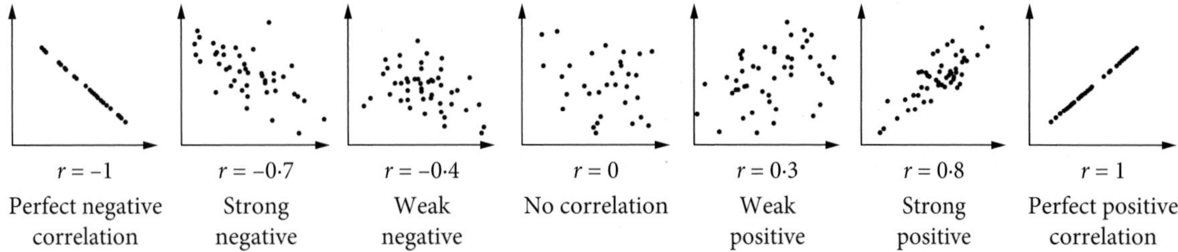

Use the following guide to help you describe a correlation:

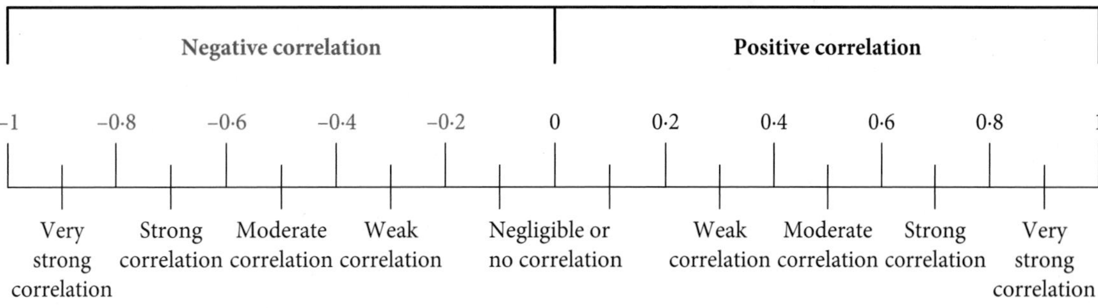

EXAMPLE

Molly thinks 'the taller you are, the bigger your shoe size'. To help prove her theory she collected some data from her classmates.

Height (cm)	Shoe size	Height (cm)	Shoe size	Height (cm)	Shoe size	Height (cm)	Shoe size	Height (cm)	Shoe size
153	5	154	6	163	6	168	9	170	9·5
154	6	155	6	164	7	170	10·5	168	10
158	5	159	7	165	7	166	10	161	5
160	6	167	9·5	167	10				

(i) How could Molly use this data to prove her claim?

(ii) Is Molly's claim correct? Justify your answer.

(iii) Estimate the correlation coefficient for the data above.

Solution

(i) Molly could prove her claim by drawing a scatterplot of this data and using it to see if there is correlation between height and shoe size.

(ii) In order to justify our answer, we will need to draw the scatter graph. This scatterplot is shown.

Molly's claim is correct because the scatter graph shows a strong positive correlation between height and shoe size. This means that as height increases shoe size increases which is what Molly claimed.

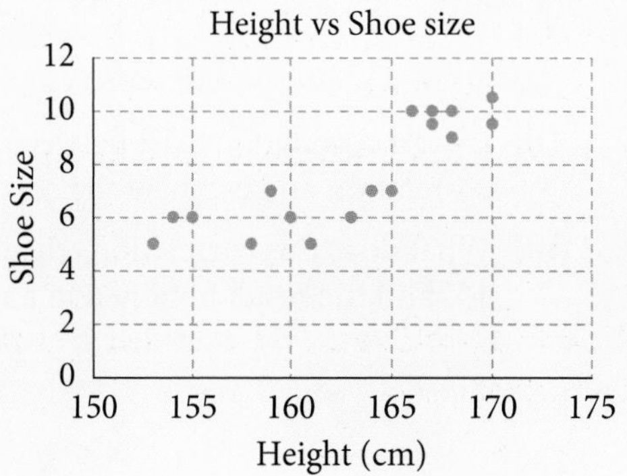

(iii) In this data we can clearly see a linear pattern so it is a strong correlation making it 0·7 or above. It is not close enough to a straight line to be 0·9. Acceptable answers would be 0·7–0·85.

Practice Questions 23.6

1. Determine whether each of the following represents a positive, negative or no correlation and determine the strength (strong, moderate, weak) for each:

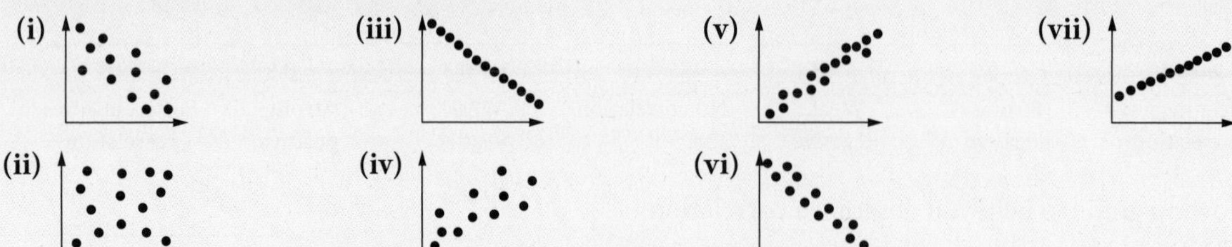

2. Match the correlation coefficient to the scatterplot.

(i) $r = 0$ (iv) $r = 0{\cdot}8$
(ii) $r = -0{\cdot}9$ (v) $r = -0{\cdot}6$
(iii) $r = 0{\cdot}3$ (vi) $r = -0{\cdot}2$

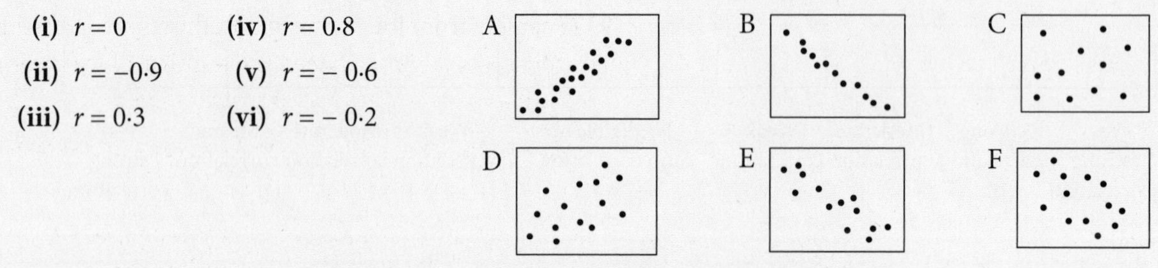

3. Suggest a value for the correlation coefficient in each of the following:
   (i) Perfect negative correlation.
   (ii) Weak positive correlation.
   (iii) Strong negative correlation.
   (iv) Moderate positive correlation.
4. Estimate the correlation coefficient for each of the following pairs of variables:
   (i) Distance travelled and time spent travelling.
   (ii) Millimetres of rain and number of umbrellas seen.
   (iii) Temperature and litres of heating oil used.
   (iv) Height and maths result.
   (v) Balance left on a gift card and cost of purchases made with the card.
5. In a recent maths test students were asked to fill in the number of hours they spent watching TV. The table shows the results of the test and the hours watching TV:

Hrs of TV	13	15	18	22	24	16	12	8	10	11	17	9	17	21	14	7	11	18	26	12
Result	78	65	56	43	48	73	75	82	53	45	69	79	97	43	88	72	40	53	38	55

   (i) Draw a scatterplot to represent this data.
   (ii) Does a correlation exist between hours spent watching TV and maths test result? If yes, describe the correlation and estimate the correlation coefficient.
   (iii) What does this correlation tell you about the relationship between the numbers of hours spent watching TV and the result obtained in a maths test?

Section 23.7: Correlation vs Causality

Learning Outcome:

You should be able to:

- understand the difference between correlation and causality

Consider the following table of data collected at a certain beach during one week in the summer:

Ice cream sales	30	110	80	40	65	125	95
No. of people swimming	25	85	70	15	90	70	80

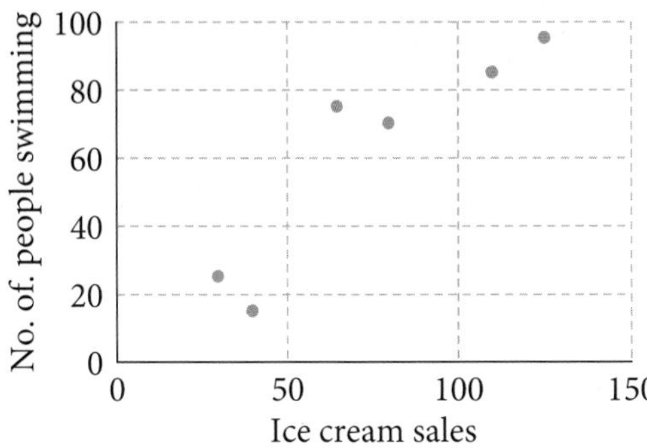

We can see from the scatter graph that there is a strong positive correlation between the number of ice creams sold and the number of people swimming.

Does this mean that buying an ice cream **causes** you to go swimming? Of course not!

Both things are more likely to happen on a sunny day but one does not **cause** the other to happen.

Sometimes when there is a correlation between two variables it is because a change in one **causes** a change in the other. In such cases a **causal relationship** is said to exist.

Causality indicates a relationship between two events where one event causes the other.

For causality to exist you should be able to say variable A **causes** an increase or decrease in variable B.

Discussion Time 

Discuss the following situations with a classmate and determine whether each of them show correlation, causality or both. Give a reason for your answer in each case.

1. Number of cars on the road and number of road traffic accidents
2. A person's age and shoe size
3. Temperature and snowfall
4. Number of firemen and size of a fire
5. Number of computer games bought and amount of money in gamer's bank account
6. Amount of rainfall and number of umbrellas up
7. Number of TVs sold and number of washing machines sold
8. Weight of a vehicle and its fuel consumption

Practice Questions 23.7

1. Decide if each of the following statements imply causality or simply correlation:
   - **(i)** Seat belts reduce the risk of serious injury.
   - **(ii)** Married people live longer than single people.
   - **(iii)** When it's raining less people walk to school.
   - **(iv)** Eating breakfast improves concentration.
   - **(v)** Texting decreases ability to spell correctly.
   - **(vi)** Bigger families have bigger cars.

2. Which of the following describes a relationship that is correlated but not causal?
   (i) The amount of rainfall received and level of water in the lake.
   (ii) The number of lights left on each day and the amount of the household electricity bill.
   (iii) World population and the cost of technology.
   (iv) The number of lates to class and the number of detentions received.
   (v) The average daily temperature and the number of water related injuries or deaths.
   (vi) A rise in temperature and the expansion of mercury within a thermometer.
   (vii) The length of the dimensions of a rectangular patio and the square footage of the patio.

3. The table below shows the number of sun loungers rented and the bucket and spade sales over a ten-day period in a popular beach resort in Spain.

Sun loungers	23	17	25	50	52	38	56	44
Bucket and spade	28	25	30	51	47	41	52	40

   (i) Draw a scatterplot to represent this data?
   (ii) Is there a correlation between sun lounger rental and bucket and spade sales?
   (iii) Describe the correlation if one exists.
   (iv) Give a reason for the correlation if one exists.
   (v) Does causality exist?

Revision and Exam Style Questions – Section A

1. Two different sets of data were collected and displayed, as shown in the graphs below.

Graph A

0 1 2 3 4 5 6 7 8

Graph B

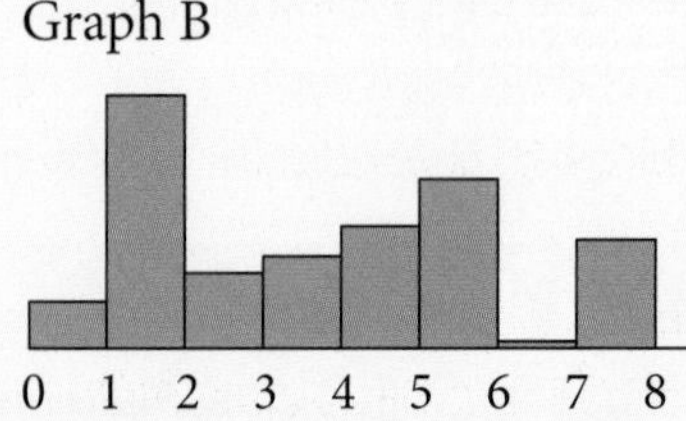

   (i) What type of data was collected? Give a reason for your answer.
   (ii) Describe the distribution of data shown in Graph A. Give an everyday example that would produce this distribution.
   (iii) Describe the distribution of data shown in Graph B. Give an everyday example that would produce this distribution.

2. Packs of party poppers are labelled with the claim, 'Contains at least 12 items'.
   Jo opens eight packs and counts the number of poppers in each pack. Her results are

   12, 13, 12, 13, 12, 12, 13, 11

   (i) Show the results on a line plot.
   (ii) Give one reason Jo might think the claim 'Contains at least 12 items' is fair.

3. The following data of foot length in 17-year-old students comes from Census at School.
   (i) What is the name for this type of graph?
   (ii) What is the largest foot length of the females?
   (iii) What is the most common foot length in males?
   (iv) Compare the distributions of the two sets of data. Include any similarities and differences in your comparison.

Male		Female
	20	0 0
	21	0 0
	22	0 0
	23	0 0 0 0 0 5
0	24	0 0 0 0 0 1 3
0 0 0	25	0 0 0 0 0 0
0 0 0 0	26	
5 0 0 0 0	27	0
0 0 0 0 0	28	1
5 2 0 0	29	

Key: 5 | 27 = 27·5 cm   Key: 23 | 5 = 23·5 cm

4. Draw a scatterplot that illustrates each of the following correlations. In each case, use a minimum of ten data points.
   (i) A weak negative correlation.
   (ii) No correlation.
   (iii) A strong positive correlation.

5. Which of the following relationships would most likely show a negative correlation?
   (i) The population of a town and the number of hospitals in that town.
   (ii) The hours spent training for a race and the time taken to complete the race.
   (iii) The price per litre of petrol and the number of people cycling bicycles to work.
   (iv) The number of pets per household and the number of computers per household.

6. Twenty students take a summer maths test. The scatter diagram shows their marks and the number of maths classes they had missed during the year.
   (i) Write down the mark of the student who missed the most classes.
   (ii) Write down the number of classes missed by the student having a mark of 46.
   (iii) One student missed many classes but still had a high mark in the test. Write down the mark and number of classes missed by this student.
   (iv) The teacher looks at the scatter diagram and concludes: 'the more maths classes a student attends, the higher the mark in the test.' Does the information in the scatter diagram support this conclusion? Give a reason for your answer.

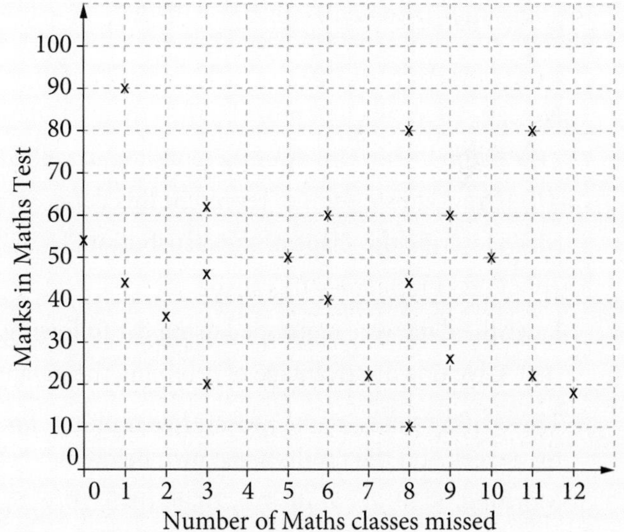

7. For a certain city, the correlation coefficient between population density and distance from the centre of the city is $r = -0{\cdot}55$ and the correlation coefficient between house size and distance from the centre of the city is $r = 0{\cdot}36$.
   (i) Describe the type and strength of each correlation.
   (ii) Explain the meaning of the correlation coefficient in each case.

Revision and Exam Style Questions – Section B

More challenging questions

1. Fourteen students and fourteen teachers took part in a race over an obstacle course at a sports day. Their times, in seconds, to complete the course were:

   Students: 53, 76, 84, 61, 86, 97, 59, 87, 65, 93, 94, 87, 68, 80

   Teachers: 91, 73, 110, 58, 74, 86, 63, 89, 95, 50, 86, 68, 92, 85

   (i) Draw a back-to-back stem-and-leaf diagram to represent this data.

   (ii) Describe the differences, if any, between the two distributions.

   (iii) Describe the similarities, if any, between the two distributions.

   (iv) The principal has to decide which team wins. What should she decide? Justify your answer.

2. On a given day a company records the number of minutes that each employee is late. The results are shown in the frequency table below.

No. of minutes late	0–5	5–10	10–15	15–20	20–25	25–30	30–35	35–40
No. of employees	41	17	22	15	7	4	2	1

   Note: 0–5 means 0 or more but less than 5, etc.

   (i) Draw a histogram to represent this data.

   (ii) Describe the distribution of the data.

3. The table shows information about the distance travelled (in kilometres) by a sample of 150 families visiting the zoo.

Distance travelled	0–10	10–20	20–30	30–40	40–50	50–60
Frequency	55	55	20	10	5	5

   Note: 0–10 means 0 or more but less than 10, etc.

   (i) Estimate how many of these visitors travelled 7 km or more.

   (ii) Draw a histogram to represent this data.

   (iii) Describe the shape of the distribution.

   (iv) Give a reason for this shape.

   Later the data were regrouped using the following classes: 0–20, 20–40, 40–60

   (v) Give one disadvantage of grouping the data using these classes.

4. The waiting times, to the nearest five minutes, for twenty patients are recorded in the morning and afternoon for a week and the results are shown below:

   Morning: 5, 10, 25, 5, 10, 5, 5, 20, 5, 10, 5, 10, 5, 5, 5, 15, 15, 20, 25, 5

   Afternoon: 10, 15, 15, 10, 15, 20, 15, 20, 20, 25, 15, 20, 20, 20, 25, 20, 20, 25, 5, 20

   (i) Draw a bar chart to represent this data and use it to make two comments on each distribution.

   (ii) When is the best time to visit the surgery? Justify your answer.

5. When blood pressure is measured both the systolic (max) and diastolic (min) pressures are recorded. The table below shows both measurements for ten people.

Systolic	121	126	141	125	122	126	119	134	121	140
Diastolic	73	75	73	73	67	74	64	77	69	76

   (i) Draw a scatter plot to represent this data.

   (ii) Is there a correlation between systolic and diastolic pressure?

   (iii) Describe the type and strength of this correlation, if one exists.

6. The table below shows the Junior Cert. Maths results for 10 students. The results show what they got in Paper 1 and Paper 2 of their examination.

Paper 1	45	56	86	75	35	76	67	83	54	74
Paper 2	48	63	89	69	42	74	66	85	55	78

(i) Draw a scatter plot to represent this data.

(ii) Is there a correlation between marks on Paper 1 and Paper 2? If so, describe the correlation.

(iii) Estimate the strength of the correlation, if one exists, by giving a suitable r value.

(iv) Discuss your findings. What conclusion can you make?

7. The following data was obtained on the heights (in cm) and masses (in kg) of 10 children:

Height	142	121	130	127	117	105	119	139	143	100
Mass	36	35	30	37	28	24	51	43	37	17

(i) Draw a scatter plot to represent this data.

(ii) One child is significantly overweight. Use your diagram to identify this child, explaining the reasons for your choice.

(iii) Describe the type and strength of correlation, if one exists, between height and mass.

8. A sports coach analyses the goal-scoring record of a large sample of Premier League Football players over a season.
Part of his analysis involves calculating values for the correlation coefficient between various variables.

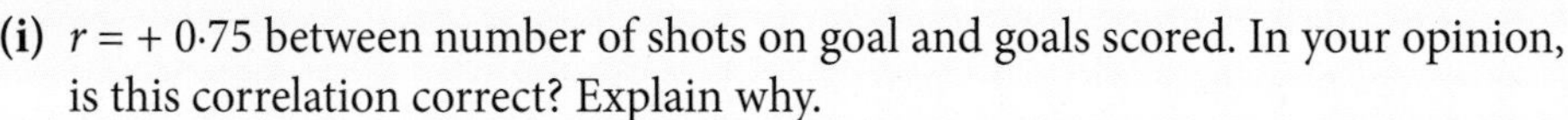
(i) $r = +0{\cdot}75$ between number of shots on goal and goals scored. In your opinion, is this correlation correct? Explain why.

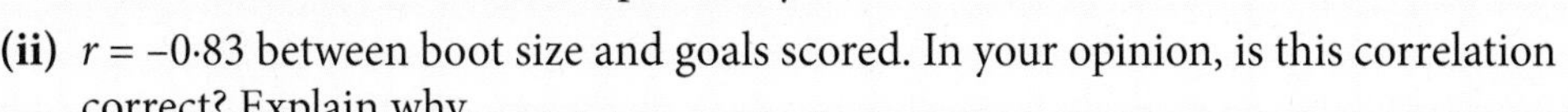
(ii) $r = -0{\cdot}83$ between boot size and goals scored. In your opinion, is this correlation correct? Explain why.

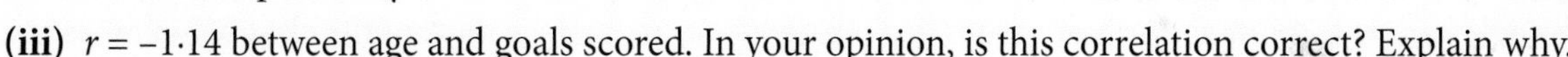
(iii) $r = -1{\cdot}14$ between age and goals scored. In your opinion, is this correlation correct? Explain why.

Now that you have completed the chapter, revisit the 'Something to think about...' question.

CHAPTER 24

Statistics III – Analysing Data

Sections covered within this chapter:

KEY WORDS

- Mode
- Outlier
- Median
- Range
- Mean
- Interquartile range
- Mid-interval value
- Standard deviation

SOMETHING TO THINK ABOUT... 

Jane has taken three tests and got 90%, 75% and 96%. She has to take a final exam and her teacher has told her that the final exam will count as two test grades. Jane really wants to achieve an A in the class, which means she needs an overall average of 85%. Jane is not sure if it is possible to get an A since she got a 75% on one of her tests. Is it possible? If not, explain why. If it is possible, what grade does she need to get?

Section 24.1: Measures of Central Tendency

Learning Outcome:

You should be able to:

- understand and calculate the mode, median and mean

One way to summarise data is to look at where the centre or middle of the data lies. This central or middle point is often called the average. The three most commonly used averages are the mode, median and mean.

The mode

The mode is the value that occurs most often.

It is possible to have more than one mode (if there are two, it is called bimodal), and it is possible to have no mode. If there is no mode, we write 'no mode' and not zero, as zero itself could be the mode.

The mode is very useful for categorical data (non-numerical) when other averages won't work. The mode is also sometimes referred to as the modal value (or class in a histogram).

Finding the mode

- In a list of data or a stem-and-leaf plot, pick the number or word that appears most often.
- In a table, look for the highest frequency (number on the bottom) and pick the value above it.
- In a bar chart, histogram or line plot, pick the value that appears as the highest 'bar'.
- In a pie chart, pick the value represented by the biggest sector.

EXAMPLE 1

The ages of the students in a Leaving Cert. maths class are as follows:

16, 17, 17, 16, 18, 17, 17, 16, 16, 18, 17, 17, 16, 17, 17, 18, 18, 18, 17, 17, 16

What is the mode?

Solution

The following solution shows four separate methods for solving this problem:

(1) From the list we can see that 17 appears most often.

(2) From the table, we can see that 17 has the highest frequency.

Age	16	17	18
Frequency	6	10	5

(3) From the bar chart we can see that 17 has the highest bar.

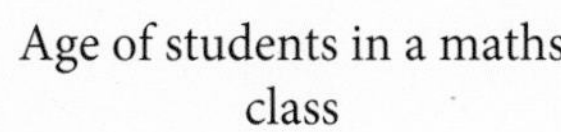

(4) From the pie chart we can see that 17 has the biggest sector.

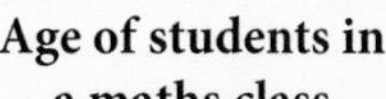

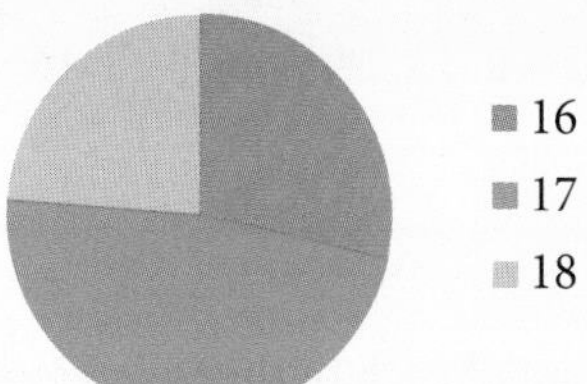

Using any of these methods, we find the mode or modal value to be 17.

The median

The **median** is the middle value, or the mean of the middle two values, when the data is arranged in ascending or descending numerical order.

Finding the median

Think of a 'median' being in the middle of a motorway.

Step 1: List the data in ascending order.

Step 2: Pick the number at the middle position for example 3, 8, (11), 15, 17. median = 11

If there are two numbers in the middle, we find the number halfway between these two values.

For example 5, 8, (9, 13), 16, 20 $\frac{9+13}{2} = \frac{22}{2} = 11$ median = 11

To find the middle position of n numbers we can use the formula $\frac{n+1}{2}$.

For example, the middle position of five numbers is $\frac{5+1}{2} = 3$, pick the value at the third position and that is the median.

The middle position of 10 numbers is $\frac{10+1}{2} = 5{\cdot}5$, pick the values at the fifth and sixth positions add them, divide by 2 and that is the median.

EXAMPLE 2

Find the median of the following set of numbers: 13 19 12 13 15 21 12 16 11 15 13 19

Solution

Step 1: Arrange the numbers in ascending order (if a number is there more than once, write it down as many times as it appears).

11 12 12 13 13 13 15 15 16 19 19 21

Step 2: Find the middle position.

$n = 12$, therefore the middle position is $\frac{12+1}{2} = 6{\cdot}5$,

pick the values at the 6th and 7th position, add them and divide by 2

6th position = 13 7th position = 15

11 12 12 13 13 [13 15] 15 16 19 19 21

Median $= \frac{13+15}{2} = 14$

EXAMPLE 3

Find the median of each of the following:

(i)

Stem	Leaf
1	0 0 1
2	3 3 4 5 5 7 8
3	2 8 9
4	0 1

(ii)

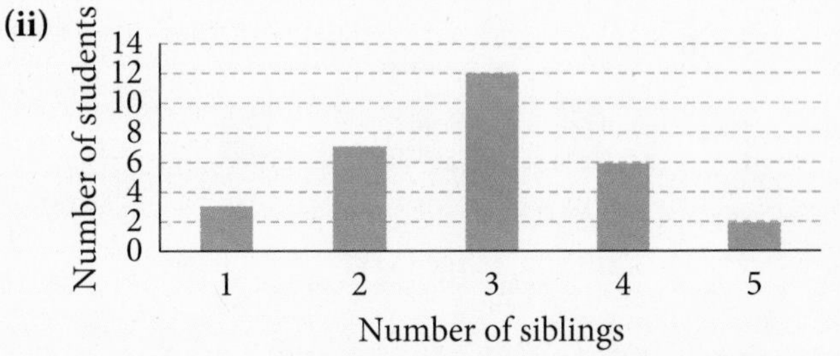

Solution

(i) Count the number of values

$n = 15$

$\frac{n+1}{2} = \frac{15+1}{2} = 8$

8th position = 25

median = 25

(ii) Find the total number of students by reading off the height of each bar.

$3 + 7 + 12 + 6 + 2 = 30$

$n = 30$

$\frac{n+1}{2} = \frac{30+1}{2} = 15{\cdot}5$

Find the bar in which the 15th position and 16th position lie.

The first three positions have 1 sibling, positions 4 to 10 have 2 siblings, positons 11 to 22 have 3 siblings.

Since the 15th and 16th position lie in the bar for three siblings, the median = 3

The mean

The **mean** of a set of values is the sum of the values divided by the number of values

The most commonly used average is the **mean**.

To find the mean of a set of numbers we add up all the numbers and divide by the number of numbers.

$$\text{Mean} = \frac{\text{Sum of the numbers}}{\text{Number of numbers}}$$

This formula is given on page 33 of the booklet of *formulae and tables*, as shown.

$\mu = \dfrac{\Sigma x}{n}$ from list of n numbers

μ = mean

Σx = the sum of all the numbers

n = the number of numbers

EXAMPLE 4

Find the mean of the following set of numbers: 13, 17, 12, 11, 16, 15, 13, 17

Solution

$$\text{Mean} = \frac{\text{Sum of the numbers}}{\text{Number of numbers}}$$

$$\text{Mean} = \frac{13 + 17 + 12 + 11 + 16 + 15 + 13 + 17}{8} = 14{\cdot}25$$

To find the mean of a frequency distribution table we add up the frequency multiplied by the values and divide by the sum of the frequencies.

$$\text{Mean} = \frac{\text{Sum of (frequency} \times \text{value)}}{\text{Sum of frequencies}}$$

This formula is also on page 33 of the booklet of *formulae and tables*, as shown.

$$\mu = \frac{\Sigma fx}{\Sigma f}$$

μ = mean

Σfx = the sum of (frequency × value),

Σf = sum of frequencies

EXAMPLE 5

Find the mean, to one decimal place, of the following table, showing the number of text messages sent by a group of students on a particular day:

No. of texts	3	5	8	10	12
No. of students	7	3	12	24	18

Solution

To find the total number of text messages sent we multiply the number of students by the number of texts that they sent and add the results:

$$\text{Mean} = \frac{\text{Total number of text messages sent}}{\text{Total number of students}}$$

If seven students sent three text messages each, then between them they sent a total of 21 texts.

$$\text{Mean} = \frac{(7 \times 3) + (3 \times 5) + (12 \times 8) + (24 \times 10) + (18 \times 12)}{7 + 3 + 12 + 24 + 18}$$

$$\text{Mean} = \frac{21 + 15 + 96 + 240 + 216}{64}$$

Mean = 9·1875

Mean = 9·2

EXAMPLE 6

Sarah's results on her last three maths tests have been 78%, 82% and 75%.

Her Christmas result will be an average of these tests and one more test result. Her mother has said that if her average is above 80% at Christmas she will buy her a new phone.

What result must Sarah get in her next test to get a new phone?

Solution

Let x be her result of the fourth test, then

$$\text{Mean} = \frac{78 + 82 + 75 + x}{4}$$

$$80 = \frac{235 + x}{4}$$

$320 = 235 + x$ (multiply both sides by 4)

$85 = x$ (subtract 235 from both sides)

Sarah must get 85% or more in her next test to be sure of getting a new phone.

Links across the syllabus

Solving equations involving fractions is covered in Chapter 3: Algebra II.

Practice Questions 24.1

Statistics III

1. Find the mode, median and mean of each of the following sets of numbers:
   - **(i)** 73, 75, 47, 42, 69, 35, 51, 29, 24, 12, 71
   - **(ii)** 68, 84, 75, 81, 77, 72, 71, 67, 71
   - **(iii)** 16, 9, 11, 23, 23, 17, 22, 4
   - **(iv)** 48, 37, 33, 39, 39, 47, 30, 33
   - **(v)** 57, 65, 72, 66, 55, 57, 58, 57, 62
2. The midday temperatures (°C) recorded over a two week period were as follows:
   10, 12, 11, 15, 14, 13, 12, 15, 11, 12, 17, 12, 16, 10
   - **(i)** What is the modal temperature?
   - **(ii)** Calculate the median temperature.
   - **(iii)** The average midday temperature for the same period the previous year was 13·5°C. Calculate the percentage increase or decrease in the mean temperature.
3. Data was collected on the number of websites visited by 15 people in an hour and presented in the following stem-and-leaf plot.
   Calculate the mode, median and mean of this data. Give your answers correct to one decimal place.

Stem	Leaf
0	1 1 3 5
1	4 4 4 4 7 8 9
2	3 5 6
3	0

Key: 2|3 = 23 websites.

4. A number of people were asked how many driving lessons they had taken before passing their test. The results are shown below:
   8, 21, 14, 21, 18, 41, 35, 12, 17,
   14, 32, 29, 38, 25, 20, 34, 13, 19
   - **(i)** Draw a stem-and-leaf diagram for this data.
   - **(ii)** Find the mean, mode and the median.
5. The table below shows the data for the number of hours' sleep received by a group of teenagers on a given night over the weekend.

Hours of sleep	4	6	8	10	12
No. of people	10	8	6	12	16

   - **(i)** Which is higher: the mode, median or mean for this data set? Justify your answer.
   - **(ii)** Suppose 3 more people say they slept for 12 hours, what affect would that have on the mode, median and mean?
6. The total weight of 8 iPad minis is 2·5 kg. The mean weight of 5 iPhones is 175 g.
   - **(i)** What is the mean weight of the iPads?
   - **(ii)** What is the total weight of the iPhones?
   - **(iii)** What is the mean weight of the 8 iPads and 5 iPhones together?

7. Find the mode, median and mean of the follow displays of data, if possible.

(i) Hours spent playing computer games.

```
                X
                X
     X          X        X
  X  X          X  X     X
  X  X  X       X  X  X  X
--+--+--+--+----+--+--+--+--
  1  2  3  4    5  6  7  8
           Hours
```

(ii) How students get to school.

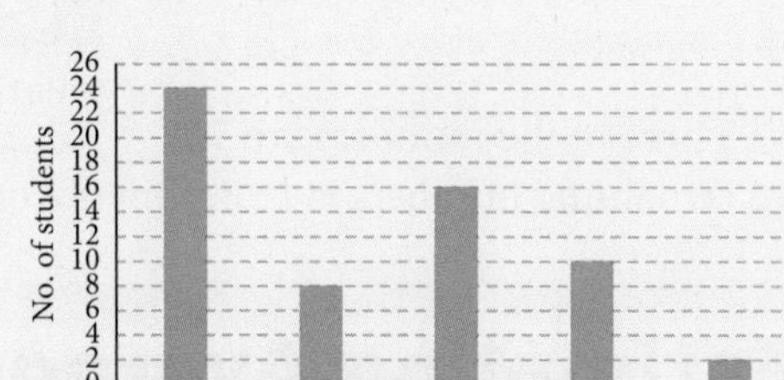

(iii) Favourite sport

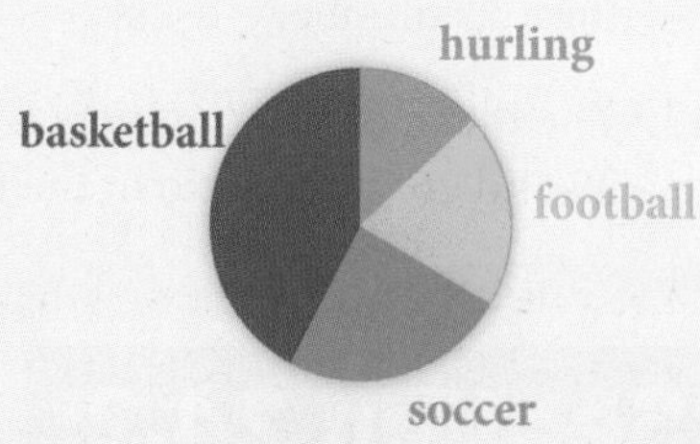

8. In a dancing competition there are five judges.
Each judge gives a score from 1 to 10 and the overall score is the mean of all five scores.
Leah is trying to remember the scores she got in the last round. She can remember the scores of four of the judges, which are as follows:

Judge 1: 7·8 Judge 2: 8·3 Judge 3: 8·1 Judge 4: 7·5

If her overall score was 8·1, work out what score the fifth judge gave her.

9. There are three different rugby teams in your area. The scores for each team for their last 5 matches are shown in the table

Team	Match 1	Match 2	Match 3	Match 4	Match 5
Lions	11	24	13	15	7
Tigers	25	6	10	33	19
Panthers	53	8	14	27	5

(i) Suppose you want to join one of the three rugby teams. You want to join the one that is doing the best so far. If you rank each team by their mean scores, which team would you join?

(ii) Instead of using mean scores, you use the median score of each team to make your decision. Which team do you join?

(iii) Pretend you are the coach of the Lions and you were being interviewed about your team for the local newspaper. Would it be better for you to report your mean score or your median score? Give a reason for your answer.

10. Three friends decide to compare how often they go to the cinema over a six-month period. The table shows how many times each of them went in each month.

Name	Jan	Feb	Mar	Apr	May	Jun
Andy	1	3	2	5	3	3
Becky	1	2	1	1	3	1
Calum	2	1	2	1	3	2

(i) By comparing modes, which person went to the cinema the most per month?

(ii) By comparing medians, which person went to the cinema the least per month?

(iii) Rank the friends in order of most movies seen to least movies seen by comparing their means.

(iv) By comparing the mean number of trips to the cinema in each month, determine which month is the most popular to go to the cinema.

(v) By comparing medians, which month is the least popular month?

(vi) What is the mean of the medians for each month?

Statistics III

11. The mean of six numbers is 5. If the mean of five of these numbers is 4·6, find the sixth number.

12. The mean of 25 numbers is 36. If the mean of the first 13 numbers is 32 and that of the last 13 numbers is 39, find the 13th number.

13. The mean of five numbers is 34. Three of the numbers are 35, 29 and 26. If the ratio of the two remaining numbers is 1 : 3, find the other two numbers.

Links across the syllabus

Ratio is covered in Chapter 8: Arithmetic I.

Section 24.2: Estimating Averages of a Grouped Frequency Table

Learning Outcome:

You should be able to:

- understand and estimate the mode, median and mean of a grouped frequency table

Results of the collection of data are often presented in a grouped frequency table such as the one shown below:

Number of training sessions per month	10–12	13–15	16–18	18–20
No. of athletes	3	8	4	2

The mean

It is not possible to get the exact mean of such a table because we do not know each value but we can estimate the mean.

Each interval has two end values e.g. 10–12 has both values 10 and 12. When finding the mean we use the middle value between the start and the end of the interval which is called the **mid-interval value.**

To do this we add the two end values and divide by two.

The mid-interval value is the middle value of the interval.

$$\frac{10+12}{2} = 11, \quad \frac{13+15}{2} = 14, \quad \frac{16+18}{2} = 17, \quad \frac{18+20}{2} = 19$$

Our table will now look like this:

Number of training sessions per month	10–12	13–15	16–18	18–20
Mid-interval values	11	14	17	19
No. of athletes	3	8	4	2

Using the mid-interval values we can now calculate the mean as we did for the frequency tables in the previous section.

$$\text{Mean} = \frac{(11 \times 3) + (14 \times 8) + (17 \times 4) + (19 \times 2)}{3 + 8 + 4 + 2} = \frac{33 + 112 + 68 + 38}{17} = \frac{251}{17} = 14{\cdot}76470....$$

Therefore, the mean number of training sessions per month, for these athletes, was 15 (to the nearest whole number).

EXAMPLE 1

The table shows the value of a number of cars in a local garage.

Value of car (€)	1,000–2,500	2,500–5,000	5,000–7,500	7,500–10,000	10,000–12,500
No. of cars	8	15	12	18	22

Note: 1,000–2,500 means 1,000 or more but less than 2,500 etc

Calculate the mean value of the cars to the nearest euro.

Solution

Find the mid-interval values

$\frac{1,000 + 2,500}{2} = 1,750$ $\frac{2,500 + 5,000}{2} = 3,750$ $\frac{5,000 + 7,500}{2} = 6,250$

$\frac{7,500 + 10,000}{2} = 8,750$ $\frac{10,000 + 12,500}{2} = 11,250$

Value of car (€)	1,000–2,500	2,500–5,000	5,000–7,500	7,500–10,000	10,000–12,500
Mid-interval value	1,750	3,750	6,250	8,750	11,250
No. of cars	8	15	12	18	22

Calculate the mean

$$\text{Mean} = \frac{(1750 \times 8) + (3750 \times 15) + (6250 \times 12) + (8750 \times 18) + (11250 \times 22)}{8 + 15 + 12 + 18 + 22}$$

$$\text{Mean} = \frac{14000 + 56250 + 75000 + 157500 + 247500}{75}$$

$$\text{Mean} = \frac{550250}{75}$$

Mean = 7,336·67 = €7,337 to the nearest euro.

Mode and median

Again we can only estimate the median and mode for grouped data. We can't find their exact value, we can only find the **median interval** and the **modal interval**.

EXAMPLE 2

The table shows the number of bars of chocolate bought by a group of students in a week

Find **(i)** the modal interval and **(ii)** the median interval.

No. of bars	0–4	5–9	10–14	15–19	19–23
No. of students	12	9	6	2	1

Solution

(i) The highest frequency is 12, so the modal interval is 0–4.

This means that 0–4 bars was the most common number of bars bought.

(ii) There are 30 students in this study so $n = 30$

Median: between the 15th and 16th position

The first 12 students bought 0–4 bars, the next 9 students, including the 15th and 16th students, bought 5–9 bars. Therefore, the median interval is the 5–9 interval.

Practice Questions 24.2

1. Estimate the **(a)** modal interval, **(b)** median interval and **(c)** mean to one decimal place for each of the following grouped frequency tables:

(i)

Score	30–40	40–50	50–60	60–70	70–80
Frequency	10	8	12	14	6

Recall: For continuous data the upper value is not included in the interval i.e. (0–10) doesn't include 10.

(ii)

Score	20–40	40–60	60–80	80–100	100–120
Frequency	5	3	1	4	6

(iii)

Score	60–70	70–80	80–90	90–100	100–110
Frequency	17	18	32	24	16

(iv)

Score	5–10	10–15	15–20	20–25	25–30
Frequency	9	15	22	11	7

2. A survey is conducted to examine the amount of money the average customer spends at a supermarket checkout. This was done with a sample of 87 people. The information was then grouped into the following intervals.

Amount Spent (€)	5–25	25–40	40–70	70–100	100–150
Frequency	10	13	12	29	23

Hint: The intervals are unequal here.

Find the **(i)** modal interval, **(ii)** median interval and **(iii)** estimated mean amount of money spent.

3. The weights of 100 objects (in kg) were measured. The results are shown in the table below.

Weight (kg)	1–5	5–10	10–15	15–20	20–25	25–30
Frequency	8	16	18	24	22	12

(i) Draw a histogram of the results shown in the table.
(ii) What is the modal interval?
(iii) Estimate the mean weight of the objects.
(iv) If the mean for a further 100 objects is 18·5, estimate the mean for the 200 objects.

4. The ages of 20 musicians are listed below.

6, 11, 14, 17, 7, 20, 19, 15, 26, 21, 13, 15, 19, 19, 29, 11, 18, 13, 8, 14

(i) Calculate the mean to one decimal place from the list.
(ii) Group the data into intervals: 6–10, 11–15, 16–20 etc., and then estimate the mean to one decimal place from the grouped data.

5. David has just moved house. In the area he has moved to there are two doctor's surgeries. David doesn't like to wait when he goes to the doctor so he decides to gather some data to help him decide which doctor to attend.

Surgery A

Waiting time (mins)	0–5	5–10	10–15	15–20	20–25
Frequency	6	18	25	19	7

Surgery B

Waiting time (mins)	0–5	5–10	10–15	15–20	20–25
Frequency	13	15	20	16	11

(i) Draw a histogram to represent both tables.
(ii) Estimate the mean for both sets of data.
(iii) Which surgery would you recommend for David to attend? Justify your answer by referring to the histograms and the estimated mean.

Section 24.3: Choosing the Most Appropriate Average

Learning Outcomes:

You should be able to:
- decide which average to use
- compare sets of data in relation to their averages
- understand the idea of outliers and the effect of these on the data

Outliers

In a set of data an **outlier** is an **extreme value**, or a value which is much greater than, or much less than, the other values.

Discussion Time 

Working with a classmate, consider the following data set: 3, 4, 5, 5, 6, 6, 6, 7, 7, 8, 9, 10

1. Find the: **(i)** mode **(ii)** median **(iii)** mean

Now add an extreme value, of 150, to your data set: 3, 4, 5, 5, 6, 6, 6, 7, 7, 8, 9, 10, 150

2. For this new data set, find the: **(i)** mode **(ii)** median **(iii)** mean

3. Comment on the effect of adding this extreme value to the **(i)** mode, **(ii)** median and **(iii)** mean.

4. Which of the three measures of central tendency is most affected by the inclusion of an outlier?

Discuss your findings with your class.

How do I know which measure of central tendency to use?

Mode

Use the mode when the data is not numerical or when asked to choose the most popular item.

Advantages:
- Extreme values (outliers) do not affect the mode.

Disadvantages:
- Not necessarily unique – may be more than one answer
- When no values repeat in the data set, the mode is every value and is useless.
- When there is more than one mode, it is difficult to interpret and compare with other data.

Median

Use the median to describe the middle for a set of data. It is useful when dealing with data that has outliers.

Advantages:
- Extreme values (outliers) do not affect the median as strongly as they do the mean.
- Useful when comparing sets of data.
- It is unique – there is only one answer.

Disadvantages:
- Not as popular or well understood as the mean.

Mean

Use the mean for a set of data that does not have an outlier.

Advantages:
- Most popular measure in fields such as business, engineering and computer science.
- It is unique – there is only one answer.
- Useful when comparing sets of data.

Disadvantages:
- Affected by extreme values (outliers).

The shape of the distribution can also affect our choice of measure of central tendency.

If the data is symmetrical:

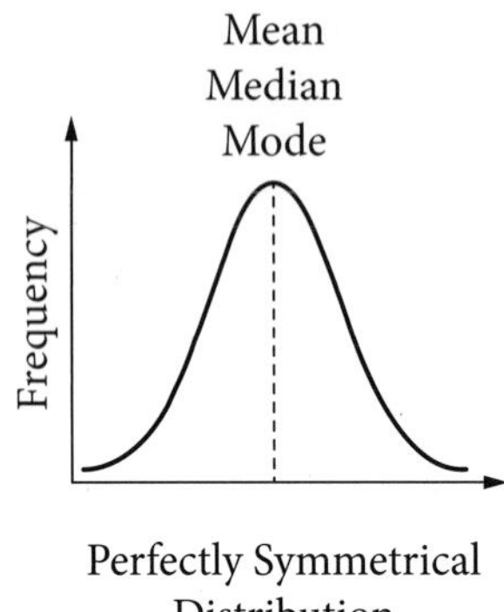

mean = median = mode

If the data is negatively skewed:

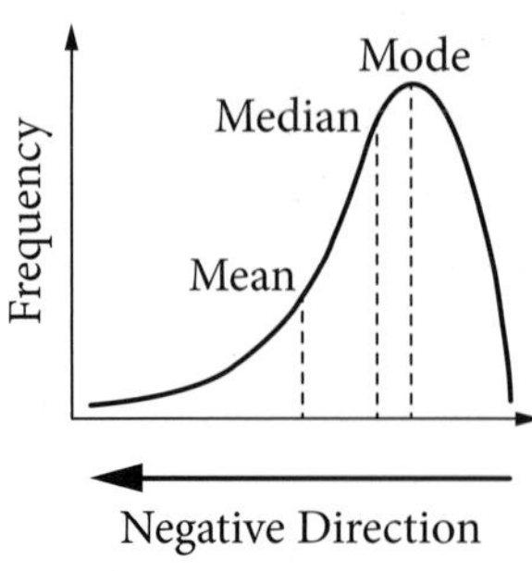

mean < median < mode

If the data is positively skewed:

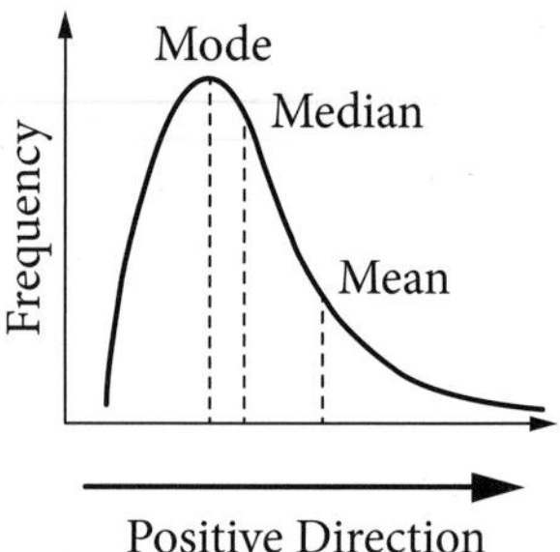

mean > median > mode

Practice Questions 24.3

1. Describe a situation where each of the following is the most appropriate measure of central tendency to use:
   - **(i)** Mode
   - **(ii)** Median
   - **(iii)** Mean
2. The following are the times (in minutes) it took 10 people to travel to work on a certain day:

   13, 58, 3, 8, 8, 68, 53, 38, 4, 12
   - **(i)** Find the mode, median and mean.
   - **(ii)** Comment on your results.
   - **(iii)** Why might some of the results to part **(i)** be higher or lower than each other?
3. Which measure of central tendency would be most appropriate to use for each of the following data sets? Explain your answers.
   - **(i)** 96, 98, 98, 105, 36, 87, 95, 93
   - **(ii)** A, B, B, B, C, A, B, B, A, B, C, B, B, B, A
   - **(iii)** 71, 69, 65, 73, 64, 66, 68
   - **(iv)** 2, 3, 4, 4, 5, 26, 1, 28, 7
   - **(v)** Blue, green, red, red, blue, yellow, black, red, white, red, green
4. The scores shown below were received by four quiz teams named A, B, C, and D in a table quiz. Each team reported an 'average' of 90.

   A: 80, 85, 90, 95, 100

   B: 93, 92, 90, 90, 91

   C: 80, 86, 95, 92, 90

   D: 85, 90, 90, 90, 90

   Which measure of central tendency was used by each team?
5. An internet company, Flash Internet, recorded the following internet speeds (in Megabits per second) following a series of tests in an area:

   1·6, 8·8, 2·9, 5·8, 3·1, 4·0, 6·5, 0·7
   - **(i)** Find the mode, median and mean
   - **(ii)** Comment on your results.
   - **(iii)** Which average would you advise Flash Internet to use in their advertising? Why?
6. The table shows the results of a group of students in a maths test.

Males	41	20	66	41	52	40	69
Females	21	89	56	27	93	51	86

   Using your knowledge of averages, compare the male and female results.

Section 24.4: Measures of Variability/Spread

Learning Outcomes:

You should be able to:
- understand and calculate the range and interquartile range
- compare the variability or spread of various sets of data

Range

Range is the difference between the highest and lowest value. It is a single value, not an interval.

We are often interested in how spread out or variable our data is.
It is generally considered that less spread out data is better.

Probably the simplest measure of how spread the data is the **range.**

Range = the highest value – the lowest value

As the range uses the highest and lowest values it can be seriously affected by extreme values or outliers.

Interquartile range (IQR)

Imagine the government was carrying out a study on household income. A sample of 1,000 people are chosen. Some will be unemployed, some will earn a typical income and there is a good chance the sample might include a small number on very high incomes.

The range would be a very big number and not very useful for establishing the variation of the majority of the population.

If the government ignored the bottom and top quarter of the sample, they would get a range that is much more representative of a majority of the population. This is what we are calculating when we find the Interquartile Range (IQR).

The **interquartile range** is a measure of variability that is not affected by outliers.

As we have seen previously the **median** **(Q_2)** is the middle value. The median therefore divides an ordered data set into two halves.

If these halves are divided in half again, we form **quartiles**.

The middle value of the lower half is called the **lower quartile** **(Q_1).** One quarter of the data has values less than or equal to the lower quartile.

The middle value of the upper half is called the **upper quartile** **(Q_3).** Three quarters of the data has values less than or equal to the upper quartile.

The **interquartile range** is the range of the middle half (50%) of the data.

interquartile range = upper quartile – lower quartile

$$IQR = Q_3 - Q_1$$

If a data set contains 20 values arranged in ascending order we could illustrate the IQR like this:

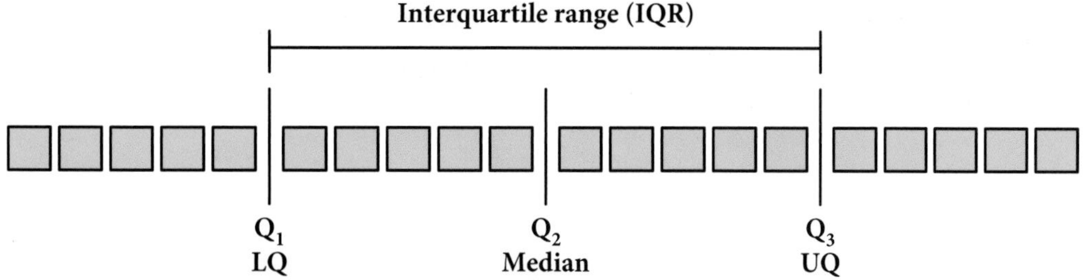

EXAMPLE 1

For the following set of data 18, 15, 12, 9, 15, 3, 33, 21; find:

(i) the lower quartile **(ii)** the upper quartile **(iii)** the IQR.

Solution

(i) Arrange the data in ascending order

3, 9, 12, 15, 15, 18, 21, 33

Q_1 is the middle value of the lower half of the data

3, 9, 12, 15

The lower quartile is halfway between the 2nd and 3rd position

$$Q_1 = \frac{9+12}{2} = \frac{21}{2} = 10{\cdot}5$$

(ii) Q_3 is the middle value of the upper half of the data:

15, 18, 21, 33

The upper quartile is halfway between the 6th and 7th position

$$Q_3 = \frac{18+21}{2} = \frac{39}{2} = 19{\cdot}5$$

(iii) $\text{IQR} = Q_3 - Q_1$

$\text{IQR} = 19{\cdot}5 - 10{\cdot}5$

$\text{IQR} = 9$

EXAMPLE 2

The following unordered stem-and-leaf plot shows the lengths, in cm, of a sample of 15 leaves from a tree.

(i) Calculate the **(a)** range and **(b)** interquartile range for this data.

(ii) Comment on the difference between these two measures of spread.

Stem	Leaf
4	3
5	4 0 7 3 9
6	3 1 4
7	6 1 6
8	
9	3 2

Key: 7|6 = 7·6 cm

Solution

(i) (a) Range = 9·3 – 4·3 = 5 cm

(b) Interquartile range = $Q_3 - Q_1$

Arrange the data in ascending order

4·3, 5·0, 5·3, 5·4, 5·7, 5·9, 6·1,
6·3, 6·4, 7·1, 7·6, 7·6, 9·2, 9·3.

The lower quartile is the middle value of the lower half of the data:

4·3, 5·0, 5·3, 5·4, 5·7, 5·9, 6·1.

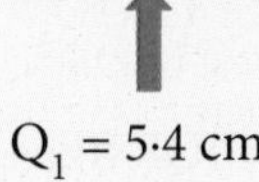

$Q_1 = 5{\cdot}4$ cm

The upper quartile is the middle value of the upper half of the data:

6·3, 6·4, 7·1, 7·6, 7·6, 9·2, 9·3

$Q_3 = 7{\cdot}6$ cm

Interquartile Range = $Q_3 - Q_1$

= 7·6 – 5·4

= 2·2 cm

(ii) The range is much larger than the interquartile range. This is due the presence of outliers 9·2 and 4·3 cm.

The interquartile range is a more reliable measure of spread since it is not affected by outliers.

Practice Questions 24.4

1. Find the range, median and interquartile range of the following data sets:
   (i) 13, 15, 9, 35, 25
   (ii) 6, 1, 3, 8, 5, 11, 1, 5
   (iii) 5, 9, 17, 25, 36, 45
   (iv) 8, 11, 32, 29, 9, 34
   (v) 3, 14, 28, 22, 5, 9

2. The ages of two families are shown below:

   Smith family: 1, 4, 7, 12, 40, 46

   Dunne family: 3, 7, 15, 18, 44, 48

   Compare the spread of the ages in both families under the headings:

   (i) Range (ii) Median (iii) Interquartile range

3. The numbers of goals scored in 10 games by the top two teams in an inter-schools soccer league are shown below:

   School A: 3, 3 2, 1, 3, 2, 1, 1, 2, 3

   School B: 1, 5, 2, 2, 4, 1, 3, 3, 2, 4

   (a) Compare the spread of the scores of each team under the following headings:
   (i) Range (iii) Interquartile range
   (ii) Median (iv) Mean
   (b) Why is the range not a very good measure of spread?
   (c) Which is the more reliable average, the mean or the median? Explain your reasoning.

4. The stem-and-leaf diagram below shows the average time (in mins) it took a group of students to solve a maths problem.

Stem	Leaf
1	1 2 5 7
2	0 1 3 4 8
3	2 9
4	3 3 5 6 8
5	0 1 6

Key: 1|1 = 11 mins

   (i) Find the range of this data.
   (ii) Find the median time to solve the problem.
   (iii) Find the interquartile range of this data set.

5. The back-to-back stem-and-leaf diagram below shows the results of two different maths classes on the same test.

Ms X's Class	Stem	Ms Y's Class
9 6 4	5	1 5
8 7 5 2	6	4 8
4 1	7	4 6 6 7
1 1 0	8	6 6 6 6
2 2 1	9	4 6 7 8 9 9

Key: 4|5 = 54% Key: 5|1 = 51%

   (i) Compare the range of both classes.
   (ii) Compare the interquartile range for both classes.
   (iii) Find the mean, correct to one decimal place, of each class.
   (iv) Which class do you think is better? Justify your answer.

6. The time spent (in minutes) by 20 people waiting at a bus stop has been recorded as follows:

   3·2, 2·4, 3·2, 1·3, 1·6, 2·8, 1·4, 2·9, 3·2, 4·8, 1·7, 3, 0·9, 3·7, 5·6, 1·4, 2·6, 3·1, 1·6, 1·1

   (i) Find the median waiting time and the upper and lower quartiles.
   (ii) Find the range and interquartile range of the waiting time.
   (iii) Copy and complete the following statements:
   (a) '50% of the waiting times were greater than .... minutes.'
   (b) '75% of the waiting times were less than ...... minutes.'
   (c) 'The minimum waiting time was .... minutes and the maximum waiting time was ..... minutes. The waiting times were spread over ...... minutes.'

7. Rory's golf scores for his last 10 rounds were:

   90, 106, 84, 103, 112, 100, 105, 81, 104, 98

   (a) Use this data to calculate:

   (i) the median **(iii)** the upper quartile

   (ii) the lower quartile **(iv)** the interquartile range.

   (b) Shane is a member in Rory's club. He has a median = 100, IQR = 7 and range = 19. Who should be picked for the last place on their club's team. Justify your answer.

Section 24.5: Standard Deviation

Learning Outcome:

You should be able to:

- understand and calculate the standard deviation by calculator only

The **standard deviation** measures the deviation between values and the mean, i.e. it is a measure of how widely spread the data is around the mean.

Probably the most commonly used measure of the spread of data is the **standard deviation.** It is given the symbol (σ), called sigma.

Imagine that you calculated the mean (μ) and standard deviation (σ) of the ages in your class at school and of the ages of all your family members including your parents.

You would expect the standard deviation for your family ages to be much higher than that of your class.

The reason for this is because the ages of your class would all be very close to the mean whereas the ages of everyone in your family would be more spread out from the mean.

The larger the standard deviation, the more widely spread the data is and vice versa.

The standard deviation provides a better measure of the spread than either the range or the interquartile range because it considers all scores in the data.

For the purpose of this course you only need to know how to calculate the standard deviation using your calculator.

EXAMPLE 1

Find the **(i)** mean and **(ii)** standard deviation of the following list of numbers:

(a) 1, 3, 5, 8, 9 **(b)** 5, 7, 12, 2, 16

(iii) Use the answers to parts **(i)** and **(ii)** to compare the two sets of data.

Solution

Using your calculator, the answers are found to be

Use your calculator to find these values.

(a) **(i)** Mean = 5·2

(ii) Standard deviation = 2.9933259....

(b) **(i)** Mean = 8·4

(ii) Standard deviation = 5·003998....

(iii) Comparing the two sets of data

Means: The first set of data has a lower mean of 5·2 compared to 8·4 for the second set.

Standard deviations: The first set of data has a lower standard deviation which means that this data is less spread out around the mean than the second set.

EXAMPLE 2

The following frequency distribution table shows the number of residents per household

Find the mean and the standard deviation (correct to one decimal place).

No. of residents	1	2	3	4	5	6
Frequency	8	12	24	18	6	4

Solution

Using your calculator you will find

Mean = 3·19444.......

Standard deviation = 1·28710......

Practice Questions 24.5

For all the questions in this section, answers should be given to two decimal places.

1. Find the mean and standard deviation of the following data sets:
   - **(i)** 2 3 4 5 6 8 9 12
   - **(ii)** 13·4 21·6 17·8 14·5 25·0 14·8 11·6
   - **(iii)** 21 99 105 38 57 76 100
   - **(iv)** 36 51 64 60 78 65 81
   - **(v)** 135 115 120 110 110 100 105 125

2. If the standard deviation of a given data set is equal to zero, what can we say about the data values included in the given data set?

3. Consider the following three data sets:
   A = 8, 4, 3 B = 7, 6, 14 C = 9, 3, 3
   - **(i)** Calculate the mean of each data set.
   - **(ii)** Calculate the standard deviation of each data set.
   - **(iii)** Which set has the largest standard deviation?
   - **(iv)** Is it possible to answer part **(iii)** without calculations of the standard deviation?

4. The results of 8 students in a maths exam were
   77, 67, 43, 90, 66, 93, 75, 62
   - **(i)** Calculate the mean and standard deviation of these marks.
   - **(ii)** Another group of eight students who sat the same exam had a mean mark of 78 and a standard deviation of 3·2.
     Make two comparisons of the marks of the two groups.

5. A gardener grows tomatoes in his greenhouse. The temperature of the greenhouse, in degrees Celsius, is recorded every day at noon for one week:
   18, 20, 23, 16, 22, 13, 15
   - **(i)** Calculate the mean and standard deviation of these temperatures.

   For best growth, the mean temperature should be 15 ± 5 °C and the standard deviation should be less than 4 °C.
   - **(ii)** Are the conditions in the greenhouse likely to result in best growth?

6. The number of pupils in each of six years in a secondary school are:
   144, 142, 166, 140, 150, 130
   - **(i)** Calculate the mean and standard deviation of the year sizes.

   In a different school the mean and standard deviation of the number of pupils in the six-year groups are 135 and 4·4 respectively.
   - **(ii)** Make two comparisons between the year group sizes in the two schools.

Statistics III

7. Find the mean and standard deviation of the following frequency distribution tables

(i)

Variable	0	1	3	4	5
Frequency	6	12	24	26	8

(ii)

Variable	1	2	3	7	9
Frequency	3	10	14	36	18

(iii)

No. of pets	0	1	2	3	4
No. of students	3	10	14	6	2

(iv)

No. of children	1	2	3	4	5
No. of families	5	22	16	9	3

8. A frozen food company uses machines to pack baby carrots into bags. A sample of six bags is taken from Machine A and the number of carrots in each bag is counted. The results are shown below:

24, 18, 20, 21, 19, 25

(i) Calculate the mean and standard deviation of this sample.

(ii) Another sample of six bags is taken from Machine B. This sample has a mean of 20 and a standard deviation of 2·5. Write down two valid comparisons between the samples.

(iii) Which machine should they use more often? Justify your answer.

9. The principal of a school records the number of minutes students arrive late, to the nearest minute, on a certain day. The results are shown on the table below:

No. of minutes late	0–4	5–9	10–14	15–19	20–24	25–29	30–34	35–39
No. of students	31	7	12	5	3	2	1	1

(i) What is the modal interval? Is this a good measure of central tendency? Give a reason for your answer.

(ii) What interval contains the median value? Is this a good measure of central tendency? Give a reason for your answer.

(iii) Use mid-interval values to calculate the mean. Is this a good measure of central tendency? Give a reason for your answer.

(iv) Use mid-interval values to find the standard deviation of this data set.

Revision and Exam Style Questions – Section A

1. Andrew has three number cards. The mode of Andrew's numbers is 8. Write three numbers that satisfy this condition.

2. Given the numbers 6, 9, 7, 8, 6; Sarah says, 'The mode is double the range.' Is Sarah correct?

3. At a ski resort the temperature, in degrees Celsius, was recorded each day at noon for the first fortnight in February.

0, −1, 2, −5, 4, 2, −3, 1, −4, 8, −6, 4, −2, 1

Calculate:

(i) the modal temperature

(ii) the mean temperature correct to two decimal places

(iii) the median temperature

(iv) the range of temperatures

(v) the lower and upper quartiles

(vi) the interquartile range

(vii) the standard deviation to 2 decimal places.

(viii) Comment on the variability of the data. Refer specifically to measures of spread in your comments.

4. A swimmer has recorded her times, in seconds, for six different lengths of the swimming pool.
23, 27, 28, 30, 25, 26
Calculate:

(i) the mean
(ii) the standard deviation to 2 decimal places.

She changes her training routine hoping to improve her consistency.
After this change, she records her times for another six lengths. The mean is 25 seconds and the standard deviation 3·2 seconds.

(iii) Has the new training routine improved her consistency? Justify your answer.

5. The weights, in kilograms, of a random sample of 12 items of cabin luggage on an airplane were as follows:

4·5, 3·7, 3·8, 4·6, 5·0, 3·5, 3·6, 5·1, 3·9, 5·0, 4·0, 3·2.

(i) Find the value of the range of this data.
(ii) Find values for the median and the interquartile range correct to two decimal places.
(iii) State why the mode is not an appropriate measure of average.

6. Emily works as a receptionist at a dentist's surgery. Each day she records the number of missed appointments. The table shows the number of missed appointments for a 90-day period.

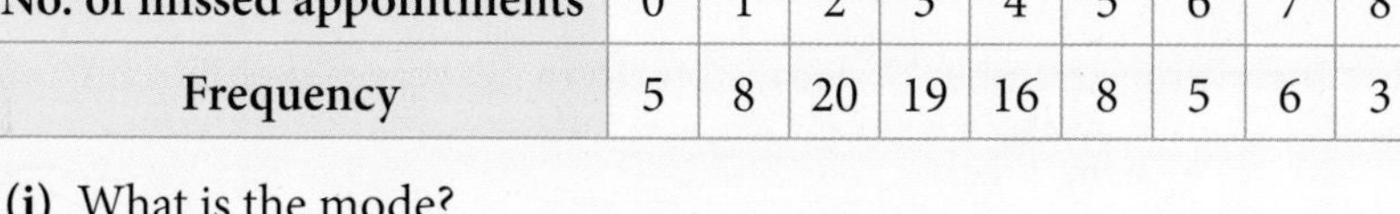

No. of missed appointments	0	1	2	3	4	5	6	7	8
Frequency	5	8	20	19	16	8	5	6	3

(i) What is the mode?
(ii) What is the range?
(iii) What is the mean to two decimal places?
(iv) What is the standard deviation, to two decimal places?
(v) Is the mean a suitable measure of average in this case? Justify your answer.

Later Emily finds that she has made some mistakes. All five of the days with 'no appointments missed' should have been recorded as 'four appointments missed'. She corrects the mistakes.

(vi) What happens to the mode, range and mean as a result of correcting this mistake?

Revision and Exam Style Questions – Section B

More challenging problems

1. The standard deviation of 1, 2, 2, 2, 8 is equal to $\sqrt{k}$. Find the value of k.

2. The number of visitors to a museum is recorded daily over a three-week period.
The results are shown in the stem-and-leaf diagram.
For the data given, calculate:

(i) the median
(ii) the lower quartile
(iii) the upper quartile.

Stem	Leaf
3	1 6
4	2 5 5 6
5	0 3 4 7 7 8
6	1 4 6 7
7	0 1 1 4
8	4

Key: 4|2 represents 42 visitors

In the same three-week period, the number of visitors to a nearby castle is recorded daily. For this data the interquartile range is found to be 5.

(iv) Make an appropriate comment comparing the distribution of visitors to the museum and the castle.

3. A personal trainer collected data from his clients over a randomly selected sample of days. From this he found that the number of glasses of water they drank in a day had a mean of 4·475.

Glasses	1	2	3	4	5	6	7
Frequency	1	4	6	10	x	9	4

(i) Find the number of days represented by x.

(ii) Find the range and the interquartile range of this data.

(iii) Calculate the standard deviation of this data, to three decimal places.

4. The table below illustrates the amount of money, to the nearest euro, saved by a group of children over the past year.

Money saved (€)	0–9	10–19	20–29	30–39	40–49	50–59	60–69	70–79
Frequency	21	42	35	46	12	23	9	14

(i) What is the modal interval?

(ii) What interval contains the median?

(iii) Calculate the mean and standard deviation, to two decimal places.

5. The stem-and-leaf plot below displays the average number of decayed teeth in 12-year-old children from 28 countries.

(i) There are errors in this ordered stem-and-leaf plot. Identify the errors and draw the stem-and-leaf plot correctly.

(ii) Describe the distribution of the data.

(iii) Calculate the median.

(iv) Calculate the interquartile range.

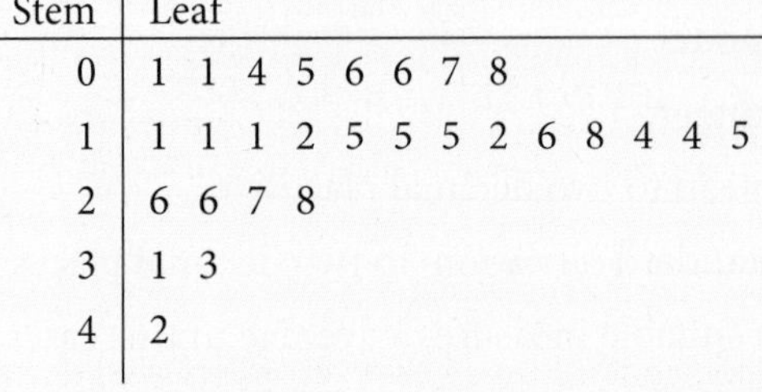

Stem	Leaf
0	1 1 4 5 6 6 7 8
1	1 1 1 2 5 5 5 2 6 8 4 4 5
2	6 6 7 8
3	1 3
4	2

Key: 0|6 = 0·6 teeth

6. A small company decides to introduce an aptitude test into their interviewing process for new employees. The test consists of solving a mechanical puzzle. The current employees were asked to solve the puzzle and their results are shown in the table below:

Time to solve (minutes)	20–40	40–50	50–60	60–80	80–90	90–100
Frequency	7	8	6	4	8	5

(i) Estimate the median interval.

(ii) Use the mid interval values, to estimate the mean and standard deviation to 2 decimal places.

The company decides not to offer a job to anyone who takes longer to complete the puzzle than the average time taken by the current employees.

(iii) Which average should be used: the mean or the median interval? Explain your choice.

Now that you have completed the chapter revisit the 'Something to think about…' question.

Statistics IV – Inferential Statistics

CHAPTER 25

Sections covered within this chapter:

KEY WORDS

- Margin of error
- Confidence interval
- Sample proportion
- Hypothesis
- Population proportion

SOMETHING TO THINK ABOUT…

A clothing store claimed that 12% of items returned were damaged. A consumer organisation wants to test this claim. They randomly select 150 returned items. Of these items, 25 are damaged.

(i) Based on this information, do you agree or disagree with the store's claim?

(ii) Can you be 100% sure that your answer to part **(i)** will always be the case?

Section 25.1: Standard Deviation and the Empirical Rule

Learning Outcome:

You should be able to:

- understand and use the empirical rule

When large amounts of continuous data, such as weights, heights or IQ values, are graphed using a histogram, a pattern is seen where most values cluster in the middle of the range and the rest taper off symmetrically toward either extreme.

This type of distribution is known as the **normal distribution** and is usually represented by the **normal curve** or **bell curve** shown.

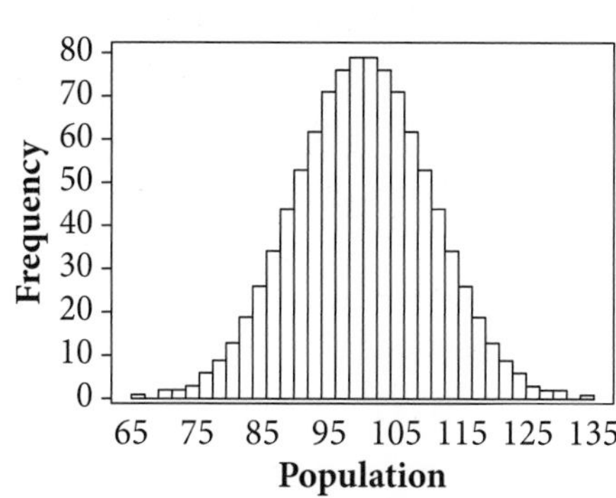

The normal distribution is a symmetrical distribution with a single central peak at the **mean, μ**.

Fifty percent of the data lies on either side of the mean.

In this type of distribution, the mean, mode and median are equal.

The Normal Distribution

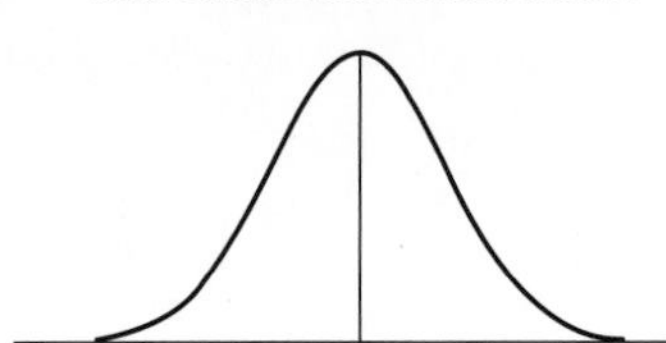

The spread of a normal distribution is controlled by the **standard deviation, σ**. The smaller the standard deviation, the more concentrated the data and the larger the standard deviation, the more spread out the data.

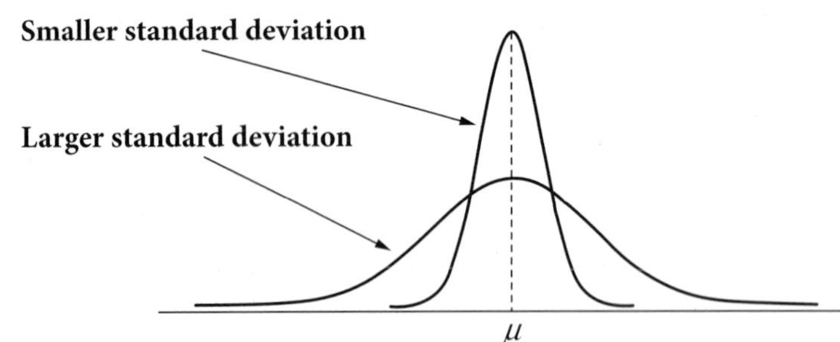

The empirical rule

The **empirical rule** states that for any normal distribution:

- approximately 68% of the distribution lies within one standard deviation of the mean; $\mu \pm 1\sigma$.
- approximately 95% of the distribution lies within two standard deviations of the mean; $\mu \pm 2\sigma$.
- approximately 99·7% of the distribution lies within three standard deviations of the mean; $\mu \pm 3\sigma$.

You must know the percentages associated with the empirical rule.

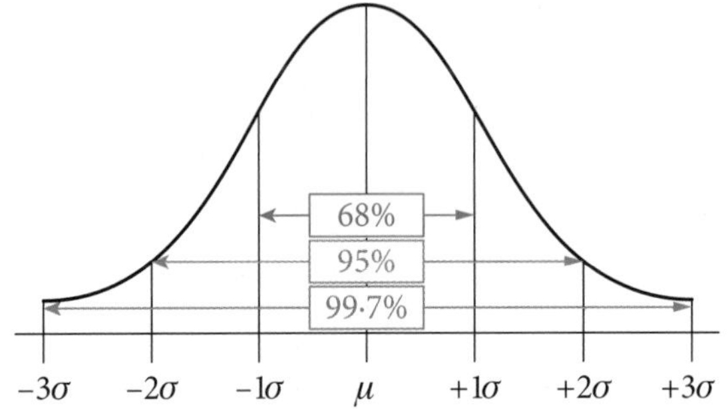

Number of standard deviations above or below the mean

EXAMPLE 1

IQ scores have a normal distribution with a mean of 100 and a standard deviation of 15.

(i) What percentage of IQ scores are between 70 and 130?

(ii) What interval contains 99·7% of all values?

Solution

(i) Draw the normal distribution curve showing 3 standard deviations to the left and right as shown.

$\mu = 100$ and $\sigma = 15$

$130 - 100 = 30$ which is 2 times 15.

Therefore, 130 is 2 standard deviations to the right of the mean.

$100 - 70 = 30$ which is 2 times 15.

Therefore, 70 is 2 standard deviations to the left of the mean.

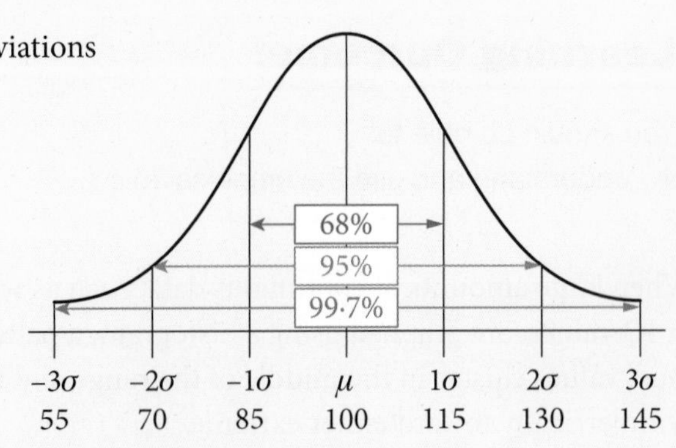

From the curve you can see 70 to 130 is within ±2 standard deviations of the mean. Therefore, 95% of the IQ scores would be between 70 and 130.

(ii) 99·7% of the data lies in the interval $\mu \pm 3\sigma$, hence, 99·7% of the data lies between 55 and 145.

The diagram on the right shows the empirical rule broken down even further. If you remember the three percentages stated in the rule, you will be able to break these down yourself as shown in Example 2, so it is not necessary to remember this diagram.

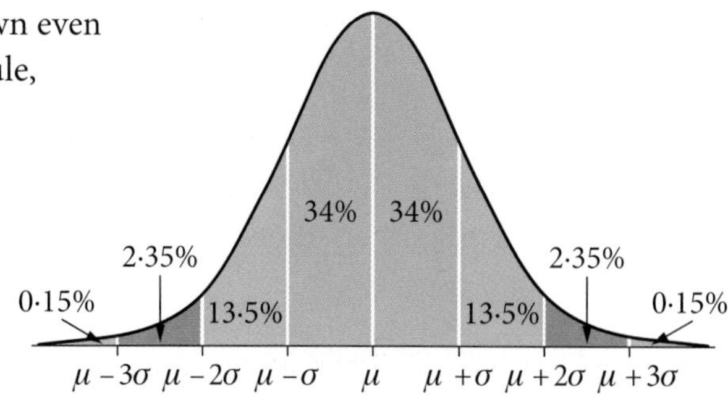

EXAMPLE 2

The height of adult males is normally distributed with a mean of 176 cm and a standard deviation of 9 cm.

(i) Draw a normal distribution curve to represent this data.

(ii) Use the empirical rule to find the following:

(a) the percentage of the population taller than 185 cm.

(b) the percentage of the population shorter than 149 cm.

(c) the percentage of the population that have a height of between 167 cm and 194 cm.

Solution

(i)

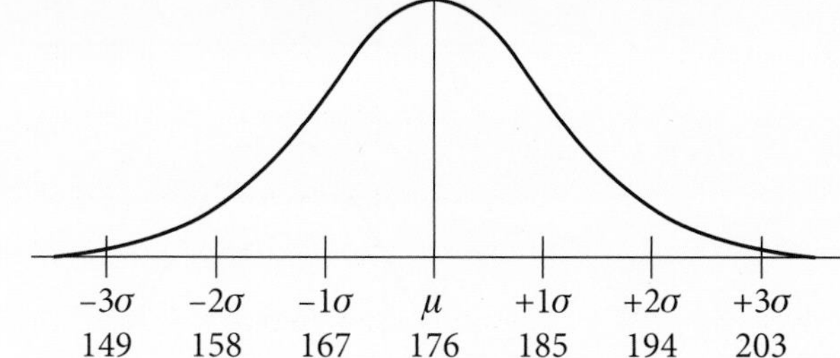

(ii) (a) 185 cm is one standard deviation above the mean.

Therefore, the portion shaded in red is equivalent to 68%.

There is 100% – 68% = 32% outside the red portion.

32% includes the part above 185 cm and below 167 cm.

Since the curve is symmetrical, 32% are divided evenly between above 185 cm and below 167 cm.

32% ÷ 2 = 16%

16% are taller than 185 cm as shown in green.

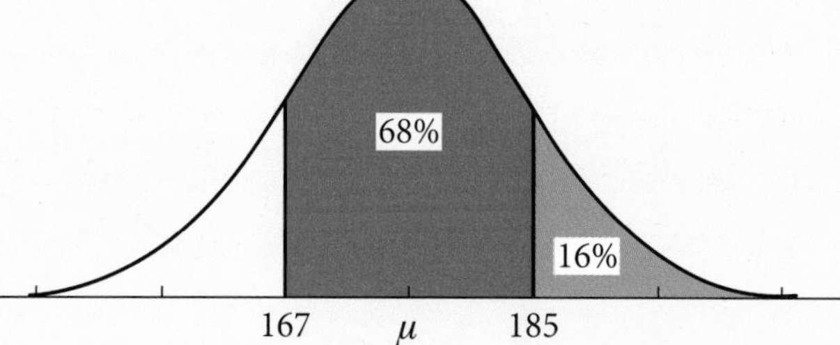

(b) 149 cm is three standard deviations below the mean.

Therefore, the portion shaded in blue is equivalent to 99·7%.

There is 100% – 99·7% = 0·3% outside of the blue portion.

0·3% ÷ 2 = 0·15% is below 149 cm.

0·15% are shorter than 149 cm.

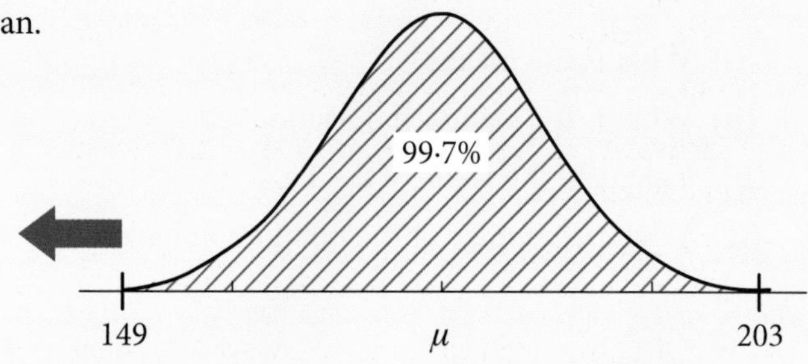

Statistics IV

(c) To find the percentage between 167 cm and 194 cm:

The portion shaded yellow contains 68% of the population as it contains the values that are within one standard deviation of the mean.

To find the portion shaded in green:

95% − 68% = 27%

27% ÷ 2 = 13·5%

68% + 13·5% = 81·5%

Therefore, the portion between 167 cm and 194 cm is 81·5%.

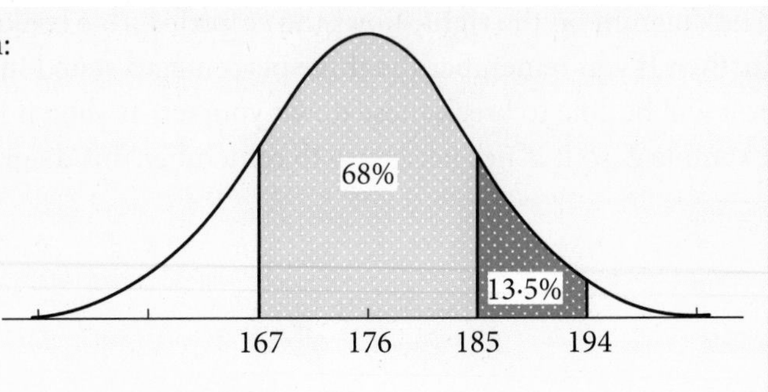

Practice Questions 25.1

1. What percentage of the following normal distribution curves is shaded?

(i)

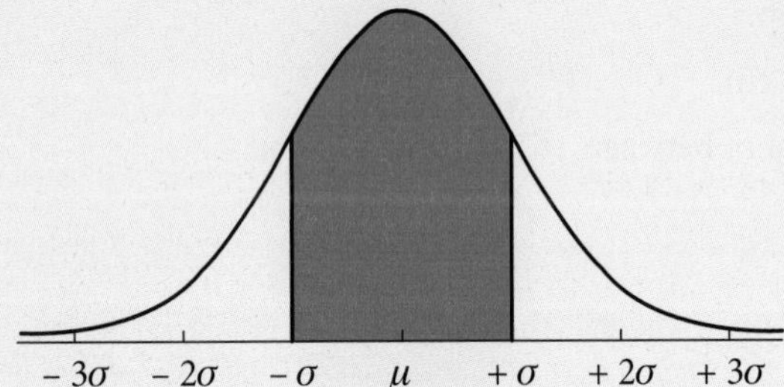

(ii)

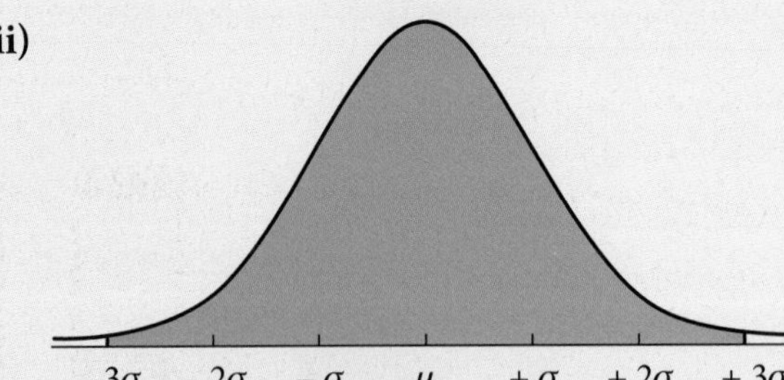

(iii)

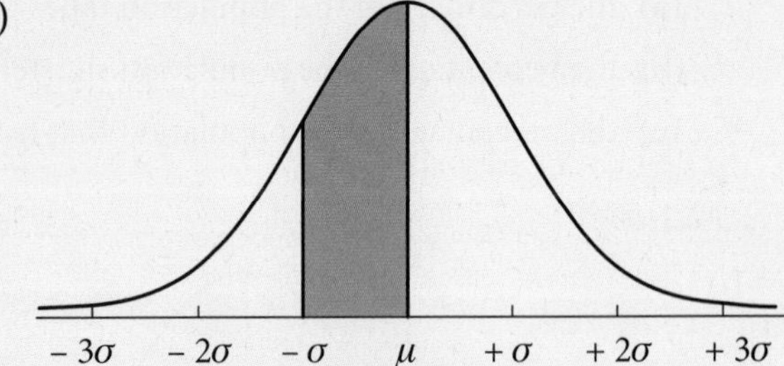

(iv)

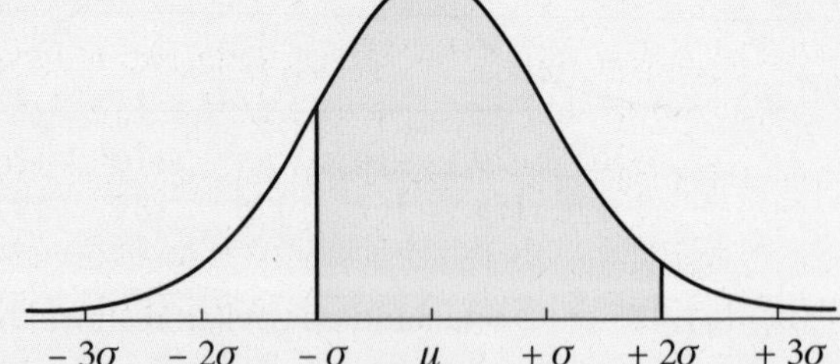

2. The normal curve shown below represents the distribution of IQ scores for a population.

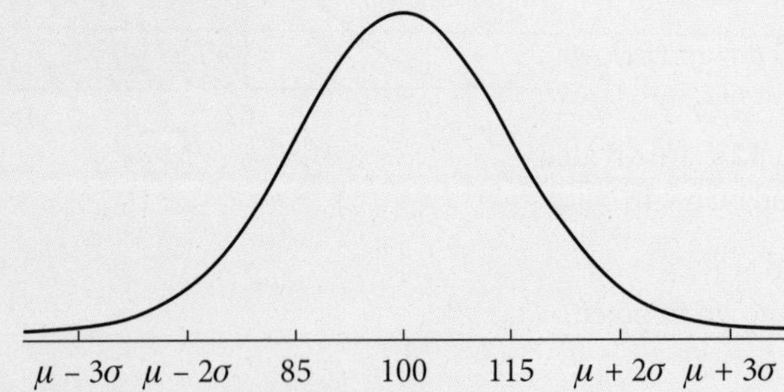

(i) What is the mean?

(ii) What is the standard deviation?

(iii) Calculate the value of $\mu - 2\sigma$.

(iv) What percentage of the population have an IQ score between 85 and 115?

3. Given an approximately normal distribution, what percentage of all values are:
   (i) above the mean?
   (ii) below the mean?
   (iii) within one standard deviation from the mean?
   (iv) within two standard deviations from the mean?
   (v) within three standard deviations from the mean?

   and

   (vi) what interval contains 99·7% of all values?

4. For each of the following, find the interval in which **(a)** 68%, **(b)** 95% and **(c)** 99·7% of data lies.
   (i) Mean = 16 Standard deviation = 3
   (ii) Mean = 5·2 Standard deviation = 0·8
   (iii) Mean = 148 Standard deviation = 6
   (iv) Mean = 68 Standard deviation = 4·6
   (v) Mean = 250 Standard deviation = 31·5

5. The heights of male students is normally distributed with a mean of 170 cm and a standard deviation of 8 cm. Find the percentage of male students whose height is:
   (i) greater than 186 cm
   (ii) between 162 cm and 186 cm
   (iii) between 154 cm and 178 cm.

6. The mean battery life of a mobile phone battery is 14 hours. Assuming that the battery life is normally distributed and the standard deviation is two hours,
   (i) what percentage of the batteries have a life of between 12 and 18 hours?

   Batteries that have a life of less than eight hours are rejected. On a particular day a mobile battery production unit makes 1,200 batteries.

   (ii) How many batteries would you expect to be rejected on this day?

7. The results of 20 students in their end-of-term maths exam were:

   45, 56, 67, 85, 28, 64, 72, 83, 48, 96, 47, 71, 59, 63, 54, 66, 79, 80, 42, 50

   (i) Find the mean of this data.
   (ii) Find the standard deviation to 2 decimal places.
   (iii) Assuming that the results are normally distributed, find the interval in which:
   (a) 68% of the data lies **(b)** 95% of the data lies **(c)** 99·7% of the data lies.

8. At a certain IT company, the ages of all new employees hired during the last five years are normally distributed. Within this curve, 95% of the ages are between 24·6 and 37·4 years. Find the mean age and the standard deviation of the data.

9. Given $\mu + 1\sigma = 247$ and $\mu + 2\sigma = 428$ find:
   (i) the standard deviation
   (ii) the mean
   (iii) the approximate percentage of the distribution that lies between 66 and 428.

Section 25.2: Margin of Error and Confidence Intervals

Learning Outcomes:

You should be able to:

- understand and calculate the margin of error
- understand and construct a 95% confidence interval

Sample surveys are generally used to estimate the percentage of people in the population that have a certain characteristic or opinion. For example, 65% of the population own a pet.

Most of these polls are based on samples of size 1,000 to 1,500 people. Why is a sample size of around 1,000 people commonly used in surveying? The answer is based on understanding what is called the **margin of error**.

The **margin of error** expresses the maximum expected difference between the true population proportion and a sample estimate of that proportion.

For example, a newspaper heading might say 65% of Leaving Cert students reported enjoying statistics, with a margin of error of 5%.

65% is known as the sample proportion. The symbol for the sample proportion is $\hat{p}$. This is called 'p hat'.

The **sample proportion** is the result of a survey polling a sample group taken from the whole population.

If we could ask every Leaving Cert student and work out the actual percentage, we would have the population proportion.

The **population proportion** (p) is the true value for the entire population.

Since it is time consuming and expensive to survey an entire population, we usually don't know the population proportion (p).

We can combine the sample proportion and the margin of error to give a good estimate for the population proportion.

If the margin of error in the example above is 5%, and we know the sample proportion is 65%, then this means that we can be fairly confident that the true population proportion lies somewhere between 60% and 70%.

On this course, the margin of error is calculated as follows:

$$E = \frac{1}{\sqrt{n}} \quad \text{where } n = \text{sample size}$$

EXAMPLE 1

Calculate the margin of error for the following samples:

(i) $n = 100$ **(ii)** $n = 400$ **(iii)** $n = 1{,}000$ **(iv)** $n = 2{,}500$

Solution

(i) $n = 100$ $\quad E = \frac{1}{\sqrt{n}} = \frac{1}{\sqrt{100}} = \frac{1}{10} = 0{\cdot}1 = 10\%$

(ii) $n = 400$ $\quad E = \frac{1}{\sqrt{n}} = \frac{1}{\sqrt{400}} = \frac{1}{20} = 0{\cdot}05 = 5\%$

(iii) $n = 1{,}000$ $\quad E = \frac{1}{\sqrt{n}} = \frac{1}{\sqrt{1{,}000}} = 0{\cdot}03 = 3\%$

(iv) $n = 2{,}500$ $\quad E = \frac{1}{\sqrt{n}} = \frac{1}{\sqrt{2{,}500}} = \frac{1}{50} = 0{\cdot}02 = 2\%$

Notice, the larger the sample size the smaller the margin of error. This means larger samples give more credible results.

Discussion Time 

Imagine you are working for a market research company. A client asks you to do a survey on the public's opinion of their new product. They want you to keep the margin of error as low as possible while also keeping costs at a minimum.

Work with a classmate to determine the best sample size to use for the survey. Try the following sample sizes: 500, 1,000, 2,000 and 4,000. Employ the 'law of diminishing returns' in your discussions.

In economics, the 'law of diminishing returns' is used to refer to a point at which the level of profits or benefits gained is less than the amount of money or energy invested.

Confidence intervals

A **confidence interval** measures the probability that a population proportion will fall between two set values.

The purpose of taking a random sample from a population and stating a value for this sample is to approximate the value for the entire population.

For example, if an opinion poll finds that 30% of those sampled would vote for the Environment Party, this means that if an election happens we would expect the Environment Party to get around 30% of the votes cast.

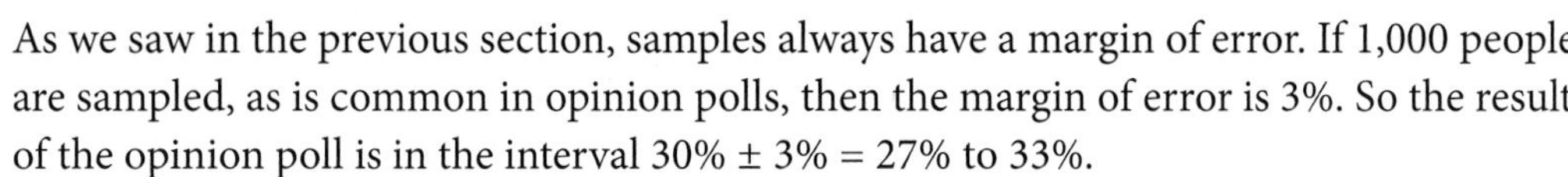

As we saw in the previous section, samples always have a margin of error. If 1,000 people are sampled, as is common in opinion polls, then the margin of error is 3%. So the result of the opinion poll is in the interval 30% ± 3% = 27% to 33%.

We add and subtract the margin of error from the sample proportion found in the survey.

This can be written as $27\% < p < 33\%$, where p is the population proportion (true value for the population).

$27\% < p < 33\%$ is called the confidence interval.

For the purposes of this course, we use a **95% confidence interval**. This is also known as a **5% level of significance**.

What this means is that if you calculate a 95% confidence interval, you can say that 95% of the true population is within the interval $\hat{p} - \textit{margin of error} < p < \hat{p} + \textit{margin of error}$.

The formula for calculating the 95% confidence interval is:

$$\hat{p} - \frac{1}{\sqrt{n}} < p < \hat{p} + \frac{1}{\sqrt{n}}$$

where $\hat{p}$ is the sample proportion, n is the sample size and p is the true population proportion.

EXAMPLE 2

In a random sample of 400 people, 250 said that they had a cat.

(i) What is the sample size?

(ii) What is the sample proportion, $\hat{p}$?

(iii) What is the margin of error?

(iv) Find the 95% confidence interval and explain what this means.

(v) What sample size should be used to get a margin of error of 4%?

Solution

(i) The sample size, n, is 400.

(ii) The sample proportion, $\hat{p}$, is $\frac{250}{400} = 0{\cdot}625$

(iii) The margin of error is $\frac{1}{\sqrt{n}} = \frac{1}{\sqrt{400}} = 0{\cdot}05$

(iv) The 95% confidence interval is $\hat{p} - \frac{1}{\sqrt{n}} < p < \hat{p} + \frac{1}{\sqrt{n}}$

$$0{\cdot}625 - 0{\cdot}05 < p < 0{\cdot}625 + 0{\cdot}05$$

$$0{\cdot}575 < p < 0{\cdot}675$$

$$57{\cdot}5\% < p < 67{\cdot}5\%$$

Explanation: 95% of the time the percentage of cat owners in the entire population lies between 57·5% and 67·5%.

(v) Margin of error = 4% = $\frac{1}{\sqrt{n}}$

$\frac{1}{\sqrt{n}} = 0{\cdot}04$

$\left(\frac{1}{\sqrt{n}}\right)^2 = (0{\cdot}04)^2$ (square both sides)

$\frac{1}{n} = 0{\cdot}0016$

$1 = 0{\cdot}0016\,n$ (multiply both sides by n)

$\frac{1}{0{\cdot}0016} = n$ (divide both sides by 0·0016)

$n = 625$

Sample size that gives a margin of error of 4% is 625.

Practice Questions 25.2

1. Calculate the margin of error (correct to two decimal places) for the following samples:

   (i) 150 **(ii)** 800 **(iii)** 1,600 **(iv)** 3,600 **(v)** 5,000

2. In a random sample of machines, 20 out of 220 were found to have been damaged in shipment.
   (i) What is the sample size?
   (ii) What is the sample proportion, $\hat{p}$, to two decimal places?
   (iii) What is the margin of error, to two decimal places?
   (iv) Find the 95% confidence interval.
   (v) If you increase the sample size to 300, what effect would this have on the margin of error?

3. An assembly line does a quality check by sampling 50 of its products. It finds that 16% of the parts are defective.
   (i) What is the sample size?
   (ii) What is the sample proportion, $\hat{p}$?
   (iii) What is the margin of error, to two decimal places?
   (iv) Find the 95% confidence interval.
   (v) How could the company decrease the margin of error?

4. 60% of a sample of 500 people leaving a shopping centre claim to have spent over €25.
   (i) What is the sample size?
   (ii) What is the sample proportion, $\hat{p}$?
   (iii) What is the margin of error, to two decimal places?
   (iv) Find the 95% confidence interval.

5. A nationwide poll was taken of 1,400 teenagers (ages 13–18). 600 of them said they have a TV in their bedroom.
   (i) Construct the 95% confidence interval by calculating $\hat{p}$ and margin of error to two decimal places.
   (ii) If the sample was increased to 2,000, but none of the additional people had a TV, find the new confidence interval.
   (iii) What happens to the confidence interval as the sample size increases?

6. What sample size, to the nearest whole number, is needed to have the following margins of error:

   (i) 1% **(ii)** 6% **(iii)** 10% **(iv)** 25% **(v)** 3·5%

7. Several factors are involved in the creation of a confidence interval. Among them are the sample size and the margin of error. Which statements are correct?

   (i) Larger samples provide smaller margins of error.

   (ii) Halving the margin of error requires a sample twice as large.

   (iii) You can get a smaller margin of error by selecting a bigger sample.

   (iv) A sample nine times as large will make a margin of error one third as big.

8. A random sample of 100 cinemas showed that the mean price of a student ticket was €7·00, with a standard deviation of €0·80. Assuming the data is normally distributed construct a 95% confidence interval for this data.

9. In an RTÉ news telephone poll of 1,012 adults, 11% of the respondents said that they were happy with the work of the current president. Construct a 95% confidence interval for the study.

   Is this a good reflection of the true population in your opinion? Justify your answer.

10. A random sample of 100 students is selected from a certain school. They are given an IQ test which has a known standard deviation of 11. The sample mean is found to be 112. Assuming the data is normally distributed, determine a 95% confidence interval for estimating the mean school intelligence.

If data is normally distributed, we can use the empirical rule to determine a 95% confidence interval. This is the interval in which 95% of the population fall.

Section 25.3: Hypothesis Testing

Learning Outcomes:

You should be able to:

- state the null and alternative hypothesis
- understand and carry out a hypothesis test

We are constantly surrounded by claims being made by advertising companies and research agencies:

'Leaving Cert students spend 20 hours a week studying.'

'New vaccine is no more effective against the flu virus than the old vaccine.'

How do we know if we can believe these claims?

A **hypothesis** is a claim or idea about a group or population.

A hypothesis may or may not be true. The process of proving the truth of a claim is called hypothesis testing.

In statistical hypothesis testing, there are always two hypotheses.

The hypothesis to be tested is called the **null hypothesis** and given the symbol $\mathbf{H_0}$.

The term 'null hypothesis' comes from the idea of a 'null effect' or 'no change', so H_0 should be stated as such, i.e. as a statement of no change.

It is the commonly accepted fact and we try to reject, nullify or disprove the null hypothesis.

We test the null hypothesis against an **alternative hypothesis**, which is given the symbol $\mathbf{H_1}$. It includes the outcomes not covered by the null hypothesis.

In our examples on the previous page: H_0: Leaving Cert students spend 20 hours a week studying
H_1: Leaving Cert students do **not** spend 20 hours a week studying
H_0: New vaccine is the same as the old one
H_1: New vaccine is **not** the same as the old one

If you set up the hypotheses correctly, then providing evidence against the null hypothesis is the same as providing evidence for the alternative hypothesis.

A statistical test can never provide evidence that the null hypothesis is true, it can only provide evidence that it is false. **We never say we accept the null hypothesis, we just fail to reject it.**

This is like the difference between saying a person is innocent and saying they are not guilty. If you are trying to prove something, you want to make sure it is stated as the alternative hypothesis, not the null hypothesis.

Steps for carrying out a hypothesis test

Step 1: State the null hypothesis (H_0) and the alternative hypothesis (H_1).
Step 2: Calculate $\hat{p}$, the sample proportion.
Step 3: Calculate the margin of error.
Step 4: Find the confidence interval.

$$\hat{p} - \frac{1}{\sqrt{n}} < p < \hat{p} + \frac{1}{\sqrt{n}}$$

Step 5: Decide whether to reject or fail to reject the null hypothesis.
- If the value of the population proportion is outside the confidence interval, we reject H_0.
- If the value of the population proportion is within the confidence interval, we fail to reject H_0.

EXAMPLE 1

A school principal claims that 40% of the students of the school come to school by bus. To test this claim a sample of 200 students were asked how they travelled to school. 75 students said they came by bus.

(i) State the null and alternative hypothesis.
(ii) Calculate $\hat{p}$.
(iii) Calculate the margin of error to two decimal places.
(iv) Set up the confidence interval.
(v) Decide whether to reject or fail to reject the null hypothesis.
(vi) What does this mean in relation to the claim?

Solution

(i) H_0: The percentage of students that come to school by bus is 40%.
H_1: The percentage of students that come to school by bus is **not** 40%.

(ii) $\hat{p} = \frac{75}{200} = 0{\cdot}38$

(iii) The margin of error is $\frac{1}{\sqrt{n}}$, $n = 200$

$$\frac{1}{\sqrt{n}} = \frac{1}{\sqrt{200}} = 0{\cdot}07$$

(iv) Confidence interval:

$$\hat{p} - \frac{1}{\sqrt{n}} < p < \hat{p} + \frac{1}{\sqrt{n}}$$

$$0{\cdot}38 - 0{\cdot}07 < p < 0{\cdot}38 + 0{\cdot}07$$

$$0{\cdot}31 < p < 0{\cdot}45$$

(v) H_0 states that the percentage of students that come to school by bus is 40% = 0·4.

Since the confidence interval goes from 0·31 to 0·45, 0·4 is inside the confidence interval and as a result we **fail to reject H_0**.

Recall: We do not accept H_0.

(vi) Since we are failing to reject H_0, we will accept the principal's claim that 40% of her students travel to school by bus.

EXAMPLE 2

The standard treatment for a disease works on 0·65 of all patients.
A new treatment is developed and the company claims it is more effective.
An initial clinical trial of 100 patients is conducted and 77 people are cured.

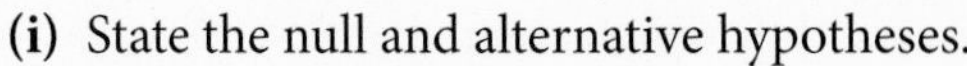

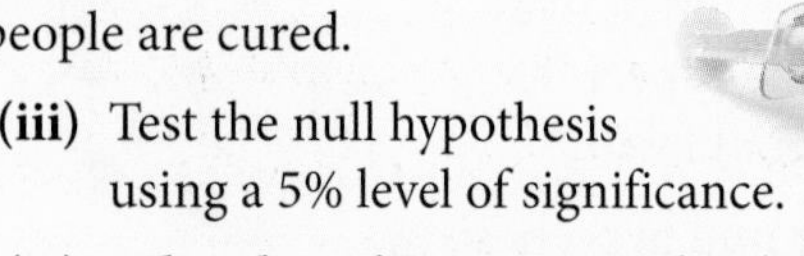

(i) State the null and alternative hypotheses.

(ii) Find the 95% confidence interval.

(iii) Test the null hypothesis using a 5% level of significance.

(iv) What does this mean in relation to the claim?

Solution

(i) H_0: The proportion of patients cured is 0·65
H_1: The proportion of patients cured is **not** 0·65

(ii) $\hat{p} = \frac{77}{100} = 0{\cdot}77$

Margin of error $= \frac{1}{\sqrt{n}} = \frac{1}{\sqrt{100}} = 0{\cdot}1$

Confidence interval:

$$\hat{p} - \frac{1}{\sqrt{n}} < p < \hat{p} + \frac{1}{\sqrt{n}}$$

$$0{\cdot}77 - 0{\cdot}1 < p < 0{\cdot}77 + 0{\cdot}1$$

$$0{\cdot}67 < p < 0{\cdot}87$$

5% level of significance means use the 95% confidence interval.

(iii) H_0 states the proportion of patients cured is 0·65

Since the confidence interval is from 0·67 to 0·77 and 0·65 lies outside the interval we **reject H_0**.

(iv) Since the 95% confidence interval is above 0·65, it would appear that the new treatment is more effective than the old one.

Practice Questions 25.3

1. State the null and alternative hypotheses used to test the following claims:
   (i) A school publicises that the percentage of its students who are involved in at least one extracurricular activity is 61%.
   (ii) A car garage announces that the mean time for a wheel change is less than 15 minutes.
   (iii) A company advertises that the mean life of its products is more than eight years.
   (iv) A drug company announces that a new vaccine is 10% more effective than its predecessor.
   (v) A skincare company advertise that 35% of people surveyed thought that their product reduced skin oiliness.

2. An advertisement states that 8 out of 10 cats prefer Catty Cat cat food.
   To test this claim, a researcher carried out an experiment using 150 cats and found that 75 cats preferred Catty Cat.
   (i) State the null and alternative hypotheses.

   (ii) Calculate $\hat{p}$.
   (iii) Calculate the margin of error to two decimal places.
   (iv) Set up the 95% confidence interval.
   (v) Decide whether to reject or fail to reject the null hypothesis.
   (vi) What does this mean in relation to the claim?

3. A hotel chain claims that 35% of its online reviews are positive. A sample of 200 reviews shows that 120 are positive.
   (i) State the null and alternative hypotheses.
   (ii) Calculate $\hat{p}$.
   (iii) Calculate the margin of error to two decimal places.
   (iv) Set up the 95% confidence interval.
   (v) Decide whether to reject or fail to reject the null hypothesis.
   (vi) What does this mean in relation to the claim?

4. An opinion poll of 1,000 voters is carried out prior to an election. 25% of those polled said they would vote for the Left Party. Left Party management believe they have 35% support.
   (i) Set up the 95% confidence interval.
   (ii) Decide whether to reject or fail to reject the null hypothesis, using a 5% level of significance.
   (iii) What does this mean in relation to the claim?

5. Evie rolled a die 360 times and got 72 fives. She suspects that the die is biased and carries out a hypothesis test to check.
   (i) What proportion of fives would Sophie expect if the die was unbiased?
   (ii) What is the null hypothesis?
   (iii) What is the alternative hypothesis?
   (iv) Use a hypothesis test at the 95% confidence level to determine if the die is biased.

6. A community sports organisation claims that it has equal numbers of males and females. A local councillor wanted to investigate this claim. He took a sample of 80 members and found that 65 of them were male. Determine whether the sports organisation's claim is true, using 5% level of significance.

7. The Irish Tourist Board claimed that 65% of the tourists who visited Ireland last year were return visitors. The Department of Transport, Tourism and Sport wanted to test this claim. They asked a random sample of 800 tourists if they had been to Ireland before. 300 responded that they had.
   (i) Using a 95% confidence interval, decide whether to reject or fail to reject the null hypothesis.
   (ii) What does this mean in relation to the Irish Tourist Board's claim?

8. A popular mobile phone provider claims that 70% of their customers are satisfied with the service provided by them. A consumer agency decides to investigate the claim. They survey 900 of the mobile company's customers and find that 650 people said they were satisfied.
   Test the company's claim using a 5% level of significance.
   As a result of your findings, what advice would you give to the mobile company?

9. A company manufacturing a new type of chocolate bar claims that 85% of the people who tried their product would recommend it to a friend. An independent study of 625 people who tried the bar, found that only 125 would recommend it.
   Use a 95% confidence interval to investigate whether the company's claim is true.

10. The Union of Secondary Students of Ireland claims that 65% of Leaving Cert students spend more than three hours a night on study or homework. The principal of a school wants to investigate this claim.
    She surveys the 200 Leaving Cert students in her school and finds that 85 of them report spending more than three hours on study or homework.
    Using a 95% confidence interval, determine whether that principal is likely to accept the claim of the Students' Union.

Revision and Exam Style Questions – Section A

1. The time, in hours, that each student spent sleeping on a school night was recorded for 550 secondary school students. The distribution of these times was found to be approximately normal with a mean of 7·6 hours and a standard deviation of 0·5 hours.
   (i) Draw the normal distribution curve to show this data.
   (ii) What amount of time did 95% of these students spend sleeping?
   (iii) What percentage of students spent between 7·1 and 8·1 hours sleeping?

2. A large group of students have a mean weight of 68 kg, with a standard deviation of 3 kg. Use the empirical rule to find the weight interval that contains 95% of the students.

3. Deirdre claims that the weather forecasts on the local radio are no better than rolling a fair die. She predicts rain if the result is odd and no rain if the result is even. She records the weather for 30 days and finds that the forecast is correct on 20 of the days.
   (i) State the null and alternative hypotheses.
   (ii) Construct the confidence interval.
   (iii) Is Deirdre's claim correct?

4. A candidate for election claims that 45% of voters will vote for him. His opponent wants to test this claim. She takes a random sample of 120 voters and finds that 48 people said they would vote for him.
   (i) State the null and alternative hypotheses.
   (ii) Calculate the confidence interval.
   (iii) Is the candidate's claim upheld?

5. An estate agent claims to have an 80% success rate for selling a house within two months. A client wants to test this hypothesis. He looks at the last 60 houses they have sold and found that 50 of them had been sold within two months.
   (i) State the null and alternative hypotheses for this test.
   (ii) Set up the confidence interval for this test.
   (iii) Is the estate agent's claim correct?

6. Adult IQ scores have a normal distribution with mean of 100 and a standard deviation of 15.
   (i) Use the empirical rule to find the percentage of adults with scores between 70 and 130.
   (ii) If 250 adults are randomly selected, about how many of them have an IQ between 85 and 130?

7. A machine fills packets with roast peanuts. The line manager takes a sample of 10 packets every hour.
   The mean weights of the samples are normally distributed with a mean of 106 g and a standard deviation of 2 g.
   (i) Write down the percentage of the samples that are likely to have a sample mean of less than 100 g.
   (ii) Write down the percentage of the samples that are likely to have a sample mean of more than 110 g.

Revision and Exam Style Questions – Section B

More challenging problems

1. The time spent by shoppers at a furniture shop on a Saturday is approximately normally distributed with a mean of 30 minutes and a standard deviation of 5 minutes. If 2,850 shoppers are expected to visit the shop on a Saturday, how many shoppers are expected to spend:
   (i) more than 40 minutes in the shop?
   (ii) between 20 and 35 minutes in the shop?

2. A machine fills packets with corn flakes. The label on each packet says the contents weigh 1·5 kg.
   At regular intervals a sample of 10 packets is taken from the machine.
   The sample mean is calculated. The sample means are normally distributed with a mean of 1,520 g and a standard deviation of 4 g.
   (i) Give one reason why it may not be practical to check the weight of each packet.
   (ii) Between what limits would you expect 95% of the sample means to lie?
   (iii) Martha takes a sample of 10 packets. She finds the weight, in grams, of each packet.
   Here are her results:
   1,517 1,525 1,534 1,527 1,531
   1,521 1,532 1,535 1,526 1,532
   The allowable limits for the weights are 1,520 g ± 3 standard deviations. How many of the sample would be rejected on these grounds?
   (iv) What could be done to ensure weights are within the acceptable range?

3. A drug company claims that the success rate of a treatment for a disease is 47%. Dr Green doubts this claim and wants to test it. He uses the treatment on 50 patients with the disease and cures 24 of them. Is the company's claim correct? Justify your answer.

4. A survey is being conducted of voters' opinions on several different issues.
   (i) What is the overall margin of error of the survey, at 95% confidence, if it is based on a simple random sample of 1,000 voters?

   A political party had claimed that it has the support of 26% of the electorate. Of the voters in the sample above, 238 stated that they support the party.
   (ii) Is there sufficient evidence to reject the party's claim? Justify your answer.

5. A manufacturing company claims that 75% of suppliers recommend their brand of product. In a survey of 42 traders, 28 said that they would recommend the company's product. Use a hypothesis test at the 95% level of confidence to decide whether there is sufficient evidence to reject the company's claim. State clearly the null hypothesis and your conclusion.

6. A boy decides to test whether a coin is fair by tossing it 20 times and recording the number of heads. He suspects that it is more likely to show a head than a tail and when he tosses it he gets 11 heads.
   (i) State suitable hypotheses to use for this test.
   (ii) Use a 5% level of significance to test whether the coin is fair.
   (iii) Do you think his results are reliable? Give a reason for the answer.

7. In general, 55% of driving tests result in a pass. It is suspected that a particular examiner is tougher than usual. To investigate this, records are kept on the next 10 people tested by this examiner. Four of them pass.
   (i) Stating your hypotheses carefully and showing your working in full, test at the 5% level whether or not the examiner is tougher than normal.
   (ii) Comment on the validity of this method of assessing the examiner.

8. On a production line in a factory, pineapple rings in syrup are put in tins. The label on each tin says that the contents weigh 415 g.
   (i) Give two reasons why it is not practical to check the weight of the contents of each tin.

   Samples of tins are taken at intervals and the weights of the contents are found.

   It has been found that the mean weight of the samples is 417 g and the standard deviation is 0·6 g. The mean weights of the samples are normally distributed.
   (ii) Between what limits would you expect 99·7% of the sample means to lie?
   (iii) A consumer authority inspects the factory and decides that the labels on the tins should be altered from 415 g. Use your answer from **(ii)** to explain why this is the case.

Now that you have completed the chapter, revisit the 'Something to think about ...' questions.

Differential Calculus I

CHAPTER 26

Sections covered within this chapter:

KEY WORDS

- Calculus
- Differentiate
- Derivative

SOMETHING TO THINK ABOUT... 

A property developer works out that the profit, in euro, he makes by selling x houses is given by

$$P(x) = 550{,}000 - 15{,}000x + 275x^2 - x^3$$

(i) Find the profit made on selling 50 houses.

(ii) Find the number of houses he should sell, in order to make the maximum possible profit.

(iii) Find this maximum profit.

Introduction

Calculus is the study of the rate at which things change.

In day-to-day life, we are often interested in the extent to which a change in one quantity affects a change in another related quantity. This is called a **rate of change**.

For example, a farmer might be interested in the extent to which a change in the amount of fertiliser used on a particular crop affects the yield of the crop. Economists want to know how a change in the price of a product affects the demand for that product.

Differential calculus is about describing the ways in which related quantities change and finding the values of those rates of change.

Links across the syllabus

While working through this chapter, you will need to be familiar with the concept of the slope (also called the gradient) of a straight line. Slope is covered in the following chapters:

Chapter 3: Algebra II

Chapter 7: Further Functions

Chapter 14: Coordinate Geometry I.

Section 26.1: Rates of Change – A Graphical Approach

Learning Outcomes:

You should be able to:
- understand what a rate of change is
- measure rates of change of a graph, by finding the slope of the graph at that point

Rates of change are used every day; for example, we measure:

- The speed at which a car is travelling in kilometres per hour or metres per second.
- The speed of a typist in words per minute.
- Pulse rate in heartbeats per minute.
- Population growth per year.

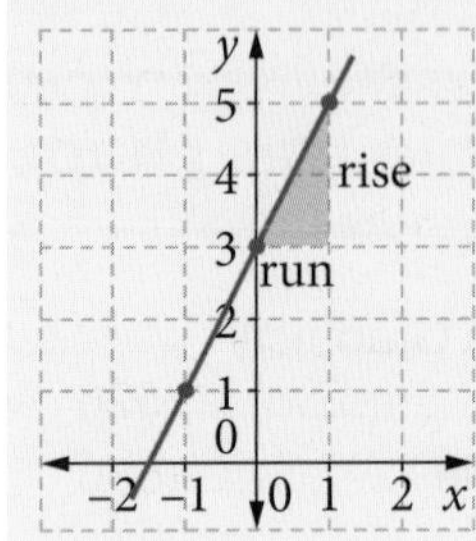

The **rate of change** is a measure of how much the graph rises or falls, for every one unit it goes across. Therefore, the rate of change of a graph, at a particular point, is equal to the slope (or the gradient) of the graph at that point. For the given graph, the rate of change = 2.

When we graph two quantities against each other, the shape of the graph indicates the rate of change between the two quantities.

A **straight line** graph indicates that there is a **constant rate of change** between the quantities, as it has a constant slope.

Recall the key points about slope:
- An increasing line has a positive slope = positive rate of change.
- A decreasing line has a negative slope = negative rate of change.
- A horizontal line has zero slope = zero rate of change.
- The steeper the line, the greater that rate of change.

Examples of straight line graphs are shown below. In each case, the slope and hence the rate of change is found:

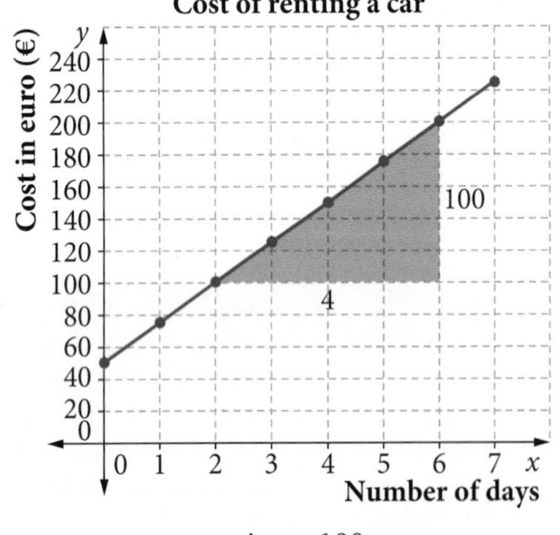

$$\text{slope} = \frac{\text{rise}}{\text{run}} = \frac{100}{4} = 25$$

Rate of change = 25
= €25 per day

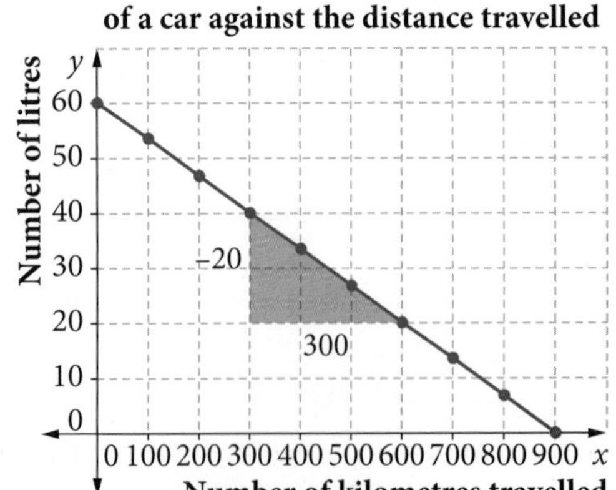

$$\text{slope} = \frac{\text{rise}}{\text{run}} = \frac{-20}{300} = -\frac{1}{15}$$

Rate of change $= -\frac{1}{15}$ of a litre per kilometre

The line is decreasing, therefore the 'rise' is a negative value.

Curved graphs

If a graph is **not a straight line**, then the rate of change is **different** at each point along the curve. For example, if a car is accelerating, its speed is constantly changing and so its rate of change will vary.

In this case, to find the rate of change at a particular point, we find the slope of the tangent to the curve at that point.

Links across the syllabus

Tangents are covered in Chapter 15: Coordinate Geometry II and Chapter 11: Geometry II.

EXAMPLE

The graph shows the height of a diver, above a swimming pool, *t* seconds after diving from the high board.

Use the graph to estimate the rate of change of the diver at the following two times.

In each case, explain what your answer means.

(i) 0·5 seconds

(ii) 4 seconds

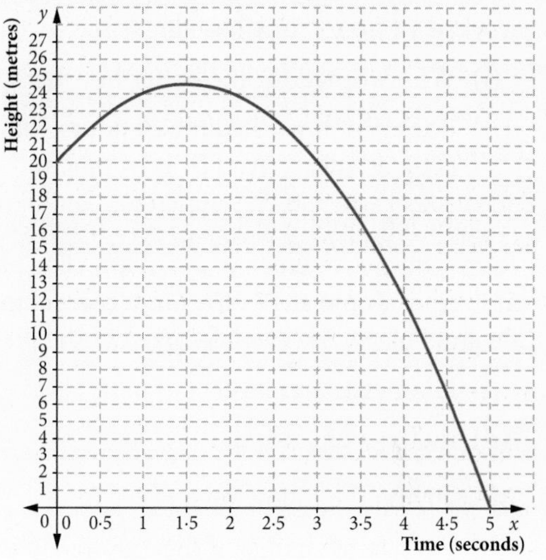

Solution

We must draw tangents. The tangent is a line which **touches** the graph at a given point and **only** at that point.

(i) Draw a tangent at the point where $x = 0{\cdot}5$ seconds (shown in green on the graph)

Find the slope of the tangent at this point.

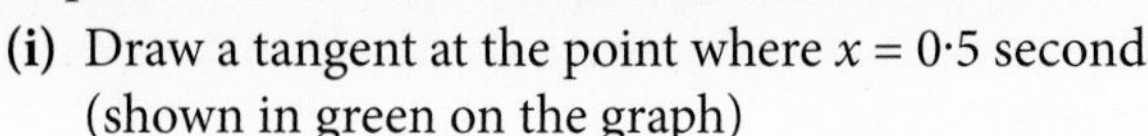

$$\text{Slope} = \frac{\text{rise}}{\text{run}} = \frac{6}{1{\cdot}5} = 4$$

Therefore, the rate of change at $t = 0{\cdot}5$ seconds is 4.

Explanation:

This means that 0·5 seconds after leaving the diving board, the diver is moving upwards (since the slope was positive) with a speed of 4 m/s.

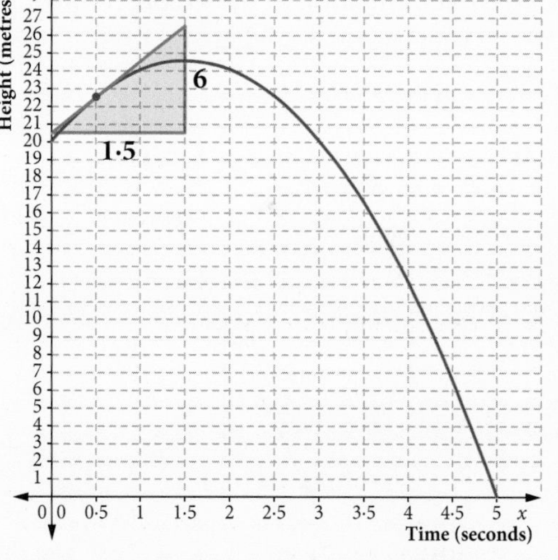

(ii) Draw a tangent at the point where $t = 4$ seconds (shown in orange on the graph)

Find the slope of the tangent at this point.

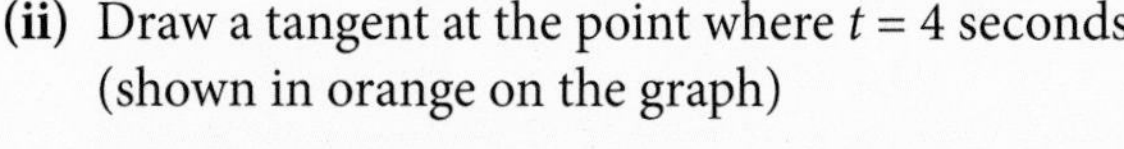

$$\text{Slope} = \frac{\text{rise}}{\text{run}} = \frac{-10}{1} = -10$$

Therefore, the rate of change at $t = 4$ seconds is -10.

Explanation:

This means that 4 seconds after leaving the diving board, the diver is moving downwards (since the slope was negative) with a speed of 10 m/s.

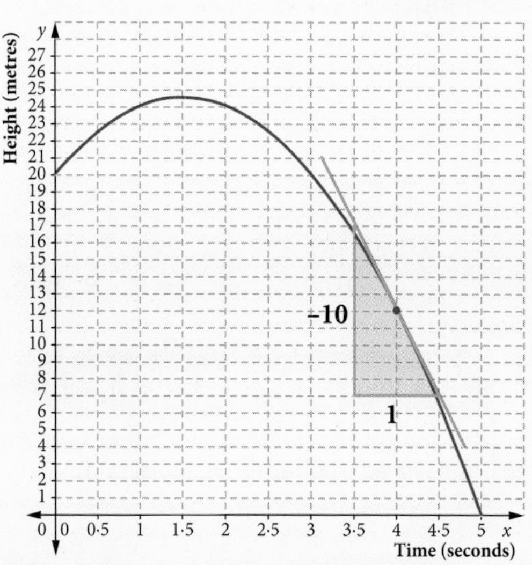

Practice Questions 26.1

1. Mike's pulse rate was measured at 72 beats per minute.
   (i) Explain exactly what this means.
   (ii) How many heartbeats would Mike expect to have in a two-hour period?

2. Alex worked 12 hours for €111, whereas Ryan worked 14 hours for €136·50.
   (i) Who worked for the better hourly rate of pay?
   (ii) If they both worked for 20 hours, who would get paid more? And by how much?

3. A plane left Dublin at 13 : 52 and travelled to Rome, Italy, a distance of 2,475 km. The plane arrived in Rome at 17 : 07. Find, correct to one decimal place, the average speed of the plane in:
   (i) kilometres per hour
   (ii) metres per second.

4. By studying the following graphs, find:
   (i) the rate of change of the graph
   (ii) the equation of the graph, in the form $f(x) = mx + c$, where $m, c \in \mathbb{R}$.

(a)

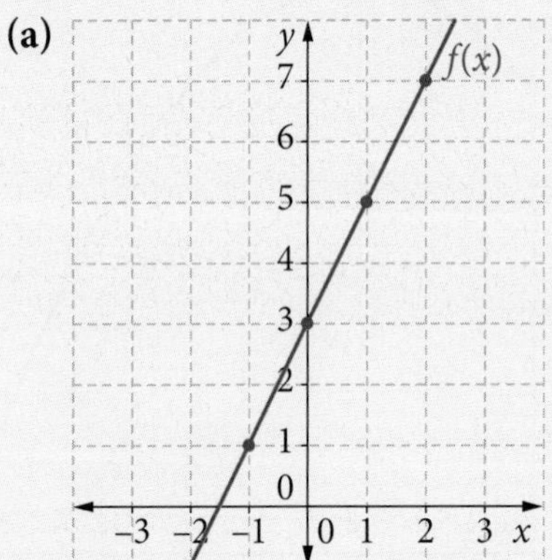

(b)

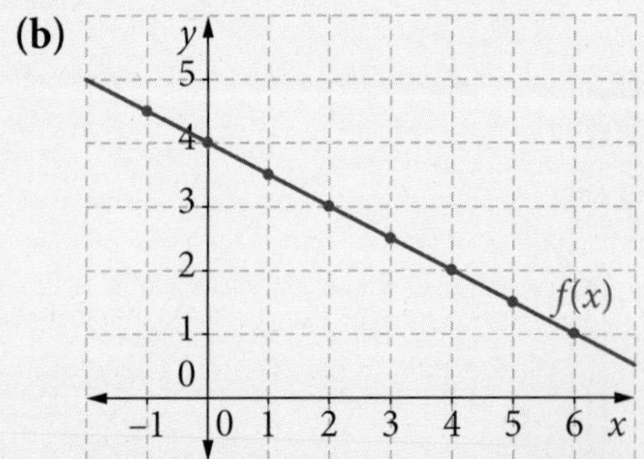

Links across the syllabus

Forming the equation of a linear function is covered in Chapter 3: Algebra II.

5. The graphs below show $y = x^2$ with tangents drawn at various points. Use the shaded triangles to find the rate of change (slope) of the tangents to the curve at the indicated point.

(i)

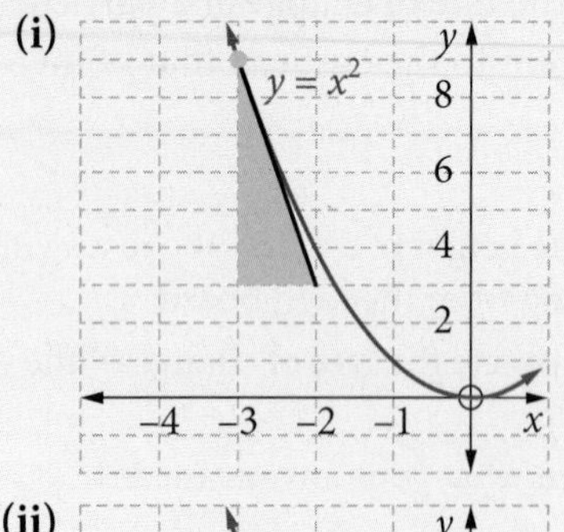

(ii)

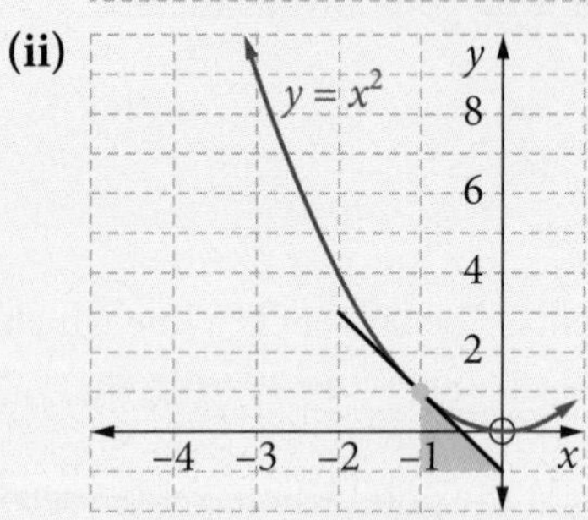

(iii)

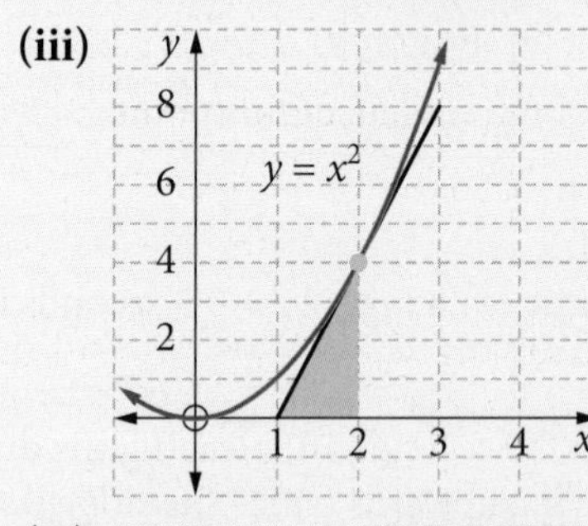

(iv)

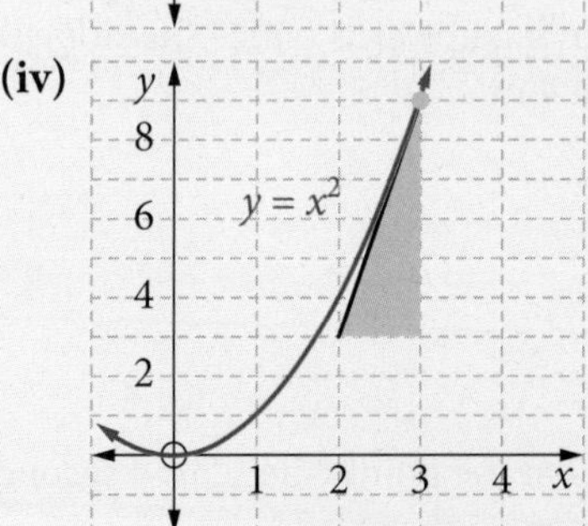

6. For each of the following graphs, use the grid to estimate the rate of change at the point indicated. Make sure to include the correct units in your answer.

(i)

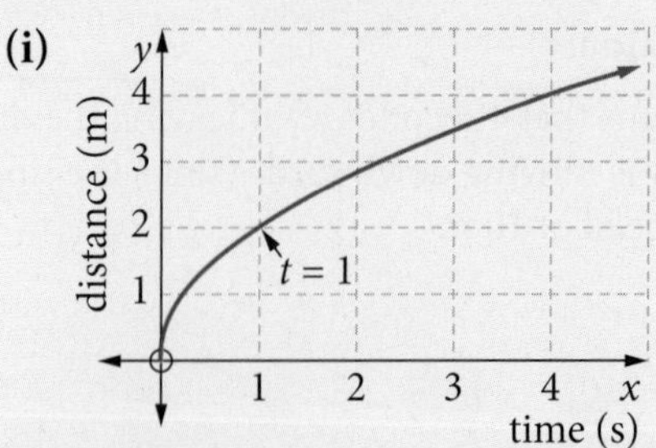

(ii)

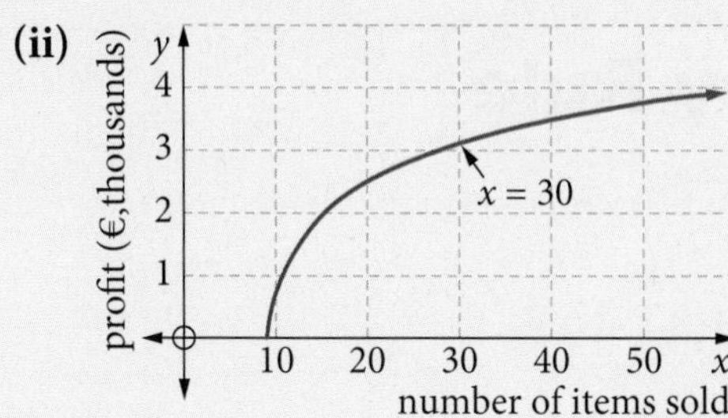

(iii)

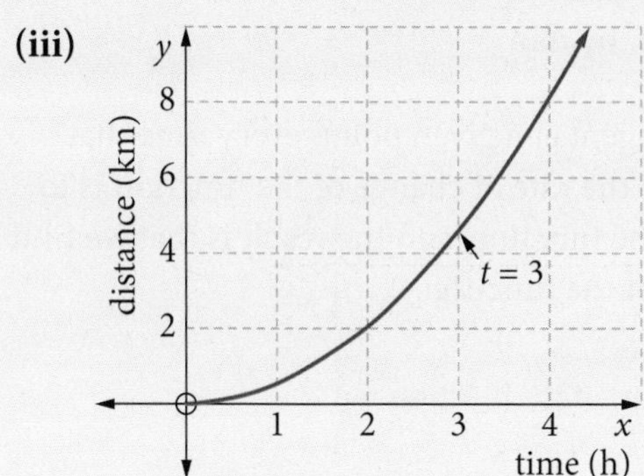

(iv)

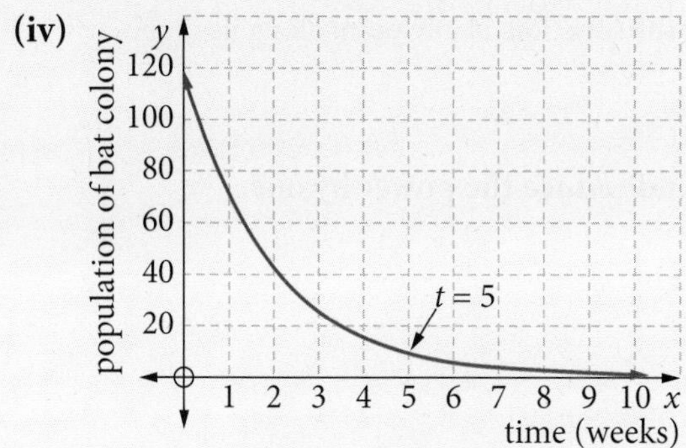

7. **(a)** The diagram shows the graph of a quadratic function.

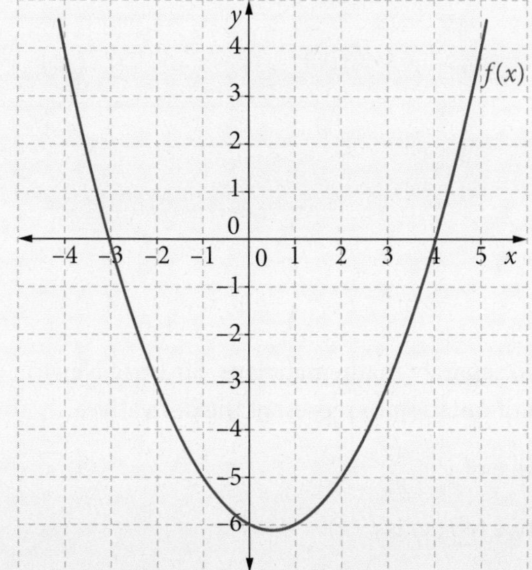

Use the grid to estimate the rate of change of the function, at the following values of x:

(i) 2 **(ii)** −2 **(iii)** 4 **(iv)** 0 **(v)** 0·5

(b) Write down the range of values of x, for which the graph is decreasing.

8. **(i)** Graph the function $g(x) = x^2 + 3x - 4$ in the domain $-5 \le x \le 2$.

(ii) Use your graph to find the rate of change of $g(x)$ at the points:

(a) $(-4, 0)$

(b) $(-1, -6)$

(c) $(2, 6)$

Links across the syllabus

Graphing quadratic functions is covered in Chapter 4: Algebra III.

9. **(a)** The diagram shows part of the graph of a cubic function.

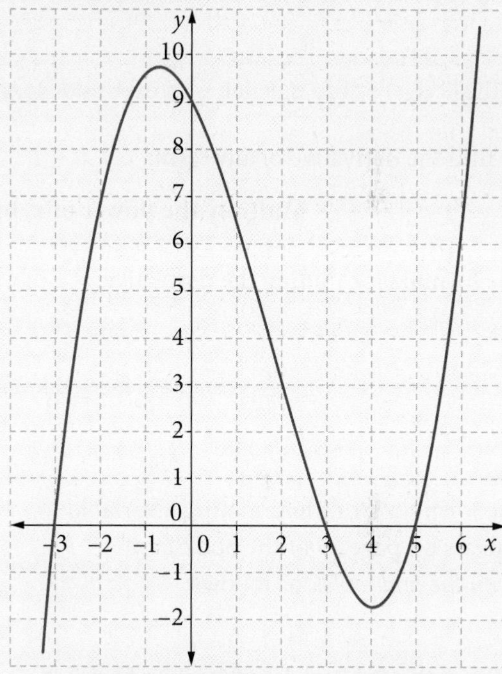

Use the grid to estimate the rate of change of the function, at the following values of x:

(i) −2

(ii) 0

(iii) 2

(iv) 4

(b) Write down the range of values of x for which the graph is increasing.

Section 26.2: Differentiation by Rule

Learning Outcomes:

You should be able to:
- find the first derivative of linear, quadratic and cubic functions, by rule
- find the second derivative of linear, quadratic and cubic functions, by rule

It is not practical for us to draw a graph and estimate the slope of a tangent at a given point, every time that we want to find the rate of change of a function. A quicker way to find the rate of change of the function is to perform a process called 'differentiation'. We are said to 'differentiate the function' and the result is that we find an expression for the rate of change, otherwise known as the 'derivative' of the function.

To **differentiate** a function means to perform a process to find the derivative of the function.

The **derivative** of a function is an expression for the rate of change of the function, at any point along its graph.

To find the derivative of any term:

Multiply the power of x, by the coefficient and reduce the power by one.

The formula for finding the derivative, $\frac{dy}{dx}$, of a function y is given by:

$\frac{dy}{dx}$ is read as 'dee y, dee x'.

If $y = ax^n$ then $\frac{dy}{dx} = nax^{n-1}$

The formula for differentiating a variable appears on page 25 of the booklet of *formulae and tables*, as follows:

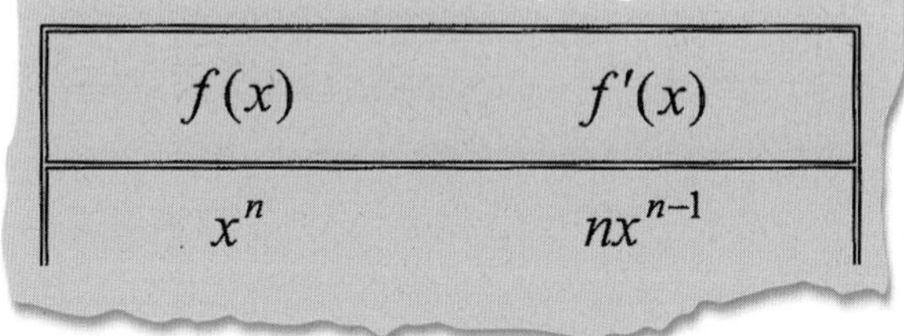

$f(x)$	$f'(x)$
x^n	nx^{n-1}

Notice that the formula in the tables book only shows what to do when the coefficient is 1.

Notation

Differential calculus was developed in the 17th century, by two separate mathematicians, Sir Isaac Newton and Gottfried Leibniz. Each mathematician used a different form of notation to represent the derivative.

Leibniz's notation: The derivative of y is $\frac{dy}{dx}$

Newton's notation: The derivative of $f(x)$ is $f'(x)$

We will use both forms of notation, when answering questions.

EXAMPLE 1

Find $\frac{dy}{dx}$ if

(i) $y = x^3$ **(ii)** $y = 5x^2$ **(iii)** $y = 3x$ **(iv)** $y = -7$

Solution

(i) $y = x^3$

Multiply the power, 3, by the coefficient, 1, and reduce the power by 1:

$$\frac{dy}{dx} = 3(1x^{3-1})$$

$$\frac{dy}{dx} = 3x^2$$

Links across the syllabus

Indices are covered in Chapter 5: Indices and Index Notation.

(ii) $y = 5x^2$

Multiply the power, 2, by the coefficient, 5, and reduce the power by 1:

$$\frac{dy}{dx} = 2(5x^{2-1})$$

$$\frac{dy}{dx} = 10x^1$$

$$\frac{dy}{dx} = 10x \quad (x^1 = x)$$

(iii) $y = 3x = 3x^1$

Multiply the power, 1, by the coefficient, 3, and reduce the power by 1:

$$\frac{dy}{dx} = 1(3x^{1-1})$$

$$\frac{dy}{dx} = 3x^0$$

$$\frac{dy}{dx} = 3(1) \quad (x^0 = 1)$$

$$\frac{dy}{dx} = 3$$

(iv) $y = -7 = -7(1)$

$y = -7(1)$

$y = -7(x^0) \quad (x^0 = 1)$

Multiply the power, 0, by the coefficient, −7, and reduce the power by 1:

$$\frac{dy}{dx} = 0(-7x^{0-1})$$

$$\frac{dy}{dx} = 0(-7x^{-1})$$

$$\frac{dy}{dx} = 0 \quad \text{(anything multiplied by 0 is 0)}$$

In general, you are not required to show all steps involved in finding the derivative, $\frac{dy}{dx}$.
In this example, it is acceptable to skip from the first line to the last.

Discussion Time 

1. Working with a classmate, use the method shown in the previous example to find the derivative of each of the following expressions:
   (i) $2x^3$ **(ii)** $-5x^3$ **(iii)** $9x^3$ **(iv)** $4x^2$ **(v)** x^2 **(vi)** $-6x^2$ **(vii)** $8x$ **(viii)** $-3x$ **(ix)** $-12x$ **(x)** 7 **(xi)** −1 **(xii)** 13
2. Based on your answers above, can you come up with a general rule for differentiating
   (i) a cubic expression.
   (ii) a quadratic expression.
   (iii) a linear expression.
   (iv) a constant.

Based on your findings from the Discussion Time above, you should be able to see that derivatives can be summarised as follows:

	y or $f(x)$	$\frac{dy}{dx}$ or $f'(x)$
Cubic	ax^3	$3ax^2$
Quadratic	bx^2	$2bx$
Linear	cx	c
Constant	d	0

EXAMPLE 2

Find the derivative of each of the following:

(i) $f(x) = 3x^2 - 4x + 5$ **(ii)** $y = 2x^3 - 6x^2 + 5x + 12$ **(iii)** $g(x) = 6x - 4x^3 - 7$

Solution

(i) $f(x) = 3x^2 - 4x + 5$

$f'(x) = 2(3x^1) - 4 + 0$

$f'(x) = 6x - 4$

(ii) $y = 2x^3 - 6x^2 + 5x + 12$

$\frac{dy}{dx} = 3(2x^2) - 2(6x^1) + 5 + 0$

$\frac{dy}{dx} = 6x^2 - 12x + 5$

(iii) $g(x) = 6x - 4x^3 - 7$

$g'(x) = 6 - 3(4x^2) - 0$

$g'(x) = 6 - 12x^2$

EXAMPLE 3

$g(k) = 4k^2 + 5k - 2$

Find:

(i) $g'(k)$ **(ii)** $g'(-2{\cdot}5)$ **(iii)** the value of k for which $g'(k) = 45$.

Solution

(i) $g(k) = 4k^2 + 5k - 2$

$g'(k) = 2(4k) + 5 - 0$

$g'(k) = 8k + 5$

(ii) $g'(-2{\cdot}5) = 8(-2{\cdot}5) + 5$

$g'(-2{\cdot}5) = -20 + 5$

$g'(-2{\cdot}5) = -15$

(iii) $g'(k) = 8k + 5$

$45 = 8k + 5$

$40 = 8k$

$5 = k$

Therefore, when $k = 5$, $g'(k) = 45$.

The variable being differentiated is not always an x. Other letters can be used, but the procedure remains the same, as shown in this example.

Second derivative

When you differentiate an expression, you find the first derivative. When you then differentiate this first derivative, you get the second derivative.

The second derivative is the rate at which the change is changing.

The notation to indicate the second derivative is: $\frac{d^2y}{dx^2}$ or $f''(x)$

The second derivative is found by differentiating an expression twice.

EXAMPLE 4

Show that the second derivative of $y = (5x + 3)(x - 2)$ is a constant.

Solution

Always expand brackets before differentiating.

Multiply out the brackets: $y = 5x(x - 2) + 3(x - 2)$

$y = 5x^2 - 10x + 3x - 6$

$y = 5x^2 - 7x - 6$

First derivative:

$y = 5x^2 - 7x - 6$

$\frac{dy}{dx} = 2(5x) - 7 + 0$

$\frac{dy}{dx} = 10x - 7$

Second derivative:

$\frac{dy}{dx} = 10x - 7$

$\frac{d^2y}{dx^2} = 10 - 0$

$\frac{d^2y}{dx^2} = 10$ which is a constant.

EXAMPLE 5

$s = 2 - 3t + 0{\cdot}4t^2 - 0{\cdot}1t^3$ is a function.

(i) Differentiate s with respect to t and evaluate it for $t = -1$

(ii) Find its second derivative, $\frac{d^2s}{dt^2}$ and evaluate it for $t = 3$

$\frac{ds}{dt}$ means to differentiate the expression for s, with respect to the letter t.

Solution

(i) First derivative, $\frac{ds}{dt}$

$s = 2 - 3t + 0{\cdot}4t^2 - 0{\cdot}1t^3$

$\frac{ds}{dt} = 0 - 3 + 2(0{\cdot}4t) - 3(0{\cdot}1t^2)$

$\frac{ds}{dt} = -3 + 0{\cdot}8t - 0{\cdot}3t^2$

When $t = -1$:

$\frac{ds}{dt} = -3 + 0{\cdot}8(-1) - 0{\cdot}3(-1)^2$

$\frac{ds}{dt} = -3 - 0{\cdot}8 - 0{\cdot}3(1)$

$\frac{ds}{dt} = -3 - 0{\cdot}8 - 0{\cdot}3$

$\frac{ds}{dt} = -4{\cdot}1$

(ii) Second derivative, $\frac{d^2s}{dt^2}$

$\frac{ds}{dt} = -3 + 0{\cdot}8t - 0{\cdot}3t^2$

$\frac{d^2s}{dt^2} = 0 + 0{\cdot}8 - 2(0{\cdot}3t)$

$\frac{d^2s}{dt^2} = 0{\cdot}8 - 0{\cdot}6t$

When $t = 3$:

$\frac{d^2s}{dt^2} = 0{\cdot}8 - 0{\cdot}6(3)$

$\frac{d^2s}{dt^2} = 0{\cdot}8 - 1{\cdot}8$

$\frac{d^2s}{dt^2} = -1$

Practice Questions 26.2

1. Differentiate each of the following:
   (i) $4x^3$
   (ii) x^2
   (iii) $-5x$
   (iv) $-2x^3$
   (v) 9
   (vi) $-6x^2$
   (vii) -4
   (viii) $8x$

2. Find $\frac{dy}{dx}$ for each of the following:
   (i) $y = x^3 + 6x$
   (ii) $y = 3x^2 - 4$
   (iii) $y = 7x^2 + 4x - 3$
   (iv) $y = 8x^3 - 5x^2 + 6$
   (v) $y = 3x - 4x^3 + x^2$
   (vi) $y = 2x^3 + 7x^2 - x - 1$

3. Differentiate each of the following:
   (i) $f(x) = 3x^2 - x$
   (ii) $s(t) = 6t - 4t^2 + 2$
   (iii) $g(k) = k(5k^2 + 2 - 8k)$
   (iv) $h(x) = 7 + x - x^2\,(3x - 1)$

4. Find $\frac{dy}{dx}$ and $\frac{d^2y}{dx^2}$ for each of the following:
   (i) $y = 6{\cdot}2x^3 - 0{\cdot}4x^2$
   (ii) $y = x(5x + 7)$
   (iii) $y = (2x + 1)(4x - 5)$
   (iv) $y = 3{\cdot}4x^3 - 8x^2 + 2{\cdot}1x - 1$

5. Find $\frac{d^2y}{dx^2}$ for each of the following:
   (i) $y = 4x^2 + 5x$
   (ii) $y = 6 - 3x$
   (iii) $y = 2x(3x^2 + 2x - 4)$
   (iv) $y = 5x^3 + 4x^2 - 7x - 4$

6. If $y = 5x^2 + 4x - 2$, find the value of $\frac{dy}{dx}$ when $x = 1$.

7. If $s = 2{\cdot}3t^3 - 0{\cdot}2t^2 + 6{\cdot}4t - 8{\cdot}1$, find the value of $\frac{ds}{dt}$ when $t = -2$.

8. If $V = 5h - 4h^2 + 3h^3$, find the value of $\frac{dV}{dh}$ when $h = 5$.

9. If $g(t) = 5t^3 - t^2 + 2t - 12$, find the value of $g'(t)$ and $g''(t)$ when $t = -1$.

10. If $h(k) = 4k^2 - 22k + 5$, find the value of k, for which $h'(k) = 2$.

11. If $f(x) = x^3 - 6x^2 - 38x + 2$, find the value of x, for which $f'(x) = -2$.

12. If $y = 2x^3 - 9x^2 - 56x + 5$, find the values of x, for which $\frac{d^2y}{dx^2} = 6$.

13. If $y = 5x^3 + 4x^2 - 21x - 2$, find the values of x, for which $\frac{d^2y}{dx^2} = -7$.

14. Let $g(x) = 5x^3 - px + 7$ for all $x \in \mathbb{R}$ and for all $p \in \mathbb{R}$.

 Given that $g'(1) = 6$, find the value of p.

15. Let $y = ax^2 + bx - 5$ for all $x \in \mathbb{R}$ and for all $a, b \in \mathbb{R}$.

 Given that when $x = -1$, $\frac{dy}{dx} = -7$ and when $x = 2$, $\frac{dy}{dx} = 11$

 (i) Form two equations in terms of a and b.

 (ii) Hence, find the values of a and b.

Links across the syllabus

Simultaneous linear equations are covered in Chapter 3: Algebra II.

16. Let $y = px^2 + qx - 1$ for all $x \in \mathbb{R}$ and for all $p, q \in \mathbb{R}$.

 Given that when $x = 1$, $\frac{dy}{dx} = 2$ and when $x = -3$, $\frac{dy}{dx} = -22$

 (i) Form two equations in terms of p and q.

 (ii) Hence, find the values of p and q.

Section 26.3: Curve Sketching

Learning Outcome:

You should be able to:

- use differential calculus to determine information about a curve and hence sketch it

There are several ways to draw the graph of a function (curve). The ones we have already met are:

- Use substitution to find points along the curve. Plot these points and join them up to draw the curve.
- Find the roots of the function and use those and the known shape of the curve to sketch the graph.

Links across the syllabus

Graphing Functions is covered in Chapter 3: Algebra II, Chapter 4: Algebra III and Chapter 7: Further Functions.

Now we will look at using differentiation to determine the shape and position of the graph of a function (curve).

Taking the graph of a function $y = f(x)$

At any point where the graph is 'going up' (reading from left to right), the graph is said to be increasing.

The slope of the tangent at any point along this section will be positive, therefore:

$\frac{dy}{dx} > 0$, when the graph is increasing

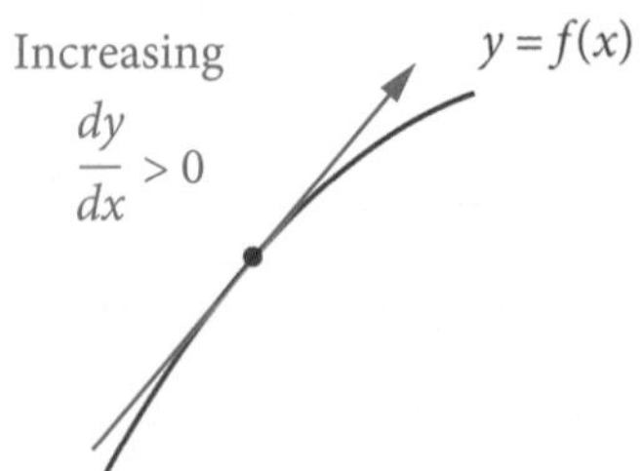

At any point where the graph is 'going down' (reading from left to right), the graph is said to be decreasing.

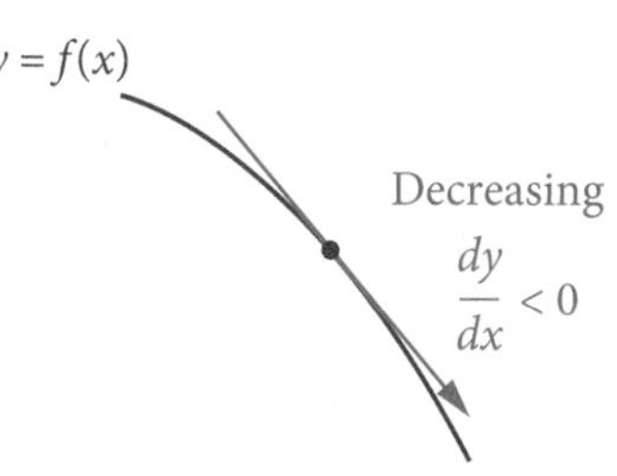

The slope of the tangent at any point along this section will be negative, therefore:

$\frac{dy}{dx} < 0$, when the graph is decreasing

Turning or stationary points

It may be the case that, at some point: the graph stops increasing and then begins to decrease, or vice versa. The point where this occurs is called a 'turning point', because the graph is changing direction and so it is turning. This point may also be referred to as a 'stationary point', because the graph has stopped moving in one direction and begun to move in a different direction.

The tangent to a graph at a turning (or stationary) point is horizontal and so has a zero slope.

Therefore:

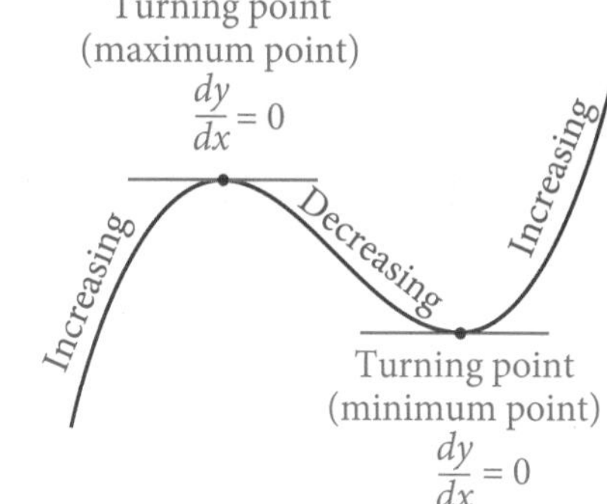

At turning (stationary) points, $\frac{dy}{dx} = 0$

Steps to finding the turning points:

Step 1: Find the derivative, $\frac{dy}{dx}$.

Step 2: Let $\frac{dy}{dx} = 0$ and solve for x.

Step 3: Substitute the x value(s) into the **original** expression to find the y coordinates of the turning points.

Determining whether a point is a local maximum or a local minimum

Before being able to sketch a graph, we need to determine whether a turning point is the maximum or the minimum. To do this, we can observe the function type, and apply logic, or we can find the second derivative of the function.

Observing the function type

Since a **linear function** is a straight line, it has no turning points.

Therefore, it is always either increasing or decreasing.

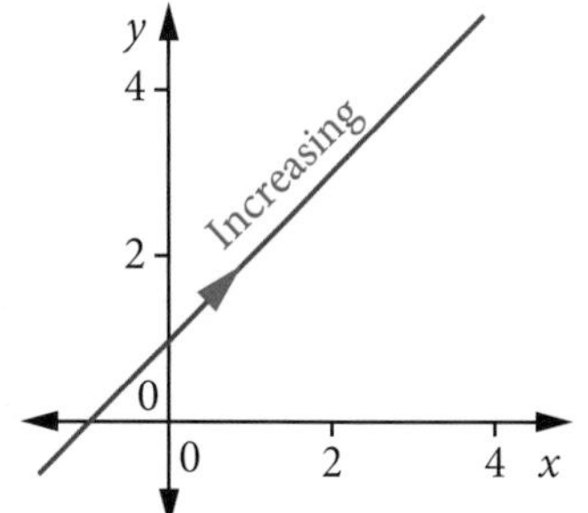

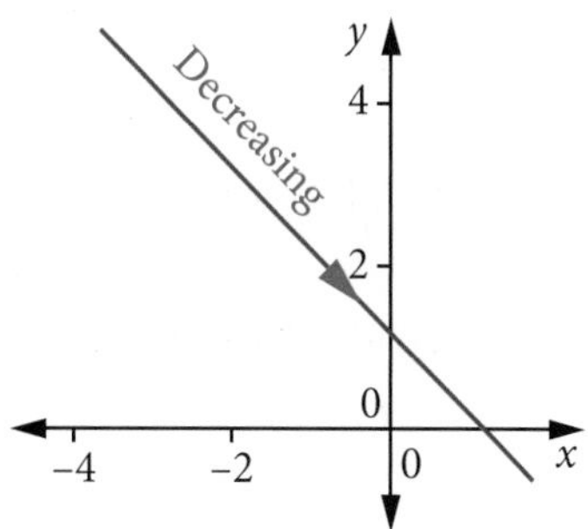

A **quadratic function** is parabolic in shape and is either a ∪ or an ∩ shape. Therefore, it will have one turning point: a minimum or a maximum.

A quadratic function, with a **positive** coefficient on the x^2, will be ∪ shaped and so have a **minimum** point only.

A quadratic function, with a **negative** coefficient on the x^2, will be ∩ shaped and so have a **maximum** point only.

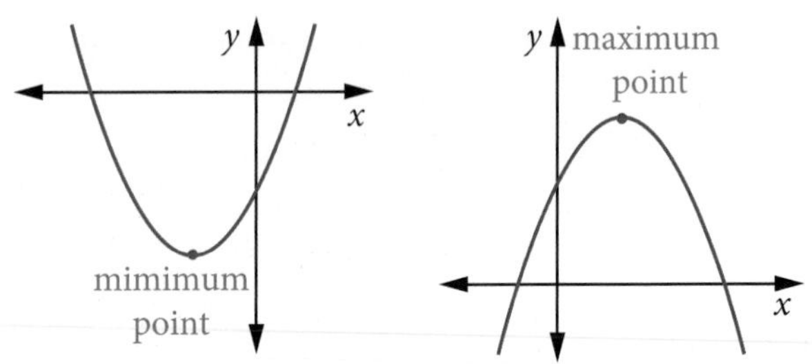

A **cubic function** is made-up or a ∪ shape and an ∩ shape. Therefore, it will have two turning points – one minimum **and** one maximum.

The maximum point will be higher than the minimum point, therefore it's y coordinate will be greater.

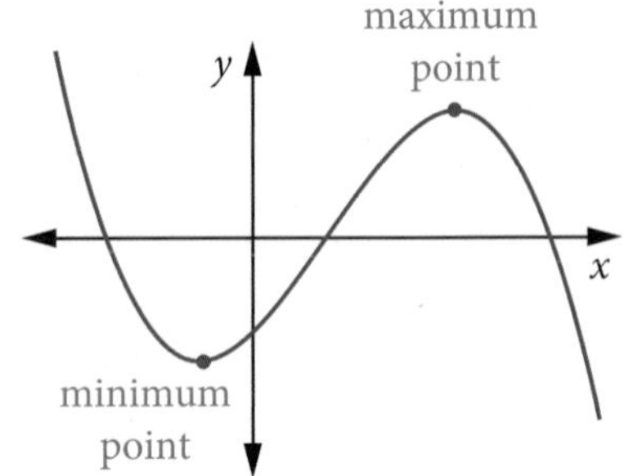

Using the second derivative

Steps to determining whether a point is a maximum or a minimum:

Step 1: Find the second derivative, $\dfrac{d^2y}{dx^2}$

Step 2: Substitute the x coordinates of the turning points into $\dfrac{d^2y}{dx^2}$

Step 3: If $\dfrac{d^2y}{dx^2} < 0$ the point is a maximum.

If $\dfrac{d^2y}{dx^2} > 0$ the point is a minimum.

If $\dfrac{d^2y}{dx^2}$ is negative, the point is a local maximum.

If $\dfrac{d^2y}{dx^2}$ is positive, the point is a local minimum.

EXAMPLE 1

(i) Find the turning points of the curve $f(x) = x^3 + 3x^2 - 9x + 13$.

(ii) Determine which point is the local maximum and which is the local minimum.

(iii) Hence, draw a sketch of the function $f(x)$.

(iv) Using your sketch, determine how many real roots $f(x)$ has.

Solution

(i) At the turning points, $f'(x) = 0$

Step 1:

$f(x) = x^3 + 3x^2 - 9x + 13$

$f'(x) = 3x^2 + 6x - 9$

Step 2:

Let $f'(x) = 0$:

$0 = 3x^2 + 6x - 9$

$0 = x^2 + 2x - 3$ (divided by 3)

$0 = (x + 3)(x - 1)$ (factorise)

$x = -3$ or $x = 1$

Step 3:

Find y coordinates:

$x = -3$: $f(-3) = (-3)^3 + 3(-3)^2 - 9(-3) + 13$

$y = -27 + 3(9) + 27 + 13$

$y = -27 + 27 + 27 + 13$

$y = 40$

$x = 1$: $f(1) = (1)^3 + 3(1)^2 - 9(1) + 13$

$y = 1 + 3(1) - 9 + 13$

$y = 1 + 3 - 9 + 13$

$y = 8$

Therefore, the turning points are $(-3, 40)$ and $(1, 8)$.

(ii) The turning points are $(-3, 40)$ and $(1, 8)$.

The first point has a y-coordinate of 40, while the second point has a y-coordinate of 8.

Therefore, we know that the $(-3, 40)$ point is higher on the coordinated plane and so it is the maximum point.

Hence, $(1, 8)$ is the minimum point.

Alternative method: To determine if a point is a maximum or a minimum, find the second derivative, $f''(x)$:

Step 1: $f'(x) = 3x^2 + 6x - 9$

$f''(x) = 6x + 6$

Step 2:

From part **(i)**, we found a turning point at $x = -3$

When $x = -3$: $f''(-3) = 6(-3) + 6$

$f''(-3) = -18 + 6$

$f''(-3) = -12 < 0$

Step 3:

Since $f''(x) < 0$, $(-3, 40)$ is the maximum point.

Step 2:

Turning point at $x = 1$:

When $x = 1$: $f''(1) = 6(1) + 6$

$f''(1) = 6 + 6$

$f''(1) = 12 > 0$

Step 3:

Since $f''(x) > 0$, $(1, 8)$ is the minimum point.

(iii) Plot the turning points and sketch the cubic function.

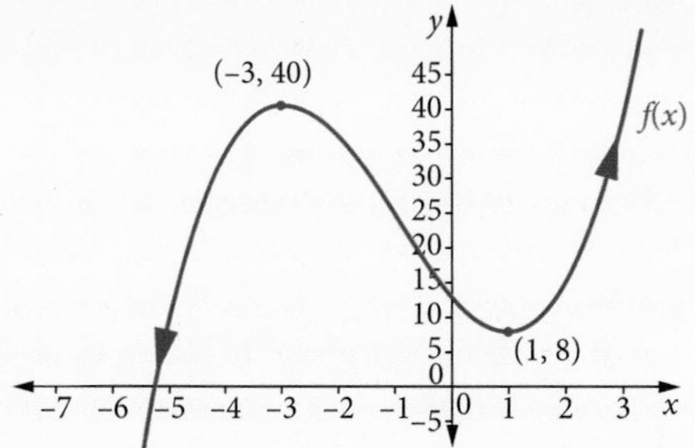

Do not just join the points and form a straight line. Recall the shape of a cubic function and take care to draw a curved line.

(iv) A real root occurs wherever the graph crosses the x-axis.

Since both turning points are above the x-axis, the graph crosses the x-axis at one point only (between -5 and -6, from the sketch)

Therefore, $f(x)$ has only one real root.

EXAMPLE 2

Find the values of x for which the function $h(x) = 3x^2 + 24x - 11$ is decreasing.

Solution

Find $h'(x)$

$h(x) = 3x^2 + 24x - 11$

$h'(x) = 2(3x^1) + 24(1) - 0$

$h'(x) = 6x + 24$

A function is decreasing when $h'(x) < 0$:

$6x + 24 < 0$

$6x < -24$ (subtract 24 from both sides)

$x < -4$ (divide both sides by 6)

Therefore, the function is decreasing for any value of $x < -4$.

EXAMPLE 3

A quadratic function $g(x) = ax^2 + bx + c$ is shown in the diagram.
The function crosses the y-axis at the point (0, 14) and has a local minimum point at (4, −18).

(i) Find the values of a, b and c and hence find the function $g(x)$.
(ii) Verify that the curve is increasing when $x = 7$.

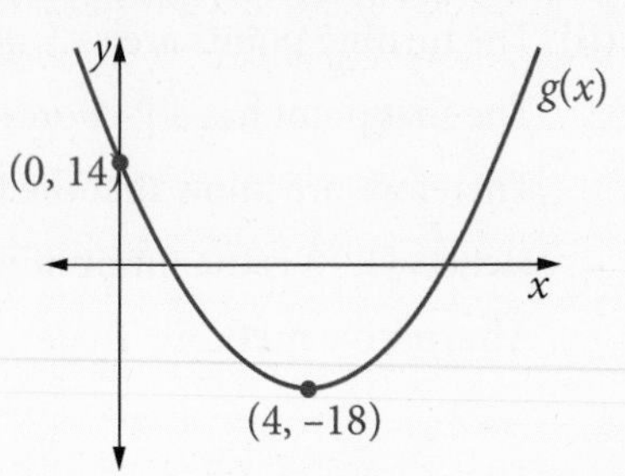

Solution

(i) The point (0, 14) is a point on the curve, so $g(0) = 14$:

$g(x) = ax^2 + bx + c$
$g(0) = a(0)^2 + b(0) + c$
$14 = 0 + 0 + c$
$14 = c$

The point (4, −18) is a point on the curve, so $g(4) = -18$:

$g(x) = ax^2 + bx + 14$
$g(4) = a(4)^2 + b(4) + 14$
$-18 = 16a + 4b + 14$
$-32 = 16a + 4b$ (subtract 14)
$-8 = 4a + b$ ① (divide by 4)

At the minimum point, $g'(x) = 0$ and $x = 4$:

$g(x) = ax^2 + bx + 14$
$g'(x) = 2ax + b$
$0 = 2a(4) + b$ ($g'(x) = 0$ and $x = 4$)
$0 = 8a + b$ ②

Solve equations ① and ②, simultaneously

$4a + b = -8$ (× −1 to eliminate b)
$8a + b = 0$

$-4a - b = 8$
$8a + b = 0$

$4a = 8$
$a = 2$

Let $a = 2$:
$8a + b = 0$
$8(2) + b = 0$
$16 + b = 0$
$b = -16$

> **Links across the syllabus**
> Simultaneous equations are covered in Chapter 3: Algebra II.

Therefore, $a = 2$, $b = -16$ and $c = 14$: $g(x) = 2x^2 - 16x + 14$

(ii) To determine if the curve is increasing or decreasing, find the value of $g'(x)$ when $x = 7$:

$g(x) = 2x^2 - 16x + 14$
$g'(x) = 4x - 16$
$g'(7) = 4(7) - 16$
$g'(7) = 28 - 16$
$g'(7) = 12$

Since $g'(x) > 0$ when $x = 7$, the graph is increasing when $x = 7$.

Practice Questions 26.3

1. Find the derivative of each of the following linear functions and hence determine whether they are increasing or decreasing. Justify your answer.
   (i) $f(x) = 2x + 6$ **(ii)** $g(n) = 8 - 3n$ **(iii)** $h(t) = 9 - 5t$ **(iv)** $k(x) = 4x - 5$

2. Find the values of x for which each of the following graphs are increasing:
   (i) $k(x) = 3x^2 - 18x + 7$
   (ii) $f(x) = 5 + 4x - 2x^2$
   (iii) $h(x) = 4x^2 + 12x - 11$
   (iv) $g(x) = -6 - 25x - 5x^2$

3. Find the coordinates of the turning point for each of the following quadratic functions. Determine if the point is a minimum or a maximum point and hence sketch the graph of the function.
   (i) $k(x) = x^2 + 8x - 9$
   (ii) $g(n) = n^2 + 2n - 35$
   (iii) $f(t) = 8 + 2t - t^2$
   (iv) $h(r) = r^2 + 6r - 9$
   (v) $g(x) = 3x^2 + 12x + 14$
   (vi) $k(n) = -4n^2 + 9n + 3$

4. A curve has equation $y = x^3 - 6x + 4$
   (i) Find the slope of the tangent to the curve at the points $(-3, -5)$, $(0, 4)$ and $(2, 0)$. Hence, decide if the graph is increasing or decreasing at each point.
   (ii) Find the coordinates of the local minimum and maximum points on the curve.
   (iii) Hence, draw a rough sketch of the curve.

Slope of the tangent = $\frac{dy}{dx}$

5. (i) Find the point where the curve $y = 2x^3 - 3x^2 + 2$ crosses the y-axis.
   (ii) Find the coordinates of the local maximum and minimum points on the curve.
   (iii) Hence, draw a rough sketch of the curve.
   (iv) Write down the range of values of x for which $\frac{dy}{dx} < 0$. Justify your answer.

6. Find the coordinates of the turning points for each of the following cubic functions. Determine which point is a minimum or a maximum point and hence sketch the graph of the function.
   (i) $h(n) = n^3 - 12n + 5$
   (ii) $f(x) = x^3 - 6x^2 - 15x + 8$
   (iii) $g(t) = -2t^3 + 3t^2 + 36t - 5$
   (iv) $k(x) = x^3 + 5x^2 - 8x + 7$
   (v) $h(x) = x^3 - 15x^2 + 48x + 7$
   (vi) $f(n) = -2n^3 + 3n^2 + 36n + 5$

7. Find the coordinates of the local maximum point of the curve $y = -x^3 + 3x - 5$.

8. Find the coordinates of the local maximum and minimum points on the curve $y = 5 + 3x^2 - x^3$. Hence, draw a rough sketch of the curve.

9. Let $f(x) = x^2 + bx + 10$ for all $x \in \mathbb{R}$ and for $b \in \mathbb{R}$.
   (i) Find $f'(x)$, the first derivative of $f(x)$.
   (ii) The minimum value of $f(x)$ is at $x = 3$. Find the value of b.
   (iii) Find the equation of the tangent to $f(x)$ at the point $(4, 2)$.

10. Let $g(x) = x^3 - px + 7$ for all $x \in \mathbb{R}$ and for $p \in \mathbb{R}$
   (i) The slope of the tangent to the curve $y = g(x)$ at $x = 1$ is -9. Find the value of p.
   (ii) Hence, find the coordinates of the local maximum point and the local minimum point on the curve $y = g(x)$.
   (iii) Write down the range of values of x, for which $g'(x) > 0$.

11. Let $h(x) = x^3 - 3x - 1$ for all $x \in \mathbb{R}$ and for $p \in \mathbb{R}$
   (i) Find $h(-2)$ and $h(2)$.
   (ii) Find $h'(x)$, the derivative of $h(x)$.
   (iii) Find the coordinates of the local minimum and local maximum points on the curve $y = h(x)$.
   (iv) Draw the graph of the function h, in the domain $-2 \leq x \leq 2$.

   Use your graph to:
   (v) estimate the range of values of x for which $h(x) < 0$ and $x > 0$
   (vi) estimate the range of values of x for which $h'(x) < 0$.

12. (i) Use the following five pieces of information to sketch the graph of the function $y = g(x)$
   - When $x = 0$, $g(x) = 6$
   - $g'(x) > 0$ for $x < 3$
   - $g'(x) = 0$ for $x = 3$
   - When $x = 3$, $g(x) = 9$
   - $g'(x) < 0$ for $x > 3$

   (ii) Hence state what type of function $g(x)$ is.

13. **(i)** Use the following six pieces of information to sketch the graph of the function $y = f(x)$

- When $x = -3, f(x) = 0$
- $f'(x) < 0$ for $x > 0$
- $f'(x) > 0$ for $-3 < x < 0$
- $f'(x) < 0$ for $x < -3$
- When $x = 0, f(x) = 4$
- $f'(x) = 0$ for $x = -3$ and $x = 0$

(ii) Hence state what type of function $f(x)$ is.

Section 26.4: Graphing the Derivative Function

Learning Outcome:

You should be able to:

- graph the derivative of a function

If we are given the equation of a function, we can find its derivative and then graph the derivative function in the given domain. However, if we are not given the function, it is important that we are able to graph the derivative function by inspection and observation only.

Discussion Time 

The diagram shows the function $f(x)$ and its derivative $f'(x)$, graphed on the same axes and scale.

Study the graphs and work with a classmate to answer the following questions:

1. What type of function is $f(x)$?
2. What type of function is $f'(x)$?
3. Identify the region where the $f(x)$ graph is increasing. Where is the $f'(x)$ graph at this time? Explain why this is the case?
4. Identify the region where the $f(x)$ graph is decreasing. Where is the $f'(x)$ graph at this time? Explain why this is the case.
5. Describe what is happening at each function when $x = 4$? Explain why this is the case.

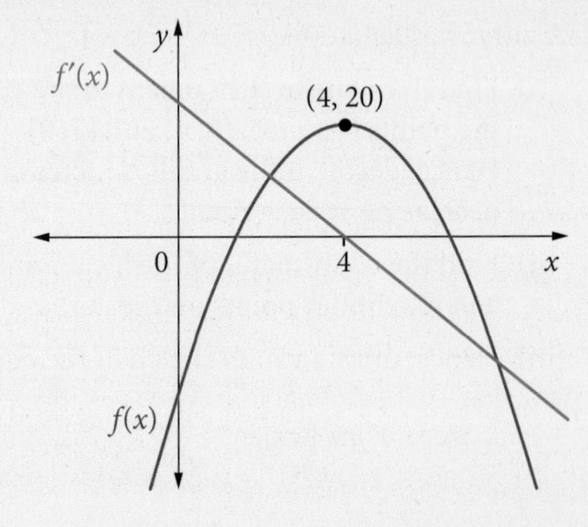

From the above discussion time, you should have deduced the following three pieces of information about the relationship between a function and the graph of its derivative:

- While the graph is **increasing**, its derivative will be **positive** and so it will be **above** the x-axis, during this time.
- While the graph is **decreasing**, its derivative will be **negative** and so it will be **below** the x-axis, during this time.
- When the graph has a **turning point**, its derivative will be **zero** and so it will be **on** the x-axis at that time.

Steps in graphing the derivative of a function

Step 1: Identify the turning point(s) of the original function and mark their positions on the x-axis. We know the derivative function will cross the x-axis at this point(s).

Step 2: Look to the left of the turning point and determine whether the graph is increasing or decreasing in this region.

If the graph is increasing – draw the derivative function above the x-axis.

If the graph is decreasing – draw the derivative function below the x-axis.

Step 3: Repeat step 2 for all remaining regions on the graph.

> It is helpful to know what shape the graph of the derivative function will be. Recall:
> - When we differentiate a cubic function, we get a quadratic function.
> - When we differentiate a quadratic function, we get a linear function.
> - When we differentiate a linear function, we get a horizontal line.

EXAMPLE 1

The diagram shows the graph of a quadratic function, $f(x)$

Using the same axes and scale, sketch the graph of $f'(x)$, the derivative of $f(x)$.

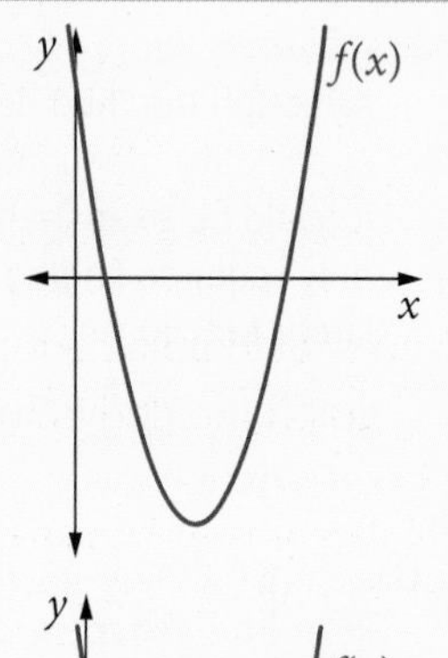

Solution

Since $f(x)$ is a quadratic function, its derivative, $f'(x)$ is a linear function (straight line).

***Step 1:* Identify the turning point**

- Start by looking at the turning point of the $f(x)$ graph.
- At a turning point, $f'(x) = 0$. Therefore, at the turning point of $f(x)$, the graph of its derivative will cross the x-axis.
- Move from the turning point up to the x-axis and mark this position on the x-axis.

***Step 2:* Determine if a region is increasing or decreasing**

- To the left of the turning point, the graph of $f(x)$ is **decreasing**. This means that it has a **negative** slope and therefore, the value of the derivative will be negative and its graph will be **below** the x-axis.
- The slope of $f(x)$ changes from a steep negative to a shallow negative, as it approaches the turning point and so the value for the derivative changes steadily from a large negative value to a small negative value and eventually to zero when it reaches the turning point.
- To graph the derivative we draw a straight line, below the x-axis, gradually rising from a large negative value to zero, at the point marked in Step 1. The graph of the derivative should begin at the same x value as the $f(x)$ function.

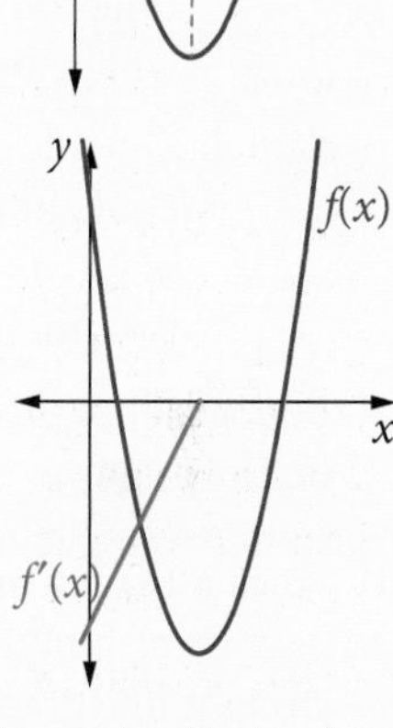

***Step 3:* Determine if a region is increasing or decreasing**

- To the right of the turning point, the graph of $f(x)$ is **increasing**. This means that it has a **positive** slope and therefore, the value of the derivative will be positive and its graph will be **above** the x-axis.
- The slope of $f(x)$ changes from a shallow positive to a steep positive and so the value for the derivative changes steadily from zero, at the turning point, to a small positive value and rises steadily to a large positive value.
- To graph the derivative we draw a straight line, above the x-axis, gradually rising from zero, at the point marked in Step 1, to a large positive value. The graph of the derivative should end at the same x value as the $f(x)$ function.

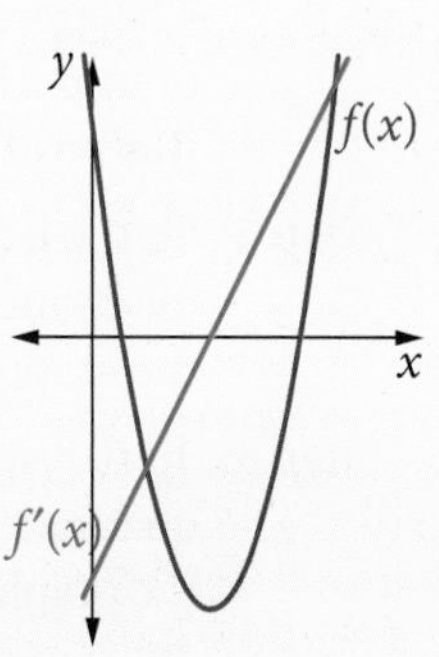

EXAMPLE 2

The diagram shows the graph of a cubic function, $g(x)$

Using the same axes and scale, sketch the graph of:

(i) $g'(x)$

(ii) $g''(x)$

(iii) $g'''(x)$ where $g'''(x)$ is the third derivative of $g(x)$.

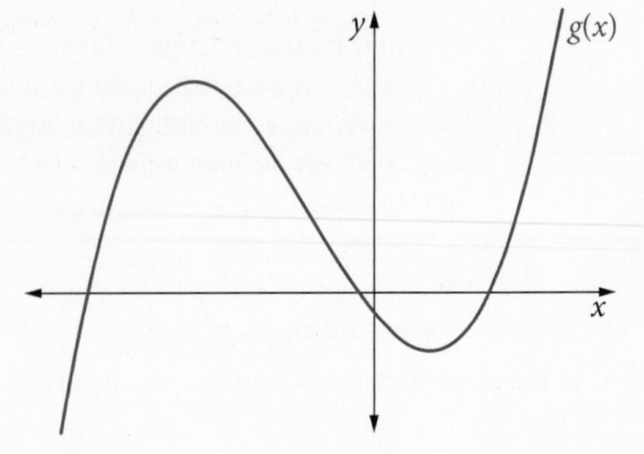

Although the third derivative is not specifically mentioned on the syllabus, it could be examinable in this case, as it only requires finding the derivative of a linear function.

Solution

(i) Since $g(x)$ is a cubic function, its derivative, $g'(x)$ is a quadratic function, so we will be expecting to draw a ∪ or an ∩ shape graph.

Step 1: At the turning points of $g(x)$, $g'(x) = 0$

Therefore, at the turning point of $g(x)$, the graph of its derivative, $g'(x)$, will cross the x-axis. Mark these positions on the x-axis.

Step 2: Between the turning points, the graph of the cubic function is **decreasing**, therefore the graph of $g'(x)$ will be **below** the x-axis between these two points.

Step 3: Outside of the turning points, the graph of the cubic function is **increasing**, therefore the graph of $g'(x)$ will be **above** the x-axis between these two points.

Putting all of this together gives the curve shown in red on the graph.

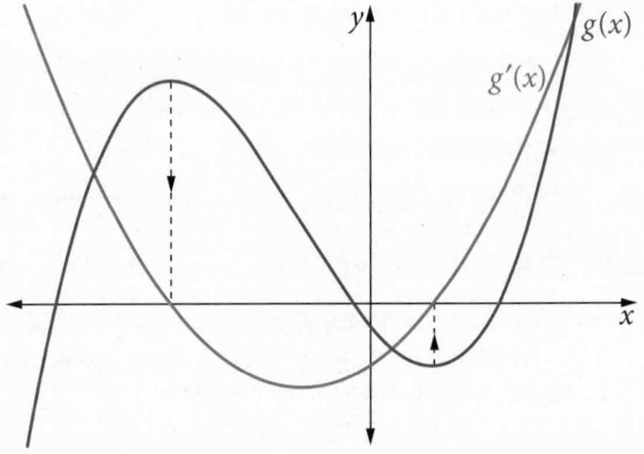

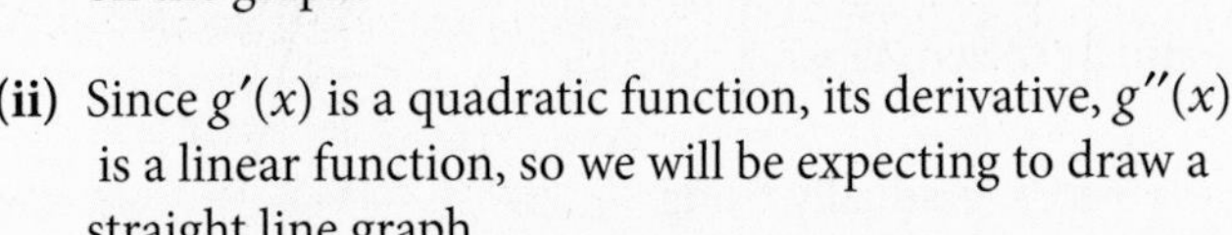

(ii) Since $g'(x)$ is a quadratic function, its derivative, $g''(x)$ is a linear function, so we will be expecting to draw a straight line graph.

Step 1: At the turning points of $g'(x)$, $g''(x) = 0$.

Therefore, at the turning point of $g'(x)$, the graph of its derivative, $g''(x)$, will cross the x-axis. Mark this position on the x-axis.

Step 2: To the left of the turning point, the graph of the quadratic function, $g'(x)$, is **decreasing**, therefore the graph of $g''(x)$ will be **below** the x-axis.

Step 3: To the right of the turning point, the graph of the quadratic function, $g'(x)$, is **increasing**, therefore the graph of $g''(x)$ will be **above** the x-axis.

Putting all of this together gives the line shown in green on the graph.

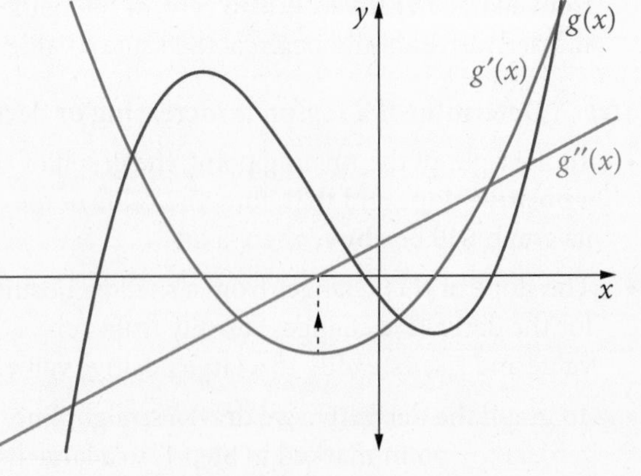

Differential Calculus I

(iii) Since $g''(x)$ is a linear function, its derivative, $g'''(x)$ is a constant, so we will be expecting to draw a horizontal graph.

Step 1: The graph of $g''(x)$ is a straight line with a positive slope and therefore it does not have any turning points.

Step 2: $g''(x)$ is **increasing** at a constant rate for all values of x, therefore its derivative will be a constant **positive** value (**above** the x-axis).

Hence, any horizontal line above the x-axis could represent $g'''(x)$. One possible answer is shown in orange on the graph.

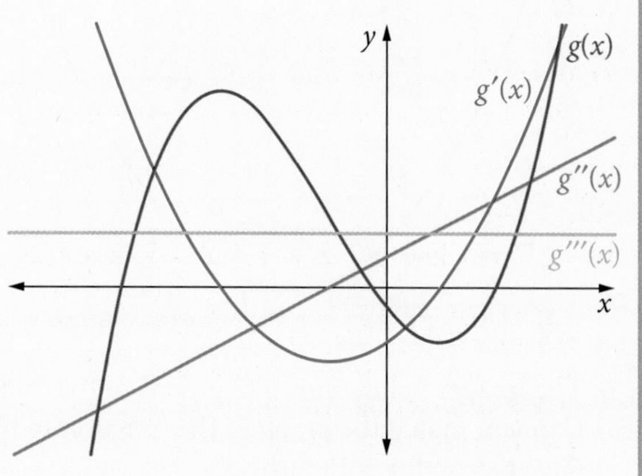

Practice Questions 26.4

1. The diagram shows the graph of a quadratic function, $f(x)$. Determine which of the graphs shown below illustrates $f'(x)$, the first derivative of $f(x)$. Give a reason for your answer.

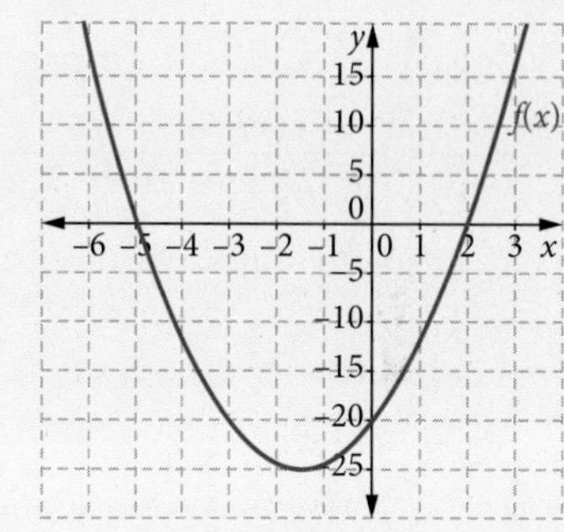

(a)
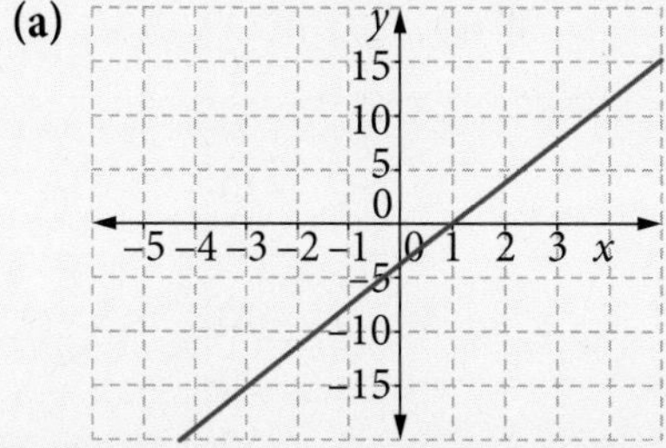

(b)
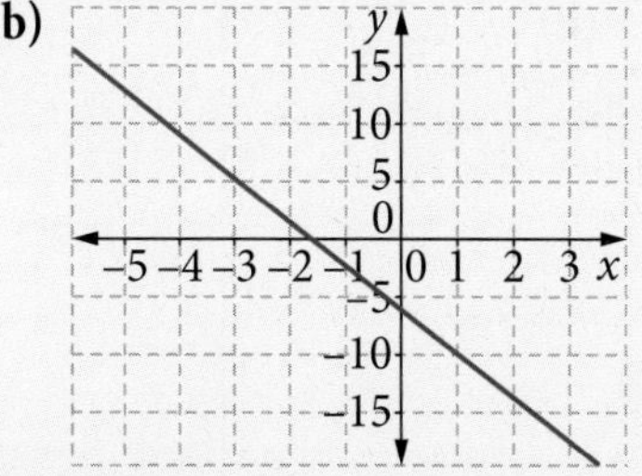

(c)
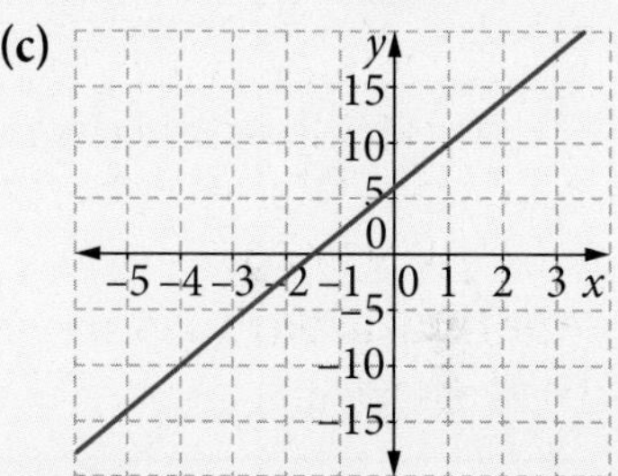

2. The diagram shows the graph of a cubic function, $f(x)$. Determine which of the graphs, **(a)**, **(b)**, **(c)** or **(d)**, shown below illustrates $f'(x)$, the first derivative of $f(x)$. Give a reason for your answer.

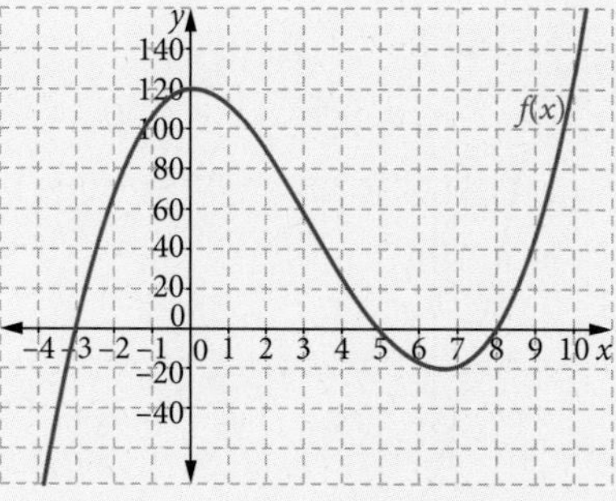

(a)
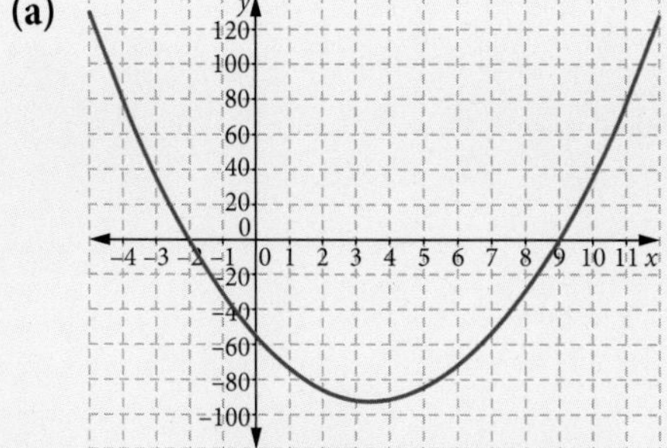

(b)
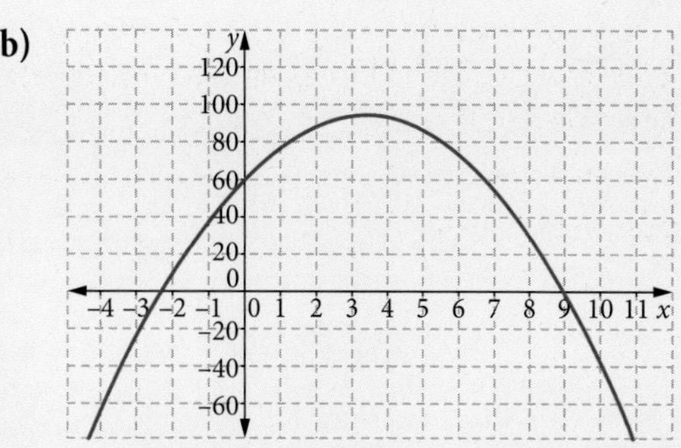

(c)

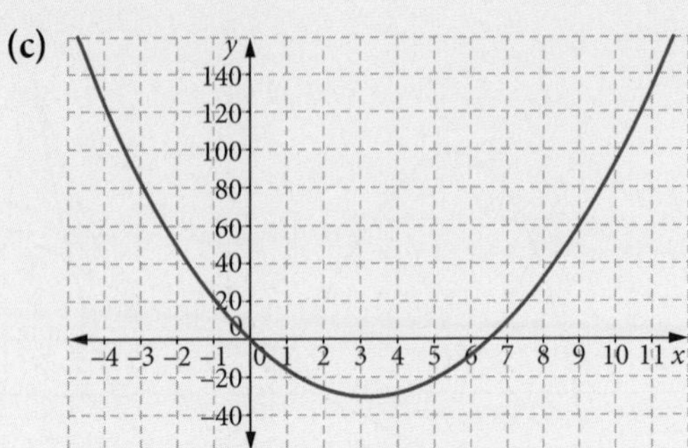

(d)

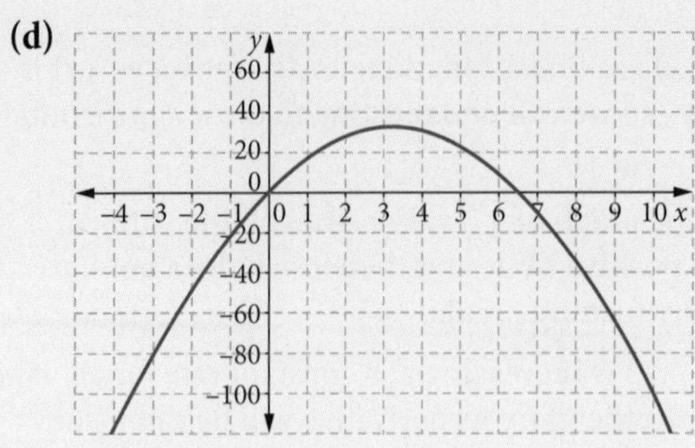

3. The images below show the graphs of five functions and their first derivatives and their second derivatives. Can you match the graph of the function to the graph of its first and second derivatives? Give reason for your answer.

Function	First derivative	Second derivative

A

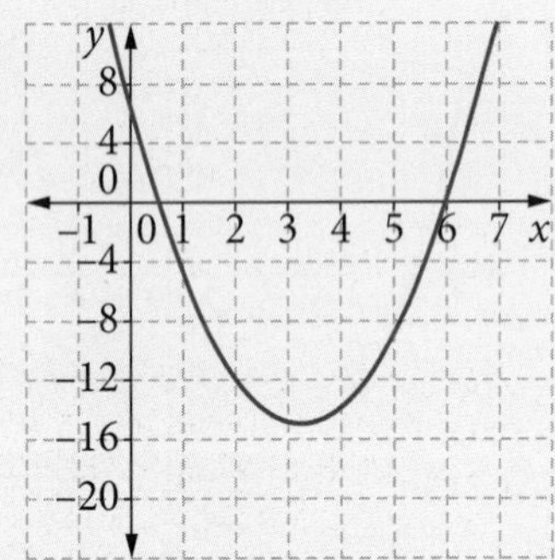

(i)

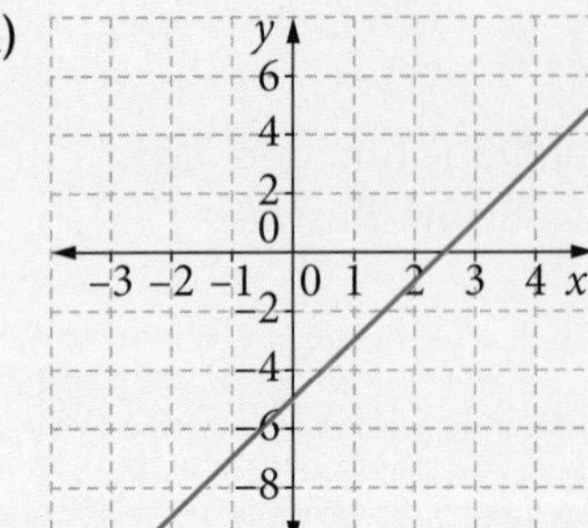

V

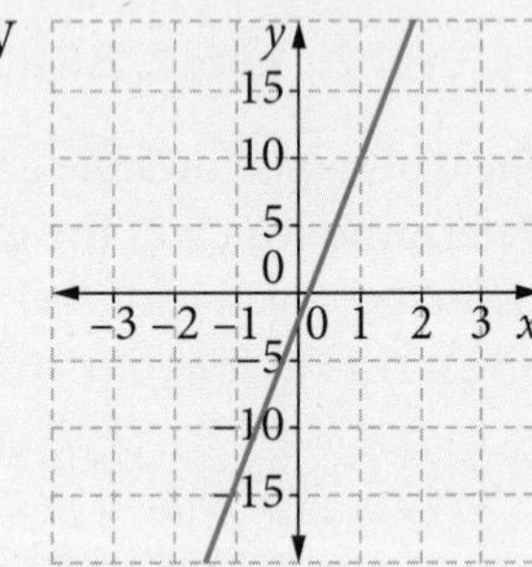

B

(ii)

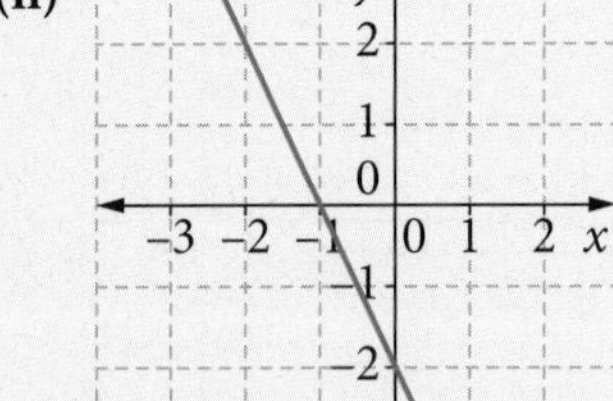

W

C

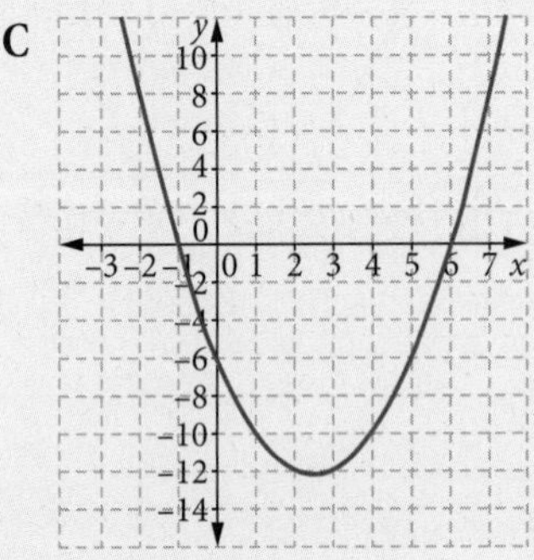

(iii)

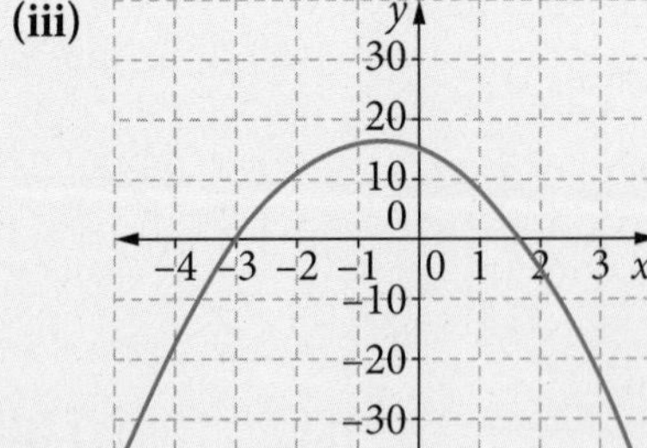

X

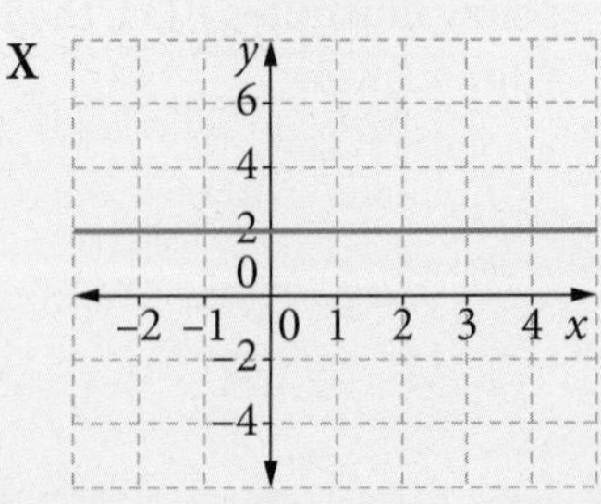

D

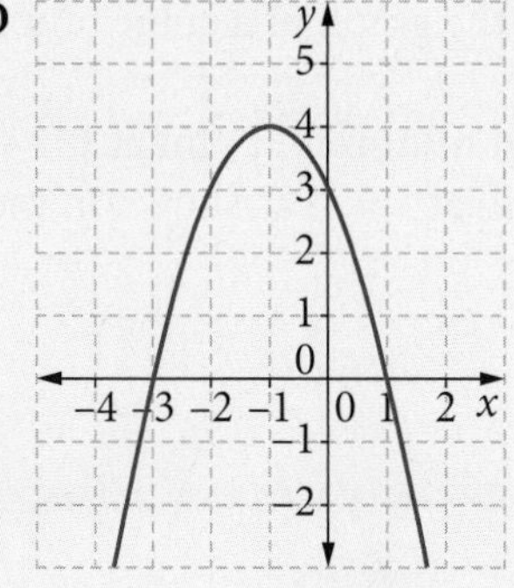

(iv)

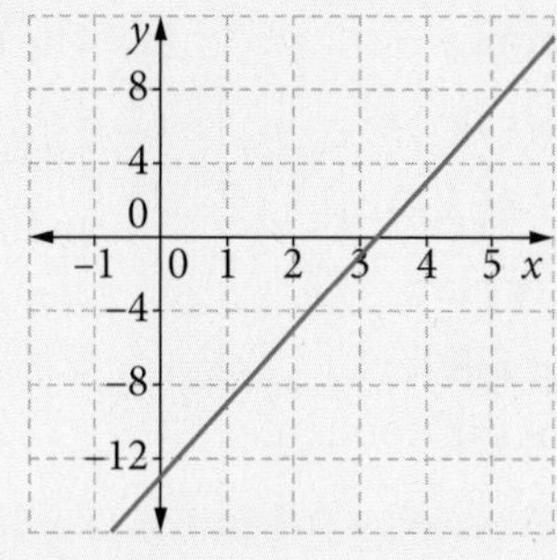

Y

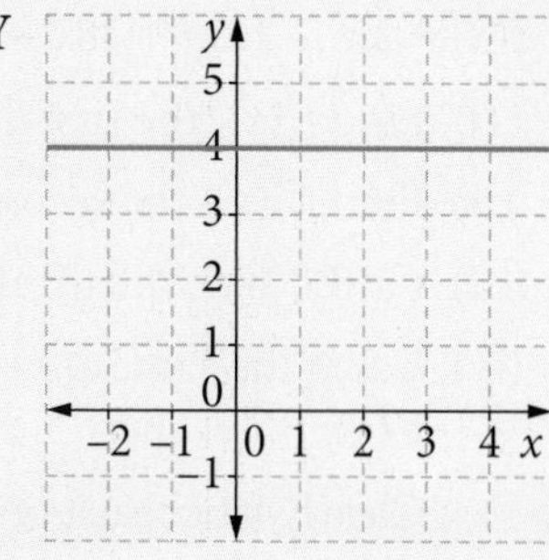

E

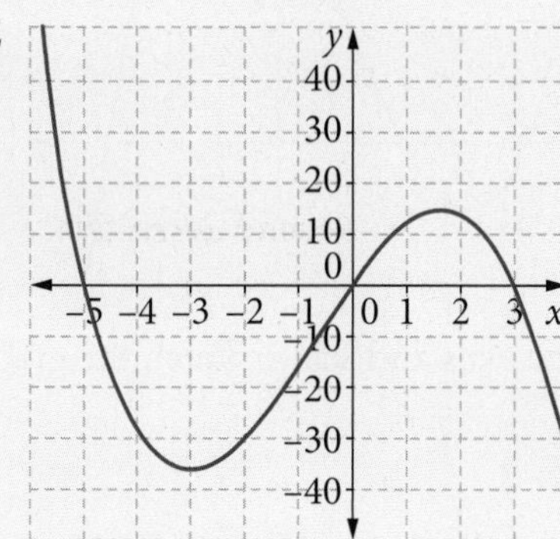

(v)

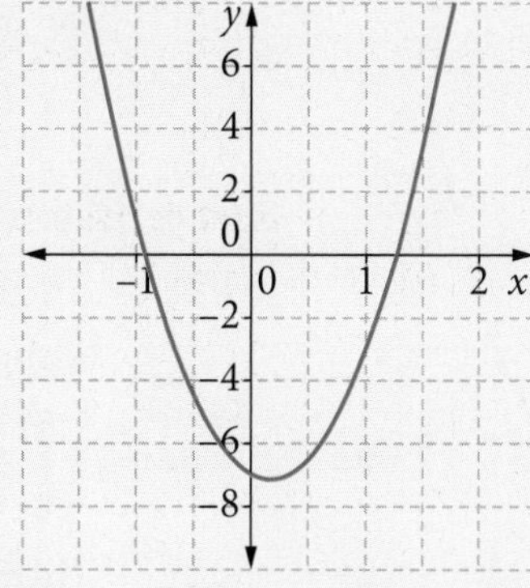

Z

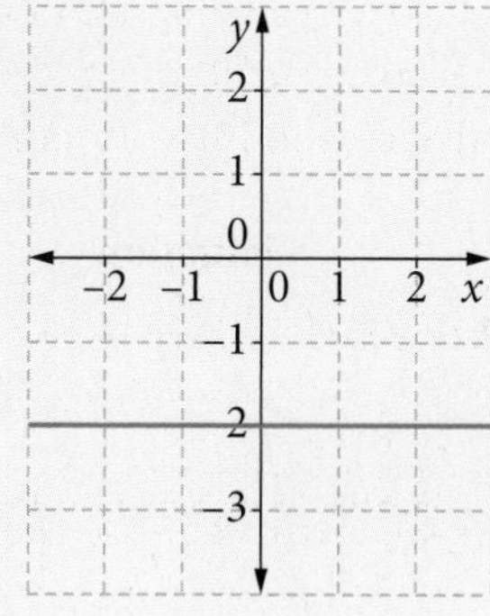

4. The diagrams show the graphs of two linear functions, $f(x)$.
Copy the sketch of each graph into your copy book. On the same axis and scales sketch the graph of $f'(x)$, the first derivative of $f(x)$.

(i)

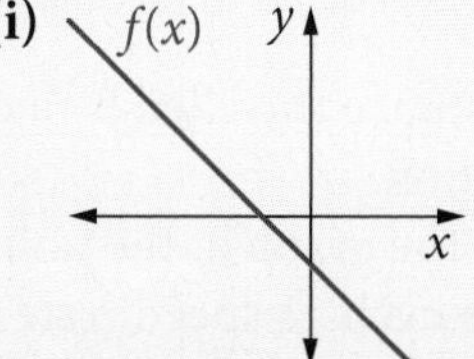

(ii)

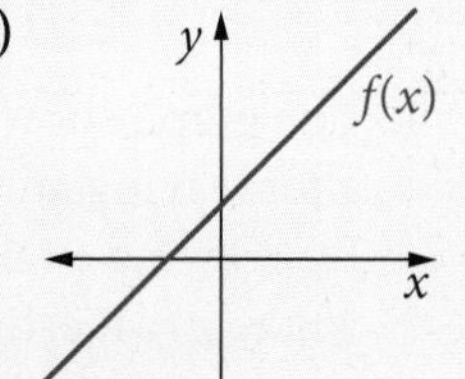

5. (i) Graph each of the following functions in the given domain.
   (a) $f(x) = 3x - 2$ in the domain $-1 \leq x \leq 3$.
   (b) $g(x) = -2x + 4$ in the domain $-1 \leq x \leq 4$.
   (c) $h(x) = \frac{1}{2}x + 1$ in the domain $-2 \leq x \leq 4$.
   (ii) Using the same axes and scale, graph the first derivative of each function.

6. The diagrams show the graph of a quadratic function, $g(x)$.

(i)

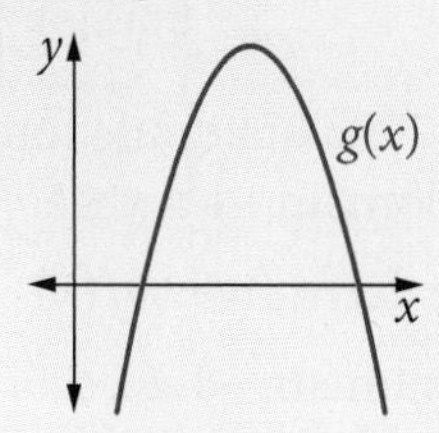

(ii)

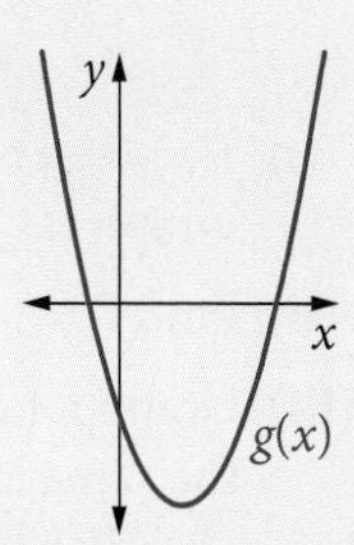

Copy the sketch of each graph into your copy book.
Using the same axes and scale, sketch the graph of:
   (a) $g'(x)$, the first derivative of $g(x)$
   (b) $g''(x)$, the second derivative of $g(x)$

7. Give three reasons why the given line represents the derivative of the given curve.

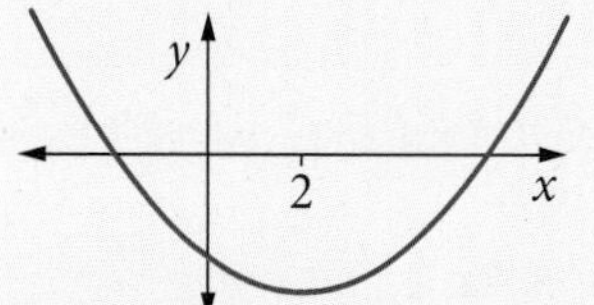

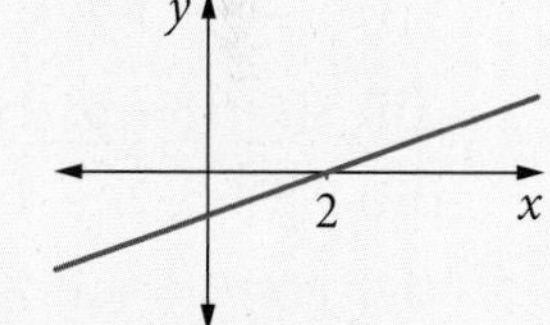

8. (i) Graph each of the following functions in the given domain.
   (a) $f(x) = 2x^2 - 8$ in the domain $-3 \leq x \leq 3$.
   (b) $g(x) = x^2 - 7x + 10$ in the domain $0 \leq x \leq 7$.
   (c) $h(x) = -3x^2 + 21x - 24$ in the domain $1 \leq x \leq 6$.
   (ii) Using the same axes and scale, graph the first derivative of each function.
   (iii) Using the same axes and scale, graph the second derivative of each function.

9. $f(x) = 2x^3 - 12x^2 + 18x - 5$ is a function.
   (i) Find $f'(x)$, the first derivative of $f(x)$.
   (ii) Find $f''(x)$, the second derivative of $f(x)$.
   (iii) Find $f'''(x)$, the third derivative of $f(x)$.
   (iv) Using the same axes and scale, graph $f(x)$, $f'(x)$, $f''(x)$ and $f'''(x)$ $0 \le x \le 4$ in the domain. Clearly label each graph.

10. The diagram shows the graph of a cubic function, $f(x)$.

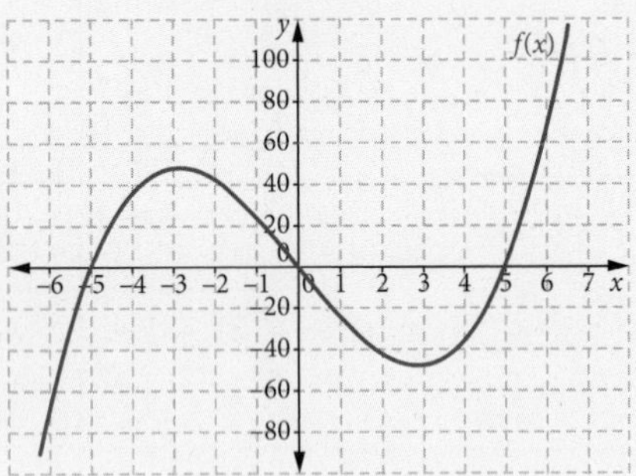

Using the same axes and scale, sketch the graph of
(i) $f'(x)$ **(ii)** $f''(x)$ **(iii)** $f'''(x)$

11. The diagram shows the graph of a cubic function, $g(x)$.
The curve has a local minimum point at $x = -4$ and a local maximum at $x = 1$, as shown in the diagram.

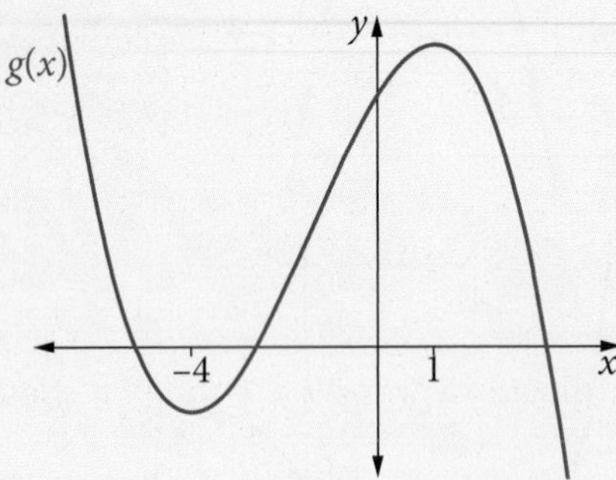

Using the same axes and scale, sketch the graph of
(i) $g'(x)$
(ii) $g''(x)$
(iii) $g'''(x)$

Revision and Exam Style Questions – Section A

1. Differentiate each of the following:
   (i) $y = 7x^2 + 2x - 5$
   (ii) $s(t) = 8 + 6t - t^2$
   (iii) $f(x) = -2x - 4x^3 + 12$
   (iv) $g(x) = 6 + x^3 - x^2 + 8x$

2. Which is greater, the derivative at the point A or the derivative at the point B?
Give a reason for your answer.

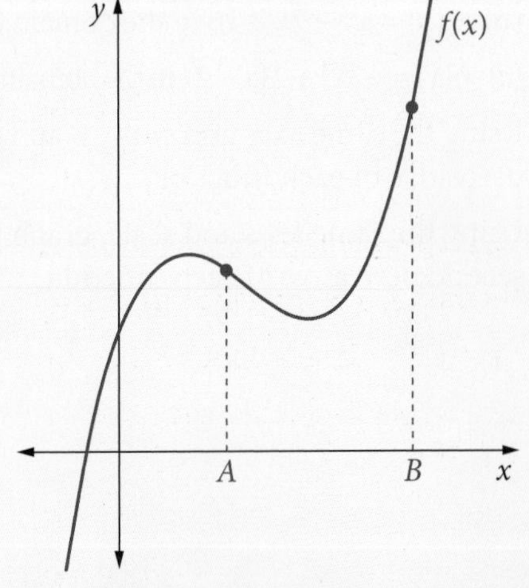

3. The graph shows the distance travelled by a cyclist after leaving an intersection.
By drawing a tangent to the graph at the point where $t = 4$, estimate the cyclist's speed (rate of change of distance, with respect to time) after 4 seconds.

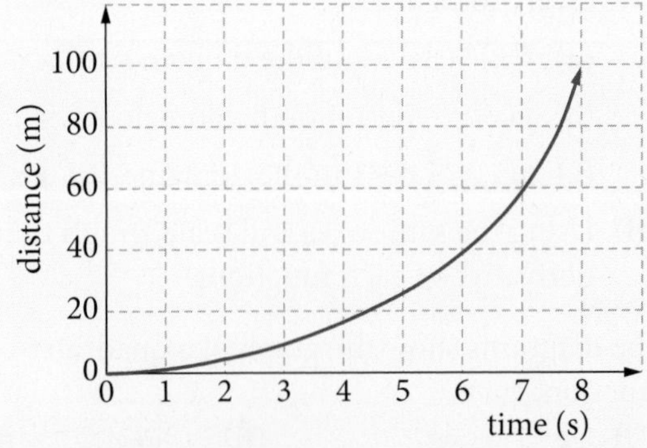

4. **(i)** $f(x) = 3x^2 - 12x - 7$ is a quadratic function. Graph $f(x)$ in the domain $-1 \le x \le 5$.
   (ii) Find $f'(x)$, the first derivative of $f(x)$.
   (iii) Graph $f'(x)$ in the domain $-1 \le x \le 5$, using the same axes and scale as part **(i)**. Clearly label each graph.

(iv) Study the two graphs and answer the following questions: Can you see a connection between them?

(a) What shape is the graph of $f(x)$?

(b) What shape is the graph of $f'(x)$?

(c) When the $f(x)$ function has a turning point, where is the $f'(x)$ graph? Explain why this is the case.

(d) When the $f(x)$ graph is decreasing, where is the $f'(x)$ graph? Explain why this is the case.

5. The diagrams show the graph of a quadratic function, $f(x)$.

(a)

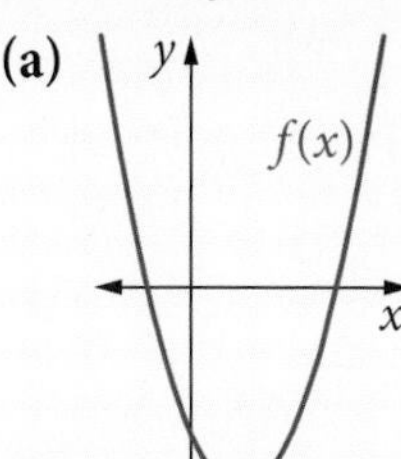

(b)

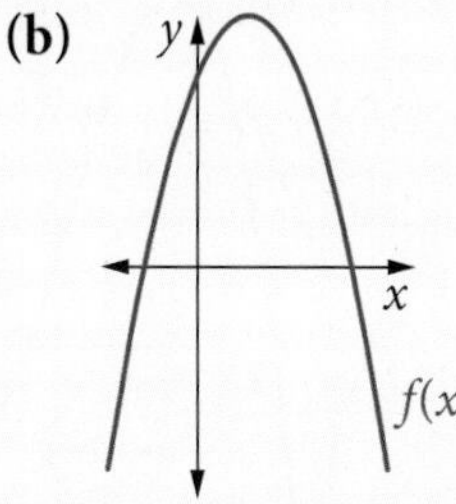

Copy the sketch of each graph into your copy book.
Using the same axes and scale sketch the graph of:

(i) $f'(x)$, the first derivative of $f(x)$

(ii) $f''(x)$, the second derivative of $f(x)$.

6. The diagram shows part of the graph of $y = x^3 - 3x - 1$.
A is a local maximum and B is a local minimum.

(i) Find the coordinates of A and B.

(ii) Hence, find the range of values of x for which $\frac{dy}{dx} < 0$.

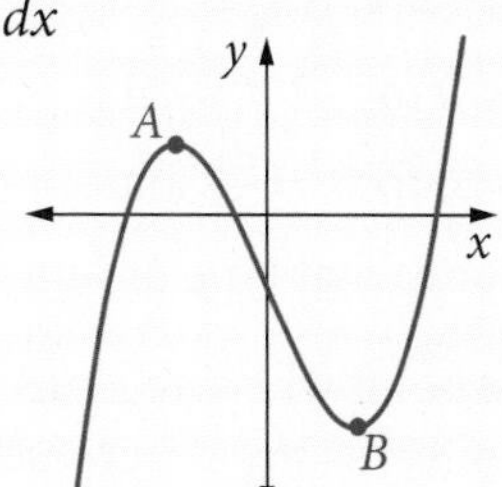

7. Oil is leaking from a tank. The volume of oil remaining in the tank over time is given in the graph shown. Use the graph to answer the following questions.

(i) How much oil was in the tank at the start?

(ii) How much oil was remaining in the tank after two hours?

(iii) Estimate the rate at which the tank was losing oil at one hour.

(iv) Estimate the rate at which the tank was losing oil at two hours.

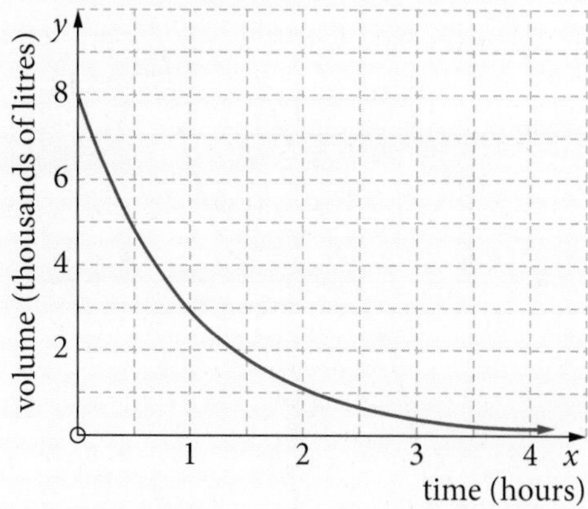

8. The tangent to $y = px^3 - 3x + 5$ at the point where $x = 2$ has a slope of 21. Find the value of p.

9. $y = 8x^3 - 2x^2 + 5x - 2$. Find the value of $\frac{d^2y}{dx^2}$ when $x = 4$.

10. **(i)** Graph the function $f(x) = 2x^3 - x^2 - 18x + 9$ in the domain $-3 \leq x \leq 3$.

(ii) Use your graph to estimate the rate of change of $g(x)$ at the points:

(a) $(-2, 25)$ **(b)** $(1, -8)$ **(c)** $(2, -15)$

(iii) Verify your answers to part **(ii)** by evaluating the following:

(a) $f'(-2)$ **(b)** $f'(1)$ **(c)** $f'(2)$

11. The diagram shows part of the graph of a function $h(x)$.

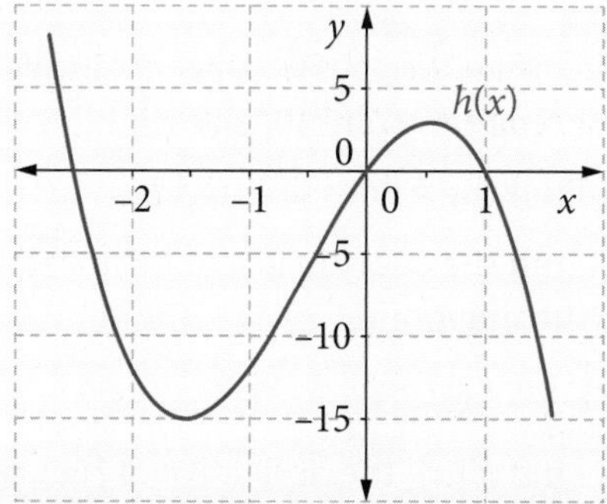

Use the graph to estimate:

(i) the values of x for which $h(x) = 0$

(ii) the values of x for which $h'(x) = 0$

(iii) the range of values of x for which $h'(x) > 0$.

Revision and Exam Style Questions – Section B

More challenging problems

1. The graph of $f(x) = x^3$ is shown. A tangent to the graph is drawn at the point $(-1, -1)$

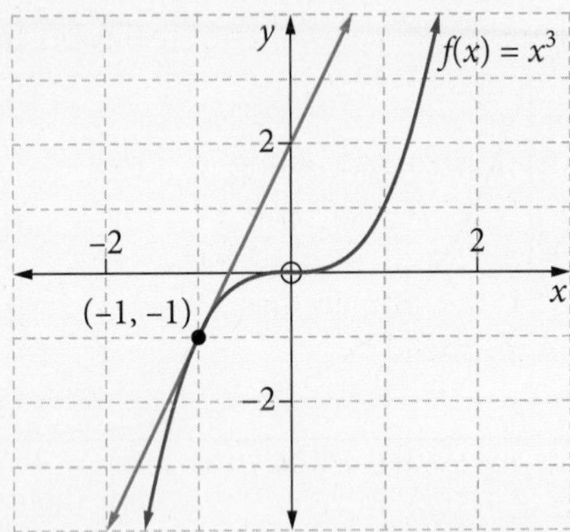

(i) Use the graph to find the slope of the tangent.

(ii) Check your answer by finding $f'(-1)$.

2. The function $f(x) = ax^2 + bx + c$, where $a, b, c \in \mathbb{Z}$ is shown.
The graph cuts the x-axis at the points $(-1, 0)$ and $(6, 0)$ and the y-axis at $(0, 24)$.

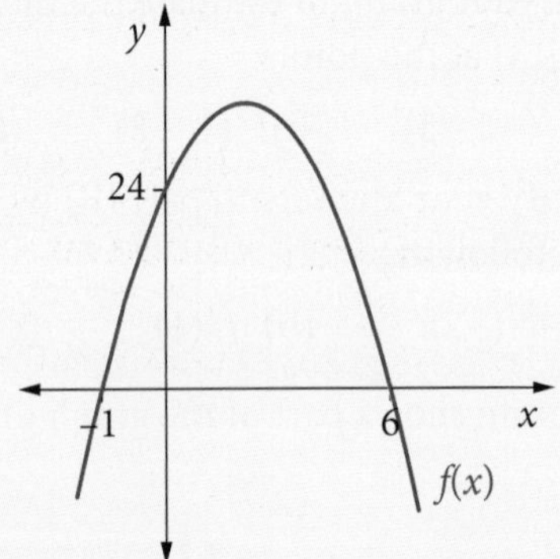

(i) Using the point $(0, 24)$, find the value of c.

(ii) Find the values of a and b.

(iii) Find the coordinates of the local maximum turning point.

3. $f(x) = 3 - 5x - 2x^2, x \in \mathbb{R}$.

(i) Find $f'(x)$, the derivative of $f(x)$, and hence find the coordinates of the local maximum point of the curve $y = f(x)$.

(ii) Find the point where $f(x)$ crosses the y-axis.

(iii) Solve the equation $f(x) = 0$.

(iv) For what range of values of x is $f'(x) > 0$.

4. Let $s(t) = t(1 - t^2)$, where $t \in \mathbb{R}$

(i) Verify that $s(-2) + s(2) = 0$.

(ii) Find the values of t for which $s'(t) = -26$.

5. The graph of $f(x) = \frac{1}{3}x^3 + \frac{3}{4}x^2 - \frac{5}{2}x - \frac{1}{4}$ is shown.

The tangents at $A(-3, 5)$ and $B(1, -\frac{5}{3})$ are given.

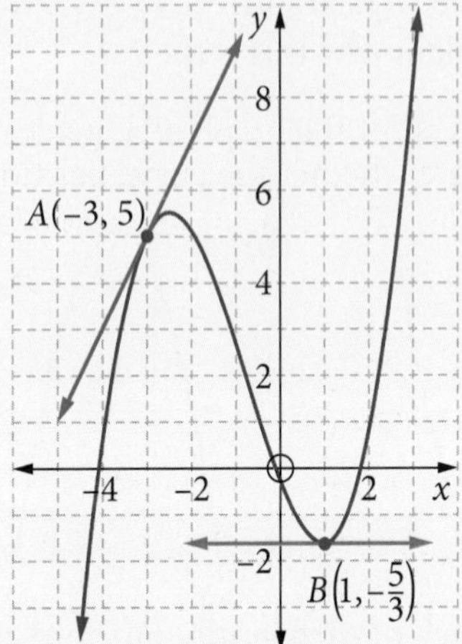

(i) Use the graph to find the slope of the tangents at the points A and B.

(ii) Verify your answers for part **(i)** by finding $f'(-3)$ and $f'(1)$.

6. (i) Use the following six pieces of information to sketch the graph of the function $y = f(x)$

- When $x = -2, f(x) = 11$
- $f'(x) > 0$ for $x < -2$
- $f'(x) > 0$ for $x > 4$
- When $x = 4, f(x) = 2$
- $f'(x) < 0$ for $-2 < x < 4$
- $f'(x) = 0$ for $x = -2$ and $x = 4$

(ii) Hence state what type of function $g(x)$ is.

7. (i) Find the point where the curve $y = 2x^3 - 3x^2 - 36x + 5$ crosses the y-axis.

(ii) Find the coordinates of the turning points on the curve and determine which is the maximum and which is the minimum.

(iii) Hence, draw a rough sketch of the curve.

(iv) Using the same axes and scale, sketch the graphs of the first and second derivatives of curve.

8. **(i)** Express the function $g(x) = (x - 1)(x - 2)(x + 3)$ in the form $g(x) = ax^3 + bx^2 + cx + d$, where $a, b, c, d \in \mathbb{Z}$.

   (ii) Find the coordinates of the turning points of $g(x)$. Give your answers in decimal form.

   (iii) Hence sketch the graph of the function.

   (iv) Using the same axes and scale, sketch the graph of the first and second derivatives of the function $g(x)$.

9. A curve has equation $y = x^3 + 3x^2 + 4x + 7$.

   (i) Find $\frac{dy}{dx}$.

   (ii) Investigate whether the curve has turning points. If so, find the coordinates of these points and if not, explain why this is the case.

10. Let $h(k) = 14 - 24k - k^3 + 9k^2$ for all $k \in \mathbb{R}$.

   (i) Find $h(1)$ and $h(5)$.

   (ii) Find $h'(k)$, the derivative of $h(k)$.

   (iii) Find the coordinates of the local minimum and local maximum points on the curve $y = h(k)$.

   (iv) Draw the graph of the function h, in the domain $0 \leq k \leq 5$.

   Use your graph to:

   (v) estimate the range of values of k for which $h(k) < 0$ and $k > 0$

   (vi) estimate the range of values of k for which $h'(k) > 0$

   (vii) determine the number of real roots the function $h(k)$ has.

11. The resistance to the flow of electricity in a metal is given by $R(T) = 20 + 0{\cdot}55T - 0{\cdot}01T^2$ Ohms, where T is the temperature in °C of the metal.

   Find:

   (i) the resistance of the wire at 20 °C and 45 °C

   (ii) the temperature for which the resistance of the wire is zero

   (iii) the rate of change of the resistance when the wire is at 30 °C

   (iv) the maximum resistance experienced by the wire and the temperature for which this occurs.

   And determine:

   (v) for what values of T does the resistance of the wire increase?

Now that you have completed the chapter, revisit the 'Something to think about…' questions.

Chapter 27 Differential Calculus II – Applications

(18 – x)

Sections covered within this chapter:

KEY WORDS

- Displacement
- Velocity
- Acceleration

SOMETHING TO THINK ABOUT... 

A sports club plans to mark out a running track on one of their pitches. The running track consists of a rectangle with a semi-circle at each end, as shown in the diagram.

The perimeter of the track must be 400 m.

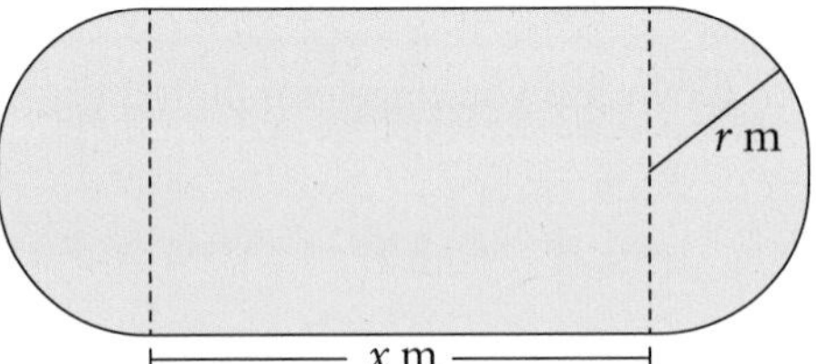

It is intended to use the inside of the rectangular part of the track for holding athletics events. Therefore, the designers want to make the rectangular part as large as possible.

Answer the following questions. Give your answers in terms of π, where appropriate.

(i) Find x in terms of r.

(ii) Hence, find the area of the rectangular part, in terms of r.

(iii) Find the dimensions of the track (x and r) which will maximise the area of the rectangle.

Section 27.1: Equation of a Tangent to a Curve

Learning Outcome:

You should be able to:

- find the equation of a tangent to a curve, at a given point along the curve

We have already seen that the rate of change of a curve, at a particular point, is equal to the slope of the tangent to the curve at that point.

Therefore, the first derivative of a function equals the slope of the tangent to the function at any point.

In short: $f'(x) = \frac{dy}{dx} = \text{slope of the tangent}$

 **Links across the syllabus**

This section is heavily linked with Chapter 14: Coordinate Geometry I. Many of the skills from that chapter are needed in answering questions in this section.

Finding the equation of the tangent to a curve, at a given value for x

Step 1: Find the derivative of the function – this gives an expression for the slope of the tangent, in terms of x.

Step 2: Substitute the given x-value into the derivative to find the value of the slope of the tangent at that point.

Step 3: Find the y-coordinate of the point (if not given) by substituting the x-value into the **original function**.

Step 4: Use the point and the slope to find the equation of the tangent, using the coordinate geometry formula $y - y_1 = m(x - x_1)$.

Some questions may require the slope of the tangent only. In this case, we would stop after step 2.

EXAMPLE

The diagram shows the graph of the function $f(x) = x^2 + 3x - 18$.
Find the equation of the tangent to the function $f(x)$, at the point where $x = 1$.

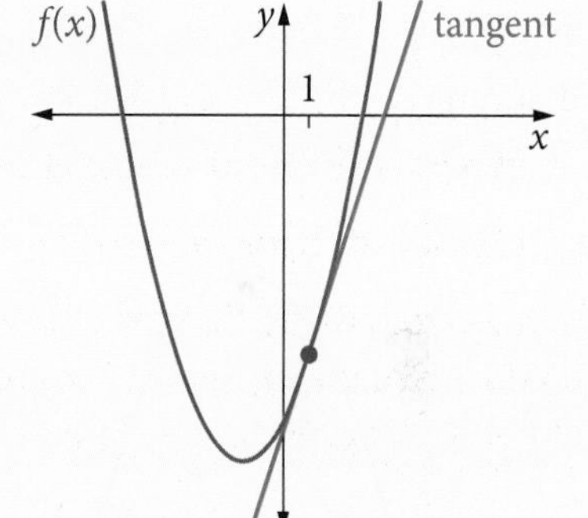

Solution

Step 1: Find $f'(x)$

$$f(x) = x^2 + 3x - 18$$
$$f'(x) = 2x + 3$$

Therefore, the slope of the tangent at any point $= 2x + 3$

Step 2: Find the value of the slope at $x = 1$: $f'(x) = \text{slope} = 2x + 3$

$$\text{slope} = 2(1) + 3$$
$$\text{slope} = 2 + 3$$
$$\text{slope} = 5$$

Step 3: Find the y coordinate by substituting $x = 1$: $f(x) = x^2 + 3x - 18$

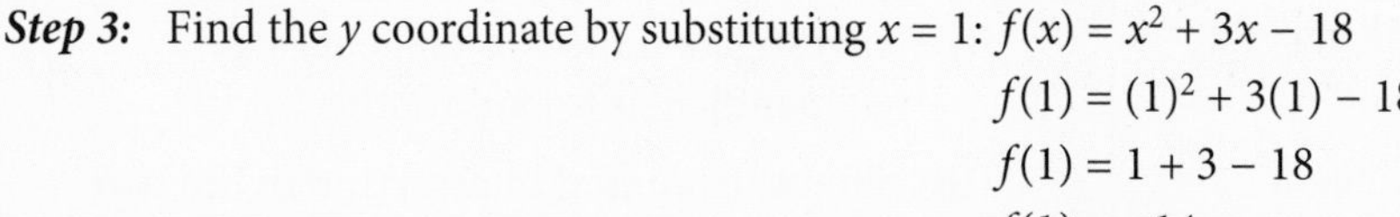

$$f(1) = (1)^2 + 3(1) - 18$$
$$f(1) = 1 + 3 - 18$$
$$f(1) = -14$$

Therefore, the point of tangency is $(1, -14)$

Step 4: Find the equation of the line, which passes through the point $(1, -14)$ and has a slope of 5:

$$y - y_1 = m(x - x_1)$$
$$y - (-14) = 5(x - 1)$$
$$y + 14 = 5x - 5$$
$$0 = 5x - y - 5 - 14$$
$$5x - y - 19 = 0$$

Differential Calculus II

Practice Questions 27.1

1. The curve $y = 3x^2 - 5x - 11$ is shown in the diagram.

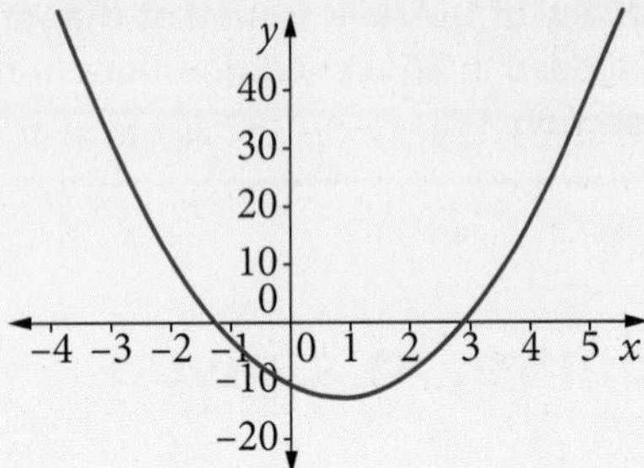

(i) Find $\frac{dy}{dx}$.

(ii) Hence, find the slope of the tangent to the curve at the point where $x = 2$.

2. (i) If $y = x^3 + x^2 - 12x$, find $\frac{dy}{dx}$

Hence, find the slope of the tangent to the curve at the point where:

(ii) $x = 1$

(iii) $x = -3$

3. The curve $y = -x^2 + 5x - 7$ is shown in the diagram.

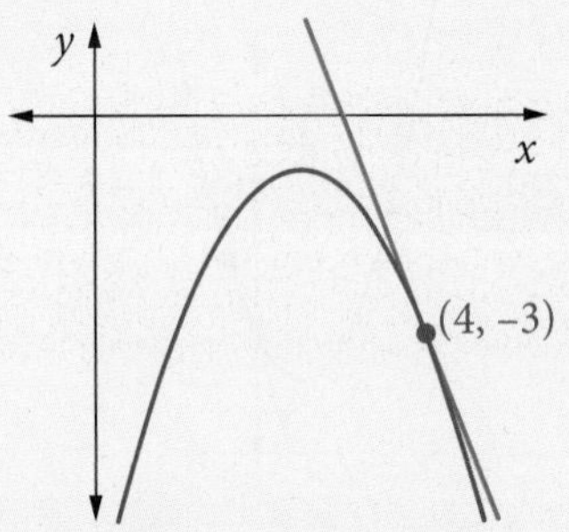

(i) Find $\frac{dy}{dx}$

(ii) Find the slope of the tangent to the curve at the point $(4, -3)$.

(iii) Hence, find the equation of this tangent.

4. (i) If $f(x) = 3x^2 + 5x + 4$, find $f'(x)$.

(ii) Hence, find the equation of the tangent to the curve at the point $(-1, 2)$.

(iii) Find the coordinates of the points where this tangent intercepts the x and y axes.

5. Find the equation of the tangent to the curve $f(x) = 5x^2 - 3x - 7$, at the point $(2, 7)$.

6. Find the equation of the tangent to the curve $g(x) = 2x^3 + x^2 - 23x + 20$, at the point $(2, -6)$.

7. Find the equation of the tangent to the curve $f(x) = -2x^2 + 7x - 5$, at the point where $x = 1$.

8. The graph of $f(x) = 5x^2 - 2x + 1$ is shown in the diagram.

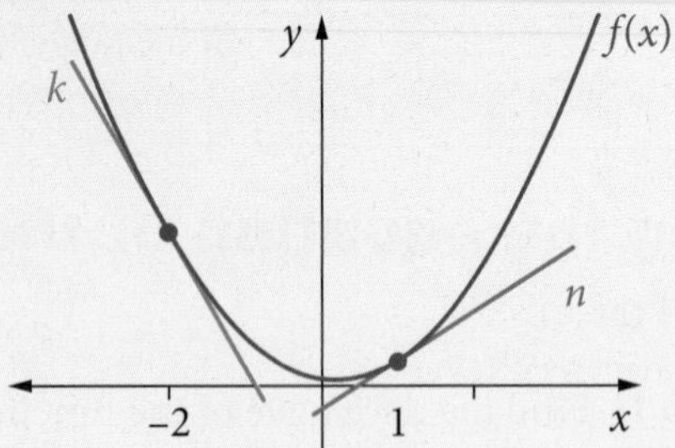

(i) Find $f'(x)$.

(ii) Find the equation of the tangent, n, to the curve at the point where $x = 1$.

(iii) Find the equation of the tangent, k, to the curve at the point where $x = -2$.

9. The diagram shows two tangents to the curve $h(x) = x^2 - 4x + 2$ at the points $(1, -1)$ and $(3, -1)$.

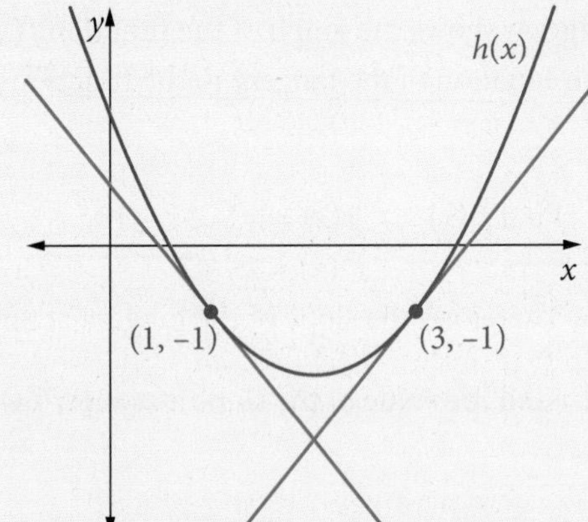

(i) Find the equations of these tangents.

(ii) Investigate if the two tangents are perpendicular to one another.

(iii) Find the point of intersection of the two tangents.

10. (i) If $f(x) = -3x^2 + 5x + 12$, find $f'(x)$.

Hence,

(ii) find the equation of the tangent, t, to the curve, at the point $(1, 14)$

(iii) find the equation of the tangent, s, to the curve, at the point $(-1, 4)$

(iv) find the point of intersection of the tangents s and t

(v) sketch the function $f(x)$ and its tangents, t and s.

11. **(i)** If $f(x) = x^2 - 5x + 8$, find $f'(x)$.
    (ii) Find the coordinates of the point, for which the slope of the tangent is zero.

12. **(i)** If $g(x) = 3x^2 + 12x - 7$, find $g'(x)$.
    (ii) Find the coordinates of the point, for which the tangent is parallel to the x-axis (i.e. its slope is zero).

13. Find the point on the curve $y = 6x^2 - 8x + 1$, where its tangent is parallel to the line $4x - y - 7 = 0$.

14. The diagram shows a sketch of the curve $y = x^3 - 3x - 1$.
    The tangents at the points A and B are parallel to the x-axis.
    Find the coordinates of the points A and B.

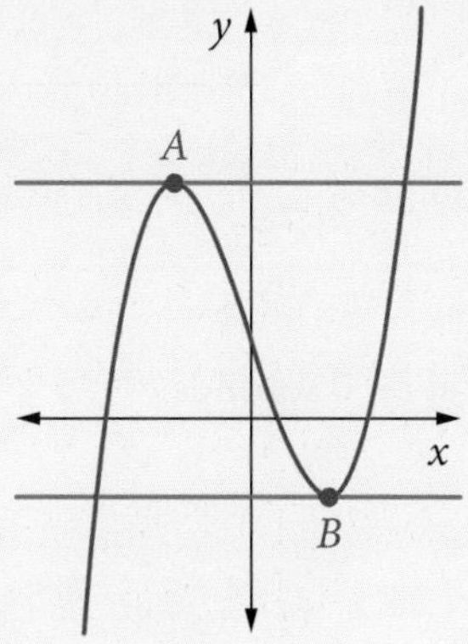

15. $h(x) = x^3 - 21x + 20$ is a function.
    (i) Find an expression for the slope of the tangent to the curve at any point x.
    (ii) Find the two values of x for which the slope of the tangent to the curve is 27.
    (iii) Hence, find the coordinates of the two points where the slope of the tangent to the curve is 27.

16. Find two points on the curve $h(x) = x^3 - 12x^2 + 39x - 28$, where the slope of the tangent is 3.

Section 27.2: Rates of Change in Context

Learning Outcomes:

You should be able to:

- find the rate of change of a quantity
- use rates of change to solve questions in context

There are many quantities in the real world that vary as another quantity varies.

For example: The height of a tree increases as time increases.

The number of bacteria in a sample changes as time increases.

The pressure on a gas increases as the volume of the gas decreases.

If we have a relationship between two quantities, A and B, we can find how one quantity changes as the other changes. This is called the rate of change of quantity A, with respect to quantity B.

As covered in the previous chapter:

> The rate of change of a quantity A, with respect to quantity B, is written as $\frac{dA}{dB}$

In a lot of cases, we will be looking for how one quantity changes as time goes on. When this is the case, quantity B will be time, t.

A special case – displacement, speed and acceleration

Displacement (s) is the distance travelled by an object, away from a certain point. Displacement or distance is often given as a function of time, $s(t)$.

The **velocity** (speed in a given direction) of the body is the rate of change of its distance, with respect to time.

velocity (or speed) $= s'(t) = \frac{ds}{dt}$.

The **acceleration** of the body is the rate of change of its velocity, with respect to time.

acceleration $= \frac{dv}{dt} = \frac{d^2s}{dt^2}$

Therefore,

Velocity or speed = first derivative.
Acceleration = second derivative.

EXAMPLE 1

A snooker ball rolls across a snooker table. It starts to move at $t = 0$ seconds. The distance, s, that it has travelled at t seconds is given by

$$s = 14t - t^2$$

where s is in centimetres.

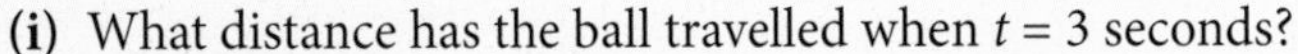

(i) What distance has the ball travelled when $t = 3$ seconds?

(ii) What is the speed of the ball at $t = 5$ seconds?

(iii) At what time is the velocity of the ball equal to zero?

(iv) What is the acceleration of the ball?

It is helpful to write down what information you have and what information you need.

Solution

(i) Find s when $t = 3$ seconds:

$s = 14t - t^2$

$s = 14(3) - (3)^2$

$s = 42 - 9$

$s = 33$

Therefore, the ball has travelled 33 cm after 3 seconds.

(ii) Velocity = speed $= \frac{ds}{dt}$:

$s = 14t - t^2$

First derivative: $\frac{ds}{dt} = 14 - 2t =$ speed

When $t = 5$ seconds:

speed $= 14 - 2(5)$

speed $= 14 - 10$

speed $= 4$ cm/s

(iii) Find t when velocity = 0 cm/s:

velocity $= 14 - 2t$

$0 = 14 - 2t$

$2t = 14$

$t = 7$ seconds

Therefore, the velocity of the ball is zero after 7 seconds.

(iv) Acceleration $= \frac{d(\text{velocity})}{dt}$:

velocity $= 14 - 2t$

Second derivative:

$\frac{d(\text{velocity})}{dt} = -2$

Therefore, the acceleration of the ball is -2 cm/s^2.

A negative acceleration means that the body is slowing down (decelerating).

EXAMPLE 2

Peter is blowing up a spherical balloon.

(i) Find a formula for $\frac{dV}{dr}$, the rate of change of the volume of the balloon, V, with respect to its radius, r.

(ii) Find $\frac{dV}{dr}$, when $r = 5$ cm. Give your answer, in terms of π.

(iii) For what volume does $\frac{dV}{dr} = 225\pi$ cm^3/cm?

Solution

(i) Volume of a sphere $= \frac{4}{3}\pi r^3$

$$\frac{dV}{dr} = 3\left(\frac{4}{3}\pi r^2\right)$$

$$\frac{dV}{dr} = 4\pi r^2 \text{ cm}^3/\text{cm}$$

(ii) Find $\frac{dV}{dr}$ when $r = 5$:

$$\frac{dV}{dr} = 4\pi(5)^2$$

$$\frac{dV}{dr} = 4\pi(25)$$

$$\frac{dV}{dr} = 100\pi \text{ cm}^3/\text{cm}$$

Links across the syllabus

Volume of a sphere is covered in Chapter 17: Volume and Surface Area.

(iii) Find volume when $\frac{dV}{dr} = 225\pi$ cm^3/cm

Step 1: Find r:

$$\frac{dV}{dr} = 4\pi r^2$$

$$225\pi = 4\pi r^2$$

$$56{\cdot}25 = r^2$$

$$\sqrt{56{\cdot}25} = r$$

$$7{\cdot}5 \text{ cm} = r$$

Step 2: Find volume when $r = 7{\cdot}5$ cm:

Now find the volume when $r = 7{\cdot}5$:

$$\text{Volume of a sphere} = \frac{4}{3}\pi r^3$$

$$\text{Volume of sphere} = \frac{4}{3}\pi(7{\cdot}5)^3$$

$$\text{Volume of a sphere} = \frac{4}{3}\pi(421{\cdot}875)$$

$$\text{Volume of a sphere} = 562{\cdot}5\pi \text{ cm}^3.$$

Motion of an object, under gravity

For an object thrown up into the air:

$\frac{dH}{dt}$ is the change in the height, with respect to time.

As its height is increasing, it is moving **upwards** and has a **positive velocity** and **positive slope**.

$$\text{velocity} = \frac{dH}{dt} > 0$$

When it reaches its maximum height, it will stop *very* briefly, before starting to fall down again.

And so, the **maximum height** reached is at the point where the **velocity of the body is zero** and so the **slope is zero**.

$$\text{velocity} = \frac{dH}{dt} = 0$$

As its height is decreasing, it is moving **downwards** and has a **negative velocity** and **negative slope**.

$$\text{velocity} = \frac{dH}{dt} < 0$$

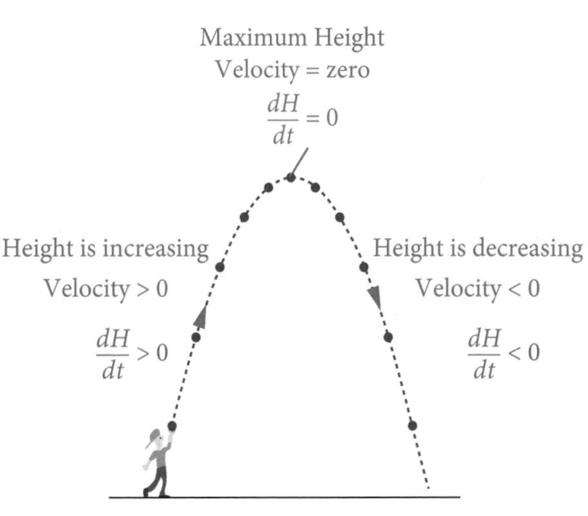

EXAMPLE 3

A firework is fired vertically upwards from the top of a building. The height, h metres, of the firework above the ground is given by $h(t) = 22 + 55t - 5t^2$

where t is the time in seconds, from the instant the firework is fired.

The firework is designed to explode 3 seconds after firing.

(i) Find the height above the ground at which the firework explodes.

(ii) Find the velocity of the firework, at the instant it explodes.

A fault occurs and the firework doesn't explode until 10 seconds after firing.

(iii) Find the height and the velocity of the firework, at this time.
Comment on what your answers tell you about the motion of the firework, at this time.

(iv) If the firework fails to explode, find the maximum height it reaches.

Solution

(i) The firework explodes after 3 seconds, so find h when $t = 3$:

$h(t) = 22 + 55t - 5t^2$

$h(3) = 22 + 55(3) - 5(3)^2$

$h(3) = 22 + 165 - 5(9)$

$h(3) = 22 + 165 - 45$

$h(3) = 142$

Therefore, the firework is at a height of 142 m, above the ground, when it explodes.

(ii) Velocity $= h'(t)$ (first derivative)

$h(t) = 22 + 55t - 5t^2$

$h'(t) = 0 + 55 - 10t$

$h'(t) = 55 - 10t$

Therefore, velocity $= (55 - 10t)$ m/s

When $t = 3$:

velocity $= 55 - 10(3)$

velocity $= 55 - 30$

velocity $= 25$ m/s

(iii) Find h when $t = 10$:

$h(t) = 22 + 55t - 5t^2$

$h(10) = 22 + 55(10) - 5(10)^2$

$h(10) = 22 + 550 - 5(100)$

$h(10) = 22 + 550 - 500$

$h(10) = 72$

Therefore, the firework is at a height of 72 m above the ground when it explodes.

Find velocity when $t = 10$:

velocity $= 55 - 10t$

velocity $= 55 - 10(10)$

velocity $= 55 - 100$

velocity $= -45$

Since the velocity is a negative value, we know that the firework is moving **downwards**, with a speed of 45 m/s.

The negative sign indicates a downward direction.

(iv) ***Step 1:***

At the maximum height, velocity = 0

velocity $= 55 - 10t$

$0 = 55 - 10t$

$10t = 55$

$t = 5{\cdot}5$ seconds

This means that the firework is at its maximum height after 5·5 seconds.

Step 2:

To find the maximum height, find h when $t = 5{\cdot}5$:

$h(t) = 22 + 55t - 5t^2$

$h(5{\cdot}5) = 22 + 55(5{\cdot}5) - 5(5{\cdot}5)^2$

$h(5{\cdot}5) = 22 + 302{\cdot}5 - 5(30{\cdot}25)$

$h(5{\cdot}5) = 22 + 302{\cdot}5 - 151{\cdot}25$

$h(5{\cdot}5) = 173{\cdot}25$

Therefore, the maximum height reached by the firework is 173·25 m above the ground.

Practice Questions 27.2

1. The pressure exerted by an electric pump is given by $p = 3t^2 + 4t + 8$, where p is the pressure in Pascals and t is the time in seconds. Find:
   (i) the pressure after 3 seconds
   (ii) the time it takes for the pressure to reach 140 Pa
   (iii) the rate of change of pressure after 8 seconds.

2. The resistance, R, in Ohms, of a piece of metal is given by $R = 5 + 20T^2$, where T is the temperature of the metal in degrees Celsius.
   (i) Find the resistance of the metal when its temperature is 8°C.
   (ii) Find the temperature of the wire when its resistance is 11,525 Ohms.
   (iii) Find the rate of change of the resistance, with respect to temperature.
   (iv) Calculate this rate of change when $T = 3$°C and explain its meaning in the context of this question.

3. As a car passes a point P, its brakes are applied. Its distance, s metres, from P after a time t seconds has elapsed is given by $s = 100t - 2t^2$.
   Find:
   (i) the car's distance from P after 3 seconds
   (ii) the speed of the car, in terms of t
   (iii) the time taken for the car to stop
   (iv) the distance the car is from P, when the car stops.

4. The area of a circle, of radius r, is given by $A = \pi r^2$.
   A stone is dropped vertically into a still pond, causing the surface to ripple with circles or increasing radius.
   (i) Find the rate of change of the area, with respect to the radius, $\frac{dA}{dr}$.
   (ii) Find $\frac{dA}{dr}$ when $r = 3$ cm. Give your answer correct to one decimal place.
   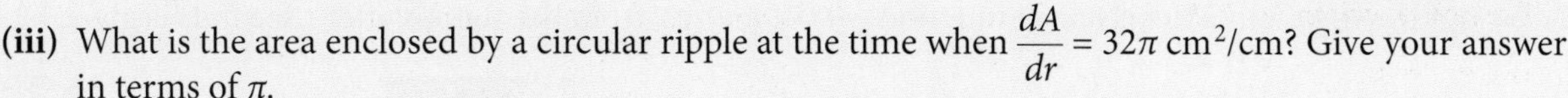
   (iii) What is the area enclosed by a circular ripple at the time when $\frac{dA}{dr} = 32\pi$ cm^2/cm? Give your answer in terms of π.

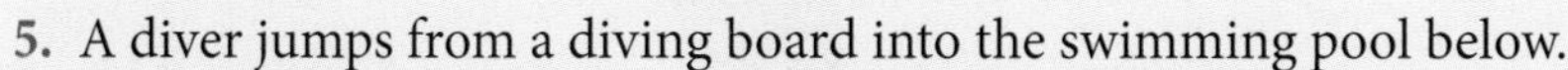

5. A diver jumps from a diving board into the swimming pool below.
   The height, h, of the diver, above the surface of the water is given by $h = 7 + 6t - t^2$, where h is the height in metres, t seconds after the diver leaves the board. Find:
   (i) the height of the diving board
   (ii) the height of the diver, after 2 seconds
   (iii) the time it takes for the diver to reach the water
   (iv) the maximum height of the diver above the water in the swimming pool
   (v) the speed with which the diver hits the water.

6. A cannon ball is fired vertically upwards. Its height above the ground, h, after a time t seconds, is given by

$$h = 1 + 24t - 3t^2$$

Find:

(i) the height of the ball after 3 seconds

(ii) the velocity of the ball, in terms of t

(iii) the velocity of the ball at 7 seconds. Is the ball rising or falling at this time? Give a reason for your answer

(iv) the acceleration of the ball

(v) the maximum possible height the ball reaches

(vi) the height of the ball, 2 seconds before it reaches its maximum height.

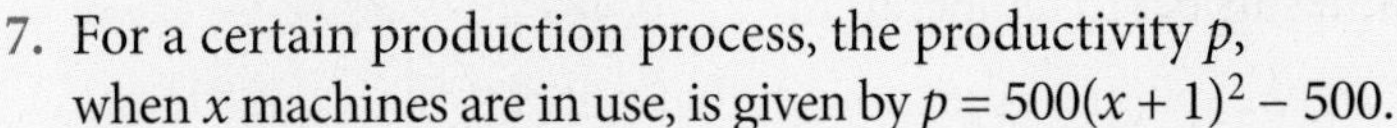

7. For a certain production process, the productivity p, when x machines are in use, is given by $p = 500(x + 1)^2 - 500$.

(i) Write p in the form $ax^2 + bx + c$, where $a, b, c \in \mathbb{Z}$.

(ii) Find an expression for the marginal productivity $\frac{dp}{dx}$.

(iii) Find the value of the marginal productivity when $x = 3$.

(iv) How many machines are required to raise the marginal productivity to 7,000?

8. The distance of a particle from a point, O, is given by $s = t^3 - 9t^2 - 11t + 190$, where s is in metres and the t is the time in seconds.

(i) How far is the particle from the point O after 10 seconds?

(ii) Find the speed, v, of the particle:

(a) at 4 seconds **(b)** at 8 seconds, and explain what your answer means.

(iii) Find the acceleration when the speed is -11 m/s.

(iv) Find the speed when the acceleration is zero.

9. As a train leaves a station, its distance function, $s(t)$ in metres, from the station after t seconds is given by

$$s(t) = t^2 + 7t.$$

Find:

(i) the distance the train has travelled after 3 seconds

(ii) the distance the train has travelled after 4 seconds

(iii) the distance travelled by the train **during** the 4th second of its journey (between $t = 3$ and $t = 4$)

(iv) the velocity of the train after 15 seconds

(v) the acceleration of the train.

(vi) Based on your answer to part **(v)**, do you think that the $s(t)$ function can be used to describe the motion of the train, as time goes on? Give a reason for your answer.

10. The distance, s metres, travelled by a particle in t seconds is given by $s = t(2t^2 - 4t + 3)$.

Find:

(i) the distance travelled in the 4th second

(ii) the speed of the particle at $t = 5$ seconds

(iii) the time at which the acceleration is zero.

11. The number of people, P, newly infected on day t of a flu epidemic is given by $P = 13t^2 - t^3$, $t \leq 13$.
   (i) Find an expression for $\frac{dP}{dt}$, the rate of change of the number of people with respect to the day number.
   (ii) Find the rate of change of P with respect to t,
      (a) on day 4 (b) on day 10
   and explain your answers in the context of this question.
   (iii) Calculate the time t for which $\frac{dP}{dt} = 0$, the value of P at this time and interpret your results.

12. A rocket is launched and its height, h metres, after t seconds is given by $h(t) = 15t^2 - 3t^3$
   (i) Find the velocity, $v(t)$, of the rocket, in terms of t.
   (ii) Find the acceleration, $a(t)$, of the rocket, in terms of t.
   (iii) Copy and complete the following table:

t	0	1	2	3	4	5
$h(t)$						
$v(t)$						
$a(t)$						

   (iv) Hence, using the same axes and scale, graph each of the following, in the domain $0 \leq t \leq 5$. Clearly label each graph.
      (a) Height, $h(t)$ (b) Velocity, $v(t)$ (c) Acceleration, $a(t)$

13. An object is thrown straight up in the air. The height of the object, in metres, above the ground is given by

$$h(t) = 20t - 2t^2$$

   (i) Copy and complete the following table:

t	0	1	2	3	4	5	6	7	8	9	10
$h(t)$				42							

   (ii) Hence, graph the height of the object against time for $0 \leq t \leq 10$.
   Using the same axes and scale, graph a function which represents:
   (iii) the velocity of the object
   (iv) the acceleration of the object
   and then
   (v) find the speed with which the object hits the ground.

14. The distance s metres travelled by a body in t seconds after it is released is given by:

$$s(t) = -t^3 + 11t^2 - 32t + 28$$

   (i) Graph the distance travelled by the body against time for $0 \leq t \leq 7$.
   Using the same axes and scale, graph a function which represents:
   (ii) the velocity of the body
   (iii) the acceleration of the body.

Section 27.3: Maxima and Minima Problems in Context

Learning Outcomes:

You should be able to:

- use differential calculus to find the value which will maximise or minimise a function
- apply this skill to questions in context

As already seen in the previous chapter, we can use differential calculus to find the values which will maximise, or minimise, a function.

The following is a summary of the main points covered in the section on curve sketching, in the previous chapter:

For any function $y = f(x)$:

- Function is increasing when $\frac{dy}{dx} > 0$ or $f'(x) > 0$
- Function is decreasing when $\frac{dy}{dx} < 0$ or $f'(x) < 0$
- Function is stationary, at a turning point, when $\frac{dy}{dx} = 0$ or $f'(x) = 0$
  - At the maximum turning point: $\frac{d^2y}{dx^2} < 0$ or $f''(x) < 0$
  - At the minimum turning point: $\frac{d^2y}{dx^2} > 0$ or $f''(x) > 0$

EXAMPLE 1

The population P (in thousands) of a certain country from 1980 through 2010 can be modelled by $P = -16t^2 + 800t + 117$, where t is the year, with $t = 0$ corresponding to 1980.

(i) Evaluate P for $t = 0$ and $t = 10$. Explain these values.

(ii) Determine the population growth rate, $\frac{dP}{dt}$.

(iii) Find the population growth rate in 2008 and interpret your results.

(iv) In what year was the population at its maximum?

(v) Hence, find the maximum population.

Solution

(i) $t = 0$:

$$P = -16(0)^2 + 800(0) + 117$$
$$P = 0 + 0 + 117$$
$$P = 117$$

Therefore, in 1980 the population was 117,000.

$t = 10$:

$$P = -16(10)^2 + 800(10) + 117$$
$$P = -16(100) + 8000 + 117$$
$$P = -1600 + 8117$$
$$P = 6517$$

Therefore, in 1990 (10 years after 1980) the population was 6,517,000.

(ii) $P = -16t^2 + 800t + 117$

$$\frac{dP}{dt} = -32t + 800$$

(iii) 2008 is 28 years after 1980, so we need to find $\frac{dP}{dt}$ when $t = 28$:

$$\frac{dP}{dt} = -32t + 800$$

$$\frac{dP}{dt} = -32(28) + 800$$

$$\frac{dP}{dt} = -896 + 800 = -96$$

A growth rate of -96 means that in 2008, the population of the country is decreasing at a rate of 96,000 people per year.

(iv) At maximum population, $\frac{dP}{dt} = 0$

$$\frac{dP}{dt} = -32t + 800$$

$$0 = -32t + 800$$

$$32t = 800$$

$$t = \frac{800}{32}$$

$$t = 25$$

Therefore, the population was at a maximum 25 years after 1980, in 2005.

(v) Find P when $t = 25$:

$$P = -16t^2 + 800t + 117$$

$$P = -16(25)^2 + 800(25) + 117$$

$$P = -10000 + 20000 + 117$$

$$P = 10{,}117$$

Therefore, the maximum population was 10,117,000.

EXAMPLE 2

A cylinder is to be made such that the sum of its radius, r, and its height, h, is 9 cm.

(i) Express h in terms of r.

(ii) Hence, show that the volume, V, of the cylinder is $V = 9\pi r^2 - \pi r^3$.

(iii) Find, in terms of π, the maximum possible volume of such a cylinder.

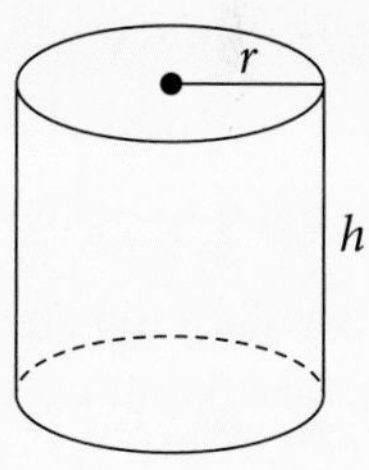

Solution

(i) radius + height = 9

$$r + h = 9$$

$$h = 9 - r$$

(ii) Volume of cylinder = $\pi r^2 h$

$$V = \pi r^2 (9 - r)$$

$$V = 9\pi r^2 - \pi r^3$$

(iii) At maximum point, $\frac{dV}{dr} = 0$:

$$V = 9\pi r^2 - \pi r^3$$

$$\frac{dV}{dr} = 2(9\pi r^1) - 3(\pi r^2)$$

$$\frac{dV}{dr} = 18\pi r - 3\pi r^2$$

$$0 = 18\pi r - 3\pi r^2$$

$$0 = 18r - 3r^2 \quad \text{(divide both sides by } \pi\text{)}$$

$$0 = 3r(6 - r)$$

$$3r = 0 \quad \text{or} \quad 6 - r = 0$$

$$r = 0 \quad \text{or} \quad r = 6$$

Since $r = 0$ will result in a cylinder which does not exist, $r = 6$ must give the maximum volume.

Alternative method to determine maximum value:

To determine which value gives the maximum, find the second derivative:

$$\frac{dV}{dr} = 18\pi r - 3\pi r^2$$

$$\frac{d^2V}{dr^2} = 18\pi - 6\pi r$$

For $r = 0$: $\frac{d^2V}{dr^2} = 18\pi - 6\pi(0)$

$$\frac{d^2V}{dr^2} = 18\pi > 0 \quad \text{(minimum value)}$$

For $r = 6$: $\frac{d^2V}{dr^2} = 18\pi - 6\pi(6)$

$$\frac{d^2V}{dr^2} = 18\pi - 36\pi$$

$$\frac{d^2V}{dr^2} = -18\pi < 0 \quad \text{(maximum value)}$$

Therefore, maximum value is when $r = 6$:

$$V = 9\pi r^2 - \pi r^3$$

$$V = 9\pi(6)^2 - \pi(6)^3$$

$$V = 9\pi(36) - \pi(216)$$

$$V = 324\pi - 216\pi$$

$$V = 108\pi \text{ cm}^3$$

Practice Questions 27.3

1. When a ball is thrown into the air, its height above the ground is given by the equation $h = 20t - 5t^2$, where h is the height in metres and t the time in seconds.

   Find $\frac{dh}{dt}$ and hence find the maximum height of the ball above the ground.

2. A particle moves in a straight line so that its displacement, s cm, from a fixed point O after time, t seconds, is given by $s = (2t + 1)(4 - t)$.
   - (i) Find the velocity of the particle after 8 seconds.
   - (ii) Show that the acceleration of the particle is a constant.
   - (iii) Find the maximum displacement of the particle from O.

3. A bird is flying at a height of 30 m above the ground. It swoops down to pick up a piece of bread from a bird table and then flies upwards again, as illustrated in the diagram.

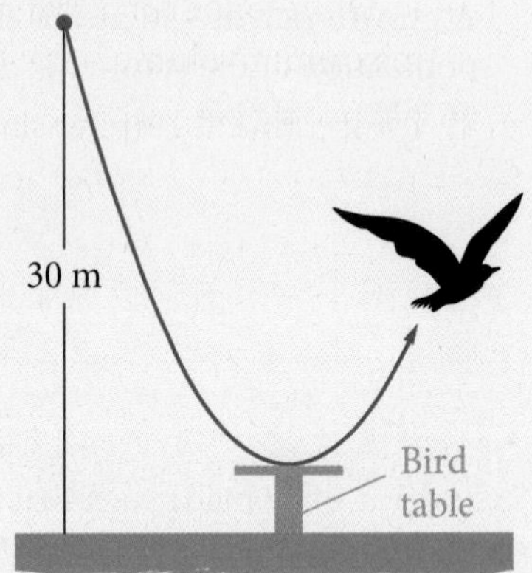

   The height, in metres, of the bird above the ground, during this time can be modelled by the function

   $$f(t) = 2{\cdot}4t^2 - 16{\cdot}8t + 30$$

   where t is the time in seconds, after the bird begins its decent. Find:
   - (i) the time taken for the bird to reach the bird table
   - (ii) the height of the bird table
   - (iii) the time taken for the bird to be back at a height of 30 m.

4. A yo-yo is a toy attached to a string, which moves in a straight line, down and up again.

   Nicole models the distance, s centimetres, of her yo-yo, from her hand at time t seconds by

   $$s(t) = 28t - 4t^2, \quad 0 \le t \le 7$$

   - (i) How far is the yo-yo from Nicole's hand after 1·5 seconds?
   - (ii) Find the speed of the yo-yo at 2 seconds and at 6 seconds. Interpret your answers.
   - (iii) What is the maximum length of the string of the yo-yo?
   - (iv) Sketch the following graphs in the interval $0 \le t \le 7$
     - (a) Distance, $s(t)$
     - (b) Velocity, $v(t)$

5. The air resistance, R, to a body moving with speed, v metres per second, is given by

   $$R(v) = 0{\cdot}01v^2 - 1{\cdot}24v + 47$$

   - (i) Find the measure of the air resistance when the body is moving at 12 m/s.
   - (ii) Find the two speeds for which the body experiences an air resistance of 10 units.
   - (iii) Find the speed which results in minimum air resistance.
   - (iv) Hence, find a minimum air resistance experienced by the body.

6. A rectangular juice carton has length $2x$ centimetres, width x centimetres and height $(18 - x)$ cm.

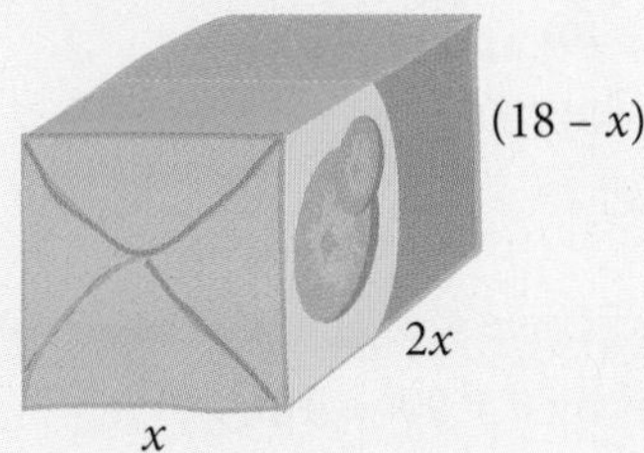

(i) Find the volume of the carton, in terms of x.

(ii) Find the value for x, which will give a maximum volume.

(iii) Hence, find the dimensions of the carton for this value of x and the maximum volume.

7. Investments can increase or decrease in value. The value of a particular investment of €500 is found by the mathematical model $V = 500 + 6t - 3{\cdot}6t^2 + 0{\cdot}4t^3$, where V is the value, in euro, and t is the time in months after the investment was made.

(i) Find the value of the investment after 4 months.

(ii) Determine whether the value of the investment is increasing or decreasing after 8 months.

(iii) Find the minimum value of the investment.

(iv) The investment was cashed out after 14 months. How much was the investment worth at this time?

(v) Tax of 30% on any profit made is deducted from the investment before the investor receives their pay out. Find the total amount this investor receives, after 14 months.

8. A retailer imports pairs of jeans to sell in their shop.

The cost, C, of importing x pairs of jeans, if given by the formula:

$$C = 18{\cdot}8x + 1150$$

The revenue brought in by the sale of x pairs of jeans is given by the formula:

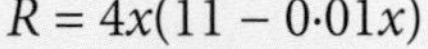

$$R = 4x(11 - 0{\cdot}01x)$$

(i) Show that the profit, P, in euro, made by the clothes shop from selling x pairs of jeans is given by:

$$P = -0{\cdot}04x^2 + 25{\cdot}2x - 1150$$

Profit = Revenue − cost

(ii) Find the profit made on the sale of 150 pairs of jeans.

(iii) Find the marginal profit, $\frac{dP}{dx}$ when $x = 100$. Interpret your results.

(iv) Find the value of x, which will maximise the profit and find this maximum profit.

9. Two industrial plants, 40 km apart, are polluting a large lake. The pollution level, P, parts per million, is given by

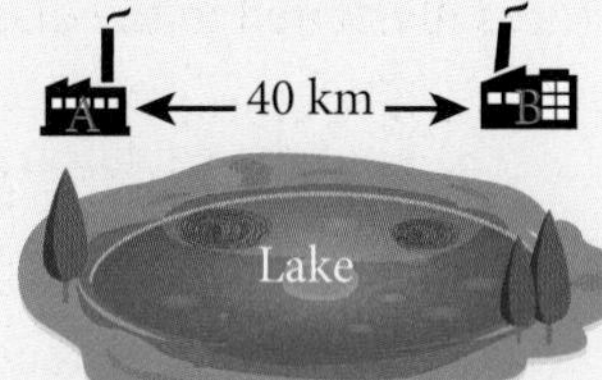

$$P = 2k(k - 24) + 400, 0 \leq k \leq 40$$

where k represents the distance from plant A towards plant B, in kilometres.

(i) Write P in the form $ak^2 + bk + c$, where $a, b, c \in \mathbb{Z}$.

(ii) Find the pollution level at a point 3 km from plant A.

(iii) Find the place between A and B where the pollution is at its lowest value.

(iv) Sketch a graph of P for $0 \leq k \leq 40$ and deduce which factory pollutes the water more.

(v) Using the same axes and scale, sketch a graph of the rate of change of the pollution for $0 \leq k \leq 40$ and explain how this graph verifies your answer to part **(iii)**.

10. A piece of cardboard has length 16 cm and breadth 10 cm. Square pieces of side x cm are removed from each corner and the flaps are turned up, so that an open box of volume V is formed.

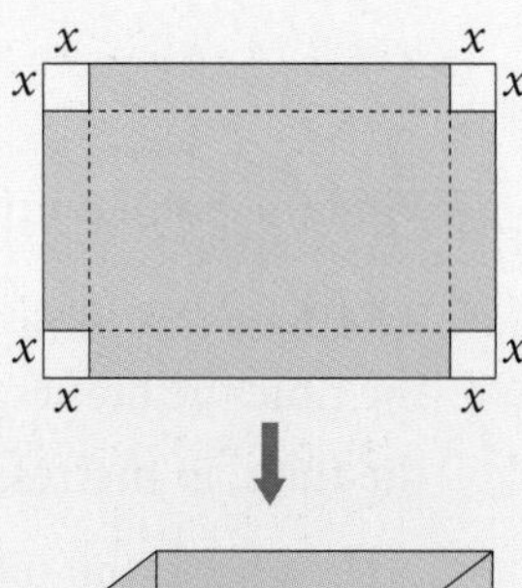

(i) Find the length and the width of the **box**, in terms of x.

(ii) Show that $V = 4x^3 - 52x^2 + 160x$.

(iii) Find the maximum possible volume.

Revision and Exam Style Questions – Section A

1. A curve has equation $y = 1 + x - 2x^2$.

   (i) Find the slope of the tangent to the curve at the points $(-2, -9)$ and $(2, -5)$. Hence, decide if the graph is increasing or decreasing at each point.

   (ii) Find the coordinates of the local turning point on the curve.

   (iii) Hence, draw a rough sketch of the curve.

2. The height, h metres, of a balloon is related to the time t seconds by $h = 90t - 10t^2$.

   Find:

   (i) its height after 2 seconds

   (ii) the maximum height reached by the balloon.

3. **(i)** If $y = -2x^2 + 7x - 5$, find $\frac{dy}{dx}$.

   Hence,

   (ii) find the equation of the tangent to the curve at the point where $x = 0$

   (iii) find the equation of the tangent to the curve at the point where $x = 3$.

4. Once an aeroplane touches down, it applies its brakes. The distance, s in metres, which it has travelled along the runway at time t seconds after touchdown is given by $s(t) = 200t - 4t^2$.

   Find:

   (i) the speed of the aeroplane at $t = 3$ seconds

   (ii) the constant deceleration of the aeroplane

   (iii) the time taken for the aeroplane to come to rest

   (iv) the distance travelled by the aeroplane before coming to rest.

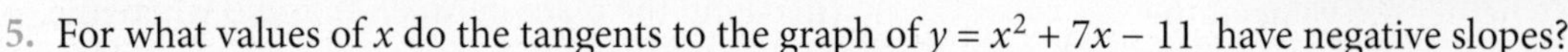

5. For what values of x do the tangents to the graph of $y = x^2 + 7x - 11$ have negative slopes?

6. Find the equation of the tangent to the curve $f(x) = 2x^2 - 3x + 5$, at the point $(-1, 10)$.

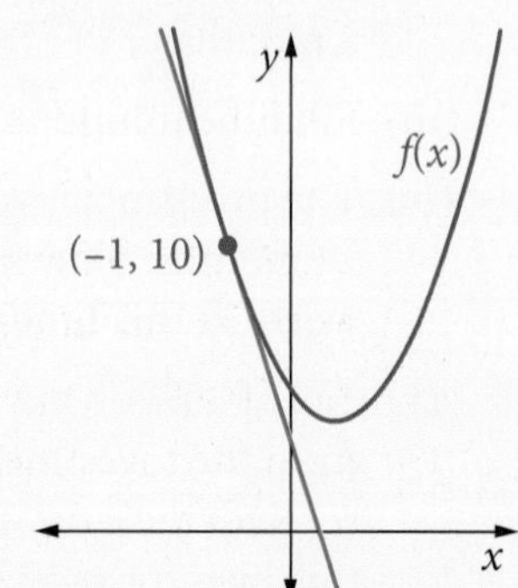

7. Find the point on the curve $y = x^2 + 12x + 6$ at which the slope of a tangent is 2.

8. A train is travelling along a track. Suddenly, the brakes are applied. From the time the brakes are applied ($t = 0$ seconds), the distance travelled by the train, in metres, is given by $s = 22t - \frac{1}{5}t^2$.

   (i) What is the speed of the train at the moment the brakes are applied?

   (ii) How many seconds does it take for the train to come to rest?

   (iii) How far does the train travel in that time?

   (iv) Find the deceleration the train undergoes.

9. A farmer has 80 m of fencing with which to make a rectangular field along the side of a river. The river will form one side of the field. The width of the two shortest sides is W.
   (i) Find the length of the field, in terms of W.
   (ii) Show that the area of the field, A, is given by $A = 80W - 2W^2$.
   (iii) Hence, find the maximum area that can be enclosed.

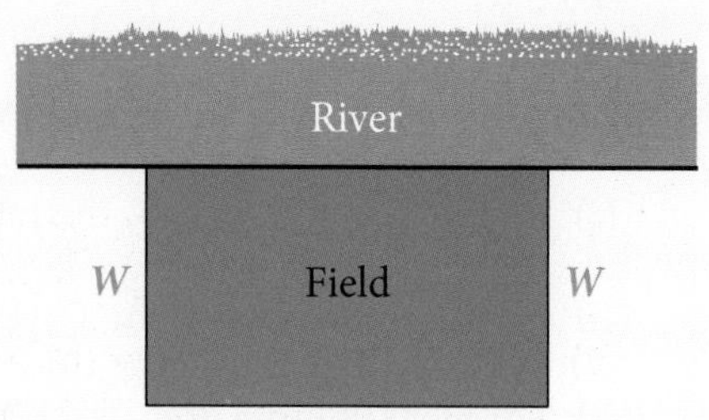

Revision and Exam Style Questions – Section B

More challenging problems

1. The speed, v, in metres per second, of an object at time t seconds is given by $v(t) = 22 + 36t - 3t^2$.
   (i) Find the two times when the speed of the object is 82 m/s.
   (ii) Find the acceleration of the object at $t = 3$ seconds. Interpret your results.
   (iii) Find the maximum speed reached by the object.
   (iv) At what value of t will the acceleration become negative?
   (v) Using your answers to parts **(i)** – **(iv)**, draw, using the same axes and scales, a sketch of the graphs of the velocity and acceleration of the object.

2. (i) If $f(x) = 4x^2 - 26x + 45$, find $f'(x)$.
   Hence,
   (ii) find the equation of the tangent, t, to the curve, at the point (3, 3)
   (iii) find the equation of the tangent, s, to the curve, at the point (5, 15)
   (iv) find the point of intersection of the tangents s and t.

3. (i) The function $g(x) = px^2 + qx$, where $p, q \in \mathbb{Z}$ passes through the point (1, 6). The tangent at $x = 2$ is parallel to the x-axis. Find p and q.
   (ii) Explain why the point of contact to the tangent at $x = 2$ is a turning point. Find the coordinates of this turning point.

4. The volume of water, V, in litres, that remains in a leaking tank after t days is given by: $V = 964 - 108t - 51t^2 - 3t^3$.
   (i) Find the volume of the water in the tank after one day.
   (ii) Find the rate of change of the volume when $t = 2$ days and interpret your results.
   (iii) Show that it takes less than three-and-a-half days for the tank to empty.
   (iv) Show that the volume is always decreasing until the tank is empty.

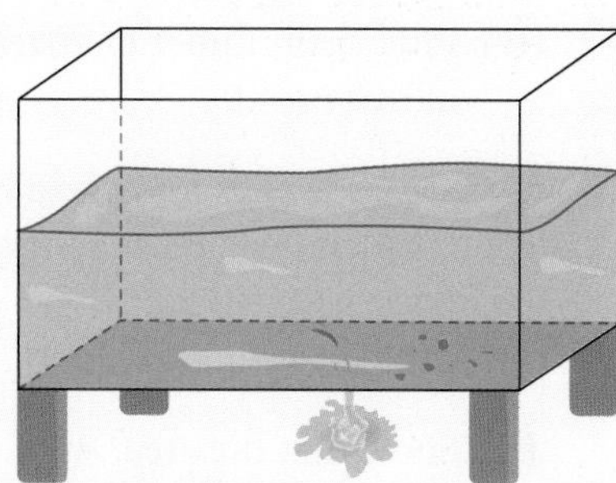

5. (i) Find where the curve $y = x^2 - 4x + 3$ crosses the x-axis and hence sketch the curve.
   (ii) Tangents are drawn to this curve at the points where it crosses the x-axis. Investigate if these tangents are at right angles to each other.

6. A particle moves along a straight line so that its distance s metres from a fixed point O, after t seconds, is given by $s = 2t^3 - 24t^2 - 3t + 12$.
   (i) How far is the particle from the point O after 25 seconds?
   (ii) Find its speed after 9 seconds.
   (iii) After how many seconds is the acceleration 24 m/s^2? Find its distance from O at this time.

7. Paul is blowing up a spherical balloon. The volume of the balloon, V, is found by using the formula: $V = \frac{4}{3}\pi r^3$ where r is the radius of the balloon.

   (i) Find a formula for $\frac{dV}{dr}$, the rate of change of volume V with respect to radius r.

   (ii) Find $\frac{dV}{dr}$ when $r = 6$ cm. Give your answer in terms of π.

   (iii) For what volume does $\frac{dV}{dr} = 1000$ cm^3/cm? Give your answer to one decimal place.

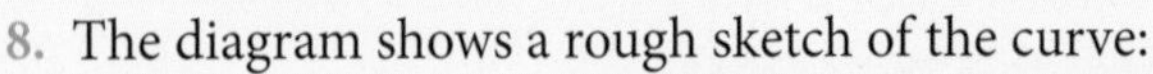

8. The diagram shows a rough sketch of the curve:

$$h(x) = x^2 - 3x + 4$$

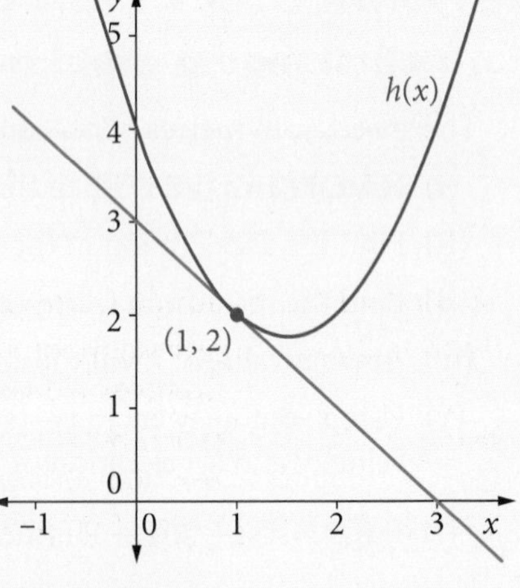

   (i) Prove that the point $P(1, 2)$ is on the curve.

   (ii) Find the slope of the tangent to the curve at P.

   (iii) Write down the slope of a perpendicular tangent.

   (iv) Find the point at which the tangent in part **(iii)** touches the curve.

   (v) Find the point of intersection of the tangents in **(ii)** and **(iii)**.

9. A letting agent rents out a number of identical apartments in a residential development. The annual revenue taken in from renting x apartments can be modelled by the formula

$$R = 2x(900 + 32x - x^2).$$

   (i) Find the annual revenue made on the rental of 12 apartments.

   (ii) The company estimates that each apartment costs €680 per year to maintain. Find an expression for the cost, C, in terms of x.

   (iii) Hence, find an expression for the annual profit, P, made by the company, in the form $ax^3 + bx^2 + cx$, where a, b and c are constants.

   (iv) Find the number of apartments which will maximise the company's profit and find the value of this profit.

10. A gardener wishes to make a rectangular flower bed. He has 24 m of wood, which he will use to make the frame. Given that the length of the flower bed is L m.

   (i) Find the width of the flower bed, in terms of L.

   (ii) Show that the area, A, of the flowerbed is given by $A = 12L - L^2$.

   (iii) Hence, find the maximum area that the flowerbed can be.

Now that you have completed the chapter, revisit the 'Something to think about…' questions.

Complex Numbers

CHAPTER 28

Sections covered within this chapter:

KEY WORDS

- Complex number
- Argand diagram
- Modulus
- Conjugate

SOMETHING TO THINK ABOUT… 

A stunt airplane pilot wants to perform a stunt where he dives towards the surface of a lake then swoops up at the last minute to avoid hitting the water.

Before attempting the stunt he decides to model the situation mathematically using a quadratic function.

With the surface of the lake as the x-axis, the model is given by the following function

$$f(x) = x^2 - 3x + 4$$

Investigate whether using this model will allow for a successful stunt.

Section 28.1: Introducing Complex Numbers

Learning Outcomes:

You should be able to:

- understand the need for complex numbers
- identify the real and imaginary parts of a complex number

Consider the following equation: $x^2 = -9$

We would usually solve this type of equation by taking the square root of both sides.

$$\sqrt{x^2} = \sqrt{-9}$$

When we try this on the calculator, we are given an error message!

Some students may say $\sqrt{-9}$ is -3, but recall $-3 \times -3 = \mathbf{+9}$.

In order to deal with the problem of finding the square root of a negative number, a new type of number was introduced.

This number is defined as the square root of -1 and is called i. So $i \times i$ or $i^2 = -1$.

i stands for imaginary but these numbers do actually exist. They are called imaginary as they are not part of the Real Number system.

$i = \sqrt{-1}$

$i^2 = -1$

Imaginary numbers are essential to the study of sciences such as electricity, quantum mechanics, vibration analysis, and cartography. They are also used in computer animations.

EXAMPLE 1

Find the value of **(i)** $\sqrt{-9}$, **(ii)** $\sqrt{-18}$ and **(iii)** $5\sqrt{-196}$, when $i = \sqrt{-1}$.

Solution

(i) $\sqrt{-9}$

Convert the number under the square root sign into a number multiplied by -1

$\sqrt{-9} = \sqrt{9 \times -1}$

Split the square root using the surd rules

$\sqrt{a \times b} = \sqrt{a} \times \sqrt{b}$

$\sqrt{9 \times -1} = \sqrt{9} \times \sqrt{-1}$

Solve each square root

$\sqrt{9} \times \sqrt{-1} = 3i$

$\sqrt{9} = 3$; $\sqrt{-1} = i$

Therefore, $\sqrt{-9} = 3i$

(ii) $\sqrt{-18}$

$= \sqrt{18 \times -1}$

We need to break 18 down further to $\sqrt{9 \times 2}$

$= \sqrt{9 \times 2 \times -1}$

$= \sqrt{9} \times \sqrt{2} \times \sqrt{-1}$

$= 3\sqrt{2}i$

(iii) $5\sqrt{-196}$

$= 5(\sqrt{-196})$

$= 5(\sqrt{196 \times -1})$

$= 5(\sqrt{196} \times \sqrt{-1})$

$= 5(14i) = 70i$

Links across the syllabus

Breaking up surds is covered in Chapter 1: Number Systems.

Discussion Time

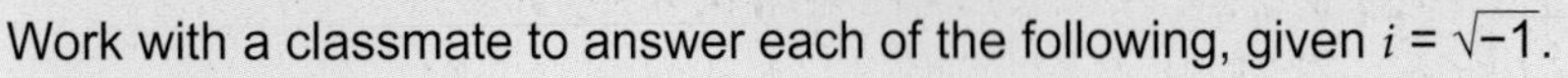

Work with a classmate to answer each of the following, given $i = \sqrt{-1}$.

1. Find the value of i^2.

2. Find the value of i^3.

3. Find the value of i^4.

4. Find the value of i^5.

5. Can you see a pattern? What is the pattern?

6. Use this pattern to find the value of i^{60} and i^{39}.

Powers of imaginary numbers

As you can see from the discussion time questions when we increase the power of i, an interesting pattern emerges.

The rules of indices are covered in Chapter 5: Indices and Index Notation.

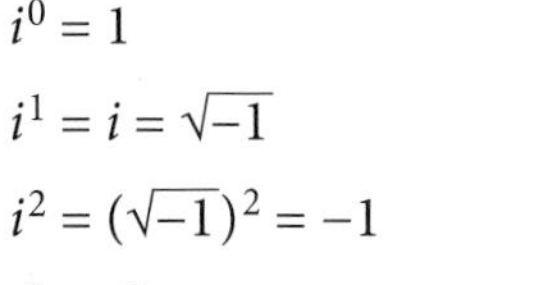

$i^0 = 1$

$i^1 = i = \sqrt{-1}$

$i^2 = (\sqrt{-1})^2 = -1$

$i^3 = i^2 \times i = -1 \times i = -i$

$i^4 = i^3 \times i = -i \times i = -i^2 = -(-1) = 1$

$i^5 = i^4 \times i = 1 \times i = i$

You can see that the pattern is repeating. Therefore, the value of any power of i will be either 1, i, −1, or $-i$.

In order to decide which of these four options is correct, we divide the given power of i by four and apply the rule shown here:

$$i^n = \begin{cases} \mathbf{1 \text{ if the remainder is } 0} \\ \boldsymbol{i} \textbf{ if the remainder is 1} \\ \mathbf{-1 \text{ if the remainder is } 2} \\ \boldsymbol{-i} \textbf{ if the remainder is 3} \end{cases}$$

For example, find the value of i^{19}. Four divides into 19 four times with remainder three. Therefore $i^{19} = -i$.

Alternatively, we can break up the given power using indices rules so that it becomes a power of i^2.

For example: $i^{10} = i^2 \times i^2 \times i^2 \times i^2 \times i^2 = (i^2)^5$ and since $i^2 = -1$ this means $i^{10} = (-1)^5 = -1$

If the power is not a multiple of two, then we convert it to a multiple of two and multiply our answer by i.

For example, $i^7 = i^6 \times i$, since $i^6 \times i = i^6 \times i^1 = i^{(6+1)}$ by indices rules.

Evaluating i to the power 7 gives

$$i^7 = i^6 \times i$$
$$i^7 = (i^2)^3 \times i$$
$$i^7 = (-1)^3 \times i$$
$$i^7 = -1 \times i$$
$$i^7 = -i$$

EXAMPLE 2

Find the value of **(i)** i^8 **(ii)** i^{42} **(iii)** i^{13} and **(iv)** i^{35}.

(v) What do you notice about the even powers when compared to the odd powers?

Solution

(i) i^8

4 divides into 8 twice with 0 remainder so the answer is 1.

$i^8 = 1$

Alternatively,

$i^8 = (i^2)^4 = (-1)^4 = 1$

(ii) i^{42}

4 divides into 42 ten times with remainder 2 so the answer is −1.

$i^{42} = -1$

Alternatively,

$i^{42} = (i^2)^{21} = (-1)^{21} = -1$

(iii) i^{13}

4 divides into 13 three times with remainder 1 so the answer is i.

$i^{13} = i$

Alternatively,

$i^{13} = i^{12} \times i$

$= (i^2)^6 \times i$

$= (-1)^6 \times i = i$

(iv) i^{35}

4 divides into 35 eight time with remainder 3 so the answer is $-i$.

$i^{35} = -i$

Alternatively,

$i^{35} = i^{34} \times i$

$= (i^2)^{17} \times i$

$= (-1)^{17} \times i = -i$

(v) The even powers give 1 or –1, the odd powers give i or $-i$.

A **complex number** is a combination of a real and an imaginary number in the form $a + bi$, where a and b are real numbers.

- a is called the **real part** and b is called the **imaginary part**. The values of a and b can be zero.
- We often use the letter z to denote a complex number; i.e. $z = a + bi$.
- The set of complex numbers is denoted by the symbol $\mathbb{C}$.

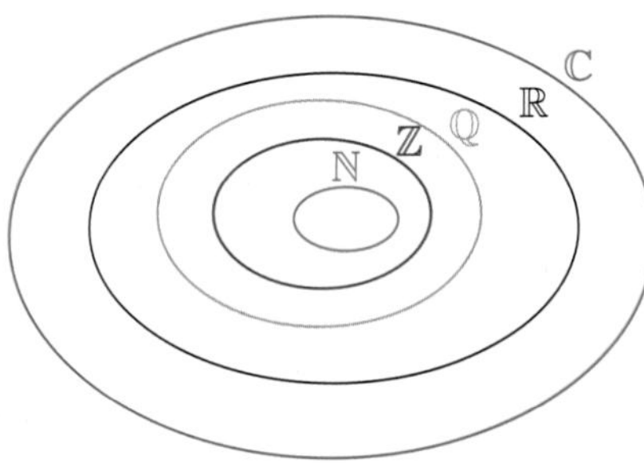

Since the value of b can be 0, all real numbers can be written as complex numbers; for example: $-2{\cdot}6 = -2{\cdot}6 + 0i$.

Therefore, all other number sets are subsets of $\mathbb{C}$.

$\mathbb{N} \subset \mathbb{Z} \subset \mathbb{Q} \subset \mathbb{R} \subset \mathbb{C}$; as shown in the diagram.

EXAMPLE 3

Identify the real and imaginary parts of the following complex numbers:

(i) $3 + i$ **(ii)** 5 **(iii)** $-6i$ **(iv)** $\frac{2i}{3} + \sqrt{2}$

Solution

(i) $3 + i$
Real = 3
Imaginary = 1

(ii) $5 + 0i$
Real = 5
Imaginary = 0

(iii) $0 - 6i$
Real = 0
Imaginary = –6

(iv) $\frac{2i}{3} + \sqrt{2}$
Real = $\sqrt{2}$
Imaginary = $\frac{2}{3}$

Don't include the i when identifying the imaginary part.

Practice Questions 28.1

1. Simplify the surds and hence express each of the following in terms of i:

   (i) $\sqrt{-1}$ **(ii)** $\sqrt{-36}$ **(iii)** $\sqrt{-81}$ **(iv)** $\sqrt{-121}$ **(v)** $\sqrt{-5}$ **(vi)** $\sqrt{-75}$ **(vii)** $\sqrt{-12}$ **(viii)** $\sqrt{-98}$

2. Express each of the following in terms of i:

   (i) $-2\sqrt{-9}$ **(ii)** $4\sqrt{-56}$ **(iii)** $3\sqrt{-16}$ **(iv)** $7\sqrt{-96}$ **(v)** $\sqrt{2}\sqrt{-32}$ **(vi)** $\sqrt{-2}\sqrt{8}$ **(vii)** $\sqrt{3}\sqrt{-48}$ **(viii)** $\sqrt{-4}\sqrt{45}$

3. Express in terms of i and simplify the following:
   (i) $\sqrt{-\frac{1}{4}}$
   (ii) $\sqrt{-\frac{16}{25}}$
   (iii) $4\sqrt{-\frac{49}{64}}$
   (iv) $\frac{3}{5}\sqrt{-\frac{100}{9}}$
   (v) $\frac{2}{3}\sqrt{-72}$
   (vi) $\frac{1}{2}\sqrt{-300}$

4. Find the value of x in each of the following equations:
   (i) $x^2 = -100$
   (ii) $x^2 = -169$
   (iii) $x^2 + 25 = 0$
   (iv) $16 + x^2 = 0$
   (v) $x^2 + 3 = -46$
   (vi) $x^2 - 13 = -157$

5. Evaluate each of the following:
   (i) i^3
   (ii) i^6
   (iii) i^{12}
   (iv) i^{15}
   (v) i^{11}
   (vi) i^7
   (vii) i^{26}
   (viii) i^{34}

6. Find the value of each of the following:
   (i) $i^8 + i^9 + i^{10}$
   (ii) $i^8 \times i^9 \times i^{10}$
   (iii) $2i^2 \times (3i)^4$
   (iv) $2i^{27} + 3i^{39}$
   (v) $4i^{99} - 2i^3$
   (vi) $i^{16} + i^6 - 2i^5 + i^{13}$

7. Identify the real and imaginary parts of the following complex numbers:
   (i) $-2 + 5i$
   (ii) $4 - i$
   (iii) $3{\cdot}5 - 0{\cdot}4i$
   (iv) $-8i$
   (v) $112i - 9$
   (vi) $\sqrt{5}i + \frac{3}{4}$

8. Write each of the following in the form $a + bi$. Hence, identify the real and imaginary parts.
   (i) $6 + \sqrt{-16}$
   (ii) $\sqrt{-48} - 5$
   (iii) $-8 - \sqrt{-4}$
   (iv) $-\sqrt{-36} - 15$
   (v) $\sqrt{-18} + 21$
   (vi) $-\sqrt{-120} - 12$

Section 28.2: The Argand Diagram and Modulus of a Complex Number

Learning Outcomes:

You should be able to:
- understand how to represent complex numbers on an Argand diagram
- understand what is meant by the modulus of a complex number
- calculate the modulus of a complex number

An **Argand diagram** is a graphical representation of a complex number.

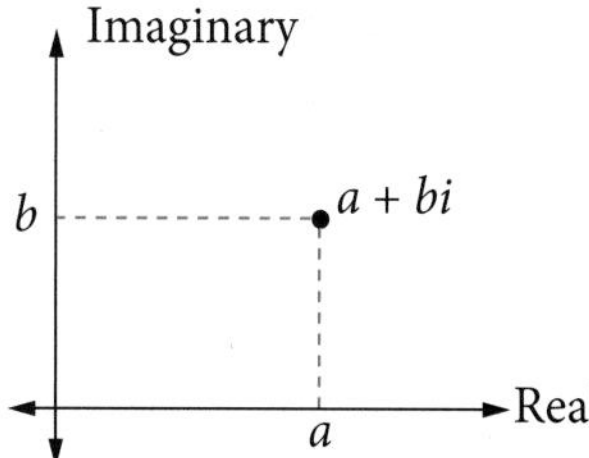

In an Argand diagram, the **horizontal** axis is the **real** axis and the **vertical** axis is the **imaginary** axis.

To plot a complex number on the Argand diagram, you express the complex number in the form $a + bi$ and plot as you would a point with the coordinates (a, b).

The modulus of a complex number

The **modulus** of a complex number is the distance between the origin $0 + 0i$ and the complex number when plotted on an Argand diagram.

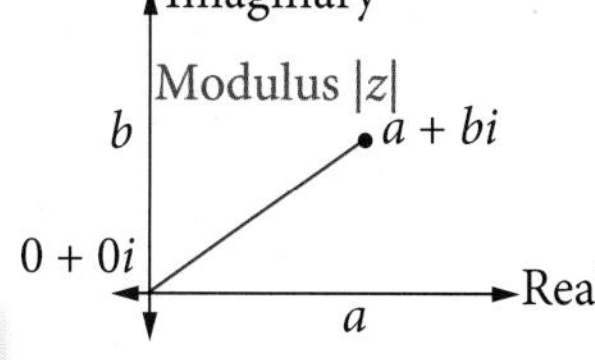

Since the modulus represents a length it will always be positive.

The modulus is given the symbol $|a + bi|$ or $|z|$.

The modulus can be calculated using the formula:

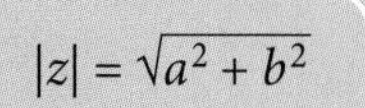

$$|z| = \sqrt{a^2 + b^2}$$

The modulus of a complex number is always a real number.

Discussion Time 

Work with a classmate to answer the following questions.

Consider the complex number $A = 8 + 6i$ shown in the diagram:

1. Use the distance formula to find $|OA|$, the distance from $0 + 0i$ to $8 + 6i$.

2. Use Pythagoras' theorem to find $|OA|$.

3. Use the modulus formula above to find $|OA|$.

4. Comment on your answers for Q**1**, **2** and **3**.

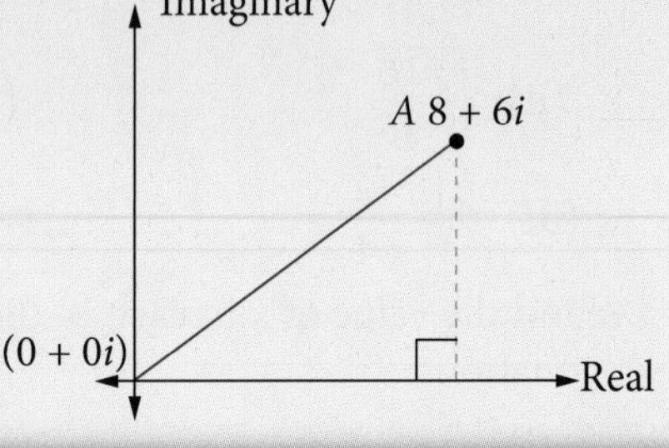

EXAMPLE 1

(a) Plot the following complex numbers on an Argand diagram:

(i) $3 + 3i$ **(ii)** $-3 + 3i$ **(iii)** $-3 - 3i$ **(iv)** $3 - 3i$

(b) Find the modulus of each complex number. What do you notice? Explain why this is the case.

Solution

(a)

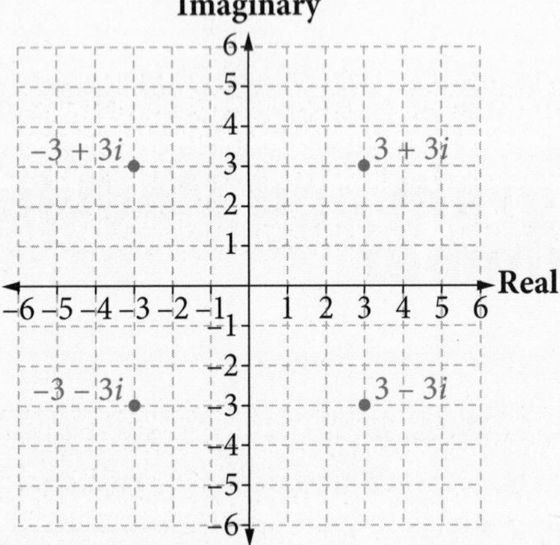

(b) **(i)** $a = 3, b = 3$

$|z| = \sqrt{(3)^2 + (3)^2}$

$= \sqrt{9 + 9}$

$= \sqrt{18} = 3\sqrt{2}$

(ii) $a = -3, b = 3$

$|z| = \sqrt{(-3)^2 + (3)^2}$

$= \sqrt{9 + 9}$

$= \sqrt{18} = 3\sqrt{2}$

(iii) $a = -3, b = -3$

$|z| = \sqrt{(-3)^2 + (-3)^2}$

$= \sqrt{9 + 9}$

$= \sqrt{18} = 3\sqrt{2}$

(iv) $a = 3, b = -3$

$|z| = \sqrt{(3)^2 + (-3)^2}$

$= \sqrt{9 + 9}$

$= \sqrt{18} = 3\sqrt{2}$

The modulus of each of these complex numbers are the same because each of the complex numbers are the same distance from (0, 0).

EXAMPLE 2

Given $|a + 3i| = 5$; find two values for a.

Solution

$|z| = \sqrt{a^2 + b^2}$ $a = a, b = 3, |z| = 5$

$5 = \sqrt{a^2 + 3^2}$

$5^2 = \left(\sqrt{a^2 + 3^2}\right)^2$ square both sides

$25 = a^2 + 3^2$

$25 = a^2 + 9$

$25 - 9 = a^2 + 9 - 9$ subtract 9 from both sides

$16 = a^2$

$\sqrt{16} = a$ take the square root of both sides

$a = \pm 4$

Practice Questions 28.2

1. Identify each of the complex numbers shown on the Argand diagram. Each marking on the axes represents one unit.

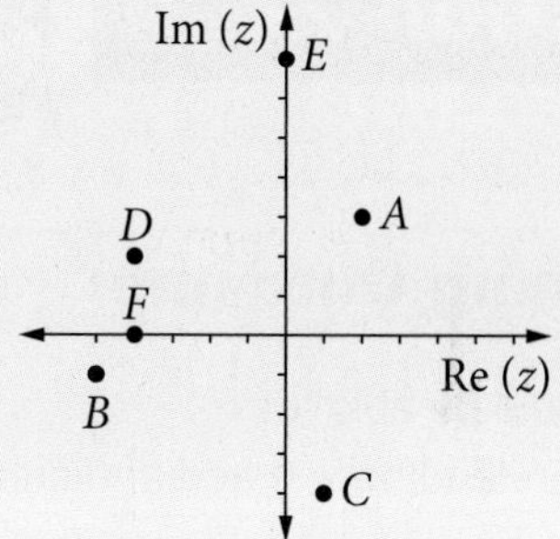

2. Plot the following complex numbers on an Argand diagram:
   (i) $3 + 2i$ **(ii)** $-1 - 5i$ **(iii)** $-4 + i$ **(iv)** $2 - 4i$ **(v)** $3i$ **(vi)** -6

3. Given that $z = 3 - 2i$ and $w = -4 + 3i$, plot the following on an Argand diagram:
   (i) z **(ii)** w **(iii)** $3z$ **(iv)** $-2w$ **(v)** $-z$ **(vi)** $\frac{w}{2}$

4. Find the modulus of each of the following:
   (i) $7 - i$ **(ii)** $10 - 2i$ **(iii)** $3 - 6i$ **(iv)** $-5 - 5i$ **(v)** $-4i$ **(vi)** $-4 - 3i$

5. $z_1 = 2 + 5i$, $z_2 = -3 - 2i$, $z_3 = -4 + 3i$ and $z_4 = 1 - i$.
   (i) Plot z_1, z_2, z_3 and z_4 on an Argand diagram.
   (ii) Calculate $|z_1|$, $|z_2|$, $|z_3|$ and $|z_4|$.

6. **(i)** Plot the following on an Argand diagram:
   (a) $-3 + \sqrt{-49}$ **(b)** $5 - \sqrt{-4}$ **(c)** $-7 + \sqrt{-121}$ **(d)** $6 - \sqrt{-196}$
   (ii) Find the modulus of each of the complex numbers above.

7. Given $|p + 4i| = \sqrt{41}$, find the value of p.

8. Given $|1 + 3i| = |-3 + bi|$, find the value of b.

9. **(i)** Plot $z = -5 - 4i$ on an Argand diagram and find $|z|$.
   (ii) Plot z_1, the image of z under axial symmetry in the real axis, on an Argand diagram and find the modulus of z_1.

(iii) Plot z_2, the image of z under axial symmetry in the imaginary axis, on an Argand diagram and find the modulus of z_2.

(iv) Plot z_3, the image of z under central symmetry in $0 + 0i$, on an Argand diagram and find $|z_3|$.

(v) What effect does reflection of a complex number in the real axis, imaginary axis or in the point $0 + 0i$ have on the modulus of the complex number?

Links across the syllabus

Transformations are covered in Chapter 13: Geometry IV.

10. $z_1 = 1 + i$ and $z_2 = 3 + 3i$.

(i) Plot z_1 and z_2 on an Argand diagram.

(ii) Calculate $|z_1|$ and $|z_2|$.

(iii) Comment on the relationship between z_1 and z_2.

(iv) Comment on the relationship between $|z_1|$ and $|z_2|$.

Section 28.3: Adding and Subtracting Complex Numbers

Learning Outcome:

You should be able to:

- understand how to add and subtract complex numbers

To add or subtract complex numbers, we use a technique that you will have seen before when doing algebra. This involves collecting together **like terms**.

By this method we first add or subtract the real terms and then add or subtract the imaginary terms.

Links across the syllabus

Adding and subtracting like terms is covered in Chapter 2: Algebra I.

Our final answer should be in the form $a + bi$.

To add or subtract complex numbers, we remove the brackets and add or subtract the like terms:

$$(a + bi) + (c + di)$$
$$= a + bi + c + di$$
$$= (a + c) + (b + d)i$$

EXAMPLE

Simplify the following:

(i) $(3 + 2i) + (1 - 5i)$

(ii) $(2 + 4i) - (1 - 2i)$

Solution

(i) $(3 + 2i) + (1 - 5i)$

$3 + 2i + 1 - 5i$ remove the brackets

$3 + 1 + 2i - 5i$ combine like terms

$= 4 - 3i$

(ii) $(2 + 4i) - (1 - 2i)$

$2 + 4i - 1 + 2i$ remove the brackets

$2 - 1 + 4i + 2i$ combine like terms

$= 1 + 6i$

Practice Questions 28.3

1. Express each of the following in the form $a + bi$:
   (i) $(3i) + (4i)$
   (ii) $(-5i) + (2i)$
   (iii) $(-6i) + (i)$
   (iv) $(-6 - 2i) + 6$
   (v) $6i + (2 - 7i)$
   (vi) $(6 - 8i) - (4i)$
2. Simplify the following:
   (i) $(7 + 3i) + (8 + 5i)$
   (ii) $(-8 + 3i) - (2 + 6i)$
   (iii) $(5 + 2i) + (6 - 7i)$
   (iv) $(1 - 3i) + (3 + 5i)$
   (v) $(8 - 4i) - (4 - 5i)$
   (vi) $(5 - i) - (7 - 6i)$
3. Simplify the following:
   (i) $(7 - 5i) + (6i) + (5 + 6i)$
   (ii) $(-7 + 7i) - (-7 - 3i) + (-7 - 8i)$
   (iii) $(-2 - 7i) - (4 + i) - (4 - 5i)$
   (iv) $(1 + 3i) + (6 - i) - (-7 + 5i)$
   (v) $(-5 + 3i) - (-6 + 4i) - (-6 + 5i)$
   (vi) $(-8 + 6i) - (6 - 6i) - (7 + 6i)$
4. Express the (i) sum and (ii) difference of $5 + \sqrt{-49}$ and $3 - \sqrt{-16}$ in the form $a + bi$.
5. $z_1 = 2 - i$, $z_2 = -3 - 5i$ and $z_3 = 4 - 6i$. Find the value of each of the following. Express your answers in the form $a + bi$.
   (i) $z_1 + 5$
   (ii) $z_3 + 4i$
   (iii) $z_2 - (3 - 2i)$
   (iv) $z_3 + z_2$
   (v) $z_3 - z_1$
   (vi) $z_1 - z_3$
6. Find a and b if $(8 + 6i) + (44 - 17i) - (a + bi) = 0$ and a and b are real.
7. $z = -3 + i$ and $w = 6i$.
   (i) Plot z, w, $z + w$ and $w - z$ on an Argand diagram.
   (ii) Find the value of $|2w - z|$.
8. A rectangular shape has a length of $5 + 2i$ cm and a width of $-3 - i$ cm. Find the perimeter of the rectangle.
9. Complex numbers u and v are represented on the Argand diagram.

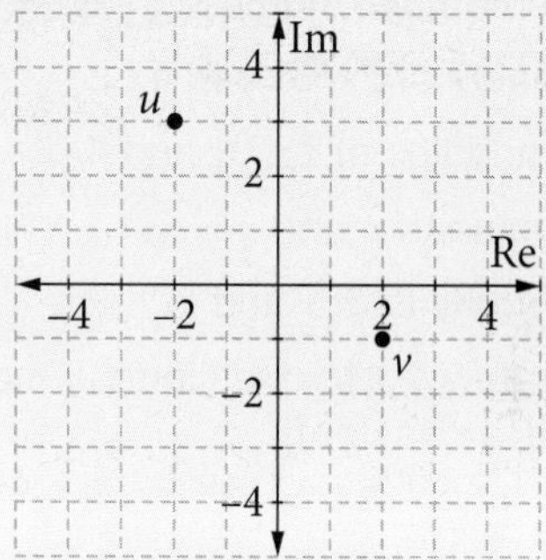

If $w = u - v$, find the value of w.
Hence, show w on an Argand diagram.

10. Given the complex numbers $u = 1 - 2i$ and $v = 2 + i$, represent the complex numbers $u + v$ and $u - v$ on one Argand diagram.

Section 28.4: Multiplying Complex Numbers

Learning Outcome:

You should be able to:
- multiply complex numbers

Multiplying a complex number by a constant

To multiply a complex number by a constant, we simply remove the brackets and multiply the constant by the real part and the imaginary part.

This is the same method used when multiplying an algebraic expression by a constant. We remove the bracket and multiply each term by the constant.

In general: $k(a + bi) = ka + kbi$

EXAMPLE 1

Simplify the following:

(i) $2(3 - 2i)$

(ii) $\sqrt{3}(1 + 4i)$

Solution

(i) $2(3 - 2i)$

$= (2 \times 3) + (2 \times -2i)$

$= 6 - 4i$

(ii) $\sqrt{3}(1 + 4i)$

$= (\sqrt{3} \times 1) + (\sqrt{3} \times 4i)$

$= \sqrt{3} + 4\sqrt{3}i$

Discussion Time 

Work with a classmate to answer the following questions.

Consider the complex number $z = 12 + 6i$.

1. Find the value of $2z$, $3z$ and $4z$.
2. Find the modulus of $2z$, $3z$ and $4z$.
3. Find the value of $\frac{z}{2}$ and $\frac{z}{3}$.
4. Find the modulus of $\frac{z}{2}$ and $\frac{z}{3}$.
5. Use your answers to questions **2** and **4** to make a statement about the effect of multiplying a complex number by a constant.

As you can see from the discussion time above, multiplying a complex number by a constant changes the modulus of the complex number.

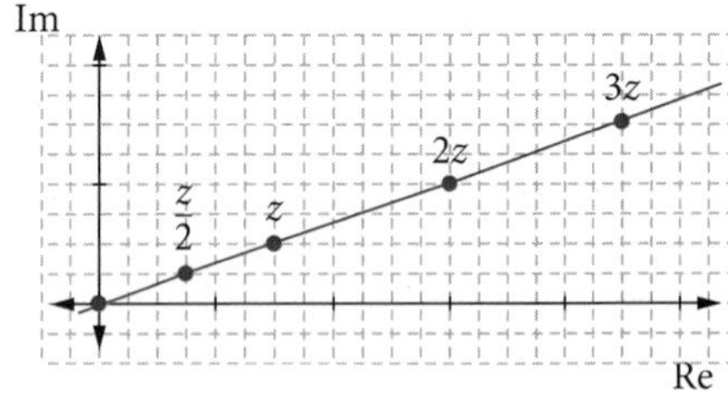

In general $|kz| = k|z|$

Multiplying by a constant (k) results in **scaling**.

As the diagram shows, the modulus increases if $k > 1$ and decreases if $k < 1$.

Multiplying a complex number by *i*

To multiply a complex number by i we remove the bracket and multiply i by the real part and the imaginary part.

This is the same method used when multiplying an algebraic expression by a variable. We remove the bracket and multiply each term by the variable.

Consider the complex number $a + bi$ being multiplied by i: $i(a + bi)$

$= ai + bi^2$

Recall, $i^2 = -1$. Substitute for i^2.

$= ai + b(-1)$

$= ai - b$

In general: $i(a + bi) = -b + ai$

EXAMPLE 2

Simplify the following:

(i) $i(-3 - 5i)$ **(ii)** $(7 + 9i)i$

Solution

(i) $i(-3 - 5i)$

$= -3i - 5i^2$

$= -3i - 5(-1)$ replace i^2 with -1

$= -3i + 5$

$= 5 - 3i$

Replacing i^2 is the same as substitution in algebra.

(ii) $(7 + 9i)i$

$= 7i + 9i^2$

$= 7i + 9(-1)$ replace i^2 with -1

$= 7i - 9$

$= -9 + 7i$

Discussion Time 

Work with a classmate to answer the following questions

1. Let $z = 6 + 2i$. Find the value of iz, i^2z, i^3z and i^4z.
2. Plot z, iz, i^2z, i^3z and i^4z on an Argand diagram.
3. Describe the effect of multiplying a complex number by the above powers of i on the position of the complex number on an Argand diagram.

As you can see from the discussion time above, multiplying a complex number by i and powers of i causes the complex number to rotate.

- Multiplication by i causes an anticlockwise rotation of 90° about the origin
- Multiplication by i^2 causes an anticlockwise rotation of 180° about the origin
- Multiplication by i^3 causes an anticlockwise rotation of 270° about the origin
- Multiplication by i^4 causes an anticlockwise rotation of 360° about the origin

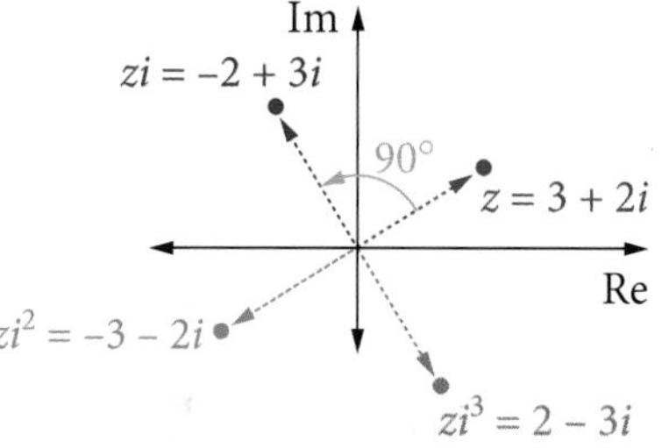

Multiplying a complex number by another complex number

To multiply a complex number by another complex number, we use the distributive law just like when we expand brackets in algebra.

$$(a + bi)(c + di) = a(c + di) + bi(c + di)$$

 **Links across the syllabus**

The distributive law is covered in Chapter 1: Number Systems, and expanding brackets is covered in Chapter 2: Algebra I.

Multiplying one complex number by another combines the effects of multiplying the complex number by a constant and multiplying it by i.

It results in scaling and rotation of the original complex number as shown in the diagram.

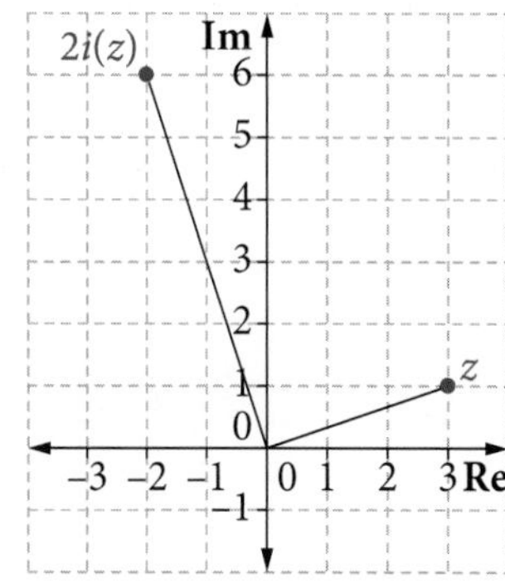

EXAMPLE 3

Find the value of **(i)** $(4 - 3i)(2 + 5i)$ **(ii)** $(7 - 2i)^2$

Solution

(i) $(4 - 3i)(2 + 5i)$

$= 4(2 + 5i) - 3i(2 + 5i)$ Distributive law

$= 8 + 20i - 6i - 15i^2$

$= 8 + 20i - 6i - 15(-1)$ Substitute -1 for i^2

$= 8 + 20i - 6i + 15$ Simplify

$= 23 + 14i$

(ii) $(7 - 2i)^2$

$= (7 - 2i)(7 - 2i)$

$= 7(7 - 2i) - 2i(7 - 2i)$ Distributive law

$= 49 - 14i - 14i + 4i^2$

$= 49 - 14i - 14i + 4(-1)$ Substitute -1 for i^2

$= 49 - 14i - 14i - 4$ Simplify

$= 45 - 28i$

Practice Questions 28.4

1. Multiply out the brackets and simplify each of the following:
   (i) $3(4i)$ **(ii)** $5(1 - 5i)$ **(iii)** $-6(-2 - 2i)$ **(iv)** $-3(-8i - 3)$
2. **(i)** Multiply $(-1 - 2i)$ by 2.
   (ii) Plot $(-1 - 2i)$ and $2(-1 - 2i)$ on an Argand diagram.
   (iii) Calculate $|(-1 - 2i)|$ and $|2(-1 - 2i)|$.
   (iv) What effect does multiplication by 2 have on $(-1 - 2i)$?
3. Multiply out the brackets and simplify each of the following:
   (i) $(i)(4 + 5i)$ **(ii)** $(2i)(3 + 2i)$ **(iii)** $(3i)(5 - 6i)$ **(iv)** $(7i)(-1 - 3i)$
4. **(i)** Plot $-8 - i$ on an Argand diagram.
   (ii) Multiply $(-8 - i)$ by $-i$.
   (iii) Plot $-i(-8 - i)$ on an Argand diagram.
   (iv) What effect does multiplication by $-i$ have on $(-8 - i)$?
5. Multiply out the brackets and simplify each of the following:
   (i) $(4 + i)(5 + 5i)$ **(iii)** $(7 - 3i)(5 + 2i)$ **(v)** $(-3 + 2i)(3 - 8i)$
   (ii) $(1 + 2i)(6 + 4i)$ **(iv)** $(-5 + 4i)(2 - 7i)$ **(vi)** $(-2 - 4i)(-1 - 5i)$
6. Simplify each of the following:
   (i) $(-4i)^2$ **(iii)** $(2 - 3i)^2$ **(v)** $(-1 - 2i)^2$
   (ii) $(4 + 7i)^2$ **(iv)** $(-6 + 5i)^2$ **(vi)** $(-5 - i)^2$
7. Simplify the following:
   (i) $3i(4 - 2i)(5 + 2i)$ **(iii)** $(1 - 3i)(3 + 4i)(-5 - 2i)$
   (ii) $2i(3 - i)(6 - 2i)$ **(iv)** $(2 + 3i)(5 - i)(4 - 3i)$
8. Find the value of z_1z_2 for each of the following:
   (i) $z_1 = -1 - i$, $z_2 = 9 + 8i$ **(iii)** $z_1 = 3 + 2i$, $z_2 = 4 - 3i$ **(v)** $z_1 = -1 + 2i$, $z_2 = -7 + i$
   (ii) $z_1 = -3 + i$, $z_2 = 5 + 7i$ **(iv)** $z_1 = 1 + i$, $z_2 = -3 + 4i$ **(vi)** $z_1 = 6 + 3i$, $z_2 = -5 - 4i$

9. If $(1 + bi)(1 - bi) = 2$, find b.

10. $z_1 = 4 - 2i$, $z_2 = -3 - i$ and $z_3 = 7 + 5i$. Find the value of each of the following. Express your answers in the form $a + bi$.

    (i) z_1z_3 (ii) $(z_2)^2$ (iii) $2z_3z_2$ (iv) $2z_13z_2$

11. If $z = 3 - 2i$ find the value of:

    (i) $2z$ (ii) $3z$ (iii) $4z$

    (iv) Plot the four complex numbers z, $2z$, $3z$ and $4z$ on an Argand diagram.

    (v) Find the modulus of each complex number z, $2z$, $3z$ and $4z$.

    (vi) Using your answers to (iv) and (v), make a statement about the effect of multiplying a complex number by a constant.

12. If $z = 2 - 3i$

    (i) show that $z^2 = -5 - 12i$

    (ii) find the value of $|z^2|$

    (iii) show z and z^2 on a single Argand diagram.

13. If $w = z^2$ find w for the following values of z:

    (i) $z = 2 + i$ (ii) $z = 4 + i$ (iii) $z = 4 + 3i$

    In each case, also find $|z|$ and $|w|$ and show w on an Argand diagram.

14. Given that $z = 2 + 2\sqrt{3}i$, show that $z^2 - 4z$ is real.

15. (i) If $z = 4 - 3i$ find the value of iz, i^2z, i^3z and i^4z.

    (ii) Plot z, iz, i^2z, i^3z and i^4z on an Argand diagram.

    (iii) Make a statement that explains what is happening when z is multiplied by i, i^2, i^3 and i^4.

Section 28.5: Dividing Complex Numbers

Learning Outcomes:

You should be able to:

- understand and find the conjugate of a complex number
- divide complex numbers

Division of complex numbers is similar to the process we used to rationalise the denominator in surds.

We must first find the **conjugate** of the denominator.

Links across the syllabus

Rationalising the denominator is covered in Chapter 1: Number Systems.

The **conjugate** of a complex number is the original number with the sign on the **imaginary** part changed. The symbol for the conjugate is $\bar{z}$.
If $z = a + bi$, the conjugate of z, $\bar{z} = a - bi$.

EXAMPLE 1

Find the conjugate ($\overline{z}$) of each of the following complex numbers:

We always change the sign of the imaginary part.

(i) $4 + 3i$ **(ii)** $-2 + i$ **(iii)** $-6i - 5$ **(iv)** $-7i$

Solution

(i) $z = 4 + 3i$
$\overline{z} = 4 - 3i$

(ii) $z = -2 + i$
$\overline{z} = -2 - i$

(iii) $z = -5 - 6i$
$\overline{z} = -5 + 6i$

(iv) $z = -7i$
$\overline{z} = +7i$
$\overline{z} = 7i$

Steps to divide complex numbers:

To divide complex numbers, you must multiply both the numerator and the denominator by the conjugate of the denominator.

Step 1: Find the conjugate of the denominator.

Step 2: Multiply both the numerator and denominator by the conjugate using the distributive law.

Step 3: Simplify the powers of i; remember that $i^2 = -1$.

Step 4: Combine like terms in both the numerator and denominator; that is, combine real numbers with real numbers and imaginary numbers with imaginary numbers.

Step 5: Write your answer in the form $a + bi$.

Step 6: Simplify your answer if you can.

When done correctly, there will be no imaginary parts in the denominator (bottom).

EXAMPLE 2

Divide: $\dfrac{3 + 2i}{-3i}$

Solution

Step 1: Find the conjugate of the denominator — Conjugate $= 3i$

Step 2: Multiply both the numerator and denominator by the conjugate using the distributive law

$$= \frac{3 + 2i}{-3i} \times \frac{3i}{3i}$$

$$= \frac{3i(3) + 3i(2i)}{3i(-3i)}$$

$$= \frac{9i + 6i^2}{-9i^2}$$

Step 3: Simplify the powers of i, remember that $i^2 = -1$

$$= \frac{9i + 6(-1)}{-9(-1)}$$

$$= \frac{9i - 6}{9}$$

Step 4: Combine like terms in both the numerator and denominator — This step is not necessary in this example.

Step 5: Write your answer in the form $a + bi$

$$= \frac{-6}{9} + \frac{9}{9}i$$

Step 6: Simplify your answer if you can

$$= -\frac{2}{3} + i$$

EXAMPLE 3

Divide: $\dfrac{1-i}{-2-2i}$

Solution

Step 1: Find the conjugate of the denominator — Conjugate $= -2 + 2i$

Step 2: Multiply numerator and denominator by the conjugate using the distributive law

$$= \frac{1-i}{-2-2i} \times \frac{-2+2i}{-2+2i}$$

$$= \frac{-2(1-i) + 2i(1-i)}{-2(-2-2i) + 2i(-2-2i)}$$

$$= \frac{-2 + 2i + 2i - 2i^2}{4 + 4i - 4i - 4i^2}$$

Step 3: Substitute −1 or i^2

$$= \frac{-2 + 2i + 2i - 2(-1)}{4 + 4i - 4i - 4(-1)}$$

Step 4: Combine like terms

$$= \frac{-2 + 2i + 2i + 2}{4 + 4i - 4i + 4}$$

$$= \frac{4i}{8}$$

Step 5: Write in the form $a + bi$

$$= \frac{0}{8} + \frac{4i}{8}$$

Step 6: Simplify

$$= 0 + \frac{1}{2}i$$

$$= \frac{1}{2}i$$

Practice Questions 28.5

1. Find the conjugate of each of the following complex numbers:
   (i) $4 + 5i$ (ii) $7 - 6i$ (iii) $-9 + i$ (iv) $-5 - 2i$ (v) $-8i$ (vi) $-3i + 4$

2. If $z_1 = 2 + i$, $z_2 = 3 - 2i$ and $z_3 = 1 + i$, find the value of:
   (i) $z_1 + \overline{z_3}$ (ii) $z_2 + \overline{z_1}$ (iii) $\overline{z_1} - \overline{z_3}$ (iv) $z_1\overline{z_1}$ (v) $\overline{z_1}\,\overline{z_2}$ (vi) $\overline{z_2}\,\overline{z_3}$

3. Given $z_1 = 2 + 3i$ and $z_2 = -1 - 2i$, investigate whether the following statements are true:
   (i) $\overline{z_1 + z_2} = \overline{z_1} + \overline{z_2}$
   (ii) $\overline{z_1 \times z_2} = \overline{z_1} \times \overline{z_2}$

4. Divide the following complex numbers and write your answer in the form $a + bi$:
   (i) $\dfrac{2}{3i}$ (ii) $\dfrac{-5}{6i}$ (iii) $\dfrac{-7}{-2i}$ (iv) $\dfrac{2+3i}{4i}$ (v) $\dfrac{-1-i}{-6i}$ (vi) $\dfrac{-1-3i}{-2i}$

5. Divide the following complex numbers and write your answer in the form $a + bi$:
   (i) $\dfrac{2+7i}{4+3i}$ (ii) $\dfrac{-3+5i}{6-4i}$ (iii) $\dfrac{-6-5i}{7-3i}$ (iv) $\dfrac{-1-8i}{7-i}$ (v) $\dfrac{-5-9i}{6+2i}$ (vi) $\dfrac{-2-3i}{-5-i}$

6. $z_1 = 2 + i$, $z_2 = 3 - 2i$, $z_3 = -4 - 5i$ and $z_4 = -1 - i$. Find the value of each of the following:
   (i) $\dfrac{z_1}{z_4}$ (ii) $\dfrac{z_4}{z_2}$ (iii) $\dfrac{z_1 + z_2}{z_4}$ (iv) $\dfrac{z_3 - z_2}{z_1}$

7. If $z = -2 + 4i$ and $w = -3 - 2i$, find the value of the following:
   (i) $\dfrac{z}{w}$ (ii) $\dfrac{\overline{z}}{w}$ (iii) $\dfrac{iz}{w}$ (iv) $\dfrac{\overline{z}}{\overline{w}}$

8. Express each of the following in the form $a + bi$:
   (i) $\dfrac{(1+2i)-(2+i)}{(2-i)(3+i)}$ (ii) $\dfrac{(2+3i)-(1-2i)}{(3+2i)(4-i)}$

9. Impedance to the flow of alternating current in an electrical circuit is measured in ohms. The impedance, Z, in a circuit is found by using the formula $Z = \frac{V}{I}$, where V is the voltage (measured in volts) and I is the current (measured in amperes).
   (i) Find the impedance when $V = 1{\cdot}8 - 0{\cdot}4i$ volts and $I = -0{\cdot}3i$ amperes.
   (ii) Find the current when $V = 1{\cdot}6 - 0{\cdot}3i$ volts and $Z = 1{\cdot}5 + 8i$ ohms.

Section 28.6: Equality of Complex Numbers

Learning Outcome:

You should be able to:

- find the value of unknown variables when two complex numbers are equal

Two complex numbers are said to be equal if their real parts and their imaginary parts are both equal.

If $z_1 = a + ib$ and $z_2 = x + iy$ are equal, then $a = x$ and $b = y$.

If $z_1 = z_2$ then $Re(z_1) = Re(z_2)$ and $Im(z_1) = Im(z_2)$

EXAMPLE

Find the value of the unknown variables in each of the following:

(i) $5 + 2yi = -x + 6i$

(ii) $7a + i(3a - b) = 14 - 6i$

Solution

(i) $5 + 2yi = -x + 6i$

Step 1: Identify the real and imaginary parts.

Re Im Re Im

$5 + 2yi = -x + 6i$

Step 2: Equate the real parts and solve for unknown.

$5 = -x$ multiply both sides by -1

$-5 = x$

$x = -5$

Step 3: Equate the imaginary parts and solve for unknown (don't include i).

$2y = 6$ divide both sides by 2

$y = 3$

(ii) $7a + i(3a - b) = 14 - 6i$

Step 1: Identify the real and imaginary parts.

Re Im Re Im

$7a + i(3a - b) = 14 - 6i$

Step 2: Equate the real parts and solve for unknown.

$7a = 14$ divide both sides by 7

$a = 2$

Step 3: Equate the imaginary parts and solve for unknown (don't include i).

$3a - b = -6$

$a = 2$ from part one

$3(2) - b = -6$ substitute 2 for a

$6 - b = -6$

$-b = -12$ subtract 6 from both sides

$b = 12$ multiply both sides by -1

Practice Questions 28.6

1. Find the value of x and y in each of the following:
   (i) $x + yi = 12 + 7i$
   (ii) $2x + 3yi = 14 - 12i$
   (iii) $(x + 5) + (y - 4)i = 3 - i$
   (iv) $(x - 6) - (y - 1)i = 2 - 8i$
2. Find the value of a and b in each of the following:
   (i) $(4a - 2) + (a - 4)i = (4 - 2b) + 2bi$
   (ii) $(3 - 2i) + (a + 5i) = 11 + bi$
   (iii) $2(a + bi) - 5(a - bi) = 9 + 14i$
   (iv) $(6i)(a + bi) = 13 + 6i$
3. Given that $z = x + iy$ and that $\bar{z}$ is the complex conjugate of z:
   (i) express $z + 2\bar{z}$ in the form $a + bi$
   (ii) find the value of z for which $z + 2\bar{z} = 9 + 2i$.
4. Let $z = 12 + 5i$.
   (i) Find $\bar{z}$.
   (ii) Find the real number p such that $2\bar{z} + p(-1 + 2i) = 13(2 - i) - i$.
5. Let $w = 1 + i$.
   Find the real numbers p and q such that $p(w + i) + wq = -5 + 2i$.
6. Find the values of x and y in the equation $x(1 + i)^2 + y(2 - i)^2 = 3 + 10i$.
7. Let $z = -3i$.
   (i) Calculate $|z|$.
   (ii) Hence, or otherwise, find the real numbers a and b such that:
   $|z|(a + bi) + (3ai - 5b) = 11 + 7i$.
8. Find the value of x and y if:
   $x + yi - 8 = 7 - 2(x - yi - 3i)$
9. Find the values of a and b for which:
   $\dfrac{a}{2 + i} + bi = 2 + 4i$
10. Let $z = a + bi$. Find the value of z such that:
   $2z - i\bar{z} = 4 + 7i$

Section 28.7: Solving Equations with Complex Roots

Learning Outcome:

You should be able to:

- solve equations with complex roots

In Chapter 4 Algebra III, we studied how to find the roots of quadratic equations using factorisation or the quadratic $(-b)$ formula.

Links across the syllabus

Finding the roots of quadratic equations is covered in Chapter 4: Algebra III.

Recall the following types of quadratic graphs.

The graph on the right has two distinct real roots as it crosses the x-axis in two places.

Example:

$$x^2 - 4x + 3 = 0$$
$$(x - 1)(x - 3) = 0$$

$x = 1, x = 3$ are the roots of this equation.

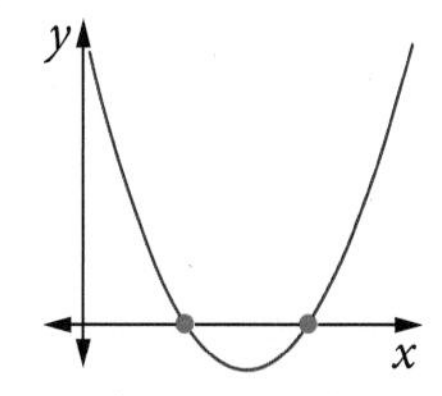

two distinct real roots

Complex Numbers

The graph on the right has two equal real roots as it crosses the x-axis in one place only.

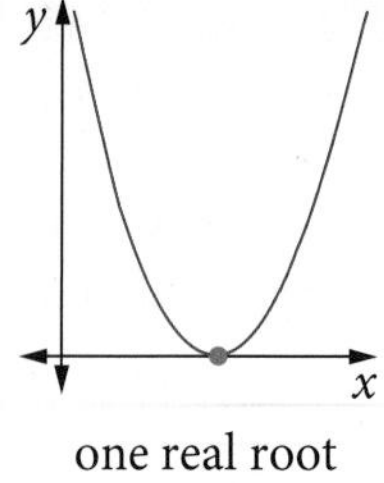

Example:

$$x^2 - 6x + 9 = 0$$
$$(x - 3)(x - 3) = 0$$

$x = 3$ and $x = 3$ are the roots of this equation.

A graph of a quadratic equation that doesn't cross the x-axis (real axis), as shown below right, has no real roots.

Such a graph has complex roots. We will now learn how to find the roots of such an equation.

Since z is used to represent complex numbers the x is replaced with a z. The x-axis becomes the real axis and the y-axis becomes the imaginary axis.

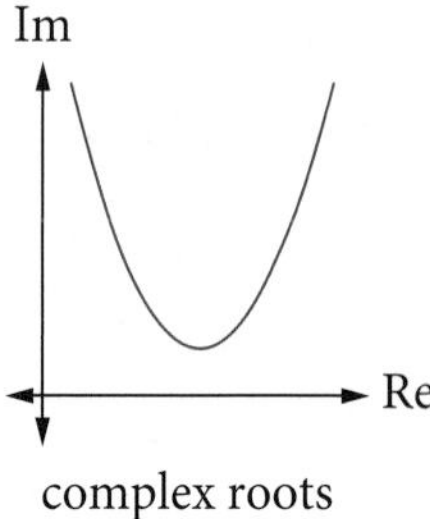

Example:

$z^2 + 2z + 10$ has no real roots as is shown in the next example.

EXAMPLE

Find the roots of the following equations:

(i) $z^2 + 2z + 10 = 0$ **(ii)** $z^2 - 3z + 12 = 0$

Solution

(i) $z^2 + 2z + 10 = 0$

$a = 1 \quad b = 2 \quad c = 10$

Using the quadratic formula:

$$z = \frac{-b \pm \sqrt{b^2 - 4ac}}{2a}$$
$$= \frac{-2 \pm \sqrt{(2)^2 - 4(1)(10)}}{2(1)}$$
$$= \frac{-2 \pm \sqrt{4 - 40}}{2}$$
$$= \frac{-2 \pm \sqrt{-36}}{2}$$
$$= \frac{-2 \pm 6i}{2}$$
$$= -1 \pm 3i$$

Roots $= -1 + 3i, -1 - 3i$

The roots occur in conjugate pairs, therefore if $a + bi$ is a root then $a - bi$ is also a root.

(ii) $z^2 - 3z + 12 = 0$

$a = 1 \quad b = -3 \quad c = 12$

Using the quadratic formula:

$$z = \frac{-b \pm \sqrt{b^2 - 4ac}}{2a}$$
$$= \frac{-(-3) \pm \sqrt{(-3)^2 - 4(1)(12)}}{2(1)}$$
$$= \frac{3 \pm \sqrt{9 - 48}}{2}$$
$$= \frac{3 \pm \sqrt{-39}}{2}$$
$$= \frac{3 \pm \sqrt{39}i}{2}$$
$$= \frac{3}{2} \pm \frac{\sqrt{39}}{2}i$$

Roots $= \frac{3}{2} + \frac{\sqrt{39}}{2}i, \frac{3}{2} - \frac{\sqrt{39}}{2}i$

Practice Questions 28.7

1. Which of the following equations have complex roots? Justify your answer.

(i)
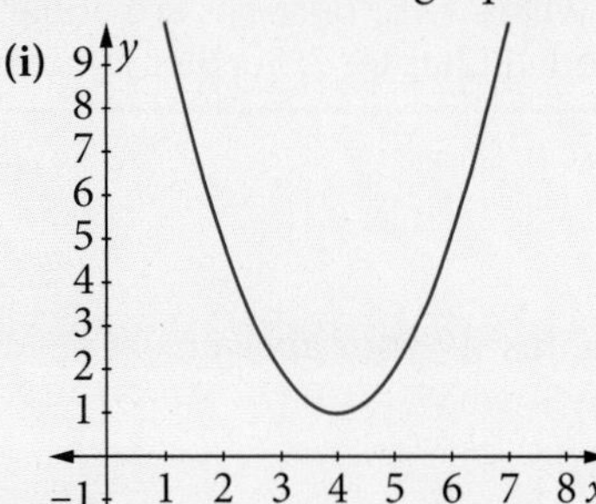

(iii)
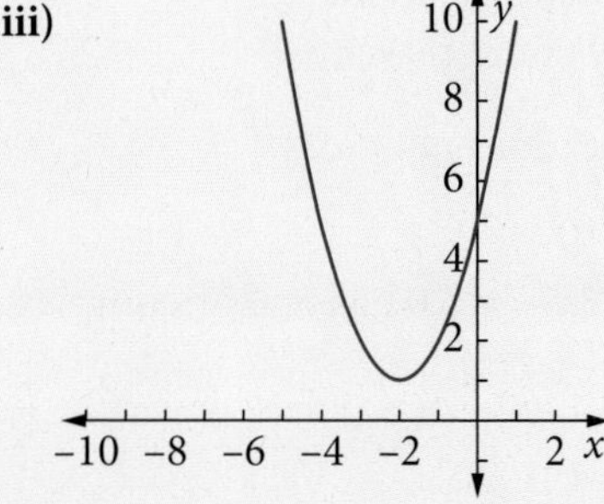

(v)
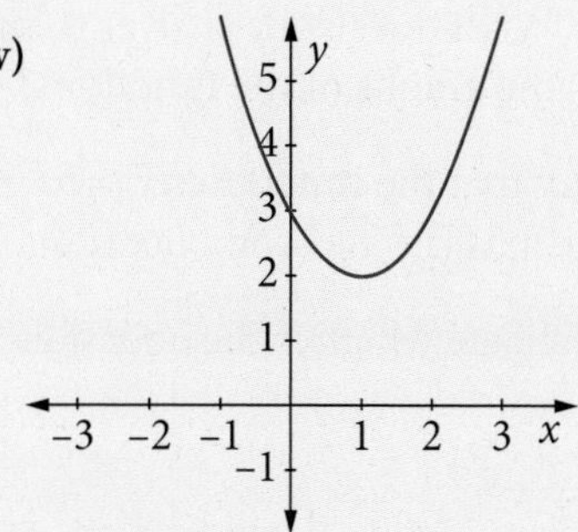

(ii)
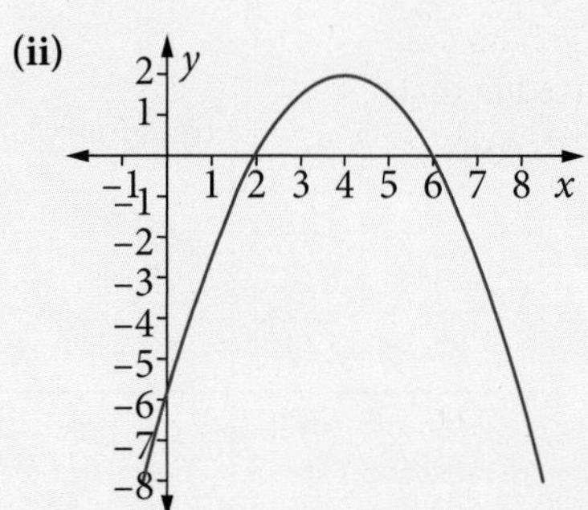

(iv)
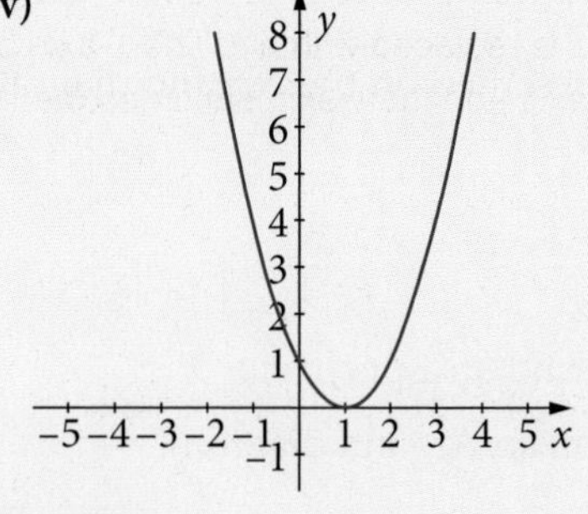

(vi)
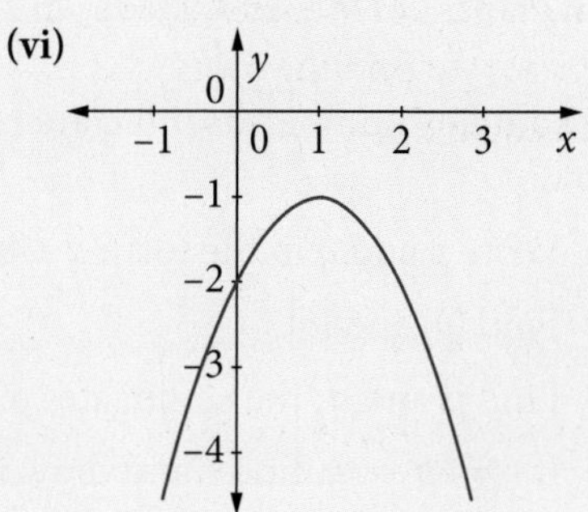

2. Find the roots of the following equations:

(i) $z^2 = -64$ (iii) $z^2 = -28$ (v) $3z^2 + 147 = 0$

(ii) $z^2 = -48$ (iv) $2z^2 + 50 = 0$ (vi) $5z^2 + 495 = 0$

3. Find the roots of the following equations:

(i) $z^2 - 10z + 34 = 0$ (iii) $z^2 - 4z + 13 = 0$ (v) $z^2 - 8z = -40$

(ii) $z^2 - 10z + 28 = 0$ (iv) $z^2 + 5 = 4z$ (vi) $z^2 = -10z - 29$

4. Find the roots of the following equations:

(i) $2z^2 - 4z + 5 = 0$ (iii) $4z^2 - 6z + 5 = 0$ (v) $9z^2 - 6z + 5 = 0$

(ii) $5z^2 + 12z + 8 = 0$ (iv) $5z^2 - 6z + 9 = 0$ (vi) $8z^2 - 12z + 5 = 0$

5. Solve the equation $z^2 + 6z + 20 = 0$
Express the solutions in the form $z = a + \sqrt{b}i$, where a and b are integers.

6. The quadratic formula for finding the roots of an equation is: $x = \dfrac{-b \pm \sqrt{b^2 - 4ac}}{2a}$

The part of the quadratic formula under the square root sign $(b^2 - 4ac)$ is called the discriminant. The value of the discriminant can be used to determine the nature of the roots of an equation as follows:

$b^2 - 4ac < 0$ means complex roots;
$b^2 - 4ac > 0$ means two distinct real roots;
$b^2 - 4ac = 0$ means two equal real roots.

(a) Use this information to determine the nature of the roots of the following equations:

(i) $6a^2 - 2a - 3 = 0$ (iii) $c^2 + 5c + 2 = 0$ (v) $4e^2 - 8e + 4 = 0$

(ii) $5b^2 + b - 2 = 0$ (iv) $9d^2 - 3d + 2 = 0$ (vi) $2f^2 - 10f - 5 = 0$

(b) Explain why $b^2 - 4ac < 0$ results in complex roots.

(c) Explain why $b^2 - 4ac = 0$ results in equal roots.

7. Show that $2 - 2i$ is a root of the equation $z^2 - 4z + 8 = 0$. Hence, or otherwise, find the other root.

8. $f(x) = 8 - 4x$ and $g(x) = x^2 - 5x - 2$ are two functions.

 (i) Solve $f(x) = g(x)$.

 (ii) What does your answer to part (i) tell you about the graphs of the functions? Justify your answer.

Finding where two functions are equal is covered in Chapter 7: Further Functions.

9. Verify that the function $f(x) = x^2 + 2x + 5$ does not cross the x-axis (i.e. has complex roots).

10. Investigate whether the equation $2x^2 - 3x - 1 = 0$ has real or complex roots. Justify your answer.

Revision and Exam Style Questions – Section A

1. The complex numbers p and q are represented on the Argand diagram below.

 (i) Write p and q in the form $a + bi$.

 (ii) Find $|p|$ and $|q|$.

 (iii) Find $\bar{p}$ and $\bar{q}$, the conjugates of p and q respectively.

 (iv) If $r = 2p - 3q$, find r and draw it on an Argand diagram.

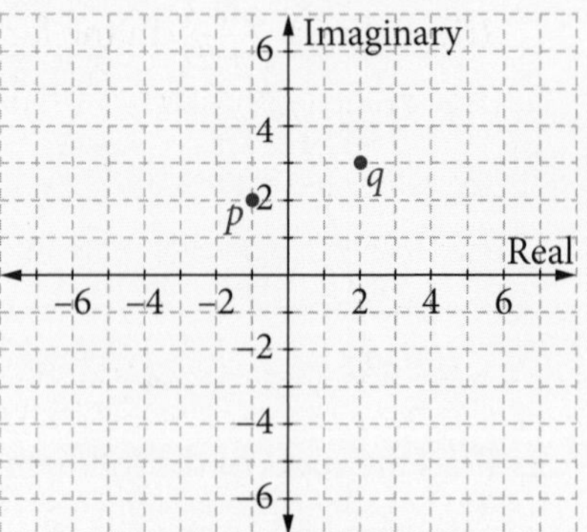

2. Given that $i^2 = -1$ and $z = -5 - 2i$:

 (i) find the value of i^{11}

 (ii) find the value of i^{11} multiplied by z

 (iii) what of the effect of multiplication by i^{11} on z?

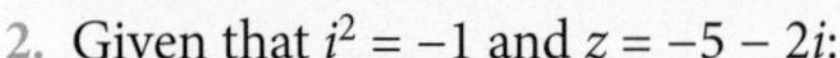

3. p and q are complex numbers, where $p = 3 + 4i$ and $q = 2 - 3i$. Find $\bar{p}q$, expressing your answer in the form $a + bi$.

4. Given the complex number $z = 2 + 3i$, represent the complex numbers z, $2z$, $\bar{z}$ and iz on one Argand diagram. Comment on their relative positions.

5. Given that $i^2 = -1$, simplify $5 + 4(6 + 3i) - i(2 - 5i)$ and write your answer in the form $x + yi$, where $x, y \in R$.

6. Let $w = 2 - 3i$ and $u = 5 - 7i$.

 (i) Plot w and u on an Argand diagram.

 (ii) Verify that $|u - w| = 5$.

7. Let $z = 4 - 2i$ and $w = \bar{z}$.

 (i) Plot z and w on an Argand diagram.

 (ii) Investigate whether $z \times w = |z|^2$.

8. The Argand diagram shows the complex number $z = 3 + 2i$.

 (i) Identify the other points P, Q and R as iz, $-z$ and $2z$.

 (ii) Explain the relationship between z and each of the points P, Q and R.

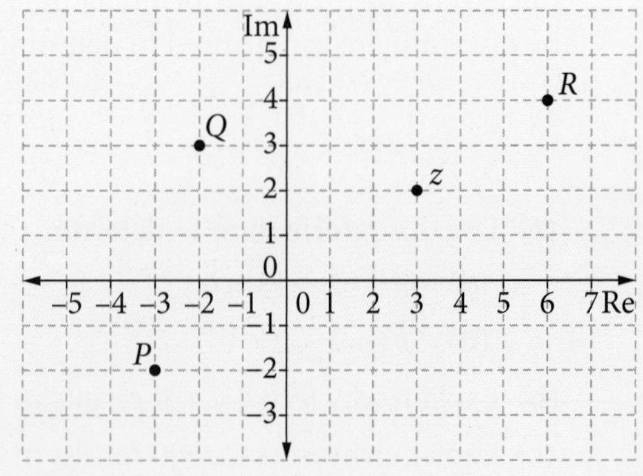

9. Let $z = \sqrt{3} + i$ and $w = 3i$.

 (i) Find $|z|$ and $|w|$, the modulus of z and w respectively.

 (ii) Simplify the expressions zw and $\frac{w}{z}$, giving the answers in the form $a + bi$.

 (iii) Investigate whether:

$$\left|\frac{w}{z}\right| = \frac{|w|}{|z|}$$

10. Let $z_1 = 1 + i$ and $z_2 = 2 - i$.
   (i) Find the imaginary part of $z_1 z_2$.
   (ii) Find the value of $|z_1 - z_2|$.
   (iii) Find the value of $i\bar{z}_2$.

11. Let $z_1 = \frac{1+i}{1-i}$ and $z_2 = \frac{1}{2} + \frac{\sqrt{3}}{2}i$.
   (i) Show that $z_1 = i$.
   (ii) Draw on an Argand diagram z_1 and z_2.
   (iii) Show that $|z_1| = |z_2|$.

12. Solve the equation $2x^2 + 98 = 0$.

Revision and Exam Style Questions – Section B

More challenging problems

1. Let $z = -2 - 5i$.
   (i) Plot $z + 3$ and $z + 2i$ on an Argand diagram.
   (ii) Express $\frac{z+3}{z+2i}$ in the form $a + bi$.
   (iii) Hence, or otherwise, calculate $\left|\frac{z+3}{z+2i}\right|$.

2. Let $w = -1 - 4i$.
   (i) Plot w, $\bar{w}$ and $w + \bar{w}$ on an Argand diagram, where $\bar{w}$ is the complex conjugate of w.
   (ii) Evaluate $2 - w$ and hence, write $(2 - w)^3 - (2 - w)^2 + 16(2 - w)$ in its simplest form.

3. Let $w = 2 - 3i$.
   (i) Express $w - 4 + 4i$ in the form $a + bi$.
   (ii) Express $w^2 + 2i + 10$ in the form $a + bi$.
   (iii) Hence, investigate whether:
   $$\left|\frac{w^2 + 2i + 10}{w - 4 + 4i}\right| = \frac{|w^2 + 2i + 10|}{|w - 4 + 4i|}$$

4. (i) Express $= \frac{1 - 18i}{2 - i}$ in the form $a + bi$.
   (ii) The complex number z satisfies the equation
   $$4z - 3\bar{z} = \frac{1 - 18i}{2 - i}$$
   Find the value of z, giving the answer in the form $a + bi$, where a and b are real numbers.

5. $z = -3 + 4i$ and $zw = -14 + 2i$.
   (i) Find the value of w in the form $a + bi$.
   (ii) Find the modulus of z and w.

6. Find the roots of the equation $z^2 - 3z + 12 = 0$.

7. Show that the graphs of the linear function $f(x) = 7 + 6x$ and the quadratic function $g(x) = x^2 + 4x + 12$ do not intersect.

8. Given that $z = 3 + 2i$, find the value of $\bar{z}^2 + \frac{169}{z^2}$, giving your answer in the form $a + b$, where a and b are integers.

9. Complex numbers can be used to describe the position of characters in computer games.
   The position of the centre of the top of the head of a character is given as $z = 1 - i$, as shown in the diagram.

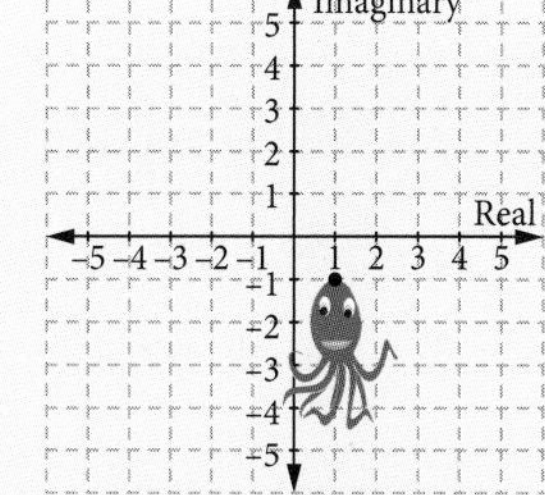

   (i) Using z and assuming that all points in the character undergo the same transformation as z, fill out the table below.
   The first one is completed for you as an example.
   (ii) Plot the transformed points on an Argand diagram to show the location of the character in each case.
   (iii) Pat wants to rotate the character by 90° anti-clockwise and double its distance from the origin. Describe the transformation of z required to do this.

Transformation	Calculation	Explanation
$z_1 = z + 2i$	$z_1 = 1 - i + 2i$ $= 1 + i$	The character moves up by two units
$z_2 = z + 2$		
$z_3 = -z$		
$z_4 = \bar{z}$		
$z_5 = i^3 z$		
$z_6 = 3z$		
$z_7 = z(3 + 2i)$		

10. The path taken by a high jumper is modelled by two quadratic functions A and B.
Function A (shown in blue) models a failure to clear the bar.
Function B (shown in red) models a successful clearance by the high jumper.
(The horizontal axis represents the bar.)

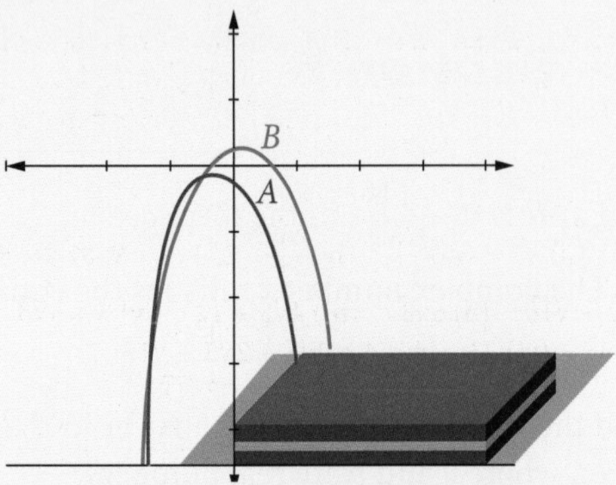

The equations representing these functions are $f(x) = -x^2 + x + 6$ and $g(x) = -x^2 + x - 6$.

(i) Which graph has real roots? Explain.

(ii) Determine which equation represents which function. Justify your answer.

11. A submarine has a radar which covers a circular area, given by the equation: $x^2 + y^2 + 4x = 14$.

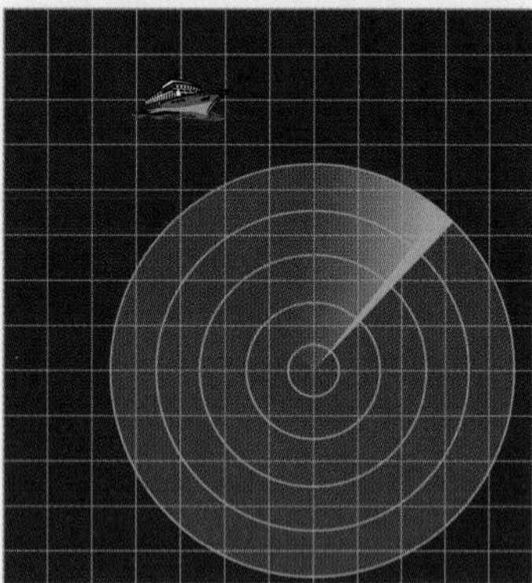

A ship is moving along the path, given by the equation $x + 2y - 12 = 0$.
Investigate whether the ship will pass through the radar of the submarine.

Now that you have completed the chapter, revisit the 'Something to think about…' question.

Answers

Chapter 1

Something to think about

(i) 12 mins (ii) 1st athlete = 3 laps 2nd athlete = 2 laps

Practice Questions 1.1

1. (i) 11 (ii) 37 (iii) 43 (iv) 163 (v) 40 (vi) 95 **2.** (i) 57 (ii) −617 (iii) 68 (iv) 78 (v) 83 (vi) 432 **3.** (i) 51 (ii) −105 (iii) 1268 (iv) 64 (v) 48 **4.** 121 **5.** 54,144 **6.** 15 **7.** (8 − (4 + 2)) = 2 **8.** 2210

Practice Questions 1.2

1. (i) Commutative (ii) Associative (iii) Distributive (iv) Associative (v) Associative **2.** (i) 7 + 11 = 11 + 7 (ii) 15 × 6 = 6 × 15 (iii) 9 + (11 + 4) = (9 + 11) + 4 (iv) 12 × (2 + 4) = (12 × 2) + (12 × 4) **3.** (i) (2 + 6) + 8 (ii) (5 × 8) × 3 (iii) 4 × 9 − 4 × 2 (iv) 2(4 + 6) + 3(4 + 6) (v) 9 + (3 + 5) (vi) 6 × (7 × 9) **4.** (i) 60 (ii) 14 (iii) −27 **5.** (i) Associative (ii) Commutative (iii) Associative and Commutative (iv) Distributive (v) Distributive **6.** (i) $3z + (4x + 2y)$; $3z + (2y + 4x)$; $(2y + 4x) + 3z$; $4x + (2y + 3z)$; $4x + (3z + 2y)$; $2y + (4x + 3z)$ (ii) $(4x + 2y) + 3z = 3z + (4x + 2y)$ shows we can swap numbers around and still get the same answer (iii) $(4x + 2y) + 3z = 4x + (2y + 3z)$ shows it doesn't matter how we group numbers **7.** 12 × (13 + 11 + 8) = 12 × 13 + 12 × 11 + 12 × 8 = 384 **8.** $n(x + y + z) = n \times x + n \times y + n \times z$. Distributive Property

Practice Questions 1.3

1. (i) $2^3 \times 3 \times 5$ (ii) 3×5^3 (iii) $2^4 \times 3 \times 13$ (iv) $2 \times 5^2 \times 29$ (v) 3 × 8263 **2.** (i)(a) 15,485,867 (b) 32,452,843 (c) 217,645,199 (d) 694,847,539 (ii) All the numbers are prime numbers. **3.** (i) 6 (ii) 5 (iii) 8 (iv) 12 **4.** 18 **5.** (i) 3 (ii) 5 (iii) 8 (iv) 2 **6.** She is incorrect **7.** (i) 42 (ii) 12 (iii) 40 (iv) 20 (v) 80 **8.** 18 **9.** 1800 **10.** 6 **11.** 18 **12.** 8

Practice Questions 1.4

1. (i) −6 (ii) −37 (iii) 41 (iv) −51 (v) −2 (vi) 6 (vii) 2 (viii) 126 **2.** (i) −12 (ii) 70 (iii) −288 (iv) −3 (v) −22 (vi) −5870 **3.** −6 × −4 = 24 **4.** 29 points **5.** (i) 16 points (ii) No.

Practice Questions 1.5

1. (i) $\frac{29}{21}$ (ii) $\frac{-25}{9}$ (iii) $\frac{1}{10}$ (iv) $\frac{1}{20}$ (v) $\frac{27}{14}$ (vi) $\frac{2}{3}$ (vii) $\frac{57}{4}$ (viii) $\frac{1420}{21}$ (ix) $\frac{4}{3}$ (x) $\frac{-20}{21}$ (xi) $\frac{83}{10}$ (xii) $\frac{121}{324}$ **2.** 36 boys **3.** €20 **4.** 480 **5.** (i) $\frac{1}{10}$ (ii) 272 **6.** Alex = 20 marbles; Betty = 8 marbles and Chris = 8 marbles **7.** €50

Practice Questions 1.6

1. (i) Rational (ii) Rational (iii) Rational (iv) Irrational (v) Rational **2.** (i) $4\sqrt{6}$ (ii) $2\sqrt{11}$ (iii) $3\sqrt{6}$ (iv) $5\sqrt{5}$ (v) $2\sqrt{7}$ (vi) $10\sqrt{2}$ (vii) $5\sqrt{2}$ (viii) $6\sqrt{2}$ **3.** (i) $\sqrt{45} = 3\sqrt{5}$; $\sqrt{20} = 2\sqrt{5}$ (ii) $13\sqrt{5}$ **4.** (i) $7\sqrt{2}$ (ii) $5\sqrt{5}$ (iii) $3\sqrt{7}$ (iv) $\sqrt{11}$ **5.** 6 m^2 **6.** Area = 12 Perimeter = $14\sqrt{2}$ **7.** (i) $\frac{3\sqrt{2}}{2}$ (ii) $\sqrt{7}$ (iii) $\frac{\sqrt{5}}{5}$ (iv) $\frac{\sqrt{6}}{2}$ **8.** $3\sqrt{2}$ **9.** 87·96 cm^2 **10.** (i) $3\sqrt{2} + \sqrt{10}$ (ii) $6\sqrt{3}$ (iii) $4\sqrt{5} + 12$ (iv) $5 + 3\sqrt{3}$ (v) $19 - 9\sqrt{5}$ (vi) 23 (vii) $4 + 2\sqrt{3} + 2\sqrt{5} + \sqrt{15}$ (viii) $1 + \sqrt{3} - \sqrt{2} - \sqrt{6}$ (ix) 62 (x) $8 + 2\sqrt{15}$ **11.** $20 + 10\sqrt{3}$ **12.** 1 **13.** $5 + 3\sqrt{3}$ **14.** (i) $\frac{3\sqrt{5}}{5}$ (ii) $\sqrt{2}$ (iii) $\frac{3\sqrt{3}}{4}$ (iv) $\frac{2 + \sqrt{2}}{2}$ (v) $\frac{\sqrt{15} - \sqrt{5}}{5}$ (vi) $\frac{-2\sqrt{2}}{3}$ (g) $\frac{\sqrt{30} + 3\sqrt{10}}{10}$ (h) $\frac{\sqrt{14} - \sqrt{7}}{7}$ (i) $\frac{1 + \sqrt{3}}{2}$ (j) $2\sqrt{6} + 4$ (k) $\frac{14 + 7\sqrt{7}}{3}$ (l) $\frac{3 - 3\sqrt{5}}{4}$ (m) $\frac{\sqrt{10} + 3\sqrt{5}}{5}$ (n) $-2 + \sqrt{5}$ (o) $\frac{5\sqrt{5} - 5\sqrt{3} + 2\sqrt{15} - 6}{2}$ **15.** $3 + 5\sqrt{2}$ **16.** $\sqrt{22}$ **17.** (i) $13\sqrt{3}$ (ii) $-12\sqrt{5}$ (iii) $3\sqrt{5}$ (iv) 180 (v) 1 (vi) $9 + 7\sqrt{5}$ (vii) $1 + 5\sqrt{15}$ (viii) $\frac{2\sqrt{3}}{3}$ (ix) $\frac{-1 + \sqrt{5}}{2}$ (x) $2 + \sqrt{3}$ (xi) $\frac{\sqrt{10} - \sqrt{5}}{2}$

Practice Questions 1.7

1. $\sqrt{5}$ **2.** $2 = \frac{2}{1} = \frac{p}{q}$; rational **3.** (i) $0{\cdot}125 = \frac{1}{8}$ (ii) $-8 = \frac{-8}{1}$ (iii) $6\frac{2}{3} = \frac{20}{3}$ (iv) $-0{\cdot}42 = \frac{-21}{50}$ **4.** $\sqrt{2}$; $\sqrt{7}$; $\sqrt{5}$

5. (i) False (ii) False (iii) False (iv) True **6.** (i) Real, rational, integer (ii) Real, rational (iii) Real, irrational (iv) Real, rational (v) Real, rational, integer (vi) Real, rational, integer, natural (vii) Real, irrational (viii) Real, rational, integer (ix) Real, rational (x) Real, rational, integer, natural **7.** (i) Real, rational, integer, natural. It must be a positive whole number. (ii) Real, rational. Can only be positive but can be a decimal. (iii) Real, rational. Can be a positive or negative whole number or decimal. (iv) Real, irrational. The circumference divided by the diameter is π, which is irrational. **8.** (i) True (ii) False (iii) False (iv) True (v) True (vi) False (vii) True **9.** (i) Irrational (ii) Irrational (iii) Natural, prime, integer, rational, terminating decimal (iv) Repeating decimal, rational (v) Integer, rational, terminating decimal (vi) Irrational (vii) Integer, rational, terminating decimal (viii) Natural, integer, rational (ix) Rational, repeating decimal (x) Rational, repeating decimal

10.

	Natural	Integer	Rational	Irrational	Real
$\frac{3\pi}{2}$	No. Not whole	No. Not whole	No. Can't be expressed as $\frac{p}{q}$	Yes. Can't be expressed as $\frac{p}{q}$	Yes. It's irrational
-4	No. Not positive	Yes. negative whole number	Yes. Can be expressed as $\frac{-4}{1}$	No. Can be expressed as $\frac{p}{q}$	Yes. It's rational
$\frac{6}{7}$	No. Not whole	No. Not whole	Yes. is in the form $\frac{p}{q}$	No. Can be expressed as $\frac{p}{q}$	Yes. It's rational
$\sqrt{225}$	Yes. $\sqrt{225} = \pm 15$ whole and positive	Yes. whole positive/ negative numbers	Yes. Can be expressed as $\frac{\pm 15}{1}$	No. Can be expressed as $\frac{p}{q}$	Yes. It's rational
$\sqrt{11}$	No. Not whole	No. Not whole	No. Can't be expressed as $\frac{p}{q}$	Yes. Can't be expressed as $\frac{p}{q}$	Yes. It's irrational

11.

Number	Rational	Irrational
p		✓
$p - 2$		✓
$(-p)^2$	✓	
$(p-1)^2$		✓
$1 - p^2$	✓	

Practice Questions 1.8

1. (i) 2 (ii) 2 (iii) 4 (iv) 1 (v) 5 (vi) 2 (vii) 2 (viii) 3 (ix) 3 (x) 3 **2.** (i) 1,570,000 (ii) 0·00277 (iii) 84,600 (iv) 0·00117 **3.** (i) 17 (ii) 0·037 (iii) 0·76 (iv) 2·9 (v) 500 **4.** (i) 1 significant figure = 30,000 4 significant figures = 26,900 (ii) 1 significant figure = 30 4 significant figures = 32·46 (iii) 1 significant figure = 200 4 significant figures = 157·0 (iv) 1 significant figure = 0·0002 4 significant figures = 0·0002399 (v) 1 significant figure = 300 4 significant figures = 293·4 (vi) 1 significant figure = 400 4 significant figures = 375·0 **5.** 71 kg **6.** (i) 41·888 cm^3 (ii) Yes or no acceptable with a valid reason. **7.** 17,000 **8.** (i) 1767 cm^3 (ii) 8660 g

Revision and Exam Style Questions – Section A

1. (i) 35 (ii) 12, 36 (iii) 36, 25 (iv) 13, 19 **2.** (i) (a) $2^4 \times 3^3$ (b) $2 \times 3^2 \times 29$ (ii) 18 **3.** 2 **4.** $\frac{5}{12}$ **5.** 42; $\frac{3}{4}$ **6.** 90 **7.** $2^4 \times 3^2 \times 5$ **8.** 12 **9.** 72 **10.** 9 and 15 **11.** π. It can't be expressed in the form $\frac{p}{q}$ **12.** $\frac{2}{3}$; $\sqrt{2}$; $(1·19)^2$; 1·6

Revision and Exam Style Questions – Section B

1.

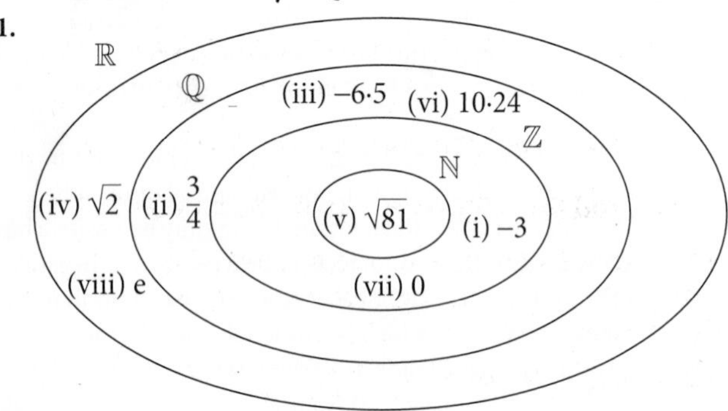

2. (i) n; $n + 1$; $n + 2$ **3.** (i) $n + 1, n + 2, n + 3$ **4.** $17 + 11\sqrt{5}$ **5.** (i) $\frac{20}{3}$ ml **6.** $2 + \sqrt{5}$ **7.** (i) {−8} (ii) {π, $\sqrt{3}$} (iii) { } **8.** Length = 44, which is a natural number **9.** 36 minutes **10.** 24 days

Chapter 2

Something to think about

$x + 5$

Practice Questions 2.1

1. (i) $6x$ (ii) $3y$ (iii) $2n + 9$ (iv) $10a + b$ (v) $21x - 1$ (vi) $3a + 4b + 5c$ **2.** (i) $7p^2 - 4p$ (ii) $y^2 + 9y$ (iii) $8x^2 + 5x - 2$ (iv) $3a^2 + 6a + 1$ (v) $-3p^2 + 5p + 7$ (vi) $5x^2 - 4x + 7$ **3.** (i) $8x^2 + 7y$ (ii) $10p + 8$ (iii) $-5k - 4$ (iv) $3x^2 + 4x + 15$ (v) $12a^2 + 2a + 1$ (vi) $12ax + 14a + 11$ (vii) $21x^2 - 19x + 6$ (viii) $-12p^2 + 4p - 1$ **4.** (i) $3x^2 + x - 2$ (ii) $4p^2 + 17p - 15$ (iii) $6x^2 - 8x - 8$ (iv) $15k^2 - 23k + 4$ (v) $4x^2 - 6$ (vi) $p^2 - 5p + 18$ **5.** (i) $x^2 - 10x + 25$ (ii) $9p^2 + 12p + 4$ (iii) $16a^2 - 16a + 4$ (iv) $49k^2 - 42k + 9$ **6.** (i) $x^2 + 7x + 12$ (ii) $5a + 5$ (iii) $-2k^2 + 2k + 17$ (iv) $a^2 + 4a - 5$ (v) $12a^2 + 2a - 11$ (vi) $13x + 13$ (vii) $-7p - 2q + 6r$ (viii) $x^2 - 9$ (ix) $y^2 - 4y + 4$ (x) $2x^2 - 4x - 9$ **7.** $3x + 4$ **8.** $3p^2 + 19x - 14$ **9.** (i) $28x + 35$ (ii) $8x + 24$ **10.** (i) $-2a^2 + 11a - 5$ (ii) $2a + 8$ **11.** $24x - 4$ **12.** $(9k^2 - 12k + 4)\pi$

Practice Questions 2.2

1. (i) 1 (ii) 15 (iii) 19 (iv) 4 (v) 12 (vi) 20 **2.** (i) 4 (ii) 31 (iii) 3 (iv) 6 (v) 2 (vi) 169 (vii) −1 (viii) 4 (ix) 9 **3.** (i) −2 (ii) −2 (iii) $\frac{19}{6}$ (iv) 0 (v) $\frac{1}{4}$ (vi) 1 **4.** $\frac{16}{5}$ **5.** $\frac{19}{2}$ **6.** 78·5 **7.** 396 **8.** 904·32 **9.** 13 **10.** 1·8 s

Practice Questions 2.3

1. (i) $\frac{11x}{12}$ (ii) $\frac{a}{10}$ (iii) $\frac{23x}{6}$ (iv) $\frac{13t - 7}{35}$ (v) $\frac{11x + 5}{15}$ (vi) $\frac{4x + 2}{3}$ (vii) $\frac{m - 4}{8}$ (viii) $\frac{k + 14}{12}$ (ix) $\frac{5x + 26}{24}$ **2.** (i) $\frac{15 + 4x}{3x}$ (ii) $\frac{a - 6}{4a}$ (iii) $\frac{2 + 2p}{3p}$ (iv) $\frac{11 - k}{6k + 6}$ (v) $\frac{3m + 41}{7m + 14}$ (vi) $\frac{2x - 2}{3x + 15}$ (vii) $\frac{13}{2x}$ (viii) $\frac{19}{5k}$ (ix) $\frac{11}{6x}$ **5.** (i) $\frac{5x - 3}{x(x - 1)}$ (ii) $\frac{-7k - 20}{k(2k + 5)}$ (iii) $\frac{11m + 3}{2m(m + 3)}$ **8.** (i) $\frac{7x + 10}{(x + 1)(x + 2)}$ (ii) $\frac{x + 2}{(x + 4)(x + 3)}$ (iii) $\frac{-2m + 13}{(m - 2)(m + 1)}$ (iv) $\frac{-20a - 23}{(3a + 1)(a - 2)}$ (v) $\frac{24k - 3}{(4k - 1)(2k + 1)}$ (vi) $\frac{5x + 10}{(3x + 4)(x + 3)}$ **9.** $\frac{12x - 36}{(x + 3)(2x - 3)}$ **10.** $\frac{19x + 7}{(3x - 1)(5x + 5)}$

Practice Questions 2.4

1. (i) $b = a - c$ (ii) $x = \frac{y - 5}{3}$ (iii) $q = \frac{5r}{p}$ (iv) $m = \frac{y - c}{x}$ (v) $w = \frac{x^2 - u}{r}$ (vi) $b = \frac{c - a^2}{ac}$ **2.** (i) $y = \sqrt{\frac{a + 2}{x}}$ (ii) $r = \sqrt{s - t}$ (iii) $b = \sqrt{\frac{a - c}{5}}$ (iv) $c = \sqrt{a} - b$ (v) $r = \sqrt[3]{x} + 2$ (vi) $s = \frac{\sqrt[4]{t} - c}{2}$ **3.** (i) $y = x^2 + 4$ (ii) $r = p^2 - 3$ (iii) $b = \frac{a^2 - 5}{2}$ (iv) $y = \frac{9x^2}{z}$ (v) $q = \frac{(p + r)^2}{4}$ (vi) $c = (b - a)^2$ **4.** (i) $a = 3b - 5$ (ii) $q = 5p + r$ (iii) $c = 3b - 24a$ (iv) $t = \frac{5}{s - 2}$ (v) $q = \frac{r + 8p}{3 - 4p}$ (vi) $c = \frac{b + 5a}{5a - 3}$ **5.** (i) $r = \frac{2pq - 3}{4q}$ (ii) $c = \frac{a}{ab - 2}$ (iii) $z = \frac{3x}{2xy - 4}$ (iv) $q = \frac{5pr}{4r + 3p}$ **6.** $r = \sqrt{\frac{V}{\pi h}}$ **7.** (i) $x = \frac{6 - 3y}{2y + 1}$ (ii) $-\frac{2}{3}$ **8.** (i) $a = \frac{v - u}{t}$ (ii) 6 **9.** (i) $r = \sqrt[3]{\frac{3V}{4\pi}}$ (ii) 6 cm **10.** (i) 50°F (ii) $C = \frac{5F - 160}{9}$ (iii) 40°C **11.** (i) 7·7 (ii) $t = \sqrt{v^2 + 5}$ (iii) 12·2 **12.** (i) $c = \sqrt{\frac{E}{m}}$ (ii) 30,000 **13.** (i) $u = \frac{2s - at^2}{2t}$ (ii) 15

Practice Questions 2.5

1. (i) $a(3 + b)$ (ii) $5x(x - 2)$ (iii) $(x + 3)(x + 5)$ (iv) $(x + 4)(x - 4)$ (v) $4p(2p - 3q)$ (vi) $(x - 5)(x - 2)$ (vii) $(x - 2)(x + 8)$ (viii) $(3a + 8b)(3a - 8b)$ (ix) $(4x + 1)(x + 5)$ (x) $(3x + 7)(x - 2)$ **2.** (i) $5x(3y - 7)$ (ii) $4x(4x + 5)$ (iii) $(a + b)(x + y)$ (iv) $3t(2mt - p)$ (v) $7p(2 + 3q)$ (vi) $(s + 2t^2)(m - n)$ (vii) $(4y + 5)(7x + 5)$ (viii) $(4y - 1)(x - 6)$ **3.** (i) $(a - 5)(a + 5)$ (ii) $(6x - y)(6x + y)$ (iii) $(x + 6)(x + 3)$ (iv) $(m + 8)(m + 5)$ (v) $(x + 9)(x - 2)$ (vi) $(7m + 8k)(7m - 8k)$ (vii) $(k - 6)(k - 4)$ (viii) $(9 + 2a)(9 - 2a)$ (ix) $(3k + 1)(3k - 1)$ **4.** (i) $(x + 2)(3x + 4)$ (ii) $(a + 4)(2a + 3)$ (iii) $(k + 4)(3k + 2)$ (iv) $(x - 10)(2x + 3)$ (v) $(p + 5)(2p - 9)$ (vi) $(2x + 5)(3x - 2)$ (vii) $(2t + 3)(5t + 1)$ (viii) $(2a - 1)(7a - 1)$ (ix) $(2x - 3)(6x + 5)$ **5.** (i) $2(x - 6)(x - 4)$ (ii) $3(x - 3)(x - 3)$ (iii) $2(x + 9)(x - 8)$ (iv) $2(3x + 1)(2x - 5)$ (v) $2(x + 8)(x - 3)$ (vi) $4(x - 8)(x + 3)$ **6.** (i) $(3x + y)(2a - b)$ (ii) $(3m - 2)(m + 5)$ (iii) $(1 - p)(1 + p)$ (iv) $(x - 10)(x + 3)$ (v) $5bc(b - 2)$ (vi) $(x - 11)(x + 7)$ (vii) $(4m + 7)(4n - m)$ (viii) $(3x + 1)(2x - 5)$ (ix) $8a(3b + 2c)$ **7.** $(x + 2)$ **8.** (i) $(x - 10)$ **9.** (i) $(2x + 5)$ m/s **10.** (i) $(3x - 1)$ s

Revision and Exam Style Questions – Section A

1. $12x + 23$ **2.** $4x(2x - 7y)$ **3.** $10a^2 + 7a - 12$ **4.** 52 **5.** $\frac{11x - 5}{15}$ **6.** $(p - 10q)(p + 10q)$ **7.** 33 **8.** $b = \frac{c - 5}{a}$ **9.** $\frac{-4x + 15}{12}$ **10.** $k = \frac{11 + 7p}{p}$ **11.** $(x + 8)(x - 3)$ **12.** (i) $x + 2$ (ii) $\frac{-x + 4}{6}$ **13.** $5p^2 + p + 6$ **14.** $(x - 9)(x + 2)$ **15.** (i) $(44 - 2T)$, $(34 - 2T)$ (ii) $4T^2 - 156T + 1496$ **16.** (i) $x + 2$, $x - 4$ (ii) $x^2 - 2x - 8$

Revision and Exam Style Questions – Section B

1. −13·5 **2.** $9x^2 - 3x - 7$ **3.** 6 **4.** $(4b - 5x)(3c - d)$ **5.** $\frac{8x + 17}{(x - 1)(x + 4)}$ **6.** 3 **7.** (i) $y = \frac{5x - 5}{3}$ (ii) −5 **8.** $(3m - 4n)(3a + c)$ **9.** (i) $a = \frac{3t - 20}{4 + t}$ (ii) $\frac{1}{11}$ **10.** $(5a - 2)(a - 2)$ **11.** $\frac{13p + 4}{(3p + 4)(p - 2)}$ **12.** (i) $q = \frac{3p}{r + 5}$ (ii) $-\frac{1}{2}$ **13.** $(4x - 5)(3x + 2)$ **14.** 2 **15.** $4(2x - 3)(x + 6)$ **16.** (i) $\text{BMI} = \frac{\text{Weight in kilograms}}{(\text{Height in metres})^2}$ (ii) 26·1 (iii) 59·05 kg (iv) 181 cm (v) 31·6

Chapter 3

Something to think about

14 years old

Practice Questions 3.1

1. (i) -10 (ii) -1 (iii) 5 (iv) 11 **2.** (i) 9 (ii) 7 (iii) 1 (iv) -1 **4.** (i) $y = x + 1$ (ii) $y = -\frac{1}{2}x + 2$ (iii) $y = -3x + 4$ (iv) $y = 2x - 1$ **5.** (3, 5) **6.** (2, 1)

7. (i)

Week number	Account balance
0	100
1	130
2	160
3	190

(ii) $B = 100 + 30W$ B = balance W = week number
(iv) The balance is €370 in the 9th week (v) €310 (vi) 17 weeks
8. (i) 30 (ii) $N = 670 + 30W$ N = number of members W = week number (iii) 1030 (iv) 61 weeks
(v) No. Some members may leave. Certain months may be busier, e.g. January **9.** (i) 1·5 (ii) $C = 4{\cdot}5 + 1{\cdot}5D$ C = cost D = distance in km (iv) A 5 km journey costs €12 (v) €28·50 (vi) 22 km
10. (i) $T = 20 + 50W$ T = time in mins W = weight in kg (iii) 95 mins (iv) 2·2 kg

Practice Questions 3.2

1. (i) 8 (ii) 6 (iii) 2 (iv) 5 (v) 5 (vi) 6 (vii) 6 (viii) 1·5 (ix) 2·5 **2.** (i) 1 (ii) -3 **3.** (i) $15x - 1 = 9x - 19$ (ii) -3 (iii) Intersect at $x = -3$ **4.** (i) 2 (ii) -6 **5.** 8 **6.** 13 **7.** 40°
8. (i) 3 (ii) 2 (iii) 6 (iv) 3·5 (v) 2 (vi) 1 (vii) $-\frac{1}{3}$ (viii) $\frac{1}{2}$
9. -1 **10.** -22 **11.** 8 **12.** 3 **13.** (i) 48 (ii) 13 (iii) 5 (iv) 8 (v) 10 (vi) 9 **14.** 16 **15.** 2 **16.** $2(x + 3) + 2(2x) = 18$; 4 cm, 5 cm **17.** 4·5 hours **18.** (i) Weight of the bag (ii) €18·75 (iii) 11 kg (iv) 19 kg **19.** (i) €7300 (ii) €165,000 (iii) €270,000
20. (i) $\frac{x}{60}h$ (ii) $\frac{x + 30}{40}h$ (iii) 60 km; 150 km **21.** (i) $2x$ (ii) $x + 1200$ (iii) $6(2x) + 10(x) + 15(x + 1200) = 27{,}472$
(iv) 512 children, 256 students, 1456 other adults

Practice Questions 3.3

1. (i) $x = 10, y = 5$ (ii) $p = 3, q = 6$ (iii) $a = 3, b = 4$ (iv) $x = 4, y = 3$ (v) $m = 6, n = 4$ (vi) $a = 2, b = 4$ (vii) $x = 4, y = 2$ (viii) $x = 3, y = 7$ (ix) $p = 3, q = -2$
2. (i) $x = -2, y = -5$ (ii) $x = 7, y = 5$ (iii) $x = 5, y = 6$ (iv) $x = \frac{1}{2}, y = -1$ (v) $x = -3, y = 5$ (vi) $x = 1, y = -3$
3. (i) $x = 15, y = 12$ (ii) $a = 2, b = 0$ (iii) $x = 6, y = -4$ (iv) $x = 10, y = -5$ (v) $a = 3, b = -1$ (vi) $p = 10, q = 5$
4. (i) $5x - 2y = 9, x - 2y = 5$ (ii) $x = 1, y = -2$
5. (i) $2x - 5y = 11, 3x + 2y = 7$ (ii) $x = 3, y = -1$ **6.** $p = 11, q = 4$
7. $a = 16, b = 12$ **8.** (i) $7x + 3y = 168, 4x + 5y = 165$ (ii) Shirt = €15, Jumper = €21 **9.** (i) $5x + 6y = 2{\cdot}5, 7x + 3y = 2{\cdot}15$ (ii) Apple = 20c, Banana = 25c **10.** Cola = 50c, Crisps = 40c
11. Adult = €15, Child = €8 **12.** (i) $3x - y = 4, 4x - 2y = 2, x - y = -2$ (ii) $x = 3, y = 5$ **13.** (ii) $-1{\cdot}9$ **14.** (i) $f(x) = -2x + 4, g(x) = 2x - 6$ (ii) 2·5 **15.** (i) $C = 50 + 30T$ C = cost T = number of trees (ii) $C = 35T$ C = cost T = number of trees (iv) B (v) A (vi) 10 trees

Practice Questions 3.4

1. (i) $x < 4$ (ii) $a > 2$ (iii) $p > -1$ (iv) $x < -\frac{1}{2}$ (v) $z > 1$ (vi) $x \geq 2$ (vii) $x \leq 3{\cdot}5$ (viii) $p < -2$ (ix) $k < 7$ (x) $z \geq -4$ (xi) $x < 3{\cdot}6$ (xii) $x > -2$ **2.** (i) $x \geq -1, x \in \mathbb{Z}$ (ii) $x \geq 1, x \in \mathbb{R}$ (iii) $x < 6, x \in \mathbb{N}$ (iv) $x < 4, x \in \mathbb{R}$ (v) $-3 \leq x \leq 1, x \in \mathbb{Z}$ (vi) $-3 < x \leq 2, x \in \mathbb{R}$ **3.** (i) 2, 4, 6 (ii) 4, 9, 16, 25, 36, 49, 64, 81 (iii) 2, 3, 5, 7, 11, 13, 17, 19, 23 (iv) 1, 3, 5 **4.** (i) 1 (ii) 18 cm^2
5. (i) (a) $x < 4$ (b) $x \geq -1$ (ii) $-1 \leq x < 4$ **6.** (i) $x > -2$ (ii) $x \leq 5$ (iii) $a = -2, b = 5$ (iv) -6 **7.** (i) $x \leq 5{\cdot}5$ (ii) $x > -4$ (iii) $a = -4, b = 5{\cdot}5$ (iv) 6·8 **8.** (i) 1, 2, 3, 4 (ii) $x \leq 6{\cdot}5$ (iii) $x \geq -3$

Revision and Exam Style Questions – Section A

1. (i) 10 (ii) -3 **2.** 6 **3.** 1, 2, 3 **4.** 5 **5.** $x \geq -4$
6. $x = 2, y = -1$ **7.** $x \geq 4$ **8.** (i) $T = 12B + 480$ Where, T = time in minutes, B = number of blades (ii) 1344 minutes (iii) 105 blades
9. 7 **10.** 12 **11.** $x \leq 4$ **12.** 1, 2, 3, 4, 5, 6, 7

Revision and Exam Style Questions – Section B

1. 2 **2.** $\frac{16}{3}$ **3.** (i) 58°C (iii) 4·5 hours (iv) 5 hours
4. $x = -2, y = 3$ **5.** $\frac{21}{8}$ **6.** (i) Weight = $115 - 1{\cdot}5W$ (ii) $-1{\cdot}5$ (iv) Kathy's weight is 107·5 kg after 5 weeks (v) 22 weeks (vi) No. It is not possible to sustain a constant weight loss over a prolonged period of time **7.** $x \leq -\frac{11}{10}$ **8.** $p = 2, q = 0$

9. (i)

Year	1	2	3	4	5	6	7	8
Murphys account balance (€)	1000	1450	1900	2350	2800	3250	3700	4150
O'Briens account balance (€)	100	700	1300	1900	2500	3100	3700	4300

(ii) Year 7 (iii) Murphys: $550 + 450n$ O'Briens: $-500 + 600n$ (v) Murphys: €7300 O'Briens: €8500 **10.** (i) $x \leq 4$ (ii) $x > -3$ (iii) $-2, -1, 0, 1, 2, 3, 4$ **11.** (i) $C = 300 + 15G$ C = cost G = number of guests (ii) $C = 25G$ C = cost G = number of guests (iii) Company B (v) Company A (vi) 30 guests

Chapter 4

Something to think about

10

Practice Questions 4.1

2. (ii) $-5{\cdot}65, -0{\cdot}35$ **3.** (i) 9, 4, 1, 0, 1, 4 (iii) 2, 2
4. (ii) $-0{\cdot}38, 4{\cdot}38$ (iii) $-1, 0, 1, 2, 3, 4, 5; -10, 5, 14, 17$
5. (ii) No real roots

Practice Questions 4.2

1. (i) $-3, 4$ (ii) $-1{\cdot}56, 2{\cdot}56$ (iii) $-4{\cdot}25$ (iv) $-7{\cdot}25$ (v) $-2{\cdot}37, 3{\cdot}37$ (vi) $(0{\cdot}5, -8{\cdot}25)$ **2.** (i) $-0{\cdot}85, 2{\cdot}35$ (ii) 6 (iii) 4 (iv) $(0{\cdot}75, 7{\cdot}125)$ **3.** (i) $-1{\cdot}43, 2{\cdot}1$ (ii) 7·25 (iii) 5·25 (iv) $-1{\cdot}23, 1{\cdot}9$ (v) $(0{\cdot}33, 7{\cdot}33)$

4. (i)

t (months)	0	4	8	12	16	20	24	28
$v(t)$ (hundreds of euro)	50	294	442	494	450	310	74	-258

(iii) €5000 (iv) €48,000 (v) 21 (vi) €494 (vii) 25 months

5.(i)

x items sold (in 100s)	0	5	10	15	20	25	30	35	40
p(X) (profit in 1000s of euro)	0	187·5	350	487·5	600	687·5	750	787·5	800

(iii) €638,000 (iv) 1350

6. (i)

t (sec)	0	0·5	1	1·5	2	2·5	3
h(t) (m)	1	16	25	28	25	16	1

(iii) 28 m (iv) 3·03 sec (v) 0·28 sec, 2·72 sec **7.** (ii) 13·6 m (iii) 12 m (iv) 5·5 m (v) 8·8 sec **8.** (i) 8·2˚C, 15·8˚C, 21·8˚C, 26·2˚C, 29˚C, 30·2˚C, 29·8˚C, 27·8˚C, 24·2˚C, 19˚C, 12·2˚C, 3·8˚C (ii) 26·2˚C is the average temperature at the start of April. (iii) February and October (iv) 30·25˚C in June

Practice Questions 4.3

1. (i) 0, 2 (ii) $0, -\frac{1}{2}$ (iii) $\frac{3}{4}, -\frac{3}{4}$ (iv) 2, 6 (v) −3, 3 (vi) −3, 4 (vii) 0, 7 (viii) −2, −8 (ix) −3, −12

2. (i) $-\frac{3}{2}, 4$ (ii) $-\frac{4}{3}, -2$ (iii) $-\frac{1}{11}, 3$ (iv) $-4, \frac{2}{3}$ (v) $-\frac{3}{2}, -1$ (vi) $-\frac{3}{2}$ (vii) $\frac{3}{4}, 5$ (viii) $-\frac{2}{3}$ (ix) $-\frac{1}{6}, -\frac{5}{2}$

3. (i) $-\frac{7}{2}, \frac{7}{2}$ (ii) −4, 4 (iii) 0, 4 (iv) $\frac{1}{7}, 2$ (v) $-5, \frac{3}{2}$ (vi) $-\frac{1}{2}, 2$ (vii) $\frac{1}{9}, 8$ (viii) $\frac{1}{3}, \frac{4}{3}$ (ix) $-\frac{2}{5}, 3$

4. (i) $-1 \pm \sqrt{3}$ (ii) $-3 \pm \sqrt{10}$ (iii) $\frac{7 \pm \sqrt{65}}{2}$ (iv) $-4 \pm 2\sqrt{5}$ (v) $\frac{-5 \pm \sqrt{17}}{4}$ (vi) $\frac{5 \pm \sqrt{10}}{3}$ **5.** (i) −4·79, −0·21 (ii) −0·30, 3·30 (iii) −9·42, 0·42 (iv) −0·53, 7·53 (v) −1·82, 0·22 (vi) −1·69, 0·44 **6.** (i) −2, 3 **7.** (i) −1, 4 **8.** (i) −1, 2·5 (ii) $2x^2 - 3x - 14 = 0$ (iii) −2, 3·5 **9.** (i) $-\frac{4}{3}, 2$ (ii) $-3x^2 + 2x + 5 = 0$ (iii) $-1, \frac{5}{3}$ **10.** (i) −3, 1 (ii) (c) **11.** (ii) $1 - \sqrt{7}$ **12.** (ii) $1 + \sqrt{10}$

Practice Questions 4.4

1. (i) $x^2 - 6x + 8 = 0$ (ii) $x^2 - 10x + 21 = 0$ (iii) $x^2 - 10x + 24 = 0$ (iv) $x^2 - 2x - 3 = 0$ (v) $x^2 - 7x - 18 = 0$ (vi) $x^2 - 6x - 16 = 0$ (vii) $x^2 - 9x - 36 = 0$ (viii) $x^2 + 8x + 12 = 0$ (ix) $x^2 + 11x + 28 = 0$ **2.** $p = -9, q = 14$ **3.** $c = 10, d = 24$ **4.** (i) $x^2 - 5x - 24 = 0$ **5.** (a) (i) −3, 1 (ii) $x^2 + 2x - 3 = 0$ (iv) $f(x) = x^2 + 2x - 3$ (b) (i) −4, 2 (ii) $x^2 + 2x - 8 = 0$ (iv) $f(x) = -x^2 - 2x + 8$ (c) (i) 5, 5 (ii) $x^2 - 10x + 25 = 0$ (iv) $f(x) = -x^2 + 10x - 25$ (d) (i) 1·5, 6 (ii) $2x^2 - 15x + 18 = 0$ (iv) $f(x) = 2x^2 - 15x + 18$ **6.** (i) $x^2 + 4x - 45 = 0$ (iv) $k(x) = x^2 + 4x - 45$ **7.** (i) $x^2 + 15x + 44 = 0$ (iv) $g(x) = -x^2 - 15x - 44$

Practice Questions 4.5

1. (i) $0, \frac{9}{4}$ (ii) $-\frac{1}{2}, \frac{3}{5}$ (iii) 0, 4 (iv) $1, \frac{3}{2}$ (v) 1, 6 (vi) $\frac{1}{7}, 2$

2. (i) 0, 1 (ii) $\frac{1}{7}, 6$ (iii) $-\frac{1}{2}, \frac{3}{2}$ (iv) $-\frac{2}{3}, 6$ **3.** (i) −0·95, 75·95 (ii) −4·25, 3·92 (iii) 0·31, 4·36 (iv) −3·81, −0·07

4. (i) $\frac{3 \pm \sqrt{89}}{2}$ (ii) $2 \pm \sqrt{3}$ (iii) $\frac{9 \pm 2\sqrt{22}}{7}$ (iv) $\frac{3 \pm \sqrt{17}}{4}$

Practice Questions 4.6

1. (i) −1, −2 and 2, 1 (ii) −1, −1 and 1, 1 (iii) 2, 3 and 3, 2

2. (i) $-\frac{27}{5}, -\frac{7}{5}$ and −1, 3 (ii) 2, −1 and 8, 11 (iii) −4, 0 and $\frac{12}{5}, \frac{16}{5}$

3. (i) −1, −7 and 4, −2 (ii) −3, 1 and 3, 4 (iii) −4, 2 and 0, −2

4. (i) (0, 2) (ii) (c) **5.** (i) (−5, 0), (4, 3) (ii) (b)

Practice Questions 4.7

1. (i) $x + 5$ (ii) $x^2 + 5x = 204$ (iii) 12 m, 17 m **2.** 8 cm **3.** (i) 28 cm^2 (ii) $k^2 + 11k - 102 = 0$ (iii) 13 cm, 10 cm **4.** (i) $35 - 2w$; $27 - 2w$ (ii) Area = $4w^2 - 124w + 945$ (iii) 2·5 m **5.** (i) $x + 2$ (ii) −8, 6 **6.** (i) 2 cm (ii) $x + 6$; $x - 4$ (iii) $V = 2x^2 + 4x - 48$ (iv) 8 cm (v) 18 cm, 8 cm **7.** (i) $300 - 2w$ (ii) Area = $300w - 2w^2$ (iii) 50 m × 200 m or 100 m × 100 m **8.** (i) €900 (ii) €7700 is the cost of producing 150 backpacks (iii) 95 **9.** (i) $\frac{45}{x}$ (ii) $\frac{24}{x-6}$ (iii) $\frac{45}{x} - \frac{24}{x-6} = \frac{1}{3}$ (iv) 15 km/h **10.** (i) €375,000 (ii) €312,000 is the revenue from selling 4000 cameras (iii) 10,000 or 20,000 **11.** (i) 160 m (ii) 118·75 m (iii) 4·8 sec (iv) 6 sec **12.** (a) (i) −€17,500,000 income made during 2005 (ii) €28,000,000 income made during 2012 (iii) 2008, 2013 (b) (i) €14,000,000 income made during 2005 (ii) 2008, 2012 **13.** (i) Density = $\frac{\text{Mass}}{\text{Volume}}$ (ii) Volume = $\frac{\text{Mass}}{\text{Density}}$ (iii) $\text{Vol}_A = \frac{3}{D}$ (iv) $\text{Vol}_B = \frac{5 \cdot 25}{D + 0 \cdot 2}$ (v) $\frac{3}{D} + \frac{5 \cdot 25}{D + 0 \cdot 2} = 6 \cdot 25$ (vi) 1·2

14. (−8, 6), (6, −8)

15. (a) (i)

t (sec)	0	1	2	3	4	5	6	7	8	9	10
h(t) (m)	0	52	87	112	127	132	127	112	87	52	7

(iii) After three seconds, the missile is at a height of 112 m (iv) 132 m (v) 2·5 s, 7·5 s (b) (i) A straight line (iii) (0, 7), (8, 87) **16.** (i) $4t^2 - 20t + 65$ (iii) In 2011 there are 90 kg of fresh vegetables consumed per person (iv) 6·7 years after 2005 (v) 104 kg **17.** (i) $\frac{75}{V+5}$ (ii) $\frac{75}{V-5}$ (iii) 20 km/hr (iv) 25 minutes faster **18.** (−13, 0), (12, 5)

Revision and Exam Style Questions – Section A

1. $x^2 - x - 12 = 0$ **2.** (i) −1·5, 5 (ii) $-\frac{1}{2}, \frac{1}{3}$ **3.** −8, 2; 175, 15 **4.** $\frac{1}{3}, 2$ **5.** (−1, 1), (5, 4) **6.** $x^2 - x = 42$; −6, 7 **7.** $3 \pm 3\sqrt{3}$ **8.** (i) 22·5 m (ii) 2·37 sec **9.** (i) $x^2 - 5x - 24 = 0$ (ii) 8 **11.** −2·23, 0·90

Revision and Exam Style Questions – Section B

1. (i) $1 \pm \sqrt{3}$ **2.** $2x^2 + 28x - 240 = 0$; 6 **3.** (i) −2, 3 and 3, −2 (ii) −13, 12 **4.** (i) $500 - 2w$ (ii) Area = $500w - 2w^2$ (iii) 200 m and 100 m or 50 m and 400 m **5.** (i) $\frac{400}{x}$ (ii) $\frac{400}{x+50}$ (iii) $\frac{400}{x} - \frac{400}{x+50} = \frac{2}{5}$ (iv) 250 g **6.** (b) 0, 6, 8, 6, 0 (c) (i) 3·5 cm^2 (ii) 8 cm^2 (iii) 2 (iv) 4 cm, 2 cm

7. (i) 1, 3 and 5, −1 (ii) (a) **8.** (i) $\frac{210}{x}$ (ii) $\frac{200}{x-3}$ (iii) $\frac{200}{x-3} - \frac{210}{x} = \frac{1}{2}$ (iv) 28

9. (i)

X	0	2	4	6	8	10	12	14	16	18	20
C(x) (€)	200	160	128	104	88	80	80	88	104	128	160

(iii) €200 (iv) 15 (v) 11 (vi) €89 (vii) $12x$ (viii) Profit $= -x^2 + 34x - 200$

Chapter 5

Something to think about

(i) $1{\cdot}2312 \times 10^{14}$ (ii) 10^2

Practice Questions 5.1

1. (i) 6^{10} (ii) 4^7 (iii) m^{10} (iv) c^{16} (v) $24a^4$ (vi) $14y^3$ **2.** (i) 6^5 (ii) $-110c^{12}d$ (iii) $84q^8r^2$ (iv) $8r^{12}$ (v) $15c^2d^3$ (vi) $14a^7$ **3.** $9a^{10}$ **4.** $15x^7$ **5.** (i) 3^3 (ii) 10^2 (iii) 2^2 (iv) 5^7 (v) k (vi) s^3 **6.** (i) 3 (ii) $4w^6x$ (iii) 8^3 (iv) $2c^{-2}d$ (v) ab^2 (vi) $8x^{-5}y^3$ **7.** $6x^5$

Practice Questions 5.2

1. (i) 1 (ii) 1 (iii) 1 (iv) 1 (v) 1 (vi) 1 (vii) 1 (viii) 1 **2.** (i) w^{12} (ii) t^{-6} (iii) 4^{42} (iv) 5^{20} (v) 2^{27} (vi) $8a^9$ (vii) $49r^8$ (viii) $27h^{12}$ (ix) $125w^{21}$ (x) $10000b^{20}$ **3.** (i) $\frac{1}{16}$ (ii) $\frac{1}{9}$ (iii) $\frac{1}{25}$ (iv) $\frac{1}{49}$ (v) $\frac{1}{32}$ **4.** (i) 5^4 (ii) 7^3 (iii) $(xy)^6$ (iv) a^2b^3 (v) $\frac{s^8}{3r}$ **5.** (i) $\frac{1}{p^2}$ (ii) $\frac{1}{t^4}$ (iii) $\frac{1}{x^5}$ (iv) $\frac{64}{a^9}$ **6.** (i) $7776p^{15}$ (ii) $-216x^{15}$ (iii) $20p^{11}q^4$ (iv) $\frac{12}{m^2}$ (v) $\frac{3}{u^{14}}$ (vi) $\frac{s^{20}}{t^{48}}$ (vii) $\frac{v^9}{64u^{16}}$ (viii) $\frac{3b^6c^2}{a^3}$

Practice Questions 5.3

1. (i) $\sqrt{y}$ (ii) $\sqrt[4]{r}$ (iii) $\sqrt[5]{a}$ (iv) $\sqrt[5]{m}$ (v) $\sqrt[6]{q}$ (vi) $\sqrt[4]{x^3}$ (vii) $\sqrt[5]{c^3}$ (viii) $\sqrt{t^3}$ (ix) ${}^{6}\sqrt{k^5}$ (x) $\sqrt{h^3}$ **2.** (i) 8 (ii) 5 (iii) 729 (iv) 9 (v) 256

Practice Questions 5.4

1. (i) $36x^6$ (ii) $64y^6z^6$ (iii) $4096h^{20}w^{12}$ (iv) $81x^{12}y^8$ (v) $49a^8b^2$ (vi) $216d^{15}$ (vii) $8192x^{21}$ (viii) $\frac{8s^9}{t^9}$ **2.** (i) $\frac{x^{12}}{y^6}$ (ii) $\frac{4b^2}{9a^2}$ (iii) $\frac{343}{64y^6}$ (iv) $\frac{32}{u^5v^5}$ (v) $\frac{6561s^8}{256r^{12}}$ (vi) $\frac{25p^6}{9q^{10}}$ (vii) $\frac{4}{g^2h^{16}}$ (viii) $\frac{1}{625a^{12}b^{24}}$ **3.** (i) x^{37} (ii) c^{12} (iii) d^{19} (iv) a^{16} (v) $\frac{1}{w^4}$ (vi) g^4 (vii) 2^{a+b} (viii) r^4s^3 **4.** (i) $8x^5y^2$ (ii) $-18a^3b^5c$ (iii) $-110c^{12}d$ (iv) $-9x^{15}y^3z^2$ **5.** (i) x^6 (ii) a^{35} (iii) y^{20} (iv) 5^6 (v) $16y^6$ (vi) $64c^{10}$ (vii) $-27h^{27}$ (viii) $c^{20}h^{24}$ (ix) $y^{32}d^{48}$ (x) k^{51} **6.** (i) y^5 (ii) b^3 (iii) m^5 (iv) cd^6 (v) $4s^4t^5$ (vi) $9e^7f^6$ (vii) a^{15} (viii) $6q^6$ **7.** (i) 3 (ii) 3 (iii) 4 (iv) $\frac{1}{4}$ (v) $\frac{1}{9}$ **8.** (i) $2^{\frac{3}{2}}$ (ii) $3m^{\frac{1}{2}}$ (iii) m^3 (iv) $10^{\frac{3}{2}}$ (v) $\frac{1}{2^4}$ **9.** (i) $3^3 \times 2^2$ (ii) $27 = 3^3$ (iii) (a) and (b) are the same

10. (i) 2^7 (ii) 3^{10} (iii) 12^{-2} (iv) 6^{-2} (v) 2^{-1} (vi) 4^{-1} (vii) 4^{-1} (viii) $\frac{b^4}{2a^4}$ (ix) x^4z **11.** 24 **12.** (ii) $\frac{1}{16}$ **13.** (i) $a = b^{\frac{1}{2}}$ (ii) $a^3 = b^{\frac{3}{2}}$

Practice Questions 5.5

1. (i) 2^6 (ii) 2^{-4} (iii) 2^0 (iv) $2^{\frac{1}{2}}$ (v) $2^{\frac{-1}{2}}$ (vi) $2^{\frac{5}{2}}$ **2.** (a) (i) $3^{\frac{3}{2}}$ (ii) 3^{-4} (iii) $3^{\frac{-5}{2}}$ (b) (i) $5^{\frac{1}{2}}$ (ii) 5^{-4} (iii) $5^{\frac{-3}{2}}$ **3.** (i) $x = 3$ (ii) $x = 8$ (iii) $x = 3$ (iv) $x = 11$ (v) $x = -1$ (vi) $x = 2$ (vii) $x = 6$ (viii) $x = 3$ **4.** (i) $x = -8$ (ii) $x = -1$ (iii) $x = -1$ (iv) $x = \frac{5}{2}$ (v) $x = -4$ (vi) $x = \frac{1}{4}$ (vii) $x = \frac{1}{3}$ (viii) $x = \frac{5}{2}$ **5.** (i) $k^{x+1} = k^{2x+\frac{1}{2}}$ (ii) $x = \frac{1}{2}$ **6.** (i) $x = 4; x = -1$ (ii) $x = \frac{1}{2}; x = -\frac{3}{2}$ (iii) $x = 2; x = 6$ **7.** (a) (i) $p = 2$ (ii) $q = -2$ (iii) $r = \frac{1}{2}$ (b) $x = \frac{-3}{2}$ **8.** (a) (i) 2^3 (ii) 2^4 (b) $x = \frac{17}{10} = 1{\cdot}7$ **9.** (i) 3^5 (ii) $3^{\frac{3}{2}}$ $x = \frac{13}{2}$ **10.** (i) $p = \frac{-1}{4}$ (ii) $p = 4$ **11.** (i) 6 (ii) $2^{\frac{5}{2}}$ (iii) $x = 2$ **12.** $3(2^2)$ $x = \frac{4}{3}$

Practice Questions 5.6

1. (i) 10^2 (ii) 10^3 (iii) 10^1 (iv) 10^5 (v) 10^{-1} (vi) 10^{-2} (vii) 10^{-5} (viii) 10^8 **2.** (i) $3{\cdot}57 \times 10^2$ (ii) $3{\cdot}57 \times 10^5$ (iii) $3{\cdot}57 \times 10^0$ (iv) $3{\cdot}57 \times 10^{-1}$ (v) $3{\cdot}57 \times 10^{-4}$ (vi) $2{\cdot}06 \times 10^3$ (vii) $2{\cdot}06 \times 10^{-3}$ (viii) $2{\cdot}06 \times 10^6$ **3.** (i) 4000 (ii) 500 (iii) 2100 (iv) 78000 (v) 0·000038 (vi) 0·86 (vii) 0·000000433 (viii) 0·00000000632 **4.** (i) $1{\cdot}495 \times 10^{11}$ (ii) 1×10^{-3} (iii) $1{\cdot}4162 \times 10^{-7}$ (iv) $1{\cdot}5 \times 10^7$ **5.** (i) 4,000,000 (ii) 0·0008 (iii) 6,380,000 (iv) 0·0000004 (v) 12,096,000 (vi) 0·000007 **6.** $8{\cdot}75 \times 10^{-12}$ grams **7.** (i) 3×10^5 (ii) 3×10^{10} km (iii) $3{\cdot}1 \times 10^6$ **8.** 18,000 km/hr

Practice Questions 5.7

1. (i) 9 (ii) 5 (iii) 4 (iv) −3 (v) −3 (vi) −6 (vii) −1 (viii) −5 (ix) 2 (x) 2 **2.** (i) −3 (ii) 24 (iii) 100 (iv) 10 (v) −5 **3.** (i) Electron: −30 Proton: −27 (ii) 10^3 **4.** (i) Earth: 10 Ireland: 6 (ii) 10^4 **5.** (i) 5 (ii) 7 (iii) 9 **6.** (i) 10^2 (ii) 10^1

Revision and Exam Style Questions – Section A

1. (i) 7 (ii) s^{12} (iii) $\frac{1}{49}$ **2.** (i) 3^6 (ii) $p = -6$ (iii) 3^4 **3.** (i) 10^{-4} (ii) $2{\cdot}3618 \times 10^{-2}$ % **4.** (i) 3×10^8 (ii) 8 **5.** $\frac{1}{n^4}$ **6.** $6{\cdot}88 \times 10^1$ **7.** (i) $1{\cdot}1 \times 10^{12}$ km^3 (ii) 50 times greater **8.** (i) $9 = 3^2 27 = 3^3$ (ii) $x = \frac{5}{2}$ **9.** $x = \frac{3}{2}$

Revision and Exam Style Questions – Section B

1. (i) 3^{-3} **2.** $3{\cdot}6875 \times 10^0$ **3.** (i) 4000 (ii) $3{\cdot}87 \times 10^3$ (iii) Difference = 130 litres; % difference = 3·36%. Rounding has made the answer higher **4.** (i) 4·52 cm^2 (ii) 787·76 cm^2 (iii) 78776 mm^2 (iv) $7{\cdot}8776 \times 10^4$ mm^2

5. An electron **6.** (i) 2^4 (ii) $2^{\frac{3}{2}}$ $x = 12{\cdot}5$ **7.** $x = \frac{3}{4}$

8. $3^{\frac{9}{2}}$ $x = \frac{31}{2}$ **9.** (a) (i) 2^2 (ii) 2^{-6} (b) $x = -3$; $x = -1$

10. $a = \frac{-11}{6}$; $b = -3$

Chapter 6

Something to think about

(i) 44, 24, 10, 8 (ii) No

Practice Questions 6.1

1. (i) Triangle, square, circle, triangle (ii) Up, right, down, left (iii) Yellow, red, black, yellow (iv) Neutral, sad, happy, neutral

2. (i) 13, 15, 17, 19 (ii) $\frac{3}{2}, \frac{3}{4}, \frac{3}{8}, \frac{3}{16}$ (iii) −15, −20, −25, −30 (iv) 9, 15, 11, 17 **3.** (i) 81, 243, 729, 2187 (ii) 25, 36, 49, 64 (iii) 8, 13, 21, 34 (iv) *N, K, H, E*

Practice Questions 6.2

1. (i) 18, 33, 38 (ii) −14, −11, −2, 1, 4 (iii) 2, 14, 18, 22, 26 **2.** (i) Yes (ii) No (iii) Yes (iv) Yes (v) No (vi) No **3.** (a) (i) 7, 3, −1 (ii) Yes (b) (i) −4, −1, 2 (ii) Yes (c) (i) 0, 3, 7 (ii) No **4.** (ii) $7n - 22$ (iii) 13, 20, 27, 34 **5.** (ii) 5, 8·5, 12, 15·5 **6.** (i) 8, 10, 12, 14, 16 (ii) 540 **7.** (i) 12, 8, 4, 0, −4 (ii) $16 - 4n$ (iii) −12, −44 (iv) −196 **8.** (i) −8 (ii) 3 (iii) Start at −8 and add 3 each time. (iv) $3n - 11$ (v) 52, 109 (vi) 13th term **9.** (i) −7 (ii) Start at 22 and subtract 7 each time. All terms are summed. (iii) $29 - 7n$ (iv) 10th (v) −675 **10.** (i) $3n + 9$ (ii) 30 (iii) 1665

11. (ii)

Pattern number	Number of blocks
1	4
2	6
3	8
4	10
5	12

(iii) Yes (iv) $2n + 2$ (v) 26 (vi) 57th (vii) 111th (viii) 340 **12.** (ii) 1, 5, 9, 13, 17 (iii) Yes (iv) $4n - 3$ (v) 109 (vi) 17th (vii) 435; €217·50

13. (ii)

Pattern number	Number of black tiles	Number of red tiles
1	1	8
2	2	13
3	3	18
4	4	23
5	5	28

(iii) (a) Yes (b) Yes (iv) n (v) $5n + 3$ (vi) $6n + 3$ (vii) 18; 93 (viii) 13th (ix) 728

Practice Questions 6.3

1. (i) 6 (ii) 41 (iii) 20 (iv) 900 **2.** (i) 4 (ii) 47 (iii) 1275 **3.** (i) 13 (ii) 1652 **4.** (i) −10, 4 (ii) 320 (iii) 10 and −4 **5.** (ii) $2n + 1$ (iii) 45 (iv) 255 **6.** (i) −11; −9 (ii) 2 (iii) $2n - 13$ (iv) 14 and −2 (v) 12 **7.** (i) 8; −3 (ii) −195 (iii) 10

8. (i) −12; 4 (ii) 660 (iii) 7 **9.** 15 **10.** 73 **11.** 72

12.

(ii)

Pattern	1	2	3	4	5
No. of tiles	4	8	12	16	20

(iii) $4n$ (iv) 48 (v) 120th (vi) $2n^2 + 2n$ (vii) 15

Practice Questions 6.4

1. (i) Yes (ii) No (iii) Yes (iv) Yes (v) No (vi) No (vii) Yes (viii) Yes (ix) No **2.** (a) (i) 4, 7, 12, 19 (ii) Yes (b) (i) 17, 6, 3, 14 (ii) No **3.** (iii) $n^2 - 3n + 5$ (iv) 75 **4.** (a)(ii) $n^2 + 2n + 3$ (iii) 171 (b) (ii) $4n^2 - 2n$ (iii) 552 (c) (ii) $-n^2 + 2n - 3$ (iii) −123

5. (ii)

Pattern number	Number of tiles
1	5
2	10
3	17
4	26

(iii) Quadratic (iv) $a = 1, b = 2, c = 2$ (v) 325 (vi) 9

6. (ii)

Pattern number	No. of green tiles	No. of red tiles	Total no. of tiles
1	4	1	5
2	4	4	8
3	4	9	13
4	4	16	20

(iii) Quadratic (iv) n^2 (v) $n^2 + 4$ (vi) 1940 (vii) 10th

7. (ii)

Pattern no.	Number of red discs	Number of green discs	Number of blue discs	Total number of discs
1	1	2	1	4
2	1	6	5	12
3	1	10	13	24
4	1	14	25	40

(iii) Linear (iv) $4n - 2$ (v) Quadratic (vi) $a = 2, b = 2, c = 0$ (vii) 1624 (viii) 1, 110, 1513 (ix) $2n^2 - 2n + 2$

Practice Questions 6.5

1. (i) Geometric (ii) Neither (iii) Geometric (iv) Arithmetic (v) Geometric (vi) Neither (vii) Neither (viii) Arithmetic (ix) Geometric **2.** (a) (i) −0·5, 0, 0·75, 1·88 (ii) Neither (b) (i) 2, 0·75, −0·5, −1·75 (ii) Arithmetic **4.** (i) −2 (ii) 1, −12, −25 (iii) −90 **5.** Geometric **6.** Neither **7.** Arithmetic

Revision and Exam Style Questions – Section A

1. 25, 21, 17, 13, 9, 5 **2.** (i) −3 (ii) 2 (iii) 18 (iv) 140 **3.** (i) $3n + 2$ (ii) 107 **4.** (i) 1, 6, 3, −2 (ii) No **5.** (i) 4 (ii) 6, 10 **6.** (i) −9, −7, −5 (ii) 6·9, 7·5, 8·1 **7.** Neither **8.** (i) 11 (ii) 19 (iii) 6 **9.** $27 - 6n$ **10.** (ii) $4n + 2$ (iii) 74 (iv) 24th (v) 1150

Revision and Exam Style Questions – Section B

1. (i) 22, 18, 14 (ii) 7th (iii) −90 (iv) 12 **2.** (i) A: 5, 2, −1, −4 B: 4, 3, 1, −3 (ii) A: Arithmetic, B: Neither **3.** (i) 2 (ii) 10 (iii) 6 (iv) 2, 8, 14, 20, 26, 32 **4.** (ii) $a = -2$, $b = 12$, $c = -5$ **5.** 21 **6.** (i) 6, 4, 2, 0 (ii) 27 (iii) −98 **7.** 92 **8.** Neither
9. (i)

Term	Value
T_1	1
T_2	6
T_3	13
T_4	22
T_5	33
T_6	46
T_7	61

(iii) $b = 2$, $c = -2$ **10.** 35
11. (ii)

	Number of red tiles	Number of blue tiles	Number of yellow tiles	Total number of tiles
Pattern 1	4	3	1	8
Pattern 2	4	6	4	14
Pattern 3	4	9	9	22
Pattern 4	4	12	16	32

(iii) Quadratic (iv) (a) 4 (b) 36 (c) 144 (d) 184 (v) $a = 1$, $b = 3$, $c = 4$ (vi) 4, 66, 484

Chapter 7

Something to think about

(i) 375 kg (ii) 40 days

Practice Questions 7.1

1. (i) Yes (ii) Yes (iii) No (iv) Yes (v) No (vi) No **2.** −10, −6, −4, 4, 8, 10 **3.** 38, 11, 3, 2, 6, 18, 27 **4.** 1, 2, 2, 2, 1, 2, 2, 2, 1, 2 **5.** (a) 1 (b) 3 (c) 1 (d) 3 (e) 1 **6.** (i) 5 (ii) 2 (iii) −3 (iv) 10 (v) 11 (vi) −11 **7.** (a) (ii) (−3, −14), (−1, −6), (3, 10), (5, 18) (iii) {−3, −1, 3, 5} (iv) {−14, −6, 10, 18} (b) (ii) (− 2, 9), (1, 3), (4, −3), (6, −7) (iii) {− 2, 1, 4, 6} (iv) {−7, −3, 3, 9} **8.** (i) −3 (ii) 3 (iii) 1·5 (iv) $f(x) = 2x - 1$ **9.** (ii) {−2, −1, 0, 1, 2} (iii) {1, 2, 5} (iv) {0, 1, 2, 3, 4, 5, 6}

Practice Questions 7.2

1. (i) 7 (ii) 13 (iii) 3 (iv) 10 (v) −3 **2.** (i) 10 (ii) −2 (iii) 2 **3.** (i) 1 (ii) −3 **4.** (i) $\frac{7}{4}$ (ii) $\frac{5}{4}$ (iii) 3 **5.** (i) −8 (ii) −7 (iii) −3 (iv) 8 (v) $-\frac{4}{3}$, 2 **6.** (i) $x^2 - 8x + 19$ (ii) 2
7. (i)

x	2·4	2·49	2·499	2·4999	…	2·5001	2·501	2·51	2·6
$g(x) = \dfrac{2x^2 + x - 15}{2x - 5}$	5·4	5·49	5·499	5·4999	…	5·5001	5·501	5·51	5·6

(ii) 5·5 **8.** $a = -2$, $b = 3$ **9.** (i) $p = -4$, $q = 3$ (ii) 3 (iii) Crosses the x-axis twice (iv) ∞ **10.** (i) 6 (ii) 9 **11.** (ii) 5·1 (iii) −1·7, 1·2 (iv) −1, 1 (v) $x < -1$, $x > 1$ **12.** (i) $p = -2$, $q = -6$ (ii) $-\frac{1}{2}$, 1 (iii) (−1, 0), (1, −4) **13.** (i) (3, 0), (5, 0) (ii) −3 (iii) $f(x)$: 3, 5; $g(x)$: 3 **14.** (ii) €67 (iii) Cost per litre (iv) $C = 1{\cdot}42L$ (v) €116·44 (vi) Line would be less steep
15. (i)

t	0	1	2	3	4	5	6
$r(t)$	0	250	400	450	400	250	0
$c(t)$	560	510	460	410	360	310	260

(ii) €400 (iii) Loss (iv) €2·50, €4·50 **16.** (ii) 10·1 km (iii) 1·6 km (iv) 10:22 am

Practice Questions 7.3

1. (i) One (ii) Three (iii) Three (iv) Three **2.** (i) −4, −1, 1·5 (ii) 18 (iii) −12 (iv) −3·4, −2, 1·9 (v) $x < -4$; $-1 < x < 1{\cdot}5$ **3.** (i) −1·6, 0·6, 3 (ii) −1·8, 1, 2·8 (iii) $-1{\cdot}6 < x < 0{\cdot}6$ **4.** (ii) (a) −3·7, −0·4, 2·1 (b) −3·8, −0·14, 1·9 (c) −8·6 (d) 5·9 **5.** (i) 12 (iii) Positive. Ends by increasing. **6.** (i) −9 (iii) Positive. Ends by increasing. **7.** (i) −18 (ii) $b - c = 17$; $3b + c = 15$; $6b + c = 39$ (iii) 8, −9; $f(x) = -x^3 + 8x^2 - 9x - 18$ **8.** (i) −4·7, −2, 1·7 (ii) $-4{\cdot}7 < x < -2$ (iii) $-2 < x < 1{\cdot}7$ **9.** (i) $2p + q = -15$ (ii) −9, 3
10. (i)

T (days)	0	1	2	3	4	5	6	7	8	9	10
$p(t)$	0	9	32	63	96	125	144	147	128	81	0

(iii) 6·7 days (iv) 10 days **11.** (ii) April until July **12.** (i) $18 - 2x$ (iv) 430 cm³ (v) If x is bigger than 9 cm, the box cannot exist. **13.** (i) €6250; €25,000 (ii) €18,750 (iii) $p(x) = 0{\cdot}5x^3 + 4x^2 - 15x + 100$ (v) At least 7 items.

Practice Questions 7.4

1. (i) Increasing (ii) Increasing (iii) Decreasing (iv) Decreasing **2.** (a) (i) (0, 6) (ii) Increasing (b) (i) (0, 3) (ii) Decreasing (c) (i) (0, 1) (ii) Decreasing (d) (i) (0, 1) (ii) Increasing (e) (i) (0, 4) (ii) Decreasing (f) (i) (0, 15) (ii) Neither **3.** (i) (0, 3) (ii) Increasing (iii) ∞ (iv) 0 **4.** 3 **5.** 3 **6.** (i) 3 (ii) 24 (iii) 1·5 (iv) Tends to infinity
7. (i)

X	−1	−0·5	0	0·5	1
$f(x)$	0·2	0·45	1	2·2	5
$g(x)$	7·5	4·74	3	1·9	1·2

(ii) (0·43, 2) (iii) $x > 0{\cdot}43$ **8.** (i) $1 = 6^x$; $2 = 4^x$; $3 = 2^x$ (ii) 6^x **9.** 2, 3 **10.** 5, 4 **11.** (ii) €10,700 (iii) 8·3 years (iv) €0 **12.** (ii) €310 (iii) 6·9 years **13.** (i) Quadratic (ii) Exponential (iii)

T (days)	0	1	2	3	4	5	6	7	8	9	10
$A(t)$	10	11·2	14·8	20·8	29·2	40	53·2	68·8	86·8	107·2	130
$B(t)$	10	13	16·9	22	28·6	37·1	48·3	62·7	81·6	106	137·9

(iv) 3·7 days, 9·2 days (v) $3{\cdot}7 < t < 9{\cdot}2$ (vi) 8 days

14. (ii) $r(t) = 2900(1{\cdot}11)^t$

(iii)

T (years)	0	1	2	3	4	5
c(t)	30000	26400	23232	20444	17990	15831
r(t)	2900	3219	3573	3966	4402	4887

T (years)	6	7	8	9	10	11	12
c(t)	13932	12260	10789	9494	8355	7352	6470
r(t)	5424	6021	6683	7418	8234	9140	10145

(iv) 10 years (v) 7 years

Practice Questions 7.5

5. (i) $(x-6)^3+2$ **6.** (i) 2 units up (ii) 3 units down (iii) 5 units to the left (iv) 3 units down (v) 1 unit to the right (vi) 2 units to the left and down 1 unit
7. B: x^2+3; C: $(x-2)^2$; D: $(x+3)^2-2$
8. $g(x) = 3f(x)$; $h(x) = f(x+2)+2$

Practice Questions 7.6

1. (i) 44 (ii) 164 (iii) 11 (iv) −1 (v) 116
2. (i) 5 (ii) 6 (iii) 13 (iv) 0 (v) $4-2x$ (vi) 17 (vii) 5 (viii) $4x+3$ **3.** (i) 5 (ii) 36 (iii) −27 (iv) 32 (v) 1 (vi) −90 (vii) $7x^2-27$ (viii) x^4-8x^2+12 **4.** (i) 3 (ii) −1 (iii) 5 (iv) 0 (v) −3 (vi) 2 (vii) −1 (viii) 1 **5.** (i) 1 (ii) 3 (iii) 0 (iv) −5 (v) −5 (vi) 1 (vii) −2 (viii) 3 **6.** (i) −4 (ii) −2 (iii) 2 (iv) 7 (v) 6 (vi) 2 (vii) 7 (viii) 6 **7.** (i) 1 (ii) 63 (iii) 13 (iv) −3
8. (i) 52 (ii) 2 (iii) 150 (iv) −974 (v) 10 (vi) 52 (vii) −63 (viii) −7954 **9.** (i) 12 (ii) 4 (iii) 64 (iv) −3 (v) 256 (vi) −48 (vii) $\frac{1}{8}$ (viii) −6·25
10. (i) (a) 11 m/s (b) 17 m/s (c) 41 m/s (d) 65 m/s (ii) (a) 24,200 J (b) 57,800 J (c) 336,200 J (d) 845,000 J (iii) $200(5+3x)^2$ **11.** (i) €525 (ii) €472·50 (iii) 37% (iv) $s(x) = 0{\cdot}7x$ (v) $d(y) = 0{\cdot}9y$ (vi) $ds(x) = 0{\cdot}63x$

Revision and Exam Style Questions – Section A

1. 3 **2.** (i) 2 sec, 4 sec (ii) 1 sec, 5 sec (iii) 6
3. (i) $P(-3, 0)$, $Q(1, 0)$, $R(0, -3)$ (ii) $-3 \le x \le 1$
4. (a) **5.** (i) 11 (ii) 26 (iii) 19 (iv) $12x^2-36x+26$
6. (i) −6 (ii) −8, −3 **7.** (ii) (a) −1, 1, 2·5 (b) 1·2, 2·4 (c) 3 (d) 4·5 **8.** (i) Decreasing (ii) 324·24 litres

(iii)

T	0	1	2	3	4	5	6	7	8	9	10
v(t)	500	470	441·8	415·3	390·4	367	345	324·2	304·8	286·5	269·3

(iv) 6 hours (2 pm) (v) 286·5 L (vi) 8 hours or 4 pm
9. (i) (0, 4) **11.** (i) $\frac{1}{2}$ sec (ii) 16·75 m (iii) 2·6 sec (iv) 82·9 m

Revision and Exam Style Questions – Section B

1. 3, −2 **2.** (i) −7, −1 (ii) $-10x-9$ (iii) −9, −1
3. (i) k^2-3k; $4k^2-2k-2$ (ii) $-1; \frac{2}{3}$
4. (i) $f(x)$ on right; $g(x)$ on left (ii) 2, 6; −3, 1 (iii) 0, 4
5. (i) $b(t) = 50{,}000{,}000(0{\cdot}92)^t$ (ii) 35,819,648 (iii) 913,662 (iv) 41 **6.** (i) $9x^2+5$ (ii) $27x^2-18x+5$ (iii) 0, 1
7. (i) $A(x) = 45x$ (ii) $B(x) = 75+25x$ (iv) A (v) B (vi) 3·75 hours **8.** (ii) A: Linear, B: Exponential (iii) €12,500; €8300 (iv) 4·5 years (v) 2·3 years; 3·4 years (vi) (a) A (b) B **9.** (i) 150 (ii) €58·90 (iii) (a) €35·10 (b) €50·50 (c) €61 (iv) $22{\cdot}5 + \frac{0{\cdot}07x}{3{\cdot}6 \times 10^6}$ (v) €80·25

Chapter 8

Something to think about

(i) 10 km/hr (ii) 9·38 km/hr (iii) 6·6%

Practice Questions 8.1

1. €520; €650 **2.** 90 cm; 120 cm **3.** (i) €56 (ii) €88 **4.** 40,000 cm³; 120,000 cm³ **5.** €300; €60; €90 **6.** (i) €240 (ii) €1,680 **7.** (i) 6 : 4 : 3 (ii) 192, 128, 96 **8.** 128 km
9. (i) 25 g (ii) 225 g (iii) 1000 ml **10.** €574,000 **11.** 101·6 cm
12. 5·6875 kg **13.** (i) 12 : 5 : 20 (ii) €120; €50; €200
14. 1224 fish **15.** 13·5 days **16.** 35 amps **17.** (i) 176·1 Hz (ii) 21,128 cm (iii) 60·4 cm **18.** (i) 13 mins (ii) 425 kg (iii) 10·5 mins (iv) 1867 W

Practice Questions 8.2

1. €149·50 **2.** 308 eggs **3.** €17,205 **4.** €7441·50 **5.** 5% **6.** €350 **7.** 6800 **8.** $6\frac{2}{3}$% **9.** €7·80 **10.** €2550 **11.** €450 **12.** Profit; 37·1% **13.** 75·6 **14.** (i) €345 (ii) 138 (iii) €1280 **15.** Shop B is cheaper **16.** €320 **17.** €320 **18.** 16·3% **19.** 224 : 210 : 175 **20.** (i) 910 units (ii) €101·37 (iii) 19% **21.** (i) $33\frac{1}{3}$% (ii) 25% **22.** (i) 18·75% (ii) 15·8% **23.** (i) €1190 (ii) €1416·67 **24.** €28 **25.** €14,340; €2340 **26.** €12,465; €3965

Practice Questions 8.3

1. (i) 235 (ii) 265 **2.** 3 days; 10% **3.** (i) 4·76% (ii) 3·83% (iii) 3·17% (iv) 10·71%; (iv) has the greatest percentage error **4.** (i) 2·8% (ii) 4·1% (iii) 2·6% (iv) 7% **5.** 2·9% **6.** (i) 980 g to 1020 g (ii) C **7.** (i) 6% (ii) 7·1% **8.** 2·4% **9.** (i) 19·2 cm (ii) 18·6 cm (iii) 3·125% **10.** (i) 0·47% (ii) 5·44% **11.** (i) 2·2125 m; 1·9 m (ii) 2·2479 m; 1·9304 m (iii) 3·12% **12.** (i) 3·04862 (ii) 3·24000 (iii) 0·19138 (iv) 1850, 1859, 1868, 1881 (v) 1866 (vi) 3·13% **13.** (i) 2756 L (ii) €3577·50 (iii) €143·10 **14.** (i) 968,000π cm^3 (ii) 1,824,637 cm^3 (iii) 1·37%

Practice Questions 8.4

1. $45·60 **2.** $165 **3.** (i) 153·6 Yuan (ii) $130 **4.** Dublin by €1·61 **5.** South Africa by €3·19 **6.** Euro. $1·75 **7.** 1 Yen = 0·6 Ruble **8.** (i) 1263 Zloty (ii) €283·82 (iii) €16·18 **9.** (i) £7912 (ii) €56·59 **10.** (i) 16,650 Yen (ii) $119·70 (iii) €648 (iv) $200 (v) 23,450·7 Yen (vi) £1116·16 **11.** €1716 **12.** $312 **13.** 3% **14.** 2·5% **15.** (i) €744 (ii) 29·4%

Practice Questions 8.5

1. 12 m/s **2.** (i) 2 m/s; 1 m/s; $\frac{4}{7}$ m/s (ii) Tiredness. Gradient of the road getting steeper. (iii) 1 m/s **3.** (ii) 900 km/h **4.** 12:37 pm **5.** (ii) 312 km **6.** (i) 43,200 m/hr (ii) 43·2 km/hr **7.** (i) 72,000 m/hr (ii) 20 m/s **8.** 2·088 × 10^8 km **9.** (ii) 7 km/hr **10.** 49·5 mph **11.** (ii) 68 km/hr **12.** (ii) 90 km/hr **13.** (i) 68 km/hr (ii) 0·8 hr (iii) 23 mins **14.** 75 s **15.** 79 s **16.** 27 s **17.** (i) 40 km (ii) $\frac{40}{x}$ hr (iii) 80 km/hr **18.** (i) B and C (ii) B

Revision and Exam Style Questions – Section A

1. (i) €22·70 (ii) €27·92 **2.** €1040 **3.** 262·4 km **4.** (i) 259 g (ii) 740 g **5.** (i) $1395 (ii) €1 = $1·25 **6.** 63 cm **7.** (i) 167% (ii) 62·5% **8.** (i) 0·002% (ii) 2·8% **9.** (i) $\frac{1}{6}$ (ii) 0·17 (iii) 17% **10.** (i) €324 (ii) €300 **11.** (i) 0·5 m/s; 1·5 m/s (ii) 0·93 m/s **12.** (i) 36 (ii) 16 (iii) 55·6% **13.** 110 km/h

Revision and Exam Style Questions – Section B

1. 11·8% **2.** (i) €420 (ii) €94·50 (iii) €416·67 (iv) 19% **3.** 23 : 33 : 60 **4.** (i) €194·81 (ii) 37% **5.** (i) 7·72 lbs (ii) 198·07 km (iii) 1·81 kg (iv) 35·46″; 23·64″ (v) 224 g; 168 g; 0·57 L; 20·3 cm **6.** €66·73 **7.** (i) $1{\cdot}5 = \frac{22}{x} + \frac{8}{x-6}$ (ii) 22 km/h; 16 km/h (iii) 20 km/hr **8.** (i) €761·20 (ii) 40·4% (iii) 11% **9.** 5 : 3 **10.** (i) £3·63 (ii) 67% **11.** (i) 5·3% (ii) 104·5 km/hr (iii) 4 h 13 mins

Chapter 9

Something to think about

(i) 21·275% (ii) 72,000

Practice Questions 9.1

1. (i) €3726 (ii) €1526 **2.** (i) €12,237·50 (ii) €8287·50 **3.** €1404·90 **4.** (i) €59·25 (ii) €22·38 (iii) €55 (iv) 8·8% **5.** (i) €231·39 (ii) €36·30 (iii) €732·31 **6.** (i) €23,898 (ii) €3522 (iii) €50,580 **7.** (i) €10,330 (ii) €2452·50 **8.** (i) €398·25 (ii) 7 hours (iii) €45 (iv) €24·70 (v) €7·22 **9.** (i) €19,359 (ii) €3224 (iii) €50·54 (iv) €787·67 **10.** 21% **11.** €3500 **12.** (i) 41% (ii) €3100 (iii) 5%

Practice Questions 9.2

1. (i) €99·89 (ii) €191·13 (iii) €934·32 (iv) €1566·18 **2.** €8598·14 **3.** 3 years at 2% by €1·54 **4.** €9362·56 **5.** €5635·20 **6.** €17,361·52 **7.** €12,287·17 **8.** €25,387·69 **9.** €22,699·01 **10.** €11,259·61 **11.** €50,000 **12.** €3200 **13.** €1800 **14.** €6268 **15.** 6·5% **16.** 3% **17.** 2·26% **18.** 2·41% **19.** 6%; €2300 **20.** (i) €68,500 (ii) 3·5% **21.** (i) €33,075 (ii) €8075 **22.** €5600 **23.** (i) 4·8% (ii) €2610

Practice Questions 9.3

1. (i)

Yr.	Value	Depreciation	Value at end of year
1	€49,000	€3920	€45,080
2	€45,080	€3606·40	€41,473·60
3	€41,473·60	€3317·89	€38,155·71

2. €11,314·49 **3.** €41,124 **4.** (i) €85,000; €78,200; €74,290 (ii) €25,710 **5.** €21,579·49 **6.** (i) €7,050·16 (ii) 21·7% **7.** €472,596 **8.** €15,250 **9.** (i) 105 years (ii) 3·5% **10.** 8% **11.** 6% **12.** 12·5% **13.** 10·21% **14.** 16·1 million **15.** 7962 cows **16.** 6% **17.** (i) 9% (ii) €750,000 **18.** (i) 12,919 people (ii) 40%

Revision and Exam Style Questions – Section A

1. €13,926·49 **2.** (i) €13,101·60 **3.** (i) €20,590 (ii) €440 **4.** (i) €2325·96 (ii) 5·2% **5.** (i) €600,000 (ii) €20,696 (iii) €159·30 **6.** (i) €8643 (ii) €28,653 **7.** (i) €1359·61 (ii) €152 (iii) Exceeded his limit (iv) 23·87% **8.** (i) €8840 (ii) 4·5% **9.** (i) 6·69 cm (ii) 3·73 cm (iii) 2·2 cm (iv) Saturday 4:30 am

Revision and Exam Style Questions – Section B

1. (i) €8867·88 **2.** (i) €37,520 (ii) €60,000 **3.** 1·88% **4.** €2989 **5.** (i) €196,691 (ii) 6% **6.** 7% **7.** (i) 1·2597*P* (ii) 1·1664*P* (iii) 1·08*P* (iv) €2500 **8.** (i) 1372 (ii) 2689 (iii) 15% **9.** (i) €24 (ii) 4% **10.** (i) €15,611·34 (ii) €10,961·27

Chapter 10

Something to think about

130°

Practice Questions 10.1

1. (i) An axiom is a statement that is taken to be true without the need for a proof. (ii) A theorem is a statement that can be proved from the axioms and other theorems by logical argument.

(iii) A proof is a step-by-step explanation that uses axioms and previously proven theorems to show another. (iv) A corollary is a statement that follows readily from a previous theorem. (v) Implies is used in a proof when we can write a fact we have proven by our previous statements. (vi) The converse of a theorem is the reverse of a theorem. **2.** (i) If two lines intersect at right angles they are perpendicular. True. (ii) If $x < 20$, then $x = 12$. False. (iii) If two lines never meet, then they are parallel. True. (iv) If a triangle is isosceles then, it has two sides of equal length. True.

3. (ii) $|DF| = \frac{1}{2}|DE|$ is true

4. (iii) cannot have two points in common
5. (ii) one unique line can be drawn through them
6. (i) 25° (ii) 60° **7.** (i) 72° (ii) 63° (iii) 99° (iv) 162°
8. $f = 35°$; $g = 81°$; $h = 44°$; $i = 75°$

Practice Questions 10.2

1. (i) 1 = 125° vertically opposite, 2 = 55° straight line, 4 = 55° vertically opposite (ii) 1 = 97° straight line, 2 = 83° vertically opposite, 3 = 97° vertically opposite (iii) $x = 55°$ vertically opposite, $y = 125°$ straight line, $z = 125°$ vertically opposite (iv) $x = 81°$ vertically opposite, $y = 21°$ straight line (v) $x = 86°$ straight line, $y = 69°$ vertically opposite (vi) $a = 38°$ straight line, $b = 64°$ vertically opposite, $c = 78°$ vertically opposite, $d = 38°$ vertically opposite a
2. (i) $a = 110°$, $b = 70°$ (ii) $a = 85°$, $b = 95°$ (iii) $a = 120°$, $b = 60°$ (iv) $a = 45°$, $b = 135°$ (v) $a = 140°$, $b = 40°$ (vi) $a = 75°$, $b = 105°$
3. (i) 130° (ii) 40° (iii) 70° (iv) 75° (v) 80° (vi) 120°
4. 2 = 65°, 3 = 70°, 4 = 110°, 5 = 65°, 6 = 115°, 7 = 110°, 8 = 70°, 9 = 115°, 10 = 65°, 11 = 70°, 12 = 110°, 13 = 65°, 14 = 115°, 15 = 110°, 16 = 70° **5.** $x = 147°$; $y = 21°$; $z = 33°$ **6.** (i) parallel (ii) not parallel **7.** 100° **8.** (i) vertically opposite (ii) alternate (iii) supplementary **9.** (i) m and n (ii) t (iii) 8 (iv) 1 = 3 = 5 = 7; 2 = 4 = 6 = 8 **10.** 2 = 68° ... corresponding
11. (i) 2 (ii) 11 (iii) 4·1 **12.** (i) 2 cm (ii) 6 cm (iii) 15 cm (iv) 23 cm.

Revision and Exam Style Questions

1. (i) An axiom is a statement that is taken to be true without the need for a proof. (ii) A theorem is a statement that can be proved from the axioms and other theorems by logical argument. (iii) The converse of a theorem is the reverse of a theorem. (iv) A proof is a step-by-step explanation that uses axioms and previously proven theorems to show another. (v) A corollary is a statement that follows readily from a previous theorem. (vi) Implies is used in a proof when we can write a fact we have proven by our previous statements. **2.** A theorem needs to be proven. An axiom is taken as fact.
3. (i) 36° (ii) 144°; 36° (iii) Angles in a straight line sum to 180°
4. (i) 1 and 3, 2 and 4, 7 and 9, 8 and 10. (ii) 1 and 7, 2 and 8, 3 and 9, 4 and 10. (iii) 2 and 10, 3 and 7 (iv) 9 = 56°; 10 = 124°
5. (i) 15° (ii) 15° (iii) 125° (iv) 140° **6.** Yes $|\angle DBA| = |\angle EBC|$
7. $x = 6$; $y = 1$ **8.** (i) 47° (ii) 47° (iii) 133° (iv) 74° (v) 106° (vi) 74° (vii) 90° (viii) 63° **9.** (i) $x = 8$; $y = 12$ (ii) If three parallel lines cut off equal segments on some transversal line, then they will cut off equal segments on any other transversal. (Theorem 11) **10.** (i) $r = 12°$, $s = 73°$, $t = 95°$, $u = 95°$.

Chapter 11

Something to think about

15 m

Practice Questions 11.1

1. (i) 75° (ii) 7 (iii) 70° (iv) 72° (v) $x = 66°$; $y = 48°$ (vi) 21° **2.** (i) 35° (ii) 70° (iii) 30° (iv) 148° (v) 143°
3. (i) smallest = $\angle A$, largest = $\angle B$ (ii) smallest = $\angle F$, Largest = $\angle E$ (iii) smallest = $\angle J$, largest = $\angle K$
4. (i) shortest = $|BC|$, longest = $|CD|$ (ii) shortest = $|MN|$, Longest = $|MO|$ (iii) shortest = $|ST|$, Longest = $|RT|$ **5.** (i) incorrect (ii) incorrect (iii) correct (iv) incorrect (v) correct (vi) correct **6.** (i) $w = 53°$; $x = 127°$; $y = 39°$ (ii) $x = 36°$ (iii) 65° (iv) $x = 30°$ **7.** $x = 40°$; $x + 7 = 47°$; $x - 9 = 31°$; $3x - 18 = 102°$; $x + 21 = 61°$; $x + 17 = 57°$; $y = 62°$ **8.** $x = 44°$
9. (i) $\angle 1 = 97°$, $\angle 2 = 83°$ (ii) No. Insufficient information.
10. (i) 8 (ii) 35 (iii) 45 (iv) 3 (v) 42 (vi) 40 **11.** (i) 5 (ii) 10 **12.** (a) (i) $|AB|$ (ii) $|BC|$ (iii) $|AC|$ (b) (i) 13 ± 0,5 cm^2 (ii) Each base × height gives approximately the same answer.

Practice Questions 11.2

1. (i) $\angle BAC = \angle ACD$ (ii) $|AD| = |BC|$ **2.** $\angle GDF = \angle EDF$; $|DF| = |DF|$; $\angle DFG = \angle DFE$ ... congruent by ASA
3. $|AB| = |AE|$; $\angle BAC = \angle DAE$, $|AC| = |AD|$ ... congruent by SAS
4 (i) No (ii) Yes for SAS (iii) Yes for RHS (iv) Yes for ASA (v) Yes for SSS (vi) No (vii) Yes for RHS (viii) Yes for SAS
5. $|XY| = |YZ|$; $\angle XYT = \angle ZYT$; $|YT| = |YT|$ ... congruent by SAS

Practice Questions 11.3

1. (i) $\angle ACE = \angle BCD$; $\angle CAE = \angle CBD$
(ii) $\angle HGF = \angle HKJ$; $\angle GHF = \angle JHK$
(iii) $\angle DFH = \angle EFG$; $\angle DHF = \angle EGF$; $\angle HDF = \angle GEF$
(iv) $\angle ACE = \angle BCD$; $\angle CAE = \angle CBD$
(v) $\angle VYU = \angle VXW$; $\angle UVY = \angle XVW$
(vi) $\angle JLK = \angle MLN$; $\angle LKJ = \angle LMN$
2. Tents are equiangular therefore similar. **3.** (i) EFB and DFC (ii) $\angle EFB = \angle DFC$; $\angle FBE = \angle FDC$; $\angle FEB = \angle FCD$ (iii) 3·75 units **4.** (i) 2·4 cm (ii) 2·8 cm (iii) 3·27 (iv) 7·2 cm (v) 7 cm (vi) 6 cm **5.** Shelf is not parallel to the floor
6. 4·61 m **7.** 3·6 m **8.** (ii) 61·83 m **9.** 1·35 m **10.** 4 m

Practice Questions 11.4

1. (i) 23·3 (ii) 91·8 (iii) 97·3 (iv) 57·3 (v) 84·4 (vi) 66·5
2. (i) No (ii) Yes (iii) Yes (iv) Yes (v) No (vi) Yes **3.** 13·6 cm
4. 13·7 cm **5.** (i) 36·6″ (ii) 1 : 1·8 **6.** 5·8 m **7.** No

Practice Questions 11.5

1. (i) 135° (ii) 98° (iii) 110° (iv) 100° (v) 23 (vi) 12·6
2. (i) 92·96 m^2 (ii) 18·7 mm^2 (iii) 37·44 m^2 **3.** (i) 15 cm (ii) 24 cm (iii) 16 cm (iv) 26 cm (v) 80° **4.** 5 ; 2 **5.** 60° ; 120°
6. (i) 14 (ii) Not right angled **7.** (ii) $x = 4$; $y = 8$ **8.** 8
9. (ii) 116 cm^2 **10.** (i) $\angle E$ decreases (ii) $|FD|$ increases (iii) Distance from the wall decreases **11.** (i) 27° (iii) 27° (iv) yes

Practice Questions 11.6

1. (i) 58° (ii) 96° (iii) 72° (iv) 256° (v) 38° (vi) $x = 114°$; $y = 132°$ **2.** (i) 51° (ii) 45° (iii) = 90°; $y = 22°$
4. (i) 105° (ii) $x = 101°$; $y = 95°$ (iii) $a = 109°$; $b = 86°$; $c = 94°$ (iv) $x = 58°$; $y = 122°$ (v) $x = 49°$ (vi) $x = 81°$; $y = 114°$ **5.** (i) 90°

(ii) $x = 90°$; $y = 15°$ (iii) $x = 90°$; $y = 36°$ **6.** (i) is a tangent (ii) is a tangent (iii) not a tangent **7.** (i) 18° (ii) 72° **8.** 6 cm **9.** (i) 54° (ii) 27° **10.** 6 cm **11.** 24 cm **12.** 29° **14.** (i) 74° (ii) 32° (iii) 37°

Revision and Exam Style Questions – Section A

1. $a = 115°$, $b = 65°$, $c = 75°$ $d = 105°$ **2.** 49° **3.** 26 cm **4.** (i) 5 cm (ii) 2·5 cm (iii) OAB and OAC (iv) $\angle AOB = 77°$; $\angle OBA = 51{\cdot}5°$ **5.** 148° **6.** 40° **7.** (i) 65° (ii) 25° **8.** 5 cm **9.** (i) $x = 8$ (ii) $y = 22$ (iii) $s = 35°$ (iv) $t = 14°$ **10.** 11·2

Revision and Exam Style Questions – Section B

1. (i) The three angles in a triangle add up to 180°.
The exterior angle is equal to the sum of the interior opposite angles. (iii) $\angle b = 60°$; $\angle c = 80°$ **3.** (i) 12·5 cm (ii) 7·2 cm **4.** $n = 8$ **6.** (i) 50° (ii) 40° (ii) 14 cm **8.** (i) cyclic quadrilateral (ii) Opposite angle add up to 180° (iii) 78° **9.** 6·4 cm **10.** 1789 km

Chapter 12

Something to think about

Circumcentre

Practice Questions 12.1

2. (i) 108° (ii) 56° (iii) 17° (iv) 6° **8.** (i) (a) False (b) True (c) True (d) False (ii) (a) $|\angle PQR| = 2|\angle RQS|$ (d) $\frac{1}{2}|\angle PQR| = |\angle PQS|$ **9.** C

Practice Questions 12.2

6. (ii) 60° (iii) equilateral (iv) 9 cm

Practice Questions 12.3

1. (i) The circumcentre is the centre of the circumcircle. It is the point at which the perpendicular bisectors of the sides of the triangle intersect. (ii) The incentre is the centre of the incircle. It is the point at which the bisectors of the angles of the triangle intersect.
(iii) The centroid of a triangle is the centre of gravity (balance point) of the triangle. It is the point of intersection of the medians of the triangle. **5.** Jack. If the street light is positioned at the circumcentre, it is equidistant from the vertices but not from each street.
6. (ii) Yes **7.** Yes. An equilateral triangle is a symmetric shape so the circumcentre and incentre are equidistant from the vertices.
9. (i) The median (ii) The centroid

Revision and Exam Style Questions – Section A

1. $|\angle ABC| = 90°$ **6.** $|\angle BAD| = 100°$

Revision and Exam Style Questions – Section B

1. (iii) If it is an acute triangle **2.** (ii) The incentre is the centre of the incircle. It is the point at which the bisectors of the angles of the triangle intersect. **3.** (iii) circumcenter **4.** (iii) Each tangent is perpendicular to the radius that goes to the point of contact. (Theorem 20) (v) equilateral **5.** (a) perpendicular bisectors (b) bisectors of the angles (c) medians
7. (i) A = circumcentre; B = centroid; C = incentre
(ii) A, the circumcentre is equidistant from the vertices of the triangle **8.** A, because you are as far from all three tracks as possible **10.** (i) He drew the perpendicular bisectors of the sides of the triangle and found their intersection point. (ii) The circumcentre (iii) it is the same distance from Kilkenny, Waterford and Wexford (iv) It is equal distance from each of the location that forms the Viking triangle, however, it is not close to the main roads so may not be easily accessible from all locations.

Chapter 13

Something to think about

Scale factor = $\frac{6000}{23}$; width = 4 m or 3704 mm

Practice Questions 13.1

1. (i) Yes (ii) Yes (iii) No (iv) Yes **2.** (i) 6 (ii) 4 (iii) 4 (iv) 8 **4.** (i) $x = 3$ (ii) $x = 2$ (iii) $x = -1$

Practice Questions 13.2

1. Object = ΔXYZ Image = $\Delta X'Y'Z'$ **2.** (i) No. One is horizontal, other is vertical. (ii) Yes. Shapes are identical, only position has changed. (iii) No. size of shape has changed. (iv) No. The shape has been reflected. **3.** (i) (−7, −1) (ii) (−2, −4) (iii) (−3, 0) (iv) (8, 5) **6.** (i) $Q' = (-6, -12)$ $R' = (-1, 3)$ $S' = (5, -9)$ (ii) $Q' = (6, -12)$ $R' = (1, 3)$ $S' = (-5, -9)$ (iii) $Q' = (6, 12)$ $R' = (1, -3)$ $S' = (-5, 9)$ (iv) $Q' = (12, 6)$ $R' = (-3, 1)$ $S' = (9, -5)$
8. (i) axial symmetry (ii) translation (iii) rotation (iv) rotation (v) axial symmetry (vi) translation **9.** A: axial symmetry in a horizontal line B: Axial symmetry in a vertical line
C: Rotation of 90° clockwise about a point **10.** (i) $\overrightarrow{DE}$, $\overrightarrow{EF}$ (ii) G (iii) ΔGEF (iv) $[EF]$ (v) $\angle EFG$ **11.** (i) ΔRPC (ii) $[RC]$ (iii) $\angle PRC$ (iv) $BQRP$, $PQRC$ (v) $\angle AQB$, $\angle QRP$ (vi) 72 cm^2 **12.** (i) $[PS]$, $[SB]$ and $[AQ]$ (ii) ΔQPA (iii) ΔPRQ (iv) $[SQ]$ (v) 40° **13.** (ii) $X' = (-2, 4)$; $Y = (-1, 1)$; $Z' = (-4, 3)$
14. (i) $A' = (5, -2)$; $B' = (5, 1)$; $C' = (2, 0)$; $D' = (2, -2)$

Practice Questions 13.3

3. (iii) The image is twice the size of the object when scale factor is 2. The image is one third (three times smaller) the size of the object when the scale factor is $\frac{1}{3}$. **5.** (i) 2 (ii) 1·5 (iii) 4 (iv) 2 (v) 3 **6.** 24 cm **7.** 5·3 cm **8.** (i) $\frac{1}{20}$ (ii) $\frac{5}{4}$ **9.** (i) $\frac{3}{2}$ (ii) 1·5 (iii) Area of A = 1868·72 cm^2 Area of B = 4204·62 cm^2
10. (i) 4·5 m (ii) 2·1 m^2

Revision and Exam Style Questions – Section A

1. A = axial symmetry, B = translation, C = central symmetry
3. (i) E (ii) A (iii) D (iv) central symmetry in O or a rotation of 180° about O (v) 90° anticlockwise rotation about O
4. (i) 2 (ii) 20 units (iii) 26 square units
5. (i) 6 (iii) 120° anticlockwise rotation (iv) translation
6. A = 90° anticlockwise rotation B = central symmetry C = axial symmetry **7.** A = central symmetry B = axial symmetry C = translation D = axial symmetry in a slanted line
8. (i) 72° (ii) Seat 9 **9.** (i) ΔFHG (ii) $[FG]$ (iii) $\angle FHG$ (iv) ΔEXH (v) $[EX]$ (vi) $\angle HEX$ (vii) $\overrightarrow{HF}$ (viii) $\overrightarrow{FG}$ (ix) $\overrightarrow{XH}$, $\overrightarrow{EF}$ **10.** (i) (−1, 1) (−1, 4) (−4, 1) (−5, 5) (ii) (−1, −1) (−4, −1) (−1, −4) (−5, −5) (iii) (1, −1) (1, −4) (4, −1) (5, −5)
11. (i) axial symmetry in y-axis (ii) central symmetry in (0, 0) (iii) translation 6 down, 2 across (iv) Axial symmetry in x axis (v) central symmetry in (1, −3) **12.** (i) 9 (ii) 12 (iii) 70·2 square units

Revision and Exam Style Questions – Section B

(iii) 147 cm^2 (iv) $\frac{3}{4}$ **2.** (iii) 111 cm^2 (iv) 0·43 **3.** (i) 1·75 (ii) 6 (iii) 32 square units **4.** (i) 2 (ii) 20 units (iii) 26 square units **5.** (iii) 8·64 cm^2 **6.** (iii) 36 cm^2 (iv) 0·91 **7.** (a) F (b) $[FE]$ (c) $\Delta\, CYE$ (d) $[DY]$ (e) $[YF]$ (f) $\angle YCD$ (ii) $XDYC$ (iii) (a) 12 cm^2 (b) 24 cm^2 (c) 48 cm^2

8. (i) (a) S (b) $[RU]$ (c) $\Delta\, STU$ (d) $\angle URS$ (ii) $\overrightarrow{QR}$ (iii) 10 cm^2 (iv) 120° **9.** (i) 1·5 square units (iii) 13·5 square units (iv) 9 : 1 (v) $k^2 = 9$ and the ratio is 9 : 1, proves that the area of B is k^2A. **10.** 20 cm

Chapter 14

Something to think about

$4\sqrt{5}$ km

Practice Questions 14.1

1. (i) 2nd quadrant (ii) 4th quadrant (iii) 3rd quadrant (iv) 1st quadrant (v) 4th quadrant **2.** (i) y-axis (ii) x-axis (iii) x-axis (iv) y-axis **3.** (i) $A = (0, 3)$, $B = (2, -1)$, $C = (-3, 1)$, $D = (-1, -3)$, $E = (3, 0)$, $F = (-2, -1)$, $G = (0, -1)$ (ii) Since F and B are on the same horizontal line, to find $|FB|$ we can count the units along the grid. Since D and B are not on the same horizontal or vertical line, to find $|DB|$ we need to use Pythagoras' Theorem or the distance formula

Practice Questions 14.2

1. (i) (4, 2) (ii) (2, 1) (iii) (−2, −1) (iv) (−3·5, 0) (v) (2·5, −4) (vi) (2·5, 0·5) **2.** (ii) (−4·5, −1) **3.** (2, 5) **4.** (−4, 7) **5.** (ii) (4, −4) **6.** (ii) (1, 4) **8.** (i) The midpoints of the diagonals are not equal, so the diagonals do not bisect each other. (ii) Not a parallelogram. **9.** (5, 6) **10.** $a = -3$, $b = 5$ **11.** $C = (2, 0)$, $D = (4, 5)$

Practice Questions 14.3

1. (i) 5 (ii) $\sqrt{26}$ (iii) $3\sqrt{2}$ (iv) 5 (v) $\sqrt{53}$ (vi) $\sqrt{10}$ **2.** (i) $\sqrt{74}$ (ii) $|BC| = 7$, $|AC| = 5$ **3.** (i) (3, 0) **5.** $|PQ| = \sqrt{26}$, $|PR| = 2\sqrt{26}$, Area = 26 units^2 **6.** (i) $\sqrt{170}$ km (ii) 15·9 km/h **7.** (i) $P = -3, 7$ **8.** $k = -6, 4$ **9.** (i) $k = 0, 6$ **10.** (i) 11,825 m (ii) 8·1 km/hr (iii) 8·8 km/hr

Practice Questions 14.4

1. (a) $\frac{2}{5}$ (b) $-\frac{2}{7}$ (c) $-\frac{3}{5}$ (d) 1 **2.** c, d, f, b, a, e **7.** $m = 0$. Horizontal line **8.** (i) $m = 5$, increasing (ii) $m = -5$, decreasing (iii) $m = -\frac{2}{3}$, decreasing (iv) $m = 13$, increasing **9.** $k = 5$ **10.** $k = 8$ **11.** $k = 5$ **12.** 1

Practice Questions 14.5

1. (i) No (ii) Yes (iii) No **2.** (i) Yes (ii) No (iii) Yes (iv) No (v) Yes (vi) No **3.** (i) $\frac{2}{3}$ (ii) $-\frac{3}{2}$ **4.** (i) $-\frac{4}{7}$ (ii) $\frac{7}{4}$ **5.** (i) −2 (ii) $-\frac{5}{3}$ (iii) $-\frac{1}{4}$ (iv) $\frac{2}{5}$ (v) 4 (vi) $\frac{1}{3}$

Practice Questions 14.6

1. (ii) $y = 4x - 3$ **2.** (ii) $y = -\frac{3}{2}x + 7$ **3.** (ii) 15·6 m (iii) $D = 4{\cdot}8M$ (iv) 216 m (v) No. Humans cannot dive underwater indefinitely. The pressure will be too great. (other possible answers here) **4.** (ii) Decrease in reaction time for every one hour of sleep (iii) 5·25 s (iv) 3·34 hours of sleep will result in a reaction time of 5 seconds. (v) $T = -0{\cdot}3H + 6$ (vi) Two possible problems: The model would create a 0 s reaction time, which is not possible. Every person is different and so will have different reaction times throughout. **5.** (ii) 55 m^2 will cost €560 to clean (iii) $C = 8M + 120$ (iv) €640 (v) 28·125 m^2 **6.** (i) $P =$ €2·80$(x) - 125$ (iii) €65·40 (iv) 45 jars

Practice Questions 14.7

1. (i) $3x - y - 5 = 0$ (ii) $2x + y - 3 = 0$ (iii) $4x + y + 7 = 0$ (iv) $x - 2y - 7 = 0$ (v) $5x - 2y + 2 = 0$ (vi) $3x + 2y - 16 = 0$ (vii) $5x - y = 0$ (viii) $5x + 7y + 6 = 0$ **2.** (i) $3x - 4y + 22 = 0$ (ii) Yes **3.** (i) $\frac{2}{5}$ (ii) $2x - 5y + 9 = 0$ **4.** (i) $3x - y = 0$ (ii) No **5.** (i) $x + 3y - 8 = 0$ (ii) $3x - y + 16 = 0$ **6.** (i) $3x - 5y + 4 = 0$ (ii) $2x + 3y - 10 = 0$ (iii) $5x - 2y + 13 = 0$ (iv) $5x + 4y - 11 = 0$ (v) $3x + y - 8 = 0$ (vi) $y + 1 = 0$ **7.** (i) $x - y - 3 = 0$ (ii) $3x + y - 1 = 0$ (iii) $5x - 2y - 14 = 0$ (iv) $2x + y = 0$ (v) $3x + 5y - 15 = 0$ (vi) $5x + 6y - 12 = 0$ **8.** (i) $x - y + 2 = 0$ (ii) Yes (iii) Yes **9.** $2x - 3y + 10 = 0$

Practice Questions 14.8

1. (i) −2 (ii) 5 (iii) −3 (iv) $\frac{3}{7}$ (v) $\frac{1}{2}$ (vi) −1 **2.** $y = 3x + 5$ (i) 3 (ii) (0, 5) **3.** (i), (ii) and (iv) **6.** $k = -6$ **7.** $k = -2$ **8.** $7x + 2y + 19 = 0$ **9.** $x + 4y - 11 = 0$ **10.** (i) $2x - 5y - 9 = 0$ (ii) $5x + 2y - 8 = 0$ **11.** (i) $3x + y + 8 = 0$ (ii) $x - 3y + 6 = 0$

Practice Questions 14.9

3. (1, 3) **4.** Lines intersect at (−3, 2) ⇒ concurrent. **5.** c, g, f, e, d, a, b

Practice Questions 14.10

1. (i) (1, 3) **2.** (i) (−1, 4) **3.** (i) (−2, 5) **4.** (i) (2, 3) (ii) (−2, 3) (iii) (4, −3) (iv) (−2, −4) (v) (−2, 4) (vi) (4, 4)
5. (i)

Distance (km)	0	1	2	3	4	5	6	7	8	9	10
Company A	3·2	4·15	5·1	6·05	7	7·95	8·9	9·85	10·8	11·75	12·7
Company B	4·5	5·3	6·1	6·9	7·7	8·5	9·3	10·1	10·9	11·7	12·5

(iii) Company A is cheaper (iv) Company B is cheaper (v) 8·7 km (vi) Company A: $C = 3{\cdot}2 + 0{\cdot}95D$
Company B: $C = 4{\cdot}5 + 0{\cdot}8D$

Practice Questions 14.11

1.(i) 3 units^2 (ii) 4 units^2 (iii) 4 units^2 (iv) 7 units^2 **2.**(ii) 5 units (iii) 4 units (iv) 10 units^2 **3.** (i) $P = (2, 4)$, $Q = (3, 1)$ **4.** (i) $B' = (6, 2)$, $C' = (4, 7)$ (ii) 17 units^2 **5.** (i) 11 units^2 (ii) 6 units^2 (iii) 8·5 units^2 (iv) 22·5 units^2 **7.** Yes. Collinear **8.** (i) 6·5 units^2 (ii) 11 units^2 (iii) 17·5 units^2

9. (i) 15·5 units^2 (ii) 18 units^2 **10.** (i) 128 units^2 (ii) 50 units^2 **11.** (i) $D = (0, -4)$ (ii) 36 units^2

Revision and Exam Style Questions – Section A

1. 3 **2.** Yes. Perpendicular **3.** $x + 2y + 1 = 0$ **4.** (ii) $3x - 4y + 18 = 0$ (iv) Not perpendicular **5.** (i) 2 (ii) (4, 0), (0, 8) **6.** (ii) 17 units^2 **7.** (i) $P = (1, 5)$, $Q = (-1, 1)$ (iii) Yes. Parallel **8.** (i) Right-angled at A (ii) 8 **9.** (i) $\frac{3}{4}$ (ii) $3x - 4y + 12 = 0$ (iv) $4x + 3y = 0$ (v) -3 **10.** (i) $P = (4, 0)$, $Q = (0, 6)$ (iii) 12 units^2 **11.** (i) $\frac{3}{4}$ (ii) $4x + 3y - 12 = 0$ (iii) (0, 4) **12.** (i) (−8, 0) (ii) $2x - y - 4 = 0$ (iii) (4·5, 5)

Revision and Exam Style Questions – Section B

1. (i) $x + y - 6 = 0$ (ii) $x - y = 0$ (iii) (3, 3) (iv) (10, 2) **2.** (i) −7 (ii) $5x - 2y + 10 = 0$ (iii) (0, −3·5), (0, 5), (2, 10), (2, 1·5) **3.** (i) $x - 2y + 2 = 0$ (ii) (0, 1) (iii) $\frac{1}{2}$ **4.** (ii) $\frac{2}{3}$ (iii) $3x + 2y + 18 = 0$ (iv) (0, −9) (vi) (6, −5) (vii) 78 units^2 **5.** (i) $F = 45 + 1{\cdot}2T$ (iii) €93 (iv) 75 minutes (v) €117 for 60 minutes work (vi) Greater rate of change. Graph would become steeper. (vii) The graph would be lower on the plane. It would start at 20 on the y-axis. **6.** (iii) 10 units^2 (iv) $H = (0, 9)$, $G = (-6, 7)$ (v) $2x - y + 9 = 0$ **7.** (i) 1 (ii) $x - y + 5 = 0$ (iii) $x + y - 3 = 0$ (iv) (−1, 4) **8.** (i) $\frac{1}{2}$ (ii) Yes. Perpendicular (iii) (0, −3) (iv) 15 units^2

Chapter 15

Something to think about

2 h 41 min

Practice Questions 15.1

1. (i) $(x - 2)^2 + (y - 5)^2 = 16$ (ii) $4x^2 + 4y^2 = 25$ (iii) $x^2 + y^2 = 20$ (iv) $(x + 4)^2 + y^2 = 81$ (v) $25x^2 + 25y^2 = 144$ (vi) $(x + 6)^2 + (y + 4)^2 = 5$ (vii) $(x + 2)^2 + (y + 5)^2 = 7$ (viii) $x^2 + y^2 = 96$ (ix) $(x + 3)^2 + (y - 7)^2 = 36$ (x) $(x - 6)^2 + (y + 1)^2 = 10$ **2.** (i) $2\sqrt{5}$ (ii) $x^2 + y^2 = 20$ **3.** (i) $\sqrt{10}$ (ii) $x^2 + y^2 = 10$ **4.** (i) $x^2 + y^2 = 16$ (ii) $(x - 3)^2 + (y - 1)^2 = 16$ (iii) $x^2 + (y - 3)^2 = 25$ (iv) $(x - 4)^2 + (y + 4)^2 = 9$ (v) $x^2 + y^2 = 9$ (vi) $(x + 4)^2 + (y + 4)^2 = 25$ (vii) $(x + 3)^2 + (y - 2)^2 = 4$ (viii) $(x + 1)^2 + y^2 = 1$ (ix) $x^2 + y^2 = 20$ **5.** (i) $x^2 + y^2 = 49$ (ii) $(x + 2)^2 + (y - 4)^2 = 18$ (iii) $(x - 3)^2 + (y - 1)^2 = 25$ (iv) $x^2 + y^2 = 34$ (v) $(x - 5)^2 + (y + 1)^2 = 32$ (vi) $x^2 + y^2 = 5$ (vii) $x^2 + y^2 = 52$ (viii) $(x + 2)^2 + (y + 1)^2 = 17$ **6.** (i) (0, 0) (ii) $\sqrt{74}$ (iii) $x^2 + y^2 = 74$ **7.** (i) 7 (ii) (14, 0) (iii) (14, 14) (iv) $(x - 14)^2 + (y - 14)^2 = 49$ (v) C_4 **8.** (i) k: (0, 0), 10, s: (3, 4), 5 (ii) k: $x^2 + y^2 = 100$, s: $(x - 3)^2 + (y - 4)^2 = 25$ **9.** (6, −2) **10.** $x^2 + (y - 1)^2 = 13$ **11.** $(x - 2)^2 + (y - 3)^2 = 17$ **12.** (i) $(x - 2)^2 + (y - 3)^2 = 25$ (ii) (−3, 3),(7, 3) (iii) $(x - 2)^2 + (y + 3)^2 = 25$ **13.** (i) (0, 0), 9 (ii) (0, 0), $2\sqrt{5}$ (iii) (5, 1), 4 (iv) (−4, −6), $\sqrt{10}$ (v) (0, 0), $4\sqrt{5}$ (vi) (3, −2), 7 (vii) (0, 0), $\frac{11}{4}$ (viii) (−1, 4), $2\sqrt{3}$ (ix) (6, 0), $3\sqrt{2}$ (x) (0, −7), $\frac{5}{2}$ **14.** 24π units^2 **15.** $\frac{11}{2}\pi$ units^2 **16.** 12π **17.** 7π **18.** s: $x^2 + y^2 = 49$, t: $x^2 + y^2 = 9$ **19.** (i) $x^2 + y^2 = 164$ (ii) $(x + 5)^2 + (y - 4)^2 = 41$ (iii) $(x - 5)^2 + (y + 4)^2 = 41$ **20.** (6, 4) **21.** (ii) $(x - 2)^2 + (y - 1)^2 = 36$ (iii) $(x + 7)^2 + (y - 1)^2 = 9$ **22.** (ii) (2, 0); $(x - 2)^2 + y^2 = 50$ **23.** (i) $\sqrt{61}$ (ii) $(x - 2)^2 + (y + 5)^2 = 61$ (iii) $P = (-4, 0)$, $Q = (-4, -10)$, $R = (8, -10)$ **24.** (i) $x - 3y + 6 = 0$ (ii) (5, 2), 5; $(x - 5)^2 + (y - 2)^2 = 25$ (iii) −3, Perpendicular to l **25.** (i) 5 (ii) $x^2 + y^2 = 4$; $x^2 + y^2 = 16$; $x^2 + y^2 = 36$; $x^2 + y^2 = 64$; $x^2 + y^2 = 100$ **26.** (i) 12 (ii) (−6, 0), 6; $(x + 6)^2 + y^2 = 36$ (iii) $A = (-6, 6)$, $B = (6, 6)$, $C = (-6, -6)$, $D = (6, -6)$ (iv) 144 units^2 (v) $x^2 + y^2 = 72$

Practice Questions 15.2

1. (i) (−5, 0), (5, 0) (ii) (−2, 0), (8, 0) (iii) (−11, 0), (1, 0) **2.** (i) (0, −7), (0, 7) (ii) (0, −1), (0, −7) (iii) (0, −9), (0, 5) **3.** 10 **4.** 12 **5.** (i) (3, 3) (ii) 3 (iii) $(x - 3)^2 + (y - 3)^2 = 9$ (iv) $(x + 3)^2 + (y - 3)^2 = 9$ **6.** (ii) 5 (iii) $(x + 5)^2 + (y - 3)^2 = 25$ **7.** (i) (1, 3) (ii) (−2, 0), (4, 0) (iii) 6 (iv) $3\sqrt{2}$ (v) $(x - 1)^2 + (y - 3)^2 = 18$ **8.** (ii) 5 (iii) $(x - 3)^2 + (y - 3)^2 = 25$ **9.** $A = (0, 6)$, $B = (8, 0)$ **10.** (ii) (−4, 0) (iii) 7 (iv) $(x + 4)^2 + y^2 = 49$ (v) $(x - 4)^2 + y^2 = 49$ **11.** (i) $(x + 3)^2 + y^2 = 34$ (ii) (0, −5), (0, 5) (iii) 10 (iv) 60 units^2

Practice Questions 15.3

1. (ii) Outside **2.** (ii) (−1, 3), (1, 3), (−1, −3), (multiple possible answers here) **3.** (i) On (ii) Outside (iii) On (iv) Inside (v) Inside (vi) Outside **5.** (i) Inside (ii) On (iii) Outside (iv) Outside (v) On (vi) Inside **6.** (i) On (ii) Outside (iii) Inside **7.** (i) (0, 0), 4 (iii) (0, 4), (4, 0), (0, −4), (−4, 0) (iv) Inside **8.** (i) (2, 1), 6 (iii) (8, 1), (2, 7), (−4, 1), (2, −5) (iv) Outside **9.** ±2 **10.** −7, 1 **11.** 7

Practice Questions 15.4

1. (i) (−3, 2), (2, −3) **2.** (i) (−3, −3), (3, 3). Not a tangent (ii) (−2, 4), (4, −2). Not a tangent (iii) (−3, −1), (1, 3). Not a tangent (iv) (−2, −1). Tangent (v) (−3, 2), (2, 3). Not a tangent **3.** (i) (−3, −2), (2, 3) (ii) $5\sqrt{2}$ (iii) Not a diameter. **4.** (i) (−3, −1), (3, 1) (ii) (0, 0) (iii) $2\sqrt{10}$ (iv) Diameter **5.** (i) (−1, −2), (2, 1) (ii) (0·5, −0·5) (iii) $3\sqrt{2}$ (iv) Not a diameter **6.** (−2, −4), (4, 2) **7.** Not a tangent **8.** (i) (−3, −1), (−1, 3), (1, −3), (3, 1) (iii) 20 units^2

Practice Questions 15.5

1. $x - y + 4 = 0$ **2.** (ii) $x - 2y - 10 = 0$ (iii) (10, 0),(0, −5) **3.** $2x + 3y - 13 = 0$ **4.** $2x + y + 3 = 0$ **5.** $x - y - 7 = 0$ **6.** (i) $4x + 3y + 25 = 0$ (ii) $3x - 4y + 25 = 0$ (iii) (−7, 1) **7.** (ii) $2x + 3y + 10 = 0$ (iii) $2x - 3y + 34 = 0$ (iv) (−11, 4) **8.** (i) $3x - 4y + 50 = 0$ (iii) $y + 10 = 0$, $y - 10 = 0$ **9.** (ii) $2x - 5y + 52 = 0$ (iii) (−2, −2) (iv) $2x - 5y - 6 = 0$ **10.** (i) $-\frac{2}{3}$ (ii) $\frac{3}{2}$ (iii) −3 (iv) $(x + 2)^2 + (y + 3)^2 = 52$

Revision and Exam Style Questions – Section A

1. (i) $x^2 + y^2 = 40$ **2.** (i) (−4, 4) (ii) (0, 9), (0, −1) **3.** (ii) (5, 4). Radius is 6 units, so any point which is further than 6 units from the origin. **4.** Yes. It can be written in the form $x^2 + y^2 = r^2$ **5.** (i) (0, 0), 10 **6.** (i) 4 (ii) $(x - 4)^2 + (y - 7)^2 = 16$ (iii) $(x - 4)^2 + (y + 7)^2 = 16$ **7.** (i) (1, 5) (ii) 6 (iii) (7, 5), (−5, 5), etc **8.** No. It cannot be written in the form $x^2 + y^2 = r^2$ **9.** (i) (−4, −3), 7 (ii) Yes (iii) $(x - 4)^2 + (y + 3)^2 = 49$ **10.** (8, 0), (−8, 0), (0, 8), (0, −8) **11.** (ii) (2, 2) **12.** (i) $(x + 4)^2 + (y - 2)^2 = 49$ (ii) (−4, 9), (−4, −5) (iii) $(x - 4)^2 + (y + 2)^2 = 49$

Revision and Exam Style Questions – Section B

1. (−1, 3) **2.** (ii) 4 **3.** (i) (1, 0), (9, 0) (iii) $(x-5)^2+y^2=16$
4. (i) $(x+1)^2+(y-2)^2=25$ **5.** (i) $x^2+y^2=26$
(ii) 0, ±1, ±2, ± 3, ±4 **6.** (i) (−4, −1), (4, 1) **7.** (ii) Yes. Justified by the diagram **8.** (i) $x^2+y^2=29$ (ii) $(x-10)^2+(y-4)^2=29$
(iii) $5x+2y-29=0$ **9.** (i) (−4, 4), (8, 4)
(ii) $x+4=0$, $x-8=0$ (iii) $(x-2)^2+y^2=36$
10. (ii) $3x+5y-44=0$ (iii) (2, −6) (iv) $3x+5y+24=0$
(v) (−8, 0), (0, −4·8) **11.** (iv) $(x-3)^2+(y-4)^2=20$
12. (i) 2·5 km/h (ii) $x^2+y^2=30{\cdot}25$ (iii) 5:12 pm (iv) 3:36 pm

Chapter 16

Something to think about

5,708 cm^2

Practice Questions 16.1

1. (i) 180 cm^2 (ii) 81 m^2 (iii) 66 cm^2 (iv) 42 mm^2 (v) 68 cm^2 (vi) 42 cm^2 (vii) 126 m^2 (viii) 270 cm^2 **2.** (i) 12 cm^2
(ii) 17·5 m^2 (iii) 30 mm^2 (iv) 27 cm^2 **3.** (i) 12 cm (ii) 42 cm
4. (i) 16 cm (ii) 256 cm^2 **5.** (i) 8 cm (ii) 80 cm^2 **6.** (i) 3 cm
(ii) 5 cm **7.** 15 cm **8.** 12 mm **9.** (i) 8·5 cm (ii) 12 cm
(iii) 10 cm **10.** (i) 192 cm^2 (ii) $\frac{64}{3}$ cm **11.** (i) $\frac{60}{13}$ cm
(ii) $\frac{48}{5}$ cm **12.** (i) A = 18 units^2 B = 24 units^2 C = 45 units^2
(ii) A = 20·49 B = 21·12 C = 28·77 **13.** (i) 52 cm^2 (ii) 98 cm^2
(iii) 110 cm^2 (iv) 52 cm^2 **14.** (i) 330 cm^2 (ii) 208·5 m^2
(iii) 568 m^2 (iv) 84 cm^2 (v) 52 m^2 (vi) 73 mm^2 **15.** (i) 42 cm^2; 28 cm (ii) 114 cm^2; 52 cm (iii) 150 cm^2; 50 cm

Practice Questions 16.2

1. (i) 113·1 cm^2; 37·7 cm (ii) 254·5 cm^2; 56·5 cm
(iii) 201·1 cm^2; 50·3 cm **2.** 2·5 m; 5π m **3.** 7 cm; 44 cm
4. 15 m; 225π m^2 **5.** 25 cm; 1,962·5 cm^2 **6.** (i) $\frac{1}{12}$ (ii) 72 cm^2
7. (i) 12·5π cm^2; 5π cm (ii) 12·25π mm^2; 3·5π mm
(iii) 24π cm^2; 4π cm (iv) 48π m^2; 12π m (v) 27π cm^2; 6π cm
(vi) 14π km^2; 7π km **8.** (i) 32·6 cm (ii) 94·8 cm **9.** (i) 13·7 cm^2
(ii) 1·9 cm^2 **10.** 769·7 cm^2 **11.** 18·8 m^2 **12.** (i) 135·03 cm^2
(ii) 147·10 m^2 (iii) 39·82 cm^2 **13.** (i) 70·28 m^2 (ii) €3,524·70
14. 312·2 cm^2 **15.** (i) 32 cm^2 (ii) 50·3 cm^2 (iii) 18·3 cm^2

Practice Questions 16.3

1. (i) 5 m (ii) 20 cm **2.** (i) 105 m (ii) 360 m **3.** (i) $2\sqrt{34}$ m
(ii) 136 m^2 **4.** (i) 1: 440,000 (ii) 96·8 km **5.** (i) 1: 2,500,000
(ii) 700 km **6.** (ii) 3·1 m; 15·5 cm (iii) 2·45 m^2; 61·24 cm^2
(iv) 1: 20 (v) 1: 400 (vi) Ratios of the areas equals the (ratio of the lengths)^2

Practice Questions 16.4

1. (i) 896 m^2 (ii) 2336 m^2 **2.** (i) 4800 m^2 (ii) 48%
3. (i) 163·8 m^2 (ii) 7% **4.** 5·95 hectares **5.** (i) 1617 m^2
(ii) 430 m^2 **6.** (i) 11·8 ± 0·4 units^2 (ii) 260 ± 5 units^2
(iii) 1270 ± 15 units^2 (iv) 910 ± 10 units^2 **7.** (i) 3600 m^2
(ii) 24 days
8. (i)

x	0	1	2	3	4
y	4	6	6	4	0

(ii) 18 units^2 (iii) 3·57%
9. (i)

x	0	1	2	3	4	5	6
y	11	6	3	2	3	6	11

(iii) 31 units^2 (iv) $3\frac{1}{3}$% **10.** (i) 35 units^2 (ii) 1·16%
11. (ii) 54,000 ± 2000 km^2 (iii) 320 km **12.** 24 m **13.** 22 m; 88 m
14. 73

Revision and Exam Style Questions – Section A

1. (i) 26 cm (ii) 60 cm **2.** 8 cm; 32 cm **3.** 37·5 m^2 **4.** (i) 82 cm
(ii) 420 cm^2 (iii) 29 cm **5.** 347 m^2 **6.** Company A
7. (i) 108π cm^2 (ii) 12π cm (iii) (36 + 12π) cm **8.** 49 cm
9. (i) 100·7 cm^2; 53·7 cm (ii) 18·8 m^2; 18·3 cm
10. 128·54 cm^2 **11.** (i) 96 cm (ii) 576 cm^2 (iii) 123·61 cm^2
12. 657 m^2 **13.** 32 ± 3 units^2

Revision and Exam Style Questions – Section B

1. (i) 18 cm (ii) 288 cm^2 **2.** 117·76 units^2 **3.** (i) 35 cm
(ii) 75 cm^2 **4.** (i) 10,148·45 m^2 (ii) 400 m (iii) 5 laps
(iv) 19·2 km/h **5.** 565·08 m^2 **6.** (i) 30π cm^2 (ii) 20π cm
7. (i)

x	−1	0	1	2	3	4	5
y	7	4	3	4	7	12	19

(ii) 43 units^2 (iii) 2·38% **8.** 331,000 ± 3000 m^2 **9.** 10 cm

Chapter 17

Something to think about

11,760 cm^3

Practice Questions 17.1

1. (i) 64 cm^3 (ii) 125 cm^3 (iii) 128 cm^3 (iv) 120 cm^3 **2.** C
3. (i) 3105 mm^3; 1374 mm^2 (ii) 343 cm^3; 294 cm^2
4. (ii) 4200 cm^3 (iii) 1720 cm^2 **5.** (i) 1728 cm^3 (ii) 864 cm^2
6. 616 cm^3 **7.** 576 mm^3 **8.** (i) *F* (ii) *C* (iii) *B* **9.** (i) 7 cm
(ii) 318 cm^2 **10.** (i) 5 m (ii) 366 m^2 **11.** (i) 9 cm (ii) 486 cm^2
12. (i) 11 m (ii) 726 m^2 **13.** 504 packets **14.** 15 cm
15. 4 cm **16.** (iii) **17.** (i) 7040 mm^3 (ii) 297 cm^3
(iii) 1860 m^3 **18.** (i) 48 cm^2 (ii) 864 cm^3 (iii) 715·60 cm^2
19. (i) 47,520 m^3 (ii) 28,118 m^3 (iii) 26,208 cm^3
(iv) 8912·5 m^3 (v) 8844 cm^3 (vi) 22,800 m^3
20. 4,062,500 litres **21.** A **22.** (i) 200 cm^2 (ii) 144 cm^3
23. (i) 480 cm^2 (ii) 576 cm^3 **24.** (i) 510 cm^2 (ii) 450 cm^3

Practice Questions 17.2

1. (i) 81π cm^3; 72π cm^2 (ii) 112π cm^3; 88π cm^2
(iii) 48π cm^3; 56π cm^2 **2.** (i) 268·1 cm^3; 201·1 cm^2
(ii) 4188·8 cm^3; 1256·6 cm^2 (iii) 1767·1 cm^3; 706·9 cm^2
3. (i) 17 cm^3; 38 cm^2 (ii) 450 cm^3; 340 cm^2 (iii) 2800 cm^3; 1100 cm^2 **4.** (i) 200·4 cm^3; 176 cm^2 (ii) 2874·67 cm^3; 1078 cm^2
(iii) 761·83 cm^3; 510·5 cm^2 **5.** (i) 3618·59 cm^3 (ii) 2915·4 cm^2
6. (i) 1150·35 cm^3 (ii) 52 cm (iii) 6902·08 cm^3 (iv) 66·67 %
7. 21,980 cm^3 **8.** (ii) 13 cm; 15·7 cm **9.** (i) 2·5 cm (ii) 80π cm^2
10. (i) 12 cm (ii) 147π cm^3 **11.** (i) 3·63 cm (ii) 52·71π cm^2
12. (i) 6·36 cm (ii) 161·8π cm^2 **13.** (i) 11 cm (ii) $1774\frac{2}{3}$ cm^3
14. (i) 6 cm (ii) 72π cm^2 (iii) 108π cm^2 **15.** (i) 12 cm
(ii) 6912 cm^3 (iii) 3292·89 cm^3 **16.** 12 cm

Practice Questions 17.3

1. (i) 36π cm^3; $46{\cdot}11\pi$ cm^2 (ii) $88{\cdot}2\pi$ cm^3; $83{\cdot}1\pi$ cm^2 (iii) 6π cm^3; $14{\cdot}4\pi$ cm^2 **2.** (ii) 12π cm^3 (iii) 24π cm^2 **3.** 377 cm^3 **4.** (i) 10 cm **5.** (i) 1·5 m (ii) 2·1 m (iii) $0{\cdot}81\pi$ m^3 (iv) $2{\cdot}97\pi$ m^2 **6.** 12 cm **7.** 3 cm **8.** (iii) 1200π mm^3 (iv) 56 mm (v) 80 mm, 20 mm, 56 mm (vi) 89,600 mm^3 **9.** (i) 1·5 cm (ii) $1{\cdot}5\pi$ cm^3 (iii) $94{\cdot}5\pi$ cm^3 (iv) 1·56% **10.** (i) 16 cm (ii) $261\frac{1}{3}\pi$ cm^3 (iii) $620\frac{2}{3}\pi$ cm^3

Practice Questions 17.4

1. (i) 11 cm (ii) 2 cm **2.** (i) 7776π mm^3 (ii) 2664π mm^2 (iii) 18 mm (iv) 1296π mm^2 (v) 37 : 18 **3.** (i) 960π cm^3 (ii) 7·75 cm **4.** (i) 148·44 cm^3 (ii) 34 candles **5.** (i) $\frac{32}{3}\pi$ cm^3 (ii) 150π cm^3 (iii) 0·43 cm **6.** (i) 39 cm^3 (ii) 2·3 cm **7.** 16·5 cm **8.** 2·6 cm **9.** (i) 50π cm^3/sec (ii) 45 seconds **10.** (i) 20π cm^3/sec (ii) 36 cm **11.** (i) 832π cm^3/sec (ii) 62·4 cm **12.** (i) 1 : 9 (ii) 1 : 27 **13.** (i) 1 : 8 (ii) 1 : 4 **14.** (i) 3 m (ii) 5 m (iii) 207·3 m^2 (iv) 83 litres (v) €1275 **15.** (i) $2\pi r^3$ (ii) 2 : 3 (iii) 1 : 1 **16.** $\sqrt{2}$: 1 **17.** (i) 377 cm^3 (ii) 8·4 s (iii) 14 s (iv) Since the value for the radius is squared, a larger radius results in a much larger volume.

Revision and Exam Style Questions – Section A

1. A **2.** (ii) 9 edges (iii) 360 cm^3 (iv) 445·7 cm^2 **3.** 4320 cm^3 **4.** 10·5 cm; 4158 cm^3 **5.** 160 litres **6.** (i) 7 (ii) 1323 cm^3 **7.** (i) 5 cm (ii) 37·7 cm^3 (iii) 47·1 cm^2 **8.** (i) 1·2 m (ii) 8·4 m^2 **9.** 400,752 cm^3

Revision and Exam Style Questions – Section B

1. (i) 6 cm (ii) 12 cm **2.** (i) 800π cm^3 (ii) 2600π cm^3 (iii) 13·7 cm **3.** (i) $30{,}375\pi$ cm^3 (ii) 22·5 cm 4(i) $300{,}000\pi$ cm^3 (ii) 28,125 (iii) 1 cm **5.** (i) $4{\cdot}5\pi$ cm^3 (ii) 125 spheres **6.** (i) 3 cm (iv) 2 cm **7.** (i) 17 cm (ii) 30 cm; 24 cm; 17 cm (iii) 36·86% **8.** (i) $\frac{160}{3}\pi$ cm^3 (ii) $\frac{10}{3}$ cm **9.** (i) $121{\cdot}5\pi$ cm^3 (ii) 3·4 cm **10.** 15·35 cm

Chapter 18

Something to think about

(i) 40,320 (ii) 8640 (iii) (a) $\frac{1}{2}$; (b) $\frac{1}{8}$; (c) $\frac{3}{8}$; (d) $\frac{1}{4}$

Practice Questions 18.1

1. 120 **2.** 24 **3.** 9; rock + rock, rock + paper, rock + scissors, paper + rock, paper + paper, paper + scissors, scissors + rock, scissors + paper, scissors + scissors. **4.** 54 **5.** 72

6.

	Chocolate bar	Muffin	Scone
Tea	T + C B	T + M	T + S
Coffee	C + C B	C + M	C + S

7. 56 **8.** 18,137,088 **9.** (i) 24 (ii) 8 (iii) 12 **10.** (ii) € 7 (iii) 6 less choices available

Practice Questions 18.2

1. (i) 3,628,800 (ii) 5040 (iii) 48 (iv) 144 (v) 60,480 (vi) 30 (vii) 720 (viii) 41,513,472,000 (ix) 360 (x) 10,080 (xi) 56 (xii) 41,580 **2.** 120 **3.** 15,120 **4.** 6 **5.** 4896 **6.** 10,897,286,400 **7.** $3{\cdot}930087096 \times 10^{20}$ **8.** 1,693,440 **9.** (i) 720 (ii) 360 (iii) 7776 **10.** (i) $3{\cdot}04140932 \times 10^{64}$ (ii) $1{\cdot}551739449 \times 10^{60}$ **11.** (i) 5040 (ii) 10,000 (iii) 4536 (iv) 2520 (v) 280 **12.** (i) 720 (ii) 240 (iii) 48 (iv) 240 **13.** (i)110 (ii) 7920 (iii) 1,663,200 (iv) 39,916,800 **14.** (i) 720 (ii) 48 (iii) 24 (iv) 240 (v) 2 **15.** (i) 3,276,000 (ii) 6,30,000 (iii) 2,948,400 (iv) 315,000 (v) 1,323,000 **16.** 4320 **17.** 1680 (i) 630 (ii) 90 (iii) 24 **18.** (i) 1,000,000 (ii) 5,31,441 **19.** (a) (i) 3,08,915,776 (ii) 1,65,765,600 (iii) 31,878,000 (iv) 84,795,480 (v) 63,756 (b) Four letter version = 456976 arrangements Five letter version = 11,881,376 arrangements Both claims are incorrect. **20.** (i) (a) 2250 (b) 2500 (c) 360 (d) 36 (ii) (a) 1,256,640 (b) 1,500,625 (iii) (a) 1,941,840,000 (b) 3,751,562,500 (iv) Add an extra character to the unique identifier.

Practice Questions 18.3

1. (i) 1 **2.** (i) *F* (ii) *A* (iii) *C* (iv) *E* (v) *B* (vi) *D* **3.** (i) *D* (ii) *A* (iii) *C* (iv) *B* **4.** *A*: $\frac{1}{2}$ *B*: 1 *C*: 0 *D*: $\frac{3}{13}$ *E*: $\frac{7}{12}$ **5.** (One possible answer shown for each part) (i) The number of cent in a euro is 150 (ii) The number of days in a week is 7 (iii) You roll an even number on a die (iv) A school day chosen at random is a Monday (v) A child chosen at random from a family of three girls and a boy is a girl.

Practice Questions 18.4

1. (i) red, blue, green (ii) *a, e, i, o, u* (iii) *p, r, o, b, a, i, l, t, y* (iv) 1, 3, 5, 7, 9 **2.** (iii) Choosing a 'G' from the 26 letters of the alphabet **3.** (i) $\frac{4}{13}$ (ii) $\frac{6}{13}$ (iii) $\frac{3}{13}$ (iv) $\frac{10}{13}$ **4.** (i) $\frac{1}{11}$ (ii) $\frac{2}{11}$ (iii) $\frac{4}{11}$ (iv) $\frac{7}{11}$ (v) $\frac{9}{11}$ **5.** (i) $\frac{1}{2}$ (ii) $\frac{1}{4}$ (iii) $\frac{1}{13}$ (iv) $\frac{1}{26}$ (v) $\frac{3}{26}$ **6.** (i) $\frac{1}{6}$ (ii) 0 (iii) $\frac{1}{6}$ (iv) $\frac{1}{2}$ (v) $\frac{1}{2}$ (vi) $\frac{1}{2}$ (vii) $\frac{1}{3}$ **7.** (i) $\frac{2}{9}$ (ii) $\frac{1}{6}$ (iii) $\frac{11}{18}$ (iv) 0 (v) $\frac{5}{6}$ (vi) $\frac{1}{2}$ **8.** A: $\frac{1}{2}$ B: $\frac{1}{6}$ C: 1 D: 0 **9.** (i) $\frac{1}{5}$ (ii) red and green

Revision and Exam Style Questions – Section A

1. (i) 120 (ii) 48 **2.** (i) 24 (ii) 18 (iii) 12 **3.** (i) Disagree. Probability can't be greater than 1. (ii) Agree. Probability = $\frac{\text{number of outcomes of interest}}{\text{total number of outcomes}} = \frac{13}{28}$ (iii) Disagree. The probability of getting a head on a fair coin is always $\frac{1}{2}$ **4.** (i) { A, B, C, D, E, F, G, H, I, J, K, L, M, N, O, P} (ii) $\frac{1}{4}$ **5.** No. $\frac{200}{600} = \frac{1}{3}$ which is twice the expected probability of $\frac{1}{6}$ **6.** (i) Spinner B. Higher probability of getting down. (ii) No. Both spinners have the same probability of forward.

7. (i)

		Disc		
		2	4	5
Card	1	3	5	6
	3	5	7	8
	4	6	8	9

(ii) $\frac{4}{9}$ (iii) $\frac{2}{5}$ **8.** (i) Disagree. Drawing pins are different shapes on either side so that may affect how they fall. (ii) Ciara dropped the most drawing pins.

Revision and Exam Style Questions – Section B

1. (a) (i) 720 (ii) 240 (iii) 48 (iv) 240 (b) (v) $\frac{1}{6}$ (vi) $\frac{5}{6}$ (vii) $\frac{1}{3}$ **2.** (i) Each person's probability is greater than $\frac{1}{2}$ (ii)(a) Leon: $\frac{13}{25}$ (b) Conor: $\frac{53}{100}$ (c) Georgia: $\frac{27}{50}$ (d) Combined results: $\frac{173}{325}$ (iii) The combined results because it involves the most coin flips **3.** (i) 18 (iii) $\frac{1}{2}$ (iv) $\frac{1}{9}$ (v) $\frac{1}{6}$ (vi) 90 **4.** (i) $\frac{3}{10}$ = 0·3 (ii) white – highest probability (iii) green – lowest probability (iv) no – no equal probability **5.** (i) $\frac{29}{50}$ (ii) $\frac{11}{25}$ (iii) No. Pass rate is lower in this centre. **6.** (ii) $\frac{5}{6}$ (iii) $\frac{1}{3}$ (iv) 1 (v) $\frac{1}{3}$

Chapter 19

Something to think about

Advise the company directors to invest. The expected value of the investment is €2250, so in the long run the company should make €2250 on this investment.

Practice Questions 19.1

1. (a) $\frac{1}{3}$ (b) $\frac{1}{2}$ (c) $\frac{1}{6}$ **2.** (a) 24 (b) $\frac{1}{4}$ (c) $\frac{1}{2}$ (d) $\frac{1}{24}$ (e) $\frac{1}{2}$ **3.** (a) $\frac{1}{2}$ (b) $\frac{1}{6}$ (c) $\frac{1}{12}$ (d) $\frac{1}{4}$ (e) $\frac{3}{4}$ **4.** (i) {head, tail} (ii) {red, green, yellow and blue} (iii) {RH, RT, GH, GT, YH, YT, BH, BT} (iv) (a) $\frac{1}{2}$ (b) $\frac{1}{4}$ (c) $\frac{1}{8}$ (d) $\frac{5}{8}$ (e) $\frac{3}{4}$ (f) $\frac{1}{4}$ (g) $\frac{3}{4}$ **5.** (a) $\frac{1}{4}$ (b) $\frac{1}{4}$ (c) $\frac{1}{4}$ (d) $\frac{3}{16}$ (e) $\frac{9}{16}$ **6.** (ii) 36 (iii) $\frac{1}{4}$ (iv) $\frac{11}{36}$ (v) No. The probability of getting a 5 is higher than of both dice being odd. (vi) (3, 5) (5, 3) (1, 5) (5, 1) (5, 5) **7.** (a) $\frac{1}{6}$ (b) $\frac{1}{4}$ (c) $\frac{5}{12}$ (d) $\frac{3}{8}$ (e) $\frac{1}{3}$ **8.** (a) $\frac{1}{9}$ (b) $\frac{2}{3}$ (c) $\frac{1}{9}$ (d) $\frac{2}{9}$ (e) $\frac{8}{27}$ **9.** (i) Tree diagram as there are more than two events. (ii) {HHT, HHX, HHB, HST, HSX, HSB, CHT, CHX, CHB, CST, CSX, CSB} (iii) (a) $\frac{1}{12}$ (b) $\frac{1}{3}$ (c) $\frac{1}{6}$ (d) $\frac{1}{2}$ **10.** (i) $\frac{1}{10}$ (ii) $\frac{1}{4}$ (iii) $\frac{16}{25}$ (iv) $\frac{3}{20}$ (v) $\frac{81}{100}$ **11.** (i) $\frac{1}{2}$ (ii) $\frac{1}{2}$ (iii) $\frac{1}{4}$ (iv) $\frac{1}{12}$ (v) $\frac{1}{24}$

Practice Questions 19.2

1. (i) Dependent (ii) Independent (iii) Dependent (iv) Independent (v) Independent (vi) Dependent **2.** $\frac{1}{36}$ **3.** (i) $\frac{16}{81}$ (ii) $\frac{20}{81}$ **4.** (i) $\frac{4}{7}$ (ii) $\frac{2}{7}$ **5.** (ii) $\frac{1}{12}$ (iii) $\frac{1}{6}$ (iv) $\frac{1}{4}$ (v) $\frac{1}{4}$ **6.** (ii) $\frac{11}{38}$ (iii) $\frac{99}{380}$ (iv) $\frac{18}{95}$ **7.** $\frac{4}{663}$ **8.** $\frac{1}{13}$ **9.** (ii) $\frac{33}{136}$ (iii) $\frac{33}{136}$ (iv) $\frac{15}{136}$ (v) $\frac{55}{136}$ **10.** $\frac{1}{36}$ **11.** (i) Independent (ii) $\frac{1}{216}$ **12.** (i) Independent (ii) $\frac{1}{169}$ **13.** (i) Dependent (ii) $\frac{32}{812175}$ **14.** $\frac{1}{15}$ **15.** (i) $\frac{8}{125}$ (ii) $\frac{12}{125}$ (iii) $\frac{27}{125}$ **16.** (i) $\frac{4}{29}$ (ii) $\frac{13}{145}$ **17.** (i) Emma. (ii) $\frac{1}{2}\times\frac{1}{2}\times\frac{1}{2}\times\frac{1}{2}\times\frac{1}{2}=\frac{1}{32}$

Practice Questions 19.3

1. (i) Not – 2 is an even number less than 3 (ii) Not – 3 and 5 are prime and odd (iii) Mutually Exclusive – a number can't be greater than 3 and less than 3 at the same time (iv) Not – a person can have both blue eyes and blond hair (v) Not – student can be in 2nd year and do business studies (vi) Not – a king can be red eg. the king of hearts **2.** (i) $\frac{1}{4}$ (ii) $\frac{1}{3}$ (iii) $\frac{1}{6}$ (iv) $\frac{2}{3}$ **3.** (i) $\frac{1}{2}$ (ii) $\frac{3}{13}$ (iii) $\frac{8}{13}$ (iv) $\frac{7}{13}$ (v) $\frac{1}{13}$ **4.** (i) $\frac{1}{4}$ (ii) $\frac{3}{10}$ (iii) $\frac{11}{20}$ **5.** 0·95 **6.** (i) $\frac{1}{2}$ (ii) $\frac{7}{10}$ (iii) $\frac{4}{5}$ (iv) $\frac{3}{5}$ **7.** (i) $\frac{29}{100}$ (ii) $\frac{1}{5}$ (iii) $\frac{9}{20}$ **8.** (i) $\frac{3}{5}$ (ii) $\frac{19}{20}$ (iii) $\frac{1}{20}$ (iv) $\frac{3}{20}$ **9.** (i) 70% (ii) 63% **10.** (ii) $\frac{22}{189}$ (iii) $\frac{2}{21}$ (iv) $\frac{2}{21}$ (v) $\frac{55}{378}$ (vi) $\frac{11}{42}$ (vii) $\frac{121}{189}$ **11.** (i) $\frac{15}{91}$ (ii) $\frac{15}{91}$ (iii) $\frac{10}{91}$ (iv) $\frac{45}{182}$ (v) $\frac{30}{91}$ (vi) $\frac{36}{91}$ **12.** (i) Independent (ii) $\frac{5}{36}$ (iii) $\frac{4}{81}$ (iv) $\frac{155}{324}$

Practice Questions 19.4

2. (i) $\frac{1}{6}$ (ii) $\frac{1}{10}$ (iii) $\frac{23}{30}$ (iv) $\frac{1}{15}$ (v) $\frac{2}{15}$ **3.** (i) $\frac{1}{2}$ (ii) $\frac{7}{13}$ (iii) $\frac{4}{13}$ (iv) $\frac{5}{26}$ (v) $\frac{6}{13}$ **4.** (i) $\frac{9}{20}$ (ii) $\frac{3}{20}$ (iii) $\frac{3}{5}$ (iv) $\frac{2}{5}$ **5.** (i) $\frac{21}{34}$ (ii) $\frac{38}{51}$ (iii) $\frac{6}{17}$ (iv) $\frac{10}{51}$ (v) $\frac{19}{102}$ **6.** (i) 0·8 (ii) 0·2 **7.** (i) 0·28 (ii) 0·82 (iv) 0·12 **8.** (ii) 42% (iii) 36%

Practice Questions 19.5

1. (i) $\frac{1}{2}$ (ii) $\frac{1}{4}$ (iii) $\frac{1}{8}$ (iv) $\frac{1}{32}$ **2.** (i) $\frac{1}{6}$ (ii) $\frac{5}{36}$ (iii) $\frac{25}{216}$ (iv) 0·0323 **3.** (i) $\frac{4}{27}$ (ii) $\frac{4}{9}$ **4.** (i) $\frac{2}{5}$ (ii) $\frac{18}{125}$ (iii) $\frac{486}{15625}$ (iv) $6{\cdot}718464 \times 10^{-3}$ **5.** (i) 0·474552 (ii) 0·401544 (iii) 0·037752 (iv) 0·010648 (v) 0·989352 **6.** (i) $\frac{1}{27}$ (ii) $\frac{2}{9}$ (iii) $\frac{8}{27}$ (iv) $\frac{2}{27}$ **7.** (i) 0·042875 (ii) 0·0274625 (iii) 0·238875 **8.** (i) $\frac{125}{512}$ (ii) $\frac{27}{512}$ (iii) $\frac{75}{512}$ (iv) $\frac{135}{512}$ **9.** (i) $\frac{3}{7}$ (ii) $\frac{36}{343}$ (iii) $\frac{64}{343}$ (iv) $\frac{316}{343}$ **10.** (i) Yes. Each question is independent and has two options; success or failure. (ii) Possible outcomes: Success – the guess is correct; Failure – the guess is incorrect (iii) P (success) = $\frac{1}{4}$; P (failure) = $\frac{3}{4}$

Practice Questions 19.6

1. 30 **2.** 64 **3.** 3 **4.** (i) (a) $\frac{11}{20}$ (b) $\frac{29}{100}$ (c) $\frac{4}{25}$ (ii) (a) 4125 (b) 2175 (c) 1200 **5.** (i) 0·64 (ii) No. Net winnings = −0·36, therefore you would expect to lose €0·36. **6.** 26 points

7. (i) €40 (ii) Expected value is the same but the perspective is switched. The customer is down but the company is up. (iii) €26,000,000 **8.** €2·25 **9.** Expect to lose €116·67 **10.** (i) €4·63 (ii) Reduce the prize money; enlarge the €2 segment; make the €5 segment smaller. **11.** (i) The mother's offer. (ii) The mothers as it has a higher expected value. **12.** (i) Speculative = €2400; Conservative = €1599 (ii) Speculative should earn more in the long run but the risk of losing everything is lower in the conservative. **13.** (i) 3·42 (ii) 'If you play the game many times with a fair die, you will win an average of €0·00 per game, but if you play with the biased die you will lose an average of €0·08 per game.

Revision and Exam Style Questions – Section A

1. (i) $\frac{2}{15}$ (ii) $\frac{7}{15}$ **2.** (ii) $\frac{16}{33}$ (iii) $\frac{17}{33}$ **3.** (i) $\frac{125}{512}$ (ii) $\frac{175}{256}$ **4.** (i) $\frac{15}{22}$ (ii) 30 **5.** (i) $\frac{16}{63}$ (ii) $\frac{47}{63}$ (iii) $\frac{31}{63}$ **6.** (i) $\frac{4}{7}$ (ii) $\frac{1}{7}$ (iii) $\frac{2}{7}$ **7.** (i) $\frac{1}{11}$ (ii) $\frac{3}{11}$ (iii) $\frac{8}{11}$ **8.** (ii) 0·0875 (iii) 0·425 **9.** (i) $\frac{1}{169}$ (ii) $\frac{1}{676}$ (iii) $\frac{4}{13}$ (iv) $\frac{100}{169}$ **10.** (i) $\frac{2}{17}$ (ii) $\frac{703}{1700}$ (iii) $\frac{169}{10200}$ (iv) $\frac{169}{1700}$ **11.** (ii) $\frac{26}{77}$ (iii) 52·6%

Revision and Exam Style Questions – Section B

1. (i) Loss of €1·50. (ii) No. The player will lose therefore it is not fair. **2.** (i) Yes. P(2 tails) = $\frac{3}{8}$, P(3 heads) = $\frac{1}{8}$ (ii) No. Each throw is independent so the probability of each throw being a tail is $\frac{1}{2}$ **3.** (i) 0·11 (ii) 0·7 (iii) $\frac{351}{50000}$ **4.** (ii) $\frac{1}{18}$ (iii) $\frac{17}{18}$ **5.** (ii) $\frac{1}{216}$ (iii) $\frac{2}{27}$ **6.** (ii) $\frac{7}{15}$ (iii) $\frac{8}{15}$ (iv) $\frac{7}{15}$ (v) $\frac{8}{15}$ **7.** $\frac{9}{64}$ **8.** (i) 0·35 (ii) 0·77 (iii) 0·73 (iv) 0·34 (b) (i) 3·21 **9.** (i) $\frac{8}{663}$ (ii) $\frac{1}{1326}$ (iii) $\frac{4}{17}$ (iv) $\frac{5}{442}$ (v) $\frac{13}{34}$ (vi) $\frac{15}{34}$ **10.** (i) $\frac{1}{4}$ (ii) $\frac{1}{2}$

Chapter 20

Something to think about

401 cm

Practice Questions 20.1

1. (i) 13 cm (ii) 15 cm (iii) $2\sqrt{13}$ mm (iv) 1·5 cm (v) 3 m (vi) 21 cm (vii) 4 mm (viii) $\sqrt{2}$ cm (ix) 8 cm **2.** (i) Right-angled (iii) Not right-angled (iii) Right-angled **3.** (i) 35 cm (ii) $8\sqrt{2}$ cm **4.** 1055 cm **5.** 2·69 m **6.** (i) 12 m (ii) 9 m (iii) 15 m (iv) Not right-angled **7.** (i) $\sqrt{65}$ mm (ii) Not right-angled **8.** (i) 15 cm (ii) 20 cm (iii) 12 cm **9.** Not square **10.** (i) Tangent is perpendicular to the radius, at the point of contact. (ii) 8

Practice Questions 20.2

1. (i) $\frac{5}{13}, \frac{12}{13}, \frac{5}{12}$ (ii) $\frac{8}{17}, \frac{15}{17}, \frac{8}{15}$ (iii) $\frac{60}{61}, \frac{11}{61}, \frac{60}{11}$ (iv) $\frac{33}{65}, \frac{56}{65}, \frac{33}{56}$ (v) $\frac{\sqrt{5}}{3}, \frac{2}{3}, \frac{\sqrt{5}}{2}$ (vi) $\frac{\sqrt{2}}{2}, \frac{\sqrt{2}}{2}, 1$ **2.** 4·8, $\frac{48}{73}, \frac{55}{73}, \frac{48}{55}$ **3.** (i) 1 (ii) 7 cm (iii) $7\sqrt{2}$ cm **4.** (i) 3 (ii) $\frac{3}{5}, \frac{4}{5}, \frac{3}{4}$ **5.** $\frac{4}{5}, \frac{4}{3}$ **6.** $\frac{35}{37}, \frac{12}{35}$ **7.** (i) $\frac{1}{2}, \frac{\sqrt{3}}{2}$ **9.** (i) $3\sqrt{5}$ (ii) 4 (iii) $\frac{\sqrt{5}}{5}$ (iv) $\frac{3}{4}$ (v) $\frac{2\sqrt{5}}{5}$ (vi) Not right-angled

Practice Questions 20.3

1. (i) 6·4 (ii) 9·4 (iii) 5·7 (iv) 5·7 (v) 13·5 (vi) 4·3 **2.** (i) 28° 37′ (ii) 51° 12′ (iii) 49° 53′ (iv) 39° 50′ **3.** (i) 12·2 cm (ii) 43·9° (iii) 1·6 cm (iv) 15·8 cm (v) 35·6° **4.** (i) $\sqrt{61}$ m (ii) 48·1° **5.** (i) 10·8 cm (ii) 53° **6.** (i) 90° (ii) 8 cm (iii) 36° 52′ **7.** (i) 12 m (ii) 67° **8.** (i) 36·9° (ii) 73·8° (iii) 5·8 (iv) 9 (v) Not right-angled **9.** (i) 11·28 (ii) 4·10 (iii) 19·03

Practice Questions 20.4

1. (ii) 26 km **2.** No. Angle is 4·3° **3.** (i) Yes. Angle is 73·5° (ii) 563 cm **4.** (i) 52° 8′ (ii) 8·0 m **5.** (i) 115 m (ii) 12,500 cm **6.** (ii) 37·83 m **7.** (i) 75 m (ii) 49° **8.** (i) 15 km (ii) 20 km (iii) 66 km **9.** (i) 48 m (ii) 52° **10.** (i) 1025 km, 700 km (ii) 1241 km **11.** (i) 34 m (ii) 3·4 m/s **12.** (ii) 7·31 km (iii) 8·8 km/h **13.** (ii) 12,807 m

Practice Questions 20.5

1. (i) $\frac{\sqrt{3}}{2}$ (ii) $\frac{1}{\sqrt{3}}$ (iii) $\frac{1}{\sqrt{2}}$ (iv) 1 (v) $\frac{\sqrt{3}}{2}$ (vi) $\frac{3}{4}$ (vii) $\frac{1}{8}$ (viii) 1 (ix) 2 **3.** 6 cm, $2\sqrt{3}$ cm **4.** $\frac{5\sqrt{3}}{2}$ cm **5.** 7 cm, $7\sqrt{2}$ cm, $7(\sqrt{3}+1)$ cm **7.** $\frac{\sqrt{6}-\sqrt{2}}{4}$

Practice Questions 20.6

1. (i) 0 (ii) $\frac{1}{\sqrt{2}}$ (iii) $-\frac{\sqrt{3}}{2}$ (iv) $\frac{1}{\sqrt{2}}$ (v) $-\frac{\sqrt{3}}{2}$ (vi) $-\sqrt{3}$ **2.** (i) −0·9063 (ii) −0·3420 (iii) 1·1918 **3.** (i) 0·3420 (ii) −0·3420 **4.** 45°, 135° **5.** 120°, 240° **6.** 135°, 315° **7.** (i) 257°, 283° (ii) 52°, 232° (iii) 112°, 248° **8.** 300° **9.** 210° **10.** $-\frac{5}{12}, -\frac{12}{13}$

Revision and Exam Style Questions – Section A

1. 665 cm **2.** (i) 180° + 45° (ii) 1 **3.** (i) $\sqrt{35}$ (ii) 29° **4.** (ii) $\sqrt{74}$ **5.** (i) 21·4 cm (ii) 69·5° **6.** (ii) 22·7 m **7.** (ii) 7·5 km (iii) 18 km **8.** 8 cm **9.** (i) $\frac{20}{29}, \frac{21}{29}$ (ii) 46° **10.** −0·8192

Revision and Exam Style Questions – Section B

1. (i) 778 cm (ii) 2684·1 cm (iii) €585 **2.** (i) $\frac{5}{13}, \frac{12}{13}$ **3.** (i) 139 cm (ii) 274 cm **4.** (i) 41° 49′ (ii) 23° 58′ **5.** 30 cm **6.** (i) 28° 4′ (ii) 6·9 m **7.** $-\frac{\sqrt{5}}{3}, \frac{2}{3}$ **8.** (i) 6 cm (ii) $\sqrt{61}$ cm (iii) 50° (iv) 39° 48′ **9.** (i) $x\sqrt{3}$ (ii) $6\sqrt{3}$ m **10.** (i) $\frac{4}{5}, \frac{12}{13}$ (ii) $\frac{63}{65}$ **11.** 210°, 330° **12.** $10\sqrt{2}$ cm

Chapter 21

Something to think about

1725 m^2; 153 m

Practice Questions 21.1

1. (i) 7·5 cm (ii) 10·5 cm (iii) 13·7 m (iv) 5·9 m **2.** (i) 17·6 cm

Answers

(ii) 6·4 cm (iii) 2·6 cm (iv) 11·1 cm **3.** (i) 44·3° (ii) 54·3° (iii) 27·8° **4.** (i) 37·8° (ii) 100·2° **5.** 118·4° **6.** (i) 72° 43' (ii) 107° (iii) 75° 32' **7.** (i) $5\sqrt{2}$ m (ii) $\sqrt{41}$ m (iii) $5(1 + \sqrt{3})$ m **8.** (i) Clinometer (ii) 246 m (iii) 219 m **9.** (i) 9 km, 14·8 km (ii) 7400 m **10.** (ii) 52 m **11.** (i) 10·6 m (ii) 4 m **12.** (i) 35°, 145° **13.** (i) 79°, 101° **14.** (i) 129·2° (ii) 50·8° (iii) 15·2 **15.** (i) 107·2° (ii) 72·8° (iii) 4·1

Practice Questions 21.2

1. (i) 110·9 cm (ii) 9·8 m (iii) 8·7 mm (iv) 18·8 cm **2.** (i) 17° 51′ (ii) 24° 13′ (iii) 120° (iv) 129° 50′ **3.** (i) 106·4° (ii) 30·6° **4.** (i) 14·4 m (ii) 29·4° **5.** (i) 29 cm (ii) Pythagoras' Theorem (iii) Cos 90° = 0 **6.** (i) 120° (ii) 12·6 cm **7.** (i) 79° (ii) 11·7 km **8.** (ii) 7·6 km **9.** (ii) 56°, 124° (iii) 14·6 cm **10.** (ii) 11·8 km (iii) N 21° W **11.** (ii) 44·17 km (iii) 9 km/h **12.** (i) 17 m (ii) 8 m **13.** (i) 22 cm (ii) 27 cm **14.** (i) S 30°, 31' E (ii) 13 minutes

Practice Questions 21.3

1. (i) $10\sqrt{3}$ m^2 (ii) $\frac{35\sqrt{2}}{2}$ cm^2 (iii) $28\sqrt{3}$ mm^2 **2.** (i) 19·6 cm^2 (ii) 43·7 km^2 (iii) 245·1 cm^2 **3.** (i) 40°; 27 cm^2 (ii) 59°; 154·3 mm^2 (iii) 105°; 77·8 cm^2 **4.** (i) 206·2 cm^2 (ii) 93·8 cm^2 (iii) 87·8 m^2 (iv) 71·7 cm^2 **5.** (i) 59·44 cm^2 (ii) 407·29 cm^2 **6.** (i) 3·9 cm (ii) 7·39 cm **7.** (i) 56·44° (ii) 57·06° **8.** 8 cm **9.** (i) 8 cm (ii) 29·9 cm^2 **10.** (i) 8 cm (ii) 14 cm (iii) 51 cm^2 **11.** (i) 10·1 cm (ii) 8·6 cm (iii) 75° **12.** (i) 43·5° (ii) 8·26 (iii) 82·6 units^2 **13.** (i) 30°, 150° (iii) 5 cm, 17·4 cm **14.** (i) 70·8°, 109·2° (iii) 17 cm, 20·8 cm

Practice Questions 21.4

1. (i) (a) 18π cm^2 (b) 3π cm (c) $(3\pi + 24)$ cm (ii) (a) $\frac{845}{12}\pi$ cm^2 (b) $\frac{65}{6}\pi$ cm (c) $\left(\frac{65}{6}\pi + 26\right)$ cm (iii) (a) 20π cm^2 (b) $\frac{20}{3}\pi$ cm (c) $\left(\frac{20}{3}\pi + 12\right)$ cm **2.** $13{\cdot}2\pi$ mm **3.** 19·3 cm^2 **4.** 23 cm^2 **5.** 48·9 cm^2 **6.** 122·5 cm **7.** (i) 9 cm^2 (ii) 24·9 cm **8.** (i) 80·4 m^2 (ii) 83·2 m **9.** (i) 165 m^2 (ii) 61 m **10.** (i) 60° (ii) 24π cm^2 **11.** (i) 40° (ii) 6π cm **12.** (i) 54 cm (ii) 1620π cm^2 **13.** 301·6 mm^2 **14.** 8π cm **15.** 141 cm^2 **16.** (i) 60° (ii) 120° (iii) 27π mm^2 (iv) 99·5 mm^2 **17.** (ii) 126 cm (iii) 691 cm (iv) 28,044 cm^2 (v) 264 cm

Revision and Exam Style Questions – Section A

1. 11·2 m **2.** (i) 66° (ii) 121 units^2 **3.** (i) 44° (ii) 36° **4.** 6·9 cm **5.** (i) 20·7 cm^2 (ii) 8 cm **6.** (i) 23 cm (ii) 39° **7.** (i) 201 cm^2 (ii) 84 cm^2 (iii) 21 cm **8.** (i) 3 m (ii) 1·55 m (iii) 106° (iv) 11·25 m (v) 29·8 m **9.** (i) 120π cm^2 (ii) 124° **10.** (i) 56° (ii) 7 cm **11.** 17·9 km **12.** (i) 14 cm^2 (ii) 3·5 cm (iii) 4 cm (iv) 61° (v) 29° **13.** (i) 12,580 m (ii) N 63° W **14.** (i) 15·4 km (ii) 14,471 m

Revision and Exam Style Questions – Section B

1. (i) 514 cm (ii) 466 cm **2.** (i) 48°, 132° **3.** (i) 4043·9 cm^2 (ii) 236·8 cm **4.** (ii) 89°, 91° (iii) 11·8 cm **5.** (i) 53·7 m (ii) 25·7 m (iii) 142 m (iv) 1154 m^2 (v) €4,820 **6.** (i) 60° (ii) 13·9 cm (iii) 8 cm (iv) 111·2 cm^2 (v) 55·3% **7.** (i) 31,650 km (ii) 31,771 km (iii) 475·9 km^2 **8.** (i) 7·39 cm (ii) 11·2 cm (iii) 25·5 cm^2 **9.** (i) 66·4 cm^2 (ii) 39·8 cm

Chapter 22

Sometimes Statistical analysis can be open to interpretation. In some cases, there may be acceptable answers, other than those shown here. For a comprehensive list of answers, see the worked solutions for this chapter.

Something to think about

Changes to make this a well-designed questionnaire:
Name – people may be more honest if answering anonymously
Age: asks for year not actual age
Do you eat a lot of junk food? – what counts as 'a lot'?
How often do you do your maths homework? – what counts as 'sometimes'?
Do you or do you not like eating at these restaurants? – two questions in one; ticking the box doesn't say which question is answered

Practice Questions 22.1

1. (i) Categorical (S, M, L, etc.) or Numerical (Size 10, 12, 14, etc.) (ii) Categorical (iii) Numerical (iv) Categorical (v) Numerical (vi) Categorical (vii) Categorical (viii) Numerical (ix) Numerical (x) Categorical **2.** (i) Discrete (ii) Continuous (iii) Continuous (iv) Discrete (v) Continuous (vi) Continuous (vii) Discrete (viii) Continuous (ix) Discrete **3.** (i) Continuous (ii) Categorical (iii) Bivariate (iv) Discrete **4.** Colour = categorical; Number of pockets = numerical **5.** (i) 5-door, €18,000, 40 km/hr (ii) Description = Categorical, Price = discrete, Speed = continuous **6.** (i) (a) Name/Transport (b) Age/Number of Siblings (c) Height (ii) Categorical ordinal

Practice Questions 22.2

1. (i) Leading question/no option for 'no'. What is your preferred platform: Xbox or PS4? (ii) No time period stated. How much TV do you watch per week? (iii) Definition of 'a lot'. How much pocket money do you get a week? €0 – €5, €5 – €10, > €10; where €0 – €5 includes €0 but does not include €5 (iv) No option for none, more than 3. How many pets do you have? None _ 1_ 2_ 3_ >3 _ (v) Leading question. What is your opinion of Mathematics? (vi) Leading statement before question. Do you think the prices are good value? **2.** (i) Population: all Irish households Sample: 1353 households sampled (ii) Population: all primary school children Sample: 2625 children surveyed (iii) Population: Everyone entering shopping centre in 3-hour period Sample: Every sixth person entering shopping centre in 3-hour period (iv) Population: visitors to 'Teen's Today' website Sample: Teenagers who responded to questionnaire **3.** Primary data is data that is collected first hand by the person carrying out the investigation. Secondary data is not collected by the person carrying out the investigation. **4.** (i) Database; not feasible to ask all teachers. (ii) Survey; easily conducted. (iii) Database; cheap/easy to access birth records. (iv) Experiment; requires scientific testing. (v) Observational study; requires observation of effects. **5.** Limited to people with access to computers. **6.** Yes; opinion given in question. **7.** (i) Assign each student on class register a number and use random number generator on calculator. (ii) Assign each student on school register a number and use random number generator on calculator. (iii) Call to every 5th house and ask for the person with the earliest month of birth. (iv) Using census data, assign each person a number and use random number generator on calculator.

8. (i) Unbiased (ii) Biased; mention of 'stories'. (iii) Unbiased (iv) Biased; use of 'willy-nilly'. (v) Unbiased (vi) Biased; use of 'mindless'. (vii) Unbiased **9.** (i) Are you in favour of widening the main street? (ii) Should the current government be re-elected? (iii) What movie should be named Movie of the Year? (iv) Are you in favour of government policies to spend money to create jobs in your community? **10.** (i) Unbiased; random. (ii) Biased; sporty students only/may be taller. (iii) Biased; only one age group. (iv) Unbiased; random. (v) Biased; no boys included. (vi) Biased; limited to students reporting to office/small sample size. **11.** (i) Randomly generate numbers between 1 and 500, go to these pages and pick every 10th person. (ii) No. Limited to people in the phone book. **12.** (i) Yes or no acceptable, depending on the reason given. (ii) No. Sample size too small. (iii) Yes or no acceptable, depending on the reason given. (iv) Yes. Trees and oranges chosen at random. Large sample size. (v) Yes. Sample was randomly chosen. **13.** (i) No. Students may be delayed getting to class for a variety of reasons. (ii) Yes. Randomly selected. (iii) Yes. Randomly selected. (iv) No. 1st nine girls are eliminated by using a two-digit number. (v) Yes. Randomly selected.

Revision and Exam Style Questions

1. Categorical nominal **2.** (i) Categorical nominal (ii) Numerical discrete (iii) Numerical continuous (iv) Categorical ordinal (never, daily etc.) or Numerical (0, 1–2 times etc.) (v) Categorical nominal (vi) Numerical discrete **3.** (i) Students in her school. (ii) No. Limited to one year group/small sample size. (iii) Every 5th person on the school register **4.** (i) Categorical nominal (ii) Numerical discrete (iii) C. Gives the most random sample. **5.** (i) People who have purchased a product/service. (ii) No. People are more likely to rate if they have had a very positive/negative experience. (iii) No. People who are unsatisfied are often more likely to review a product. **6.** (i) The intervals overlap. (ii) 0, $< €5$, $\geq €5$, Don't know **7.** (i) Secondary (ii) Primary (iii) Primary (iv) Secondary (v) Primary (vi) Primary
8. (i) Sample size too small, excludes rural population, limited to people in the phonebook, only one member per household. (ii) A gives clearer data, easier to analyse; B gives more information.
9. (i) Advantage: all people asked so data more accurate; Disadvantage: too much data, a lot of work, expensive. (ii) No. Biased towards people using a similar facility. (iii) Select every 8th household and ask a random occupant to complete the survey. (iv) Interview: Advantages: high response rate, questions can be explained; Disadvantages: expensive, time consuming, less honest responses, influence of interviewer.
Questionnaire: Advantages: easy to carry out, cheaper, anonymous; Disadvantages: lower response rate, sample limited by administration method e.g. phone, internet etc.
(v) Clear, concise, provides relevant data

Chapter 23

Sometimes Statistical analysis can be open to interpretation. In some cases, there may be acceptable answers other than those shown here. For a comprehensive list of answers, see the worked solutions for this chapter.

Something to think about

Some suitable answers:
Sport is what the highest number of males want to be famous for.
Entertainment is what the highest number of females want to be famous for.
More males than females wanted to be famous in sport, engineering, innovation, business and politics.
More females than males wanted to be famous in entertainment, media, arts and culture, science and medicine.

Practice Questions 23.1

1. (i) Discrete. It is countable and can only take certain values.

(ii) October (iii) €2500 (iv) Yes.

2. (i) 148 (ii) 17 (iii) 15 (iv) Maths and Irish **3.** (i) (a) False. Instagram. (b) True (c) False. Facebook. (ii) 21 (iii) 41 **4.** (i) 2nd Wednesday (Day 8) (ii) 1st Friday (Day 5) (iii) 8 (iv) In both weeks the most lates are on Friday. Both weeks have lowest lates on Wednesday. 2nd half of the week has more lates in both weeks. (v) Week 1 **5.** (i) Discrete. Time is continuous but data is given to the nearest hour. (iii) 4 hours. (iv) 9 hours. (v) 7 hours. **6.** Chocolate 105°, Vanilla 66°, Strawberry 138°, Chocolate chip 51° **7.** (i) 10 people (ii) Piano 10, Guitar 8, Violin 6, None 6 (iii) 20%

Practice Questions 23.2

1. (i) Key: 13|2 = 132 cm (ii) 6 (iii) 132, 133, 133, 134, 136, 137 cm **2.** (i) 1, 2, 3, 4, 5 (ii) 0, 1, 2, 3, 4, 5 (iii) 21, 22, 23, 24 (iv) 3, 4, 5, 6, 7, 8, 9 **3.** (i) 100% (ii) 30 students (iii) 2 students (iv) 61% (v) 39% **4.** (i) 25 (ii) largest = 106 smallest = 38 (iii) 60, 61, 63, 63, 65, 65, 69 (iv) none (v) 9 (vi) 9 (vii) 14 **6.** (ii) largest = 52 smallest = 5 **7.** (ii) 9 students (iii) Most of the students scored in the 80's.
8. Most of the car journeys are between 10 and 20 minutes. Most of the bus journeys are between 10 and 30 minutes. The difference between the shortest and longest journey time is greater in the bus data. **9.** (ii) 30 people (iii) Youngest = 12 Oldest = 48 (iv) 16 year olds **10.** (ii) Girls = 23 Boys = 35 (iii) Boys, because more than half of the boys completed 35 or more puzzles. Only approximately $\frac{1}{3}$ of the girls completed 35 or more puzzles.

Practice Questions 23.3

1. (i)

Points	0 – 9	10 – 19	20 – 29	30 – 39	40 – 49
Frequency	1	4	8	4	3

(ii) 20 – 29 (iii) 35% **2.** (ii) Continuous. It is measured and can take 'in between' values. (iii) 66 (iv) 41 **3.** (ii) 29% (iii) (a) maximum: 16 + 3 = 19 (b) minimum: 3 **4.** (ii) A: more evenly spread, 20 – 30 is most common interval, few > 60
B: majority < 30 **5.** (i) 96 students (ii) 60 students (iii) 13.5% (iv) maximum = 63 minimum = 23
(v) Divide the intervals in half to give more detail.

6. (i) 140–145 cm (ii) 2 students (iii) There are no students of these heights. (iv) No. Sample size too small.

Practice Questions 23.4

1. (a) (i) positive skewed (ii) population age (b) (i) symmetric (ii) exam results (c) (i) uniform (ii) slopes of the line $x = 2$ (d) (i) negative skewed (ii) salary expectancy **2.** (i) negative skewed (ii) positive skewed (iii) negative skewed (iv) uniform (v) negative skewed **3.** (i) Test 1: negative skewed Test 2: symmetric (ii) Test 1 appears to have been easier as more people got higher grades, >80% **4.** Data is positive skewed. Dublin has the highest population and the data is graphed in descending order.
5. (i) uniform distribution (ii) positive skewed. Younger people are more likely to use social media. **6.** (i) 72 (ii) skewed towards the heavier weights (iii) skewed towards the lighter weights (iv) No. The majority of the girls' bags weigh 3–4 kg; the majority of the boys' bags weigh 9–10 kg.

Practice Questions 23.5

1. (i) increases (ii) decreases (iii) random **2.** (i) no correlation (ii) negative correlation (iii) positive correlation
3. (i) 90 kg (ii) 6.5 km (iii) 85 kg (iv) 4 km (v) negative correlation **4.** (i) positive – children grow as the get older (ii) positive – larger cars use more fuel
(iii) negative – students who miss class tend to do worse in tests
(iv) positive – high calorie intake causes weight gain
(v) no correlation – house number has no impact on intelligence
(vi) negative correlation – lower temperatures increase sales of gloves (vii) positive – more study should ensure better results
(viii) negative – the faster the cyclist the shorter the journey time
(ix) no correlation – shoe size doesn't impact wages
(x) negative – car's value decreases with age
5. (i) A – increased exposure to sun increases sunburn
(ii) C – hair length doesn't affect nail length
(iii) A – the more students in a school the more teachers needed
(iv) B – the longer a person runs for, generally, the slower they get, as they get tired
(v) A – as children grow, they need bigger clothes
(vi) B – as exercise increases, weight decreases
(vii) C – time spent on social media doesn't affect family size
(viii) B – as it gets colder your wear more layers of clothes
(ix) C – distance from school doesn't affect test results
6. (ii) Yes. There is a positive correlation on the graph.
7. (ii) negative correlation (iii) Spending more time on social media leaves less time to spend on watching TV.

Practice Questions 23.6

1. (i) weak negative (ii) no correlation (iii) strong negative (iv) weak positive (v) moderate positive (vi) moderate negative (vii) strong positive (perfect) **2.** A = 0.8 B = −0.9 C = 0 D = 0.3 E = −0.6 F = −0.2 **3.** (i) $r = -1$ (ii) $r = 0.2$ (iii) $r = -0.8$ (iv) $r = 0.5$ **4.** (i) $r = 1$ (ii) $r = 0.5$ (iii) $r = -0.8$ (iv) $r = 0$ (v) $r = -1$ **5.** (ii) Yes. Weak negative. $R = -0.2$ (iii) Students who watched more TV generally got lower results.

Practice Questions 23.7

1. (i) Causality (ii) correlation (iii) causality (iv) correlation (v) correlation (vi) causality **2.** (iii), (iv) and (v) **3.** (ii) Yes (iii) strong positive (iv) The correlation may be because of increased numbers on the beach (v) No.

Revision and Exam Style Questions – Section A

1. (i) Continuous. Histograms (no gaps) are used to display continuous data. (ii) Slightly positively skewed. Age of getting first driving license. (iii) negatively Skewed. Hours spent online over the week.
2. (ii) Only one packet had less than 12 in it. **3.** (i) Stem and leaf (ii) 28.1 cm (iii) 28 cm (iv) Females have smaller feet, smallest 15 cm and largest 28.1 cm, so spread is 13.1 cm; majority have feet between 24 and 25 cm. Males have larger feet, smallest 24 cm and largest 29.5 cm, so spread is 5.5 cm; majority have feet 28 cm.
5. (ii) **6.** (i) 18 marks (ii) 3 classes missed (iii) 11 classes missed and 80 marks (iv) No. The graph doesn't show a clear correlation.
7. (i) $r = -0.55$ is a moderate negative correlation $r = 0.36$ is a weak positive correlation (ii) Population density decreases moderately as the distance from the city increases House size increases slightly as distance from the city centre increases

Revision and Exam Style Questions – Section B

1. (ii) Teachers' fastest time is faster than the students. Half the teachers' times are greater than 84; half the students' times are greater than 79. The spread of the teachers' times is 50; the spread of students' times is 44. (iii) The lowest scores are both in the 50's. Half of both sets of data are ≥ 80 seconds. (iv) The teachers should win because half the teachers' times are > 84, their fastest time is faster and their middle value is higher than that of the students.
2. (ii) positive skewed **3.** (i) 111 (iii) positive skewed
(iv) People who live nearer are more likely to visit more often.
(v) The graph will give a less accurate picture.
4. (ii) Morning. Highest frequency in the shortest waiting time (5 mins) **5.** (ii) Yes (iii) Moderate positive. **6.** (ii) Yes. Strong positive. (iii) $r = 0.8$ (iv) Students who do well in Paper 1 are very likely to do well in Paper 2 also. **7.** (ii) The student who has a mass of 51 kg and height of 119 cm. This point is away from all the rest. (iii) Strong positive **8.** (i) Yes. Premier league footballers would be expected to take every opportunity to score a goal.
(ii) No. This indicates a strong negative correlation but there should be no correlation between boot size and goals scored.
(iii) No. A correlation must be between −1 and 1.

Chapter 24

Sometimes statistical analysis can be open to interpretation. In some cases, there may be acceptable answers, other than those shown here. For a comprehensive list of answers, see the worked solutions for this chapter.

Something to think about

It is possible. She needs to get at least 82% on her final exam to ensure she gets an A overall.

Practice Questions 24.1

1. (i) Mode: none Median: 47 Mean: 48 (ii) Mode: 71 Median: 72 Mean: 74 (iii) Mode: 23 Median: 16·5 Mean: 15·6 (iv) Mode: 33 and 39 Median: 38 Mean: 38·3 (v) Mode: 57 Median: 58 Mean: 61
2. (i) 12° (ii) 12° (iii) 4% decrease **3.** Mode: 14 Median: 14 Mean: 14·9 **4.** (ii) Mode: 14 and 21 Median: 20·5 Mean: 22·8
5. (i) The mode (ii) Mode: stays the same Median: stays the same Mean: increases **6.** (i) 0·3125 kg / 3125 g (ii) 875 g (iii) 259·6 g
7. (i) Mode: 5 hrs Median: 5 hrs Mean: 4·7 hrs (ii) Mode: Walk Median: Cycle Mean: not possible to calculate

(iii) Mode: Basketball Median: not possible to calculate Mean: not possible to calculate **8.** 8·8 **9.** (i) Panthers. They have highest mean (ii) Tigers. They have highest median (iii) Better to report the mean score as it is higher than the median score **10.** (i) Andy (ii) Becky (iii) Andy, Calum, Becky (iv) May (v) January and April (vi) 1·8 **11.** 7 **12.** 23 **13.** 20; 60

Practice Questions 24.2

1. (i) (a) Modal interval: 60 – 70 (b) Median interval: 50 – 60 (c) Mean: 54·6 (ii) (a) Modal interval: 100 – 120 (b) Median interval: 80 – 100 (c) Mean: 73·2 (iii) (a) Modal interval: 80 – 90 (b) Median interval: 80 – 90 (c) Mean: 85·4 (iv) (a) Modal interval: 15 – 20 (b) Median interval: 15 – 20 (c) Mean: 16·9 **2.** (i) Modal interval: 70 – 100 (ii) Median interval: 70 – 100 (iii) Mean: €75·55 **3.** (ii) 15 – 20 kg (iii) 16·1 kg (iv) 17·3 kg **4.** (i) 15·8 (ii) 15·8 **5.** (ii) Mean surgery A: 12·7 mins Mean surgery B: 12·3 mins (iii) Surgery B. According to the mean waiting time Surgery A has a slightly longer wait.

Practice Questions 24.3

1. (i) Mode: Categorical data (ii) Median: Data with outliers (iii) Mean **2.** (i) Mode: 8 Median: 12·5 Mean: 26·5 (ii) There is a large variation in the measures of central tendency. This may be due to the very small sample size. (iii) The data is very spread out and increases dramatically above the median which increases the mean. The mode is based on two pieces of data so isn't very reliable. **3.** (i) Median: the outlier (36) would affect the mean (ii) Mode: data is categorical. (iii) Mean: no outliers (iv) Median: data has outliers (v) Mode: categorical data **4.** A: Median and mean B: Mode C: Median D: Mode and median **5.** (i) Mode: none Median: 3·55 Mean: 4·175 (ii) No repeats so no mode. Data is skewed to the positive so the mean is higher than the median. (iii) Mean. It is higher. **6.** Mode: Males = 41, Females = none Median: Males = 41, Females = 56 Mean: Males = 47, Males = 60·4 Both the median and the mean show the average female result is higher than the average male result.

Practice Questions 24.4

1. (i) Range: 26 Median: 15 Interquartile range: 19 (ii) Range: 10 Median: 5 Interquartile range: 5 (iii) Range: 40 Median: 21 Interquartile range: 27 (iv) Range: 26 Median: 20 Interquartile range: 23 (v) Range: 25 Median: 11·5 Interquartile range: 17 **2.** (i) Range: Smith = 45, Dunne = 45 Both families have the same range of ages. (ii) Median: Smith = 9·5, Dunne = 16·5 The Dunne family has a higher median age which indicates the children are older. (iii) Interquartile range: Smith = 36, Dunne = 37 The IQR of both is very similar. The spread of the middle 50% of the ages is similar for both families. **3.** (a) (i) Range: School A = 2, School B = 4 School B has more varied results. (ii) Median: School A = 2, School B = 2·5 School B has higher median which means they have higher scores on average than School *A*. (iii) Interquartile range: School A = 2, School B = 2 Without outliers the schools have the same range of results. (iv) Mean: School A= 2·1 School B = 2·7 School B has a higher mean which shows the effect of outliers on the mean. (b) Affected by outliers. (c) Median. Not affected by outliers **4.** (i) 45 minutes (ii) 32 minutes (iii) 26 minutes **5.** (i) Range: Ms X = 38, Ms Y = 48 Ms Y's class has a larger range of results. (ii) Interquartile range: Ms X = 19, Ms Y = 22 The range of the middle 50% of Ms Y's results is larger than Ms X's. (iii) Mean: Ms X = 72·9, Ms Y = 81·6 (iv) Ms Y's class have better average results but the higher IQR means their results are more varied. **6.** (i) Median = 2·7; lower quartile = 1·5; upper quartile = 3·2 (ii) range = 4·7; interquartile range = 1·7 (iii) (a) 2·7 (b) 3·2 (c) 0·9; 5·6 minutes; 4·7 **7.** (a) (i) 101·5 (ii) 90 (iii) 105 (iv) 15 (b) Rory. Median higher. Shane's lower IQR indicates less variable and therefore more consistent results.

Practice Questions 24.5

1. (i) mean = 6·13, standard deviation = 3·14 (ii) mean = 16·96, standard deviation = 4·46 (iii) mean = 70·86, standard deviation = 30·68 (iv) mean = 62·14, standard deviation = 14·3 (v) mean = 115, standard deviation = 10·61 **2.** The values are all equal to the mean. **3.** (i) A = 5, B = 9, C = 5 (ii) A = 2·16, B = 3·56, C = 2·83 (iii) B (iv) Yes. By inspecting the differences from the mean in each case. **4.** (i) mean = 71·63, standard deviation = 15 (ii) The first group has a lower mean. First group has much higher standard deviation which means the results of this group are more varied. **5.** (i) mean = 18·14, standard deviation = 3·44 (ii) Yes **6.** (i) mean = 145·33, standard deviation = 10·99 (ii) The mean of the first school is higher. So, the average size of the years in this school is bigger. Standard deviation of second school is much lower so there is less variation between the numbers in each year. **7.** (i) Mean = 3 Standard deviation = 1·45 (ii) Mean = 5·91 Standard deviation = 2·63 (iii) Mean = 1·83 Standard deviation = 1 (iv) Mean = 2·69 Standard deviation = 1·02 **8.** (i) Mean = 21·17 Standard deviation = 2·54 (ii) Machine B has a lower mean. Machine B has a lower standard deviation. (iii) Machine B; number of carrots in each bag is more consistent. **9.** (i) 0 – 4; No; less accurate (ii) between 0 – 4 and 5 – 9 interval; No; not clear for this data (iii) 8·53; Yes; takes all values into account (iv) 8·45

Revision and Exam Style Questions – Section A

1. Any combination with minimum two 8s. **2.** Yes. Mode = 6, Range = 3 **3.** (i) 1, 2 and 4 (ii) 0·07 (iii) 0·5 (iv) 14 (v) lower quartile = –3, upper quartile = 2 (vi) 5 (vii) 3·75 (viii) The data doesn't show a large level of variability. The range, interquartile range and standard deviation are all relatively low. **4.** (i) 26·5 (ii) 2·22 (iii) No. Standard deviation is higher so consistency has decreased. **5.** (i) 1·9 (ii) median = 3·95; interquartile range = 1·15 (iii) 5 is the mode which is the highest weight not the average. **6.** (i) 2 (ii) 8 (iii) 3·89 (iv) 1·96 (v) Yes. There are no outliers. (vi) Mode now = 4 (frequency 21) Range: no change Mean now = 3·61

Revision and Exam Style Questions – Section B

1. 40·96 **2.** (i) 57 (ii) 45·5 (iii) 68·5 (iv) There is a much larger range in the number of visitors to the museum. **3.** (i) $x = 6$ (ii) range = 6; interquartile range = 3 (iii) 1·581 **4.** (i) 30 – 39 (ii) 30 – 39 (iii) mean = 32·47; standard deviation = 19·81 **5.** (i) skewed to the lower numbers (ii) 14 (iii) 14·5 **6.** (i) 50 – 60 (ii) mean = 61·45 Standard deviation = 22·77 (iii) The mean. It's an exact value.

Chapter 25

Something to think about

(i) Agree; (ii) No. 95% of the time true percentage lies between 9% and 25%.

Practice Questions 25.1

1. (i) 68% (ii) 99·7% (iii) 34% (iv) 81·5% **2.** (i) 100 (ii) 15 (iii) 70 (iv) 68% **3.** (i) 50% (ii) 50% (iii) 68% (iv) 95% (v) 99·7% (vi) $\mu - 3\overline{\sigma} \to \mu + 3\overline{\sigma}$ **4.** (i) (a) 13 → 19 ; (b) 10 → 22; (c) 7 → 25 (ii) (a) 4·4 → 6; (b) 3·6 → 6·8; (c) 2·8 → 7·6 (iii) (a) 142 → 154; (b) 136 → 160; (c) 130 → 166 (iv) (a) 63·4 → 72·6; (b) 58·8 → 77.2; (c) 54·2 → 81·8 (v) (a) 218·5 → 281·5; (b) 187 → 313; (c) 155·5 → 344·5 **5.** (i) 2·5% (ii) 81·5% (iii) 81·5% **6.** (i) 81·5% (ii) 1·8 **7.** (i) 62·75 (ii) 16·54 (iii) (a) 46·21 → 79·29; (b) 29·67 → 95·83; (c) 13·13 → 112·37 **8.** Mean = 31; standard deviation = 3·2 **9.** (i) 181 (ii) 66 (iii) 47·5%

Practice Questions 25.2

1. (i) 0·08 (ii) 0·04 (iii) 0·03 (iv) 0·02 (v) 0·01 **2.** (i) 220 (ii) 0·10 (iii) 0·07 (iv) $0{\cdot}03 < p < 0{\cdot}17$ (v) Decreases margin of error from 0·07 to 0·06. **3.** (i) 50 (ii) 0·16 (iii) 0·14 (iv) $0{\cdot}02 < p < 0{\cdot}3$ (v) Increase the sample size. **4.** (i) 500 (ii) 0·6 (iii) 0·04 (iv) $0{\cdot}56 < p < 0{\cdot}64$ **5.** (i) $0{\cdot}4 < p < 0{\cdot}46$ (ii) $0{\cdot}28 < p < 0{\cdot}32$ (iii) The confidence interval shrinks. **6.** (i) 10,000 (ii) 278 (iii) 100 (iv) 16 (v) 816 **7.** (i) Yes (ii) No (iii) Yes (iv) Yes **8.** €5·40 < p < €8·60 **9.** $0{\cdot}08 < p < 0{\cdot}14$ Yes. The sample size is quiet large. **10.** $90 < p < 134$

Practice Questions 25.3

1. (i) H_0: The percentage of students involved in at least one extracurricular activity is 61%.
H_1: The percentage of students involved in at least one extracurricular activity is not 61%.
(ii) H_0: The mean time for a wheel change is less than 15 minutes.
H1: The mean time for a wheel change is not less than 15 minutes.
(iii) H_0: The mean life of the products is more than 8 years.
H1: The mean life of the products is not more than 8 years.
(iv) H_0: The new vaccine is 10% more effective.
H1: The new vaccine is not 10% more effective.
(v) H_0: The percentage of people who thought the product reduced oiliness is 35%.
H_1: The percentage of people who thought the product reduced oiliness is not 35%.
2. (i) H_0: The proportion of cats who prefer Catty Cat is 0·8. H_1: The proportion of cats who prefer Catty Cat is not 0·8
(ii) 0·5 (iii) 0·08 (iv) $0{\cdot}42 < p < 0{\cdot}58$
(v) 0·8 falls outside the confidence interval so we reject H_0.
(vi) It appears the claim is untrue.
3. (i) H_0: The percentage of positive reviews is 35%. H_1: The percentage of positive reviews is not 35%.
(ii) 0·6 (iii) 0·07 (iv) $0{\cdot}53 < p < 0{\cdot}67$
(v) 0·35 falls outside the confidence interval so we reject H_0
(vi) The claim is untrue. It appears the number of positive reviews are actually higher than the company claims.
4. (i) $0{\cdot}22 < p < 0{\cdot}28$ (ii) 0·35 falls outside the confidence interval so we reject the null hypothesis. (iii) The claim is incorrect.
5. (i) $\frac{1}{6} = 0{\cdot}1\dot{6}$ (ii) H_0: the die is unbiased (fair). (iii) H_1: the die is biased. (iv) $0{\cdot}15 < p < 0{\cdot}25$, $0{\cdot}1\dot{6}$ falls inside the confidence interval so we fail to reject the null hypothesis. This implies the die is unbiased (fair). **6.** H_0: The percentage of members that are male is 50% (0·5). H_1: The percentage of members that are male is not 50%. Confidence interval: $0{\cdot}7 < p < 0{\cdot}92$, 0·5 falls outside the confidence interval so we reject the null hypothesis. The claim that there are equal numbers of males and females is untrue.
7. (i) H_0: The percentage of first time visitors to Ireland is 65% (0·65). H_1: The percentage of first time visitors to Ireland is not 65%. Confidence interval: $0{\cdot}34 < p < 0{\cdot}42$, 0·65 falls outside the confidence interval so we reject the null hypothesis
(ii) The claim is untrue. The percentage is lower than 65%.
8. H_0: The percentage of satisfied customers is 70%
H_1: The percentage of satisfied customers is not 70%
Confidence interval: $0{\cdot}69 < p < 0{\cdot}75$, 0·7 falls inside the confidence interval so we fail to reject the null hypothesis. It appears the companies satisfaction rate is higher than claimed. They should continue providing the services they do. **9.** H_0: The percentage of customers who would recommend the bar is 85%. H_1: The percentage of customers who would recommend the bar is not 85%. Confidence interval: $0{\cdot}16 < p < 0{\cdot}24$, 0·85 falls outside the confidence interval so we reject the null hypothesis. The claim is untrue. **10.** H_0: The percentage of students studying more than 3 hours is 65%. H_1: The percentage of students studying more than 3 hours is not 65%. Confidence interval: $0{\cdot}36 < p < 0{\cdot}5$, 0·65 falls outside the confidence interval so we reject the null hypothesis. The principal is unlikely to accept the claim.

Revision and Exam Style Questions – Section A

1. (ii) 6·6 hrs → 8·6 hrs (iii) 68% **2.** 62 kg → 74 kg
3. (i) H_0: The percentage of times her forecast is correct is 50%.
H_1: The percentage of times her forecast is correct is not 50%.
(ii) Confidence interval: $0{\cdot}49 < p < 0{\cdot}85$ (iii) Yes
4. (i) H_0: The percentage of voters that will vote for the candidate is 45%. H_1: The percentage of voters that will vote for the candidate is not 45%. (ii) Confidence interval: $0{\cdot}31 < p < 0{\cdot}49$ (iii) Yes
5. (i) H_0: The percentage of houses sold within two months is 80%.
H_1: The percentage of houses sold within two months is not 80%.
(ii) Confidence interval: $0{\cdot}7 < p < 0{\cdot}96$ (iii) Yes **6.** (i) 95% (ii) 203 **7.** (i) 0·15% (ii) 2·5%

Revision and Exam Style Questions – Section B

1. (i) 71 (ii) 2322 **2.** (i) Time-consuming and expensive (ii) 1512 g → 1528 g (iii) 2 (iv) The machine could be set to a lower weight. **3.** H_0: The success rate is 47%,
H_1: The success rate is not 47%. Confidence interval: $0{\cdot}34 < p < 0{\cdot}62$. 0·47 falls inside the confidence interval so we fail to reject the null hypothesis and say the company's claim appears to be true. **4.** (i) 0·03 (ii) H_0: Support for the party is 26%. H_1: Support for the party is not 26%. Confidence interval: $0{\cdot}21 < p < 0{\cdot}27$, 0·26 falls inside the confidence interval so we fail to reject the null hypothesis and say the party's claim appears to be true. **5.** H_0: The percentage of suppliers that would recommend the product is 75%, H_1: The percentage of suppliers that would recommend the product is not 75%. Confidence interval: $0{\cdot}52 < p < 0{\cdot}82$, 0·75 falls inside the confidence interval so we fail to reject the null hypothesis. No. The company's claim appears to be true. **6.** (i) H_0: The coin is fair and the chance of a head is 0·5.
H_1: The coin is unfair and the chance of a head is not 0·5.
Confidence interval: $0{\cdot}33 < p < 0{\cdot}77$ (ii) 0·5 falls inside the confidence interval so we fail to reject the null hypothesis and say the coin is fair. (iii) No. The number of tosses is very small.
7. (i) H_0: The examiners pass rate is 55%.
H_1: The examiners pass rate is not 55%. Confidence interval: $0{\cdot}08 < p < 0{\cdot}72$, 0·55 falls inside the confidence interval so we fail to reject the null hypothesis and say the examiner is not tougher than normal. (ii) The sample size is very small and as a result the margin of error is high. **8.** (i) Time consuming and expensive. (ii) 415·2g → 418·8 g (iii) Only 0·15% will fall below 415·2 g therefore the majority of the tins weight ≥ 415 g.

Chapter 26

Something to think about

(i) €362,500 (ii) 150 (iii) €1,112,500

Practice Questions 26.1

1. (i) Every minute, Mick's hear beats 72 times. (ii) 8640 beats **2.** (i) Ryan (ii) Ryan, by €10 **3.** (i) 761·5 km/h (ii) 211·5 m/s **4.** (a) (i) 2 (ii) $f(x) = 2x + 3$ (b) (i) $-\frac{1}{2}$ (ii) $f(x)= -\frac{1}{2}x + 4$ **5.** (i) −6 (ii) −2 (iii) 4 (iv) 6 **6.** (i) 1 ± 0·1 m/s (ii) €50 ± 5 profit/item (iii) 3 ± 0·3 km/h (iv) −4 ± 0·4 bat colonies/week **7.** (a) (i) 1·5 ± 0·1 (ii) −2·5 ± 0·2 (iii) 3·5 ± 0·3 (iv) −0·5 ± 0·1 (v) 0 ± 0·1 (b) $x < \frac{1}{2}$ **8.** (ii) (a) −5 ± 0·5 (b) 1 ± 0·1 (c) 7 ± 0·5

9. (a) (i) 4·6 ± 0·25 (ii) −1·8 ± 0·1 (iii) −3·4 ± 0·3 (iv) −0·2 ± 0·05 (b) $x < -0{\cdot}75$ and $x > 4{\cdot}1$

Practice Questions 26.2

1. (i) $12x^2$ (ii) $2x$ (iii) −5 (iv) $-6x^2$ (v) 0 (vi) $-12x$ (vii) 0 (viii) 8 **2.** (i) $3x^2 + 6$ (ii) $6x$ (iii) $14x + 4$ (iv) $24x^2 - 10x$ (v) $3 - 12x^2 + 2x$ (vi) $6x^2 + 14x - 1$ **3.** (i) $6x - 1$ (ii) $6 - 8t$ (iii) $15k^2 + 2 - 16k$ (iv) $1 - 9x^2 + 2x$ **4.** (i) $18{\cdot}6x^2 - 0{\cdot}8x$; $37{\cdot}2x - 0{\cdot}8$ (ii) $10x + 7$; 10 (iii) $16x - 6$; 16 (iv) $10{\cdot}2x^2 - 16x + 2{\cdot}1$; $20{\cdot}4x - 16$ **5.** (i) 8 (ii) 0 (iii) $36x + 8$ (iv) $30x + 8$ **6.** 14 **7.** 34·8 **8.** 190 **9.** 19; −32 **10.** 3

11. −2, 6 **12.** 2 **13.** $-\frac{1}{2}$ **14.** 9 **15.** (i) $-2a + b = -7$; $4a + b = 11$ (ii) $a = 3, b = -1$ **16.** (i) $2p + q = 2$; $-6p + q = -22$ (ii) $p = 3, q = -4$

Practice Question 26.3

1. (i) 2; increasing (ii) −3; decreasing (iii) −5; decreasing (iv) 4; increasing **2.** (i) $x > 3$ (ii) $x < 1$ (iii) $x > -1{\cdot}5$ (iv) $x < -2{\cdot}5$ **3.** (i) (−4, −25); minimum (ii) (−1, −36); minimum (iii) (1, 9); maximum (iv) (−3, −18); minimum (v) (−2, 2); minimum (vi) $\left(\frac{9}{8}, \frac{129}{16}\right)$; maximum

4. (i) 21, increasing; −6, decreasing; 6, increasing (ii) $(\sqrt{2}, 4 - 4\sqrt{2})$, $(-\sqrt{2}, 4 + 4\sqrt{2})$ **5.** (i) (0, 2) (ii) (0, 2), (1, 1) (iv) $0 < x < 1$ **6.** (i) (2, −11), (−2, 21) (ii) (5, −92), (−1, 16) (iii) (−2, −49), (3, 76) (iv) $\left(\frac{2}{3}, \frac{113}{27}\right)$, (−4, 55) (v) (8, −57), (2, 51) (vi) (−2, −39), (3, 86) **7.** (1, −3) **8.** (2, 9), (0, 5) **9.** (i) $2x + b$ (ii) −6 (iii) $2x - y - 6 = 0$ **10.** (i) 12 (ii) (−2, 23), (2, −9) (iii) $x < -2, x > 2$ **11.** (i) − 3, 1 (ii) $3x^2 - 3$ (iii) (1, −3), (−1, 1) (v) $0 < x < 1{\cdot}9$ (vi) $-1 < x < 1$ **12.** (ii) Quadratic **13.** (ii) Cubic

Practice Questions 26.4

1. (c) **2.** (c) **3.** A, (iv), Y; B, (v), V; C, (i), X; D, (ii), Z; E, (iii), W **7.** Turning point at $x = 2$; Decreasing before $x = 2$, so derivative is below the x-axis when $x = 2$. Increasing before $x = 2$, so derivative is above the x-axis when $x = 2$. **9.** (i) $6x^2 - 24x + 18$ (ii) $12x - 24$ (iii) 12

Revision and Exam Style Questions – Section A

1. (i) $14x + 2$ (ii) $6 - 2t$ (iii) $-2 - 12x^2$ (iv) $3x^2 - 2x + 8$ **2.** B **3.** 8 ± 0·5 m/s **4.** (ii) $6x - 12$ (iv) (a) U-shaped (b) Straight line (c) On the x-axis (d) Below the x-axis. **6.** (i) $A = (-1, 1)$, $B = (1, -3)$ (ii) $-1 < x < 1$ **7.** (i) 8000 litres (ii) 1000 litres (iii) −3000 ± 250 litres/h (iv) −1170 ± 100 litres/h **8.** 2 **9.** 188 **10.** (ii) (a) 10 ± 0·5 (b) −14 ± 0·5 (c) 2 ± 0·25 **11.** (i) −2·5, 0, 1 (ii) −1·6, 0·5 (iii) $-1{\cdot}6 < x < 0{\cdot}5$

Revision and Exam Style Questions – Section B

1. (i) 3 **2.** (i) 24 (ii) $a = -4, b = 20$ (iii) (2·5, 49) **3.** (i) $-5 - 4x$; (−1·25, 6·125) (ii) (0, 3) (iii) $-3, \frac{1}{2}$ (iv) $x < -1{\cdot}25$ **4.** (ii) −3, 3 **5.** (i) 2; 0 **6.** (ii) Cubic function **7.** (i) (0, 5) (ii) (−2, 49); (3, −76) **8.** (i) $x^3 - 7x + 6$ (ii) (1·5275, −1·128), (−1·5275, 13·128) **9.** (i) $3x^2 + 6x + 4$ (ii) No turning points **10.** (i) −2, −6 (ii) $24 - 3k^2 + 18k$ (iii) (2, −6), (4, −2) (v) $0{\cdot}8 < k < 5$ (vi) $2 < k < 4$ (vii) One **11.** (i) 27 Ohms, 24·5 Ohms (ii) −25° C, 80° C (iii) −0·05 Ohms/degree (iv) 27·5625 Ohms, 27·5° C (v) $T < 27{\cdot}5°$ C

Chapter 27

Something to think about

(i) $200 - \pi r$ (ii) $400r - 2\pi r^2$ (iii) $x = 100$ m; $r = \frac{100}{\pi}$ m

Practice Questions 27.1

1. (i) $6x - 5$ (ii) 7 **2.** (i) $3x^2 + 2x - 12$ (ii) −7 (iii) 9 **3.** (i) $-2x + 5$ (ii) −3 (iii) $3x + y - 9 = 0$ **4.** (i) $6x + 5$ (ii) $x + y - 1 = 0$ (iii) (1, 0), (0, 1) **5.** $17x - y - 27 = 0$ **6.** $5x - y - 16 = 0$ **7.** $3x - y - 3 = 0$ **8.** (i) $10x - 2$ (ii) $8x - y - 4 = 0$ (iii) $22x + y + 19 = 0$ **9.** (i) $2x + y - 1 = 0$; $2x - 1 - 7 = 0$ (ii) Not perpendicular (iii) (2, −3) **10.** (i) $-6x + 5$ (ii) $x + y - 15 = 0$ (iii) $11x - y + 15 = 0$ (iv) (0, 15) **11.** (i) $2x - 5$ (ii) (2·5, 1·75) **12.** (i) $6x + 12$ (ii) (−2, −19) **13.** (1, −1) **14.** $A = (-1, 1)$, $B = (1, -3)$ **15.** (i) $3x^2 - 21$ (ii) −4, 4 (iii) (−4, 40), (4, 0) **16.** (2, 10), (6, −10)

Practice Questions 27.2

1. (i) 47 Pa (ii) 6 s (iii) 52 Pa/s **2.** (i) 1285 Ohms (ii) −24°C, 24°C (iii) 40T Ohms/degree (iv) 120 Ohms/degree; at this temperature the resistance of the metal is increasing at a rate of 120 Ohms per degree. **3.** (i) 282 m (ii) $100 - 4t$ m/s (iii) 25 s (iv) 1250 m **4.** (i) $2\pi r$ (ii) 18·8 cm²/cm (iii) 256π cm² **5.** (i) 7 m (ii) 15 m (iii) 7 s (iv) 16 m (v) 8 m/s **6.** (i) 46 m (ii) $24 - 6t$ (iii) −18 m/s; falling (iv) −6 m/s² (v) 49 m (vi) 37 m **7.** (i) $500x^2 + 1000x$ (ii) $1000x + 1000$ (iii) 4000 (iv) 6 machines **8.** (i) 180 m (ii) (a) −35 m/s (b) 37 m/s (iii) 18 m/s² (iv) −38 m/s **9.** (i) 30 m (ii) 44 m (iii) 14 m (iv) 37 m/s (v) 2 m/s² (vi) No. Train cannot accelerate forever.

10. (i) 49 m (ii) 113 m/s (iii) $\frac{2}{3}$ s **11.** (i) $26t - 3t^2$ (ii) 56 people/day (b) – 40 people/day (iii) $8\frac{2}{3}$ days; 325 people **12.** (i) $30t - 9t^2$ (ii) $30 - 18t$

(iii)

t	0	1	2	3	4	5
$h(t)$	0	12	36	54	48	0
$v(t)$	0	21	24	9	−24	−75
$a(t)$	30	12	−6	−24	−42	−60

13. (i)

t	0	1	2	3	4	5	6	7	8	9	10
$h(t)$	0	18	32	42	48	50	48	42	32	18	0

(v) 20 m/s

Practice Questions 27.3

1. $20 - 10t$; 20 m **2.** (i) -25 cm/s (ii) -4 cm/s^2 (iii) $\frac{81}{8}$ cm
3. (i) 3·5 s (ii) 0·6 m (iii) 7 s **4.** (i) 33 cm
(ii) 12 cm/s; -20 cm/s (iii) 49 cm **5.** (i) 33·56
(ii) 50 m/s, 74 m/s (iii) 62 m/s (iv) 8·56 **6.** (i) $36x^2 - 2x^3$
(ii) 12 cm (iii) 24 cm, 12 cm, 6 cm; 1728 cm^3
7. (i) €492 (ii) Increasing (iii) €490 (iv) €976
(v) €833·20 **8.** (ii) €1,730 (iii) €17·20 (iv) 315
9. (i) $2k^2 - 48k + 400$ (ii) 274 (iii) 12 km from A
(iv) B (v) Rate of change is zero at $k = 12$. **10.** (i) $16 - 2x$, $10 - 2x$
(iii) 144 cm^3

Revision and Exam Style Questions – Section A

1. (i) 9, increasing; -7, decreasing (ii) $\left(\frac{1}{4}, \frac{9}{8}\right)$ **2.** (i) 140 m
(ii) 202·5 m **3.** (i) $-4x + 7$ (ii) $7x - y - 5 = 0$
(iii) $5x + y - 13 = 0$ **4.** (i) 176 m/s (ii) -8 m/s^2 (iii) 25 s
(iv) 2500 m **5.** $x < -3{\cdot}5$ **6.** $7x + y - 3 = 0$ **7.** $(-5, -29)$
8. (i) 22 m/s (ii) 55 s (iii) 605 m (iv) $-\frac{2}{5}$ m/s^2
9. (i) $80 - 2W$ (iii) 800 m^2

Revision and Exam Style Questions – Section B

1. (i) 2 s, 10 s (ii) 18 m/s^2 (iii) 130 m/s (iv) $t > 6$ s
2. (i) $8x - 26$ (ii) $2x + y - 9 = 0$ (iii) $14x - y - 55 = 0$
(iv) (4, 1) **3.** (i) $p = -2$, $q = 8$ (ii) Point where $g'(x) = 0$; (2, 8)
4. (i) 802 litres (ii) -348 litres/day **5.** (i) 1, 3
(ii) Not perpendicular **6.** (i) 16,187 m (ii) 51 m/s
(iii) 6 s; -438 m **7.** (i) $4\pi r^2$ cm^3/cm (ii) 144π cm^3/cm
(iii) 2973·5 cm^3 **8.** (ii) -1 (iii) 1 (iv) (2, 2) (v) (1·5, 1·5)
9. (i) €27,360 (ii) $680x$ (iii) $-2x^3 + 64x^2 + 1120x$ (iv) 28; €37,632
10. (i) $12 - L$ (iii) 36 m^2

Chapter 28

Something to think about

The stunt will be successful since this function has no real roots.

Practice Questions 28.1

1. (i) i (ii) $6i$ (iii) $9i$ (iv) $11i$ (v) $\sqrt{5}i$ (vi) $5\sqrt{3}i$ (vii) $2\sqrt{3}i$
(viii) $7\sqrt{2}i$ **2.** (i) $-6i$ (ii) $8\sqrt{14}$i (iii) $12i$ (iv) $28\sqrt{6}$i (v) $8i$
(vi) $4i$ (vii) $12i$ (viii) $6\sqrt{5}i$ **3.** (i) $\frac{1}{2}i$ (ii) $\frac{4}{5}i$ (iii) $\frac{7}{2}i$ (iv) $2i$
(v) $4\sqrt{2}i$ (vi) $5\sqrt{3}i$ **4.** (i) $10i$ (ii) $13i$ (iii) $5i$ (iv) $4i$ (v) $7i$
(vi) $12i$ **5.** (i) $-i$ (ii) -1 (iii) 1 (iv) $-i$ (v) $-i$ (vi) $-i$
(vii) -1 (viii) -1 **6.** (i) i (ii) $-i$ (iii) -162 (iv) $-5i$
(v) $-2i$ (vi) $-i$ **7.** (i) Real = $-$ 2 Imaginary = 5 (ii) Real = 4
Imaginary = -1 (iii) Real = 3·5 Imaginary = $-0{\cdot}4$ (iv) Real = 0
Imaginary = -8 (v) Real = -9 Imaginary = 112 (vi) Real = $\frac{3}{4}$
Imaginary = $\sqrt{5}$ **8.** (i) Real = 6 Imaginary = 4 (ii) Real = -5
Imaginary = $4\sqrt{3}$ (iii) Real = -8 Imaginary = -2
(iv) Real = -15 Imaginary = -6 (v) Real = 21 Imaginary = $3\sqrt{2}$
(vi) Real = -12 Imaginary = $-2\sqrt{30}$

Practice Questions 28.2

1. $A = 2 + 3i$ $B = -5 - i$ $C = 1 - 4i$ $D = -4 + 2i$ $E = 0 + 7i$ $F = -4 + 0i$
3. (i) $3 + 2i$ (ii) $-4 + 3i$ (iii) $9 - 6i$ (iv) $8 - 6i$ (v) $-3 + 2i$
(vi) $-2 + \frac{3}{2}i$ **4.** (i) $5\sqrt{2}$ (ii) $2\sqrt{26}$ (iii) $3\sqrt{5}$ (iv) $5\sqrt{2}$ (v) 4
(vi) 5 **5.** (ii) $|z_1| = \sqrt{29}$ $|z_2| = \sqrt{13}$ $|z_3| = 5$ $|z_4| = \sqrt{2}$
6. (i) (a) $-3 + 7i$ (b) $5 - 2i$ (c) $-7 + 11i$ (d) $6 - 14i$
(ii) (a) $\sqrt{58}$ (b) $\sqrt{29}$ (c) $\sqrt{170}$ (d) $2\sqrt{58}$ **7.** $p = \pm 5$
8. $b = \pm 1$ **9.** (i) $\sqrt{41}$ (ii) $z_1 = -5 + 4i$; $|z_1| = \sqrt{41}$
(iii) $z_2 = 5 - 4i$; $|z_2| = \sqrt{41}$ (iv) $z_3 = 5 + 4i$; $|z_3| = \sqrt{41}$
(v) The modulus stays the same. **10.** (ii) $|z_1| = \sqrt{2}$; $|z_2| = 3\sqrt{2}$
(iii) $z_2 = 3z_1$ (iv) $|z_2| = 3|z_1|$

Practice Questions 28.3

1. (i) $7i$ (ii) $-3i$ (iii) $-5i$ (iv) $-2i$ (v) $2 - i$ (vi) $6 - 12i$
2. (i) $15 + 8i$ (ii) $-10 - 3i$ (iii) $11 - 5i$ (iv) $4 + 2i$ (v) $4 + i$
(vi) $-2 + 5i$ **3.** (i) $12 + 7i$ (ii) $-7 + 2i$ (iii) $-10 - 3i$
(iv) $14 - 3i$ (v) $7 - 6i$ (vi) $-21 + 6i$ **4.** (i) $8 + 3i$ (ii) $2 + 11i$
5. (i) $7 - i$ (ii) $4 - 2i$ (iii) $-6 - 3i$ (iv) $1 - 11i$ (v) $2 - 5i$
(vi) $-2 + 5i$ **6.** $a = 52$; $b = -11$ **7.** (i) $z + w = -3 + 7i$; $w - z = 3 + 5i$
(ii) $\sqrt{130}$ **8.** $4 + 2i$ **9.** $w = -4 + 4i$ **10.** $u + v = 3 - i$;
$u - v = -1 - 3i$

Practice Questions 28.4

1. (i) $12i$ (ii) $5 - 25i$ (iii) $12 + 12i$ (iv) $9 + 24i$ **2.** (i) $-2 - 4i$
(iii) $|-1 - 2i| = \sqrt{5}$; $|2(-1 - 2i)| = 2\sqrt{5}$
(iv) Increased the modulus by a factor of 2 **3.** (i) $-5 + 4i$
(ii) $-4 + 6i$ (iii) $18 + 15i$ (iv) $21 - 7i$ **4.** (ii) $-1 + 8i$
(iv) Rotates it 90° clockwise **5.** (i) $15 + 25i$ (ii) $-2 + 16i$
(iii) $41 - i$ (iv) $18 + 43i$ (v) $7 + 30i$ (vi) $-18 + 14i$
6. (i) -16 (ii) $-33 + 56i$ (iii) $-5 - 12i$ (iv) $11 - 60i$
(v) $-3 + 4i$ (vi) $24 + 10i$ **7.** (i) $6 + 72i$ (ii) $24 + 32i$
(iii) $-85 - 5i$ (iv) $91 + 13i$ **8.** (i) $-1 - 17i$ (ii) $-22 - 16i$
(iii) $18 - i$ (iv) $-7 + i$ (v) $5 - 15i$ (vi) $-18 - 39i$ **9.** $b = \pm 1$
10. (i) $38 + 6i$ (ii) $8 + 6i$ (iii) $-32 - 44i$ (iv) $-84 + 12i$
11. (i) $6 - 4i$ (ii) $9 - 6i$ (iii) $12 - 8i$ (v) $|z| = \sqrt{13}$; $|2z| = 2\sqrt{13}$;
$|3z| = 3\sqrt{13}$; $|4z| = 4\sqrt{13}$ (vi) Multiplying a complex number by a constant multiplies its modulus by the same constant.
12. (ii) 13 **13.** (i) $w = 3 + 4i$ $|z| = \sqrt{5}$ $|w| = 5$
(ii) $w = 15 + 8i$ $|z| = \sqrt{17}$ $|w| = 17$ (iii) $w = 7 + 24i$ $|z| = 5$ $|w| = 25$
14. $-16 \in R$ **15.** (i) $iz = 3 + 4i$; $i^2z = -4 + 3i$; $i^3z = -3 - 4i$;
$i^4z = 4 - 3i$ (iii) Multiplying by i rotates the complex number by 90°; by i^2 rotates 180°; by i^3rotates 270° and by i^4 rotates 360°

Practice Questions 28.5

1. (i) $4 - 5i$ (ii) $7 + 6i$ (iii) $-9 - i$ (iv) $-5 + 2i$ (v) $8i$
(vi) $4 + 3i$ **2.** (i) 3 (ii) $5 - 3i$ (iii) 1 (iv) 5 (v) $8 + i$
(vi) $5 - i$ **3.** (i) True (ii) True **4.** (i) $\frac{-2i}{3}$ (ii) $\frac{5i}{6}$ (iii) $-\frac{7}{2}i$
(iv) $\frac{3}{4} - \frac{1}{2}i$ (v) $\frac{1}{6} - \frac{1}{6}i$ (vi) $\frac{3}{2} - \frac{1}{2}i$ **5.** (i) $\frac{29}{25} + \frac{22}{25}i$ (ii) $-\frac{19}{26} + \frac{9}{26}i$
(iii) $-\frac{27}{58} - \frac{53}{58}i$ (iv) $\frac{1}{50} - \frac{57}{50}i$ (v) $-\frac{6}{5} - \frac{11}{10}i$ (vi) $\frac{1}{2} + \frac{1}{2}i$
6. (i) $-\frac{3}{2} + \frac{1}{2}i$ (ii) $-\frac{1}{13} - \frac{5}{13}i$ (iii) $-2 + 3i$ (iv) $-\frac{17}{5} + \frac{1}{5}i$
7. (i) $-\frac{2}{13} - \frac{16}{13}i$ (ii) $\frac{14}{13} + \frac{8}{13}i$ (iii) $\frac{16}{13} - \frac{2}{13}i$ (iv) $-\frac{2}{13} + \frac{16}{13}i$
8. (i) $-\frac{4}{25} + \frac{3}{25}i$ (ii) $\frac{3}{17} + \frac{5}{17}i$ **9.** (i) $\frac{4}{3} + 6i$ (ii) $-0{\cdot}2\,i$

Practice Questions 28.6

1. (i) $x = 12$ $y = 7$ (ii) $x = 7$ $y = -4$ (iii) $x = -2$ $y = 3$ (iv) $x = 8$
$y = 9$ **2.** (i) $a = 2$ $b = -1$ (ii) $a = 8$ $b = 3$ (iii) $a = -3$ $b = 2$
(iv) $a = 1$ $b = -\frac{13}{6}$ **3.** (i) $3x - yi$ (ii) $x = 3$; $y = -2$
4. (i) $\bar{z} = 12 - 5i$ (ii) $p = -2$ **5.** $p = 7$; $q = -12$ **6.** $x = 7$; $y = 1$
7. $|z| = 3$ $a = \frac{17}{6}$; $b = -\frac{1}{2}$ **8.** $x = 5$; $y = -6$ **9.** $a = 5$; $b = 5$

10. $z = 5 + 6i$

Practice Questions 28.7

1. (i), (iii), (v) and (vi) have no real roots as the graphs do not cross the x axis. **2.** (i) $z = \pm 8i$ (ii) $z = \pm 4\sqrt{3}\,i$ (iii) $z = \pm 2\sqrt{7}i$ (iv) $z = \pm 5i$ (v) $z = \pm 7i$ (vi) $z = \pm 3\sqrt{11}\,i$ **3.** (i) $z = 5 \pm 3\,i$ (ii) $z = 5 \pm \sqrt{3}\,i$ (iii) $z = 2 \pm 3i$ (iv) $z = 2 \pm i$ (v) $z = 4 \pm 2\sqrt{6}\,i$ (vi) $z = -5 \pm 2i$ **4.** (i) $z = 1 \pm \frac{\sqrt{6}}{2}i$ (ii) $z = -\frac{6}{5} \pm \frac{2}{5}i$ (iii) $z = \frac{3 \pm \sqrt{11}\,i}{4}$ (iv) $z = \frac{3 \pm 6i}{5}$ (v) $z = \frac{1 \pm 2i}{3}$ (vi) $z = \frac{3 \pm i}{4}$ **5.** $z = -3 \pm \sqrt{11}\,i$ **6.** (a) (i) $76 > 0$; two real roots (ii) $41 > 0$; two real roots (iii) $17 > 0$; two real roots (iv) $-63 < 0$; complex roots (v) $0 = 0$; one real root (vi) $140 > 0$; two real roots (b) The number under the square root is negative which means the roots will be complex. (c) $\pm\sqrt{0} = 0$; getting rid of the $\pm$ leaves only one root

7. Other root $= 2 + 2i$ **8.** (i) $x = \frac{1 \pm \sqrt{41}}{2}$ (ii) The graphs intersect because $f(x) = g(x)$ has real roots.
9. $b^2 - 4ac = -16$; $-16 < 0$ so the function has complex roots. Roots are $-1 \pm 2i$
10. $b^2 - 4ac = 17$; $17 > 0$ so the function has two real roots. Roots are $\frac{3 \pm \sqrt{17}}{4}$

Revision and Exam Style Questions – Section A

1. (i) $p = -1 + 2i$; $q = 2 + 3i$ (ii) $|p| = \sqrt{5}$; $|q| = \sqrt{13}$ (iii) $\overline{p} = -1 - 2i$; $\overline{q} = 2 - 3i$ (iv) $r = -8 - 5i$ **2.** (i) $-i$ (ii) $-2 + 5i$ (iii) Rotation anti clockwise by 270° **3.** $-6 - 17i$
4. $2z = 4 + 6i$ and is twice as far away from $(0 + 0i)$ as z
$\overline{z} = 2 - 3i$ and is the image of z by axial symmetry in the real axis
$iz = -3 + 2i$ and is z rotated anticlockwise by 90° **5.** $24 + 10i$
7. $w = 4 + 2i$ **8.** (i) $P = -z$; $Q = iz$; $R = 2z$
(ii) P is the image of z through central symmetry in $0 + 0i$ or a rotation of z by 180° Q is an anticlockwise rotation of z by 90° R is z scaled by 2 **9.** (i) $|z| = 2$; $|w| = 3$ (ii) $zw = -3 + 3\sqrt{3}i$; $\frac{w}{z} = \frac{3 + 3\sqrt{3}i}{4}$ (iii) True **10.** (i) 1 (ii) $\sqrt{5}$ (iii) $-1 + 2i$
12. $x = \pm 7i$

Revision and Exam Style Questions – Section B

1. (i) $z + 3 = 1 - 5i$, $z + 2i = -2 - 3i$ (ii) $1 + i$ (iii) $\sqrt{2}$
2. (i) $\overline{w} = -1 + 4i$; $w + \overline{w} = -2$ (ii) $2 - w = 3 + 4i$ (iii) $-62 + 84i$

3. (i) $-2 + i$ (ii) $5 - 10i$ (iii) $\left|\frac{w^2 + 2i + 10}{w - 4 + 4i}\right| = 5$; $\frac{|w^2 + 2i + 10|}{|w - 4 + 4i|} = 5$; true **4.** (i) $4 - 7i$, (ii) $a = 4$; $b = -1$ $z = 4 - i$

5. (i) $w = 2 + 2i$ (ii) $|z| = 5$; $|w| = 2\sqrt{2}$ **8.** $z = \frac{3 \pm \sqrt{39}\,i}{2}$

9. Roots are complex $(1 \pm 2i)$ so these functions don't intersect.

10. $10 - 24i$

11. (iii) multiply z by $2i$

Transformation	Calculation	Explanation
$z_1 = z + 2i$	$z_1 = 1 - i + 2i$ $= 1 + i$	The character moves up by two units
$z_2 = z + 2$	$3 - i$	Moves 2 places to the right
$z_3 = -z$	$-1 + i$	Rotates 180° anticlockwise
$z_4 = \overline{z}$	$1 + i$	Moves under axial symmetry in real axis
$z_5 = i^3 z$	$-1 - i$	Anticlockwise rotation of 270°
$z_6 = 3z$	$3 - 3i$	Moves 3 times further from $0 + 0i$
$z_7 = z(3 + 2i)$	$5 - i$	Moves four units to the right

11. (i) $f(x) = -x^2 + x + 6$ has real roots;
$g(x) = -x^2 + x - 6$ has complex roots;
(ii) $f(x) = -x^2 + x + 6$ is function B as it cuts the x axis
$g(x) = -x^2 + x - 6$ is function A as it doesn't cuts the x axis
12. Roots are complex so the ship will not pass through the radar.